Biology Today

ACKNOWLEDGMENTS

CONTENT ADVISORS

Thomas Armentano, Ph.D.
Director, Biotic Resources Program
Holcomb Research Institute
Butler University
Indianapolis, Indiana

Gary M. Aron, Ph.D.
Professor of Biology
Southwest Texas State University
San Marcos, Texas

Richard K. Boohar, Ph.D.
Associate Professor and Chief
    Biological Sciences Advisor
Department of Biological Science
University of Nebraska
Lincoln, Nebraska

John R. Bristol, Ph.D.
University of Texas
Vice President for Academic Affairs
El Paso, Texas

Robert D. Burke
Director, Sexually Transmitted
    Diseases Control Division
Tennessee Department of Health
    and Environment
Nashville, Tennessee

Dorothy E. Croall, Ph.D.
Assistant Professor of Biochemistry
University of Maine
Orono, Maine

Mapi M. Cuevas, Ph.D.
Adjunct Instructor
Santa Fe Community College
Gainesville, Florida
Gainesville High School Science
    Instructor

Beth DiDomenico, Ph.D.
Principal Scientist
Department of Molecular Genetics and
    Chemotherapy
Schering-Plough Research
Bloomfield, New Jersey

Betsy L. Dresser, Ph.D.
Director of Research
Cincinnati Zoo and Botanical Garden
Center for Reproduction of
    Endangered Wildlife
Cincinnati, Ohio

William Eickmeier, Ph.D.
Department of Biology
Vanderbilt University
Nashville, Tennessee

Thomas Kantz, Ph.D.
Chair, Professor of Biology
Department of Biological Sciences
California State University
Sacramento, California

David E. Lemke, Ph.D.
Associate Professor of Biology
Southwest Texas State University
San Marcos, Texas

Georgia E. Lesh-Laurie, Ph.D.
Professor of Biology
Interim Provost
Cleveland State University
Cleveland, Ohio

C. Owen Lovejoy, Ph.D.
University Professor of Anthropology
Kent State University
Kent, Ohio

Henry A. Robitaille, Ph.D.
Director, Science and Technology
The Land, EPCOT Center
Lake Buena Vista, Florida

Carol A. Simon, Ph.D.
Department of Biology
City College of the City University
    of New York
Department of Herpetology and
    Ichthyology
The American Museum of Natural
    History

Beryl B. Simpson, Ph.D.
Botany Department
The University of Texas at Austin
Austin, Texas

Ethel Sloane, Ph.D.
Chair, Department of Biological
    Sciences
University of Wisconsin—Milwaukee
Milwaukee, Wisconsin

Patton Smith, M.D.
Family Practitioner
Forsyth, Georgia

Samuel Tarsitano, Ph.D.
Assistant Professor of Biology
Southwest Texas State University
San Marcos, Texas

Diane TeStrake, Ph.D.
Department of Biology
University of South Florida
Tampa, Florida

Curtis A. Williams, Ph.D.
Professor of Biology
State University of New York
Purchase, New York

Alfred Zweidler, Ph.D.
Fox Chase Cancer Center
Philadelphia, Pennsylvania

Biology Today

Harvey D. Goodman
Principal, Catherine and
  Count Basie Junior High School
  Rockdale Village, New York

Linda E. Graham
Associate Professor, Department
  of Botany
University of Wisconsin
Madison, Wisconsin

Thomas C. Emmel
Professor, Department of Zoology
University of Florida
Gainesville, Florida

Yaakov Shechter
Professor, Department of
  Biological Sciences,
  and Chairperson,
  Natural Sciences Core
  Curriculum
Herbert H. Lehman College
  of the City University
  of New York
Lecturer, College of Physicians
  and Surgeons,
  Columbia University
  New York, New York

SENIOR EDITORIAL ADVISORS

Tommy E. Wynn, Ph.D.
Associate Professor of Botany
North Carolina State University
Raleigh, North Carolina

Mary E. Kayusa
Biology Teacher
North Fort Myers High School
North Fort Myers, Florida

 Holt, Rinehart and Winston, Inc.
Harcourt Brace Jovanovich, Inc. HBJ
Austin · Orlando · San Diego · Chicago · Dallas · Toronto

CURRICULUM ADVISORS

Stephanie Baron
Science Educator
Patrick Henry High School
San Diego Unified School District
San Diego, California

Lowell Bethel, Ed.D.
Professor
Science Education Center
The University of Texas at Austin
Austin, Texas

Linda Bostick
Specialist, Talented and Gifted
Riverwood High School
Atlanta, Georgia

Dorothy Chang-Van Horn
Science Advisor
Senior High Schools Division
Los Angeles Unified School District

Jody Cunningham
Biology Teacher
Williamstown High School
Williamstown, West Virginia

Delmous R. Ingram
Former Biology Teacher and
  Science Department Chairperson
Needham B. Broughton High School
Raleigh, North Carolina

Janis W. Lariviere
Biology-Chemistry Teacher
Anderson High School
Austin, Texas

Robert L. Lehrman
Former Science Teacher and
  Department Chairperson
Roslyn High School
Roslyn, New York

Sarah Longino
Biology Teacher
Colonial High School
Orlando, Florida

Karen M. Nein
Science Consultant
Englewood, Colorado

Barney Parker
Developmental Research School
Florida State University
Tallahassee, Florida

Carl M. Raab
Curriculum Advisor
Chairperson, Biology Department
Fort Hamilton High School
Brooklyn, New York

Barbara Rothstein, Ph.D.
Adjunct Professor
Southeastern University of Allied
  Health Sciences
College of Osteopathic Medicine
North Miami Beach, Florida
Chairperson
Science Department
Dade County Public Schools
North Miami Beach, Florida

Daniel S. Sheldon, Ph.D.
Associate Professor
Science Education Center
University of Iowa
Iowa City, Iowa

Frances M. Slowiczek, Ed.D.
Science Curriculum Coordinator
San Diego City Schools
San Diego, California

Mary Ulrich
District Science Department Chairperson
Biology Teacher
Provine High School
Jackson, Mississippi

Thomasena Woods, Ed.D.
Science Supervisor
Newport News Public Schools
Newport News, Virginia

Robert Wright
Biology Teacher
MacArthur High School
Lawton, Oklahoma

READING SPECIALISTS

Patricia Bowers, Ph.D.
Science and Reading Coordinator
Division of Curriculum and Instruction
Chapel Hill-Carrboro City Schools
Chapel Hill, North Carolina

Judy Nichols Mitchell, Ph.D.
Chair, Division of Language, Reading, and
  Culture
College of Education
University of Arizona
Tucson, Arizona

FEATURE WRITERS AND CONTRIBUTORS

Eve Cech
Science Writer and Editor
Gainesville, Florida

William R. Collien
Biology and Botany Instructor
Triton College
River Grove, Illinois

Vicki Werner Hoffman
Former Biology Teacher
Coral Gables Senior High School
Coral Gables, Florida

Joanne Ingwall, Ph.D.
Associate Professor of Physiology
  and Biophysics
Department of Medicine
Harvard Medical School and
  Brigham and Women's Hospital
Boston, Massachusetts

Irving Kent Loh, M.D., F.A.C.C.
Medical Director, Ventura Heart
  Institute
Los Robles Regional Medical Center
Thousand Oaks, California

Glenn K. Leto
Biology Teacher
Barrington High School
Barrington, Illinois

Karen M. Nein
Science Consultant
Englewood, Colorado

Kenneth Nelson
Biology Teacher
Lyons Township High School,
  South Campus
Western Springs, Illinois

James D. Oilschlager
Biology Teacher
Libertyville High School
Libertyville, Illinois

Henry A. Robitaille, Ph.D.
Agricultural Director
The Land, EPCOT Center
Lake Buena Vista, Florida

Kenneth W. Weidlich
Biology Teacher
Hillsborough High School
Belle Mead, New Jersey

Contents

INVESTIGATIONS

BIOTECH

ISSUES IN BIOLOGY

BIOLOGY AND YOU

THINKING ABOUT BIOLOGY

A Challenge to Students

When you were beginning to talk, people around you pointed to things and told you what they were. Then, most likely, they asked you, "*What* is this?" and "*What* is that?" You delighted them when you responded, "Nose," "Ear," "Door," and "Airplane." Next, they watched as you experimented, sometimes messily, with spoons and drinking cups and found out *how* they worked. About the same time, you were probably ready to ask the question *why,* and you asked this question about almost everything. "*Why* is the sky blue?" "*Why* can't I go out to play?" "*Why* do I have to eat that?"

Scientists, too, ask the questions *what, how,* and *why*. An astronomer asks, *what* is a star, *how* does a star produce light, and *why* is a star where it is. A chemist asks *what* a compound is, *how* it is put together, and *why* it combines with some compounds and not others. A physicist asks about forces—*how* they hold things in place and *why* they operate in one situation and not in another. A mathematician asks questions, too, and expresses the answers in numbers and symbols.

Biology, the subject of this textbook, asks the question "What is life?" This question has probably been in the minds of some humans since humans first walked on this planet. In case you're wondering, it is still unanswered. The formal framing of the question, "What is life?" for purposes of scientific study, is recent. The word *biology* was coined less than 200 years ago.

Biology is a science in its infancy. But, like a very bright child learning from others, biology has gathered information from many sciences in an attempt to understand what life is and how living things work. Astronomy and chemistry have shown biologists that life forms contain some of the same elements as Earth, the stars, and the atmosphere. Physics has taught biologists theories about light, and biologists have used these theories to understand processes such as how plants make food and how the human eye works. Mathematics has taught biologists the laws of probability, and biologists have used these laws to understand how genetic traits are passed from one generation to another. All the sciences have contributed and continue to contribute pieces of the answer to the question of what life is.

The second question, *how,* is concerned with the processes of science. "How do things work?" How do muscles work, how do cells use the energy from food for their life activities, how does a virus destroy the immune system of a human being, and how could life—as we know it—arise on this planet? Biologists make these inquiries and seek information, answers, and solutions through processes that involve both reason and creativity, logic and insight—a scientific method.

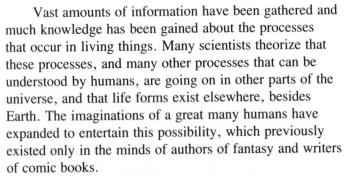

Vast amounts of information have been gathered and much knowledge has been gained about the processes that occur in living things. Many scientists theorize that these processes, and many other processes that can be understood by humans, are going on in other parts of the universe, and that life forms exist elsewhere, besides Earth. The imaginations of a great many humans have expanded to entertain this possibility, which previously existed only in the minds of authors of fantasy and writers of comic books.

Because biology draws information from so many other sciences, it stimulates the curious student and challenges the very brightest. This textbook presents information about and insight into the questions of what living things are and how they work. And, it presents some of the principles, theories, and laws of chemistry, physics, astronomy, and mathematics that have been used by biologists in their efforts to understand living things.

There are some questions, however, that biology, as a science, cannot answer but that the study of life has forced humans to confront. Many of these questions come from new possibilities generated by scientific knowledge. If humans know how something works, then, chances are, humans can make it themselves. If humans can know how a heart works, for example, humans can design one that works in the human body—and they have. If humans can understand the physics and chemistry of vision, they can, perhaps, design an eye that works in a human body. If humans can understand the structure of the AIDS virus, humans can then determine how to defeat the virus. If humans can know how the chemistry of the brain changes when humans experience fear, pleasure, and pain, then humans can find ways to produce pleasure or alleviate pain by altering the brain's chemistry.

The wedding of biology and the other sciences has allowed the development of a technology so advanced that surgery can be performed with lasers, the fetus can be monitored as it develops in the womb, and many human organs can be replaced with artificial ones. The question, then, is whether humans should do all the things that the study of biology has allowed them to do. And, if so, who will do them and who will make the decisions about how, when, and to whom they are done? As scientists uncover more and more information about the processes of life, more and more decisions will have to be made about whether or not to use this knowledge and how it is to be used.

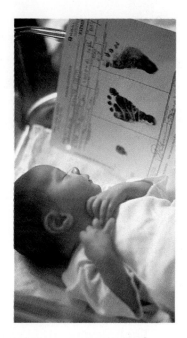

The study of life is a challenging subject. If you succeed in mastering it, you have much to gain. Few sciences have affected or contributed more than biology to the philosophical and physical aspects of the society in which you now live and in which you will live in the future. Biology, as a formal science, may still be too young to answer the question *why,* but it will tell you much about how you and other living things work and interact with the physical world. It is a challenge to you to understand the questions, the concepts, and the processes presented in this textbook. Accepting the challenge will help you make decisions that affect your life now and in the future. You may even find that you will be able to answer the question *why* yourself. The rest is up to you!

UNIT

1

THE STUDY OF LIVING THINGS

Unit Outline

Unit Focus

There is no doubt that the tiger in the photograph is a living thing. However, the question "What makes the tiger, or any other living thing, alive?" is a difficult and challenging one. This question has fascinated most humans at one time or another. Some humans have pursued the question as their life's work. Although many insights have been gained by asking questions about life forms, the question has never been answered.

■ *How do you recognize the tiger as a living thing?*

■ *What tools and processes are needed to find out more about what life is?*

All living things share certain characteristics of life.

Biology: The Study of Life

Outline

Wildlife near a water hole in Kenya, Africa

Focus

Many dictionaries define **biology** as "the study of life." However, the word *life* is difficult to define. Therefore, the definition of biology is often modified as "the study of living things." This study includes examining the characteristics that all the diverse forms of life share.

■ *What characteristics do the living things in this photograph of an African plain show?*

■ *Name the characteristics that these living things share with humans.*

Characteristics of Living Things

The scientific term for a complete, individual living thing is **organism.** Butterflies, trees, bacteria, sponges, and elephants are all organisms. The characteristics shared by these and other organisms define what it means to say that something is alive.

1.1 Organisms Are Made of Cells

One of the most important discoveries biologists have made is that all organisms are made up of the same basic kind of building blocks. These building blocks are called **cells.** Most cells are so small that they are invisible to the unaided eye. You can see some cells, however, if they are magnified. If you gently scrape the moist skin inside your mouth with a toothpick and look at the scraping through a microscope, you can see one type of skin cell. If you look at a drop of your blood under the microscope, you will see red blood cells suspended in the fluid.

Because all organisms are made of cells, cells are called the *structural* units of living things. Cells are not just structural units, however. They are also the *functional* units of organisms. In other words, cells are the smallest units that can carry on the activities of life. All the things that an organism can do are made possible by what its cells can do.

Some organisms, called **unicellular** (yoo nuh SEHL yoo luhr) **organisms,** are single cells. You will study many organisms of this type later in this book. Among those you may already be familiar with are bacteria. Other living things, called **multicellular** (muhl tih SEHL yoo luhr) **organisms,** are made up

Section Objectives
- *List* eight characteristics shared by organisms.
- *Explain* the relationship between organization and energy.
- *Distinguish* between long-term and short-term adaptation.
- *Define* homeostasis and give an example.

Identifying characteristics of living things is the subject of the Investigation on page 23.

Figure 1–1. The cells of a plant (left), a rat (center), and a human being (right) appear to be quite different. In fact, they have many similarities, and each plays an important role in the structure and function of the organism.

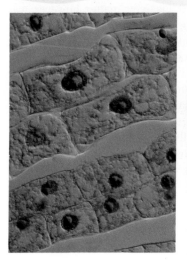 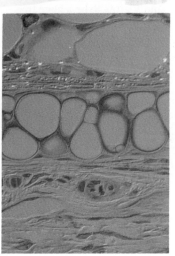 

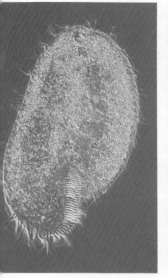 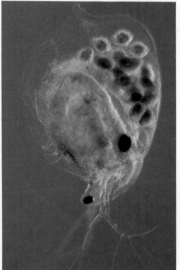 

Figure 1–2. A unicellular *Oxytricha* (left), a simple, multicellular water flea (center), and a complex animal like a whale (right) are all composed of cells. The more complex an organism, the more diverse are the structures and functions of its cells.

of more than one cell. Some multicellular organisms have only a few cells. Others, such as whales or humans, consist of trillions of cells. Most cells in more complex organisms are highly specialized. That is, each of the many types of cells has its own special functions to perform.

Organisms Are Highly Organized   *Every living cell is a highly complex structural and chemical system.* It consists of thousands of substances, many of which have never been made in the laboratory. Organisms make these substances from simpler substances in their surroundings.

Consider a green plant. Starting from a tiny seed, it may eventually grow to be a huge tree. All this living matter, however, was produced from simple, nonliving materials: carbon dioxide from the air, plus water and a few minerals from the soil. In fact, all organisms consist of the same chemical raw materials as nonliving things. The only difference lies in the way in which these raw materials are organized into more complex substances.

Inside a living cell are many complex structures that the cell uses to stay alive. These structures perform many functions. For example, they enable the cell to manufacture substances it needs. Each cell is, in fact, a complete chemical factory. Unlike other factories, however, a cell constructs all its own tools and machinery—even its own building. A cell conducts all its own repairs and even generates its own power. In short, a cell controls and regulates all its own activities. Just as a factory can come in many sizes and shapes, cells also come in many shapes and sizes.

Reading Critically

Inferring Conclusions   What is the advantage of the cell's ability to manufacture the substances it needs?

Organisms Use Energy   No work of any kind can be done without some form of **energy.** No machine, for example, will run without some source of energy. To get an air conditioner to function, you must plug it in so that it can draw electrical energy. To get a car to run, you must supply gasoline, a source of chemical energy.

Like an automobile engine, you too run on chemical energy. That energy is provided by the food you eat. In the cells of your body, foods are chemically "burned" to release their energy. Cells use the energy to carry out their activities.

What is true of you is true of all organisms. *All living things use energy.* You need energy to walk, to talk, to breathe—even to think. A bird needs energy to fly, a spider needs energy to spin its web, and a plant needs energy to produce a flower.

Unlike an engine, organisms need energy constantly. An engine that runs out of gas will stop, but it will not be damaged. An organism, however, will die if it goes without food for very long, because it must do a great deal of work just to stay alive. Even while you sleep, your heart beats, you breathe, and your brain sends messages to all parts of your body. In fact, every cell of your body is working and using energy.

Every living thing is constantly building the substances that it needs. Generally, such chemical building requires energy. However, cells are also constantly breaking down other substances, and this process releases energy. This chemical

---

THINKING ABOUT BIOLOGY: It Takes Energy to Stay Organized

You may be wondering why organisms must use energy even when they don't seem to be doing anything in particular. Energy is needed to maintain the organization that exists within all living things. A basic law of physics states that any organized system that undergoes change requires energy to maintain itself.

As an illustration of this concept, think about a library. A library is tightly organized, yet undergoes constant change. It is organized because all the books are located in specific places according to their subjects. It is changing because users borrow and return books. An active library changes from day to day.

If librarians did not expend energy to catalog, shelve, and reshelve the books, the library would quickly become so disorganized that it could not be used.

The same is true for the cells of all living things. They are organized and perform a variety of chemical reactions that require energy. If energy is not constantly supplied to a cell it becomes disorganized and dies.

■ **Predicting Results**   What do organisms do when they take in more energy than they use?

building up and breaking down is **metabolism** (muh TAB uh lihz uhm). You can also look at metabolism as the sum of all the ways in which an organism gets and uses energy.

1.2 Organisms Grow and Develop

A glance at the family photo album reminds you that you were once much smaller than you are now. One of the main ways organisms use food is for growth. The growth of an organism is of a special kind, however. Some nonliving things, such as a fire or a salt crystal, can also grow. This type of growth is just "more of the same." You can grow a salt crystal as large as you want, but except for size it will never change as it grows.

An organism, on the other hand, grows by using materials from its surroundings to make more of itself. A baby does not grow by adding little bits of baby to itself. It grows by drinking milk. Substances in the milk are broken down chemically and made into other substances. Eventually, they become part of new cells of the growing baby.

In addition, the growth of organisms does not occur at a constant rate. Most growth takes place during certain parts of an organism's life. A baby generally doubles its weight during the first five months of life. You wouldn't want to double your weight in the next five months, and fortunately you won't. You are probably now nearly as tall as you are likely to get and also nearly as heavy, unless you overeat. Like you, most animals reach a full adult size and then stay about that size.

Most organisms do not become adults just by growing larger. An adult human being does not look like a giant baby. You can compare the growth of an organism with the growth of a university. When a university has to expand, it does not simply increase the size of all its buildings by 10 percent. The growth is planned and orderly. One year a new science building may be constructed. Later a new gym may be built, and the old one converted to a new cafeteria.

Organisms grow in much the same way. *Growth always takes place in a specific way, which is different for each kind of organism.* Different parts grow at different rates. Sometimes

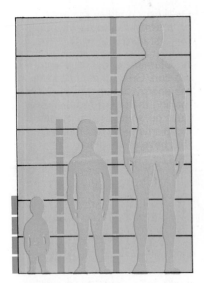

Figure 1–3. As humans grow, they also change. For example, the head of an infant represents about one-fourth of its total body length. The head of an adult, however, represents about one-seventh of total body length.

Infant   Six-year-old   Adult

Figure 1–4. Three months after beginning life as a single cell, a human fetus is more than 7.5 cm (3 in.) long and weighs nearly 28 g (1 oz.).

new structures appear, and old ones take on new functions. In short, organisms do not simply grow—they develop. The **development** of a living thing includes all the changes that it undergoes as it matures.

Some developmental changes are dramatic, as when a caterpillar becomes a butterfly or when a tadpole becomes a frog. You may think these cases are unusual, but actually they are not. Consider your own existence before birth. You began as a single cell. Now your body consists of trillions of cells, most of them highly specialized. A liver cell, for example, cannot do the work of a brain cell, and a nerve cell cannot do the work of a muscle cell. The taking on of special functions by different groups of cells is an important part of development.

Organisms Have a Life Span Development does not stop when an organism reaches its adult form. Even after growth has stopped, repair, rebuilding, and replacement go on continuously throughout an organism's life span. No organism, however, can keep renewing itself forever. In time the repair processes become less efficient. As a result, the organism deteriorates and eventually it dies.

Most organisms have a fixed length of life. The average length of life for an organism is its **life span.** In the late 1700s, the average human life span in most parts of the world was less than 40 years. Today it is about 70 years in the developed nations. The life spans of other organisms vary greatly. Certain

Figure 1–5. Among the most spectacular of all developmental changes are those that transform this caterpillar into a spicebush swallowtail butterfly.

122	
72	
60	
23	
21	
15	
13.5	
11	
3	

Figure 1–6. The life spans of organisms vary. Some turtles live to be 122 years old, whereas most snakes live only about 12 years. Humans average about 70 years in developed countries.

insects live only for a single day as adults. At the opposite extreme, one bristlecone pine tree in California is about 4,600 years old. For some other examples of life spans of organisms, see Figure 1–6.

Organisms Reproduce Themselves   *One of the most vital activities of living things is the production of offspring.* The process of producing offspring, or new individuals, is called **reproduction.** Since no organism lives forever, reproduction is necessary for the continued existence of a **species,** or kind of living thing.

New individuals are always like their parents in *kind* but different in *detail*. A baby may or may not inherit its father's brown hair or its mother's blue eyes. Nevertheless, it is sure to have a human nose, not a trunk like an elephant. It will have two eyes, not eight like some spiders.

1.3 Organisms Respond to Stimuli

All organisms respond to conditions in their surroundings. Any condition to which an organism can react is called a **stimulus.** What the organism does as a result of the stimulus is a **response.** *The ability to respond to stimuli is typical of all living organisms*. Biologists call this property **irritability.**

Human beings and other higher organisms detect stimuli through senses that include sight, hearing, and smell. What organisms detect affects their behavior. A baby who hears a loud noise may respond by crying. A dog that smells food may sit up, wag its tail, drool, or perhaps run to the place where it expects to be fed. Far simpler organisms also respond to stimuli. Tiny,

stimulus (plural, *stimuli*)

single-celled creatures can "taste" chemicals in the water in which they live. They will swim toward particles of food and away from harmful substances.

1.4 Organisms Adjust to Their Environments

To survive, an organism must adjust to changes in its environment. The **environment** includes everything in an organism's surroundings that affects it in any way. The environment of a trout, for example, includes the temperature of the water, the amount of dissolved oxygen, and the composition of the bottom (sand, mud, or rock). The environment also includes the organisms that the trout might eat, such as insects or worms, as well as any animals that might eat the trout, such as birds or otters.

Any environment can support only a limited number of each type of organism. Hundreds of birch seedlings may sprout in a meadow, but not all will live long enough to become trees. Some may be destroyed by hungry insects or other animals. Harsh weather may kill others. The remaining seedlings will have to compete with one another for moisture, sunlight, and space to grow. The survivors will be the individuals best adjusted to their environment.

Environmental conditions change, however. Some changes are sudden and dramatic: a flood, a drought, a forest fire, a volcanic eruption. Other, much slower changes can be even more important in the long run. Several times, great sheets of ice have covered large parts of Europe and North America. Mountains have been pushed up by tremendous forces within the earth and then worn down by erosion over millions of years. To survive, organisms must adjust, or *adapt,* to such changes. Any change in an organism that makes it better suited to its environment is called an **adaptation.**

Individual organisms can adapt to many short-term changes in their environments. They can cope with changes in the weather or with the passage of the seasons. As winter comes on, for example, the brown fur of an arctic hare is replaced by white fur. The white coat makes it difficult for enemies to spot the hare in a snow-covered landscape. Any response like this one that increases an individual's chances of surviving is called an *adaptive response.*

Groups of organisms can also adapt to long-term changes. This process occurs over many generations and does not depend on changes by individual organisms during their lifetimes. It depends entirely on the **traits,** or characteristics, received by new individuals from their parents. These traits are **inherited,** or passed from generation to generation.

Figure 1–7. The short-tailed weasel has an adaptive response to winter: Its coat changes color from brown to white.

You can jump from a sauna at 70°C (160°F) into a cold lake at 15°C (60°F). Yet your body temperature will change by only a degree or so from its normal 37°C (98.6°F). You can visit La Paz, Bolivia (altitude 3,630 m, or 11,900 ft.), where the air has 30 percent less oxygen than at sea level. You may feel unusually tired for a few days, but your cells will still get enough oxygen to function normally.

These examples illustrate an important property of living things. Although their surroundings may change greatly, organisms maintain a nearly constant internal environment. It is vital that they do so,

because the cells of a multicellular organism are extremely delicate. Cells cannot tolerate much change in temperature. The concentration of chemicals in the surrounding fluid also cannot change much. If it does, the cells will shrivel up like raisins, or swell and burst.

The environment within a complex organism can be compared to the controlled environment in a greenhouse. Outside, the weather changes and the seasons come and go. Inside the greenhouse, the temperature and humidity are always maintained at the ideal level for the plants

Some **variation,** or set of differences, generally exists among individuals in a group of organisms. In a pack of wolves, for example, one animal may have longer legs, another a warmer coat, and another keener hearing. Many such differences are inherited.

If the environment changes, certain traits may take on special importance. They may give the individual that has them an edge in competition with others of its kind. If the climate is growing colder, for example, wolves with exceptionally thick coats will be most likely to survive. Such animals may at first be few in number. In each generation, however, a high proportion of the thin-coated animals will die before they have a chance to reproduce. Many of the thick-coated individuals will survive and pass this trait on to their offspring. The number of thin-coated individuals will be very few. Thus the valuable trait will become more common in each new generation. Eventually it growing there. The plants have just the right kind of soil, the right amount of water, light, and fertilizer. Maintaining such a change-less environment takes work. Similarly, your body works hard to keep its internal environment constant.

Adjusting to the external environment is only part of the problem. An organism must also adjust its life functions to fit its activities at a given moment. If you are running a race, for instance, your muscles are working at top capacity. They need extra fuel and oxygen. They are also producing wastes at a high rate. As a result, your heart and lungs must work harder than usual. Since fuel is being used up so rapidly, much heat is also being released. Your body must get rid of this heat, or your cells will "roast" them-selves. One method of temperature control is sweating. The evaporation of moisture from your skin helps cool the body.

To keep its internal environment stable, an organism must maintain a delicate balance between its life functions and its activities and environment. This self-adjusting balance of life functions, environ-ment, and activities is known as **homeostasis** (hoh mee oh STAY sihs.)

You may already have recognized an important link between homeostasis and adaptation. Organisms constantly monitor both their internal and external environments. Any change in the external environ-ment that threatens the organism calls for a response. The organism adapts and so fits better into its changing environ-ment. A change in the internal environment also calls forth a response. Through homeostasis, the organism changes its life functions and so restores the original conditions.

■ **Inferring Relationships** How do heavy coats aid in the maintenance of homeo-stasis during winter?

■ **Synthesizing Information** Why could a high fever be dangerous?

will be the rule rather than the exception. Over a long period, the group of organisms will have adapted to the new, colder conditions.

Section Review

1. **Relating Ideas**   List eight characteristics that are shared by all organisms.
2. **Analyzing Relationships**   Explain how a cell is both the structural and functional unit of organisms.
3. **Relating Ideas**   Relate metabolism to energy.
4. **Inferring Relationships**   Why is sweating after strenuous exercise an example of homeostasis?
5. **Predicting Outcomes**   What long-term changes might occur in a group of insects if spraying them with insecticide killed only 90 percent of them?

⟨ **Thinking Critically** ⟩

Section Objectives

- *Name* six elements commonly found in living things.
- *Describe* levels of organization found in living things.
- *Distinguish* between tissues, organs, and systems.
- *Name* examples of communities, ecosystems, and biomes.

Biofact

Q: *How many kinds of molecules are present in the human body?*

A: No one knows exactly, but 10,000 to 15,000 is probably a good estimate.

Organization of Living Things

Biology is the study of living things, but biologists do not limit their study to complete, individual organisms. To understand how a car functions, you must study its parts, such as the carburetor, the engine, and the transmission. You may even have to study the parts of the parts. Similarly, to understand organisms, biologists study the workings of organisms, of their parts, and of the parts of their parts.

1.5 Atoms and Molecules

The building blocks of all matter—living and nonliving alike—are called **atoms.** Atoms themselves are composed of still smaller parts. In organisms, however, atoms are never broken down. Instead, they are only rearranged into new combinations.

Ninety-two kinds of atoms are found naturally on the earth. They correspond to the ninety-two natural **elements,** substances that cannot be broken down chemically into simpler substances. Six elements are especially important to life: carbon, hydrogen, oxygen, nitrogen, sulfur, and phosphorus. About twenty others play lesser roles.

How can complex living cells be made up of only about two dozen kinds of atoms? To help answer this question, ask yourself another one: How is it possible that so many different pieces of music—from the classics to the latest pop songs—could have been composed using the same few dozen notes? In each case, a few simple parts can be put together in many different patterns.

Atoms join together and form larger structures called **molecules.** A molecule of water, for instance, contains two hydrogen atoms and one oxygen atom. In living things, many molecules are made up of millions of atoms.

1.6 Organelles and Cells

Organelles are structures that perform specific functions within living cells. Each organelle is made up of many large molecules. Some organelles serve as the cell's waste disposal units. They store and break down harmful substances produced by the cell. Other organelles serve as the cell's power plants, providing energy for the cell. Still others are chemical factories that make many of the molecules of life.

Organelles can perform some but not all life functions. They can exist only as part of a living cell. Thus the cell is truly the "frontier of life." Cells exhibit all the properties of life discussed earlier in this chapter. Indeed, some cells are complete organisms.

1.7 Tissues, Organs, and Systems

In most multicellular organisms, cells are organized into tissues. A **tissue** is a group of similar cells that perform a common function. Your body contains many kinds of tissues. Nervous tissue consists of cells specialized for carrying messages. Muscle tissue is made up of cells that contract. This specialization of cells makes possible much *division of labor*. Like people with different jobs, the cells of the body depend on one another.

Tissues are organized into organs. An **organ** is a structure composed of a number of tissues that work together to perform a specific task. The eye, for example, is an organ. Muscle tissue controls its movement and focus. Nervous tissue responds to light and sends messages to the brain. Other types of tissue protect and nourish the eyeball. All these tissues are necessary if the eye is to perform its special function of seeing.

In a complex multicellular organism, many tasks are too great for a single organ. They require a **system**—a group of organs that cooperate in a series of related functions. For example, the digestive system carries out the complex job of digesting food. Human beings eat a wide variety of foods. These foods require many kinds of special processing before they can be used by the body. Each organ of the digestive system has its own part to play in the process of digestion. They all must function together to perform the function.

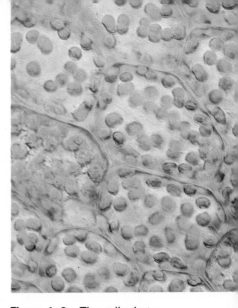

Figure 1–8. The cells that make up a leaf, shown here magnified 400 times, are themselves made up of many parts. Each organelle helps the cell function.

To compare the systems of different living things, see pages 890–905.

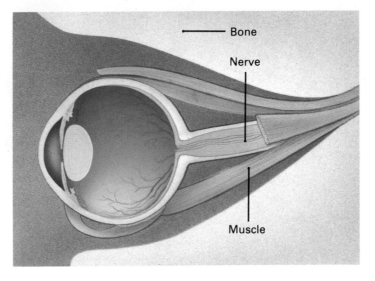

Bone

Nerve

Muscle

Figure 1–9. The eye is an organ of the nervous system. It is made of many kinds of tissues, such as muscle and nerve tissue. Each of these tissues, in turn, consists of similar kinds of cells.

1.8 Organisms

Most multicellular organisms have several systems. Keep in mind, though, that many organisms are unicellular. They depend on organelles to perform specialized functions that tissues, organs, and systems perform in multicellular organisms.

Some organisms, called **colonial organisms,** live in groups that resemble multicellular organisms. In reality, however, each cell is a separate organism, independent from all the other cells in the organism. Like the residents of an apartment house, they are merely neighbors who get certain advantages from living near one another.

Biologists are also interested in how living things interact with one another and with their environments. Information about the interaction of organisms may lead to the discovery of previously unknown relationships. For this reason, biologists study organisms in a series of larger and larger groups.

Populations A **population** is a group of organisms of the same species living in a particular place at a particular time. The place may be large or small, and so may the size of the population. A population may consist of a billion bacterial cells in a tiny puddle of water. In contrast, a few dozen elephants in a huge African game preserve may also be a population.

Biologists often limit the meaning of the term *population* somewhat. They define a population as a group of organisms that **interbreed**—that is, that mate within the population.

Reading Critically

Evaluating Ideas What are the benefits of living as a colonial organism?

Figure 1–10. Similar organisms living in the same area and sharing the same habitat make up a population. Some populations, such as this penguin colony in Antarctica, are composed of hundreds or thousands of individuals.

Blood—The Liquid Tissue

If asked to identify the tissues in their bodies, most people might name the most abundant tissue, muscle. With a little thought, nervous tissue might be named. Usually, only those who have studied anatomy could name epithelial and connective tissues.

What about a large tissue that is not a solid, but a liquid? Blood is considered a type of connective tissue, and makes up 7 to 8 percent of the weight of the human body. Because of its physical form, however, it is often overlooked as a tissue.

Blood is a complex mixture of specialized cells that are suspended in a solution that is mostly water. It has two major components: the fluid and cellular fractions. The fluid portion is called the *plasma*. Plasma is mostly water containing proteins and dissolved inorganic salts.

Red blood cells, or *erythrocytes*, make up the largest part of the cellular portion of blood. The remainder contains several types of white blood cells and platelets.

Blood performs many critical functions in the body. As part of the circulatory system, its main task is to carry oxygen and nutrients to all the cells of the body and remove the waste products. Blood also transports hormones to specific tissues or organs. Another function of the blood is to help the body fight against infection. Specialized blood cells recognize, attack, and destroy viruses, bacteria, and other foreign invaders.

The circulation of blood helps to distribute heat and, therefore, aids in keeping the environment inside the body constant. The body's organs operate most efficiently when kept within a

very narrow range of temperature and acid-base (pH) balance. The average human body temperature is 37°C (98.6°F). If the internal temperature rises four or five degrees Celsius, even for a few moments, permanent damage can result.

Communities Different populations that live in the same area and interact with one another make up a **community.** Like populations, communities can be large or small. The community of organisms in and around a pond, for example, would probably include populations of many kinds of plants, fish, insects, shellfish, and amphibians.

Populations in a community interact in many ways. The most obvious form of interaction is eating or being eaten. Each animal population depends on other plant or animal populations for its food. Populations may also depend on one another for shelter. Many animals live in hollow trees, and birds use twigs and grass to build their nests.

Ecosystems A community of living things and its physical environment make up an **ecosystem.** A biologist might study a forest, a prairie, or a coral reef as an ecosystem. Living things, naturally, are greatly affected by their environments. However, the physical environment is also affected by the organisms that inhabit it. Beavers dam streams, creating lakes and ponds. Lakes gradually fill up with decaying matter from dead plants and animals. Eventually the lakes become meadows. Dead organisms and animal wastes enrich the soil, making it more fertile for new plants.

Over long periods, organisms can produce great environmental changes. Evidence indicates that billions of years ago the earth's atmosphere had no oxygen. Today it is one-fifth oxygen. All the oxygen was released by green plants over millions of years. Only after this oxygen was released could animal life develop.

Biomes Ecosystems can be grouped together into still larger units called biomes. A **biome** is a large geographic area that has the same major forms of life. The nature of a biome is shaped

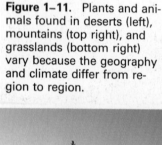

Figure 1–11. Plants and animals found in deserts (left), mountains (top right), and grasslands (bottom right) vary because the geography and climate differ from region to region.

largely by the geography of the region and its climate, especially the temperature and amount of rainfall. These features determine the types of plant life that can flourish in the region. The kinds of plants, in turn, largely determine what kinds of animals will be found in the area.

Biomes are generally identified by their climate, their vegetation, or both. For example, the most familiar of the major kinds of biomes include tropical rain forest, grassland, and desert.

The Biosphere All the ecosystems on Earth together make up the **biosphere.** *The biosphere includes all the life-supporting environments on this planet, together with all the organisms that inhabit them.*

The biosphere may seem vast to you, but from a spacecraft you would see that the realm of life is actually very limited. A few birds have been observed at altitudes of 8,000 m (26,000 ft.) above sea level. A few organisms inhabit depths of the oceans, about 10,000 m (33,000 ft.) below the surface. Seen from space, however, the entire region between these two extremes is only a tiny fraction of the 6,400–km (4,000–mi.) radius of the Earth. Proportionally, it is no thicker than the peel of an apple.

Most life is actually confined to a far narrower region. The vast majority of organisms live in the top 100 m (330 ft.) of the ocean, the bottom 100 m of the atmosphere, on the Earth's solid surface, or a few meters deep in the soil. This 200–m "skin" on the surface of the planet is home for about 5 million kinds of organisms. Whether the Earth's biosphere is the only home for living things in the universe is one of today's great unanswered questions.

Figure 1–12. The Earth's biosphere is home for about 5 million kinds of organisms.

Section Review

1. **Organizing Ideas** Which six elements are the most important to living things?
2. **Analyzing Ideas** What is meant by specialization of cells?
3. **Comparing Ideas** How is a tissue different from an organ and how is an organ different from a system?
4. **Comparing Ideas** How does an ecosystem differ from a community?
5. **Comprehending Ideas** What factors affect the characteristics of a biome?
6. **Drawing Conclusions** What advantages are there to having specialized cells and tissues?

> **Thinking Critically**

The Science of Biology

Section Objectives

- *List* some reasons why people study biology.
- *Explain* how the study of biology helps promote human welfare.
- *Name* some major fields of modern biology and describe the subject matter of each.

Now that you have some basic knowledge about living things, you are ready to consider the study of living things—biology. What is the value of biology? Why do people study biology at all?

1.9 Biology and Human Welfare

People study biology for many reasons. Some people choose to study biology chiefly as a way of helping humans to live longer and healthier lives. Biological research has laid the foundations of modern medicine. It has brought about the conquest of many diseases. It is basic to our knowledge of nutrition. It has helped us to raise more and better food. In these and many other ways, biology has made a tremendous contribution to human well-being.

1.10 The Diversity of Life

Some people study biology simply for the pleasure of learning about the world of living things. You may think that by now biologists must know everything there is to know about living things. In fact, millions of species of organisms have not even been named yet, let alone studied. Those that are well known show us that life is far from predictable. Nothing that you can read in works of fantasy or science fiction is as strange as some of the creatures that actually live on this planet. Consider the following examples:

- A plant, a variety of bamboo, flowers only once every 120 years or so. All plants of this species flower at exactly the same time, whether they are growing in Japan, Great Britain, or the United States.
- A certain type of albatross may fly over ocean waters for three years, apparently without alighting on land. These birds fly nearly a million miles before they settle down to raise a family.
- A frog that must remain moist at all times lives in the bone-dry deserts of Australia. On the rare occasions when it rains, this frog soaks up water through its skin like a sponge. It then buries its swollen body in the earth and seals itself up in a waterproof, plasticlike material of its own making. It can live for two years or more until the rains come again.

Figure 1–13. This Australian frog encases itself in a water-proof membrane that prevents water-loss during dry weather.

Some people study biology because they are curious about themselves. They wish to know more about the human body and the human brain. How do these amazing "machines" work? What keeps the heart continuously beating? How can people remember thousands of names and faces? Why do people sleep? Are there really certain foods you can eat to live longer? Biology is the science that seeks answers to questions such as these as well as many other questions.

Reading Critically

Evaluating Ideas Why would it be useful to know why people sleep?

1.11 The Web of Life

Another reason for studying biology is especially important for everyone today. Biology helps us understand our place in the living world. *All organisms in the biosphere are interrelated and affect one another in many ways.* The phrase "the web of life" expresses this idea well. This web cannot be torn without harming the human species. People too are part of the biosphere and depend for their day-to-day survival on countless other living things.

Living things supply all food. They provide important raw materials, such as wood, cotton, and wool. Plants replenish the life-giving oxygen in the air, and they also help prevent erosion and control floods. Many medicines and drugs were first obtained from living things, and hundreds of others almost certainly remain to be discovered. Human fate is tied up with the fate of all these organisms.

1.12 Biology and the Future

An extremely important reason for studying biology is to help people understand, and perhaps play a constructive role in, the future. In the near future, new medical techniques may wipe out many diseases, while disease caused by polluted environments may increase sharply. Scientists may soon be able to create entirely new organisms in the laboratory, but many thousands of existing species are faced with extinction. New agricultural technologies may make it possible to raise more food, but the number of people to be fed is rising rapidly. People may establish settlements in space or on other planets, but the environment on the Earth is seriously threatened by pollution and the wasteful use of natural resources.

As citizens of this world of the future, you will have to understand both its promises and its problems. A knowledge of biology is essential to this understanding. Making responsible decisions will be easier for you when those decisions are based on a thorough understanding of biology.

Figure 1–14. Destruction of natural habitats, like this rain forest in New Guinea, threatens the existence of many kinds of plants and animals. Such damage to the environment could ultimately threaten human existence.

1.13 Some Fields of Modern Biology

Biology is a large, complex, and rapidly growing science. A couple of centuries ago, there were only two main areas of biology: **zoology,** the study of animals; and **botany,** the study of plants. Today, new specialties are constantly emerging. Table 1–1 lists some of the major divisions of biology.

Table 1–1: Some Major Fields of Biology

Anatomy	The study of the external and internal structure of organisms
Biochemistry	The study of the chemical makeup and processes of organisms
Botany	The study of plants
Cell biology	The study of the structure and activities of living cells
Ecology	The study of how organisms interact with one another and with their environments
Evolutionary biology	The study of how organisms have changed through time
Genetics	The study of heredity, or how traits are transmitted from generation to generation
Microbiology	The study of organisms too small to be seen without a microscope
Physiology	The study of how organisms carry on their life processes and how various parts of the organisms perform their special functions
Zoology	The study of animals

The various fields of modern biology are closely interrelated. For example, a thorough knowledge of biochemistry is important for anyone who is studying cell biology, genetics, or physiology.

Section Review

1. **Comprehending Ideas** What are some reasons why people decide to study biology?
2. **Interpreting Ideas** How does the study of biology help promote human welfare?
3. **Identifying Relationships** Why is it important to understand the role that human beings have in the web of life?
4. **Summarizing Ideas** What were originally the two main areas into which biology was divided?
5. **Inferring Relationships** Why is it necessary for an ecologist to know physiology?

> **Thinking Critically**

INVESTIGATION 1:
What Characteristics Can Be Observed in Living Things?

Objectives
- To *observe* living things
- To *identify* characteristics of life

Materials
lens paper, microscope slide, coverslip, compound light microscope, medicine dropper, pond water, toothpick, petroleum jelly

Prelab Preparation
1. List the characteristics of living things. Identify those characteristics that might be easily observed in microscopic organisms. Explain why some characteristics are difficult to observe.
2. Read the information about the use and care of a compound light microscope on pages 908–909. How should the microscope be carried? Explain your answer. What power of objective must be used to make your first observations? State the reasons why this objective must be used first. Name the adjustment that should never be used when you are focusing with the high power objective. Explain your answer.
3. Use only lens paper to clean the microscope mirror and lenses.

Inquiry: Exploration
4. Using a toothpick, make a thin ring of petroleum jelly about the size of a dime on the glass slide.
5. Place a drop of pond water inside the ring.

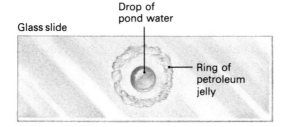

Glass slide
Drop of pond water
Ring of petroleum jelly

6. Carefully place the coverslip on top of the pond water and petroleum jelly. *What is the function of the petroleum jelly?*
7. Use low power to observe the pond water. Move the slide, as necessary, to inspect the entire drop.
8. Make a drawing of each thing you observe that appears to be alive. List the characteristics of life shown by each thing that you draw.
9. Compare your work with that of three other students. *What purpose does a comparison of results serve in a scientific investigation?*
10. Pool the information obtained by the members of your group and prepare a composite list of the characteristics of life that were seen in pond organisms.

Analysis
1. **Analyzing Information** What characteristics of life can be used to identify the things that are seen with the compound light microscope?
2. **Analyzing Conclusions** List the characteristics of life that were not evident in the pond water organisms and explain why these characteristics cannot be seen when using a compound light microscope.
3. **Inferring Conclusions** Why is movement an indication that an organism has certain other characteristics of life?
4. **Inferring Conclusions** You find a purple and green mass in a field. How can you determine whether or not it is a living thing?

Chapter 1 Review

Summary

The millions of different organisms on Earth share certain characteristics. All are composed of complex structural and chemical units called cells. Organisms begin life as a single cell, develop into adults, and eventually, die. They all use energy to perform functions that include reproducing, responding to stimuli, and maintaining a constant internal environment. Organisms that survive and reproduce are generally well suited to their environments.

To understand organisms, biologists study parts of organisms, including organelles, cells, tissues, organs, and systems. They also study organisms in larger and larger groups to learn how organisms relate to one another.

Dozens of fields of biology have emerged from botany and zoology, the original areas of biological study. Today, specialists find new species, improve human life, and may also hold the key to solving future problems.

BioTerms

adaptation (11)	environment (11)	reproduction (10)	tissue (15)
atom (14)	homeostasis (13)		trait (11)
biology (4)	inherited (11)	response (10)	unicellular
biome (18)	interbreed (16)	species (10)	organism (5)
biosphere (19)	irritability (10)	stimulus (10)	variation (12)
botany (22)	life span (9)	system (15)	zoology (22)
cell (5)	metabolism (8)		
colonial	molecule (14)		
organism (16)	multicellular		
community (17)	organism (5)		
development (9)	organ (15)		
ecosystem (18)	organelle (14)		
element (14)	organism (5)		
energy (7)	population (16)		

For each pair of terms, explain the differences in their meanings.

1. botany, zoology
2. organ, organelle
3. population, community
4. adaptation, response

BioQuiz   (Write all answers on a separate sheet of paper.)

Completion

1. A group of organs that share a series of related functions is a _____ .
2. No organism lives forever, so _____ is necessary for the species to continue.
3. To be classified as living, an organism must grow and _____ .
4. Tissue specialized for contraction is called _____ .
5. All living things require _____ in order to function.

Multiple Choice

6. When a cow swishes its tail to brush away insects, it is displaying   a) a stimulus.   b) an adaptation.   c) variation.   d) irritability.
7. Perspiring and shivering are ways to maintain   a) metabolism.   b) homeostasis.   c) irritability.   d) reproduction.
8. The _____ includes all life-supporting environments on Earth and the organisms that live in them.   a) community

b) biome   c) biosphere   d) ecosystem
9. If you wanted to know why puppies do not always resemble their mother, you may want to consult a book on a) zoology.   b) genetics.   c) anatomy.   d) cell biology.
10. All molecules must contain   a) carbon.   b) elements.   c) atoms.   d) hydrogen.
11. A geographic area that has the same major forms of life is   a) a community.   b) a biome.   c) a population.   d) an ecosystem.
12. Green plants are responsible for the increase in _____ in the environment over time.   a) species   b) sulfur   c) oxygen   d) ecosystems
13. Only multicellular organisms contain   a) organs.   b) cells.   c) energy.   d) traits.

14. A condition to which an organism can react is called   a) a trait.   b) an adaptation.   c) an environment.   d) a stimulus.
15. A _____ is a group of organisms of the same species living in a particular place at a particular time.   a) community   b) population   c) colony   d) ecosystem

Writing Critically

16. Distinguish growth from development.
17. What is the difference between long-term and short-term adaptation?
18. What makes colonial organisms unique?
19. Why are plants essential to all organisms?
20. In what ways may environmental temperature be considered a stimulus?

Application/Critical Thinking

1. **Interpreting Ideas** When a skunk encounters a threatening organism, it sprays out a stream of foul-smelling liquid. In what way is the skunk's response to danger an adaptive response?
2. **Evaluating Experiments** During the 1970s, the *Viking* craft analyzed samples of soil from Mars. How could the scientists determine whether there was any life on Mars base on this examination of soil?
3. **Analyzing Viewpoints** How could the work of an evolutionary biologist help promote human welfare or help people to understand better the significance of their place in the web of life?
4. **Synthesizing Ideas** When you exercise on a hot day, you may both sweat and become thirsty. Explain both the sweating and the thirst in terms of the mechanism of homeostasis.

Cross-Discipline Connection

Biology and History   Work in groups to create a large mural that shows when major scientific discoveries were made. Use the information on pages 912–913 of the appendix as a guide.

Discovery Through Reading

Read "A Stupid Cell with All the Answers," *Discover* (November 1986):70. This article provides a lively look at yeast-cell research. How can this research help answer questions in cell biology?

"Not Your Average Terrarium," *Newsweek* (June 1, 1987):60, describes a Texas oil billionaire's project—a self-contained world called Biosphere II. How could this be a model for a base on Mars?

Science and Problem Solving

Outline

A scientist collecting alligator eggs in a swamp

Focus

The word **science** is used to describe both the body of knowledge that exists about the world and the processes that are used to arrive at that knowledge. Scientists expand this knowledge by a process of inquiry that seeks answers to questions about the world around them.

■ *With what process is the scientist in the photograph involved?*

■ *How might the activities of this scientist add to the body of knowledge that makes up science?*

A Scientific Method

The goal of science is to establish principles and thereby to acquire knowledge about the natural world. Scientists establish principles through a logical, organized method of study called a **scientific method.** Many different procedures, performed in varying order, are part of a scientific method, but all of them draw on the following series of logical steps.

2.1 Defining the Problem

Usually the first step in a scientific method is to identify the problem. For example, a scientist might be interested in acid rain. This pollutant forms when chemicals released by cars and factories mix with moisture in the air and fall as rain. Acidity of rain is represented on a scale of 0 to 7, where 0 represents high acidity and 7 represents no acidity.

A scientist might be curious about the effect of acid rain on wildlife. However, trying to investigate all the animals that make up "wildlife" would be impossible. Instead, the scientist would focus on a smaller group of organisms. For example, the researcher might pose the question, "Does acid rain affect the development of salamanders?"

2.2 Collecting Background Information

After stating the problem as a clear question, the scientist collects information about the problem. The scientist studying the effects of acid rain would need to understand normal salamander development and the characteristics of areas affected by acid rain. He or she would also want to know whether anyone had studied this question or a related one.

The scientist could find information in books and scientific journals. He or she could also use a computer to search the scientific information published each year. In this way, the scientist could avoid duplicating the work of others and benefit from recent discoveries.

2.3 Formulating a Hypothesis

Next the scientist may offer a **hypothesis** (hy PAHTH uh sihs), which is a proposed answer to the question. The hypothesis can be based on information available to the scientist. It can also be an educated guess. *The hypothesis is a statement that can be tested.* The scientist studying salamanders might state the

Figure 2–1. To understand the biology of a salamander, a scientist first collects information on its environment. The scientist studies the geographical area where the animal lives and its habitat within that area.

To learn how to design a controlled experiment, see page 35.

Figure 2–2. This scientist is using a computer to analyze the data he has collected through his experiments.

following hypothesis: "Salamanders that develop under acid rain conditions show a greater number of developmental abnormalities than salamanders that develop in unpolluted waters."

2.4 Testing the Hypothesis

A hypothesis can be tested in an **experiment.** In an experiment, one variable, or condition, is changed and the response of another variable is measured. The condition that is varied is called the **independent variable.** The condition that responds to changes in the independent variable is called the **dependent variable.** In the salamander experiment, the independent variable is the acidity of the water where salamanders develop and the dependent variable is the number of abnormal salamanders.

Scientists often perform experiments that require two identical groups of subjects. One group is exposed to changes in the independent variable and is called the **experimental group.** The other group is not exposed to changes in the independent variable and is called the **control group.** In the salamander example, the control group is raised in water with normal acidity. The experimental group is raised in water with the same acidity as polluted water. An experiment that uses both a control group and an experimental group is called a **controlled experiment.**

To be valid, an experiment must show that only the independent variable produces changes in the dependent variable. In addition, other scientists must be able to repeat the experiment.

2.5 Making and Recording Observations

In order for an experiment to be reproduced by other researchers, a scientist must keep careful records. These records must state how the experiment was planned, how it was carried out, what equipment was used, and how long it took. In addition, the scientist must record all the observations made during the experiment. Such information may include drawings, tables, graphs, diagrams, written observations, photographs—even sound recordings.

2.6 Drawing Conclusions

The answer to a scientific question is formulated by drawing a conclusion based on **data,** which are scientific facts collected during the experiment. Often, scientists form their conclusions with the help of **statistics** (stuh TIHS tihks), a mathematical method of evaluating numerical data. Statistical tests help determine whether important differences exist between data obtained from the experimental and control groups. In the salamander study, the scientist found that of 1,000 eggs raised in normal water, 6 were abnormal. Of 1,000 eggs raised in acidic water, 440 were abnormal. From this, the scientist could conclude that more salamanders develop abnormally in acidic water.

Before accepting conclusions, scientists retest their hypoth-eses several times. Later other scientists repeat the experiment until the hypothesis and the conclusion are supported or rejected. When a hypothesis explains how an event occurs, it becomes a **scientific principle** or **law.** When a hypothesis explains why events occur, it becomes a **theory.** At all times, however, theories and principles are subject to revision or replacement by a new theory or principle that provides a better or more complete explanation.

Scientists often use **operational definitions,** definitions that are limited to repeatable and observable phenomena. An opera-tional definition of a polluted lake could be: a lake containing an above average number of abnormal salamanders.

Section Review

1. **Summarizing Ideas**   Name six steps of a scientific method.
2. **Relating Ideas**   How do scientists use hypotheses?
3. **Recognizing Relationships**   Identify an applied science.
4. **Analyzing Experiments**   Why are two identical groups of subjects used in a controlled experiment?

Thinking Critically

Section Objectives

- *Compare* the theories of biogenesis and abiogenesis.
- *List* Redi's hypotheses and *explain* how he tested them.
- *Compare* Needham's and Spallanzani's experiments.
- *Explain* how Pasteur's experiment discredited abiogenesis.

Using a Scientific Method

Through the ages people have developed theories that explained a great many natural occurrences. The following investigation shows how one long-accepted scientific theory was discredited by scientific experimentation and how the theory that replaced it is being modified.

2.7 The Question of Spontaneous Generation

Today the theory of **biogenesis** (by oh JEHN uh sihs) is part of the definition of living things. *The theory of biogenesis states that all living things arise from other living things.*

The theory of biogenesis may seem obvious to you, but it was a very controversial issue until only about 100 years ago. As recently as the late 1800s, many people believed that some organisms form from nonliving materials. This concept is referred to as **spontaneous generation,** or **abiogenesis** (ay by oh JEHN uh sihs).

The idea of abiogenesis can be traced to the Greek philosopher Aristotle, whose major work was done during the 300s B.C. Aristotle stated that some fish were produced by mud at the bottom of rivers and oceans. Aristotle had previously seen the release and development of fish eggs. However, he could not explain how they arose from the mud where no fish had been for some time. Over the centuries, people explained other events through abiogenesis. In the 1600s, the Belgian physician Jean van Helmont stated that mice arose from a dirty shirt and a few grains of wheat placed in a dark corner. According to another belief, decaying meat produced tiny white wormlike creatures called maggots. This belief persisted because no one saw flies laying eggs on decaying food or the eggs hatching into maggots.

2.8 Testing the Theory of Abiogenesis

The theory of abiogenesis states that some organisms arise from nonliving materials. It took nearly 200 years of experimentation to replace abiogenesis with a more accurate theory.

The Debate Begins In 1668 an Italian physician named Francesco Redi challenged the belief that decaying meat will eventually turn into flies. He began with the following hypothesis: "Flies come from eggs laid by other flies on decaying flesh. The decaying flesh serves as a source of food for the developing flies."

Figure 2–3. This engraving, done in 1552, shows "barnacle geese" being hatched from trees. Scientists quickly dispelled this and other myths, but struggled for centuries with the question of spontaneous generation.

To test this hypothesis, Redi filled two sets of four jars with chunks of veal, snake, fish, or eel. He sealed one set of jars and left the other set open to the air. *The variable in Redi's experiment was whether or not the jars were sealed.* The sealed set of jars composed the experimental group. The control group consisted of jars left open to the air.

During the next few days, Redi observed flies entering and leaving the open jars. Several days later, the open jars contained rotting or decaying flesh and maggots. The covered jars also contained decaying flesh but no maggots. Based on these observations, Redi concluded that maggots do not arise through spontaneous generation but that they come from eggs laid by flies on rotting meat.

Other scientists of Redi's day did not agree. They believed that Redi had prevented spontaneous generation by keeping air out of the jars. They felt there was an "active principle" present in air needed for abiogenesis.

Redi answered his critics with a second experiment that began with the following hypothesis: "Flies arise from eggs, not rotten flesh, and the presence or absence of air is not a deciding factor." In this second experiment Redi did not seal the experimental group of jars. Instead, he covered them with fine mesh. The mesh allowed air to enter the jars but kept the flies out.

As before, Redi observed that flies entered the open jars and that maggots developed in the rotting flesh. He also observed that flies landed on the mesh covering the experimental jars but

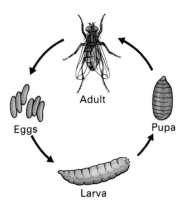

Figure 2–4. Redi showed that eggs and maggots, natural parts of a fly's life cycle (above), were not spontaneously generated in jars of meat. By covering jars with a screen (below), he excluded flies and proved that maggots did not arise from a mixture of air and meat.

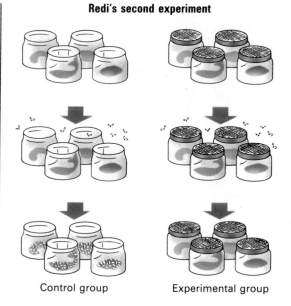

Redi's first experiment

Control group   Experimental group

Redi's second experiment

Control group   Experimental group

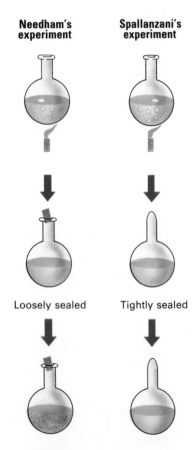

Needham's experiment　　**Spallanzani's experiment**

Loosely sealed　　Tightly sealed

Figure 2–5. Needham's experiment (above left) seemed to show that microorganisms could spontaneously generate after the broth in a corked flask had been boiled. Spallanzani's experiment (above right) showed that Needham had not sealed his flasks correctly. Spallanzani sealed his flasks completely, and no organisms grew in the broth.

Reading Critically

Comparing Ideas What was the important difference between Needham's experiment and Spallanzani's experiments?

that no maggots appeared on the meat inside. Again, Redi concluded that maggots did not arise by spontaneous generation but hatched from eggs laid by flies.

Most scientists of the time could not deny Redi's experimental data, yet some clung to the principle of abiogenesis. These scientists pointed out that what was true for flies was not necessarily true for all organisms.

Needham and Spallanzani By the 1700s many scientists were using the microscope to study bacteria and other tiny organisms. In the mid-1700s, an English scientist named John Needham used microscopic observations to support the theory of abiogenesis.

To test the theory, Needham boiled meat broth for several minutes in loosely sealed flasks. Immediately after boiling, Needham examined the broth under a microscope and saw no living things. Then Needham used cork stoppers to loosely reseal the flasks and allowed them to cool.

After a few days, Needham reexamined the broth and found it was teeming with microorganisms. He concluded that the microorganisms had spontaneously generated from the nonliving materials of the broth.

About 25 years later, an Italian priest and biologist named Lazzaro Spallanzani challenged Needham's work. Spallanzani felt that Needham's experiment was flawed in two ways. First, Spallanzani believed that Needham had not boiled the broth long enough to kill all the life it contained. Thus new organisms could have been produced by organisms that survived the boiling. Secondly, Spallanzani thought that fresh microorganisms could have entered the flasks through the loose seals and reproduced once inside.

Spallanzani designed an experiment to disprove abiogenesis for microorganisms. He boiled seeds in water for one hour to produce a broth. Then he sealed the flasks by melting their glass necks closed. Finally, he placed the flasks in boiling water for several hours and then left them to rest.

Several days later Spallanzani broke the necks of the flasks and examined the broth under a microscope. He found no signs of life. Spallanzani concluded that microorganisms do not arise spontaneously. The supporters of abiogenesis were quick to disagree. They argued that the long period of boiling had destroyed the ''active principle'' in the broth.

In response to the critics, Spallanzani tested a new hypothesis: ''If boiling destroys some active principle, longer boiling will destroy more active principle.'' In his experiment, Spallanzani filled flasks with broth and covered them with loose seals. Each flask was boiled for a different period of time, from 30 minutes to two hours. Then Spallanzani allowed the sealed flasks to sit undisturbed.

After eight days Spallanzani examined the broth in the flasks with a microscope and found living organisms in each one. He also discovered that the broth boiled the longest had the most organisms. Spallanzani concluded that boiling did not destroy the ''active principle'' in broth. He also incorrectly concluded that longer boiling actually made the broth more supportive for microorganisms.

Pasteur Settles the Question

The abiogenesis debate continued until 1864 when Louis Pasteur, a French chemist, began his investigations. As a result of earlier studies, Pasteur hypothesized that microorganisms are carried on dust particles in the air.

Pasteur developed a two-part experiment to test this hypothesis. First, he sealed flasks filled with broth and boiled them long enough to kill all the microorganisms present. Then he took the flasks to places with varying amounts of dust, such as mountain meadows and country roads. At each place Pasteur exposed a different flask to the air.

Several days later Pasteur examined each flask and found microorganisms in each one. The flasks that were exposed to dustier areas contained the most microorganisms. Pasteur concluded that microorganisms were carried in the air in differing amounts depending on the area.

Next Pasteur retested his hypothesis in the laboratory. First he filled a series of flasks with broth, melted the neck of each one, and bent it in an S-shaped curve. In this way, air could move in and out of the flasks, but dust was caught in the curves. Then Pasteur boiled the flasks, forcing the air out and killing microorganisms in the broth.

As the broth cooled, air flowed into the flasks but the curves in the neck prevented dust from reaching the broth. After several days, Pasteur saw no microorganisms in the flasks, although the broth in each one was exposed to the air. Then Pasteur tipped a flask, allowing some broth to come into contact with dust trapped in the S-shaped curve. In a few days, Pasteur saw microorganisms in the broth.

Pasteur's experiment showed that although air was allowed to enter the flasks, it produced no life. At the same time, Pasteur proved that boiling broth did not affect its ability to support life. *Instead, Pasteur showed that the microorganisms in the flasks came from microorganisms carried on dust particles, not from the air itself.*

Pasteur's experiment

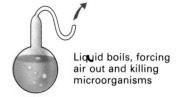

Liquid boils, forcing air out and killing microorganisms

Liquid cools, drawing air and dust in and trapping dust

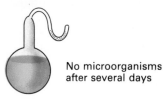

No microorganisms after several days

One flask tipped, mixing dust with liquid

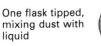

Liquid contaminated

Figure 2–6. To silence critics who claimed that air was necessary for spontaneous generation, Pasteur heated broth in an open, swannecked flask. No microorganisms grew in the broth. By tilting the flask, Pasteur then proved that microorganisms in the neck of the flask, and in the air, could contaminate the broth.

Fake Science

Many statements that are presented as scientific fact are really pseudoscientific. They are hypotheses that have never been tested by scientists using a scientific method.

Pseudoscientific assertions are based neither on scientific investigation nor on valid references. Rather, evidence is often unverifiable, such as eyewitness testimony and hearsay. In addition, conflicting evidence is ignored.

There are also differences between scientific and pseudoscientific literature. Before a scientist publishes his or her work, it is assessed by other scientists. This process is known as *peer review*. Standards that must be met before publication of a scientist's work are rigorous. In addition, other scientists must be able to repeat the published experiments and obtain the same results.

There is no peer review, demand for accuracy, or scrutiny of the methods used to obtain results in pseudoscientific literature. In addition, there is no requirement that results or observations must be reproducible.

The information in pseudoscientific books relies heavily on opinion, testimony that cannot be veri-

fied, and ideas that have not been tested using a scientific method. Therefore, these books are often supported only by those who do not require objective evidence to support a claim.

Scientific literature, however, is always open to scrutiny and even to the addition of new material that may provide new insights into existing ideas.

The work of Redi, Spallanzani, Pasteur, and others provided enough evidence to convince scientists that organisms do not arise from nonliving things. By discrediting the theory of abiogenesis, they contributed to the development of the theory of biogenesis.

Today, however, the principle of biogenesis may have to be modified. When considering the origin of life on Earth, some scientists have hypothesized that the first cells arose from nonliving materials. In Chapter 15 you will read more about this hypothesis and experiments performed to test it.

Section Review

1. **Comparing Ideas**   How do the theories of abiogenesis and biogenesis differ?
2. **Analyzing Experiments**   How did Spallanzani improve Needham's experiment?
3. **Synthesizing Information**   What was the independent variable in Pasteur's experiment?

Thinking Critically

INVESTIGATION 2:
How Do You Design an Experiment?

Objectives
- To *design* a controlled experiment
- To *evaluate* experimental data

Materials
lima bean seeds, glass beakers or small flower pots, potting soil, sand, gravel, powdered clay, water

Prelab Preparation
1. Define the terms hypothesis, controlled experiment, experimental group, control group, independent variable, and dependent variable.
2. A scientist interested in how soil conditions affect seed germination frames the question: "How do humus, sand, gravel, and clay soils affect lima bean germination?" Why does the scientist frame a specific question rather than a general one to investigate?
3. List the properties of soil that might affect seed germination.
4. Lima bean seeds will usually germinate when planted about 2 cm below the surface of the soil and adequately watered.
5. Discuss the question in step 2 with your partner. What information, in addition to that given in steps 3 and 4, do you need to collect in order to form a hypothesis?
6. After you have the necessary information, construct a hypothesis that addresses the question in step 2. Discuss this hypothesis with your partner and modify the hypothesis so that it reflects the thinking of both of you. Explain how you arrived at the hypothesis.

Inquiry: Experimentation
7. Work with your partner. Use the materials in this Investigation and the information below to design a controlled experiment that tests the hypothesis.
   a. List the steps, in order, that you will use in your experiment.
   b. For each step, specify the materials you will use, the amounts that will be used, how measurements will be made, and the conditions under which the procedures will take place.
   c. Explain why your experiment is a controlled experiment. *What will be the control group and experimental groups in your experiment?*
   d. Use the chart below as an example to construct a chart for recording data.

Observations on Germination and Growth of Seeds

Soil type	Day 1	Day 2	Day 3	Day 4	Day 5
Humus					
Sand					
Gravel					
Clay					

8. After having your design approved by your teacher, conduct your experiment.
9. Write a summary of your experiment. Explain how your data either support or do not support your hypothesis. If your data show the need to modify your hypothesis, state a new hypothesis. Explain why you changed your hypothesis.
10. Compare the results of your experiment with the results of the experiments of other teams in your group.

Analysis
1. **Analyzing Information** Why is it necessary to construct a hypothesis when using a scientific method of problem solving?
2. **Analyzing Information** Why was a control group included in your experiment?
3. **Analyzing Procedures** Why are specific procedures used in an experiment?
4. **Evaluating Ideas** What is the importance of keeping careful records when doing an experiment?
5. **Evaluating Ideas** Why is an experiment valuable even when it proves that a hypothesis is incorrect?
6. **Inferring Ideas** What is the value of comparing the results of your team's experiment with the results of the other teams' experiments?

Chapter 2 Review

Summary

Science is a body of knowledge about the world around us. Science is also a process of inquiry. This process, called a scientific method, includes the following steps: defining the problem, collecting background information, formulating a hypothesis, conducting a controlled experiment, observing and recording data, and formulating a conclusion. This method of study sets science apart from all other areas of study.

The abiogenesis-biogenesis debate illustrates the scientific method at work. Prior to the 1800s, many people believed in abio-genesis, the ability of nonliving things to produce certain forms of life. In the seventeenth century, Francesco Redi's experiments challenged abiogenesis by showing that maggots arose not from decaying meat but from eggs laid by flies. In the eighteenth century, John Needham designed an experiment to support abiogenesis, but Lazzaro Spallanzani's work uncovered flaws in Needham's experiment. The theory of abiogenesis was finally disproved by Louis Pasteur's work in 1864. Today aspects of biogenesis are being explored as scientists study the origin of life on Earth.

BioTerms

abiogenesis **(30)**
applied science **(29)**
biogenesis **(30)**
control group **(28)**
controlled
  experiment **(28)**
data **(28)**
dependent
  variable **(28)**
experiment **(28)**

experimental
  group **(28)**
hypothesis **(27)**
independent
  variable **(28)**
law **(29)**
operational
  definition **(29)**
pure science **(29)**
science **(26)**

scientific method **(27)**
scientific principle **(29)**
spontaneous generation **(30)**

statistics **(28)**
theory **(29)**

For each pair of terms, explain the differences in their meanings.

1. scientific method, scientific principle
2. abiogenesis, biogenesis
3. hypothesis, theory
4. pure science, applied science

BioQuiz   (Write all answers on a separate sheet of paper.)

Completion

1. Redi, Spallanzani, and Pasteur all wanted to disprove the theory of _____ .
2. Scientific facts collected during an experiment are called _____ .
3. An essential factor in testing a hypothesis is to test only one _____ at a time.
4. Mathematical methods of evaluating data using _____ help determine whether important differences exist.
5. A _____ is a statement of why events occur the way they do.

Multiple Choice

6. The practical use of scientific knowledge is known as   a) an observation. b) applied science.   c) statistics. d) a scientific principle.
7. The group that is not exposed to the independent variable is the   a) experimental group.   b) control group.   c) variable group.   d) scientific group.
8. The test of a hypothesis is   a) an experiment.   b) a conclusion.   c) a theory. d) a principle.

9. The theory of _____ states that all living things must arise from other living things. a) abiogenesis b) spontaneous generation c) biogenesis d) evolution
10. A variable is a) a proposed answer to a scientific question. b) the factor tested in an experiment. c) a scientific explanation of known facts. d) an established scientific truth.
11. The belief that fish were produced by river mud is an example of a) biogenesis. b) science. c) abiogenesis. d) evolution.
12. Experiments conducted by Pasteur disproved a) scientific principles. b) active principles. c) biogenesis. d) abiogenesis.
13. The S-shape in Pasteur's bottle captured a) microorganisms. b) maggots. c) fish eggs. d) mice.

14. Maggots in decaying meat are produced by a) an active principle. b) eggs laid by flies. c) microorganisms. d) mice.
15. In an experiment, the group that is exposed to the variable is called the a) control group. b) experimental group. c) scientific principle. d) data.

Writing Critically

16. How does a control group affect an experiment?
17. Why must a scientist's e.periments be reproducible?
18. In what ways did Louis Pasteur show that dust particles carried microorganisms?
19. How did the mesh screens over the jars affect Redi's experiments?
20. What factor in Needham's experiment caused his erroneous result?

Application/Critical Thinking

1. **Designing Experiments** Design an experiment to test one of the following hypotheses: (a) A plant flowers faster in wet soil than in dry soil, (b) A seed germinates faster in light than in darkness.
2. **Analyzing Experiments** A biologist thinks that trees treated with fertilizer 1 produce more apples than those treated with fertilizer 2. The biologist uses fertilizer 1 on a red delicious apple tree and an equal amount of fertilizer 2 on a Rome apple tree. At the season's end, the delicious apple tree had produced 45 apples and the Rome apple tree had produced 86 apples. Evaluate the experiment that was used to test the hypothesis.

Cross-Discipline Connection

Biology and Writing Write a report for the experiment on page 35 that includes all the information necessary for another student to repeat the experiment. Ask a classmate to evaluate whether or not the experiment could be repeated using the information provided in your report.

Discovery Through Reading

Read "What's Killing the Palm Trees?" *National Geographic* (July 1988):120–130. How was the scientific method used to discover what is killing coconut palm trees in the Caribbean?

Read the article "Evidence vs. Nonsense: A Guide to the Scientific Method," *FDA Consumer* 19 (June 1985):26–30. How is the scientific method used in medicine?

Tools and Techniques of the Biologist

Outline

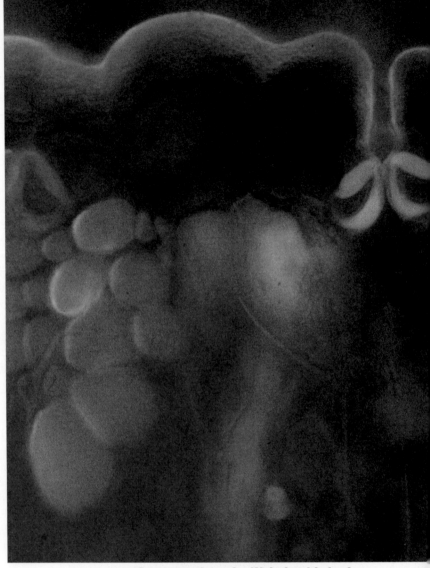

Cross section of a *Welwitschia* leaf, with fluorescent staining, × 100

Focus

A scientific method involves observation of objects and events. Powerful microscopes and staining techniques have made it possible for scientists to observe objects that are far too small to be seen by the unaided eye. Researchers use computer technology to process data, including the information provided by microscopes and other sophisticated tools.

■ *Why is observation a critical step in a scientific method?*

■ *In what ways can computers contribute to the accumulation of scientific knowledge?*

The Microscope

Without the help of a magnifying glass, your eyes see only a limited amount of detail. For example, two dots less than 0.1 mm (0.004 in.) apart blur into a single fuzzy dot. When you consider that many of your body cells are one-fourth the size of the smallest dot you can see, the importance of the microscope becomes clear. *By allowing scientists to see what the unaided eye cannot see, the microscope greatly increases the amount of data available for scientific inquiry.*

3.1 The Light Microscope

The microscope most often used in biological research today is the *light microscope*. This microscope uses light to form an enlarged image of the *specimen,* or object being viewed.

The magnifying glass, called a **simple microscope,** is the most basic light microscope. It is a single lens, or curved piece of glass. The lens bends light rays as they pass through it, causing the specimen to appear between 2 and 20 times its actual size. This apparent increase in the object's size is called **magnification.** Objects that are invisible to the naked eye can often be observed with a microscope. The ability of a microscope to increase the visible detail of a specimen is called **resolving power.**

The most commonly used light microscope is the **compound light microscope,** which contains two kinds of lenses. The **ocular** lens set is positioned near the viewer's eye. It forms part of the **eyepiece** of the microscope. The **objective** lens set is positioned near the specimen. As Figure 3–1 shows, light travels through the specimen and the lenses and into the eye of the viewer.

The lenses of the compound light microscope determine its degree of magnification. Each lens is marked with a number and the symbol ×, which stands for *times.* Thus a lens marked 20× magnifies an object 20 times. To calculate the total magnification, multiply the power of the objective by the power of the ocular. A 43× objective and a 10× ocular can therefore magnify the image of a specimen 430 times. Compound light microscopes are used to view living organisms as well as preserved cells mounted on glass slides.

Biologists also use a variety of other light microscopes. The **stereomicroscope,** used to study large specimens, has an ocular lens and an objective lens for each eye. This arrangement of lenses provides a three-dimensional view of the specimen's surface magnified 5 to 60 times. The **phase contrast microscope**

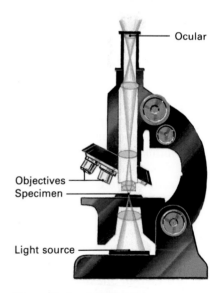

Ocular

Objectives

Specimen

Light source

Figure 3–1. A light microscope uses lenses to focus light and create a magnified image of a specimen. Objects to be viewed under a light microscope usually require special preparation.

To learn about advances in microscopes, see page 138.

Reading Critically

Why would a light microscope be useless for studying atoms?

clarifies features inside living cells. As the beam of light passes through the specimen, the edges of cell structures bend the waves of light. The bent light waves cross, or interfere with, the unbent light waves. The special lenses of the phase contrast microscope use this interference to reveal boundaries between cell parts, which appear brighter to the viewer.

Light microscopes are important tools, but they have one major drawback. These microscopes can magnify an object by any desired amount, but eventually the details of the object become fuzzy. Why does this occur? The resolving power, or the ability of a microscope to provide clear details, depends on the objective lens. The best objective lens can distinguish objects as close together as 0.2 micrometers (μm) when used with a 10X ocular. A **micrometer** is a unit of measure that equals one-millionth of a meter (0.000039 in.). A magnification of 1,000 times is needed for the eye to distinguish objects that are

THINKING ABOUT BIOLOGY: A Look at Early Microscopes

When you think of microscopes, probably the last thing that comes to mind is the Middle Ages. Yet historians believe the first microscopes came into use during the mid-1400s. These microscopes, the familiar magnifying glasses now called *simple microscopes,* were used by scientists to study insects.

About 140 years after the first simple microscopes were introduced, several inventors in Europe discovered that one magnifying lens could be used to enlarge the image produced by another lens. Two of these inventors—Dutch eyeglass makers named Hans and Zacharias Janssen—are credited with using this fact to develop the first

compound light microscope in 1590. Their compound microscope had a lens at each end of a tube.

Although early compound microscopes provided greater magnification than simple microscopes, they produced distorted images. For this reason, most scientists preferred high quality single lenses. The finest such lenses were produced by a Dutch merchant named Anton van Leeuwenhoek in the 1670s and 1680s. During that time, Leeuwenhoek ground more than 400 lenses with magnification powers of 50 to 300 times. Leeuwenhoek designed each of his lenses for a specific purpose. For example, Leeuwenhoek used the lens shown in the

picture to view pond water, where he saw bacteria and other tiny organisms he called "cavorting beasties." Leeuwenhoek was the first person to produce drawings of microscopic organisms. His work eventually led to *microbiology,* the study of microscopic life.

■ **Evaluating Ideas** Why was the development of microscopes so important to science?

0.2 micrometers (μm) apart. Since the resolution is limited by the objective lens, increasing the magnification beyond 1,000 times will not improve the resolution.

3.2 The Electron Microscope

Physicists who wanted to solve the problem of achieving higher resolution knew they could do so only by using an energy beam with a shorter wavelength than that of light. Certain atomic particles called *electrons* have such a wavelength. The **electron microscope** creates enlarged images with a beam of electrons instead of a beam of light. Scientists introduced the first commercial electron microscope in 1935.

Modern electron microscopes produce both high magnification and high resolution, but they too have a major limitation. Living things cannot be viewed under an electron microscope because they cannot survive the techniques used to prepare them for viewing. Even if they could, they would die in the airless interior of the microscope. The air is removed because electrons cannot travel very far in air.

Today scientists use two kinds of electron microscopes. The **transmission electron microscope (TEM)** sends a beam of electrons through the specimen. The beam creates a clear, detailed image on a televisionlike screen magnified 200,000 times or more.

The **scanning electron microscope (SEM)** sends a beam of electrons across the specimen from left to right, a process called *scanning*. As the beam moves, electrons bounce off the specimen in different directions. These electrons produce a three-

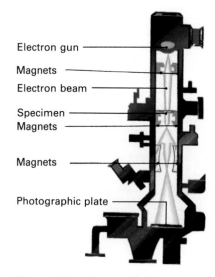

Electron gun

Magnets

Electron beam

Specimen
Magnets

Magnets

Photographic plate

Figure 3–2. A transmission electron microscope uses magnets to focus an electron beam.

Figure 3–3. A diatom looks different under a light microscope (left), a transmission electron microscope (center), and a scanning electron microscope (right).

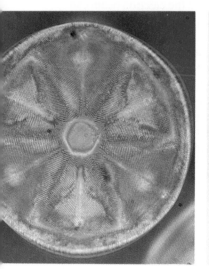
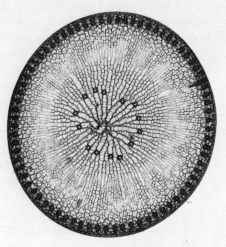
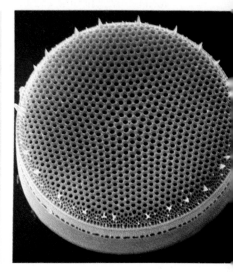

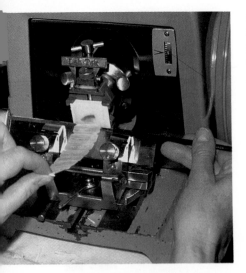

Figure 3–4. A microtome like this one is used to cut thin slices of a specimen to be viewed under a light microscope.

For an example of cell-staining technique, see page 45.

Biofact

Q: *In everyday terms, how thin must specimens be for viewing with a transmission electron microscope?*

A: Specimens must be about 60 times thinner than a page of this book.

Thinking Critically

dimensional view of the specimen's surface on a televisionlike screen. The scanning electron microscope magnifies objects as much as 100,000 times—not as much as the transmission electron microscope. The advantage of the SEM lies in its three-dimensional views of the object's surface features.

3.3 Preparation of Specimens

For study under the light microscope, cells must be thin enough for light to pass through them. However, cell parts would remain invisible unless they were made to reflect some of the light. For this reason, most cells must be prepared for viewing. The first step in this process is to treat cells with substances that hold their parts firmly in place. Thick tissues are sometimes embedded in wax and sliced into very thin pieces with a cutting instrument called a **microtome** (MY kruh tohm). To ensure that structures in the cell will reflect light and become visible, biologists color them with dyes called **stains.** For instance, *safranin* colors some tissues red. *Crystal violet* colors certain tissues blue. Because certain cell parts can absorb only certain stains, biologists can highlight specific structures without staining the entire cell.

Obviously these processes kill cells or disturb their contents, possibly giving scientists a distorted picture of organisms and their structures. To avoid this problem, scientists have developed a few **vital stains** which are dyes that highlight structures in living tissues.

Specimens to be viewed using electron microscopes are prepared differently. TEM specimens are embedded in plastic and sliced into ultrathin sections through which the electron beam can pass. They are then stained with a chemical containing metal molecules. These molecules block electrons, just as the dyes used to stain specimens for light microscopy block light, causing certain cell parts to stand out from the others. Specimens are prepared for the SEM by drying tissues thoroughly and then coating the surface with a thin layer of metal. The electron beam bounces electrons off of this metal replica that covers the specimen.

Section Review

1. **Comparing Ideas** Distinguish between a simple microscope and a compound microscope.
2. **Comprehending Ideas**   Why do scientists stain cells?
3. **Evaluating Ideas**   When might a scientist use a scanning electron microscope rather than a transmission electron microscope?

Other Tools and Techniques

Section Objectives

- *Describe* the process of centrifugation.
- *List* three tools of microdissection.
- *Name* three ways in which biologists use computers.

Microscopes enable scientists to see minute cells and organisms. To understand how these units of life work, biologists use other tools and techniques. Among the most important are centrifugation, microdissection, and the use of computers.

3.4 Centrifugation

Cells and microscopic organisms are very small, but they are made up of many substances. Scientists can separate the substances that make up cells by spinning cell parts at high speeds, a process called **centrifugation** (sehn trihf yuh GAY shuhn). Cells, which may be suspended in a sugar solution, are broken apart in a blender. The resulting liquid is placed in a tube. A machine called a *centrifuge* spins the tube at speeds of up to 20,000 revolutions per minute. This rotation forces the cell parts to settle in layers, with the heaviest parts at the bottom of the tube and the lightest ones at the top. Then scientists can remove each layer and study its contents to determine what materials make up cells.

3.5 Microdissection

To learn what the structures within cells do, biologists remove or add structures to cells through a kind of surgery called **microdissection.** By removing the nucleus from one organism and replacing it with a nucleus from another organism, for example, biologists can learn what functions the nucleus performs.

The cell surgeon uses special tools to perform surgery on a single cell. One of these tools is the *micromanipulator,* a special machine that translates large movements of the hand into microscopic movements. A variety of tools may be attached to the micromanipulator. *Microelectrodes* measure electric currents within the cell. A *micropipette,* a glass syringe with a tip much finer than a human hair, is used to remove materials from the cell or to insert new material. Together, these instruments form an operating room the size of your thumbnail.

3.6 Computers

The computer has many applications in biology today. Some biologists, for example, use computers to determine how atoms are arranged within complex molecules that are necessary for life. Computers are also used to create visual models of these

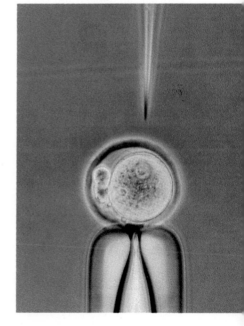

Figure 3–5. Using a micropipette, a biologist injects nucleic acid into this mouse cell. This procedure allows scientists to study the biochemistry of the mouse cell nucleus.

Ingestible Medical Monitors?

Technology developed for outer space may soon be used for hospital patients. Researchers are developing tiny medical monitors that, when swallowed, can collect information about a person's "inner space."

Advanced, space age technology has made it possible to develop these three-quarter inch battery-powered monitors that act as sensors and can collect information about some body functions, such as body temperature.

The monitor transmits information to a special receiving coil worn on the clothing. This receiver can collect an entire day's worth of medical statistics which is transferred to a computer for storage. The information can then be retrieved and analyzed. A radio signal pinpoints the capsule's precise location at all times.

As small as they are, the capsules are large enough so that they may be equipped with several electronic sensors.

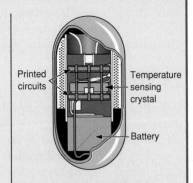

Printed circuits

Temperature sensing crystal

Battery

Advanced models of these monitors may be able to keep track of a patient's heart rate, measure changes in stomach acidity, and monitor other bodily functions.

Reading Critically

Evaluating Relationships
Name some other uses of computers in biology.

complicated molecules. In addition, many scientists use computers to help them analyze data. A computer helps a scientist make sense of hundreds or even thousands of individual bits of information. For example, a biologist may want to learn how wing size affects the flight speed of hawks. The scientist collects data by measuring the wings and speeds of many individual hawks. The scientist then enters this raw, or unprocessed, data into a computer. The computer processes the data into logical chunks of information, such as average wing size and range of flight speeds. Then the scientist can more easily draw conclusions from the information available.

Section Review

1. **Summarizing Ideas**   How does centrifuging affect a specimen?
2. **Interpreting Ideas**   Describe the uses of a micromanipulator and a microelectrode.
3. **Synthesizing Conclusions**   What are three ways a biologist can use a computer?

Thinking Critically

INVESTIGATION 3:
How Are Biological Specimens Stained?

Objectives
- To *develop* skills needed to stain biological specimens
- To *observe* stained biological specimens

Materials
lens paper, microscope slide, coverslip, compound light microscope, forceps, medicine dropper, distilled water, paper towel, Lugol's iodine, onion

Prelab Preparation
1. Describe the pathway of light as it passes from the mirror or lamp to the ocular lens of the microscope. Why is the proper intensity of light necessary when viewing a specimen?
2. Explain how a biological stain aids in observing a microscopic specimen.
3. Describe how specimens are prepared for microscopic examination with a light microscope.
4. Read the microscope procedure on pages 908–909. Summarize the procedure for observing a specimen first at low power and then at high power.
5. Read the procedure on page 909 for making a wet mount slide. Summarize the steps.

Inquiry: Lab Technique
6. Use lens paper to clean the microscope lenses and mirror.
7. Obtain a small piece of onion. Hold the piece with the concave side up. Without pulling it completely apart, snap the piece in half by folding it toward you. Using the forceps, gently pull only one half of the broken piece toward you. A very thin layer of onion should come free from the inside surface of the other half. Completely separate this thin layer of tissue from both halves of the piece of onion.
8. Carefully place the thin layer of tissue on the slide so that it lies as flat as possible. Prepare a wet mount of this tissue.
9. Using low power, observe the specimen.

Make a labeled drawing showing what you observe. Include the name of the specimen and the magnification at which you made your observations.
10. Use proper technique to switch to high power. Make a labeled drawing that shows the specimen at high power magnification.
11. Switch to low power. Raise the body tube four or five centimeters. Leave the slide in place and carefully place a drop of Lugol's iodine along one edge of the coverslip. Place a small piece of paper towel along the opposite edge of the coverslip. Describe what happens.

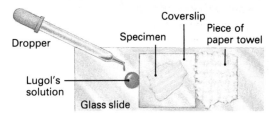

12. Use low power to observe the specimen. Switch to high power and use the diaphragm to adjust the light. Make a second series of labeled drawings that illustrates the stained specimen.
13. Dispose of the specimen as directed by your teacher. Carefully clean and dry the slide and coverslip. Return your laboratory materials to their proper places.

Analysis
1. **Summarizing Observation** Summarize the similarities and differences between stained and unstained onion tissue.
2. **Analyzing Information** What is the advantage of using a biological stain?
3. **Inferring Causes** Suggest possible causes for each of the following problems:
   a. The specimen is too dark.
   b. The coverslip is cracked and the specimen appears to be crushed.
   c. The specimen cannot be seen clearly under high power.

Chapter 3 Review

Summary

Microscopes are among the most important biological tools. The compound light microscope has an objective lens and an ocular lens. Together, these lenses can magnify up to 2,000 times. Other light microscopes include the single-lens simple microscope, or magnifying glass; the stereomicroscope with lenses for both eyes; and the phase contrast microscope for defining features inside cells.

Electron microscopes use beams of electrons to greatly enlarge images. Transmission electron microscopes magnify specimens up to 200,000 times. Scanning electron microscopes produce three-dimensional images of the surface of a specimen.

Most specimens viewed with a microscope are not alive. They are prepared by processes such as staining and slicing. However, vital stains enable biologists to study living cells under a light microscope.

Biologists use a wide variety of other tools and techniques, including centrifugation. Microdissection enables biologists to manipulate various cell parts. Computers perform a wide range of tasks, from drawing images of complex molecules to analyzing data.

BioTerms

centrifugation (**43**)
compound light
   microscope (**39**)
electron
   microscope (**41**)
eyepiece (**39**)
magnification (**39**)
microdissection (**43**)
micrometer (**40**)
microtome (**42**)

objective (**39**)
ocular (**39**)
phase contrast
   microscope (**39**)
resolving
   power (**39**)
scanning electron
   microscope (**41**)
simple
   microscope (**39**)

stain (**42**)
stereomicroscope (**39**)

transmission electron
   microscope (**41**)
vital stain (**42**)

For each pair of terms, explain the differences in their meanings.

1. ocular, objective
2. magnification, resolving power
3. centrifugation, microdissection
4. microtome, micrometer

BioQuiz   (Write all answers on a separate sheet of paper.)

Completion

1. The instrument that is used to measure the electric current within cells is a _____ .
2. A cell can be separated into heavier and lighter parts by _____ .
3. A _____ is a unit of measure equal to one-millionth of a meter.
4. The apparent increase of an object's size is its _____ .
5. Biologists use _____ to analyze data.

Multiple Choice

6. The ability of the microscope to provide clear details depends on the
  a) objective lens.   b) ocular lens.
  c) eyepiece.   d) All choices are correct.
7. A magnifying glass is an example of a
  a) stereomicroscope.   b) compound light microscope.   c) simple microscope.
  d) phase contrast microscope.
8. The study of microscopic life is called
  a) microbiology.   b) cell biology.

c) microdissection.   d) resolving power.
9. The first microscopes came into use in the   a) Middle Ages.   b) 1500s.   c) 1600s.   d) 1800s.
10. Specimens viewed with an electron microscope are coated with   a) plastic.   b) oil.   c) stain.   d) metals.
11. The maximum magnification of a scanning electron microscope is   a) 200,000 times.   b) 100,000 times.   c) 50,000 times.   d) 150,000 times.
12. A microscope with a $56 \times$ objective and a $12 \times$ ocular can magnify a specimen   a) 67 times.   b) 762 times.   c) 76 times.   d) 672 times.
13. An instrument used to thinly slice tissues embedded in wax or plastic is a   a) vital stain.   b) microtome.   c) microforceps.   d) microdissector.
14. Which of the following cannot be done by a computer?   a) make visual models   b) perform microdissection   c) analyze data   d) determine atomic arrangement
15. The ability to increase visible detail is   a) centrifugation.   b) microdissection.   c) resolving power.   d) magnification.

Writing Critically

16. When can a simple microscope be more useful than a compound microscope?
17. What is the value of staining cells before examining them?
18. Describe each type of microscope discussed in the chapter in order of increasing magnification.
19. When would you use a stereomicroscope?
20. How do images produced by a transmission electron microscope and a scanning electron microscope differ?

Application/Critical Thinking

1. **Analyzing Experiments**   Collect a sample of pond water. Observe drops of the sample with a compound light microscope. Do library research to find the names of three organisms in the water.
2. **Communicating Ideas**   Prepare a poster illustrating the means by which electron microscopes produce images.
3. **Summarizing Conclusions**   Using Table 1–1 on page 20, pick one of the careers in biology and write a paragraph about how the computer is used in that field of study.
4. **Evaluating Experiments**   *Artifacts* are data produced by experimental manipulation. For example, an air bubble trapped in a glass slide is an artifact that could be mistaken for the nucleus of a cell. How does the preparation of cells for viewing increase the dangers of producing artifacts?

Cross-Discipline Connection

Biology and Mathematics   The magnification of a microscope is calculated by multiplying the power of the objective by the power of the ocular. Calculate the possible magnifications of a microscope with a $10 \times$ ocular and a $43 \times$ objective.

Discovery Through Reading

Read the article "Electron Microscope Inventors Share Nobel Prize," *Science* 234 (November 14, 1986): 821. How were electron microscopes used by Nobel Prize winners in physics?

4

Basic Chemistry

Outline

The Nature of Matter

Energy and Chemical Change

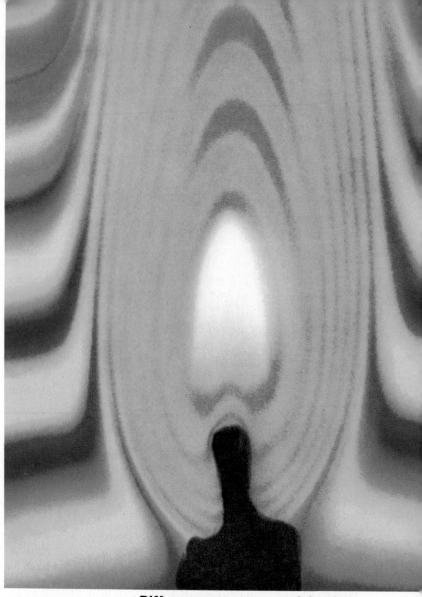

Different temperature and density zones within a candle flame

Focus

Living things, like nonliving things, are made of chemicals. Living things are constantly changing and require constant sources of energy. Humans, for example, convert food and water into muscle, bone, and skin. Chemical reactions release energy that is needed for life processes.

■ *What evidence is there that chemical reactions occur in organisms?*

■ *What life processes require energy?*

The Nature of Matter

Ask a scientist what makes up the universe and you are likely to get a very simple answer—matter and energy. **Matter** is anything that takes up space. *Energy* is the capacity to move matter. Before learning about how energy affects matter, you will need to know the basic properties and composition of matter.

4.1 Properties of Matter

Every object contains a certain amount of matter. The measure of the amount of matter in an object is its **mass.** The *weight* of an object measures the pull of gravity on its mass. The more mass something has, the more it weighs.

Each kind of matter has specific properties, or characteristics, that distinguish it from every other kind of matter. Scientists generally divide the properties of matter into two classes. **Physical properties** are characteristics that can be determined without changing the basic makeup of the substance. Physical properties include the size, shape, texture, and color of a substance. **Chemical properties** describe how a substance acts when it combines with other substances to form entirely different kinds of matter.

Physical Properties and Physical Change The physical properties of a substance include its odor, its hardness, and its ability to conduct heat and electricity. The temperature at which a substance melts, boils, or freezes is also a physical property.

A substance can undergo changes in its physical properties without changing its chemical properties. One simple kind of physical change occurs when a substance changes in size or shape. Quartz boulders on a beach are ground into tiny grains of sand by the waves. The sand has all the chemical properties the boulders had, but some of the physical properties have changed.

A more complex physical change occurs when matter changes state. The three common **states of matter** are solid, liquid, and gas. In all three states, matter consists of tiny particles. The particles in a solid are held tightly together. A solid therefore has a definite shape. It also has a definite *volume*—a given amount of a solid takes up a definite amount of space.

The particles in a liquid are held together less tightly than in a solid. They are free to tumble over one another, and so a liquid assumes the shape of any container. Like a solid, however, a given amount of a liquid at constant temperature maintains a constant volume.

Figure 4–1. Water, like all matter, exists in three states. The solid state is ice; the gaseous state is steam. Liquid water is an important part of all organisms.

Basic Chemistry **49**

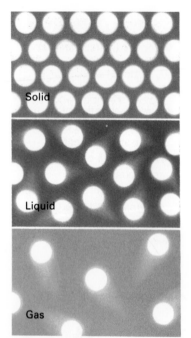

Figure 4–2. The atoms in a solid vibrate slowly around a fixed point. In a liquid, they move more quickly. Atoms in a gas move most rapidly of all.

The particles in a gas are held so loosely that they disperse to fill any given volume. A gas can also be compressed into a smaller space. That is why a small tank of compressed helium can hold enough gas to fill hundreds of balloons.

Matter commonly changes from one state to another. Such a change of state usually results from a change in temperature. When you remove ice from the freezer, heat from the surrounding air causes the frozen water to melt, or change into its liquid state. When you heat that water in a pan on the stove, the liquid changes into a gas called water vapor. Heating gives particles more energy, causing them to move faster and spread farther apart. Cooling causes particles to move more slowly and so to move closer together.

Chemical Properties and Chemical Change Although the physical properties of a substance are relatively simple to study, determining its chemical properties requires complex observations. When chemists study chemical properties, they try to determine how one substance breaks down into other substances. They also experiment to see how different substances combine.

When a substance undergoes a chemical change, it is changed into one or more different substances. For example, an explosive chemical change occurs when the metal sodium comes in contact with water, converting these two substances into hydrogen gas and sodium hydroxide.

You experience chemical changes every day, although you may be unaware of them. For example, every time you eat, the food you consume goes through complex chemical changes. These changes convert much of the food into energy your body can use to produce new cells, run, or think. The clues to how these changes occur lie in the basic composition of matter.

4.2 Atoms

The basic building blocks of all matter are **atoms.** They are so small that only the most powerful electron microscopes can detect individual atoms. The largest known naturally occurring atom, the uranium atom, is just over one angstrom (one ten-billionth of a meter) wide.

Atoms are made of still smaller components called **subatomic particles.** The atom's central core, called the **nucleus,** consists of two types of subatomic particles— protons and neutrons. **Protons** carry a positive electrical charge (+1). **Neutrons,** as their name suggests, are electrically neutral. The nucleus thus has an overall positive charge.

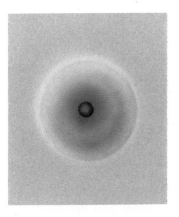

Figure 4–3. Many types of illustrations are used to represent an atom. One (left) shows the nucleus surrounded by a "cloud" of electrons. Another (right) portrays the nucleus, electrons, and electron orbits.

Negatively charged particles called **electrons** move around the nucleus at tremendous speeds. They do not follow well-defined paths, and so they are said to form a cloud around the nucleus. Each electron has a negative electrical charge (-1) equal to a proton's positive charge. In all atoms, the number of electrons equals the number of protons. Thus the atom is electrically neutral.

Under certain conditions, an atom may gain or lose electrons. An atom that has gained or lost one or more electrons is called an **ion.** When an atom loses electrons, it becomes an ion with a positive charge. When an atom gains electrons, it becomes an ion with a negative charge.

4.3 Elements

Each basic type of atom makes up an **element,** a substance that cannot be changed into a simpler substance by chemical means. For example, carbon is made entirely of carbon atoms. If you try to break down a lump of carbon—by heating it, for example—you will find that the carbon does not turn into any other substance. Ninety-two elements occur naturally on the earth. At least 16 others have been artificially created in laboratories and may exist in the cores of certain stars.

About 25 of the 92 naturally occurring elements are found in living things. Most organisms are made chiefly of the elements carbon, hydrogen, oxygen, nitrogen, sulfur, and phosphorus. Iron, iodine, and other *trace elements* make up less than 0.1 percent of the human body but must be present for the body to function normally.

Some of the basic information about elements appears in the periodic table on pages 52 and 53. Scientists use the periodic table as a tool to classify elements and their properties and to predict the behavior of elements. Notice in the table that each

Figure 4–4. Atoms can be seen only as tiny bumps even when magnified over 500,000 times as in this scanning tunneling microscope image.

element is represented by a symbol, usually the first letter or two of its common name. For example, the letter H stands for hydrogen, and Ca stands for calcium. The symbols for some elements come from other languages. For example, the symbol for iron is Fe from the Latin *ferrum,* and the symbol for sodium is Na from Latin *natrium.*

Elements in the periodic table are arranged in rows in order of their **atomic number,** which is the number of protons in the nucleus of one atom of the element. A nitrogen atom (N) has seven protons, so nitrogen has an atomic number of seven. What is the atomic number of iron?

The periodic table also shows each element's **mass number,** which equals the number of protons plus the number of neutrons in an atom. This number tells you the approximate mass of an atom relative to other kinds of atoms. Protons and neutrons are roughly equal in mass. The mass of an electron is so slight that it is not figured into the mass number of the atom. The mass number of ordinary oxygen, therefore, is 16 (8 protons + 8 neutrons).

Table 4–1: Periodic Table of the Elements. The columns are referred to as groups and the rows are referred to as periods.

Common Elements in Living Things	
Name	Symbol
Calcium	Ca
Carbon	C
Chlorine	Cl
Chromium	Cr
Cobalt	Co
Copper	Cu
Fluorine	F
Hydrogen	H
Iodine	I
Iron	Fe
Magnesium	Mg
Manganese	Mn
Molybdenum	Mo
Nitrogen	N
Oxygen	O
Phosphorus	P
Potassium	K
Selenium	Se
Silicon	Si
Sodium	Na
Sulfur	S
Tin	Sn
Vanadium	V
Zinc	Zn

52   Chapter 4

4.4 Compounds and Molecules

Two or more elements that are chemically combined form a **compound.** Although thousands of compounds occur in the nonliving world, most are made by living things. The basic materials of living tissues are complex compounds.

Each compound has its own special properties, which differ from the properties of the individual elements in that compound. Recall, for example, that sodium is a metal that reacts explosively with water. Chlorine is a poisonous green gas. Yet when sodium and chlorine combine chemically, they form a compound called sodium chloride—ordinary table salt.

Elements vary greatly in their ability to form compounds. Sodium, chlorine, and other elements in Groups 1 and 17 of the periodic table are extremely reactive elements. They have such a strong tendency to combine that it is difficult to keep them as pure elements. In contrast, helium and other elements in Group 18 ordinarily do not form compounds. Under normal conditions, Group 18 elements are gases.

													18
Elements making up 99.3% of living things													2 **He** 4
Elements making up about 0.7% of living things			13	14	15	16	17						
Trace elements making up less than 0.01% of living things			5 **B** 11	6 **C** 12	7 **N** 14	8 **O** 16	9 **F** 19	10 **Ne** 20					
8	9	10	11	12	13 **Al** 27	14 **Si** 28	15 **P** 31	16 **S** 32	17 **Cl** 35	18 **Ar** 40			
26 **Fe** 56	27 **Co** 59	28 **Ni** 59	29 **Cu** 64	30 **Zn** 65	31 **Ga** 70	32 **Ge** 73	33 **As** 76	34 **Se** 79	35 **Br** 80	36 **Kr** 84			
44 **Ru** 101	45 **Rh** 103	46 **Pd** 106	47 **Ag** 108	48 **Cd** 112	49 **In** 115	50 **Sn** 119	51 **Sb** 122	52 **Te** 128	53 **I** 127	54 **Xe** 131			
76 **Os** 190	77 **Ir** 192	78 **Pt** 195	79 **Au** 197	80 **Hg** 200	81 **Tl** 204	82 **Pb** 207	83 **Bi** 209	84 **Po** (209)	85 **At** (210)	86 **Rn** (222)			
108 •	109 •												

• Elements synthesized, but not officially named

61 **Pm** (145)	62 **Sm** 150	63 **Eu** 152	64 **Gd** 157	65 **Tb** 159	66 **Dy** 163	67 **Ho** 165	68 **Er** 167	69 **Tm** 169	70 **Yb** 173	71 **Lu** 175
93 **Np** 237	94 **Pu** (244)	95 **Am** (243)	96 **Cm** (247)	97 **Bk** (247)	98 **Cf** (251)	99 **Es** (252)	100 **Fm** (257)	101 **Md** (258)	102 **No** (259)	103 **Lr** (260)

All the atoms of an element have the same number of protons. The number of neutrons, however, can vary. Atoms of an element with different numbers of neutrons are **isotopes** (EYE suh tohps).

Elements naturally occur as mixtures of isotopes. Because each isotope has a different number of neutrons, an isotope is identified by its mass number. Tin, for example, has ten isotopes ranging from tin-112 to tin-124.

Some isotopes are unstable and release energy or particles, in a process called *radioactive decay,* which can be detected easily by radiation detection devices.

Radioactive isotopes, or *radioisotopes,* are used widely in scientific research. Using a process called "labeling," a small amount of a radioisotope is injected into a living organism and is traced as it circulates through the organism.

The radioisotope phosphorus-32 has been used to test how plants absorb fertilizer. Scientists showed that applying nutrients directly onto leaves can be more effective than feeding plants through the roots.

Physicians use iodine-131 to diagnose the condition of the thyroid gland. Since iodine naturally concentrates in the thyroid gland, the radioactive tracer also accumulates in the gland. Radiation scanners can then detect the gland's shape and size, and can monitor its activity.

■ **Inferring Relationships** How could radioisotopes be used to detect tumors?

The smallest particle of a compound or element that has the properties of that element or compound is called a **molecule.** A molecule of an element may consist of one, two, or more atoms of that element. Each molecule of a compound contains two or more different atoms.

The number of atoms of each element in a molecule is indicated by a **molecular formula.** For example, the molecular formula for hydrogen is H_2. The number 2 in the formula is a subscript. It tells you that two *atoms* of hydrogen make up one *molecule* of hydrogen. Any molecule that contains exactly two atoms is called a *diatomic molecule.* CO is the molecular formula for another diatomic molecule, carbon monoxide.

A molecular formula also shows the proportions of each kind of atom found in a compound. *Atoms combine in specific ratios to form molecules.* For example, a water molecule (H_2O) always contains hydrogen and oxygen in a ratio of two hydrogen atoms to one oxygen atom. Add one more atom of oxygen and you have a molecule of hydrogen peroxide (H_2O_2), a syrupy, corrosive compound used in bleaches, antiseptics, and rocket fuel. You could say that the proportion of atoms in a compound gives that compound its distinctive chemical personality.

Reading Critically

Comprehending Ideas How could you tell from the molecular formula whether or not an element was diatomic?

Using a molecular formula, you can also determine a molecule's molecular weight. The **molecular weight** equals the sum of the mass numbers of all the atoms in the molecule. Glucose is a simple sugar with the molecular formula $C_6H_{12}O_6$. What is the molecular weight of this molecule?

4.5 Mixtures

In nature, elements and compounds rarely exist in a pure state. They are normally found mixed together. In a **mixture,** the molecules of different substances mingle without combining chemically.

Each substance in a mixture retains all its chemical properties. The components of a mixture also retain their physical properties, which makes it possible to separate them physically. For example, you can use a paper filter to separate smoke from air. Mixtures can contain solids, liquids, and gases. Unlike compounds, mixtures can be composed of substances in varying ratios. The three kinds of mixtures most important to living things are solutions, suspensions, and colloids.

Solutions   When you stir sugar into a glass of water, the sugar granules break up into individual molecules that disperse throughout the water. The resulting mixture is called a solution. A **solution** forms when the particles of one substance are dispersed in another substance to make a uniform mixture. Solutions can be mixtures of gases, mixtures of liquids, mixtures of gases and liquids, or mixtures of gases, liquids, or solids in a solid. For example, fish get the oxygen they need from the oxygen dissolved in water.

A substance that can dissolve other substances is called a **solvent.** The substance that dissolves in the solvent is called the **solute.** Water is often called the "universal solvent" because it can dissolve a great variety of substances. Most of the chemical processes of living things take place in water solutions. In fact, life on Earth would not be possible without water.

When a solute such as salt dissolves, the individual ions of the solute separate from one another and then disperse in the solvent. The separation of ions in solution is called *dissociation.* The sodium and chloride ions in salt dissociate when the salt dissolves in water.

The amount of solute dissolved in a given amount of solvent is called the **concentration** of the solution. For example, the normal salt solution that doctors give patients to replace lost body fluids has a concentration of 0.9 percent, or 9 parts of salt per 1,000 parts of water. Every solution has a maximum possible concentration. The solution becomes *saturated* when the

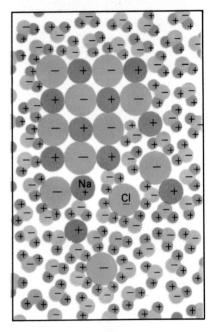

Figure 4–5. When the solute sodium chloride (NaCl) is dissolved in the solvent water (H_2O), it dissociates and forms the ions Na^+ and Cl^-.

To investigate the difference between compounds and mixtures, see page 63.

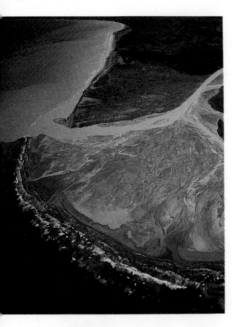

Figure 4–6. A suspension is formed when a river picks up millions of dirt particles on its way to the sea.

solvent holds all the solute it can. A glass of iced tea, for example, can hold only a certain amount of sugar in solution. Additional sugar settles to the bottom of the glass without dissolving.

Suspensions   A mixture in which particles are temporarily mixed together is called a **suspension.** You can distinguish a suspension from a solution by its appearance. Suspensions look cloudy; solutions are clear.

The particles in a suspension are larger than molecules. For example, fine dirt mixed in water forms a suspension. The water will appear murky and discolored while dirt particles are suspended in it. If you let the water stand for several minutes, the dirt particles will gradually settle to the bottom of the glass. You can also separate the particles from a suspension by passing the mixture through a filter.

Suspensions are important to living things. For example, blood cells are suspended in the liquid portion of blood. The bloodstream's constant circulation keeps the blood cells from settling out in any one location.

Colloids   A **colloid** is a mixture in which the suspended particles are smaller than those in an ordinary suspension but larger than the particles of solute in a solution. Colloidal particles cannot be filtered out through paper, and they do not settle to the bottom of a container. Unlike most suspensions, a colloid will last indefinitely if left undisturbed.

Powdered gelatin forms a colloid when it is mixed with warm water. As long as the particles of gelatin remain uniformly dispersed in the warm water, the colloid is said to be in the *sol* state. A sol behaves much like a liquid. When the gelatin mixture is chilled, the gelatin particles join together to form a tangled network. Water is trapped within this network, giving the colloid a semisolid consistency called the *gel* state.

Colloids are important to living organisms. The interior of a living cell is a colloid. The functioning parts of the cell, as well as particles of food, remain dispersed throughout the cell rather than settling in any one area.

Thinking Critically

Section Review

1. **Comparing Ideas**   Explain the difference between the physical and chemical properties of matter.
2. **Summarizing Ideas**   What are three subatomic particles?
3. **Comparing Ideas**   How do compounds and elements differ?
4. **Inferring Relationships**   Why are colloids particularly suited for use in living cells?

Energy and Chemical Change

All living things must constantly use energy to stay alive. Organisms obtain the energy they need by converting food into various forms of energy within their cells. To understand how these conversions occur, you will first need to understand the basic nature of energy.

4.6 Forms of Energy

Both food energy and the energy of a falling object demonstrate one of the basic principles of energy: *Any process of change involves the conversion of one form of energy into another.* A book resting on the edge of a shelf has a form of energy called potential energy. **Potential energy** is energy an object possesses because of its position or its composition. When the book falls off the shelf, its potential energy is converted into **kinetic energy,** the energy of motion.

Water backed up behind a dam has a great deal of potential energy because of the force of gravity acting on the water. As the water flows down through the dam, its potential energy is converted into kinetic energy. The dam's turbines in turn convert this kinetic energy into electricity. The potential chemical energy in wood, gasoline, and other fuels is converted into heat and other forms of kinetic energy as the fuel burns.

4.7 Energy Levels in the Atom

The energy used by living things is chemical potential energy. This chemical energy is actually the energy of electrons within atoms. Electrons speed around the nucleus within specific regions of space. These regions are called **energy levels** because the electrons in each region have a specific amount of energy. Electrons in the first level—that is, in the level closest to the nucleus—have the least amount of energy. The more energy an electron has, the farther it is from the nucleus.

Each energy level can hold only a certain number of electrons. The first level can hold only 2 electrons. The second level can hold up to 8 electrons, and the third can hold up to 18 electrons. Atoms may have over 6 energy levels.

Atoms fill their energy levels from the inside out. For example, the first level must be filled before any electrons will occupy the second level. Neon, with 10 protons and 10 electrons, has 2 electrons in the first level and 8 in the second. Both levels are filled to capacity.

Figure 4–7. When moving down an incline, the slider's energy of position is converted into kinetic energy, the energy of action.

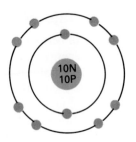

Figure 4–8. A Bohr model of a neon atom shows that it has 10 electrons. The first energy level contains 2 of these electrons. The second energy level contains the other eight. The presence of 8 electrons in the outer energy level makes neon extremely stable. Under normal circumstances, neon rarely forms molecules.

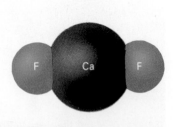

Figure 4–9. When regularly arranged, millions of molecules of calcium fluoride (top) form large crystals of fluorite (bottom).

Like neon, all elements in Group 18 of the periodic table have their outer energy level filled. Generally, an atom is most stable when its outer energy level is filled to capacity. This fact explains why atoms of neon and other similar elements rarely combine with other atoms. Atoms with two or more energy levels are most stable with 8 electrons in the outer level. Atoms tend to interact in ways that result in stable, complete energy levels.

4.8 Formation of Chemical Bonds

Atoms in any molecule or compound are held together by forces called **chemical bonds.** Chemical bonds result from the interaction of electrons in the outer energy levels of atoms. Two different kinds of interaction between atoms may produce chemical bonds. In one kind of interaction, an atom with "extra" electrons in its outer energy level may transfer them to an atom that needs electrons in its outer level. In another kind of interaction, atoms that need electrons in their outer energy levels may share the electrons available.

A transfer of electrons makes each atom an ion but gives it a stable outer energy level. The electrical attraction between the positively and negatively charged ions forms a bond called an **ionic bond.** Sharing electrons also creates stable outer levels. Two atoms that share electrons are held together by a **covalent bond.** Both kinds of interactions produce stable electron arrangements and lead to bonding between atoms.

Ionic Bonds The interaction of sodium and chlorine illustrates how ionic bonds are formed. Both sodium and chlorine are unstable elements because their outer energy levels are incomplete. A sodium atom has one electron in its outer level. A chlorine atom has seven electrons in its outer level. Sodium tends to enter chemical reactions in which it will lose its outer electron, while chlorine tends to enter reactions in which it will gain an electron. When sodium and chlorine atoms combine, as shown in Figure 4–10, the sodium atom transfers its single outer electron to the chlorine atom. This transfer gives each atom a stable outer energy level of eight electrons.

The loss of an electron makes the sodium atom a positively charged ion, symbolized as Na^+. At the same time, the gain of an electron makes the chlorine atom a negatively charged ion, Cl^-. The electrical attraction between the oppositely charged ions forms an ionic bond between them. The resulting compound, NaCl, or table salt, is called an *ionic compound* because it consists of ions held together by an ionic bond.

Covalent Bonds When salt dissolves in water, the sodium and chlorine ions dissociate and disperse through the water. This dissociation indicates that some ionic bonds can be easily broken. Covalent bonds are relatively strong bonds. Covalent bonds do not break easily because the bonded atoms share electrons.

Water is the most common example of a covalent compound. A water molecule is composed of an oxygen atom and two hydrogen atoms that share electrons. An oxygen atom has six electrons in its outer energy level. It needs two more for a stable outer level. In a water molecule, each of the two hydrogen atoms shares its single electron with the oxygen atom, completing the oxygen's outer level. At the same time, the oxygen shares one of its electrons with each of the hydrogen atoms, completing their outer levels. Altogether, four electrons are shared in a water molecule—one contributed by each of the two hydrogen atoms and two contributed by the oxygen atom.

Figure 4–10. A carbon atom (top) forms a covalent bond with each of four hydrogen atoms to form methane (CH₄). When sodium donates an electron to chlorine (bottom), the resulting ions, Na⁺ and Cl⁻, attract each other and form an ionic bond.

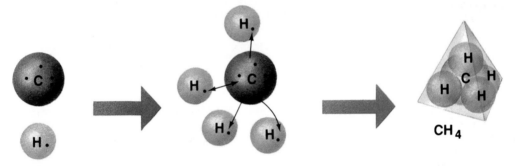

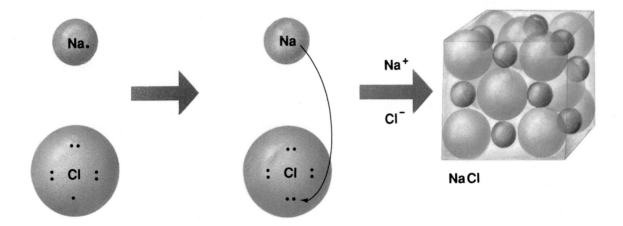

Reading Critically

Interpreting Graphics How many electrons are shared in methane gas?

Carbon has four outer electrons available for sharing. In the gas methane, each carbon atom completes its outer energy level by bonding with four separate hydrogen atoms, as Figure 4–10 shows. In this bond, each hydrogen atom also completes its own outer shell. Like water, methane is a compound with *single bonds*. That is, each bond consists of one pair of electrons. Atoms may share more than one pair of electrons. A covalent bond in which atoms share two pairs of electrons is called a *double bond*.

BIOLOGY AND YOU:

Elements Used in Body Building

About 99.2 percent, by weight, of the human body is made from four elements: hydrogen, carbon, oxygen, and nitrogen. Although quite different, these four elements share some important common features, which explains why they, and not some other elements, are important in living things.

The importance of carbon, hydrogen, oxygen, and nitrogen in living things may be related to the way these atoms bond with other atoms. They are the lightest elements able to form covalent bonds. Because bond strength is inversely related to atomic weight, these elements form extremely strong bonds. This strong bonding ability makes these four elements suitable for forming important organic compounds.

Carbon, oxygen, and nitrogen can also form multiple bonds. For this reason, each of these elements can form a large number of different compounds.

Carbon is one of the most important elements found in living things. Since carbon atoms have the ability to form four covalent bonds, carbon can bond with more kinds of atoms than any other element can. Carbon also bonds readily with other carbon atoms to form the chains and rings that are the backbones of many organic molecules. Biological molecules, such as proteins, carbohydrates, lipids, nucleic acids, and steroids owe a large part of their structure to this ability of carbon atoms.

Lipids, for example, are

important organic molecules that contain chains of carbon atoms. Animal fats and vegetable oils, as well as the oils that are secreted by human skin, are examples of familiar lipids. Lipids function as energy storage reservoirs, heat insulators, lubricants, nerve insulators, and even as hormones.

The models in the illustration show carbon-containing chains that are found in lipids. In the models, red represents oxygen, yellow represents hydrogen, and black represents carbon.

4.9 Chemical Reactions

By filling outer energy levels, chemical bonds between atoms make compounds relatively stable. However, adding energy to a compound can break the bonds. The atoms may then form new bonds with other atoms to make new compounds. The process of breaking existing chemical bonds and forming new bonds is called a **chemical reaction.**

Because bonds break only when sufficient energy is supplied, every chemical reaction requires an input of energy to get started. The energy required to start a chemical reaction is called **activation energy.** Heat is the most common form of activation energy. For example, when sugar is exposed to high heat it bubbles, turns black, and gives off water vapor and carbon dioxide. The chemical explanation for this change is that the heat energy causes the sugar molecules to collide faster and faster. These collisions break the existing bonds between the carbon, hydrogen, and oxygen atoms in the sugar. As the bonds break, the atoms form new bonds which result in carbon dioxide, water vapor, and pure carbon. Energy is also released in the forms of heat and light from this activity. No energy is lost; it only changes form.

Atoms do not change into other atoms in a chemical reaction; they are only rearranged into different combinations. The *products* of the reaction described above—water vapor, carbon dioxide, and pure carbon—contain the same total number of atoms as the sugar originally contained. This fact illustrates one of the basic laws of chemistry: All the atoms that enter into a chemical reaction will be present in the products of the reaction.

As new bonds form, some amount of energy is released. In some cases, this energy helps keep a reaction going. Chemical reactions that release more energy than they use up are called

Figure 4–11. A spark, a flame, and a fire are the results of exergonic chemical reactions in which energy is released as heat and light. The exergonic chemical reactions that occur in cells release energy far more gradually than the exergonic reactions shown below.

Scientists use a special shorthand called **chemical equations** to describe what happens in chemical reactions. The substances entering the reaction, called *reactants,* are symbolized on the left side of the equation. An arrow points in the direction of the products that result from the reaction, symbolized on the right side.

A chemical equation also shows the relative amount of each substance that will take part in the reaction. For example, the equation

$$H + H \rightarrow H_2$$

states that one atom of hydrogen combines with another atom of hydrogen to make one molecule of hydrogen.

The same number of hydrogen atoms are present on both sides of the equation. An equation is *balanced* if the numbers of each kind of atom are equal on both sides. Balanced equations demonstrate the **law of conservation of mass,** which states that matter cannot be created or destroyed.

The equation below shows hydrogen and oxygen combining to form water. The equation

$$H_2 + O_2 \rightarrow H_2O$$

is not balanced—only one atom of oxygen appears in the product. You cannot add a subscript to the product because subscripts are fixed numbers that tell the number of atoms of an element in one molecule of a substance. Instead, numbers called *coefficients* show the correct proportion of substances in the reaction. The balanced equation for water reads

$$2H_2 + O_2 \rightarrow 2H_2O$$

The coefficient, 2, multiplies all the numbers that follow it. The balanced equation shows four hydrogen atoms and two oxygen atoms on each side.

■ **Relating Ideas** Explain how chemical equations illustrate the law of conservation of mass.

exergonic (ehk suhr GAHN ihk) **reactions.** Wood burns in an exergonic reaction that sustains itself and gives off heat and light energy. Reactions that use up more energy than they release are called **endergonic** (ehn duhr GAHN ihk) **reactions.** Many cellular reactions are endergonic. Living things need a constant supply of energy to stay alive because the endergonic reactions within their cells use more energy than they release.

Section Review

1. **Comparing Ideas**   Compare potential and kinetic energy.
2. **Comparing Ideas**   Compare covalent and ionic bonds.
3. **Drawing Conclusions**   What happens to chemical bonds during reactions?
4. **Balancing Equations**   How would you balance $Al + O_2 \rightarrow Al_2O_3$?

> **Thinking Critically**

5. **Inferring Relationships**   Why are atoms with eight electrons in the outermost level unreactive?

INVESTIGATION 4:
How Do Mixtures and Compounds Differ?

Objectives
- To *apply* a scientific method
- To *distinguish* between a mixture and compound

Materials
iron filings, sulfur, triple-beam balance, bar magnet, three heat-resistant test tubes, test-tube rack, test-tube holder, water, small spoon, spatula, filter paper, Bunsen burner, matches

Prelab Preparation
1. Define the terms mixture and compound.
2. Give three examples each of mixtures and compounds used in everyday life.
3. List the physical properties that could be used to describe a chemical substance.
4. Are sulfur and iron found on the periodic table? What does that tell you about these substances?

Inquiry: Observation
5. Make a table similar to the one shown. Record your observations in the table.

Characteristics of Iron and Sulfur

Element	Iron	Sulfur
Color		
Texture		
Density		
Magnetism		
Solubility		

6. **CAUTION: Put on safety goggles, a laboratory apron, and rubber gloves for this Investigation.**
7. Label one piece of filter paper "Iron" and another "Sulfur." Use the balance to find the mass of each piece of filter paper. Record your results.
8. Place one level spoonful of iron and one of sulfur on the appropriate piece of filter paper. Compare the color and texture of these substances.

9. Find the mass of each substance. Although measuring in level spoonfuls is not precise, mass per level spoonful can be used as a measure of the density.
10. Use the periodic table on pages 52–53 to find the atomic mass numbers of iron and sulfur. *What is the relationship between atomic mass number and density?*
11. Use the magnet to test the response of each substance to a magnetic field. Record your observations.
12. Add 10 mL of water to each of two test tubes. Use the tip of a small spatula to place a small amount of each substance into a separate test tube. Compare the solubility in water of the two substances.
13. Mix the remainder of the two substances on a piece of filter paper. *Based on your results thus far, how might you separate these substances?* Test your hypothesis and describe the results.
14. **CAUTION: Open flames and hot chemicals can cause injury.** Mix the iron and sulfur together again and use the spatula to place a small amount of the mixture into a clean, dry 50-mL or larger test tube. In a well-ventilated area or under a ventilation hood, gently heat the tube over the Bunsen burner. Make sure that you keep the mouth of the tube pointed away from everyone.
15. Remove the test tube from the heat as soon as the sulfur has melted. *Have the sulfur and iron combined? How does this substance compare with the original substances? How does this substance compare with the substances mixed together in step 13?*

Analysis
1. **Analyzing Observations** How do the substances formed in steps 13 and 14 differ? How do the methods of combining the elements differ in each step?
2. **Inferring Relationships** What is the relationship between physical and chemical changes, and mixtures and compounds?

Chapter 4 Review

Summary

All matter is composed of atoms that consist of protons, neutrons, and electrons. Each chemically different type of atom makes up a different kind of element.

Elements combine in fixed ratios to form compounds. Molecules are the smallest particles of an element or compound that can exist independently.

Energy is the capacity to move matter from one location to another. Energy transfer in the atom involves electrons as they interact to form chemical bonds. In chemical reactions, existing bonds between atoms are broken and new bonds are formed. Activation energy is necessary to start a chemical reaction.

BioTerms

activation energy **(61)**
atom **(50)**
atomic number **(52)**
chemical bond **(58)**
chemical equation **(62)**
chemical property **(49)**
chemical reaction **(61)**
colloid **(56)**
compound **(53)**
concentration **(55)**
covalent bond **(58)**
electron **(51)**
element **(51)**
endergonic
    reaction **(62)**

energy level **(57)**
exergonic reaction **(62)**
ion **(51)**
ionic bond **(58)**
isotope **(54)**
kinetic energy **(57)**
law of conservation
    of mass **(62)**
mass **(49)**
mass number **(52)**
matter **(49)**
mixture **(55)**
molecular formula **(54)**
molecular weight **(55)**
molecule **(54)**

neutron **(50)**
nucleus **(50)**
physical property **(49)**
potential energy **(57)**
proton **(50)**
solute **(55)**

solution **(55)**
solvent **(55)**
states of matter **(49)**
subatomic
    particle **(50)**
suspension **(56)**

For each pair of terms, explain the differences in their meanings.

1. covalent bond, ionic bond
2. solute, solvent
3. kinetic energy, potential energy
4. chemical property, physical property

BioQuiz   (Write all answers on a separate sheet of paper.)

Completion

1. Electrons speed around the nucleus in specific regions of space called _____ .
2. Particles that cannot be filtered and do not settle out of a solution are _____ .
3. Electrically neutral particles found within the central core of an atom are _____ .
4. If you know the _____ of the atoms in a molecule, then you can determine its molecular weight.
5. When a solvent contains all the solute it can, it is said to be _____ .

Multiple Choice

6. A flower pot that is resting on a third-story windowsill is an example of _____ energy.   a) potential   b) kinetic   c) physical   d) chemical
7. The bond between Na and Cl is   a) a covalent bond.   b) an ionic bond.   c) a compound bond.   d) a simple bond.
8. The smallest particle that can be identified as a particular element is   a) a proton.   b) a neutron.   c) an electron.   d) an atom.

9. Five parts of salt per 1,000 parts of water describes the _____ of a solution.
   a) concentration   b) mass number
   c) molecular weight   d) mixture
10. A _____ has no definite volume.
   a) solid   b) liquid   c) gas   d) solution
11. Which of the following is not a physical change?   a) melting   b) boiling
   c) freezing   d) burning
12. Which subatomic particle has no charge?
   a) proton   b) ion   c) electron   d) neutron
13. The periodic table is divided into _____ groups.   a) 16   b) 12   c) 18   d) 14
14. The most stable elements have _____ electrons in their outermost shell.   a) 6
   b) 8   c) 4   d) 0

15. The amount of matter in an object is referred to as   a) weight.   b) atomic weight.   c) mass.   d) atomic number.

Writing Critically
---

16. What do the numbers on the periodic chart tell you about each element?
17. How are chemical changes and physical changes different?
18. Why do Group 18 elements rarely form compounds?
19. What is the difference between a suspension and a colloid?
20. Why does salt dissolve in water?

Application/Critical Thinking

1. **Interpreting Ideas**   Use your school or public library to research deuterium. Discover how this isotope was vital during World War II. Write a report about how its uses have changed and how it is used today.
2. **Comprehending Ideas**   Iron is mined and brought to the Earth's surface as a mixture of iron and other ores. Discover what techniques are used to separate the minerals in the process of purifying ore.
3. **Drawing Conclusions**   Crude oil comes from the ground as a mixture of many

different compounds called *grades* of oil. Heat is used to separate the grades and purify them into gasoline, kerosene, and other petroleum products. What physical property must therefore vary between the grades of oil? Write a brief paragraph to explain your answer.

4. **Inferring Conclusions**   Water is a very unusual compound. Most compounds contract as they freeze; water expands. As a result, ice weighs less than water. What would happen to a lake and the organisms in it if ice were heavier than liquid water?

Cross-Discipline Connection

Biology and Language Arts   The name of each element was derived from an interesting fact. Use references in the school library to find out the origins of these names.

Discovery Through Reading

The article "Searching for Strange Matter," *Science News* (March 4, 1989): 138–139, focuses on the nature of strange matter and the probability of its existence. Name one place where strange matter may be found.

"Penned-in Positrons," *Science News* (March 11, 1989): 154, tells of the creation of the first antimatter plasma on Earth. What is the most common form of matter in the universe? What is plasma?

Biostereometrics

A biologist taps the keys of a computer keyboard, bringing an image of the structure of a skin cell to the computer screen. A paleontologist examines the computer-generated image of a fossil skull. A physician studies a computer image of a small section of a patient's artery. All three scientists are using new technological processes called *biostereometrics*—the study of biological form and function in three dimensions. Biostereometrics allows biologists in many fields of study to see things in entirely new ways. The cell, for example, can be examined in ways never before possible.

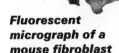

Fluorescent micrograph of a mouse fibroblast

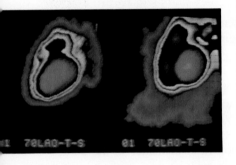

Cine CT provides stop-action photographs of the heart as it is pumping

Positron emission tomography (PET) is among the newest of the biostereometric techniques. PET scans provide color-coded pictures of brain activity. These pictures are used to study the effects of drugs in the treatment of mental disorders such as schizophrenia and neurological disorders such as Parkinson's disease. PET scans are also being used to map the activity of neurotransmitters to better understand the function of the brain.

The *cine CT* (computerized tomography) is an advanced medical device that takes stop-action photographs of the beating heart. It can be used to measure blood flow through grafted coronary arteries, to weigh different parts of the heart, and to find congenital defects in the heart, all without surgery.

Magnetic resonance imaging (MRI) provides

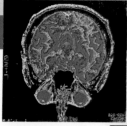

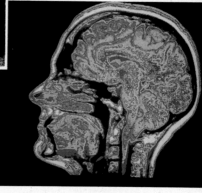

MRI magnet consists of four rings that generate a magnetic field. The pulse from a radio frequency coil provides data for a computer image, such as a human head (above) and a human spine (below).

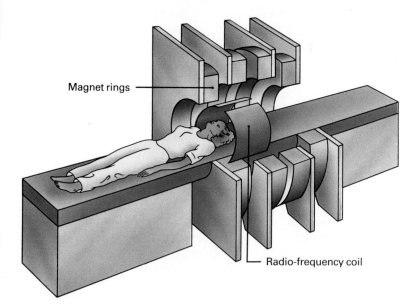

Magnet rings

Radio-frequency coil

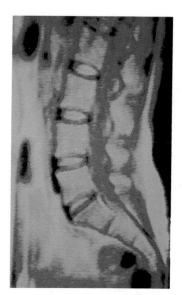

a way to obtain cross-sectional pictures that show differences among tissues at the chemical level. Recent advances in MRI technology like the **MRI microscope** allow researchers to monitor

Biostereometrics allow biologists to see living things in new ways.

the development of a cell while it is still in the organism. *MRI spectroscopy* is being used to study changes in blood fats which one day may help detect cancer before it develops.

The Chemistry of Living Things

Outline

Bioluminescent coral on the Great Barrier Reef, Australia

Focus

By the beginning of the nineteenth century, scientists had begun to ask questions about the chemical reactions that occur in organisms. The answers to these questions formed the basis of the science of *biochemistry*. Biochemistry explores how the properties of chemicals make life possible and how these chemicals help determine the characteristics of living things.

■ *What evidence of chemical activity does the sea coral in the photograph show?*

■ *What is the relationship between chemical activity and an organism's need for energy?*

Inorganic Compounds and Life

One of the earliest discoveries about the chemistry of living things was that most compounds made by organisms contain carbon. Scientists therefore came to classify most of the thousands of carbon compounds as **organic compounds. Inorganic compounds** are those not made by living things.

Many inorganic compounds are essential to life. Nitrogen compounds and minerals such as sodium, potassium, and iron provide elements that all organisms need. Water is also an inorganic compound.

Section Objectives

- *Differentiate* between organic and inorganic compounds.
- *Explain* why water is an excellent solvent and why it has a high heat capacity.
- *Compare* the chemical characteristics of acids and bases.

5.1 Water

Water is the most important inorganic compound for living organisms. Most cellular activities take place in water solutions. Water is important to living things because it is an excellent solvent and has a high *heat capacity*. Water has a high heat capacity because it can absorb and release a great deal of heat energy before changing temperature. This property of water protects organisms from overheating or freezing.

The chemical structure of a water molecule (Figure 5–1) explains its effectiveness as a solvent and its high heat capacity. The single oxygen atom in a water molecule strongly attracts the electrons of the two hydrogen atoms. As a result, the oxygen atom in a water molecule has a slight negative charge, while each of the two hydrogen atoms has a slight positive charge. The opposite charges found at either end of the molecule make water a **polar compound.** Polarity makes water an excellent solvent. Its polar ends attract the ends of other polar molecules as well as ions such as the sodium and chloride ions in salt.

Water has a high heat capacity because water molecules also attract each other. When water is heated, most of the heat energy is used first in breaking the bonds between water molecules. Then only a relatively small amount of heat energy is available to increase the movement of the molecules and raise the water's temperature.

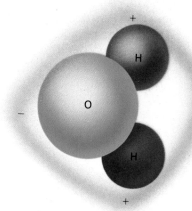

Figure 5–1. The unequal distribution of positive and negative charges around a water molecule causes water to be polarized. Its polarity makes water an excellent solvent.

5.2 Acids and Bases

The vast majority of water molecules always remain as H_2O. However, the attraction between water molecules causes a few molecules to *dissociate,* or separate, into a positively charged hydrogen ion (H^+) and a negatively charged hydroxide ion (OH^-). In pure water the number of hydrogen ions equals the

Just Add Water

Researchers are studying the tardigrade, a millimeter-long invertebrate, to find out how this animal can become almost completely dried out and then revive when water becomes available. A tardigrade's body is normally 85 percent water by weight. When dehydrated, however, this animal contains less than 2 percent water. Tardigrades can survive for several years—far beyond their normal life spans—in this inactive, dehydrated state. Just add water and the tardigrade expands and becomes active again.

Normally when an organism loses large amounts of water, its dehydrated cellular membranes collapse and the organism may die.

Scientists have learned that tardigrades produce the sugar *trehalose* when they dehydrate. Researchers have concluded that trehalose molecules insert themselves between the lipid molecules of the tardigrade's cell membranes. This allows the cells to maintain their integrity even though the water is mostly gone.

The properties of trehalose may someday be applied to preserving human tissues. If this can be achieved, body tissues and substances such as hemoglobin may be preserved, stored, and transported easily, without refrigeration.

number of hydroxide ions. Certain compounds called **acids,** however, release hydrogen ions in water and so increase the concentration of H^+ in a solution. **Bases,** on the other hand, accept hydrogen ions and release hydroxide ions in solution.

The relative concentration of hydrogen ions in a substance is measured by the **pH scale.** The strongest acids have a pH near 0, the strongest bases a pH near 14, and a neutral solution a pH of 7. Pure water has a pH of 7. Each kind of organism has particular pH balances that must be maintained at all times. Human blood, for example, has a pH of 7.4; stomach acid a pH of 2.0. Changes in pH can alter the rate and nature of internal chemical reactions and can endanger an organism's life.

Reading Critically

Synthesizing Information
How could you neutralize a strong acid in the laboratory?

Thinking Critically

Section Review

1. **Comparing Ideas**   How do organic and inorganic compounds differ?
2. **Recognizing Relationships**   Explain the difference between an acid and a base.
3. **Relating Ideas**   How does the chemical structure of water explain its special properties?

Organic Compounds

Although many inorganic substances are essential to life, the vast majority of substances in living things are organic compounds. ***Carbon forms the structural backbone of all organic molecules.*** Of all the elements, only carbon is versatile and stable enough to make up the tremendous variety of molecules found in living things. A carbon atom can bond with up to four atoms at once. Carbon atoms can also bond with one another to form rings or long chains.

Most organic molecules are constructed of basic units that repeat over and over. These units are called **monomers.** When two monomers combine chemically, a new compound is formed. The reaction often releases two hydrogen atoms and one oxygen atom that unite to form a molecule of water. A reaction that produces water in this way is called a **condensation reaction,** or a *dehydration synthesis*. The condensation of many monomers produces a complex molecule called a **polymer.** Many organic molecules are polymers.

The most common organic compounds in living things are classified in four major groups. These groups are carbohydrates, lipids, proteins, and nucleic acids.

5.3 Carbohydrates

Carbohydrates are organic compounds that contain carbon and hydrogen and oxygen in the same ratio as in water—two hydrogen atoms for each oxygen atom. Familiar carbohydrates include sugars and starches. Some carbohydrates, such as cellulose, are used as structural materials. Others, such as sugars, provide quick energy or store energy in cells.

The monomers that make up all carbohydrates are single-sugar molecules. These simple molecules are called **monosaccharides.** Two common monosaccharides, glucose and fructose, are shown in Figure 5–2. They both have the same molecular formula, $C_6H_{12}O_6$, but differ in the arrangement of their atoms. Compounds such as these, in which the same atoms are arranged differently, are called **isomers.** Most monosaccharides are five- or six-carbon sugars. Each molecule is built on a chain of five or six carbon atoms. Both plants and animals use monosaccharides for energy. These compounds, however, may enter the body not as monosaccharides but as compounds formed from the condensation of monosaccharides.

The condensation of two monosaccharides produces a **disaccharide,** or double-sugar molecule. Maltose, known as malt

Section Objectives

- *Summarize* what happens in a condensation reaction.
- *Identify* the chemical similarities and differences among the four main kinds of organic compounds.
- *Explain* how chemists use structural formulas.
- *Describe* the basic structure of an amino acid and *explain* how amino acids form proteins.
- *Summarize* the interaction between an enzyme and its substrate.

To see how different organic compounds can be identified, see page 77.

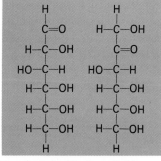

Figure 5–2. Glucose (left) and fructose (right) are isomers. They have the same molecular formula, $C_6H_{12}O_6$, but their atoms are arranged differently and they have different chemical properties.

THINKING ABOUT BIOLOGY: Structural Formulas

If you have ever drawn stick figures to represent people, then you already know how chemists represent molecules. Just as a stick figure shows the basic parts of a human body, so **structural formulas** show the parts of a molecule.

The lines between letters represent the bonds between atoms. Below is the formula for a water molecule. Each line represents a single covalent bond between a hydrogen atom and the oxygen atom.

$$H \diagdown O \diagup H$$

Double bonds, like those in a molecule of carbon dioxide,

$$O = C = O$$

are represented by two lines (=). Three lines (≡) represent triple bonds. One of the values of structural formulas is that they enable a scientist to picture the differences between isomers. Compare the formu-

las for glucose and fructose (a). Many organic molecules are more accurately drawn as a ring. This method shows the structures of glucose and fructose even more clearly (b).

■ **Interpreting Graphics** In what ways do structural formulas illustrate the differences between isomers?

sugar, is made of two condensed glucose molecules. Lactose, or milk sugar, is a molecule of glucose combined with a molecule of galactose. Both human milk and cow's milk contain lactose, composed of glucose and galactose. Sucrose, common table sugar, is made of glucose joined to fructose.

The largest carbohydrates are **polysaccharides.** These molecules may consist of thousands of monomers. Plants store food in the form of *starch*, a polysaccharide that is a polymer of glucose (Figure 5–3). Animals store excess sugars as *glycogen,*

Reading Critically

Comprehending Ideas How could you tell by looking at the formula if two monosaccharides were isomers?

another polymer of glucose, in liver and muscle tissue. When you are active, stored glycogen is broken down to release glucose for quick energy. **Hydrolysis,** the reaction that breaks down complex molecules, is the reverse of a condensation reaction. In hydrolysis, water molecules combine with parts of the long glycogen molecules to form molecules of glucose.

Changing just a few atoms in a large molecule can dramatically alter the molecule's chemical behavior. Both starch and cellulose have almost the same kinds of atoms. Both are polymers of glucose, but the atoms are arranged differently in each. Because of this, the chemical behavior of the two polymers is different. Starch is a storage molecule that most organisms can easily break down into glucose. Most organisms cannot break down cellulose. Instead, cellulose forms the tough, fibrous tissues that support plant stems and transport water in plants.

5.4 Lipids

Lipids are a chemically diverse group of substances that include fats, oils, and waxes. Beef fat, butter, and olive oil are examples of lipids. Like carbohydrates, lipids contain carbon, hydrogen, and oxygen. Lipids are classified together because they are all insoluble in water. In living things, lipids serve mainly as storage of energy. Lipids are also part of cell membranes and thus help regulate what enters and leaves cells.

Lipid molecules are somewhat more complex than carbohydrate molecules. The backbone of many lipids is a three-carbon molecule called *glycerol,* to which three *fatty acids* are attached. Fatty acids are chainlike molecules that typically contain between 14 and 22 carbon atoms. Each chain bonds with the glycerol molecule through a condensation reaction.

5.5 Proteins

Egg whites, gelatin, hair, and muscle, among many other materials, are made of proteins. **Proteins** are the basic building materials of all living things. Protein molecules contain carbon, hydrogen, and oxygen. Unlike lipids and carbohydrates, they also contain nitrogen as well as sulfur and other elements. All proteins are made of monomers called **amino acids.**

Amino Acids All amino acids have the same basic structure. As shown in Figure 5–5, in an amino acid four groups of atoms are bonded to a central carbon atom. Each group has distinctive chemical characteristics. The *acid group,* COOH, tends to give up a hydrogen ion. The *amino group,* NH_2, acts as a base

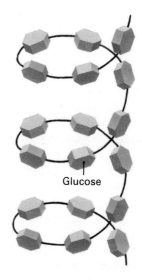

Figure 5–3. Starch is a polymer, a polysaccharide formed from many glucose units. When glucose is needed by cells, starch molecules are broken down by hydrolysis.

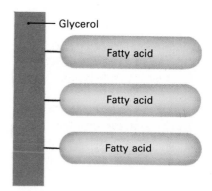

Figure 5–4. Many lipids consist of a single glycerol molecule and three fatty acids.

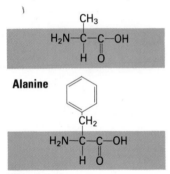

Alanine

Phenylalanine

Figure 5–5. The amino acids alanine and phenylalanine have similar structures. The tinted portion is the same in almost all amino acids.

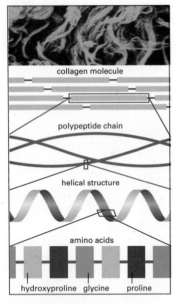

collagen molecule

polypeptide chain

helical structure

amino acids

hydroxyproline glycine proline

Figure 5–6. Collagen fibers from human skin (top) are composed of collagen molecules, polypeptide chains wound around each other. Each chain has a helical structure composed of a repeating sequence of the amino acids glycine, proline, and hydroxyproline.

because it tends to combine with hydrogen ions. The third group consists of a single hydrogen atom.

The three groups listed so far are identical in all amino acids. Variety is introduced in the fourth group, called the *R group*. The R group can be a single hydrogen atom or a complex chain of atoms. Each of the 20 amino acids has its own specific R group.

Protein Structure A protein molecule is formed through a series of condensation reactions. In each reaction, an acid group combines with an amino group from another amino acid. The bond that holds these two groups together is called a **peptide bond.** A molecule formed by two bonded amino acids is a *dipeptide.* Three or more amino acids bonded together form a *polypeptide.* All proteins consist of polypeptides.

The sequence of amino acids and the resulting shape of the protein molecule give each protein its unique characteristics. In *fibrous proteins,* for example, the polypeptide chains are long and stretched out. They may wrap around each other like strands of a rope, or they may be interwoven to form flexible layers. Fibrous proteins form muscles, spider webs, wool, nails, hooves, horns, and beaks. Collagen, for instance, a major component of skin and muscle tissue, is composed of interwoven polypeptide chains (Figure 5–6). *Globular proteins* twist and fold into complex patterns because of the attraction between the electrically charged groups along the polypeptide chain. Hemoglobin and other globular proteins make up 90 percent of the solid matter in blood.

Enzymes Some proteins act as **catalysts**—that is, they speed up chemical reactions in cells. Protein catalysts called **enzymes** control the rate of reactions without themselves being affected by the reactions. Some reactions occur up to one million times faster with enzymes than without them.

You can think of an enzyme as a key that fits only one lock. The "lock" is a specific molecule, called the enzyme's **substrate.**

When an enzyme and its substrate come into contact, chemical bonds form between them at a special place on the enzyme called the **active site.** Bonding of the enzyme to the substrate at the active site weakens, or "unlocks," some of the bonds in the substrate. As a result the substrate can more easily enter into chemical reactions. When two or more substrates are involved in the reaction, the enzyme holds the molecules together at the point where the reacting molecules will connect. Some reactions also require the presence of small, nonprotein molecules called *coenzymes* that help the enzyme bind to the substrate.

Many vitamins act as coenzymes. Vitamins are complex molecules that are smaller than proteins. Some are soluble in water and others are not. Vitamins are grouped according to similar chemical characteristics. Vitamins of the B group are water soluble. Vitamin A is not water soluble.

Substances called *inhibitors* act to regulate enzyme activity. Inhibitors may block the active site of an enzyme. They may also distort the enzyme's shape by bonding with it elsewhere. Some poisons act as enzyme inhibitors.

Enzymes are marvels of biological efficiency. Most chemical reactions require a large amount of energy to get started. The action of enzymes lowers the energy required to start reactions so that the reactions can take place at normal body temperature. Enzymes also speed up reactions to the rates necessary to sustain life. Enzymes are also biologically efficient because they are not used up during chemical reactions. They can be used repeatedly. Thus the cell does not have to use extra energy to make new enzymes each time an enzyme is involved in a reaction.

5.6 Nucleic Acids

How do cells know which proteins, lipids, or carbohydrates to manufacture at any given time? Considering the huge number of different kinds of cells, the information must be extremely detailed and precise. Yet it must also be passed along to each new cell and each new organism, so it must be stored in compact form.

All instructions for cellular activity are carried by a class of organic compounds called **nucleic acids.** There are two kinds of nucleic acid. **Deoxyribonucleic acid, or DNA,** records the instructions and transmits them from generation to generation. **Ribonucleic acid, or RNA,** "reads" the instructions and carries them out. Both DNA and RNA are made of complex monomers called **nucleotides.** DNA is found primarily in the nucleus. RNA is found in both the nucleus and the cytoplasm. The nature and function of nucleic acids are discussed in Chapter 12.

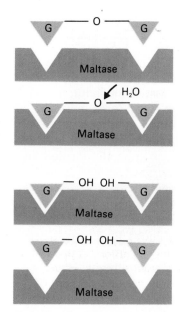

Figure 5–7. The enzyme maltase catalyzes the reaction that hydrolyzes the disaccharide maltose to form two glucose molecules.

Section Review

1. **Comparing Ideas**   What do the four major groups of organic compounds all have in common?
2. **Evaluating Ideas**   Why are structural formulas useful?
3. **Summarizing Ideas**   How do amino acids form proteins?
4. **Relating Ideas**   How do enzymes and substrates interact?
5. **Identifying Relationships**   Why is a condensation reaction also called a dehydration synthesis?

〈 **Thinking Critically** 〉

The Vanishing Rain Forests

Most of the living things in a rain forest exist among the tops of the trees in the upper level of lush vegetation called the *canopy.* So lush is the canopy that most of the light is screened out, leaving the forest floor in twilight. Rain forests contain an amazing diversity of living things. However, only about 5 percent of the species have been identified and studied by scientists. These species include plants that contain chemicals used to treat diseases such as Hodgkin's disease and leukemia.

Over the past few years, developers have been destroying rain forests at an average rate of about 50 acres a minute. They clear the forest for farming and grazing by cutting and burning the vegetation, a method called *slash and burn.* Yields from the crops that are planted in the poor soil dwindle after one or two seasons and the developer then moves to another area in the forest and begins the cycle anew. Farming and grazing provide food for a country's population and earn money through exportation of products.

However, destruction of rain forests may have global consequences. In addition to loss of species, destruction of rain-forest plants may affect global weather patterns. The plants use carbon dioxide from the atmosphere to manufacture sugars and starches in the process called *photosynthesis.* Destruction of vegetation reduces photosynthesis, and carbon dioxide levels in the atmosphere may increase. Some scientists predict that this may contribute to a *greenhouse effect*—a global warming of the Earth's surface. Weather experts warn that the loss of rain forests may alter global rainfall patterns.

Some solutions have been suggested to save rain forests from destruction. These solutions include giving rewards in the form of reduced debts, called *conservation credits,* to countries that preserve their rain forests. The credits would be given by countries to whom the debts are owed. Other solutions include replacing trees

that are destroyed and designating areas that could never be developed.

Analyze the Issue

1. What arguments could a person in the Amazon and a person in the United States present both for and against the replacement of rain forests with farm and grazing land?

2. Describe solutions that may both conserve rain forests and allow for their development for farming and grazing.

3. Is the fact that rain forest environments are almost totally unexplored by scientists enough reason to prevent destruction of these forests? Support your view.

INVESTIGATION 5:
How Can Organic Compounds Be Identified?

Objectives
- To *test* for the presence of certain organic compounds
- To *apply* laboratory skills and techniques

Materials [icons]
Benedict's solution, hot plate, water bath, test tube holder, test-tube rack, test tubes, Lugol's iodine, brown paper, Biuret reagent, albumin solution, glucose solution, starch solution, white potato, cooking oil, centimeter ruler, scalpel

Prelab Preparation
1. List four major types of organic compounds.
2. Distinguish among monosaccharides, disaccharides, and polysaccharides.
3. Explain how lipids and carbohydrates differ.
4. Make an Investigation Summary Table like the one shown.

Investigation Summary Table

Test used	Substance identified	Procedure	Results
Condensation			
Incineration			
Brown paper			
Benedict's solution			
Iodine			
Biuret reagent			

Inquiry: Lab Technique
5. **CAUTION: Put on safety goggles, a laboratory apron, and rubber gloves. Leave them on for the entire Investigation.** Summarize your work for each test in your Investigation Summary Table.
6. **Condensation Test** Place a 3 cm cube of potato into a test tube. Hold the test tube over a Bunsen burner with its mouth pointing away from everyone. *As you heat the potato, what appears to condense on the walls of the test tube?*
7. **Incineration Test** Carefully continue heating the potato until it is completely incinerated. The residue in the tube consists of mineral salts that were present in the potato. Record your results.
8. **Brown Paper Test** Rub a few drops of cooking oil (a lipid) onto a small piece of brown paper. Onto a second piece of brown paper, rub an equal amount of water. After 10 to 15 minutes compare the papers. Record your results.
9. **Benedict's Test CAUTION: Use rubber gloves. Do not get Benedict's solution on your skin. If you do, wash it off immediately.** Add 10 drops of Benedict's solution to each of three test tubes. Next, add 40 drops of glucose (a monosaccharide) to the first tube, 40 drops of starch (a polysaccharide) to the second tube and 40 drops of water to the third. Heat the tubes in a boiling water bath for five minutes. Record the results.
10. **Iodine Test** Add 40 drops of starch to a clean test tube. Add 40 drops of glucose to a second test tube and 40 drops of water to a third. Next, add two drops of Lugol's iodine solution to each of the test tubes. Record the results.
11. **Biuret Test** Add 40 drops of albumin solution (a protein) to a clean test tube. Add 40 drops of water to a second test tube. Next, add three drops of Biuret reagent to each tube. Record the results.

Analysis
1. **Analyzing Procedures** Why was the Benedict's test used with both starch and water?
2. **Inferring Relationships** Biuret reagent reacts with proteins but not with carbohydrates or lipids. Which part of an amino acid molecule most likely reacts with Biuret reagent?

Chapter 5 Review

Summary

Biochemistry is the study of how the properties of atoms and molecules make life possible. For living things, water is the most important inorganic compound. Certain properties of water are essential for life. The polarity of water makes it an excellent solvent and gives it a high heat capacity. Acids and bases are also important to living things because of the part they play in the body's chemical balance.

All organic compounds contain carbon. Organic molecules typically form from two or more monomers. Monosaccharides, the monomers that form carbohydrates, contain carbon, hydrogen, and oxygen. Cellulose and starch are polysaccharides.

Lipids are complex compounds that are insoluble in water. Fats and oils are lipids that store concentrated energy and protect cells.

Proteins are highly complex molecules that contain nitrogen. They are built of amino acids. Enzymes are proteins that catalyze chemical reactions within organisms. The instructions for all cellular activity are carried by nucleic acids.

BioTerms

acid **(70)**
active site **(74)**
amino acid **(73)**
base **(70)**
carbohydrate **(71)**
catalyst **(74)**
condensation
  reaction **(71)**
deoxyribonucleic
  acid (DNA) **(75)**
disaccharide **(71)**
enzyme **(74)**

hydrolysis **(73)**
inorganic
  compound **(69)**
isomer **(71)**
lipid **(73)**
monomer **(71)**
monosaccharide **(71)**
nucleic acid **(75)**
nucleotide **(75)**
organic compound **(69)**
peptide bond **(74)**
pH scale **(70)**

polar
  compound **(69)**
polymer **(71)**
polysaccharide **(72)**
protein **(73)**

ribonucleic
  acid (RNA) **(75)**
structural
  formula **(72)**
substrate **(74)**

For each pair of terms, explain the differences in their meanings.

1. acid, base
2. nucleic acid, amino acid
3. polysaccharide, monosaccharide
4. organic compound, inorganic compound

BioQuiz   (Write all answers on a separate sheet of paper.)

Completion

1. A condensation reaction produces a new compound and releases a molecule of _____ .
2. _____ is the reverse of a condensation reaction.
3. An enzyme bonds to a _____ to control the rate of a chemical reaction.
4. Proteins that speed up chemical reactions in cells are called _____ .
5. Proteins consist of monomers called _____ .

Multiple Choice

6. Enzymes and substrates make contact at
   a) an active site.   b) a glycerol.
   c) a peptide bond.   d) a catalyst.
7. Which of the following will prevent an enzyme from catalyzing a reaction?
   a) a monomer   b) monosaccharides
   c) inhibitor   d) proteins
8. Single-sugar molecules are called
   a) monomers.   b) monosaccharides.
   c) carbohydrates.   d) proteins.

9. Hair, muscle, and gelatin are all examples of a) carbohydrates. b) lipids. c) acids. d) proteins.
10. Amino acids differ only in their a) acid group. b) amino group. c) hydrogen ion. d) R group.
11. Which of the following is a coenzyme? a) vitamin A b) gelatin c) water d) fatty acid
12. Glucose and fructose are examples of a) lipids. b) isomers. c) acids. d) proteins.
13. All proteins consist of a) polypeptides. b) nucleotides. c) polysaccharides. d) fatty acids.
14. Organic compounds that carry all instructions for cellular activity are called a) proteins. b) amino acids.

c) nucleic acids. d) carbohydrates.
15. A reaction that releases two hydrogen atoms and one oxygen atom that unite to form one molecule of water is called a) hydrolysis. b) a polar compound. c) a condensation reaction. d) a catalyst.

Writing Critically

16. How is water's polarity related to its excellent qualities as a solvent?
17. What are the four parts of an amino acid?
18. Why must living things maintain a fairly constant pH balance?
19. How do enzymes lower the amount of energy needed for chemical reactions?
20. How do the functions and locations of DNA and RNA differ?

Application/Critical Thinking

1. **Inferring Conclusions** Honeycombs are made of wax, a kind of lipid. What might happen if a honeycomb were made of a carbohydrate such as sucrose?
2. **Identifying Relationships** When proteins are cooked, their structure is permanently changed. If the protein is an enzyme, it ceases to function. This process is called *denaturation*. Why, do you suppose, is denaturation used to preserve foods? Which foods does it preserve?
3. **Synthesizing Conclusions** Fats and oils store up to six times more energy per gram than carbohydrates. How might differences in plant and animal life explain why plants store energy as starches and animals store energy as fats and oils? Why do arctic animals store much of their food as oil?

Cross-Discipline Connection

Biology and Nutrition Research common foods that are high in fats, in carbohydrates, or in proteins. Write a report that summarizes recent research about how the requirements of these compounds differ between children and adults.

Discovery Through Reading

"Bigfoot or Bust," *Discover* (March 1988): 44–53, describes an unusual field of biology—cryptozoology. The recent discovery of what animal provides some credibility to the field of cryptozoology?

The article "A Frustrating Start for Life on Earth," *Science News* (March 5, 1988):152, explains a theory about why is was difficult for life to begin on Earth. What event may have repeatedly exterminated early life?

Summary

Living things share characteristics that include organization, energy use, growth and development, a life span, reproduction, and both long-term and short-term adaptation. The cells of multicellular organisms are organized into tissues, organs, and organ systems that perform a variety of functions. Organisms of the same species in an area form a population. The different populations in an area form a community that interacts with the physical environment to form an ecosystem.

All scientists use a scientific method of inquiry that includes defining a problem, collecting information, hypothesizing, experimenting, analyzing data, and drawing conclusions. Scientists also use a variety of tools and techniques including computers, centrifuges, and staining. Various kinds of compound light microscopes and electron microscopes allow biologists to study microscopic structures.

Living matter consists of atoms that combine to form molecules. These molecules can be found together as three kinds of mixtures that are important in living things: solutions, suspensions, and colloids. Chemical reactions occur in the cells of all living things. These reactions result in the synthesis and breakdown of materials as well as the storage and release of energy.

Biochemistry is the study of how the properties of atoms and molecules make life possible. Water is the most important inorganic molecule in living things. Carbohydrates, lipids, proteins, and nucleic acids are the four main groups of organic compounds. These organic compounds contain carbon, oxygen, and hydrogen atoms. In addition, proteins and nucleic acids all contain nitrogen.

The work of biologists and other scientists often creates controversy. For example, before 1800, many people believed in abiogenesis, the ability of nonliving things to produce life. In 1864, Louis Pasteur performed experiments that disproved abiogenesis. However, many questions still remain about how living things arose on Earth.

Synthesis

Synthesis Statement

Living things are diverse. Yet all organisms share certain characteristics. In addition, organisms are made up of chemicals that are formed from elements found in the physical world. The laws of chemistry apply to the chemical reactions that occur in organisms.

Biology, the scientific study of organisms, involves a scientific method, knowledge of chemistry and the other sciences, and mathematics. The ability to make observations of living things and the processes that occur within them is aided by the use of tools such as microscopes and computers and techniques such as staining and centrifugation.

Synthesis Questions

Apply your understanding of this unit to the following questions.

1. How could you be sure that differences exist between the experimental group and the control group in an experiment? How could you ensure that others could repeat your experiment?

2. Discuss the reasons why a conclusion cannot claim to be scientific if a scientific method was not used to reach the conclusion. How does the application of a scientific method ensure scientific validity?

3. How might biologists differ from physicists, archaeologists, chemists, and geologists in how they would design an experiment and collect and analyze data?

4. Identify the points at which scientists using a scientific method could make an error. Describe the possible consequences of such an error.

5. Organisms show a tremendous amount of diversity yet share certain characteristics. What major characteristics do all organisms share? In what ways are organisms diverse?

6. How do scientists use the light microscope and the electron microscope to learn more about the organization of living things?

7. How does a knowledge of chemistry allow biologists to achieve a better understanding of living organisms?

8. Use a separate piece of paper to draw a concept map like the one shown. The figures represent the steps used in a scientific method. Place each of the following terms inside the appropriate figure: conclusions, data, experiment, control group, experimental group, observations, background information. Draw an arrow to the step to which you will return if your conclusions do not support your hypothesis.

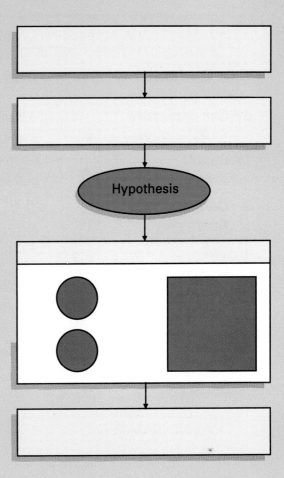

THE CELL

Unit Focus

All of the activities of living things also take place within the cell. Whether an organism is composed of trillions of cells or only one, the cell is the basic unit of structure and function of all living things.

- *What activities of living things also apply to the cell?*

- *What are the similarities and differences between a microcomputer chip and a cell?*

A nerve cell on a computer chip

Cell Structure and Function

Outline

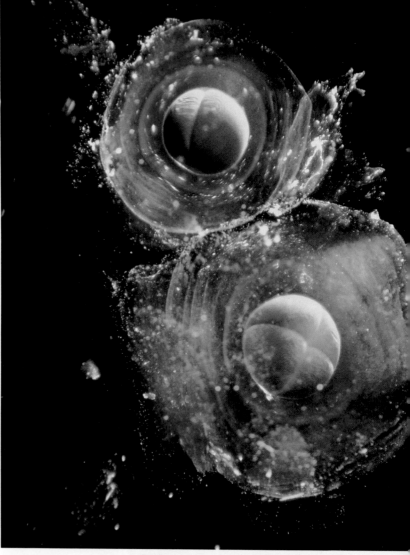

**Early embryos of the leopard frog,
*Rana pipiens***

Focus

Every cell represents a collection of chemicals that consist of elements known to humans. However, questions still remain about how the atoms and molecules that make up a cell are organized and interact. As these questions are answered, biologists gain more and more insight about the qualities and characteristics of life.

- *What elements are most common in living things?*

- *What kinds of tools would be required to find out how cells are constructed and how they work?*

The Discovery of Cells

Most cells are too small to be seen with the unaided eye. The development in the seventeenth century of the compound light microscope gave biologists the tool they needed to study cells. The first compound light microscopes magnified an object 270 times. Today's light microscopes can magnify objects up to 2,000 times. Electron microscopes can magnify objects more than 200,000 times. Even with these modern tools, however, some details of cell structures are much too small to be seen.

6.1 Early Microscopic Observations

One of the first records of observations using the compound light microscope was made by the English scientist Robert Hooke. During the 1660s Hooke made a simple but significant discovery. Hooke carefully shaved a thin section of cork from a plant stem and looked at it using his microscope. In his book *Micrographia,* Hooke recorded, "I could . . . plainly perceive it to be perforated and porous, much like a honeycomb, but the pores were not regular . . . ." *Hooke named the structures that he saw by using a microscope "cells."* These small boxlike units reminded him of the small rooms of a monastery where monks lived. Hooke was not looking at living cells. He was looking at the nonliving outer walls of what once had been living cork cells. Nonetheless, this was a significant discovery about the structure of living things.

During the next 160 years, microscopes and their lenses gradually improved. In the 1820s, a French botanist named René Dutrochet became one of the first to make a generalized statement about the structure of living things. He examined parts from many animals and plants with the microscope and concluded that various parts of organisms are composed of cells. To rephrase Dutrochet, the leaves of a tree and the skin on your hand are each made of cells.

The 1830s brought a flurry of activity in cell study. Pieces of all sorts of organisms were studied using the microscope. In Scotland, Robert Brown announced that a cell contains a large, central part, or **nucleus.** A French scientist, Felix Dujardin, reported that cells are not hollow, empty structures. He described them as full of a clear, jellylike fluid.

A great wealth of information was accumulating. What did these seemingly isolated facts about cells mean? By the late 1830s, two German scientists working separately began to formulate a general theory about cells. After extensive research

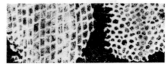

Figure 6–1. In the 1660s, Robert Hooke used this microscope (top) to view the microscopic world for the first time. He observed and illustrated thinly sliced cork (bottom) and called the structures he saw "cells."

on plants, Matthias Schleiden concluded that all plants and plant parts are composed of living cells. Theodore Schwann came to the same conclusion about animals. The separate conclusions of Schleiden and Schwann, when considered together, meant that all living things are composed of cells. Cells are the basic building blocks of living things, just as bricks are the basic structural units of many buildings.

The last bit of information required to complete the general theory of cells was supplied by the German physician, Rudolph Virchow. Virchow advanced the idea that existing cells give rise to new cells. He stated, "All cells come from living cells." Life is an unbroken chain of cells going all the way back to the first living thing.

6.2 The Cell Theory

The conclusions of Schleiden, Schwann, and Virchow are summarized in the **cell theory,** which has three parts:

1. *All organisms are composed of cells.*
2. *Cells are the basic units of structure and function in organisms.*
3. *All cells come from preexisting cells.*

Like most theories, this one has some exceptions. If every cell comes from a parent cell, where did the first cell come from? Billions of years ago the environmental conditions on the earth were much different than they are today. Could conditions at that time have enabled the first living cell to form from non-living materials?

Another exception to the cell theory is the virus. A virus is a package of nucleic acid wrapped in a protein coating. It possesses only a few of the structures of a cell. In fact, a virus must invade and occupy a cell in order to reproduce. Without a host cell, a virus is as lifeless as a grain of sand. A virus is not a cell. Is a virus alive, or is it somewhere between life and nonlife?

6.3 Size and Shape of Cells

Cells exist in a great variety of sizes and shapes. The smallest cells are bacterialike organisms called *mycoplasmas.* Some of these organisms cause diseases that infect the respiratory system. Mycoplasmas are about 0.1 to 0.3 micrometer (μm) in diameter. One micrometer equals one-millionth of a meter (0.000039 in.). Mycoplasmas can be seen only with an electron microscope. The smallest cells that can be seen with a light microscope are larger bacteria, from 1 to 5 μm in diameter. At

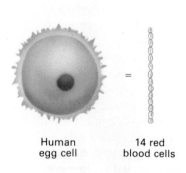

Human egg cell | 14 red blood cells

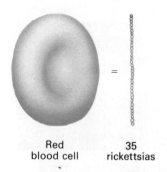

Red blood cell | 35 rickettsias

Figure 6–2. One human egg cell has a diameter equal to that of 14 human red blood cells. The diameter of one red blood cell equals that of 35 microorganisms called rickettsias.

THINKING ABOUT BIOLOGY: The Size of Cells

Certain factors limit the longest diameter of most cells to between 2 and 200 μm. One factor that affects cell size is the relationship between the surface area and the volume of a cell. Two cube-shaped cells of different sizes can be used to illustrate how this relationship changes as cells increase in size.

The volume of a cube equals length times width times height. The surface area is calculated by multiplying width times length times six—the number of sides of a cube. In our example, the smaller cell measures one unit on a side, and the larger cell is twice that size, or two units on a side.

Doubling the size of the cube increases the volume eight times. The surface area, however, increases only four times.

The smaller of the two cells in the example has six units of surface area for one unit of volume. This can be expressed as a surface area to volume ratio of 6:1. When the width of the cell is doubled, as occurs in the larger cube in this example, the ratio of surface area to volume drops to 3:1. If the cell grew to a cube four units on a side, the ratio of surface area to volume would then drop to 1.5:1.

The chemicals inside a cell that are required to keep the cell alive must enter and leave the cell through its surface. It follows that the cell must have a sufficiently large surface area to keep the living material inside the cell supplied. In addition, the surface of the cell must be large enough to permit the waste materials that result from the cell's chemistry to leave before they "pollute" the cell.

As a cell increases in size, its volume increases faster than its surface area. Cells cannot grow so large that their surface areas become too small to supply materials to the inner parts of the cell and to get rid of wastes.

An ostrich egg, like a hen's egg, is a large cell that contains mostly yolk. Yolk is food for the active parts of the cell. Yolk does not use energy; it supplies energy to the developing embryo, which at its early stages is a small point on the surface of the yolk. Since food materials are already stored inside the egg cell, an ostrich egg can remain alive even with a low surface area to volume ratio.

- **Inferring Relationships** Describe several shapes that have large surface areas in relation to their volumes.

the opposite extreme is the ostrich egg cell, which measures about 100 mm (4 in.) in diameter. The volume of an ostrich egg cell is approximately one million trillion times greater than that of the smallest mycoplasma. In everyday terms, this is like comparing the sizes of a whale and a flea.

Cells exhibit an even greater variety in shape than in size. Some *unicellular,* or one-celled organisms, such as a paramecium or a euglena, have a definite shape. Others, such as amoebas, are constantly changing in shape. Even within the human body, cells exhibit a great variety of shapes. Cells near the surface of the skin are flattened, irregularly shaped disks a few

Reading Critically

Inferring Relationships Why would you be unable to detect a mycoplasma under a light microscope?

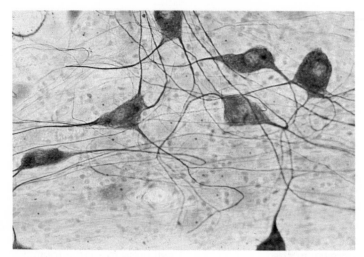

Figure 6–3. Cells are often modified in ways that reflect their functions. The cell of a unicellular organism, such as a paramecium (left), is adapted to meet all the organism's needs. Human nerve cells have unusual shapes related to the task they perform.

micrometers across. In contrast, nerve cells are long, thin, and stringlike. Some human nerve cells are over a meter in length.

Why is there such diversity in the size and shape of cells? You might as well ask why balls are round and tennis rackets flat. The shapes of many objects in the everyday world reflect the functions the objects perform. This same principle holds true for cells. Skin cells function as a covering for the body just as shingles on a roof cover a house. The similarity of the broad, flat shape of skin cells and shingles is related to their similarity in function. Is it just a coincidence that nerve cells are long and thin? Nerve cells function as transmission lines throughout the body. Shape is related to function in nerve cells just as it is in telephone wires.

Biological structure is closely related to the function that is performed by that structure. This basic principle holds true for the structures composed of cells, the cells themselves, and the parts that make up the cells.

Section Review

1. **Relating Ideas**   What were the contributions of Schleiden, Schwann, and Virchow to the development of the cell theory?
2. **Summarizing Ideas**   State the cell theory.
3. **Interpreting Ideas**   How do the shapes of nerve cells reflect their function?
4. **Evaluating Ideas**   How are cells that vary in shape an advantage to an organism?
5. **Inferring Conclusions**   Describe what might happen if each cell in your body increased to twice its normal size?

Thinking Critically

Basic Parts of the Cell

A "typical" cell cannot be described any more successfully than can a "typical" animal. Nevertheless, most cells do have certain characteristics in common. The structure of most cells can be divided into three basic parts: the nucleus, or control center; the cell membrane, or outer boundary of the cell; and the cytoplasm, or everything between the nucleus and the membrane.

The nucleus and its component parts form the control center of the cell. The **cytoplasm** (SYT uh plaz uhm) is the material between the nucleus and the outer boundary. Within the cytoplasm are found cellular **organelles**—tiny structures that perform specialized functions in the cell. Organelles function in the cell in much the same way as organs function in the human body. Each organelle has a special task that helps maintain the life of the cell.

You can think of the cell as a microscopic factory. The cell takes in raw materials and manufactures products much as factories do in human society. Consider an automobile factory, for example. Such a factory can be very large and spread out over a square kilometer or more. To produce a car, a great many different tasks must be performed. One part of the factory may make the engine and another part the body. A large factory also has departments that contribute indirectly to the final product. The maintenance department makes sure that the factory itself is in good working order. The janitorial service sees that the factory is clean. Management makes sure that everything is done correctly and on time.

6.4 The Nucleus

Using the analogy of the factory, the cell nucleus represents management. In many cells the nucleus is the most prominent internal structure. Many nuclei are spherical, but some are cylindrical and others disklike.

The nucleus performs two important functions for the cell. *First, the nucleus controls most activities that take place in the cell.* The nucleus provides the instructions for building proteins. It determines not only how they will be made but which proteins will be made and when. Proteins, in turn, regulate most of the other chemical processes in the cell.

Second, the nucleus transmits hereditary information. Each generation of cells must have the appropriate directions for maintaining all life's functions. The nucleus is responsible for

Section Objectives

- *Identify* the three basic parts of most cells.
- *Compare* the structure of the cell membrane with the cell wall.
- *State* the function of each organelle.
- *State* the difference between organelles and cytoplasmic inclusions.

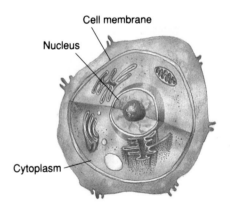

Figure 6–4. A typical animal cell has a cell membrane, cytoplasm, a nucleus, and various organelles. Each component functions in an important role in the cell's biology.

Figure 6–5. The large, circular area with the dark patches around the perimeter in the photomicrograph is the cell nucleus. The smaller dark body inside the nucleus is the nucleolus, where ribosomes are assembled. The nucleus directs cell activities and is often called the control center of the cell.

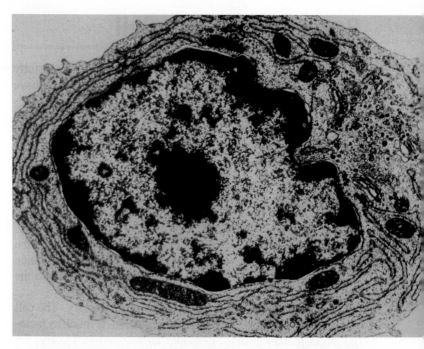

the orderly transfer of that information to the next generation of cells. The nucleus contains the hereditary material. This material consists of the nucleic acid DNA and, with proteins, is formed into rod-shaped or rope-shaped bodies called **chromosomes.** The chromosomes are clearly visible only when the cell is dividing. In between cell divisions the hereditary material is no longer rod-shaped. In this more diffuse state the material is referred to as **chromatin.** *Chromosomes carry the hereditary information from one generation of cells to the next.*

The nucleus of most cells has one or more spherical bodies called **nucleoli** (noo KLEE uh ly). A nucleolus is most prominent in cells that actively make proteins. Nucleoli are made of DNA, another type of nucleic acid called RNA, and proteins.

The chromosomes and nucleoli are surrounded by a two-layered nuclear membrane, or the **nuclear envelope,** that forms a boundary with the cytoplasm. This envelope is a double layer of lipids and proteins with openings, or **nuclear pores,** scattered throughout. The pores allow some materials to pass between the cytoplasm and the nucleus.

6.5 Cell Membrane and Cell Wall

A fence and security system enclose the outer boundary of many large factories. The security department regulates what enters and leaves the factory. The cell, like the factory, has an outer

Grow—or Make—Your Own Cells

The human kidneys are essential organs. Human kidney cells filter waste products from the blood. If the kidneys fail, toxins rapidly accumulate in the bloodstream and death follows quickly.

At present, two main alternatives exist for persons suffering from kidney failure. These alternatives are kidney transplants and the artificial kidney machine, or *hemodialyzer,* which is also known as the dialysis machine. When the dialysis machine is used, blood is shunted from an artery and passes through a membrane that filters waste products from the blood. The filtered blood is then returned to the body.

Researchers are trying to mimic the kidney's natural cleansing system by developing cell-like sacs that can change the chemistry of the body's cellular wastes

to make them less toxic. The "artificial cell" consists of enzymes, detoxicants, and catalytic chemicals. These materials are encapsulated within a semipermeable membrane.

The sacs are about the size of cells: 10 microns in diameter. When placed in blood filters, along with blood-cleanup sacs that contain activated charcoal, the "artificial cells" could eventually assist victims of kidney and liver failure.

Scientists are also experimenting with bone marrow cells. Researchers are learning to culture these cells outside the body. These cultured cells can then be transplanted into cancer patients. Presently, many cancer patients must undergo bone-marrow extraction, a painful ordeal that is necessary to protect the marrow from radiation or chemotherapy.

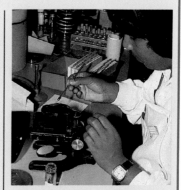

Researchers hope to be able, someday, to extract a tablespoon of bone marrow cells, grow a batch of new cells, and transplant the cultured cells into the patient at the end of cancer treatment. The greatest challenge in this research is finding ways to foster growth of the stem cells that perform bone marrow's most important function: manufacturing the body's different blood cells.

Producing artificial kidney cells and culturing bone marrow cells that can be transplanted may extend lives in the future.

boundary composed of lipids and proteins, called the **cell membrane.** The membrane, sometimes called the *plasma membrane,* holds the cell together. It encloses the contents of the cell and helps give the cell a shape. ***The cell membrane regulates what enters and leaves the cell.***

The cells of plants, algae, fungi, and some bacteria possess a **cell wall** in addition to a cell membrane. ***The cell wall aids in the protection and support of the cell.*** The wall is very porous and so allows water and dissolved substances to pass through

Secondary
cell walls

Middle lamella

Primary cell wall

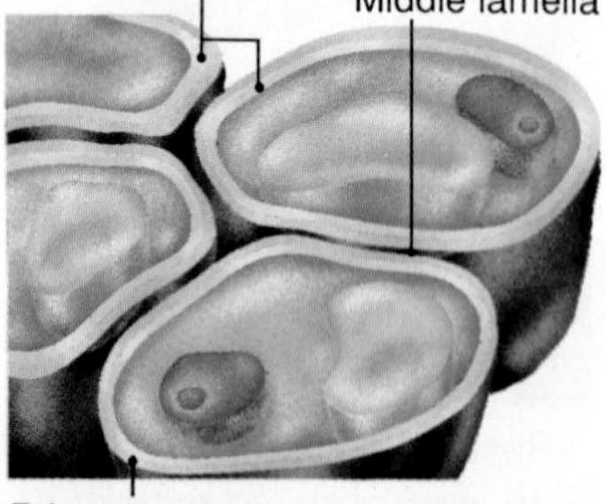

Figure 6–6. Unlike an animal cell, a typical plant cell is surrounded by a multilayered cell wall. Adjacent plant cells are usually joined by a sticky substance called a middle lamella.

The BioTech on pages 138–139 describes how electron microscope technology has changed biologists' view of cells.

easily. As Figure 6–6 shows, the cell wall lies outside the cell membrane.

Cell walls of plants are built in a series of steps. First, a partition called the **middle lamella** (luh MEHL uh) forms between two newly formed cells. This partition contains a gluey substance, *pectin*, that helps hold the cells together.

Each of the cells then forms a *primary cell wall* on its side of the middle lamella. This structure is composed of *cellulose*, a fibrous material. The elasticity of the cellulose fibers allows the wall to stretch as the cell grows.

When the cell is completely grown, most plants add a *secondary cell wall*. This wall is composed of cellulose and *lignin*, a substance that stiffens the cellulose. Wood is a material that consists mainly of rigid secondary cell walls.

6.6 The Cytoplasm and Organelles

The term *cytoplasm* is generally used to describe everything within the cell except the nucleus. Today, scientists know that this material is more than the clear jellylike fluid first observed by Dujardin. With powerful electron microscopes, scientists have discovered that cytoplasm is a highly complex material. It is not as uniform in consistency as jelly. The cytoplasm contains numerous organelles, many of them *membrane-bound*, or enclosed by a membrane.

If you look at living cells through a microscope, you will see that the cytoplasm is in constant motion. This flow of cytoplasm is called **cytoplasmic streaming.** The cytoplasm is more than just a place where things happen. It is part of the living material of the cell. Cytoplasmic streaming is one mechanism that moves materials from one place to another in the cell.

Endoplasmic Reticulum A series of canals or channels called the **endoplasmic reticulum** (ehn duh PLAZ mihk rih TIHK yuh luhm), or **ER,** winds through the cytoplasm. This network of interconnecting, flattened sacs and tubes is made up of a thin, delicate membrane. *The endoplasmic reticulum is the cell's internal transport system.* The ER connects with the nuclear envelope. It serves as a transportation route for materials moving between various parts of the cytoplasm and the nucleus of the cell.

The amount of ER within a cell varies with the cell's function. Cells that produce large quantities of proteins for use outside the cell have the most ER. For example, cells that line the stomach and produce enzymes and those that produce regulatory hormones possess a large, complex ER.

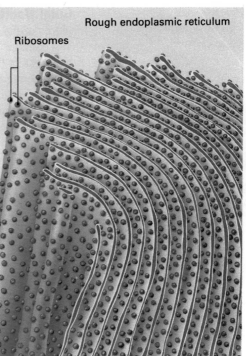

Rough endoplasmic reticulum

Ribosomes

There are two types of endoplasmic reticulum—*smooth ER* and *rough ER*. Smooth ER plays an important role in building the lipids that will be used in the plasma membrane of the cell. Smooth ER also helps neutralize poisons. Drugs such as amphetamines and morphine are broken down within the smooth endoplasmic reticulum. Rough ER gets its name from the presence of ribosomes attached to it.

Ribosomes Tiny, knoblike organelles called **ribosomes** (RY buh sohmz) are manufacturing centers of the cell. They are not enclosed by a membrane. ***Ribosomes are sites of protein synthesis.*** Proteins used within the cell are formed on "free" ribosomes scattered throughout the cytoplasm. Proteins exported out of the cell are synthesized on the "bound" ribosomes attached to the membrane of the rough ER. Because these manufacturing units lie along the transport system, the products can be more easily collected for relocation.

Proteins are vital to life—all cells must produce them. Ribosomes, accordingly, are the most numerous of all the organelles. The proteins produced by the rough ER collect in large fluid-filled sacs. These sacs are like warehouses along the transport systems. When a quantity of protein has accumulated, it may be released from the cell or transferred to a packaging area.

Figure 6–7. Magnified 20,000 times, endoplasmic reticulum resembles folded strings winding through the cytoplasm (left). The illustration shows that ER consists of sheets of membranes (right). Rough ER is covered with ribosomes; smooth ER is not.

Biofact

Q: *Is hair made of cells?*

A: Hair is made of cells that have flattened and died. The cells that produce a hair are found in the skin at the base of the hair.

Golgi bodies

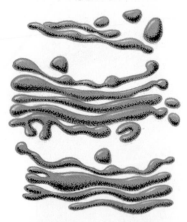

Figure 6–8. Golgi bodies are stacks of membranes that float in the cytoplasm. The small, membrane-bound sacs around the edge of each Golgi body store chemicals.

Figure 6-9. The folding of the inner membrane of the mitochondrion is illustrated below. These same structures are magnified 70,800 times in the photograph below right.

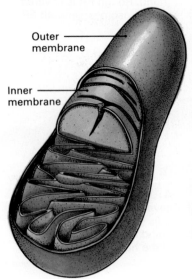

Outer membrane

Inner membrane

Golgi Bodies

As chemicals collect in the ER, small saclike pieces of the membrane are pinched off. These tiny sacs gradually combine to form **Golgi** (GOHL jee) **bodies,** which appear to be stacks of tubes with membranous sacs at the ends. As Figure 6–8 shows, they look like tiny flattened balloons in the cytoplasm. Golgi bodies get their name from the scientist who first described them, the Italian biologist Camillo Golgi. They are also known as the *Golgi complex* or *Golgi apparatus.*

Golgi bodies are areas for the storage and packaging of chemicals. The accumulated chemicals are secreted from the cells. As with the ER, the number and size of the Golgi bodies are greater in cells that produce large quantities of chemicals. Cells that make saliva and other materials that aid digestion have large numbers of Golgi bodies. Mucus, the substance that coats the nasal passages, is packaged and stored in the Golgi bodies of the mucus-producing cells.

Mitochondria

The organelles that release energy from the nutrients taken into the cell are **mitochondria** (myt uh KAHN dree uh). The mitochondria are the cell's powerhouses. They vary in shape from almost spherical to sausagelike. As Figure 6–9 shows, mitochondria are composed of two membranes. The structure of each membrane is similar to that of the cell membrane. The outer membrane is a smooth enclosure, while the inner membrane has many folds. This folding of the membrane greatly increases the internal surface area. A complex series of energy-releasing chemical reactions takes place on the surface of this inner membrane. *Chemical activity in the mitochondria provides energy for the cell.*

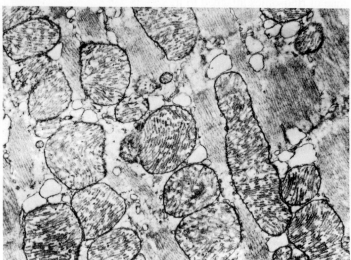

Mitochondria are most common in cells that require large amounts of energy. A liver cell may have as many as 2,500 mitochondria. A heart muscle cell has even more. Mitochondria contain DNA and ribosomes. They originate within the cytoplasm from materials already in the cytoplasm or imported through the cell membrane and reproduce by binary fission.

Plastids Another group of specialized organelles that can reproduce themselves are **plastids.** They are found only in plants and in some algae. *Some plastids contain food; others contain pigments.* Like mitochondria, each type is composed of an outer membrane surrounding a complex system of inner membranes.

Leucoplasts (LOO kuh plasts) are colorless plastids that store food. The cell of roots and stems may contain many leucoplasts. *Chromoplasts* contain the pigments responsible for orange and yellow color in fruit, flowers, and autumn leaves. *Chloroplasts* contain the green pigment chlorophyll. Chloroplasts are the site of food production in plants and algae.

Vacuoles A factory has a warehouse or a storeroom. Some cells, especially plant cells, require a storage area for certain substances. **Vacuoles** are bubblelike structures that store water, other liquids, waste materials, or food particles. A membrane keeps the contents of the vacuole separate from the cytoplasm. This membrane functions in much the same way as the cell

Reading Critically

Inferring Relationships How effective would a mitochondrion be if the inner membrane had no folds?

Figure 6–10. The photograph below left shows a plant cell with a large central vacuole magnified 610 times. Water in the central vacuole exerts pressure on the cell that helps it retain its shape (below right). The central vacuole is also the site of waste storage for plant cells.

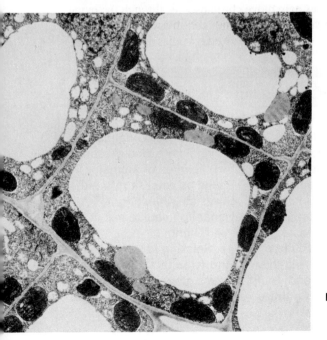

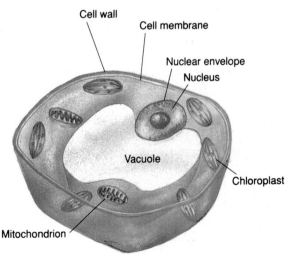

Cell wall

Cell membrane

Nuclear envelope

Nucleus

Vacuole

Chloroplast

Mitochondrion

membrane. It regulates the passage of materials between the cytoplasm and the contents of the vacuole.

The interior of many plant cells contains one large water-filled vacuole, as Figure 6–10 shows. The pressure exerted by the water in the vacuole helps maintain the shape of the cell. When the plant is deprived of water, the vacuoles collapse and the plant wilts. Animal cells have only small vacuoles or none at all.

Lysosomes   Membrane-bound organelles that are formed in the Golgi bodies are **lysosomes** (LY suh sohmz). Loaded with strong destructive enzymes, lysosomes digest large particles found in the cell.

One example of lysosomes at work can be seen in the action of white blood cells. These cells engulf bacteria and other foreign objects in the blood. When the cell encircles a bacterium, the cell membrane becomes a vacuole around it. Lysosomes fuse with the vacuole membrane and dump their chemical contents inside. The powerful enzymes destroy the bacterium.

Other Organelles   Cells are made more rigid by long, slender tubes called **microtubules** (my kroh TOOB yoolz). These hollow cylinders of protein often lie just beneath the cell membrane. They help support the cell and maintain its shape. **Spindle fibers** are microtubules that appear during cell division. These temporary structures help move chromosomes through the cytoplasm. Microtubules are used during cell division to construct **centrioles** (SEHN tree ohlz), small dark bodies located outside

Figure 6–11.   Centrioles generally occur in pairs (upper left). The microtubular structure of a centriole is shown in the cross-section (bottom right).

THINKING ABOUT BIOLOGY: Cytoplasmic Inclusions

Each of the cellular structures discussed in this chapter is an active participant in the functioning of a cell. Each has a specific task to perform to maintain everyday life in the cell.

Cells also may contain materials that do not participate in the everyday functions of cell life. These materials are called *cytoplasmic inclusions.* Lipid droplets, starch grains, and yolk granules are examples of cytoplasmic inclusions that function as a cellular food supply.

Crystals of a substance called *guanine* are often found as inclusions in the skin cells of fish and amphibians, giving these animals their silvery appearance. Guanine crystals are also present in the eyes of animals such as cats. At night, the crystals reflect light, enabling cats to see in dim light.

■ **Relating Ideas**   Explain how the fact that cats' eyes glow in the dark is related to the presence of guanine crystals.

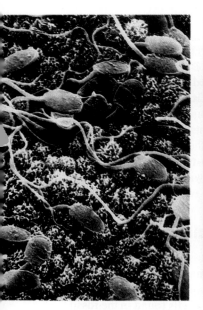
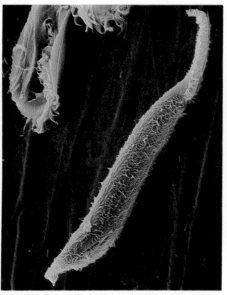
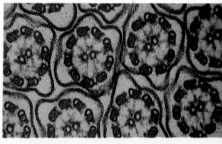
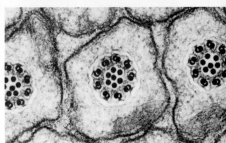

the nucleus in many cells. These cylindrical structures generally exist in pairs. Each centriole contains nine triplets of lengthwise microtubules arranged in a circle. Centrioles function during cell division.

Cilia (SIHL ee uh) and **flagella** (fluh JEHL uh) are extensions of a cell that project from the cell's surface. Cilia are short, threadlike organelles. When present in a cell, they are usually numerous. Flagella are longer than cilia and less numerous. Flagella aid in the locomotion of unicellular organisms. Cilia aid in locomotion and in the movement of substances across the cell's surface. Both cilia and flagella contain nine pairs of microtubules surrounding two central microtubules. This arrangement of microtubules is called a *"9 + 2" arrangement*.

Figure 6-12. The flagella of spermatozoa (left) and the cilia of *Euplotis* (center) enable these cells to move. Cross sections of cilia (top right) and flagella (bottom right) magnified 20,000 times show microtubules arranged in some variation of the "9 + 2" scheme.

Section Review

1. **Listing Structures**   Name the three basic parts of a cell.
2. **Comparing Structures**   How do a cell membrane and a cell wall differ?
3. **Organizing Information**   Name and describe the function of five organelles.
4. **Analyzing Information**   How do lysosomes destroy bacteria?
5. **Analyzing Relationships**   How do the products of "free" ribosomes and those on the ER differ?
6. **Inferring Conclusions**   Why would a cell die if it lost its ribosomes?

⟨ **Thinking Critically** ⟩

- *Distinguish* between prokaryotes and eukaryotes.
- *Give* examples of prokaryotic organisms and eukaryotic organisms.
- *State* the differences in structure between plant and animal cells.

Differences in Cells

Not all of the organelles discussed thus far are present in all cells. A cell's structure is closely related to the function it performs. The organelles found in a cell reflect its function. Muscle cells, for example, have large concentrations of mitochondria because of the high energy requirements of muscles.

Cells can be grouped according to their similarities and differences. All cells can be divided into two large categories—**eukaryotes** (yoo KAR ee ohts), or cells with a nucleus, and **prokaryotes** (proh KAR ee ohts), or cells without a true nucleus.

6.7 Cells Without a True Nucleus

Prokaryotes have nuclear material that is not surrounded by a nuclear membrane. The DNA, or hereditary material, of prokaryotic cells is not arranged into chromosomes. Rather, the DNA is a single circular molecule. The earliest cells found in the fossil record did not have a nucleus surrounded by a nuclear membrane. Today, prokaryotes include bacteria and cyanobacteria.

Figure 6–13. Prokaryotic cells, such as the cells of bacteria and cyanobacteria, lack a true nucleus. They also lack the mitochondria, Golgi bodies, lysosomes, and other components that characterize eukaryotic cells.

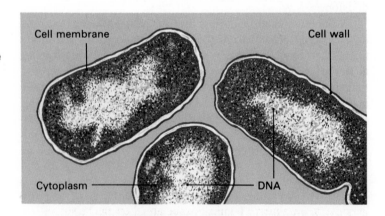

Cell membrane

Cell wall

Cytoplasm

DNA

Prokaryotic cells differ from eukaryotic cells in several other ways. They have no mitochondria, chloroplasts, or endoplasmic reticulum. They do not possess Golgi bodies, lysosomes, and vacuoles. Thus they do not have any membrane-bound organelles. Prokaryotic cells do have a cell membrane and a cell wall, although these walls differ from the walls of plant cells. The flagella of bacteria are also quite different in structure and mode of action, though their function is the same as for eukaryotes. Prokaryotic cells also have ribosomes and these are much like those of the highest eukaryotic organisms.

Table 6–1: Comparison of Prokaryotic and Eukaryotic Cells

Structures and Characteristics	Prokaryotic Cells	Eukaryotic Cells
Nuclear membrane	Absent	Present
Chromosomes	Single circular molecule of nucleic acid	Multiple, composed of nucleic acid and protein
Membrane-bound organelles	Absent	Present
Cell membrane	Present	Present
Cell wall	Present, contains muramic acid	When present, does not contain muramic acid
Ribosomes	Present	Present
Chlorophyll	When present, not contained in chloroplasts	When present, contained in chloroplasts
Flagella	Lack 9 + 2 microtubular structure	Have 9 + 2 microtubular structure
Cytoplasmic streaming	Does not occur	Occurs

6.8 Cells with a Nucleus

All other cells are eukaryotes. *Eukaryotes are cells that possess a well-defined nucleus surrounded by a nuclear membrane.* The complex chromosomes of eukaryotic cells can be seen during cell division. All of the membrane-bound organelles can be found in eukaryotic cells. Each organelle is specialized to perform its task well. The many organelles of eukaryotic cells allow for a greater division of labor. For example, the ER forms a route to transport chemicals that are then packaged by the Golgi body. The greater efficiency that results makes it possible for eukaryotic organisms to be multicellular and to grow larger than prokaryotic organisms.

6.9 Animal and Plant Cells

If you were to compare a tree with a cat, you would find them very different. When the individual cells of these organisms are compared, however, they have many characteristics in common. Cells are the basic structural and functional units of both

Reading Critically

Evaluating Information
How could you quickly tell whether a cell was a prokaryote or a eukaryote?

Animal and plant cells are observed and compared in the Investigation on page 101.

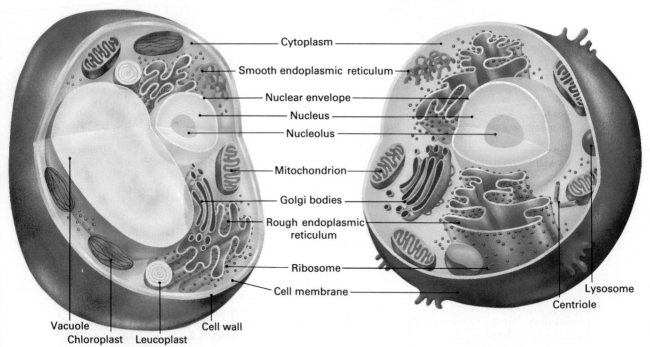

Generalized plant cell

Generalized animal cell

Cytoplasm

Smooth endoplasmic reticulum

Nuclear envelope

Nucleus

Nucleolus

Mitochondrion

Golgi bodies

Rough endoplasmic
reticulum

Ribosome

Cell membrane

Vacuole

Chloroplast   Leucoplast

Cell wall

Lysosome

Centriole

Figure 6-14. Plant and animal cells are similar but have some structural differences. Plant cells have cell walls, large central vacuoles, and chloroplasts. Animal cells lack these structures.

plants and animals. They share many characteristics: both are multicellular organisms; all plant and animal cells are eukaryotic; and most organelles are present in both types of cells. Some characteristics, however, are unique to the cells of each type of organism.

Plant cells may contain three structures not found in animal cells. Cell walls, large central vacuoles, and plastids are characteristic of plant cells. These structures are not found in animal cells. Centrioles are found in some but not all types of plant and animal cells.

Section Review

1. **Comparing Ideas**   Give an example of a prokaryote and explain how it differs from a eukaryote.
2. **Comparing Structures**   What structures are found in plant cells that are not found in animal cells?
3. **Analyzing Ideas**   What allows eukaryotes to be multicellular and to grow larger than prokaryotes?

> **Thinking Critically**

INVESTIGATION 6:
How Do Cells Differ?

Objectives
- To *observe* cell structures.
- To *compare* cells of animals and plants.
- To *construct* a table that summarizes observations.

Materials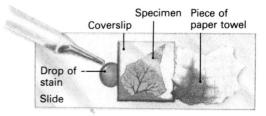
compound light microscope, lens paper, glass slides, coverslips, plant and animal specimens, forceps, scalpel, medicine dropper, paper towels, water, Lugol's iodine, methylene blue

Prelab Preparation
1. As directed by your teacher, bring to class a variety of plant and animal specimens.
2. Review the procedures on pages 908–909 for the proper use of the microscope.
3. Review the procedures on page 909 for making a wet mount.
4. Review the procedures on page 43 for staining cells.
5. State which cell structures you can expect to see with the aid of a compound light microscope.
6. Explain how a cell wall differs from a cell membrane.

Inquiry: Exploration
7. Make a wet mount of one of your specimens.
8. Observe your specimen, using the low power objective. If necessary, use Lugol's iodine or methylene blue stain to make the details of your specimen easier to observe. Observe the specimen using the high power objective.
9. Draw and label your specimen as it appears at each magnification. Indicate the power of the objective lens used to view the specimen on your drawing.
10. Write a detailed description of your observations.
11. Repeat steps 7 through 10 for each of your remaining specimens.
12. Repeat steps 9 and 10 for any prepared

specimens that your teacher assigns. At least one specimen will be labeled "Unknown."
13. Make a table that summarizes your observations. Your table should include a separate column for each specimen that you have observed. Each cell structure that you observed should have a row of its own.
14. Use the table to write a summary that describes the differences between the plant and animal cells you observed.

Analysis
1. **Comparing Structures** Compare the size and shape of plant and animal cells.
2. **Making Generalizations** Based on your observations, describe a generalized plant cell, a generalized animal cell, and a generalized cell.
3. **Analyzing Structures** Identify the unknown specimens as animal or plant and give reasons for your decisions.
4. **Evaluating Ideas** What is the benefit of making generalizations? What is the danger of making generalizations?
5. **Evaluating Methods** Describe some of the problems that you had when preparing slides and viewing them. Based on your experience, how will you solve these problems the next time you prepare a slide and use a microscope?

Chapter 6 Review

Summary

The cell theory states that all living things are composed of cells, cells are the basic unit of structure and function in living things, and cells come only from preexisting cells.

Generally, cells have a nucleus, cytoplasm, and a cell membrane. The nucleus acts as the control center of the cell. The cell membrane regulates what materials pass in and out of a cell. The chemical reactions required to maintain life occur in the cytoplasm. Organelles in the cytoplasm perform specific functions within the cell.

Prokaryotic cells lack a nuclear membrane. Prokaryotic cells have ribosomes and cell walls, but lack the other organelles found in eukaryotic cells.

Eukaryotic cells have a nucleus, surrounded by a layered membrane. Organelles in these cells include mitochondria, endoplasmic reticulum, Golgi bodies, ribosomes, and lysosomes. Plant cells also have plastids, large vacuoles, and cell walls which animal cells lack. Certain types of plant and animal cells have centrioles.

BioTerms

cell membrane (91)
cell theory (86)
cell wall (91)
centriole (96)
chromatin (90)
chromosome (90)
cilia (97)
cytoplasm (89)
cytoplasmic streaming (92)

endoplasmic reticulum (ER) (92)
eukaryote (98)
flagella (97)
Golgi body (94)
lysosome (96)
microtubule (96)
middle lamella (92)
mitochondria (94)
nuclear envelope (90)
nuclear pore (90)

nucleolus (90)
nucleus (85)
organelle (89)
plastid (95)

prokaryote (98)
ribosome (93)
spindle fiber (96)
vacuole (95)

For each pair of terms, explain the differences in their meanings.

1. cell membrane, cell wall
2. eukaryote, prokaryote
3. ribosome, mitochondria
4. flagella, cilia

BioQuiz   (Write all answers on a separate sheet of paper.)

Completion

1. Plant cells have a partition between cell walls called the _____ .
2. The structures that store water, other liquids, or food particles are _____ .
3. Chromoplasts contain the _____ responsible for orange and yellow color in fruits, flowers, and autumn leaves.
4. According to the cell theory, all cells come from _____ cells.
5. _____ are structures that perform specialized functions within the cell.

Multiple Choice

6. All cells have   a) a cell membrane.
   b) a nucleus.   c) a cell wall.
   d) chlorophyll.
7. Which of the following structures is not found in an animal cell?   a) ribosome
   b) chloroplast   c) lysosome   d) nucleoli
8. The cell wall is composed of cellulose and   a) lignin.   b) cilia.
   c) lysosomes.   d) organelles.
9. Ribosomes are   a) manufacturing centers of the cell.   b) sites of protein

synthesis. c) vital to life. d) All choices are correct.

10. Organelles that release energy from nutrients taken into the cell are a) mitochondria. b) Golgi bodies. c) plastids. d) vacuoles.

11. Which organelle contains both food and pigments? a) Golgi bodies b) ribosomes c) plastids d) vacuoles

12. Materials in the cell that are not part of the everyday function of the cell are called a) cytoplasmic streamers. b) cytoplasmic inclusions. c) plastids. d) lysosomes.

13. Golgi bodies form a) lysosomes. b) ribosomes. c) ER. d) centrioles.

14. Threadlike organelles that aid in locomotion are called a) flagella.

b) microtubules. c) lysosomes. d) spindle fibers.

15. Which of the following structures is not found in a prokaryotic cell? a) nuclear membrane b) ribosome c) cell membrane d) cell wall

Writing Critically

16. Why do cells not grow indefinitely?

17. How could you distinguish a plant cell from an animal cell?

18. Why are lysosomes essential to the continuing health of an organism?

19. Why do cells that make saliva contain a large number of Golgi bodies?

20. If a cell had to be deprived of one type of organelle, which one should it be? Justify your answer.

Application/Critical Thinking

1. **Inferring Conclusions** Would you expect to find more lysosomes in a skin cell or a nerve cell? Why?

2. **Evaluating Conclusions** How long could a cell live without nuclear pores? Explain.

3. **Relating Ideas** What function does cytoplasmic streaming perform?

4. **Recognizing Relationships** Use your public or school library to research the nature of viruses and how they are classified. Then write a report on how viruses differ from cells.

5. **Synthesizing Conclusions** New technologies are making it possible to introduce new characteristics into cells. If an animal's cells were given the ability to produce cell walls, how might this affect the animal's survival?

Cross-Discipline Connection

Biology and Art Before photographs were commonly used in the study of biology, artistic renderings of cells and organisms were the best and most accurate way to share information. Compare the detail of the drawings in this chapter with that of the photographs. Write a report on the benefits and disadvantages of using artwork instead of a photograph.

Discovery Through Reading

Read the article "New Microscope Images Ions' Ins and Outs," *Science* (February 3, 1989): 609. This article focuses on the uses of the scanning ion-conductance microscope (SICM). How is it used in biology?

"Mom's Mitochondria May Hold Mutation," *Science News* (July 30, 1988): 70, describes how the DNA in mitochondria may cause a mutation that causes blindness in humans. What do mitochondrial DNA usually code for?

Cellular Transport

Outline

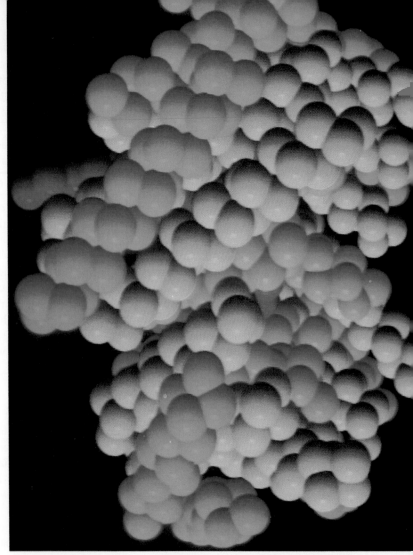

Computer-generated image of a sodium transport molecule

Focus

A cell must constantly exchange materials with the environment. This exchange occurs through a cell membrane that regulates the passage of materials in much the same way that a nation regulates materials that pass across its borders. As with nations, what moves in and out of a cell affects the cell's health and well-being.

■ *What kinds of materials must be constantly supplied to a cell from its environment?*

■ *What kinds of materials must be constantly eliminated from a cell?*

The Movement of Materials

Section Objectives
- *Compare* the movement of molecules in solids, liquids, and gases.
- *Define* the terms *concentration gradient* and *diffusion.*
- *Explain* the effects of temperature, pressure, and concentration on diffusion rate.

Whether part of a living system or not, all molecules are governed by the same physical laws. A knowledge of the physical properties that affect molecular movement will help you better understand the movement of materials in a living cell.

7.1 Molecular Movement

In solid and liquid matter, molecules are packed closely together. In a gas, however, molecules are relatively far apart. In all substances—solids, liquids, and gases—molecules are in constant motion. Even in solids, molecules vibrate in a fixed space.

In liquids and gases, molecular motion is totally random. Imagine a room full of table-tennis balls that are in constant motion. A ball moves in one direction until it collides with another ball, then each flies off in a new direction. In the same way, the movement of molecules in liquids and gases has no plan or design.

This constant random movement of molecules is referred to as *Brownian movement,* after Robert Brown, the nineteenth-century Scottish scientist who first described it. If you look through a microscope at a particle of dust suspended in a drop of water, you can see the result of Brownian movement.

The study of cells is primarily concerned with the movement of molecules in the liquid state. All the substances important to life are most often part of a **solution,** a mixture in which the molecules of one substance are evenly dispersed in another. The substance that makes up the greater part of the solution is called the **solvent,** and the substance dissolved in the solvent is called the **solute.** *Water is the solvent of most solutions involved in cell activities.*

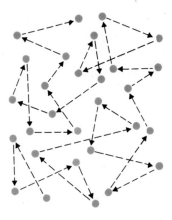

Figure 7–1. Molecules undergoing Brownian movement move in random paths. This natural movement of molecules allows solutes to disperse throughout solvents and create solutions.

7.2 Diffusion

Consider what happens if you place a drop of food coloring into a beaker of water. All of the molecules are in constant, random motion. As they move about, the food coloring molecules spread farther and farther apart until they are evenly spaced throughout the beaker of water.

Diffusion is the process by which molecules of a substance move from areas of higher concentration of that substance to areas of lower concentration. The dispersal of a drop of food coloring through the beaker of water is an example of diffusion

---

Reading Critically

Synthesizing Ideas How is diffusion related to Brownian movement?

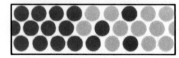
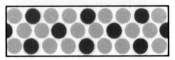

Figure 7–2. When food coloring is placed in water (left), it starts to diffuse. It moves with the concentration gradient (center), diffusing from high to low concentration until it is evenly distributed throughout the water (right). The illustrations show diffusion at the molecular level.

Biofact

Q: *When you smell the aroma of turkey on Thanksgiving Day, what is actually entering your nose?*

A: The heat of the oven causes some molecules that make up the turkey to break free. These molecules diffuse through the air and some stimulate the sense receptors in your nose.

in liquids. Diffusion continues until the molecules of food coloring are evenly distributed throughout the molecules of water in the container. The net, or overall, movement of the molecules results in a uniform concentration of the food coloring through the substance. Molecular movement continues, but the random motion of molecules will not change their overall distribution. ***Diffusion is one of the major mechanisms of molecular transport in cells.*** Many materials move into, out of, and through cells by the process of diffusion.

The difference in concentration of molecules of a substance from the highest to the lowest number of molecules is called the **concentration gradient.** Molecules of a substance that are moving from areas of high concentration of that substance to areas of low concentration are moving with the concentration gradient.

Diffusion only takes place from areas of high concentration to areas of lower concentration. The steeper the grade from high to low, the more rapid the diffusion rate.

Concentration is not the only factor that affects the rate of diffusion. When the temperature of a liquid or gas is raised, the molecules move faster and rebound farther after collisions. An increase in the temperature of a substance thus increases the rate of diffusion. Consider how much faster a spoonful of sugar dissolves in a cup of hot tea than in iced tea.

An increase in pressure also results in an increase in the rate of diffusion. The molecules of substances under high pressure

Receptor Sites May Determine the Shape You're In

Despite the promises of diet and exercise programs, bodies tend to retain fat in certain areas even when weight is lost.

Scientists are beginning to understand why some fat cells retain fat longer than others, and why, if weight is gained, fat is not distributed equally all over the body.

The reason that fat tends to accumulate in some places faster than others may be linked to receptor sites on the fat cells themselves. Researchers have identified two kinds of receptors on fat cells called $alpha_2$ and $beta_1$ receptors. When $beta_1$ receptors are stimulated, fat cells lose their stores of fat. When $alpha_2$ receptors are stimulated, cells store fat.

Most women and most men have proportionately the same $alpha_2$ activity in the buttocks. Therefore, both men and women tend to gain weight equally in that region in proportion to their size. Most men, however, have proportionally more $alpha_2$ receptors in the abdominal area than women have in this body region. Consequently, overweight men tend to become apple-shaped. Overweight women are

often pear-shaped because they tend to add pounds to their hips and thighs.

If more can be found out about how the activity of fat receptor sites could be regulated, selective slimming might be possible.

are squeezed more closely together than those under low pressure. Under high pressure, a molecule has less empty space through which it can move before a collision sends it in a new direction. Conversely, molecules under low pressure diffuse slowly because there is less chance of collision.

Section Review

1. **Comparing Ideas** Compare the movement of molecules in solids, liquids, and gases.
2. **Comprehending Ideas** What is the meaning of the terms *concentration gradient* and *diffusion?*
3. **Inferring Conclusions** Why would you expect diffusion to occur more rapidly in a system at high temperature and pressure than in a system at low temperature and low concentration?

Thinking Critically

Section Objectives

- *Describe* the process of diffusion through a selectively permeable membrane.
- *Define* the terms *isotonic*, *hypotonic*, and *hypertonic*.
- *Describe* the behavior of cells in isotonic, hypotonic, and hypertonic solutions.
- *Discuss* the cause of turgor pressure and its effect on plant tissues.
- *Explain* how cytolysis is used to study cells.

For information about a career that involves both the physical sciences and the biological sciences, see pages 924–925.

Figure 7–3. The cell membrane is composed of a double layer of lipids in which proteins are embedded. Because both lipids and proteins are in motion, the membrane is called fluid-mosaic.

Diffusion Through Membranes

The cell and many organelles within the cell are surrounded by a membrane. Any material that moves into or out of the cell or these organelles must pass through the membrane.

7.3 Characteristics of Cell Membranes

The cell membrane acts as a barrier, isolating the cell from its environment. This barrier must allow some materials to pass through, however, or the cell would die. ***Membranes regulate the passage of material into and out of the cell.*** Cell membranes are **selectively permeable**—that is, only certain substances can pass through them. Water, for example, passes through cell membranes, but the substances dissolved in the water may or may not pass through.

The cell membrane is an active, living part of the cell, visible only through an electron microscope. The membrane's structure is generally described as a double layer of lipid molecules with proteins scattered through the lipid layers. As Figure 7–3 suggests, some proteins are partially embedded in one layer of the lipids like icebergs. Other proteins rest on the surface of the lipids or poke completely through the double layer. The lipids are fluid and some of the proteins are free to move about, forming different patterns. For this reason, this model of the cell membrane is called the *fluid-mosaic model.*

Oxygen and carbon dioxide can dissolve in lipids and so pass right through the cell membrane. Water molecules are also able to pass through the cell membrane. Some other small molecules pass into the cell through openings formed by proteins in the lipid layers. Although water molecules diffuse no differently than any other molecules, the diffusion of water through a membrane is called **osmosis** (ahz MOH suhs). ***Water diffuses into cells by osmosis.***

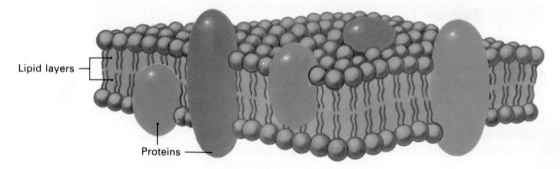

Lipid layers

Proteins

7.4 Osmosis and Living Cells

Water makes up 70 to 95 percent of a living cell. Since water is the most abundant substance in cells, its movement into and out of cells is of vital importance. The cell has no control over osmosis. Water will flow into or out of the cell depending on the concentration of water molecules on either side of the membrane. If the concentration of two solutions separated by a membrane is the same, the two solutions are in a state of **equilibrium.** *Water will continue to diffuse back and forth across a cell membrane even after equilibrium is reached.* However, when water molecules reach equilibrium the number of molecules that moves into the cell equals the number moving out.

The movement of water across a cell membrane depends on the concentration gradient of the water across that membrane. The concentration of water on each side of the membrane, in turn, is determined by the concentration of solutes in that water solution. In an **isotonic** (eye suh TAHN ihk) **solution** the concentration of solutes outside the cell is the same as that inside a cell. In a **hypotonic solution** the concentration of solutes outside the cell is lower than that inside the cell. In a **hypertonic solution** the concentration of the solutes outside the cell is greater than that inside the cell. An easy way to remember the differences among these three solutions is to recall that *iso-* means "equal," *hypo-* means "less than," and *hyper-* means "more than."

Isotonic Solutions   If a cell is placed in an isotonic solution, the rate of osmosis into the cell is exactly the same as the rate of osmosis out of the cell. As a result, no net movement of water takes place. Isotonic solutions are important to living organisms. Plasma, the liquid portion of whole blood, is an isotonic solution with respect to blood cells. Accident victims who have lost large amounts of blood often receive transfusions of plasma instead of whole blood. This increases the volume of the victims' blood without upsetting the balance between the plasma and the blood cells.

Hypotonic Solutions   Because the concentration of solutes in a hypotonic solution is lower, the concentration of water is relatively higher in the solution than in a cell placed in the solution. Water moves from the solution into the cell—that is, from an area of higher concentration of water to an area of lower concentration of water.

Freshwater plants often exist in hypotonic solutions. As water diffuses into the cell, the cell swells and increases its

Biofact

Q: *Can osmosis affect the taste of foods?*

A: Yes. When a steak is salted before cooking, water moves out of its cells. The water is boiled away during cooking, making the meat dry and tasteless.

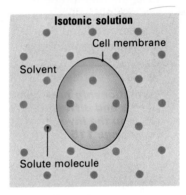

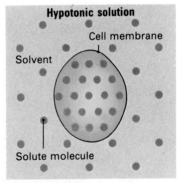

Figure 7–4. A cell placed in an isotonic solution has the same solute concentration inside and outside the cell. A cell placed in a hypotonic solution has a higher solute concentration than that of the surrounding medium.

The relationship between enzymes and diffusion is studied in the Investigation on page 115.

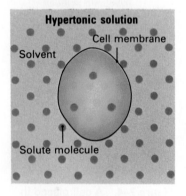

Figure 7–5. A cell placed in a hypertonic solution has a lower solute concentration than that of the surrounding medium. Water diffuses out of the cell until equilibrium is reached.

internal pressure. The pressure that builds in a plant cell as a result of osmosis is called **turgor** (TUHR guhr), or *turgor pressure.* The excess water entering a plant cell is often stored in a large central vacuole. Increase of the turgor pressure forces the cytoplasm and the cell membrane against the plant cell wall, causing the cell to become stiff. The cell wall prevents the cell from bursting. In this way, turgor makes the soft tissues of stems and leaves more rigid. Water will continue to diffuse into the plant until the solutions inside and outside the cell are in equilibrium.

Animal cells do not have a cell wall and therefore cannot reach equilibrium in a hypotonic solution. As water flows in, the cell swells and bursts. Clearly, it is very important for a cell to be able to remove excess water efficiently. A number of mechanisms have developed to remove excess water from cells. As a general rule, energy is needed to pump excess water from cells before any damage results. Unicellular organisms living in fresh water have **contractile** (kuhn TRAK tuhl) **vacuoles,** which actively pump excess water out of the cell. Freshwater fish and some other animals with gills remove excess water from their bodies through excretion.

Hypertonic Solutions   In a hypertonic solution, the concentration of solutes is higher than that inside a cell placed in the solution. As a result, the concentration of water is lower in the solution surrounding the cell than it is inside the cell itself.

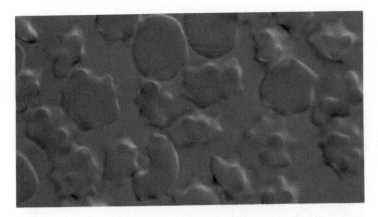

Cells placed in a hypertonic solution shrivel up and lose their shape because more water flows out of the cells than into the cells.

Drinking sea water is dangerous because the salt water of the ocean is hypertonic relative to human cells. If people drank sea water, their cells would lose more water through osmosis than the cells would take in. Some animals, however, have developed ways of living part of their lives in salt water and part in fresh water. Salmon, for example, regulate the level of salt in their body cells. These fish actively excrete salt through their gills when in salt water. In fresh water, salmon excrete urine, or waste fluids, with a low concentration of salt.

The flow of water out of the cells in a hypertonic solution can cause the loss of turgor pressure in plant cells. In northern climates, salt is often spread on roads, driveways, and sidewalks to melt ice in winter. As the ice melts, a hypertonic solution of salt and water forms and is carried away as runoff. This solution does not disappear harmlessly. Instead, it collects at the side of the road or along the edge of the driveway. If the concentration of salt collected in the soil is high enough, the plants in the affected area will wilt and die.

Reading Critically

Relating Ideas What is one method by which the human body solves the problem of excess salt in the body?

Section Review

1. **Comprehending Ideas** What is a selectively permeable membrane?
2. **Summarizing Ideas** Summarize the effects of hypotonic, hypertonic, and isotonic solutions on animal cells.
3. **Identifying Relationships** Under what conditions would a plant begin to wilt?
4. **Analyzing Conclusions** Explain why freshwater unicellular organisms must use energy to rid themselves of excess water.

Thinking Critically

- *Compare* the processes of simple diffusion and facilitated diffusion.
- *Compare* active transport and passive transport.
- *Define* the terms *endocytosis* and *exocytosis*.
- *Describe* phagocytosis and pinocytosis.

Other Means of Transport

Osmosis and diffusion take place without any use of energy by cells. For this reason, osmosis and diffusion are considered *passive* processes. These processes are not the only ways materials move across the cell membrane, however. The transport of some materials involves the active participation of the cell and in some cases the use of cell energy. Transport methods that involve work by the cell are considered *active* processes.

7.5 Carrier Transport

Carrier molecules are proteins in the cell membrane that transport large molecules or molecules that do not dissolve in the lipids that make up the cell membrane. Carrier molecules function like moving vans. They pick up other molecules on one side of the membrane, carry them across, and deposit them on the other side of the membrane.

Each carrier molecule is highly specific in its function. A carrier may transport one type of molecule and not carry another almost identical one. Although biologists do not completely understand the details of this transport method, they do know that transport by carrier molecules occurs in two ways.

Facilitated diffusion involves the use of a carrier molecule but follows the rules of simple diffusion. *In facilitated diffusion, substances move with the concentration gradient from high to low, but carrier molecules speed up the movement of diffusing substances.* The cell does not expend energy in this process. Glucose enters most cells through facilitated diffusion.

Active transport is a second transport method using carrier molecules. *Active transport involves the movement of materials against the concentration gradient.* In active transport, molecules are moved from regions of low concentration to

Figure 7–7. The diagrams below show the active transport of a sodium ion across a membrane. The sodium ion first attaches to a carrier protein (left). The protein then changes shape (center) and delivers the ion across the membrane (right).

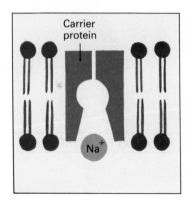
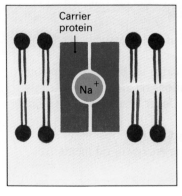
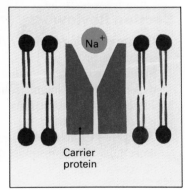

regions of higher concentration. Moving a molecule against the concentration gradient requires the use of energy. Liver cells store glucose and have a higher concentration of glucose than the surrounding bloodstream has. Thus active transport is required to move glucose into liver cells.

Many models have been proposed to show how active transport actually works. The currently preferred model suggests that a solute such as a sodium ion enters an opening in a carrier molecule located in the membrane. The carrier molecule changes its shape, channeling the sodium to the other side of the membrane, where the sodium ion is released.

7.6 Bulk Transport

Often materials that cannot pass through the membrane are transported into or out of the cell. The molecules may be so large or they may be present in such great quantities that movement through the membrane is not possible. *Bulk transport* methods allow droplets of fluid, particles of food, or globules of protein to move across the cell boundary without actually passing through the membrane. **Endocytosis** (ehn doh sy TOH sihs) is the bulk transport of substances *into* the cell. *Endo-* means "into." **Exocytosis** (ehk soh sy TOH sihs) is the bulk transport of substances *out of* the cell. *Exo-* means "out of." Cells use energy in these methods of transport.

Endocytosis Endocytosis begins as the cell membrane encloses a substance or particle, forming a pouch. The pouch is drawn into the cell and then pinched free of the cell membrane. **Phagocytosis** (fag oh sy TOH sihs) is the term used to describe the movement of solids or large particles into the cell. Amoebas use this method of taking in food. After the food particle is surrounded, the cell membrane fuses and forms a vacuole within

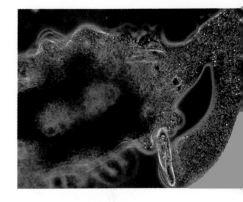

Figure 7–8. When an amoeba engulfs a paramecium (top), it does so by endocytosis. The illustration below shows the steps in this process. The cell membrane first forms a pocket (left), then pinches off (center), and food is taken into the cell (right).

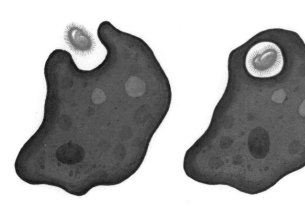
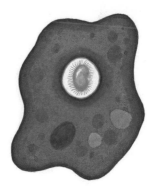

Figure 7–9. During pinocytosis (top), liquids and small particles are taken into the cell in small membrane packets. In exocytosis (bottom), materials leaving the cell are packaged in membrane sacs, transported to the cell membrane, and dumped outside the cell.

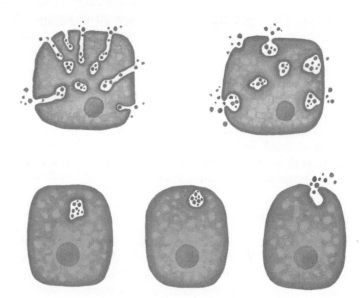

the cell. Once the food is inside the cell, lysosomes fuse with the vacuole and dissolve its contents. **Pinocytosis** (pihn oh sy TOH sihs) refers to the movement of liquids with solutes and small particles into the cell. A small region of the cell membrane forms a pocket or channel. The liquid flows into this pocket. The membrane near the entrance of the pocket comes together, leaving the membrane-enclosed vacuole inside the cell.

Exocytosis   Exocytosis is essentially the reverse of endocytosis. Substances to be removed from the cell are enclosed in membrane vacuoles. The vacuoles then move to the surface of the cell, where the membrane of the vacuole fuses with the cell membrane. The contents of the vacuole are then expelled from the cell through the opening in the membrane.

Biofact

Q: *How does a cell membrane increase in size?*

A: A cell membrane increases in size in a process similar to exocytosis. A membrane-enclosed vacuole manufactured by the Golgi bodies moves to the surface of the cell, where it fuses with the cell membrane.

Thinking Critically

Section Review

1. **Contrasting Ideas**   How is facilitated diffusion different from simple diffusion?
2. **Relating Ideas**   What is the difference in energy expenditure between active and passive transport?
3. **Identifying Relationships**   How do endocytosis and exocytosis differ? How can that difference be seen?
4. **Analyzing Ideas**   Explain the difference between facilitated diffusion and pinocytosis.

INVESTIGATION 7:
How Can an Enzyme Affect Diffusion Through a Membrane?

Objectives
- To *demonstrate* enzyme function using a selectively permeable membrane
- To *interpret* data

Materials
dialysis tubing, string, starch solution, Benedict's solution, Lugol's iodine, diastase solution, hot plate, two 250-mL beakers, 400-mL beaker water bath, water, medicine dropper, eight test tubes

Prelab Preparation
1. Distinguish between a starch and a simple sugar.
2. Explain how a cell membrane regulates the flow of molecules.
3. State the function of enzymes.
4. Name chemical tests that indicate the presence of sugars and starch.
5. Make a table, similar to the one shown.

		Starch	Sugar
Initial Test	Starch solution		
	Enzyme solution		
	B 1: Water		
	B 2: Water		
Final Test	B 1: Water		
	B 2: Water		

Inquiry: Lab Technique
6. **CAUTION: Put on safety goggles, a laboratory apron, and rubber gloves and leave them on throughout this Investigation.**
7. Use a wax pencil to label one 250-mL beaker "B 1: Starch and Enzyme" and another "B 2: Starch." You will need two sets of four test tubes. Label one test tube in each set "Starch," "Enzyme," "B 1 Water," and "B 2 Water," respectively.
8. Add 40 drops of water to each test tube. Add 20 drops of starch to each tube labeled "Starch" and 20 drops of enzyme to each tube labeled "Enzyme." Put the tubes aside.
9. Obtain two 15-cm lengths of dialysis tubing. Use string to tie off one end of each piece of tubing to make two bags.
10. Pour starch solution into each bag until it is two-thirds full. Into only one bag add 20 drops of enzyme solution. Use string to seal each bag. Rinse the bags with water.
11. Place each bag into the appropriately labeled beaker and cover each bag with water.
12. Add 20 drops of liquid from the "B 1: Starch and Enzyme" beaker to each test tube labeled "B 1: Water." Add 20 drops of liquid from the "B 2: Starch" beaker to each test tube labeled "B 2: Water."
13. Set the beakers aside for 15 minutes.
14. Using one set of test tubes and Lugol's iodine, test the liquid in each beaker for the presence of starch.
15. **CAUTION: Use goggles and rubber gloves. Do not get Benedict's solution in your eyes or on your skin. Immediately rinse any exposed area.** Using the second set of test tubes and Benedict's solution, test the liquid in each beaker for the presence of sugar.
16. Clean all the test tubes before continuing with this Investigation.
17. After 15 minutes, test samples from each beaker for the presence of both starch and sugar.

Analysis
1. **Evaluating Methods** Why was it necessary to make initial tests of the starch solution, enzyme solution, and beaker water?
2. **Analyzing Observations** Describe the contents of each dialysis bag and explain how the data support your description.
3. **Analyzing Ideas** Explain how the dialysis membrane demonstrates selective permeability.

Chapter 7 Review

Summary

Both the speed of molecules and the distance between them increase as matter changes from solid to liquid to gas. The motion of molecules in liquids and gases is random.

Molecules diffuse from areas of higher concentration to areas of lower concentration. A rise in temperature, pressure, or concentration increases the rate of diffusion.

Osmosis is the diffusion of water. Diffusion and osmosis do not require that the cell use energy. An isotonic solution has the same concentration of solutes as that of a cell immersed in the solution. No net movement of solutes or water takes place across the cell membrane. A hypotonic solution has a lower concentration of solutes than the concentration of those solutes inside the cell. As a result, water moves into the cell. A hypertonic solution has a higher concentration of solutes than the cell, causing water to move out of the cell.

Turgor pressure increases as water flows into a plant cell. Turgor stiffens plant tissues.

Some substances are transported across the cell membrane by carrier molecules. Facilitated diffusion does not require energy; active transport does. Large molecules are moved in and out of the cell by bulk transport. Bulk transport methods require the use of energy.

BioTerms

active transport (**112**)
carrier molecule (**112**)
concentration
    gradient (**106**)
contractile
    vacuole (**110**)
diffusion (**105**)
endocytosis (**113**)
equilibrium (**109**)
exocytosis (**113**)

facilitated
    diffusion (**112**)
hypertonic
    solution (**109**)
hypotonic
    solution (**109**)
isotonic solution (**109**)
osmosis (**108**)
phagocytosis (**113**)
pinocytosis (**114**)

selectively
    permeable (**108**)
solute (**105**)

solution (**105**)
solvent (**105**)
turgor (**110**)

For each pair of terms, explain the differences in their meanings.

1. osmosis, diffusion
2. pinocytosis, phagocytosis
3. hypotonic solution, hypertonic solution
4. solute, solvent

BioQuiz   (Write all answers on a separate sheet of paper.)

Completion

1. Turgor pressure builds up in a plant cell as a result of _____ .
2. Wastes move out of cells by _____ .
3. A _____ membrane allows some substances to pass through but prevents others from doing so.
4. The dissolved substance in a solution is a _____ .
5. The bulk transport of substances out of a cell is called _____ .

Multiple Choice

6. Cells swell in _____ solution.
   a) a hypertonic   b) a hypotonic
   c) an isotonic   d) an aqueous
7. Active transport moves substances against   a) the cell membrane.
   b) equilibrium.   c) the concentration gradient.   d) selective permeability.
8. _____ moves liquids into a cell.
   a) Pinocytosis   b) Phagocytosis
   c) Exocytosis   d) Hemolysis

9. Which of the following affects the rate of diffusion? a) temperature b) pressure c) concentration d) All choices are correct.
10. The diffusion of water into cells is called a) bulk transport. b) osmosis. c) phagocytosis. d) pinocytosis.
11. Some organisms pump water out of the cell via a) contractile vacuoles. b) turgor pressure. c) phagocytosis. d) pinocytosis.
12. Water is vital to cellular transport because it a) contains necessary oxygen. b) is lightweight. c) is the most common solvent. d) is isotonic.
13. The cytolysis of red blood cells is known as a) pinocytosis. b) hemolysis. c) exocytosis. d) diffusion.
14. Some proteins in the cell membrane function as a) carrier molecules. b) solvents. c) contractile vacuoles.
d) concentration gradients.
15. Materials that pass across the cell boundary but not through the membrane do so by a) diffusion. b) osmosis. c) equilibrium. d) bulk transport.

Writing Critically

16. Describe the characteristics of the cell membrane that account for its selective permeability.
17. Will a teaspoon of salt dissolve more quickly in a cup of fresh water or a cup of salt water? Why?
18. How do freshwater fish rid themselves of excess water?
19. Why do raisins plump up more quickly in hot water than in cold water?
20. How do scientists prepare samples of cell membranes for study?

Application/Critical Thinking

1. **Drawing Conclusions** Cells taken from a frog and a human are placed in an 0.8 percent salt solution. The frog cells swell and burst, while the human cells shrink. Explain these results.
2. **Identifying Relationships** Why might overfertilization result in wilted plants?
3. **Analyzing Results** Chemicals that dissolve easily in fat pass through the cell membrane more quickly than fat-insoluble molecules of similar size and weight. Suggest an explanation for this phenomenon.
4. **Evaluating Experiments** Determine the concentration of salt that is isotonic to plant cells, such as *Elodea*, by placing leaves of the plant in solutions that vary in salt concentration. What should you look for?

Cross-Discipline Connection

Biology and Language Increase your science vocabulary by studying the meaning of prefixes in "Building a Science Vocabulary" on pages 938–942 of the appendix.

Discovery Through Reading

Read the article "Gatekeeper Protein Pictured in Profile," *Science News* (November 19, 1988): 327. This article focuses on the discovery of the shape of an ion channel in the cell membrane. What is the function of the ion channel within the cell membrane? Describe the shape of the ion channel. What kinds of drugs might researchers be able to produce as a result of the research reported in this article?

Cells and Energy

Outline

**The cells of plants capture energy
from sunlight**

Focus

Like a machine, a cell does work and requires energy. The cell requires a specialized form of energy called *chemical energy*. Some cells can convert sunlight energy to chemical energy. All cells carry on processes that make energy available to carry on life activities.

■ *What life activities performed by cells require energy?*

■ *Does diffusion through a cell membrane require energy?*

Energy for Living Cells

Cells require chemical energy to undertake the many tasks necessary for life. This energy is stored in the form of chemical bonds in food. However, food molecules cannot deliver energy directly to living systems. The energy stored in food's chemical bonds must first be transferred to molecules capable of providing energy where and when it is needed.

8.1 Energy Transfer in Cells

Like all chemical reactions, the reactions that take place within cells require energy to get started. This extra energy, called *activation energy*, enables molecules to collide with enough force to break existing chemical bonds. Within cells, proteins called *enzymes* lower the amount of activation energy needed to start reactions. Enzymes allow reactions to occur that normally could not take place in a cell. Enzymes come in many different shapes. Figure 8–1 is a model that shows how enzymes combine briefly with the reacting molecules, then are released unchanged. Enzymes themselves are not used up in a reaction.

Many reactions within cells are *endergonic*. That means that in addition to activation energy, these reactions require a steady input of energy to keep them going. In most cases, this energy is supplied by a molecule called **ATP** (adenosine triphosphate). ATP consists of a base, a sugar, and a chain of three phosphates. The base is *adenine* and the sugar is *ribose*. Together they form *adenosine*. Attached to the adenosine are three phosphates. Adenosine with one phosphate, represented as Ⓟ, is called AMP (adenosine monophosphate). Adenosine with two phosphates is called ADP (adenosine diphosphate).

The bond that joins the second and third phosphates in ATP is easily broken. Enzymes allow ATP to readily transfer the third phosphate to another molecule. ***By transferring a phosphate, ATP provides energy that can be used to drive endergonic reactions in the cell.*** ATP is the transfer molecule that allows the energy in food molecules to be delivered to cells wherever needed.

To understand this process more clearly, consider a hypothetical reaction:

$$W + X \rightarrow Y + Z$$

If the products of this reaction, Y and Z, have more energy in their chemical bonds than do the reactants, W and X, then this reaction is an endergonic one. It will not take place without the

Section Objectives

- *State* the function of ATP in cells.
- *Diagram* and *explain* the ATP-ADP cycle.
- *Explain* the role of enzymes in chemical reactions.

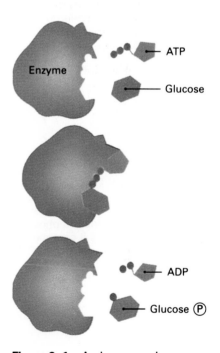

Figure 8–1. A glucose molecule is activated when it receives a phosphate group from ATP. This reaction requires an enzyme that brings the molecules close to one another.

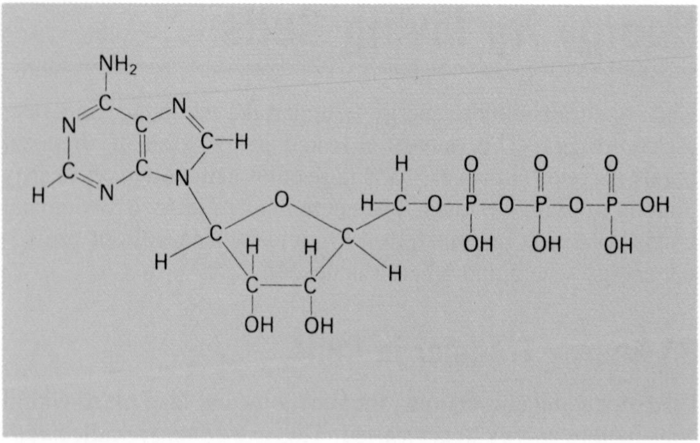

Figure 8–2. ATP, ADP, and AMP differ only in the number of phosphate groups that are attached to the adenosine molecule. ATP has three phosphate groups, ADP has two, and AMP has one.

Reading Critically

Evaluating Relationships
What part of the equation provides the necessary energy for the endergonic reaction shown?

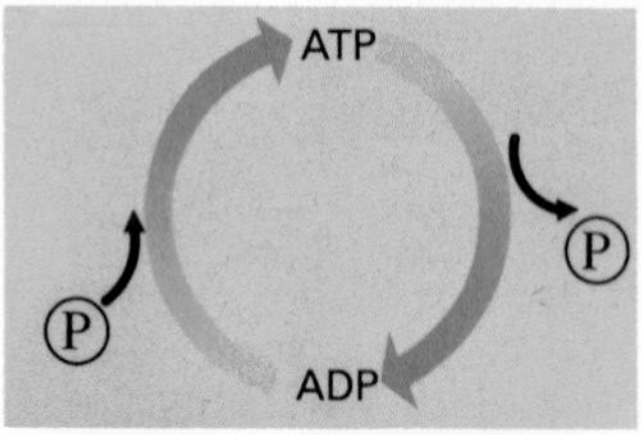

Figure 8–3. ATP becomes ADP when it loses a phosphate group as it contributes energy to cell reactions. ATP is then reformed from ADP during cellular respiration.

Thinking Critically

input of energy. This energy is supplied by the transfer of a phosphate from ATP to one of the reactants:

$$ATP + W \rightarrow ADP + W-\textcircled{P}$$

W has formed a new bond with $\textcircled{P}$, so $W-\textcircled{P}$ has more energy than W. In fact, $W-\textcircled{P}$ and X have more energy than Y and Z. As a result, the reaction can now proceed as follows:

$$W-\textcircled{P} + X \rightarrow Y + Z + \textcircled{P}$$

8.2 ATP-ADP Cycle

For ATP to be an effective energy transfer molecule, it must lose its final phosphate group. The phosphate group is returned to ATP by adding a $\textcircled{P}$ to ADP. The series of reactions between ATP and ADP form a cycle; the products of the first reaction are used for the second. In terms of energy, the ATP-ADP cycle can be compared to a battery that would be able to continually recharge itself. The reforming of ATP recharges the battery.

The phosphate group is returned to ATP by adding a $\textcircled{P}$ to ADP during the process of **cellular respiration.** Glucose is broken down and the energy in its chemical bonds transferred to the energy bonds of ATP. The glucose used is produced through **photosynthesis,** a process in which green plants convert the energy from sunlight into chemical energy.

Section Review

1. **Summarizing Ideas**   What is the function of ATP?
2. **Summarizing Ideas**   Explain the ATP-ADP cycle.
3. **Inferring Conclusions**   How would cellular reactions be affected by the absence of enzymes?

Capturing Energy

The ultimate source of the energy that powers cells is the sun. Green plants and certain other organisms capture the light energy of the sun through the process of photosynthesis.

8.3 Requirements for Photosynthesis

Photosynthesis requires light, chlorophyll, and raw materials. Enzymes are needed for the reactions to proceed. The chlorophyll present in plants traps light from the sun. Carbon dioxide from the air and water absorbed through the roots are the usual raw materials for photosynthesis. Glucose, a six-carbon sugar, is the end product of photosynthesis. Oxygen and water are byproducts. A summary of the process of photosynthesis can be written as the equation:

$$6CO_2 + 12H_2O \xrightarrow{\text{light, enzymes, chlorophyll}} C_6H_{12}O_6 + 6O_2 + 6H_2O$$

This equation summarizes the overall process of photosynthesis. It does not show the many individual reactions.

The rate of photosynthesis depends on factors such as the availability of the raw materials, the intensity of the sunlight, and the temperature. If water becomes scarce, as when a severe drought occurs, photosynthesis may stop altogether. The greater the intensity of sunlight, in general, the higher the rate of photosynthesis. A temperature range of between 20°C (68°F.) and 35°C (95°F.) is best. Above 35°C and below 0°C, the activity of the enzymes required for chemical reactions is lessened and the rate of photosynthesis decreases.

Light Light provides the energy for photosynthesis. To understand how this energy is converted into chemical energy, you must understand something about the nature of light.

The visible portion of the sun's light is but a small part of the radiation emitted by the sun. When white light passes through a prism, the light spreads out into an array of colors called the **visible spectrum.** This effect can also be observed when water droplets in the atmosphere act as a prism, producing a rainbow.

Light energy comes in packets, or units, called **photons.** The energy is not the same for all kinds of light. A photon of violet light, for example, has almost twice the energy of a photon of red light.

Section Objectives

● *State* the function of each of the pigments involved in photosynthesis.
● *List* the requirements for photosynthesis to occur and the products that result from this process.
● *Summarize* the main events of the light and dark reactions of photosynthesis.

Biofact

Q: *Does photosynthesis always use carbon dioxide and water as raw materials?*

A: No. Some forms of bacteria use hydrogen sulfide in place of water to complete photosynthesis.

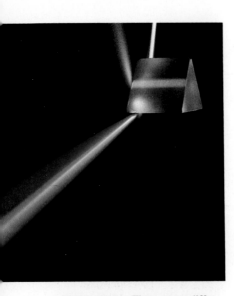

Figure 8–4. The many different wavelengths that make up sunlight are revealed when light passes through a prism. Green plants reflect some wavelengths but use others for processes such as photosynthesis.

The color of an object seen by the eye is the color of light reflected by the object. A red dress, for example, absorbs all of the visible spectrum except red, which is reflected. Green plants reflect the green portion of the spectrum, while absorbing other colors. The violet, blue, and red portions of the spectrum provide the most energy for photosynthesis.

Chlorophyll and Other Pigments Substances that absorb light are called **pigments.** Early investigators demonstrated that only the green parts of plants performed photosynthesis. **Chlorophyll** (KLAWR uh fihl), the green pigment present in plants, is necessary for photosynthesis to begin. Chorophyll absorbs energy from all but the green portion of the visible spectrum. Several types of chlorophyll are active in the presence of light. Plants contain *chlorophyll a* and *chlorophyll b*; other types of chlorophyll are found in other photosynthetic organisms.

Chlorophyll acts as a "light trap" during photosynthesis. When a photon strikes a chlorophyll molecule and is absorbed, the photon's energy is transferred to an electron of the chlorophyll molecule. The electron is raised to a higher energy level. Energized electrons are like stretched rubber bands—they cannot remain for long in this "excited" state. As the electron returns to its original energy level, it releases the absorbed energy, which is then used in chemical reactions.

Xanthophylls (ZAN thuh fihlz) are yellow pigments that absorb light energy in other parts of the spectrum and pass it on to chlorophyll. **Carotenes** are orange pigments that perform the same function. These two pigments are present in most green plants but in lesser amounts than chlorophyll, which usually masks their presence. In the fall when many leaves stop producing chlorophyll, xanthophyll and carotene become more prominent. As a result, the foliage changes to its autumn colors of red, yellow, and orange. The red leaves of brown algae and plants such as coleus and begonias also are due to the presence of accessory pigments, which mask the presence of chlorophyll.

In blue-green bacteria, which are prokaryotes, pigments involved in photosynthesis are part of a membrane system found throughout the cytoplasm. Green plants, however, are eukaryotes. Their chlorophyll and other photosynthetic pigments are found in chloroplasts.

Figure 8–5 shows that a chloroplast consists of flattened structures enclosed by a double membrane. Photosynthesis begins in the **grana,** stacks of tiny disklike sacs. These stacks look like dark dots when seen under an electron microscope. A fluid-filled space, the **stroma,** is found between the grana and the outer membranes.

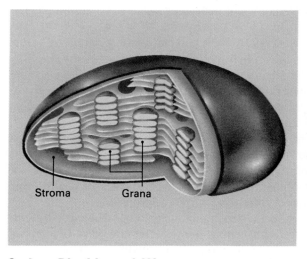

Stroma   Grana

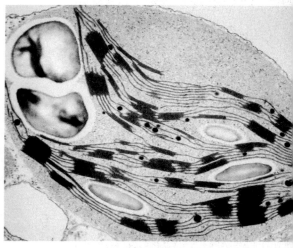

Carbon Dioxide and Water   Carbon dioxide (CO_2) is the source of the carbon and oxygen atoms used in constructing glucose. Plants use water (H_2O) as the source of the hydrogen atoms needed in making glucose. Plants release oxygen from the water molecule into the air. This process is the source of most of the oxygen found in the atmosphere.

8.4 The Process of Photosynthesis

Biochemists divide the process of photosynthesis into two phases. The first phase is called the **light reactions,** or light phase. As the name implies, this phase uses light energy. *Light reactions involve the trapping of light energy and the formation of materials required in the next phase of the process.* Light reactions can proceed only in the presence of light.

The **dark reactions** comprise the second phase of photosynthesis. *The dark reactions use the products from the light reactions to form glucose.* Thus the light reactions must take place for the dark reactions to proceed. The two phases together form one continuous process. The reactions of the dark phase are not part of the light-trapping process. The dark reactions can occur with or without light; they do not require light.

The Light Reactions   The light reactions of photosynthesis use some of the trapped energy to convert ADP into ATP, which stores the energy for later use. Some energy is also used to split water molecules into hydrogen and oxygen.

The light reactions can be described as a series of steps. Some of these steps happen simultaneously. Follow these steps in Figure 8–6 on the next page as you read.

Figure 8–5.   Disklike membranes inside the chloroplasts are stacked atop one another to form grana (above left). Magnified 44,000 times (above), grana appear as dense, membranous layers embedded in the stroma. The light reactions of photosynthesis take place in the grana, the dark reactions in the stroma.

The Investigation on page 135 explores the effect of temperature on the rate of photosynthesis.

For information about a career as a plant physiologist, see pages 934–935.

1. The chlorophyll molecules in the grana absorb photons of light.
2. The energy from the photons boosts electrons (e⁻) from the chlorophyll molecules to a higher energy level.
3. The energized electrons move from one molecule to another in a series of reactions called an **electron transport chain.** Each time a transfer is made, some energy is released.
4. The energy released from the electrons as they move down the electron transport chain is used ultimately to form ATP molecules by uniting ADP molecules and phosphates. Both ADP and phosphates are readily available in the stroma of the chloroplast.
5. The electrons lost from the chlorophyll molecule are replaced by electrons from a water molecule. This process splits the water molecule into hydrogen ions and oxygen gas. The hydrogen combines with a *hydrogen acceptor* molecule, a molecule that readily accepts hydrogen ions. The oxygen escapes into the atmosphere.

The release of energy as electrons are transferred from molecule to molecule in the electron transport chain can be compared to water falling from a height. The water can fall free in a waterfall, its energy unharnessed. The falling water can also be directed so that it hits the paddles of a wheel. The water hitting the paddles turns the wheel. Each time the water hits another

Figure 8–6. The light reactions of photosynthesis take place in the parts of the plant that contain chlorophyll. Light energy is used to split water into hydrogen ions and oxygen gas. In the process, electrons are released and ATP is formed. ATP and the hydrogen ions are then used in the dark reactions.

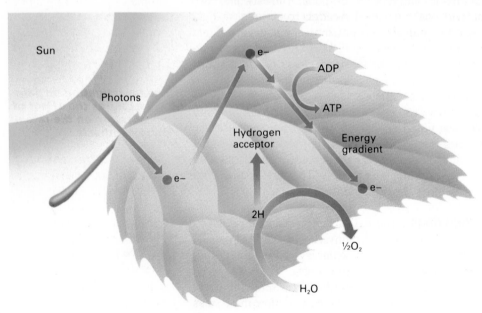

paddle, it holds less energy. By the time the water reaches the bottom of the wheel, the water is almost still. Its original energy has been captured to do the work of turning the wheel. In the same way, the energy of electrons is captured for the work of the cell.

The Dark Reactions The second phase of photosynthesis uses the energy stored in ATP and the hydrogen locked into the hydrogen acceptor to form glucose. This phase uses carbon

---

dioxide as a source of carbon for the glucose. The dark phase requires several enzymes and forms several byproducts. This second phase of photosynthesis takes place in the stroma of the chloroplasts.

The dark phase is also known as the *Calvin cycle*. This name recognizes the work of Melvin Calvin, the American scientist who first identified the process in the 1950s. The cycle begins and ends with a five-carbon sugar, **RuBP** (ribulose bisphosphate), which is abundant in chloroplasts. There are four major steps in the cycle. As you read, follow these steps in Figure 8–7.

1. Carbon dioxide from the atmosphere combines with RuBP in a series of reactions. These reactions use ATP as the energy source and form a substance called *PGA* (phosphoglyceric acid), a molecule containing three carbon atoms.
2. PGA reacts with hydrogen from the light reactions to form **PGAL** (phosphoglyceraldehyde).
3. Most of the PGAL formed during the dark reactions is used to make more RuBP. This RuBP then unites with more carbon dioxide, beginning another cycle of dark reactions.
4. Some of the PGAL is combined to form glucose. Two three-carbon molecules of PGAL are required to form one molecule of glucose ($C_6H_{12}O_6$).

Figure 8–7. The dark reactions begin when carbon dioxide from the atmosphere unites with the five-carbon sugar ribulose bisphosphate (RuBP). The resulting six-carbon molecule is then broken down into phosphoglyceraldehyde (PGAL). Some PGAL is used to synthesize glucose—food for plants and animals.

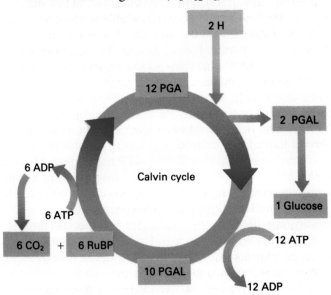

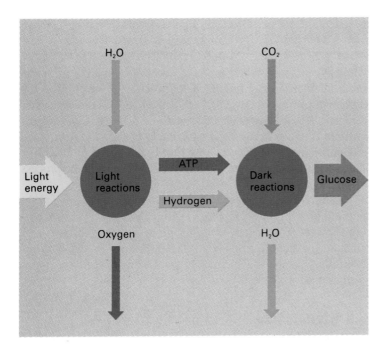

Figure 8–8. Photosynthesis consists of two sets of reactions. The light reactions are driven by the energy of sunlight, which is captured by chlorophyll. The dark reactions use ATP and hydrogen ions from the light reactions to convert atmospheric carbon dioxide into glucose.

Glucose formed in photosynthesis is often not immediately used by the plant. Some glucose is stored by plants in the form of starch, a polysaccharide made of thousands of glucose molecules. When glucose is needed, the cell breaks down starch and releases just as much glucose as is demanded. In this way, plants regulate the amount of glucose available to the cells. If large amounts of starch must be stored, the plant often forms a special storage organ. A white potato, for example, is a plant stem that is modified to hold excess amounts of starch.

Plants also combine glucose molecules to form other carbohydrates, including sucrose, the commonly used table sugar. Cellulose, the material that makes up plant cell walls, is also formed from the union of many glucose molecules.

Section Review

1. **Summarizing Ideas** Describe the functions of chlorophyll, xanthophyll, and carotene in photosynthesis.
2. **Organizing Ideas** List the requirements for photosynthesis and the resultant products.
3. **Identifying Relationships** How is PGAL formed during the dark reactions, and how is it used?
4. **Inferring Relationships** What steps must be accomplished during the light reactions before the dark reactions can proceed?

Thinking Critically

Section Objectives

- *Summarize* the process of glycolysis.
- *Contrast* fermentation with aerobic respiration and state uses for each.
- *State* the overall role of the Krebs cycle and electron transport chain in aerobic respiration.
- *Identify* the relationship between autotrophs and heterotrophs.
- *List* some commercial uses of fermentation.

Releasing Energy

Although respiration and breathing are often thought of as the same, they are in fact two different processes. Breathing is the exchange of gases between an organism and its external environment. Respiration occurs within all living cells. ***Cellular respiration involves breaking the chemical bonds of organic food molecules and releasing energy that can be used by the cells.*** These food molecules are produced in plants during the process of photosynthesis.

Cellular respiration may be compared in some ways to the burning of a log in a fireplace. Both release energy. Burning a log, however, is an uncontrolled process that gives off large amounts of heat energy. Cellular respiration is an enzyme-controlled process in which amounts of energy are given off and then trapped in molecules of ATP.

8.5 Glycolysis

The first step in cellular respiration is a process called **glycolysis** (gly KAHL uh sihs). In glycolysis, a glucose molecule is broken in half to form two three-carbon molecules of a substance called **pyruvic** (py ROO vihk) **acid.**

Glycolysis takes place in the cytoplasm of the cell. The process involves a series of nine enzyme-controlled reactions. Two reactions early in the process are endergonic; each requires the input of one molecule of ATP. The later reactions release enough energy to combine four molecules of ADP and four molecules of free phosphate to get four molecules of ATP. Thus, glycolysis produces an overall gain of two molecules of ATP for each molecule of glucose.

In addition to producing two three-carbon molecules of pyruvic acid and two ATPs, glycolysis also releases four hydrogen atoms. These hydrogens then combine with a hydrogen acceptor, as in the light reactions of photosynthesis. The following equation summarizes the overall reaction:

$$C_6H_{12}O_6 \rightarrow 2C_2H_3OCOOH + 4H$$
$$\text{glucose} \qquad \text{pyruvic acid}$$

Glycolysis is an **anaerobic** (an ehr OH bihk) process—that is, no oxygen is required for the process to take place. Glycolysis is followed by one of two processes. If oxygen is present in the cell, the pyruvic acid is broken down further through the process of **aerobic** (ehr OH bihk) **respiration.** This process results in an additional gain of ATP molecules. Without oxygen,

All life on Earth is locked together in a never-ending cycle of construction and destruction. Green plants use the energy of the sun to turn carbon dioxide and water into glucose and oxygen. Both plants and animals consume the glucose and oxygen and in turn give off carbon dioxide and water. The plants use these products to continue the cycle.

Green plants and other organisms that can use inorganic molecules to produce organic food molecules are called **autotrophs** (AWT uh trahfs). Many organisms cannot produce their own food molecules from inorganic substances. They are called **heterotrophs** (HEHT

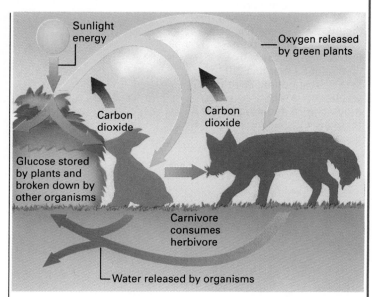

Sunlight energy

Oxygen released by green plants

Carbon dioxide

Carbon dioxide

Glucose stored by plants and broken down by other organisms

Carnivore consumes herbivore

Water released by organisms

uhr uh trahfs). Heterotrophic organisms must rely on autotrophs for energy. All life depends on autotrophs, because only autotrophs are able to convert

light and energy into food.
■ **Identifying Relationships** Explain why humans are heterotrophs even though they grow their own food crops.

the pyruvic acid cannot be used to release more energy. However, the hydrogen acceptor molecules must release the hydrogen atoms, or else glycolysis could not continue. Hydrogen atoms are removed through **fermentation,** an anaerobic process that breaks down pyruvic acid into ethyl alcohol or lactic acid. Together, the processes of glycolysis and fermentation make up **anaerobic respiration.**

8.6 Fermentation

Fermentation occurs in some of the less complex organisms, such as some bacteria and yeasts. Most microorganisms ferment pyruvic acid to ethyl alcohol, while some animal cells and other microorganisms produce lactic acid.

In *alcoholic fermentation* the hydrogen and the pyruvic acid formed during glycolysis combine to produce ethyl alcohol.

Reading Critically

Comparing Processes What are the differences between fermentation and photosynthesis?

Figure 8–9. This diagram summarizes the reactions of cellular respiration, which occur in the mitochondria. First, two ATPs are produced as glucose is broken down by glycolysis to pyruvic acid. The pyruvic acid is then further broken down by fermentation (anaerobic), or aerobic respiration. Aerobic respiration is highly efficient, producing 36 additional ATPs for every glucose molecule used.

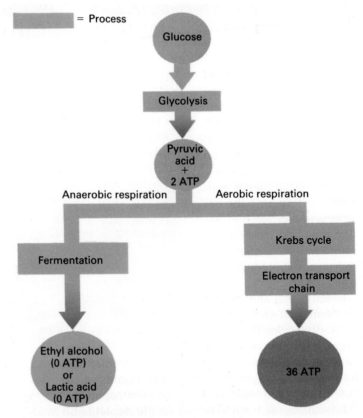

Carbon dioxide is given off as a byproduct. The general equation of the process can be written:

$$2C_2H_3OCOOH + 4H \rightarrow 2C_2H_5OH + 2CO_2$$
pyruvic acid   ethyl alcohol

Most of the energy originally stored in the glucose remains in the bonds of the ethyl alcohol molecule. For this reason, alcohol is a good fuel.

In *lactic acid fermentation* pyruvic acid and hydrogen from glycolysis combine to form lactic acid. The general equation for this process can be written:

$$2C_2H_3OCOOH + 4H \rightarrow 2CH_3CHOHCOOH$$
pyruvic acid   lactic acid

Lactic acid fermentation occurs in animal muscle cells. When oxygen is available, these cells carry on aerobic respiration. During strenuous exercise, oxygen concentration diminishes, and muscle cells are forced to use lactic acid fermentation. This process uses the hydrogen stored by the hydrogen acceptor molecule and makes the acceptor molecule available

Biofact

Q: *How many ATP molecules are used by a human cell in a minute?*

A: It is estimated that each cell in a human body uses 1 billion to 2 billion molecules of ATP each minute.

for reuse in glycolysis to obtain more energy. The accumulation of lactic acid in the cells is one of the causes of muscle soreness. When the oxygen concentration returns to normal, the lactic acid is converted back to pyruvic acid, aerobic respiration is begun again, and the soreness fades.

8.7 Aerobic Respiration

Like fermentation, aerobic respiration also begins with the pyruvic acid produced through glycolysis. Although glycolysis takes place in the cytoplasm of the cell, aerobic respiration takes place on the folded membranes inside the mitochondria. Associated with these folded membranes are all the enzymes and coenzymes needed in the reactions that make up the process of aerobic respiration.

The equation for aerobic respiration is essentially the reverse of that for photosynthesis:

$$C_6H_{12}O_6 + 6O_2 \xrightarrow{\text{enzymes}} 6CO_2 + 6H_2O + \text{energy}$$
glucose

Aerobic respiration results in a maximum energy gain of 38 molecules of ATP from each molecule of glucose—that is, 36

ATPs are produced in the mitochondria in addition to the 2 gained from cytoplasmic glycolysis. Some cells, because of a high metabolic rate, must produce a greater amount of energy. Brain cells and muscle cells, for example, contain large numbers of mitochondria.

Aerobic respiration delivers higher energy yields than anaerobic respiration. The highly active and complex organisms that inhabit the Earth today may not have evolved without the energy provided by aerobic respiration.

Pyruvic Acid Conversion The first step of aerobic respiration is the breakdown of pyruvic acid into carbon dioxide, hydrogen, and a two-carbon acetyl group. The carbon dioxide is released as a waste product, and the hydrogen combines with a hydrogen acceptor. The acetyl group then combines with a molecule called *coenzyme A* (CoA) and forms **acetyl CoA.** The function of coenzyme A is to carry the acetyl group into the next stage of respiration, the Krebs cycle.

Krebs Cycle The acetyl CoA produced from pyruvic acid transfers its acetyl group to a four-carbon molecule to form a six-carbon molecule called **citric acid.** The citric acid then enters a series of reactions called the **Krebs cycle,** or *citric acid cycle*. This reaction series involves many enzymes and coenzymes found within the mitochondria. The Krebs cycle occurs in a series of steps that begin and end with the same substance, citric acid. In other words, some of the molecules required to begin the cycle are re-formed by the reactions that end the cycle.

The reactions of the Krebs cycle involve breaking the chemical bonds between carbon and hydrogen atoms and forming

Figure 8–10. The Krebs cycle is the heart of aerobic respiration. Pyruvic acid from glycolysis is converted to an acetyl group that enters the cycle after combining with coenzyme A. As the cycle turns, hydrogen ions are released. These ions are picked up by hydrogen acceptors and carried to the electron transport chain.

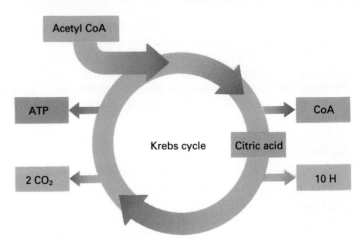

new compounds. As Figure 8–10 shows, one turn of the cycle produces two molecules of carbon dioxide as a waste product. The hydrogen atoms removed during the cycle combine with hydrogen acceptors. Some of the energy released during one turn of the cycle is used to convert one molecule of ADP to ATP. Most of the rest of the energy is in the form of electrons in the hydrogen atoms transferred to the hydrogen acceptors.

Electron Transport Chain   By the end of the Krebs cycle, energy from the original glucose molecule has been used to produce four molecules of ATP—two during glycolysis and two during the Krebs cycle. Most of the energy of the glucose, however, remains in the hydrogen atoms transferred to acceptor molecules. There are 24 of these hydrogens—2 from glycolysis, 2 from the conversion of pyruvic acid, and 20 from the Krebs cycle.

In the final stage of aerobic respiration, energy from the 24 hydrogen atoms is released and used to produce ATP. This process occurs in an electron transport chain similar to the one in photosynthesis. The process begins as the 24 hydrogen atoms form 12 pairs of hydrogen ions and 12 pairs of electrons. The electrons are then passed in pairs from molecule to molecule in the electron transport chain. Each transfer is accompanied by a small loss in energy for the electron. The energy released is used to form ATP.

At the end of the chain, the electrons combine with hydrogen ions and oxygen atoms to form water. The oxygen comes from the air and is the final hydrogen acceptor in the process of aerobic respiration.

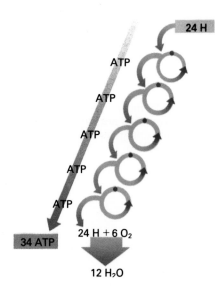

Figure 8–11. The electron transport chain consists of a series of molecules that accept and donate hydrogen ions arriving from the Krebs cycle. As ions pass down the chain they release energy and ATP is formed.

Table 8–1: A Comparison of Respiration and Photosynthesis

	Photosynthesis	**Respiration**
Result of reactions	Production of organic carbon compound	Breakdown of organic carbon compound
Where reactions occur	Chlorophyll-containing cells	All living cells
When reactions occur	In the presence of light (some reactions take place in the dark)	All the time
Gases and compounds required	Carbon dioxide, water	Oxygen, organic carbon compounds
Gases and compounds produced	Oxygen, organic carbon compounds	Carbon dioxide, water
Energy source	Light	Chemical bonds
Energy result	Energy stored in chemical bonds	Energy released from chemical bonds

Figure 8–12. During the processes of glycolysis and aerobic respiration, the energy present in the chemical bonds of one glucose molecule is transferred to the energy in the phosphate bonds of 38 molecules of ATP. The processes are structured so that energy is released a little at a time.

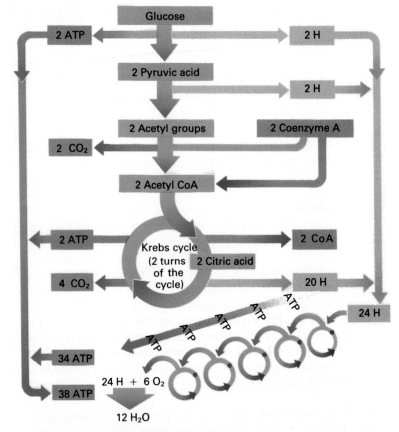

Summary of ATP Produced As Figure 8–12 shows, *the complete breakdown of one molecule of glucose results in a maximum net yield of 38 molecules of ATP.* Glycolysis and the Krebs cycle each yield a net gain of 2 ATP. The electron transport chain produces 34 ATP molecules.

Section Review

1. **Organizing Ideas** Describe the process of glycolysis.
2. **Comparing Ideas** How are fermentation and aerobic respiration different? Give examples of each.
3. **Evaluating Ideas** Describe the net gain of ATP molecules from one glucose molecule by each of the following: glycolysis, conversion of pyruvic acid, Krebs cycle, electron transport chain.
4. **Listing Ideas** Name three commercial uses of fermentation.

> **Thinking Critically**

5. **Inferring Relationships** Explain why heterotrophs can not live without autotrophs.

INVESTIGATION 8:
Does Temperature Affect the Rate of Photosynthesis?

Objectives
- To *measure* the rate of photosynthesis
- To *evaluate* the effect of temperature on the rate of photosynthesis

Materials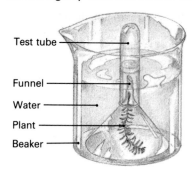

water, 1000-mL beaker, sodium bicarbonate, *Elodea,* glass funnel, test tube, thermometer, watch with second hand, single-edge razor blade

Prelab Preparation

1. Write a summary equation of photosynthesis.
2. Name the product of photosynthesis that would be easiest to measure in an aquatic plant. Explain your answer.
3. List physical factors that might affect the rate of photosynthesis.
4. Discuss the problem stated in the title of this Investigation with your partner. Then state a hypothesis that relates to this problem. Explain how you arrived at your hypothesis.

Inquiry: Experimentation

5. Pour water into the beaker until it is half full. Dissolve 3 g of sodium bicarbonate in the water. Record your observations.
6. Cut off the end of a fresh sprig of *Elodea* at a 45° angle. Insert the cut end into the stem of the funnel. Place the funnel, upside down, into the beaker. Add water to the beaker until the funnel is submerged.
7. Fill a test tube with water. Placing your thumb tightly over the mouth of the test tube, invert the tube and place it over the narrow end of the funnel.
8. Use a thermometer to find the temperature of the water in the beaker.
9. Set the beaker in direct sunlight or under a bright light. After five minutes observe the funnel. Record your observations.
10. Count the bubbles for 210 seconds. Record the total number of bubbles for each 30-second interval.
11. Measure the water temperature again. If it has changed by more than three degrees, find the average of the two temperatures. Use this average as the water's temperature.
12. *How might the identity of the gas collecting in the test tube be confirmed?*
13. Pour the water from the beaker and replace it with water differing in temperature by five to eight degrees.
14. Add 3 g of sodium bicarbonate to the water and repeat steps 6–11.
15. Graph your data. Use a separate line for data collected at each temperature.

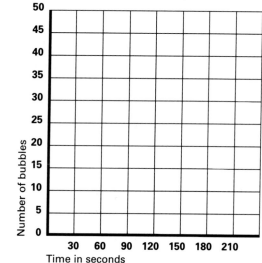

Test tube
Funnel
Water
Plant
Beaker

Analysis

1. **Summarizing Data** Use your graph to write a summary of your results.
2. **Inferring Ideas** Explain how your data support your hypothesis.

Chapter 8 Review

Summary

Cell processes depend on the transfer of energy. A special molecule, ATP, stores, carries, and releases energy as needed in the cell.

All energy used by cells originally comes from sunlight. Through photosynthesis, green plants trap light energy and convert it into chemical energy stored in the bonds of glucose. The light reactions of photosynthesis use light energy to produce ATP and to split water into hydrogen ions, oxygen, and electrons. The dark reactions utilize the ATP and hydrogen ions in the formation of glucose.

Cellular respiration releases the ATP energy that was trapped during photosynthesis. Anaerobic respiration takes place without oxygen. The process begins with glycolysis. During fermentation, pyruvic acid is converted to alcohol or lactic acid. This process does not produce any additional ATP, but is required for glycolysis to continue. Aerobic respiration requires free oxygen. The pyruvic acid produced during glycolysis is broken down further in the Krebs cycle and the electron transport chain. The final product is a maximum additional 36, or a total of 38, molecules of ATP.

BioTerms

acetyl CoA (132)
aerobic respiration (128)
anaerobic (128)
anaerobic respiration (129)
ATP (119)
autotroph (129)
carotene (122)
cellular respiration (120)
chlorophyll (122)

citric acid (132)
dark reactions (123)
electron transport chain (124)
fermentation (129)
glycolysis (128)
grana (122)
heterotroph (129)
Krebs cycle (132)
light reactions (123)
PGAL (126)

photon (121)
photosynthesis (120)
pigment (122)
pyruvic acid (128)

RDP (126)
stroma (122)
visible spectrum (121)
xanthophyll (122)

For each pair of terms, explain the differences in their meanings.

1. aerobic respiration, anaerobic respiration
2. autotroph, heterotroph
3. light reactions, dark reactions
4. fermentation, glycolysis

BioQuiz   (Write all answers on a separate sheet of paper.)

Completion

1. The electron transport chain allows electrons to release _____ .
2. Photosynthesis begins in the _____ of the chloroplast.
3. During the dark reactions, some _____ is used to form glucose.
4. Cellular respiration cannot take place without catalysts called _____ .
5. During glycolysis, glucose is broken down into two _____ molecules.

Multiple Choice

6. During alcoholic fermentation, pyruvic acid is converted to   a) glucose.
   b) ethyl alcohol.   c) ATP.   d) ADP.
7. The activation energy of some chemical reactions is lowered by   a) glycolysis.
   b) chlorophyll.   c) enzymes.
   d) fermentation.
8. Aerobic respiration of one molecule of glucose produces a net of _____ molecules of ATP.   a) 0   b) 2   c) 36   d) 38

9. The Krebs cycle begins and ends with
   a) citric acid. b) glucose.
   c) phosphate. d) oxygen.
10. Energy for the cell's use is released when ATP gives up a phosphate, forming
   a) ATP and Ⓟ. b) pyruvic acid.
   c) ADP and Ⓟ. d) acetic acid.
11. Chlorophyll absorbs energy from all the visible spectrum except a) red.
   b) green. c) orange. d) yellow.
12. Photosynthesis produces glucose and releases water and a) sucrose.
   b) hydrogen. c) citric acid. d) oxygen.
13. To begin the Krebs cycle, an acetyl group and a four-carbon molecule form
   a) citric acid. b) acetic acid.
   c) adenine. d) ribose.
14. Light energy comes in packets, or units, called a) ATP. b) ADP. c) photons.
   d) electrons.
15. The fluid-filled space between the grana and the outer membranes is called
   a) carotenes. b) stroma.
   c) xanthophyll. d) pigments.

Writing Critically

16. What causes muscle fatigue?
17. How do electrons in chlorophyll become energized?
18. What is the importance of the RDP in the dark reactions of photosynthesis?
19. Through what three processes do organisms break down pyruvic acid?
20. How do plants and animals compare as consumers and producers?

Application/Critical Thinking

1. **Analyzing Conclusions** Of what advantage is it that muscle cells can carry on both aerobic and anaerobic respiration?
2. **Evaluating Conclusions** Are vegetarians the only heterotrophs that get all their energy from plants? Explain your answer.
3. **Recognizing Relationships** Make a table comparing aerobic respiration, alcoholic fermentation, and lactic acid fermentation after glycolysis. Include the materials with which each process begins, the products, and the net gain of ATP molecules.
4. **Inferring Relationships** Organisms that make up plankton have the ability to both float and sink in the water. Why is this an advantage?
5. **Synthesizing Conclusions** Why are ATP-ADP conversion, dark reactions, and the Krebs reactions all described as cyclical processes?

Cross-Discipline Connection

Biology and Social Studies Use library resources to find out how people around the world have used fermentation to produce bread; dairy products such as yogurt and cheese; and soybean products such as tofu and soy sauce.

Discovery Through Reading

"Keys to Help Unlock Photosynthesis," *Science News* (March 14, 1987): 168, is about the discovery of the photosynthetic reaction center (PRC) and the structure of the enzyme RuBP-Case. What function does the PRC perform?

The article "The Children of Mother Earth," *Discover* 6 (June 1985): 11, describes the discovery at the Ames Research Center that clay has the ability to store and transfer energy. What applications might this discovery have?

Uncovering the World of the Cell

The nucleus of a cell

Most cells are very small. An average cell is about 40 micrometers (μm) in diameter. Even smaller are organelles, the structures inside a cell. A mitochondrion, for example, is about 1 μm in diameter. If one could flatten the membranes of 10 million mitochondria and spread them out, they would cover a surface area equivalent to that of a postage stamp. A ribosome is about 0.025 μm in diameter. Relatively speaking, an average ribosome inside an average cell is like a marble inside a very large high-school auditorium.

Technological advances have made it possible for cell biologists to study organelles as small as ribosomes. In fact, electron microscopes can be used to view objects 0.0002 μm in diameter. The electron microscope magnifies cell structure so well that it can show only a very limited area at one time. Imagine using the electron microscope to photograph the surface of one side of a penny. About 200,000 7.5-by-10-cm prints would be needed to assemble the entire image.

To study a structure like a mitochondrion, a cell biologist must first use a machine called an *ultramicrotome.* This device

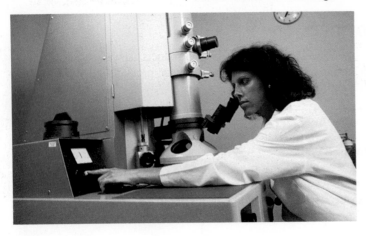

Conventional electron microscopes offer detailed views of cell structures.

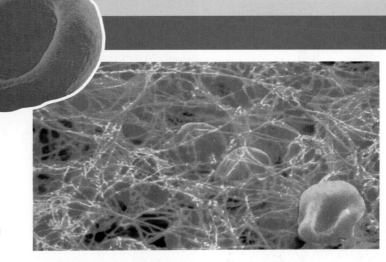

A blood clot is composed of red blood cells (inset) tangled in fibrin fibers.

can slice material very fine, to less than 0.02 μm in thickness. Then the scientist is able to view the material through a microscope.

Two new types of microscopes have been developed that are revolutionizing scientific study. They are the *scanning tunneling microscope* (STM) and the *tandem scanning reflected light microscope* (TSRLM). Both microscopes can provide three-dimensional images with greater resolution than ever before.

The STM has a fine-tipped probe with a diameter that can be as small as a single atom. The probe can trace an outline of a sample's atoms and the depressions between them. Dozens of such tracings are combined to create a three-dimensional image of the sample's surface with

Electron microscope technology has dramatically changed biologists' view of cells.

extremely high resolution.

Unlike the STM, the TSRLM is used to study living tissue. The TSRLM allows a viewer to see one very thin, undistorted plane at a time. Only the light from that plane is allowed to pass into the eyepiece, thus screening out all the layers of cells above and below that would otherwise obscure the region.

With the TSRLM, scientists can observe, for the first time, the interior of living tissue without damaging it, and they can make computerized, three-dimensional pictures of the tissue in its true colors.

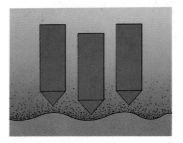

The scanning needle of the STM floats above the surface of the specimen.

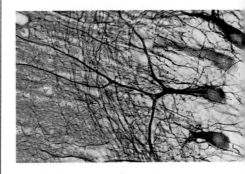

Nerve cells in the brain

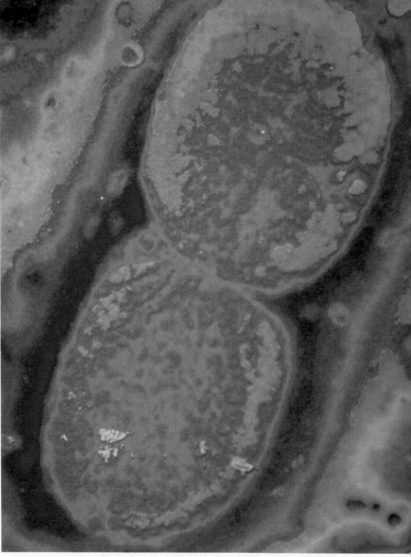

Bacterial cells, *Escherichia coli*, dividing

Focus

Reproduction is possible in all living things only because individual cells can reproduce. The *parent cell* divides and forms new cells called *daughter cells*. Unicellular organisms reproduce by cell division and multicellular organisms grow and repair themselves through this process. A special type of cell division produces sex cells that may in turn combine and form new organisms.

- *What evidence of cell reproduction do you see in the photograph?*

- *How many cells are shown in the photograph?*

Cell Division

The materials a cell needs for maintenance and growth move into the cell through the cell membrane. Waste materials leave through the cell membrane. As the cell grows, its volume increases at a greater rate than its surface area. If growth were unchecked, the surface area would become too small to accommodate the transfer of materials in and out of the cell. *To maintain a workable ratio of volume to surface area, a cell must divide or stop growing.*

When a cell reaches a certain size, it divides into daughter cells. The daughter cells in turn grow and increase in size until they too divide. The daughter cells produced during cell division are similar in structure to the parent cell. The daughter cells receive portions of the cytoplasm and organelles of the parent cell. Each daughter cell also receives a copy of the hereditary information possessed by the parent cell.

9.1 Growth and Repair Require Cell Division

Multicellular organisms grow by increasing the number of their cells through cell division. Cell division also produces new cells that replace worn out or damaged cells. Thus human bodies rely on cell division to heal cuts, repair broken bones, and replace cells that have a short life span.

The frequency of cell division varies greatly among organisms and among cells within an organism. Bacteria may divide every 20 minutes, while many human cells require 18 to 22 hours to divide. Many cells, such as cells found in the skin and in the lining of the human intestine, continue to divide throughout the life of the individual. Many cells in the human body, such as nerve cells, do not divide.

9.2 Reproduction Depends on Cell Division

Cell division is necessary for reproduction of a single cell or of an entire multicellular organism. Organisms reproduce in two basic ways—asexually and sexually. **Asexual reproduction** is the production of offspring from one parent. Offspring formed asexually have some of the cytoplasm and organelles of the parent cell and genetic material identical to the parent. **Sexual reproduction** is the formation of a new individual from the union of two specialized parental cells. In almost all cases, sexual reproduction requires two parents, and the offspring usually show some characteristics of each parent.

Biofact

Q: *How many cells are produced by the human body in a day?*

A: About 2 trillion additional cells are produced by the body of an adult human during one day, or about 25 million new cells per second.

A New You Every Day

Until the 1930s, it was commonly believed that cell proteins lasted an organism's entire lifetime. Despite the large amount of time and energy required to manufacture them, proteins are dynamic structures that are constantly being built, torn down, and rebuilt.

Most macromolecules, carbohydrates and lipids included, undergo the same type of metabolism. These molecules are assembled from a combination of newly-eaten raw materials and recycled older components. Some are continuously rebuilt every few hours while others remain stable for months. The rate at which these com-

pounds are regenerated is called the *metabolic turnover rate.*

Cells also have turnover rates. Of the estimated 60 trillion cells in the human body, about one to two percent are replaced daily. Outer skin cells live for approximately two weeks before they are replaced. The surface epithelium of the stomach is regenerated every three days while the entire epithelium of the small intestine changes about once a week. Liver cells usually last 18 months.

Considering cellular turnover rates for all tissues, some scientists estimate that we renew our bodies every seven years. This is just a statistical

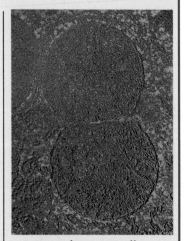

average since not all mature cells divide. The brain stabilizes at a constant size a few years after birth. And some human nerve cells can live throughout the average human life span and never regenerate. This explains why many spine and head injuries can be so devastating.

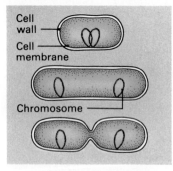

Cell wall

Cell membrane

Chromosome

Figure 9–1. Three stages in the process of binary fission are shown in the illustration above.

Asexual Reproduction   The simplest form of asexual reproduction is **binary fission,** in which the cell splits in two. Binary fission is the primary means of reproduction in prokaryotes, such as blue-green algae (cyanobacteria) and bacteria, which are organisms that lack a true nucleus. First the single, circular chromosome in a prokaryote duplicates, a process called **replication.** Both chromosomes then attach themselves to sites on the cell membrane. As the cell grows, a new cell membrane forms between the attachment sites, and the two chromosomes are forced apart. Then the cell membrane constricts in the center, ultimately separating the cell into two identical parts.

A second method of asexual reproduction is through the production of tiny, asexual reproductive cells called **spores.** A single spore will develop into an adult without combining with another cell. After a spore is produced by the parent organism, the spore can remain inactive until environmental conditions are favorable for the growth of the organism. The spore will then germinate. Molds and other fungi reproduce asexually through the formation of spores. Spores also play an important role in the life cycles of plants.

Some organisms, such as yeast, reproduce asexually through a process called **budding.** The cell nucleus and cytoplasm divide into two cells of unequal size. The bud, the daughter cell, pinches off to become a new individual.

Some plants produce organisms that are initially attached to the parent plant and then separate to become individual plants. This process is called **vegetative propagation.** Plants such as strawberries send out "runners," or horizontal aboveground stems. The runners root and develop into new, individual plants when they contact fertile soil. Tuber plants such as potatoes propagate through underground runners that develop from "eyes." Some plants form tiny plants on the edges of their leaves. The new plants drop off the leaves and root in the soil.

Some animals have the ability to develop lost body parts or even to form new individuals from a single fragment. The development of a new animal from its parts is called **regeneration.** For example, consider what happens if a starfish is cut into several pieces and thrown back into the water. Each of the pieces that contains a portion of the central body will regenerate into a new complete starfish.

Sexual Reproduction Sexual reproduction results from the joining of two specialized sex cells called **gametes** (GAM eets). The male gamete is called a **sperm** cell and the female gamete an **ovum,** or egg cell. In the process of **fertilization,** a sperm and an ovum combine to form a cell called a **zygote** (ZY goht). Because both parents contribute the same number of chromosomes to the zygote, the offspring is usually not identical to either parent but may have some characteristics of each.

Section Review

1. **Relating Ideas** Explain why cells have growth limits.
2. **Comparing Ideas** Differentiate between asexual reproduction and sexual reproduction.
3. **Organizing Ideas** List and describe four methods of asexual reproduction.
4. **Synthesizing Information** Why does sexual reproduction result in a greater variety of offspring than does asexual reproduction?

Reading Critically

Evaluating Relationships
What would be the best form of asexual reproduction in a climate that had extreme changes in rainfall and sunlight? Why?

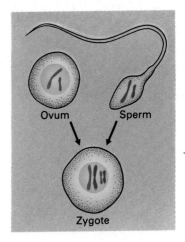

Figure 9–2. Sexual reproduction occurs when gametes, such as a sperm cell and an ovum, fuse to form a zygote.

Thinking Critically

A prokaryotic cell reproduces by replicating its single chromosome and then simply dividing in two. The reproduction of eukaryotic cells is more complex because it involves replication of a greater amount of genetic material and the division of the nucleus as well as the cell. Cell division of eukaryotic body cells involves a process of nuclear division called **mitosis** (my TOH sihs). *As a result of mitosis, each daughter cell receives an exact copy of the chromosomes present in the parent cell.* Before mitosis, the chromosomes in the nucleus of the parent cell replicate. They then divide into identical sets. Mitosis is generally followed by division of the cytoplasm.

Each kind of organism has a specific number of chromosomes in its **somatic** (soh MAT ihk) cells. These are all of the body cells except those that give rise to gametes. Every somatic cell within the body of a multicellular organism contains the same number of chromosomes. Somatic cells of humans, for example, possess 46 chromosomes. Somatic cells of mosquitoes have 6 chromosomes; those of corn plants have 20; those of goldfish have 94.

9.3 Preparation for Mitosis

Cell replication is not a single process but a complex series of events. It involves the duplication of the chromosomes, growth of the cytoplasm, and division of the nucleus and cytoplasm. While most cells may require 20 hours to go through the entire cycle of replication and growth, the actual distribution of the nuclear duplicates into two daughter cells may occur in less than an hour. The time between the formation of a cell through mitosis and the beginning of the next mitosis is called **interphase.** During interphase the cell prepares for division by duplicating genetic material, by producing the necessary numbers of organelles, and by assembling the structures needed for mitosis. Interphase itself is not a part of mitosis.

During interphase chromosomes are not distinguishable under a light microscope. The hereditary material—the nucleic acid DNA and protein—appears as *chromatin,* dense patches within the nucleus. At the start of mitosis, the chromatin begins coiling up, condensing into short, thick rods that become visible under a microscope. Each chromosome, as it is now called, consists of two joined strands called **chromatids** (KROH muh tihdz). Each chromatid is a duplicate of its partner. The point at which the chromatids are held together is called the **centromere** (SEHN truh mihr).

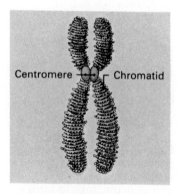

Centromere — Chromatid

Figure 9–3. A chromosome consists of two coiled chromatids that are joined at the centromere.

9.4 Phases of Mitosis

Biologists divide mitosis into four phases: prophase, metaphase, anaphase, and telophase. *Actually, mitosis is a continuous process in which each phase merges into the next.* Here the process is described as it occurs in an animal cell.

You will observe the phases of mitosis in the Investigation on page 153.

Prophase   The first stage of mitosis is called **prophase.** This stage takes up about 60 percent of the total time required for mitosis. Prophase can be divided into early, middle, and late stages. During early prophase, the chromosomes begin to coil up into short rods. The nucleoli break down and begin to disappear. Two pairs of centrioles appear to one side of the nucleus, outside the nuclear membrane.

The centrioles move apart, signaling the beginning of middle prophase. Protein tubes called *spindle fibers* form between

---

THINKING ABOUT BIOLOGY: The Cell Cycle

Many events in the natural world follow a regular, recurring pattern. One cycle basic to all living organisms is the cycle of the cell.

The **cell cycle** is the sequence of cell growth and division that occurs in a cell between the beginning of one mitosis and the beginning of the next mitosis. The cell cycle has four stages. The first stage includes mitosis and the division of the cytoplasm, called **cytokinesis** (syt oh kih NEE sihs). The remaining stages make up interphase. In a multicellular organism, many cells are permanently in interphase.

Following mitosis, the cell enters a period of intense cellular activity and growth known as the G_1 phase. The cell doubles in size, and organelles such as the ribosomes and mitochondria double in number. The production of enzymes is at a high level to accommodate the increased chemical activity.

Those cells that stop growing remain in the G_1 phase. Cells that go on to divide next enter the S, or DNA synthesis, phase. During this period the chromosomes replicate. The S phase is followed by a second period of growth, G_2. During G_2, the spindle fibers are assembled.

Temperatures and other external environmental factors can affect the duration of the cell cycle,

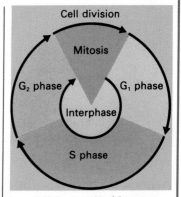

In addition, other factors may influence the length of the cycle, which may last from hours to days. In bean cells, seven hours are spent in S phase, five hours in each of the two growth phases, and two hours in mitosis.

■ **Predicting Outcomes** What would happen if a cell had no S phase?

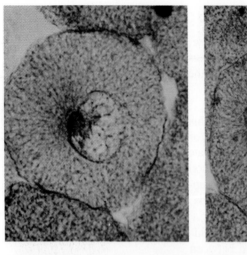
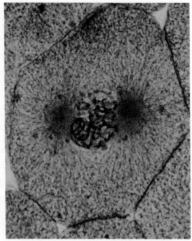
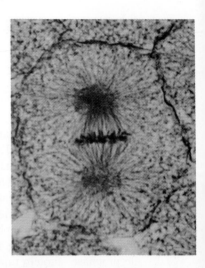

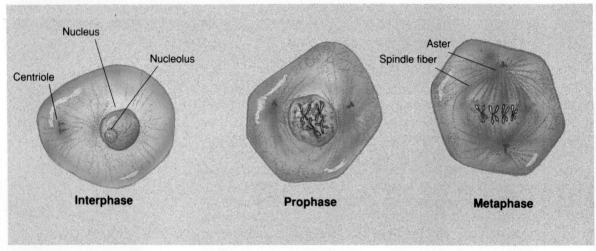

Nucleus

Nucleolus

Centriole

Aster

Spindle fiber

Interphase

Prophase

Metaphase

Figure 9–4. The process of mitosis results in two cells that have the same number of chromosomes as the original cell. Six phases in the process of mitotic cell division are shown above: interphase, prophase, metaphase, anaphase, telophase, and cytokinesis.

the centrioles. Additional fibers radiating outward from each centriole form the **aster,** visible in Figure 9–4. The exact function of the aster is not yet known. Plant cells develop spindle fibers, but they lack centrioles and asters. At this stage the nuclear membrane has broken down and disappeared.

By late prophase, the centriole pairs are at opposite ends of the cell. Each centriole is fully formed into a three-dimensional, football-shaped structure. The chromosomes are attached to the centrioles by some of the spindle fibers. Other spindle fibers stretch across the cell from one centriole to the other. Animal cells have centrioles; most plant cells do not.

Metaphase During **metaphase,** the chromosomes are pushed and pulled by the spindle fibers. Finally they become arranged

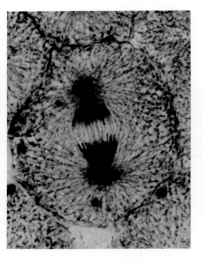
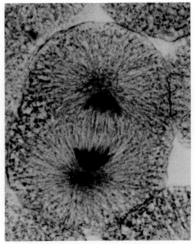
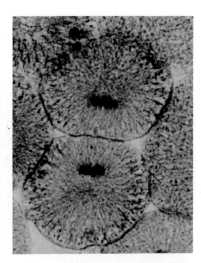

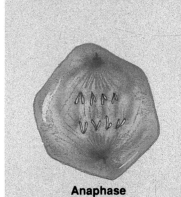
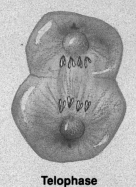
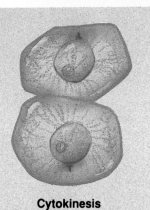

Anaphase　　　　　**Telophase**　　　　　**Cytokinesis**

along the cell's midplane, called the *equator*. The centromere of each chromosome is attached to a separate spindle fiber.

Anaphase　Anaphase begins with the separation of the centromeres followed by the separation of the chromatids in each pair. The spindle fibers appear to shorten, pulling the chromatids apart at the centromere. Each chromatid is now called a chromosome. As Figure 9–4 shows, the two sets of separated chromosomes then move through the cytoplasm to opposite ends, or poles, of the cell.

Telophase　The last stage of mitosis is **telophase**. After the individual chromosomes have reached the opposite poles of the cell, the spindle fibers disappear. A nuclear membrane forms

Reading Critically

Identifying Function　What may be the function of spindle fibers?

Figure 9–5. Plant cells do not undergo the same kind of cytokinesis as animal cells. Plants form a cell plate, a structure made from membranes synthesized by Golgi bodies.

See pages 926–927 for career information.

around each set of chromosomes as the chromosomes uncoil and once more return to a threadlike mass. The nucleoli also re-form within each newly formed nucleus.

9.5 Cytokinesis

Mitosis is followed by cytokinesis, the division of the cytoplasm. Cytokinesis begins during telophase. In an animal cell, the cell membrane pinches together, and a furrow or groove forms along the equator. The groove deepens until the cell membrane separates, forming two daughter cells. A plant cell has a relatively rigid cell wall that prevents the cell from dividing by pinching. In plant cells, a **cell plate** is formed in the middle of the dividing cell from membrane vesicles produced by the cell's Golgi bodies. Just before cytokinesis, the Golgi bodies migrate to the area where the cell plate will form. Then the membrane vacuoles formed by the Golgi bodies fuse into a membrane that separates the cells. The cell plate extends outward until it separates the two daughter cells. Each of the new cells then forms a cell wall on its side of the cell plate.

Section Review

1. **Identifying Relationships**   State the relationship between the chromosome number of parent and daughter cells.
2. **Summarizing Ideas**   Summarize the events of mitosis.
3. **Comparing Ideas**   Compare cytokinesis in plants and animals.
4. **Listing Ideas**   Name the stages of the cell cycle.
5. **Inferring Relationships**   What would result if chromosomes did not replicate during interphase?

Thinking Critically

Meiosis

All cells produced through mitosis have the same number of chromosomes as their parent cells. Consider what would happen if two cells formed through mitosis combined in sexual reproduction. The offspring would have twice as many chromosomes as its parents. As this process continued, each succeeding generation would have double the chromosome number of its parents. Sexual reproduction does not increase the number of chromosomes, because gametes have only half the number of chromosomes found in somatic cells.

The chromosomes in somatic cells occur in pairs called **homologous** (hoh MAHL uh guhs) **chromosomes.** The chromosomes in a pair are alike in appearance and in the type of genetic information they carry. The 46 chromosomes in human cells, for example, form 23 homologous pairs. Cells that have homologous chromosomes are said to have the **diploid** (DIHP loyd) **number (2n)** of chromosomes. A gamete, however, has only one member from each pair of homologous chromosomes of its parent cell. Thus gametes have half the diploid number, or the **haploid number (n).** Gametes are formed by a type of nuclear division called **meiosis** (my OH sihs). *Meiosis reduces the number of chromosomes to half the number in somatic cells.*

9.6 Phases of Meiosis

The process by which haploid daughter cells are formed from a diploid parent cell requires two successive cell divisions. During the first division, meiosis I, the homologous chromosomes separate. During meiosis II, the chromatids of each chromosome separate.

Meiosis I   As in mitosis, meiosis is preceded by the synthesis of DNA and replication of the chromosomes. During meiosis I, the homologous chromosomes come together, a process called **synapsis** (sih NAP sihs). The chromosomes lie next to each

Table 9-1: Comparison of Mitosis and Meiosis

Nuclear division	No. of daughter cells	Parent cell type	Daughter cell type	Genetic likeness of daughter cells to parent
Mitosis				
1	2	diploid	diploid	identical
Meiosis				
2	4	diploid	haploid	different

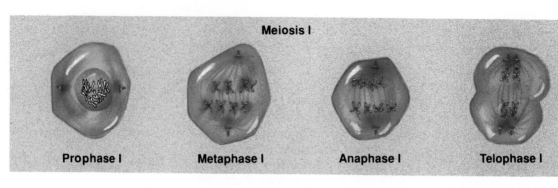

Meiosis I

Prophase I | Metaphase I | Anaphase I | Telophase I

Figure 9–6. In the first meiotic division, homologous chromosomes separate. The second division results in four cells, each with half the number of chromosomes present in the original cell.

other, forming a structure called a **tetrad** (TEHT rad). Meiosis I can be divided into the same four phases as mitosis:

- *Prophase I:* The chromatin begins to coil into short rods, the spindle appears, and the nucleoli break down. By the end of prophase I, the nuclear membrane has completely disappeared and, as Figure 9–6 shows, synapsis of homologous chromosomes has occurred, and tetrads consisting of two pairs of chromatids are visible.
- *Metaphase I:* Each tetrad lines up along the equator of the cell.
- *Anaphase I:* The homologous chromosomes that form each tetrad are pulled apart. One pair goes to one end of the cell, and the other pair moves to the other.
- *Telophase I:* The chromosomes reach the ends of the cell. Cytokinesis takes place and the cell divides into two daughter cells.

At the end of meiosis I, each daughter cell contains half the number of chromosomes found in the parent cell. That is, one chromosome of each homologous pair is present in each daughter cell. *Meiosis I is reductive division; it reduces the number of chromosomes from the diploid (2n) to the haploid (n) number.*

Meiosis II Each daughter cell produced in meiosis I undergoes another nuclear and cytoplasmic division in meiosis II. *Meiosis II is similar to mitosis but is not preceded by the replication of DNA.* Meiosis II also has four stages:

- *Prophase II:* Telophase I leads directly into prophase II. A new spindle forms around the chromosomes.
- *Metaphase II:* The chromosomes line up along the equator, attached at their centromeres to spindle fibers.
- *Anaphase II:* The centromeres divide and the chromatids separate. Each chromatid now becomes a new chromosome with its own centromere.

Biofact

Q: *When does meiosis begin to form egg cells within the human female?*

A: The cells that produce human egg cells begin meiosis during fetal development. These cells remain in prophase I for many years. The completion of meiosis I and meiosis II takes place after sexual maturity.

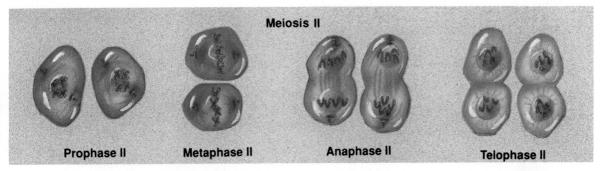

Meiosis II

Prophase II   Metaphase II   Anaphase II   Telophase II

• *Telophase II:* The nuclear membrane forms around each set of chromosomes. The spindle breaks down and the cell undergoes cytokinesis.

Each of the daughter cells formed in meiosis I has divided in two, resulting in a total of four daughter cells produced in meiosis II. *Each of the daughter cells produced in meiosis II is haploid.* The cell in Figure 9–6 began with a diploid number of eight. It contained four homologous pairs of chromosomes. As a result of meiosis, four haploid cells have been produced. Each cell has four chromosomes, one from each of the homologous pairs of the parent cell.

9.7 Meiosis in Males and Females

Meiosis in male animals results in four cells that *differentiate,* or change, into sperm cells. Meiosis in female animals results in four cells, only one of which becomes an egg. During meiosis I in females, the cytoplasm divides unequally. The smaller of the two cells, called the **first polar body,** may divide again but its cells will not survive. In meiosis II, the division of the egg cell is again unequal. The smaller cell, the **second polar body,** dies. Because of its larger share of cytoplasm, the mature ovum has a rich storehouse of nutrients. These nutrients nourish the young organism that may develop if the ovum is fertilized.

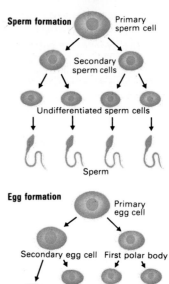

Sperm formation — Primary sperm cell — Secondary sperm cells — Undifferentiated sperm cells — Sperm

Egg formation — Primary egg cell — Secondary egg cell — First polar body — Second polar bodies — Undifferentiated egg cell — Egg cell (ovum)

Figure 9–7. Meiosis of a primary diploid sperm cell (top) yields four haploid sperm. Meiosis of a primary diploid egg cell (bottom) results in only one functional haploid egg cell.

Section Review

1. **Analyzing Ideas**   Why is meiosis essential to sexual reproduction?
2. **Comparing Ideas**   Compare diploid and haploid cells.
3. **Identifying Relationships**   How does anaphase I in meiosis differ from anaphase in mitosis?
4. **Analyzing Outcomes**   How do the daughter cells that result from mitosis and meiosis differ?

⟨**Thinking Critically**⟩

Cells for Sale

Currently, it is illegal to buy or sell a human organ, such as a liver or kidney, for transplant. However, the cells and tissues from some human organs may be sold. For example, cells from tumors and other surgically removed tissue that would otherwise be discarded, can be cultured so that they divide to produce a *cell line* of identical cells. These cell lines are used by medical and research laboratories to gain information about diseases and possible ways to control and cure diseases.

The almost complete absence of laws that regulate the sale of human cells and tissues presents a problem to both researchers and patients. In 1984, a leukemia patient sued a research hospital for using a cell line that was derived from his spleen cells. The hospital had signed contracts with a biotechnology company to develop drugs that were tested on the patient's cell line. A court denied the patient's demand for a share in the profits that were made.

Legal problems concerning human cells also arise when human embryos are produced through *in vitro* fertilization, fertilization that takes place outside the human body. There is a question of ownership of the embryos. One couple asked that the embryos produced by *in vitro* fertilization be transferred to a facility in another state. The clinic refused, claiming that the couple had no rights of ownership of the embryos outside the clinic. The couple won the court battle for ownership.

Analyze the Issue

1. What is a cell line? What are the issues involved in determining who owns a cell line?

2. How does ownership of a whole kidney differ from ownership of diseased kidney tissue that has been removed surgically?

3. What are the similarities and differences between using a person's donated blood and using a patient's cells and tissues?

4. What are the advantages and disadvantages of paying a person for his or her cells and tissues? Support your view.

INVESTIGATION 9:
What Events Occur During Mitosis?

Objectives
- To *observe* cells in various stages of mitosis
- To *organize* data

Materials
compound light microscope, prepared slide of longitudinal sections of onion root tip

Prelab Preparation
1. Review the events that occur in each stage of mitosis.
2. State the results of mitosis.
3. Where in a growing plant would you expect to observe mitosis?
4. Explain how an interphase cell differs in appearance from cells undergoing mitosis.

Inquiry: Observation
5. Obtain a prepared slide of an onion root tip. *Why is the root tip selected for study in this Investigation?*
6. There are usually several root-tip sections on each slide. Using low power of the microscope, focus on one of these sections.
7. Just above the root cap, locate the meristematic zone, which is the area of fastest growth.
8. Find an interphase cell and switch to high power. Describe the appearance of this cell. Make a drawing of this cell labeling the nuclear membrane, nucleolus, cell membrane, cell wall, and chromatin.
9. Using low power, find a cell in early prophase. Switch to high power and make a labeled drawing of this cell. Label the nuclear membrane and chromatin.
10. Using low power, find a metaphase cell. Switch to high power and make a drawing of this cell. Label the chromatids, spindle and spindle fibers. *To what do the spindle fibers appear to attach?*
11. Using low power, find an anaphase cell. Switch to high power and make a draw-ing of this cell. Label the chromosomes and spindle fibers. *How does the num-ber of chromosomes on one side of the cell compare to the number on the oppo-site side?*
12. Using low power, find a cell in late telophase. Switch to high power and make a drawing of this cell. Label the nuclear membrane, chromatin, cell plate, and cytoplasm.

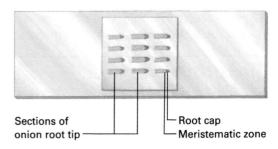

Sections of onion root tip — Root cap
— Meristematic zone

Analysis
1. **Analyzing Observations** What hap-pens to the nuclear membrane and the nucleolus during mitosis?
2. **Inferring Functions** What appears to be the function of the spindle fibers? What evidence do you have for this?
3. **Analyzing Observations** What evi-dence indicates that the cells produced by mitosis are duplicates?
4. **Analyzing Observations** How do daughter cells compare to the parent cell?

Chapter 9 Review

Summary

Replacement of worn-out cells, increase in the size of organisms, and reproduction are possible because cells can divide. Asexual reproduction produces genetically identical offspring from one parent. Binary fission, spore formation, vegetative propagation, and fragmentation are forms of asexual reproduction. Sexual reproduction involves the fusion of gametes supplied by two parents. It produces offspring that are not identical to either parent.

Mitosis is the process of nuclear division that results in the reproduction of body cells and in asexual reproduction in eukaryotes.

Meiosis forms the gametes necessary for sexual reproduction. Meiosis reduces the number of chromosomes in gamete cells through two successive nuclear divisions.

Meiosis in a male animal produces four haploid sperm cells, while meiosis in a female produces one haploid egg cell. Fertilization results in the formation of a diploid zygote that may then develop into a new organism.

BioTerms

anaphase (**147**)
asexual
   reproduction (**141**)
aster (**146**)
binary fission (**142**)
budding (**143**)
cell cycle (**145**)
cell plate (**148**)
centromere (**144**)
chromatid (**144**)
cytokinesis (**145**)
diploid number (**149**)
fertilization (**143**)

first polar body (**151**)
gamete (**143**)
haploid number (**149**)
homologous
   chromosome (**149**)
interphase (**144**)
meiosis (**149**)
metaphase (**146**)
mitosis (**144**)
ovum (**143**)
prophase (**145**)
regeneration (**143**)
replication (**142**)

second polar body (**151**)
sexual
   reproduction (**141**)
somatic cell (**144**)
sperm (**143**)
spore (**142**)

synapsis (**149**)
telophase (**147**)
tetrad (**150**)
vegetative
   propagation (**143**)
zygote (**143**)

For each pair of terms, explain the differences in their meanings.

1. asexual reproduction, sexual reproduction
2. diploid number, haploid number
3. mitosis, meiosis
4. gamete, zygote

BioQuiz   (Write all answers on a separate sheet of paper.)

Completion

1. Cytokinesis always results in two _____ cells.
2. Chromosomes form into tetrads during _____ .
3. Binary fission and regeneration are both forms of _____ reproduction.
4. The point at which the _____ are held together is called the centromere.
5. The union of a male and a female gamete produces a _____ .

Multiple Choice

6. Two homologous chromosomes move together during   a) anaphase.
   b) cytokinesis.   c) synapsis.
   d) interphase.
7. The process by which a prokaryote duplicates is   a) binary fission.
   b) sexual reproduction.   c) vegetative propagation.   d) meiosis.
8. A cell plate forms during the _____ of plant cells.   a) metaphase

b) interphase   c) telophase   d) cytokinesis

9. The chromosomes become arranged along the equator during   a) metaphase. b) anaphase. c) telophase. d) interphase.

10. Yeast cells reproduce asexually in a process called   a) regeneration. b) vegetative propagation.   c) budding. d) binary fission.

11. If a cell did not complete interphase, a) the cell would die.   b) DNA would not replicate.   c) the nuclear membrane would break up.   d) the nucleolus would take over the nucleus.

12. In diploid cells, homologous chromosomes are   a) harmful mutations.   b) matching pairs of chromosomes.   c) evidence of division.   d) found only in humans.

13. If an organism could not carry out meiosis, it would   a) stop growing. b) fail to produce gametes.   c) grow

faster.   d) shrivel up and die.

14. During the G_1 phase of the cell cycle, the cell   a) structures for mitosis are assembled.   b) nucleus divides.   c) size doubles.   d) chromosomes replicate.

15. A _____ reproduces asexually.   a) mold b) bacterium   c) strawberry   d) All choices are correct.

Writing Critically

16. What is the function of mitosis in most animals?

17. Why is meiosis sometimes called a "reduction division"?

18. Describe the major events that occur during each stage of mitosis.

19. Why must cells divide?

20. What happens during the interphase of the cell cycle?

Application/Critical Thinking

1. **Interpreting Graphics** Illustrate the phases of meiosis through a series of labeled drawings. Represent the process as it would appear in a parent cell with a diploid number of eight.

2. **Synthesizing Conclusions** Some hereditary illnesses are a result of abnormal numbers of chromosomes. Explain how it might happen that a human offspring with 47 chromosomes could be produced.

3. **Inferring Relationships** In humans, the egg is larger than the sperm. Explain how it is possible that a child inherits equally from its mother and father.

4. **Analyzing Conclusions** A horse and a donkey can produce a mule, but the mule is almost always sterile. Horses have a diploid number of 60, and donkeys a diploid number of 66. Offer an explanation for the fact that the mule is sterile.

Cross-Discipline Connection

Biology and Theater Arts   Write a play, complete with stage directions, in which the actors and actresses play the roles of chromosomes that are in a cell that is undergoing the process of mitosis. Choreograph a chromosome dance for the play. Produce the play and invite groups of students from your school to view your production.

Discovery Through Reading

"Nature's Single Parents," *Omni* (October, 1988): 72–77, 218, describes asexual organisms. Are asexually reproductive organisms considered to be all male or all female?

Summary

As microscopes improved between the late 1600s and the early 1800s, scientists' understanding about cellular organization increased. This understanding eventually led to the formulation of the cell theory. This theory states that organisms are composed of cells, cells are the basic unit of structure and function in living things, and cells come only from preexisting cells.

Most cells have a nucleus in addition to a cell membrane, and numerous organelles within the cytoplasm. Cells without a membrane surrounding the nuclear area are prokaryotic and those with a membrane around the nucleus are eukaryotic.

Materials are exchanged between a cell and its environment through the cell membrane. The major passive method by which molecules are transported is diffusion. Osmosis is the diffusion of water through a selectively permeable membrane. Active methods of transport require that the cell use energy.

Green plants trap sunlight energy through photosynthesis and store this energy in glucose molecules. Cellular respiration releases the energy in glucose and stores it in small amounts in energy-rich bonds of ATP molecules. The first step of cellular respiration is the anaerobic process of glycolysis. In the cells of most organisms, aerobic respiration follows and pyruvic acid is broken down into carbon dioxide and water.

Mitosis is a process in which a cell divides and forms two daughter cells that are identical both to each other and to the original parent cell. Some organisms reproduce by mitosis, and cell replacement and growth occur through mitosis. Meiosis is a process of cell division that results in haploid cells that may combine in sexual reproduction.

Asexual reproduction involves one parent. The offspring that are produced by asexual reproduction are genetically identical to the parent. Sexual reproduction involves the joining of sex cells from two parents. The offspring that are produced by sexual reproduction are not genetically identical to either parent.

Synthesis

Synthesis Statement

The cell is a dynamic structural and functional unit that is common to all living things. The sum of all cellular chemical activities—the cell's metabolism—requires constant transformations of energy. Cells that contain chlorophyll trap energy from sunlight to satisfy their energy requirements. Most other cells depend, directly or indirectly, on these chlorophyll-containing cells for energy.

The process of mitosis results in genetically similar cells from one generation to the next. Meiosis provides the opportunity for recombination of hereditary information.

Synthesis Questions

Apply your understanding of this unit to the following questions.

1. Some unicellular organisms, such as paramecium, have a definite shape, while others, such as amoeba, do not. The cells of the human body also show many different shapes. Offer an explanation for the variety of shapes seen among cells.

2. Why are cell transport mechanisms essential for multicellular organisms?

3. Compare the amounts of ATP generated by anaerobic and aerobic respiration.

4. Plant cells and animal cells have different ways of obtaining energy. Describe how these differences are reflected in differences in the cell structures of plants and animals.

5. How do the parts of the cell resemble the different divisions of a human business organization or a school? In what ways does a cell resemble an automobile or a computer?

6. Among animals, egg cells are typically much larger than sperm cells. Offer an explanation that may account for the differences in size. Why is the sperm cell more motile than the egg cell?

7. Plants and animals have very different ways of obtaining energy. Compare and contrast the advantages and disadvantages of the photosynthetic lifestyle of plants with the heterotrophic lifestyles of animals.

8. Sexual reproduction is characteristic of larger, more complex organisms. Simple unicellular organisms often rely upon asexual reproduction. Discuss the advantages and disadvantages of asexual reproduction and sexual reproduction.

9. Use a separate piece of paper to draw a concept map like the one below. Place each of the following terms inside the appropriate figure: waste products, chemical reactions, materials from the environment, mitosis, daughter cell.

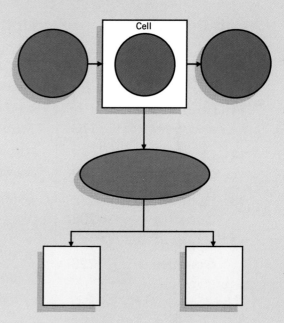

CONTINUITY OF LIFE

Unit Outline

Unit Focus

The offspring of each species of organism share a large number of characteristics. Yet, in sexually reproducing organisms, each offspring is unique. Many of the questions about how members of a species can be both similar and diverse have their answers in the study of inheritance.

■ *What features of snow monkeys allow humans to recognize them as snow monkeys?*

■ *What characteristics would allow you to identify two snow monkeys of the same sex and age as different individuals?*

Female snow monkeys with their offspring

Fundamentals of Genetics

Outline

Four generations of a family

Focus

Only in this century have scientists begun to understand the molecular basis of **heredity,** the study of how parents pass certain traits to their offspring. Information that influences these traits is transmitted in molecules called *DNA*. Knowledge gained from the continuing study of DNA has had, and will continue to have, great impact on biology, technology, and society.

- *Where is DNA found in a cell?*

- *What kinds of physical traits may members of the same family show?*

The Origin of Genetics

The scientific study of heredity is called **genetics.** Modern genetics is based on the knowledge that traits are transmitted by means of **chromosomes,** rod-shaped structures within the nucleus of a cell. Offspring resemble parents because the chromosomes in sperm cells and egg cells contain units of hereditary information. These units are called **genes.** As an individual formed by a sperm cell and an egg cell grows into an adult, the genes influence its development. The genes cause it to resemble the parents who supplied the chromosomes.

Long before people understood the basis of heredity, they bred animals and plants for certain desirable traits. Many breeds of dogs, for example, were developed during the Middle Ages. In the 1800s biologists began to study heredity through scientific experiments. Discoveries made by one of these biologists, Gregor Mendel, became the basis of modern genetics.

10.1 Gregor Mendel: A Pioneer of Genetics

Gregor Mendel was born July 22, 1822, in a small Austrian village. Mendel was an outstanding student and eventually entered a monastery to become a high school teacher. As part of his education, he spent two years at the University of Vienna, where he developed an interest in plant-breeding experiments. When Mendel returned to the monastery, he devoted much of his time to plant-breeding research. Through his experiments, Mendel discovered the basic principles of heredity.

Although scientists before Mendel had performed breeding experiments, none had unlocked the secrets of heredity. Why did Mendel succeed where other scientists had failed? *One important factor in Mendel's success was his choice of garden pea plants for his experiments.* The seeds of these plants were readily available, and the plants could be cultivated quickly in the small garden at the monastery. The large number of offspring produced provided abundant data for Mendel to analyze.

The way in which pea plants reproduce also made them ideal for experimentation. The flower of the garden pea contains *stamens* that produce pollen. The pollen contains the sperm cells—the male **gametes,** or reproductive cells. The same flower also has a *pistil* that contains the eggs, or female gametes. The petals of the flower trap the pollen, which then falls on the pistil and fertilizes the eggs. This process is called **self-pollination.** After many generations of self-pollination, offspring are genetically identical and show the same traits.

- *Explain* why Mendel succeeded in discovering the principles of heredity when other biologists had failed
- *Describe* Mendel's experiments.
- *State* each of Mendel's principles of heredity and give examples of each one.
- *Tell* how Mendel's work was rediscovered.
- *Distinguish* between genotype and phenotype.

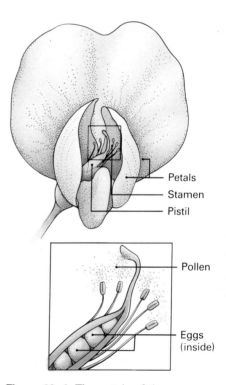

Figure 10–1. The petals of the garden pea plant completely enclose the stamen and pistil, protecting them from foreign pollen. The petals do not open until the plant has self-pollinated.

Petals
Stamen
Pistil

Pollen

Eggs (inside)

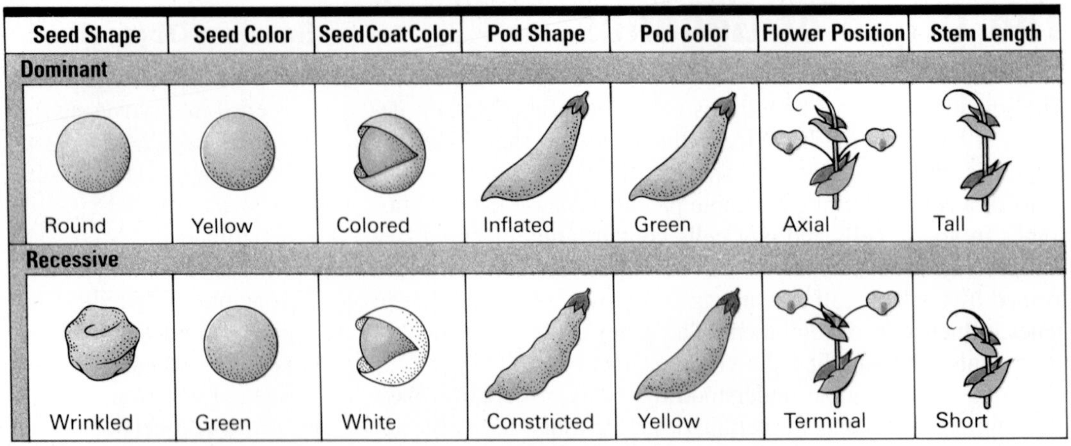

Seed Shape	Seed Color	SeedCoatColor	Pod Shape	Pod Color	Flower Position	Stem Length
Dominant						
Round	Yellow	Colored	Inflated	Green	Axial	Tall
Recessive						
Wrinkled	Green	White	Constricted	Yellow	Terminal	Short

Figure 10–2. Of the many characteristics in the garden pea plant, Mendel chose to study these seven contrasting pairs of traits.

Reading Critically

Evaluating Conclusions
Why would humans have been a poor choice for Mendel in his experimental studies?

The pea plants were also a good choice because they displayed several traits in one of two contrasting forms. For example, the seeds of the pea plant were either round or wrinkled, never a blend of the two. The plants themselves were either tall or short, never of medium height. Figure 10–2 shows the seven contrasting traits that Mendel studied in pea plants. The choice of plants with distinct traits enabled Mendel to discover how traits are passed from generation to generation. Earlier scientists had studied traits with several intermediate forms and had falsely concluded that all inheritance involved blending of traits.

In addition, Mendel's success resulted from his logical experimental methods and his careful record keeping. First Mendel studied the inheritance of only one trait, then of two traits, and finally of three traits at a time. He also studied the appearance of these traits in three generations. Furthermore, Mendel counted the results of experiments and kept accurate records of them. Later Mendel used these records to calculate the mathematical ratios in which traits appeared. Unlike scientists before him, Mendel believed that inherited traits would appear in some mathematical pattern.

10.2 Mendel's Experiments

Mendel knew that after many generations of self-pollination, pea plants produce offspring identical to themselves. Short plants always produce short offspring. Yellow-seeded plants always produce yellow-seeded offspring.

Mendel wondered what would happen if he crossed two pure-breeding plants with contrasting traits, such as tallness and shortness. To find out he crossed two pea plants. Mendel called these plants the **parental,** or **P, generation.** He performed the parental cross by means of **cross-pollination**, or taking pollen from one plant and dusting it on the pistil of another plant. The results of the parental cross appeared in the first generation of offspring, called the **first filial** (FIHL ee uhl), or **F₁, generation.**

Three possible traits could have appeared in the F₁ generation of offspring. The plants could have been tall, short, or of medium height. Mendel soon discovered, however, that all of the F₁ generation plants were tall. The contrasting trait—shortness—seemed to have disappeared.

Mendel continued making parental crosses for each of the seven pairs of contrasting traits. A cross between yellow-seeded plants and green-seeded plants produced F₁ generation seeds that were all yellow. Similarly, a cross between round-seeded plants and wrinkled-seeded plants produced F₁ generation seeds that were all round. *After testing all seven pairs of traits, Mendel discovered that one trait in each pair showed up in the F₁ generation. He noticed that the other trait in each pair seemed to have disappeared.*

Next, Mendel allowed the members of the F₁ generation to self-pollinate, producing the **second filial,** or **F₂, generation.** The results were striking. About three-fourths of the plants in the F₂ generation were tall. However, about one-fourth were short—the trait that had not appeared in the F₁ generation. Expressed in mathematical terms, the ratio of tall to short plants was about 3:1. When Mendel checked the remaining six traits in the F₂ generation, he found that every pair of traits appeared in roughly the same 3:1 ratio.

Mendel proposed that traits that had "disappeared" in the F₁ generation were not lost. Instead, each one was somehow prevented from being expressed. Based on this idea, Mendel reasoned that a pair of elements, which he called *factors,* governs the expression of traits in each individual. Today these factors are called *genes.* According to Mendel, every plant has a pair of genes for each trait. The genes of each trait are of two types. For example, the pair of genes that determines height in pea plants includes one gene for tallness and one gene for shortness. For some reason, however, only one of each pair of traits appears in the F₁ generation.

10.3 The Principle of Dominance

From his idea of factors, or genes, Mendel developed the **principle of dominance.** *The principle of dominance states that one factor (gene) in a pair may prevent the other factor (gene) in the pair from being expressed.* For example, an F₁ generation seed produced by a cross between a yellow-seeded plant

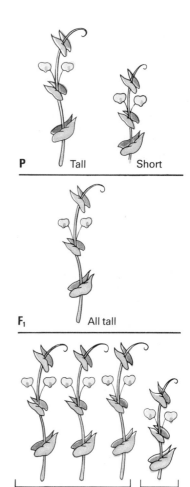

Figure 10–3. When Mendel crossed pea plants with contrasting traits, one trait in each pair disappeared in the F₁ generation and reappeared in the F₂.

Q: *The basenji is a breed of dog noted for its inability to bark. Why can't a basenji bark?*

A: The ability to bark is a dominant trait in dogs. All basenjis have two recessive genes for this trait, and so they cannot bark.

and a green-seeded plant contains both a gene for yellow seed color and a gene for green seed color. The gene for yellow seed color prevents the gene for green seed color from being expressed. According to Mendel's principle, a gene that masks the other gene in a pair is **dominant.** The gene that is hidden by the dominant gene in the F_1 generation is **recessive.** The recessive gene may reappear, however, in the F_2 generation.

Geneticists use symbols to represent genes. A dominant gene is symbolized by a capital letter. For example, Y represents the gene for yellow seed color. The recessive gene in a pair is indicated with the same letter in lowercase. Thus y represents the recessive gene for green seed color. When the two genes in a pair are identical—YY or yy—the individual is **homozygous** (hoh moh ZY guhs), or **purebred** for that particular trait. If both genes are dominant (YY), the individual is **homozygous dominant.** If both genes are recessive (yy), the individual is **homozygous recessive.** Individuals who have a dominant gene and a recessive gene (Yy) are said to be **heterozygous** (heht uhr oh ZY guhs), or **hybrid,** for that trait.

THINKING ABOUT BIOLOGY: The Fate of Mendel's Ideas

In 1865 Gregor Mendel presented his findings to a meeting of scientists, but they showed little interest in his work. A report of his experiments was published in 1866 and gathered dust on library shelves for the next 35 years.

There were many reasons why the scientific community neglected Mendel's discoveries, one being his mathematical approach. Combining biology and mathematics was not popular at that time. Scientists of the day believed that biological processes were too complex to be explained by mathematics.

Another reason for the neglect of Mendel's findings was that biologists had not yet discovered the physical basis of heredity. In 1866 there was no workable theory of the cell and its functions. Chromosomes had not yet been observed. Thus it was the fate of Mendel's ideas to await a time when biologists were better able to understand and accept them.

That time came in 1900. Within the brief period of four months, Mendel's work was rediscovered by three botanists: Hugo DeVries, Carl Correns, and Erich Tschermak. All three

came across Mendel's paper while working independently on problems like those Mendel had solved 35 years earlier. Because of the advances that had taken place in biology during those 35 years, the three scientists immediately recognized the importance of Mendel's discoveries. After these men brought his experiments to the attention of the world, genetics truly got under way.

■ **Synthesizing Relationships** How is the development of the cell theory linked to the discovery of Mendel's work?

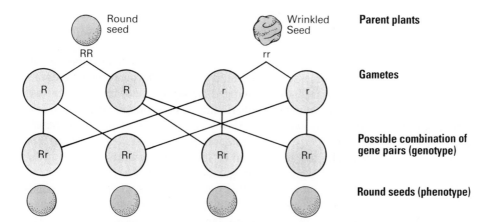

Round seed		Wrinkled Seed	Parent plants
RR		rr	

Gametes

Possible combination of gene pairs (genotype)

Round seeds (phenotype)

10.4 The Principle of Segregation

Mendel's experiments revealed that a parental trait, such as shortness, can disappear in the F_1 generation. His experiments also showed that the same trait can reappear in the F_2 generation in roughly a $3:1$ ratio. To explain how traits can disappear and reappear in a certain pattern from generation to generation, Mendel proposed the **principle of segregation.** *The principle of segregation states that the members of each pair of genes separate, or segregate, when gametes are formed.*

Today biologists know that the principle of segregation describes what happens during *meiosis,* the nuclear division in which the chromosome number is halved. As a result of meiosis, each gamete receives one member of each pair of chromosomes found in body cells. When gametes from two parents unite, new pairs of chromosomes are formed. Mendel, however, did not have the benefit of this knowledge. Chromosomes had not yet been discovered, and the process of meiosis was not observed until about 30 years after Mendel completed his research.

10.5 The Principle of Independent Assortment

Mendel developed his first two principles through experiments involving the inheritance of a single pair of traits. He arrived at his third principle by crossing pea plants with two or more pairs of contrasting traits. For example, he crossed a purebred plant with yellow, round seeds and a purebred plant with green, wrinkled seeds. Seeds produced from this cross were all yellow and round. This result illustrated the principle of dominance.

When these seeds grew into plants and self-pollinated, they produced four types of F_2 generation seeds. The yellow, round seeds and the green, wrinkled seeds resembled the seeds of the P

Figure 10–4. According to the principle of segregation, the two genes in a pair separate when gametes form. One gene goes to one gamete and the other gene goes to a different gamete. The uniting of two gametes in fertilization creates a new gene pair.

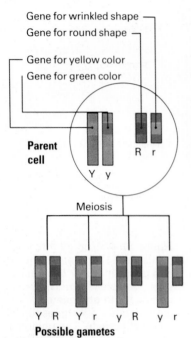

Gene for wrinkled shape
Gene for round shape

Gene for yellow color
Gene for green color

Parent cell

R r

Y y

Meiosis

Y R   Y r   y R   y r
Possible gametes

Figure 10–5. The principle of independent assortment states that two or more gene pairs separate independently. Thus gametes may contain a combination of dominant and recessive genes.

generation. However, the F₂ generation also included round, green seeds and yellow, wrinkled seeds. From this experiment, Mendel realized that two traits produced by recessive genes did not have to appear in the same offspring. For example, green color, a recessive trait, could appear with round seeds, a dominant trait. Mendel formulated the **principle of independent assortment** to explain this finding. *The principle of independent assortment states that two or more pairs of genes segregate independently of one another during gamete formation.* For example, the segregation of the genes for seed color does not affect the segregation of genes for seed shape.

Today it is known that most gene pairs segregate independently if they are located on different chromosomes. Traits determined by two genes on the same chromosome tend to be inherited together. Mendel, however, was able to choose seven contrasting traits, each determined by a gene pair on a different pair of chromosomes.

10.6 Other Genetic Terminology

Since the time of Mendel, the language of genetics has become more precise. As you know, scientists use the term *gene* instead of *factor* to describe the unit of heredity. They also use the term **allele** (uh LEEL) to refer to either member of a pair of genes that determines a single trait. For example, the dominant allele for seed color in peas (Y) produces yellow seeds. The recessive allele (y) produces green seeds.

The pairs of alleles in the cells of an organism make up its **genotype** (JEE nuh typ). These pairs of genes are represented with capital and lowercase letters, such as YY, Yy, and yy. A trait that is actually expressed in an organism's appearance is called a **phenotype** (FEE nuh typ). Although environment may affect many visible traits, most phenotypes are largely determined by an organism's genotype. For example, a pea plant with the genotype YY will have the phenotype of yellow seeds. What other genotype can produce the phenotype of yellow seeds?

Section Review

1. **Interpreting Ideas**   How did Mendel show the principle of dominance?
2. **Comparing Ideas**   How is Mendel's principle of segregation different from the principle of independent assortment?

> **Thinking Critically**

3. **Analyzing Relationships**   How is phenotype distinguished from genotype?

Genetics and Probability

Mendel's principles of heredity help geneticists today predict the likely results of genetic crosses. For example, Mendel's experiments revealed that when two plants heterozygous for yellow seeds (Yy) are crossed, about one of every four resulting seeds will be green. Mathematicians would say that the likelihood of such a cross producing green seeds is $\frac{1}{4}$, or 25 percent. Mathematicians use the term **probability** to refer to the fraction or percentage that describes the likelihood of an event taking place. Geneticists use probabilities in predicting the phenotypes and genotypes that may result from genetic crosses.

10.7 The Principles of Chance and Probability

If you flip a coin, it can land in only one of two ways—heads or tails. Thus, there is an equal chance that the coin will come up heads or tails. Expressed in mathematical terms, the probability of the coin landing heads or tails is $\frac{1}{2}$ heads : $\frac{1}{2}$ tails. In other words, there is a 50 percent chance of getting heads and a 50 percent chance of getting tails.

It is important to note that probability predicts what is likely to happen, not what must happen. You might toss a coin six times and have it come up heads every time. This can happen because the result of one toss does not influence the outcome of any other toss. Each toss is an independent event. Thus, the probability of a coin coming up heads on the seventh toss is still $\frac{1}{2}$, or 50 percent. The larger the number of tosses, however, the less likely that heads will turn up every time. The probability of 50 percent indicates that if you toss the coin many times you are likely to get roughly equal numbers of heads and tails.

Section Objectives

- *Predict* the outcome of a genetic cross by using probability.
- *Diagram* a genetic cross using a Punnett square.
- *Explain* why a genetic experiment should include a large sample.
- *State* the purpose of a testcross.

You will learn more about probability on page 175.

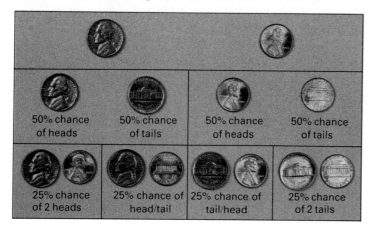

50% chance of heads | 50% chance of tails | 50% chance of heads | 50% chance of tails

25% chance of 2 heads | 25% chance of head/tail | 25% chance of tail/head | 25% chance of 2 tails

Figure 10–6. If you toss two coins, the chance that both coins turn up heads is $\frac{1}{4}$, or 25%. The chance that both turn up tails is also $\frac{1}{4}$, or 25%. The chance that one coin turns up heads and the other turns up tails is $\frac{1}{4} + \frac{1}{4}$, or 50%.

Biofact

Q: *The probability of any one child being a girl is $\frac{1}{2}$. What is the probability of all five children in a family being girls?*

A: The product rule provides the answer. The probability of all five being girls is $(\frac{1}{2})(\frac{1}{2})(\frac{1}{2})(\frac{1}{2})(\frac{1}{2})$, or $\frac{1}{32}$.

$$\left(\tfrac{1}{2}\mathrm{R} + \tfrac{1}{2}\mathrm{r}\right) \times \left(\tfrac{1}{2}\mathrm{R} + \tfrac{1}{2}\mathrm{r}\right)$$

$$\downarrow$$

$$\begin{array}{rrrrr}
 & & \tfrac{1}{2}\mathrm{R} & + & \tfrac{1}{2}\mathrm{r} \\
 & \times & \tfrac{1}{2}\mathrm{R} & + & \tfrac{1}{2}\mathrm{r} \\
\hline
 & & \tfrac{1}{4}\mathrm{Rr} & + & \tfrac{1}{4}\mathrm{rr} \\
+\ \tfrac{1}{4}\mathrm{RR} & + & \tfrac{1}{4}\mathrm{Rr} & & \\
\hline
\tfrac{1}{4}\mathrm{RR} & + & \tfrac{1}{2}\mathrm{Rr} & + & \tfrac{1}{4}\mathrm{rr}
\end{array}$$

Figure 10–7. Using the product rule is a quick way to calculate the probable results of a genetic cross.

Suppose you toss two coins at the same time. What is the probability that both will turn up heads? Figure 10–6 shows that if you toss two coins, the chance of the first one turning up heads is $\frac{1}{2}$ and the chance of the second one turning up heads is $\frac{1}{2}$. The probability that both coins will turn up heads is the product of the two independent probabilities, or $\frac{1}{2} \times \frac{1}{2} = \frac{1}{4}$. This example illustrates the **product rule.** ***The product rule states that the probability of two or more independent events occurring together is the product of the individual probabilities of each event occurring alone.***

10.8 Predicting the Results of Genetic Crosses

Geneticists make two assumptions when applying the principles of probability to genetic crosses. First, they assume that a pair of alleles will segregate in a 1:1 ratio during meiosis. Each gamete produced by an individual with an Rr genotype has an equal chance of receiving an R or an r allele. Thus, the gamete possibilities from one Rr parent can be expressed as $\frac{1}{2}$R and $\frac{1}{2}$r.

Second, geneticists assume that gametes combine randomly during fertilization. This means that any male gamete has an equal chance of combining with any female gamete. Consider the possible combinations of gametes resulting from a cross between two parents heterozygous for round seeds (Rr). We already know that 50 percent of the gametes produced by each parent have the R allele and the other 50 percent have the r allele. To determine the probable combinations of these alleles in F_1 generation offspring, you can apply the product rule and multiply ($\frac{1}{2}$R + $\frac{1}{2}$r) ($\frac{1}{2}$R + $\frac{1}{2}$r).

As Figure 10–7 shows, the product of this cross is $\frac{1}{4}$RR + $\frac{1}{2}$Rr + $\frac{1}{4}$rr. Thus, the F_1 offspring will probably contain three genotypes in a ratio of approximately 1:2:1. This ratio is called the *genotypic ratio*. The *phenotypic ratio*, however, is 3:1. About $\frac{3}{4}$ of the offspring are round seeds ($\frac{1}{4}$RR and $\frac{1}{2}$Rr), and only about $\frac{1}{4}$ are wrinkled seeds (rr).

Remember that predictions based on probability are accurate only if a large number of events are involved. For this reason, the actual outcome of any one genetic cross that produces few offspring is unlikely to match perfectly the predicted genotypic and phenotypic ratios. For example, a single cross between cats heterozygous for short hair (Ss) might produce only short-haired offspring. A large number of crosses would be more likely to reflect the predicted 3:1 ratio of short- to long-haired cats. ***In order to apply the principles of probability, geneticists use very large samples, sometimes conducting thousands of trials in each experiment.***

Reading Critically

Analyzing Data What would be the phenotypic ratio of a cross between a long-haired cat and a heterozygous short-haired cat?

10.9 The Punnett Square

To visualize the probable results of genetic crosses, it is helpful to use a grid, or chart, that shows all the possible gene combinations for a cross. This grid is called a **Punnett square.** It is named for Reginald Punnett, the British geneticist who developed it in the early 1900s.

In a Punnett square, symbols for all the possible gametes from the male (♂) parent appear across the top of the grid. Those from the female (♀) parent appear along the left side of the grid. By combining the symbol for each male gamete with the symbol for each female gamete, all the possible gamete combinations can be found.

Figure 10-8 shows a Punnett square for a cross involving a human trait. In humans free earlobes (E) are dominant over attached earlobes (e). In the cross illustrated, 50 percent of the male gametes carry the allele for free earlobes (E). The other 50 percent of the male gametes carry the allele for attached earlobes (e). The female gametes carry the same contrasting alleles. As the Punnett square shows, there is a 25 percent chance that the offspring will be homozygous dominant (EE). There is a 50 percent chance the offspring will be heterozygous (Ee), and a 25 percent chance the offspring will be homozygous recessive (ee).

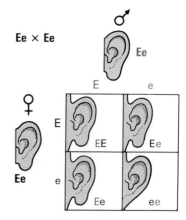

Figure 10–8. Punnett squares can be used to determine the probable results of a genetic cross. Symbols representing male and female gametes appear along the top and left sides of the square. All the possible gamete combinations appear in the boxes of the square.

THINKING ABOUT BIOLOGY: The Testcross

The results of a cross between two pea plants with the genotype Rr can be predicted by using probability. But how can a biologist tell whether a round seed is homozygous or heterozygous?

The genotype of a plant with round seeds can be determined by crossing it with a plant with wrinkled seeds. If the plant with round seeds is heterozygous (Rr), about half of the offspring will also be heterozygous and round.

The other half will be homozygous recessive (rr) and wrinkled. If all of the offspring are round, the parent plant with round seeds was homozygous (RR).

This procedure, called a **testcross,** makes it possible to determine the genotype of any individual whose phenotype is dominant. Mendel used testcrosses to verify the results of his experiments and to support his principle of segregation. Today, plant and animal breeders often

perform testcrosses to determine if an individual is "pure" dominant or a hybrid.

■ **Relating Ideas** Why is it unnecessary to testcross a wrinkled seed to determine its genotype?

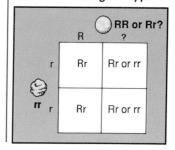

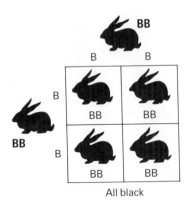

Figure 10–9. A genetic cross between homozygous individuals results in identical genotypic and phenotypic ratios in the F₁ generation.

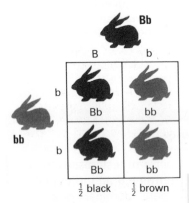

½ black   ½ brown

Figure 10–10. A cross involving a heterozygous individual and a homozygous individual results in genotypic and phenotypic ratios of 1:1.

Thinking Critically

These genotypes result in only two phenotypes, however. There is a 75 percent chance the offspring will have free earlobes and a 25 percent chance for attached earlobes.

10.10 Crosses Involving One Trait

A cross involving one trait is called a **monohybrid cross.** You have already seen the probable results of a cross between two parents heterozygous for free earlobes (Ee). Many other monohybrid cross combinations are possible.

Some of the possibilities can be illustrated by considering various monohybrid crosses between rabbits. In rabbits, the allele for black coat color (B) is dominant over the allele for brown coat color (b). Figure 10–9 shows a cross between a homozygous dominant black male (BB) and a homozygous dominant black female (BB). As you can see, the genotypes in the F₁ generation are all BB and the phenotypes are all black. The same genotypic and phenotypic ratios occur when two homozygous recessive brown parents (bb) are crossed. All the F₁ genotypes are bb, and all the offspring are brown. Offspring with identical genotypes and phenotypes also result when a homozygous dominant black male (BB) is crossed with a homozygous recessive brown female (bb). All the F₁ phenotypes are black, and all the genotypes are heterozygous (Bb).

The pattern changes when a heterozygous black male (Bb) is crossed with a homozygous recessive brown female (bb). Half the offspring have a genotype of Bb and are black. The other half have a genotype of bb and are brown.

Section Review

1. **Predicting Results**   What is the probability of tossing a coin seven times and getting heads every time?
2. **Interpreting Ideas**   Why is it more accurate to draw conclusions from a large sample than from a small sample?
3. **Predicting Conclusions**   What phenotypic ratio would you expect from a cross between a heterozygous tall pea plant (Tt) and a homozygous short pea plant (tt)? Find your answer by using the product rule.
4. **Interpreting Graphics**   A black male rabbit is mated with a brown female rabbit (bb). Their offspring are black and brown in a 1:1 ratio. Use a Punnett square to determine the genotype of the black male parent.
5. **Inferring Relationships**   How can a biologist determine the genotype of an organism that is showing a dominant phenotype?

Extending Mendel's Principles

You have seen how Mendel's principles and the principles of probability apply in crosses involving one pair of alleles. These same principles also govern crosses between parents with two or more contrasting traits.

10.11 Crosses Involving Two Traits

A cross involving two pairs of alleles is called a **dihybrid cross.** The study of this type of cross eventually caused Mendel to develop the principle of independent assortment. *The same principles that govern monohybrid crosses also apply to alleles in dihybrid crosses.*

Figure 10–11 shows a dihybrid cross between two watermelon plants. In watermelons, solid green color (G) is dominant over striped pattern (g), and short shape (S) is dominant over long shape (s). As Figure 10–11 shows, each parent possesses two alleles for each trait, so the cross is expressed as GGSS (green, short) × ggss (striped, long).

According to the principle of independent assortment, each pair of alleles will segregate independently of the other pair. The green, short parent will produce only GS gametes because it has only dominant alleles in its genotype. The striped, long parent will produce only gs gametes because it has only recessive alleles. All members of the F_1 generation will have the genotype GgSs and the phenotype green color and short shape.

Section Objectives

- *Diagram* a dihybrid cross using a Punnett square.
- *Determine* the phenotypic ratio from a dihybrid cross.
- *Predict* the results of a dihybrid cross using the product rule.
- *Explain* what the term *incomplete dominance* means.

Figure 10–11. The F_2 generation of a dihybrid cross shows nine genotypes and four phenotypes in a 9:3:3:1 ratio. This ratio represents 9 green, short; 3 green, long; 3 striped, short; and 1 striped, long.

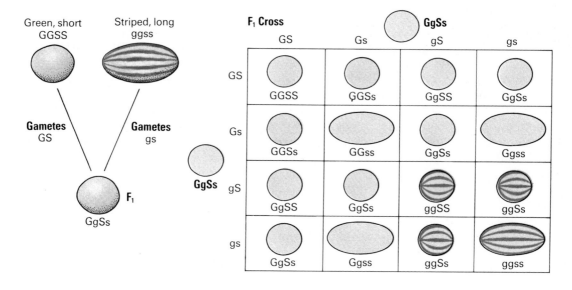

Reading Critically

Why do all members of the F₁ generation discussed here have the genotype GgSs?

The F_2 generation is found by crossing two members of the F_1 generation, GgSs × GgSs. Remember that the Gg and Ss alleles segregate independently. As Figure 10–11 shows, each parent produces four different kinds of gametes—GS, Gs, gS, and gs. Notice that the Punnett square has 16 boxes and that each of the offspring has two alleles for each trait.

Look at Figure 10–11. How many different genotypes are produced from this cross? What are the phenotypes produced? Because of dominance, the nine genotypes produce just four phenotypes: green, short watermelons; green, long watermel-

BIOLOGY AND YOU:

The Punnett Square and Human Inheritance

Many human traits are governed by a single gene. Some, such as earlobe shape, are inconsequential. Others may be far more serious. One example is the disease cystic fibrosis.

Cystic fibrosis is a disease in which the lungs, pancreas, and liver become clogged with a sticky mucus. Persons who suffer from CF usually die in childhood or adolescence. It is the most common inherited disease among Caucasians. The inheritance of CF follows the single-gene pattern described by Mendel. Individuals suffering from CF are homozygous recessive for a single defective allele.

The Punnett square shows how traits governed by one gene, like CF

are passed from one generation to the next. Cystic fibrosis is transmitted by individuals who are carriers for CF. A carrier is a heterozygote who carries a recessive allele but does not express it. One out of every 20 Caucasians carries the CF gene.

The Punnett square drawn here shows the possible offspring of two heterozygous carriers. When two carriers marry and have a child, the chances are 25 percent that the child will inherit the defective gene from each parent and thus suffer the disease. The chances are 50 percent that the child will be a heterozygous carrier. There is a 25 percent chance that the child will not inherit the allele for

♂ ♀	C	c
C	CC Normal individual	Cc Carrier
c	Cc Carrier	cc Individual with cystic fibrosis

CF. These probabilities are the same for every child these two heterozygous carriers may have.

The genes for cystic fibrosis and several other diseases can now be detected through genetic analysis. Couples with CF in their family history can, through genetic counseling, gain information about the probability that they will have children with cystic fibrosis.

ons; striped, short watermelons; and striped, long watermelons. The phenotypic ratio of the F_2 generation can be expressed as 9:3:3:1.

10.12 Incomplete Dominance

As genetics has progressed, geneticists have learned that the principle of dominance does not hold in all cases. *Not all phenotypes result from dominant or recessive genes. In many cases both alleles for a trait are expressed.* Such alleles show **incomplete dominance,** a situation in which neither allele is completely dominant or recessive. Incompletely dominant alleles produce an intermediate phenotype between the two contrasting ones. Incomplete dominance is a modification of Mendel's principle of dominance.

Incomplete dominance may be observed in short-tailed cats. These cats have two alleles for tail length—one for long tail and one for no tail. A Manx cat is homozygous for no tail ($T^N T^N$). Figure 10–12 shows a cross between a Manx cat and a cat homozygous for long tail ($T^L T^L$). Such a cross produces short-tailed offspring. The short-tailed cat is an intermediate phenotype having alleles for both long tail and no tail. Figure 10–12 also shows what happens when two short-tailed cats are crossed. There is a 25 percent chance the offspring will have no tail; a 25 percent chance for a long tail; and a 50 percent chance for a short tail. In this case, both the genotypic and phenotypic ratios are 1:2:1, because neither allele is dominant.

Figure 10–12. In cats, alleles for long tail and no tail demonstrate incomplete dominance and result in a short-tailed cat. The offspring of two short-tailed cats may include cats with no tail, short-tailed cats, and long-tailed cats in a ratio of 1:2:1.

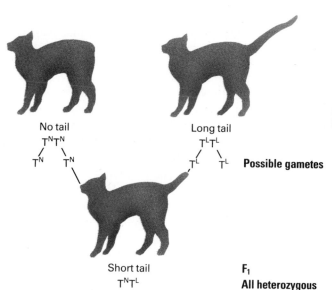

No tail
$T^N T^N$
T^N T^N

Long tail
$T^L T^L$
T^L T^L **Possible gametes**

Short tail
$T^N T^L$

F_1
All heterozygous

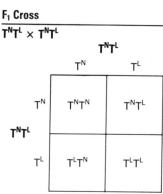

F_1 Cross

$T^N T^L \times T^N T^L$

		$T^N T^L$	
		T^N	T^L
$T^N T^L$	T^N	$T^N T^N$	$T^N T^L$
	T^L	$T^L T^N$	$T^L T^L$

Figure 10-13. Both the Andalusian chicken and the pink snapdragons are phenotypes that result from incomplete dominance.

As you may have noticed in Figure 10-12, incompletely dominant alleles are represented differently from dominant and recessive alleles. In cats the symbol T^N represents the allele for no tail. The symbol T^L represents the allele for a long tail. The genotype T^NT^N produces a cat with no tail, and the genotype T^LT^L produces a cat with a long tail. The short-tailed cat, therefore, has the genotype T^NT^L. The raised, small capital letter in these symbols is called a *superscript*. Why are lowercase letters not used to represent incompletely dominant alleles?

Incomplete dominance also shows up in chickens. The Andalusian breed has one allele for black feathers and one for white feathers. Because neither allele is dominant, an Andalusian chicken has both black and white feathers. This combination causes the chicken to appear blue. Breeding two blue Andalusians results in offspring that are black, blue, or white in a ratio of 1:2:1. Another example of incomplete dominance is pink flower color in snapdragons. Pink-flowering snapdragons are heterozygous. Red or white snapdragons are homozygous.

Section Review

1. **Comprehending Graphs** In pea plants, red flowers (R) are dominant over white flowers (r). Tall plants (T) are dominant over short plants (t). Diagram a dihybrid cross between a plant with the genotype Rrtt and a plant with the genotype rrTt. How many genotypes and phenotypes are found in the offspring?
2. **Predicting Results** Use the product rule to predict the results of a dihybrid cross between a plant with the genotype YyRR and a plant with the genotype Yyrr.
3. **Inferring Relationships** Can a plant breeder produce only pink snapdragons by crossing pink snapdragons and white snapdragons? Explain your answer.

Thinking Critically

INVESTIGATION 10:
How Is Probability Determined?

Objectives
- To *formulate* operational definitions
- To *apply* the rules of probability

Materials
red die, white die, red and blue pencils

Prelab Preparation
1. What are operational definitions and how are they useful in a scientific method?
2. Using red and blue pencils, make a Punnett square similar to the one shown.

	White die					
	1	2	3	4	5	6
Red die 1	1 + 1	2 + 1	3 + 1	4 + 1		
2	1 + 2	2 + 2	3 + 2			
3	1 + 3	2 + 3				
4	1 + 4					
5						
6						

Inquiry: Lab Technique
3. Each roll of a die can be thought of as an *event*. A desired event is a result that you want to happen. For example, if you want to roll a "six", then six is the *desired event*. Each number that could be rolled is a *possible event*. How many possible events can occur when rolling a die? Probability is the relationship between the number of desired events and the number of possible events.
4. *How many sixes are on the die? What is the probability of rolling a six? What is the probability of rolling each of the other numbers on the die?* Express this probability as a percentage. Complete the Punnett square.
5. Using a small cup, roll the die 80 times, recording your results in a data table. Calculate the percentage of times each number appeared.

6. Compare the observed results, obtained in step 5, to the expected results. *How can differences between observed and expected results be explained?*
7. Use the Punnett square to find the number of different red-white combinations that can occur when rolling a pair of dice.
8. When rolling a single die, the probability of rolling a "one" is one-sixth. *When rolling a red die and white die together, how many combinations total two? What is the probability of rolling a combination that totals two?*
9. *Using only the individual probabilities of rolling a red one and a white one, how can the probability of rolling a combination that totals two be calculated?*
10. Use the Punnett square to find the number of combinations that involve rolling a red three. *What is the probability of rolling a red three? What is the probability of rolling a white two?*
11. Find the number of combinations that involve rolling either a red three or a white two. *What is the probability of rolling either a red three or a white two with a pair of dice?* Explain how the individual probabilities can be used to calculate the probability of rolling either a red three or a white two.

Analysis
1. **Making Generalizations** State an operational definition of probability based on your observations.
2. **Making Generalizations** State an operational rule for finding the probability that two or more independent events will occur together.
3. **Making Generalizations** State an operational rule for finding the probability that either or any of a number of events will occur.
4. **Applying Principles** Explain how to find the probability of rolling a combination totaling seven with a pair of dice.

Chapter 10 Review

Summary

Gregor Mendel inferred the fundamentals of genetics through research with garden peas. Mendel found that each trait he studied is influenced by a pair of factors, which are now called genes. Mendel established the principle of dominance, the principle of segregation, and the principle of independent assortment.

The two genes in a pair are called alleles. If the alleles are the same, the individual is homozygous. If the pair consists of contrasting alleles, the individual is heterozygous.

Geneticists use probability to predict the results of genetic crosses. Punnett squares are used to display the results of genetic crosses.

A cross involving one trait is called a monohybrid cross. A cross involving two traits is a dihybrid cross. When neither allele is dominant, the result is an intermediate trait.

BioTerms

allele (**166**)
chromosome (**161**)
cross-pollination (**163**)
dihybrid cross (**171**)
dominant (**164**)
first filial
    generation (**163**)
gamete (**161**)
gene (**161**)
genetics (**161**)
genotype (**166**)
heredity (**160**)
heterozygous (**164**)
homozygous (**164**)

homozygous
    dominant (**164**)
homozygous
    recessive (**164**)
hybrid (**164**)
incomplete
    dominance (**173**)
monohybrid
    cross (**170**)
parental
    generation (**162**)
phenotype (**166**)
principle of
    dominance (**163**)

principle of
    independent
    assortment (**166**)
principle of
    segregation (**165**)
probability (**167**)
product rule (**168**)

Punnett square (**169**)
purebred (**164**)
recessive (**164**)
second filial
    generation (**163**)
self-pollination (**161**)
testcross (**169**)

For each pair of terms, explain the differences in their meanings.

1. homozygous, heterozygous
2. genotype, phenotype
3. dominant, recessive
4. dihybrid cross, monohybrid cross

BioQuiz   (Write all answers on a separate sheet of paper.)

Completion

1. A cross involving two pairs of alleles is called a _____ .
2. The fraction that describes the likelihood of an event's taking place is the _____ .
3. The gene that is hidden by a dominant gene in the F_1, generation is _____ .
4. If both genes are dominant, then the individual is _____ .
5. A grid used to visualize possible gene combinations for a cross is a _____ .

Multiple Choice

6. A plant with a genotype of Rr is a) homozygous dominant. b) heterozygous. c) homozygous recessive. d) homozygous.
7. The color pink in snapdragons is due to a) dominance. b) incomplete segregation. c) blending. d) incomplete dominance.
8. The cross GgSs × GgSs yields what phenotypic ratio? a) 3:1 b) 2:4 c) 9:3:3:1 d) 6:3:3:1

9. Given a cross between individuals with TT and tt genotypes, what would be the genotype of the first filial generation? a) TT. b) tt. c) Tt. d) TTTt.
10. The genotype of an individual with a dominant phenotype can be determined using a) a Punnett square. b) a test cross. c) a dihybrid cross. d) probability.
11. The formation of an equal number of R and r gametes from an Rr individual demonstrates a) independent assortment. b) dominance. c) segregation. d) incomplete dominance.
12. The probability of a coin's turning heads up six times in a row is a) 1/4. b) 1/8. c) 1/32. d) 1/64.
13. The probable phenotypic ratio resulting from the cross Rr × rr is a) 2:4. b) 1:3. c) 2:2. d) 1:2.

14. If a phenotype expresses a recessive trait, then the genotype is a) heterozygous. b) homozygous. c) hybrid. d) self-pollinating.
15. The genotype for a Manx cat with no tail is a) $T^L T^L$. b) $T^L T^N$. c) $T^N T^L$. d) $T^N T^N$.

16. Explain how cross pollination was an important part of Mendel's experiments.
17. Describe how the product rule applies to the study of genetics.
18. Draw a Punnett square to show the genotypes of the offspring of a ggSS watermelon and a GgSs watermelon.
19. What is the product rule?
20. Why is it impossible to produce pure-breeding pink snapdragons?

Application/Critical Thinking

1. **Inferring Relationships** In cattle a recessive gene is responsible for the appearance of horns. The dominant allele causes a hornless condition. Would it be easier for a farmer to establish pure-breeding stock of hornless cattle or horned cattle? Explain your answer.
2. **Synthesizing Information** One dihybrid cross involves two pairs of *complementary genes* that are inherited separately but influence the same trait. Do library research on complementary genes that produce purple color in sweet pea flowers. Then use Punnett squares to determine the phenotypic ratio in the F_2 generation. How does this ratio differ from the phenotypic ratio of the F_2 generation in a cross where one allele is dominant?

Cross-Discipline Connection

Biology and History Investigate and report on the work of the following scientists: Wilhelm Johannsen, Carl E. Correns, and Hugo DeVries. How did the work of these three scientists differ from that conducted by Mendel?

Discovery Through Reading

"A Genetic Gender Gap," *Science News* (May 20, 1989): 312–315, questions Mendel's principles that have been the basis of genetics for 100 years. What is genomic imprinting and why was it not noticed for such a long time? How might genomic imprinting be used?

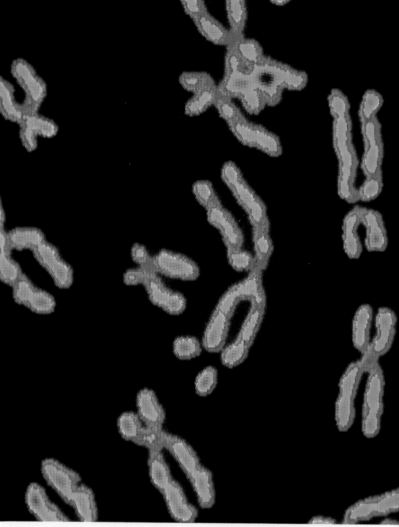

CHAPTER

11

Chromosomes and Genetics

Outline

Normal human chromosomes, stained to show detail

Focus

Gregor Mendel derived the basic principles of heredity by applying simple arithmetic to the results of his garden pea experiments. By the late 1800s, scientists had observed chromosomes and the processes of mitosis and meiosis. These observations and the rediscovery of Mendel's work in 1900 led scientists to conclude that the mysteries of heredity could be solved by studying the cell nucleus.

■ *What clue in the photograph indicates that each chromosome carries two sets of identical information?*

■ *In what stage of mitosis does one set of information separate from the other?*

The Chromosome Theory

Section Objectives
- *Describe* the observations that led Walter Sutton to propose the chromosome theory.
- *State* the chromosome theory.
- *Describe* the relationship Sutton believed existed between a gene and a chromosome.

In 1882 the German scientist Walther Flemming first observed chromosomes during mitosis. About ten years later, August Weismann, another German scientist, hypothesized that chromosomes are responsible for heredity. However, scientists did not accept the fact that chromosomes are the carriers of heredity until the rediscovery of Gregor Mendel's work in 1900.

11.1 The Work of Walter Sutton

In 1903 Walter S. Sutton was a professor at Columbia University in New York City. During his studies, Sutton noticed a strong similarity between Mendel's principles and his own observations of meiosis in grasshoppers. These similarities led Sutton to propose the **chromosome theory**. *The chromosome theory states that hereditary factors, or genes, are carried on chromosomes.*

What observations led Sutton to state the chromosome theory? First Sutton noticed that the chromosomes in each grasshopper cell line up in pairs during meiosis. He also observed that the members of each chromosome pair are homologous, or alike in shape and size. Thus, Sutton noted that chromosomes in the body cells occur in pairs, corresponding to Mendel's pairs of factors.

Next Sutton observed that homologous chromosomes segregate during meiosis. As a result, each gamete receives one half of the chromosomes—one member from each pair. In addition, Sutton saw that the way in which members of one pair segregate seems to have no effect on how members of another pair segregate. Finally Sutton observed that a sperm and an egg cell, each

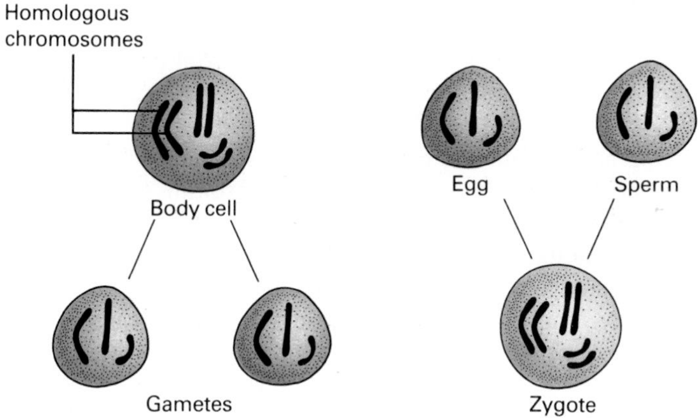

Homologous chromosomes

Body cell

Gametes

Egg   Sperm

Zygote

Figure 11–1. As Walter Sutton noted, the separation of homologous chromosomes into different gametes follows Mendel's principle of segregation. The formation of new homologous pairs in the zygote is consistent with the principle of independent assortment.

DNA Fingerprints—The Genetic Crime Stopper

One of the newest tools used in solving crimes is a result of the technology developed in DNA research. The technique is DNA fingerprinting. DNA fingerprints are made from skin, blood, and other body tissues. When even a small amount of body tissue or a strand of hair is discovered at a crime scene, its DNA content can be analyzed and compared to the DNA of a suspect.

In more than a dozen states, criminal suspects have been convicted or acquitted primarily on the basis of DNA fingerprints. The procedure has been used most often in cases of rape, where the only physical evidence may be sperm.

DNA fingerprinting can also help resolve paternity suits by comparing a child's DNA to that of the man who has been charged with paternity.

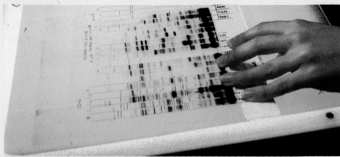

DNA fingerprinting is done by first extracting DNA from bits of body tissue. These DNA strands are cut into sections through the use of enzymes. Scientists then add a radioactive substance to the DNA sample. The substance adheres to specific parts of the individual's DNA and produces a pattern of stripes. These stripes, or bands, are similar to a bar code on a store product. This "bar code" is unique to the individual. It is his or her DNA fingerprint.

The probability that identical DNA fingerprints will be obtained from two different people has been estimated at one in a billion. So far, experts in genetics who have testified in court have convinced juries that DNA fingerprints can be used to identify a suspect. The uniqueness of a person's DNA, together with the fact that only a small sample of tissue is needed to make a "fingerprint," has provided law enforcement professionals with a valuable tool. One state has proposed DNA typing of all convicted criminals as a deterrent to crime.

carrying half the number of chromosomes found in body cells, unite during fertilization. Therefore, the resulting zygote has a complete set of homologous chromosomes.

After Sutton observed meiosis, he realized that chromosomes behave in a manner that agrees with Mendel's principles of heredity. This fact, along with certain other observations Sutton made, contributed to his belief that chromosomes carry the information of heredity. The major points that supported Sutton's hypothesis include the following:

1. Egg and sperm cells provide the only physical link between one generation and the next. For this reason, the hereditary material must be carried in these cells.
2. Hereditary material is probably located in a cell's nucleus rather than in its cytoplasm. Sutton knew that both parents contribute equally to the genetic makeup of offspring. With this idea in mind, Sutton noted that sperm cells have far less cytoplasm than egg cells have. However, the nuclei of the two cell types are about the same size.
3. During meiosis, chromosomes tend to behave according to Mendel's principles. Following Mendel's principle of segregation, each pair of homologous chromosomes separates independently of one another. Each gamete thus receives only one of the genes of the allelic pair.

Interestingly, a German scientist named Theodore Boveri arrived at similar conclusions at about the same time as Sutton. Boveri's work was done on parasitic roundworms. Sutton's findings, however, were published first. Thus Sutton generally receives credit for establishing the chromosome theory.

11.2 Genes and Chromosomes

Scientists quickly realized that organisms have many more traits than they have chromosomes. For example, in the grasshoppers that Sutton observed, only 12 pairs of chromosomes seemed to be responsible for producing hundreds of traits. Sutton reasoned that each chromosome must carry hundreds, perhaps thousands, of smaller particles that contain hereditary information.

In 1909 a Danish biologist named Wilhelm Johannsen first used the word *gene* to describe these tiny particles of inheritance. The demonstration that a particular gene is located in a specific chromosome, however, did not come until several years later.

Section Review

1. **Relating Ideas**   What similarity did Sutton observe between meiosis and Mendel's principles?
2. **Identifying Ideas**   What is the chromosome theory?
3. **Comprehending Ideas**   What led Sutton to think that each chromosome carried many factors?
4. **Synthesizing Relationships**   Why was the fact that Mendel published his findings important to the progress of genetic research?

Biofact

Q: *How did chromosomes get their name?*

A: Walther Flemming used dyes to stain cell parts for study. He found that a certain dye revealed threadlike material in the nucleus. He called this material *chromatin* after the Greek word for *color*. Later the threads were called *chromosomes*, based on a Greek word meaning "colored bodies."

Reading Critically

Interpreting Information
How can an individual have more traits than chromosomes?

The search for human gene locations is described on pages 224–225.

The search for human gene locations is described on pages 224–225.

Thinking Critically

- *Explain* how chromosomes determine the sex of an individual.
- *State* what is meant by a sex-linked trait.
- *Diagram* a cross using a Punnett square to show sex-linked inheritance.

The Sex Chromosomes

The chromosome theory suggested that genes are located on chromosomes. Although Sutton's theory was accepted, it was Thomas Hunt Morgan, an American zoologist, who demonstrated that a specific gene was located on a specific chromosome.

11.3 Chromosomes and Sex Determination

In the early 1900s, Morgan began genetic research at Columbia University using the fruit fly, *Drosophila melanogaster*. Morgan selected *Drosophila* because they are easy to maintain and breed. Just 3 mm (0.1 in.) long, *Drosophila* are so tiny that hundreds can be kept in a jar. In addition, *Drosophila* have a reproductive cycle of just 10 to 15 days. Therefore, they can produce many generations of offspring in a matter of weeks.

Morgan and his colleagues found another important characteristic: *Drosophila* have only four pairs of chromosomes. The researchers further observed that one pair of chromosomes in males is different from the corresponding pair in females. In males, the two chromosomes in this pair are not the same size or shape. One chromosome is large and rod-shaped; the other is small and hook-shaped. The rod-shaped chromosome is called an *X* chromosome. The hook-shaped one is called a *Y chromosome*. The corresponding pair of chromosomes in females consists of two X chromosomes. Morgan and his colleagues had determined the action of the **sex chromosomes**—the chromosomes that determine the sex of an individual. All other chromosomes in an individual are called **autosomes**.

Figure 11–2 shows how sex is determined in *Drosophila*. The sex chromosomes separate during meiosis. Each egg has only an X chromosome. Each sperm has either an X or a Y chromosome. When a sperm carrying an X chromosome fertilizes an egg, the offspring will be female (XX). If the sperm that fertilizes the egg carries a Y chromosome, the offspring will be male (XY). Roughly equal numbers of male and female offspring will be produced. *In most organisms, including both fruit flies and humans, sex is determined by gametes from the male parent.*

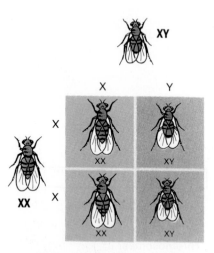

Figure 11–2. This Punnett square shows that a female fruit fly can contribute only an X chromosome to all her offspring. Therefore, sex is determined by the male gamete, which contributes either an X or a Y chromosome.

Reading Critically

Inferring Relationships Why is sex always determined by the male parent?

11.4 Sex-Linked Traits

Morgan's observation of sex chromosomes was the first of several important findings. Another discovery resulted from crosses that Morgan made with red-eyed fruit flies and white-eyed fruit flies. Red is the normal eye color in wild-type *Drosophila*. By this time, Morgan and his associates knew that the allele for red eye color, R, was dominant over the allele for white eye color, r.

Morgan crossed the white-eyed male with a red-eyed female. Following the principle of dominance, all members of the F_1 generation had red eyes. Then Morgan allowed the F_1 generation to mate. The F_2 generation showed about a 3:1 ratio of red-eyed flies to white-eyed flies. Surprisingly, however, all the F_2 generation flies with white eyes were males. Why were there no females with white eyes?

Morgan concluded that the alleles for eye color are carried only on the X chromosome. Thus, eye color in fruit flies is an example of a **sex-linked trait.** A sex-linked trait is one that is determined by alleles carried only on an X chromosome. A sex-linked trait has no alleles on the Y chromosome.

Punnett squares illustrate how sex-linked traits appear in offspring. Figure 11–3 shows Morgan's parental cross between a white-eyed male and a red-eyed female. Each female gamete carries a dominant allele (X^R) for eye color. Each male gamete, however, has either an X chromosome carrying a recessive allele (X^r) for eye color or a Y chromosome with no allele for eye color. The F_1 generation, then, consists of females heterozygous for red eyes and males with one dominant allele for red eyes. Figure 11–3 also shows the results of the F_1 generation cross. About one-fourth of the offspring are male flies with white eyes. Each of these white-eyed males resulted from the union of a female gamete carrying the recessive allele and a male gamete carrying only a Y chromosome.

Morgan's experiments confirmed Sutton's hypothesis that genes are found on chromosomes. In addition, the discovery of sex-linked traits explained why some characteristics caused by recessive genes appear far more often in males. Since males have only one X chromosome, any recessive allele present on that chromosome will be expressed. Only females have two X chromosomes, and therefore, they are more likely to be heterozygous, carrying a dominant allele that masks the expression of a recessive allele.

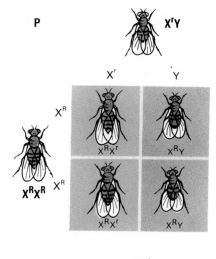

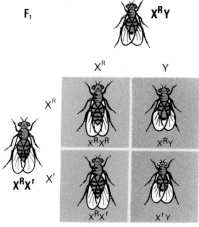

Figure 11–3. In fruit flies, the alleles for red eyes (R) and for white eyes (r) are carried only on the X chromosome.

Section Review

1. **Summarizing Ideas** How is the sex of most organisms determined? Use a Punnett square to illustrate your answer.
2. **Inferring Relationships** Explain how Morgan's experiments confirmed Sutton's hypothesis. What kind of cross is needed to confirm this?

⟨ **Thinking Critically** ⟩

Section Objectives

- *Explain* how the idea of gene linkage developed.
- *Describe* the process of crossing over.
- *Explain* how chromosome maps are made.
- *Discuss* gene mapping.

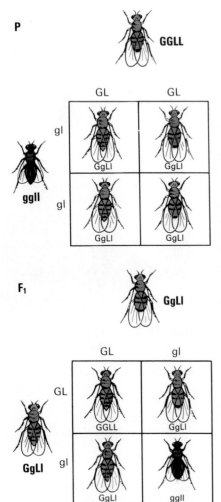

Figure 11–4. In *Drosophila*, alleles for body color and wing length are linked.

The Behavior of Genes

Thomas Hunt Morgan's work revealed that genes for certain traits are carried on the X chromosomes, and that chromosomes and their genes segregate during meiosis. Later, Morgan demonstrated that specific genes are also carried on specific autosomes. In addition, his research showed that genes may be exchanged between homologous chromosomes.

11.5 Gene Linkage

In later experiments, Morgan studied other traits in fruit flies. One of his most important experiments involved two contrasting traits produced by dominant alleles—gray body color (G) and long wings (L). The corresponding recessive alleles determine black body color (g) and short wings (l).

Morgan crossed flies homozygous for gray bodies and long wings (GGLL) with flies homozygous for black bodies and short wings (ggll). As predicted by Mendel's principles, all of the F_1 flies were heterozygous and had gray bodies and long wings.

According to Mendel's principle of independent assortment, the F_2 generation phenotypes should have shown a 9:3:3:1 ratio. However, when Morgan crossed flies from the F_1 generation, the F_2 generation phenotypes appeared in roughly a 3:1 ratio. About three-fourths had gray bodies and long wings, and about one-fourth had black bodies and short wings. From these results, Morgan concluded that the alleles for gray body and long wings were located on the same chromosome. The Punnett squares in Figure 11–4 illustrate the results of Morgan's crosses.

As a result of Morgan's experiments and the work of certain other scientists, it became clear that genes are linked on all chromosomes. The situation in which two or more genes occur on the same chromosome is called **gene linkage**. Genes that occur together on a chromosome represent a **linkage group**. Fruit flies have 4 pairs of chromosomes and therefore have 4 linkage groups. Humans have 23 pairs of chromosomes and thus 23 linkage groups.

11.6 Crossing Over

Morgan then did a testcross of the F_1 and a homozygous recessive and he found several offspring with a mixture of dominant and recessive traits. A few flies had gray bodies and short

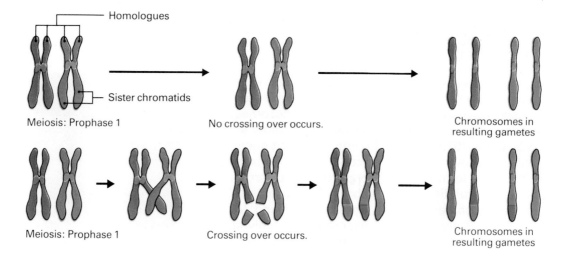

Homologues

Sister chromatids

Meiosis: Prophase 1

No crossing over occurs.

Chromosomes in resulting gametes

Meiosis: Prophase 1

Crossing over occurs.

Chromosomes in resulting gametes

wings. A few others had black bodies and long wings. These individuals could not have been produced if the alleles G and L were always inherited together. Morgan proposed that alleles from two homologous chromosomes had exchanged places. This process by which alleles exchange places is called **crossing over.** Later experiments confirmed that crossing over does regularly take place in almost all organisms.

Figure 11–5 illustrates how crossing over occurs. During prophase I of meiosis, the duplicated chromosomes pair up with their homologues. Each duplicated chromosome is made up of two identical sister chromatids. Together, the two chromosomes consist of four chromatids. At this time, breaks may occur in the same spot on two nonsister chromatids. The broken ends of one chromatid then fuse with those of the other chromatid. As a result, each chromatid contains parts from its homologue.

11.7 Chromosome Mapping

The discovery of crossing over revealed that genes are found at certain fixed positions on the chromosomes. The alleles for eye color in fruit flies, for instance, always occupy the same position on homologous chromosomes.

Alfred H. Sturtevant, a graduate student in Morgan's laboratory, proposed that genes are located on the chromosomes in a line, like beads on a string. Sturtevant suggested that the frequency of crossing over would be affected by the distance between two genes on a chromosome. He reasoned that widely spaced genes would be more likely to cross over than closely spaced genes. Sturtevant proposed that this assumption could be used to develop a chromosome map like that in Figure 11–6.

Figure 11–5. Crossing over occurs after homologous chromosomes have paired during meiosis. A segment of one chromatid is exchanged with a segment from a non-sister chromatid.

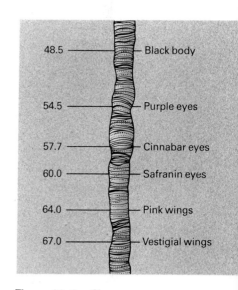

48.5	Black body
54.5	Purple eyes
57.7	Cinnabar eyes
60.0	Safranin eyes
64.0	Pink wings
67.0	Vestigial wings

Figure 11–6. Chromosome mapping was used to determine the position of genes on this chromosome taken from the salivary gland of *Drosophila.*

Chromosomes in most organisms are so small that microscopes can reveal only a few of their details. In the 1930s, scientists discovered that the immature form, or larva, of the fruit fly has giant chromosomes in the cells of its salivary glands. These chromosomes are more than 1,000 times larger than the same chromosomes in the cells of the adult fruit fly. They are large because the chromosomes duplicate many times but do not separate. The duplicates line up close to one another, forming the giant chromosome you see here.

Giant chromosomes, easily visible under a compound light microscope, gave scientists an opportunity to learn more about chromosomes. Researchers found, for example, that applying stain to these chromosomes produced sequences of dark and light bands. Gene mapping revealed that specific genes were located in specific bands. Giant chromosomes also enabled scientists to learn more about minute changes in chromosomes

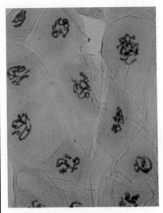

that produce severe problems in offspring.

■ **Evaluating Relationships** What is the value of knowing the location of specific genes on a chromosome?

To learn how to make chromosome maps, see the Investigation on page 187.

To learn how to make chromosome maps, see the Investigation on page 187.

A **chromosome map** is a graphic device that shows where genes are located on a chromosome.

Sturtevant determined the location of genes on a chromosome by calculating the percentage of offspring showing the crossing over of genes. For example, if the two dominant traits produced by linked genes A and B appeared together in 85 percent of the offspring of a testcross ($F_1 \times$ aabb), then crossing over must have occurred in the other 15 percent. According to Sturtevant's system, genes A and B would then be considered 15 units apart. Sturtevant and other scientists used many such percentages to develop a chromosome map of *Drosophila*.

Reading Critically

Inferring Relationships How could a chromosome map help predict the probability of crossing over between genes?

Thinking Critically

Section Review

1. **Summarizing Ideas** What event led Thomas Hunt Morgan to suggest the idea of gene linkage?
2. **Recognizing Relationships** How does crossing over explain mixtures of recessive and dominant traits?
3. **Inferring Relationships** How is the percentage of crossing over used to map genes?

INVESTIGATION 11:
How Are Chromosomes Mapped?

Objectives
- To *determine* patterns of heredity
- To *analyze* data

Materials
paper, pencil

Prelab Preparation
1. Define the terms linkage group, crossing over, and chromosome map.
2. Explain how crossing over is used to develop a chromosome map.

Inquiry: Experimentation
3. The table below summarizes four traits for a certain fictitious insect.

Trait	Possible Phenotypes
Body Color	Blue White
Eye Color	Green Brown
Antennae	Long Short
Bristles	Straight Curly
Number of Chromosomes	2 pairs

A young geneticist wishes to test the following two hypotheses.

Hypothesis 1: Blue body, green eyes, long antennae, and straight bristles are dominant traits.

Hypothesis 2: The genes for body color and bristle texture form one linkage group; the genes for antenna length and eye color form another linkage group.

4. Study the data collected from the crosses described below to complete the analysis.

Cross #1   white-bodied ♂ × blue-bodied ♀
F₁ All blue-bodied
F₂ 62 blue-bodied
   21 white-bodied

Cross #2   blue-bodied, green-eyed ♂ × blue-bodied, green-eyed ♀
F₁ 21 blue, green
    7 white, green

8 blue, brown
2 white, brown

Cross #3   blue-bodied, short-antennaed ♂ × white-bodied, long antennaed ♀
F₁ All blue-bodied, short antennaed
F₂ 66 blue, short
   19 white, long
    1 blue, long
    1 white, short

Cross #4   curly-bristled, blue-bodied ♂ × straight-bristled, white-bodied ♀
F₁ All curly-bristled, blue-bodied
F₂ 80 curly, blue
   27 straight, white
    3 curly, white
    4 straight, blue

Analysis
1. **Analyzing Data** Explain whether or not the evidence supports the geneticist's first hypothesis.
2. **Analyzing Data** What do the results of Cross #2 indicate about the parents?
3. **Making Predictions** What results would be expected for Cross #2, if the genes for body color and eye color are not linked?
4. **Identifying Relationships** Which of Mendel's principles is demonstrated by Cross #1? Which is demonstrated by Cross #2?
5. **Making Predictions** What results would be expected for Cross #3 and for Cross #4 if the genes are not linked?
6. **Analyzing Data** Explain whether or not the evidence supports the geneticist's second hypothesis.
7. **Making Inferences** Suppose the following cross-over percentages are correct:
   - 39 percent between the genes for body color and bristle texture
   - 23 percent between the genes for bristle texture and antenna length
   - 16 percent between the genes for body color and antenna length.

Diagram the arrangement of these genes on a chromosome and their relative distances from each other.

Chapter 11 Review

Summary

Great strides were made in genetic research following the improvement of the compound light microscope and the rediscovery of Mendel's work in 1900. In 1902, Walter Sutton observed that, during meiosis, chromosomes behave according to Mendel's principles. These observations led Sutton to propose the chromosome theory. Sutton's chromosome theory states that hereditary information is carried from generation to generation by hereditary factors located on chromosomes.

Thomas Hunt Morgan furthered the study of genetics using the fruit fly. His early observations revealed one pair of chromosomes in male flies that do not match a pair of chromosomes in female flies. These chromosomes, called the sex chromosomes, are designated XY in the male and XX in the female. Morgan showed that the sex chromosomes carry genes for sex-linked traits. Chromosomes other than sex chromosomes are called autosomes.

Morgan also demonstrated that genes are linked on chromosomes. In addition, he discovered that, during meiosis, homologous chromosomes regularly exchange genes in a process called crossing over. Alfred Sturtevant determined that the percentage of time genes cross over is related to the distance between the genes on a chromosome. Sturtevant used these percentages to draw chromosome maps showing the location of genes for different traits.

BioTerms

autosome (**182**)
chromosome
   map (**186**)
chromosome
   theory (**179**)
crossing over (**185**)
gene linkage (**184**)
linkage group (**184**)
sex chromosome (**182**)
sex-linkage trait (**183**)

For each pair of terms, explain the differences in their meanings.

1. crossing over, gene linkage
2. autosome, sex chromosome

BioQuiz   (Write all answers on a separate sheet of paper.)

Completion

1. Chromosomes that do not determine sex are _____ .
2. A trait that is determined by alleles carried only on an X chromosome is said to be _____ .
3. The occurrence of two or more genes on the same chromosome is an example of _____ .
4. The exchanging of alleles on chromosomes is called _____ .
5. A graphic device that is useful in showing the positions of genes on chromosomes is called a _____ .

Multiple Choice

6. Sutton studied the behavior of grasshopper chromosomes during
   a) meiosis.   b) fertilization.
   c) mitosis.   d) embryo growth.
7. Morgan's genetic discoveries came from the study of   a) pea plants.   b) fruit flies.   c) houseflies.   d) sunflowers.
8. The word _____ is now used to refer to Mendel's factors.   a) autosome
   b) trait   c) gene   d) chromosome
9. In humans, if the sperm carries a Y chromosome, the offspring will be   a) male.
   b) female. c) homozygous. d) dominant.

10. In fruit flies, which of the following genotypes represents a female?
    a) XX b) XY c) YO d) YY
11. Crossingover occurs during a) meiosis.
    b) mitosis. c) fertilization. d) replication.
12. The chromosome theory was first proposed by a) Mendel. b) Morgan.
    c) Sutton. d) Flemming.
13. Hereditary material is located in the cell's
    a) cytoplasm. b) plastids.
    c) ribosomes. d) nucleus.
14. The number of homologous pairs of chromosomes in an organism determines the number of a) linked traits.
    b) linkage groups. c) genes. d) gametes.
15. The number of linkage groups in an organism is equal to the number of

a) chromosome pairs. b) autosomes.
c) traits. d) genes.

16. What observation led Walter Sutton to conclude that chromosomes carry the hereditary information?
17. What characteristics make *Drosophila* well suited for genetic study?
18. How did the discovery of sex-linked traits support the chromosome theory?
19. How did Thomas Hunt Morgan explain the fact that linked genes are sometimes inherited separately?
20. Why are genes that are far apart on a chromosome more likely to cross over than genes that are closer together?

Application/Critical Thinking

1. **Synthesizing Conclusions** Two dominant traits in fruit flies are long legs (L) and long antennae bristles (B). The recessive traits are short legs (l) and short bristles (b). Design an experiment to find out whether the genes for these traits are linked. Use Punnett squares to determine the phenotypic ratio that would occur if the traits were not linked.
2. **Evaluating Relationships** In cats, the X chromosome carries the genes for coat color. The allele for yellow coat (Y) is dominant over the allele for black coat (y). A cross between a yellow male and a black female produces three male kittens. What color are the kittens? How do you know?
3. **Relating Ideas** In 1961, geneticist Mary Lyon proposed that one X chromosome in each cell of a female mammal becomes inactive early in the organism's development. Research the Lyon hypothesis. Then use it and the information from question 2 above to explain why almost all calico, or yellow and black, cats are female.

Cross-Discipline Connection

Biology and Reading The Nobel Prize winner, Barbara McClintock, researched the genetic makeup of Indian corn. Read current articles about this scientist and her work.

Discovery Through Reading

Read "A Genetic Gender Gap" *Science News* (May 20, 1989): 312–315 which raises questions about Mendel's principles, especially the principle of segregation. What is genomic imprinting?
    "The Gene Hunt," *Time* (March 20, 1989): 62–67, focuses on how gene mapping techniques are being used to develop a map of the entire human genome. What is one long-range benefit of the genome project? What is one early benefit?

Chemical Basis of Genetics

Outline

Computer-generated model of DNA

Focus

In the 40 years after Thomas Hunt Morgan's experiments with fruit flies in 1910, scientists began to answer fundamental questions about genes. The answers came from *biochemical molecular genetics,* the study of the chemistry of genes. Experiments in this field supplied information about the chemical structure of genes and how these genes influence both the chemical processes and physical structure of all living things.

■ *How might knowing about the chemical nature of genes provide ways of curing diseases?*

■ *What does the term biochemistry mean?*

The Discovery of DNA

Biochemists provided some early insights into the nature of genes by analyzing the chemical makeup of chromosomes. They found that chromosomes are composed of two different substances. One substance is protein. The other substance is **DNA,** or **deoxyribonucleic** (dee AHK sih ry boh noo KLEE ihk) **acid,** a complex compound classified as a nucleic acid. For years, scientists believed that the protein in chromosomes was the genetic material. Experiments in the 1940s and 1950s, however, showed that the genetic material is DNA.

12.1 Early Proof of DNA's Role

The first evidence that DNA is the genetic material came in 1944 from the research of Oswald Avery, Colin MacLeod, and Maclyn McCarty. These scientists were working at Rockefeller Institute in New York City. Their work was based on a puzzling situation discovered earlier by the English bacteriologist Frank Griffith.

In 1928 Griffith was experimenting with two strains of *Streptococcus,* a type of bacterium. One of these strains (called S, or smooth) is surrounded by a protective capsule and causes fatal cases of pneumonia in mice. The other strain (called R, or rough) has no protective capsule and does not produce pneumonia in mice. In his experiments, Griffith killed the deadly strain S bacteria with heat. When the killed strain S bacteria were injected into mice, the bacteria did not cause pneumonia. However, mice injected with both heat-killed strain S and living

Figure 12–1. The illustrations below show the results of Griffith's experiments. Why did mice die when infected with a mixture of heat-killed S-strain bacteria and live R-strain bacteria?

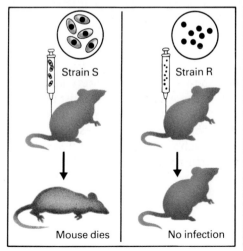

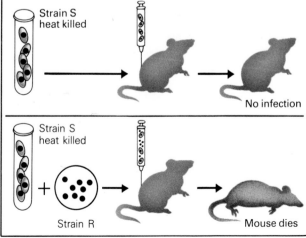

The Investigation on page 205 gives a procedure for extracting DNA.

Pyrimidines

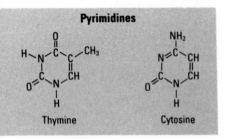

Thymine   Cytosine

Purines

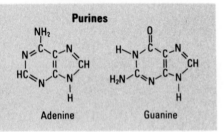

Adenine   Guanine

Figure 12–2. Thymine and cytosine are pyrimidines. Each contains a single ring of carbon and nitrogen atoms. Adenine and guanine are purines, which have a double carbon-nitrogen ring.

strain R bacteria developed pneumonia and died. What had happened? The strain S bacteria could not have come back to life.

After years of complicated chemical studies, Avery and his associates found the answer to Griffith's question. In their most important experiment, they managed to remove DNA from strain S bacteria and place it in a culture of strain R bacteria. Inside the cells of the strain R bacteria, DNA of the strain S apparently took over and caused the strain R bacteria to develop capsules. Furthermore, the strain R bacteria passed on the genetic instructions of strain S DNA to their offspring. The offspring of the changed strain R bacteria developed protective capsules as well. *As a result of their tests, Avery and his associates identified DNA as the genetic material.*

In 1952 biologist Alfred Hershey and his laboratory assistant Martha Chase conducted experiments that supported Avery's findings. Their research showed that a certain type of virus could inject a substance into bacteria and that minutes later, new viruses would appear. Hershey and Chase further showed that the substance injected into the bacteria was DNA. From this observation, Hershey and Chase concluded that DNA was the genetic material because it took control of the bacterial cell and forced it to make new viruses.

12.2 Structure of DNA

The next major breakthrough in genetic research took place in 1953 at Cambridge University in Great Britain. This breakthrough was one of the most important of all scientific discoveries. *James D. Watson, an American biologist, and Francis H. C. Crick, a British biophysicist, described the structure of DNA.* Watson and Crick also developed a model of DNA. Their now famous model explains how DNA works.

Existing Knowledge of DNA Watson and Crick had substantial information to draw on as they pieced together the structure of DNA. First, they knew that DNA is a very long, thin molecule. From the work of the American biochemist Phoebus A. Levene in the 1920s, they also knew the chemical makeup of DNA. DNA contains four nitrogen-carrying bases. These four bases are called **adenine** (AD uh neen), **guanine** (GWAH neen), **thymine** (THY meen), and **cytosine** (SYT uh seen). Adenine and guanine are compounds called *purines* (PYOOR eenz). Thymine and cytosine are compounds called *pyrimidines* (pih RIHM uh deenz). In Figure 12–2 you can see that purines have a double ring of carbon and nitrogen atoms; pyrimidines have a single ring of carbon and nitrogen atoms.

DNA also contains a phosphate group and a five-carbon sugar called **deoxyribose** (dee ahk sih RY bohs), from which DNA gets its name. Each nitrogen-carrying base is attached to a sugar molecule and a phosphate group. A unit made up of a nitrogen-carrying base, a sugar molecule, and a phosphate group is called a **nucleotide.**

In addition to the clues provided by Levene's research, Watson and Crick had information about the bases in DNA. Erwin Chargaff of Columbia University had shown through chemical analyses that the amount of guanine (G) always equals the amount of cytosine (C). The amount of adenine (A) always equals the amount of thymine (T).

Finally, Watson and Crick had the images of DNA made in 1951 by two British biophysicists, Maurice Wilkins and Rosalind Franklin. These images indicated that the shape of DNA is a *helix* (HEE lihks), or spiral.

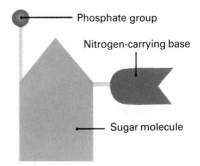

Figure 12–3. A nucleotide consists of a phosphate, a sugar, and a nitrogen-carrying base.

THINKING ABOUT BIOLOGY: Watson and Crick's Major Clue

The DNA model created by Watson and Crick was based on the work of many scientists. In 1869 Friedrich Meischer, a German scientist, isolated a substance from cell nuclei and called it *nucleic acid.* This substance is now known as DNA. In 1914 Robert Feulgen, another German scientist, discovered that DNA could be stained with a red dye, *fuchsin.* This helped scientists learn that DNA is located in chromosomes.

Rosalind Franklin and Maurice Wilkins of King's College in London, provided a major clue to the structure of DNA when they produced

images of DNA using *X-ray diffraction.* These two scientists prepared DNA fibers and then directed a beam of X rays at the fibers. Some X rays passed through the fibers. Others were scattered onto photographic film. The scattered rays produced a pattern of dark images on the film.

In the winter of 1952–1953, Rosalind Franklin produced the photograph that is reproduced here. The photograph experimentally confirmed that DNA was helical—the form indicated by the cross pattern of X-ray reflections in the photograph. The dark

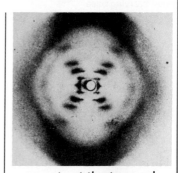

crescents at the top and bottom of the photograph show that the purine and pyrimidine bases are stacked next to each other in a regular pattern. Watson and Crick used this information to explain the structure of DNA in detail.

■ **Analyzing Information** Why was it necessary to prepare fibers of DNA before X-raying it?

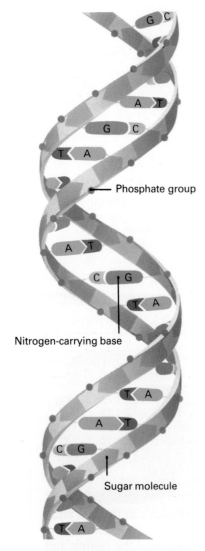

Phosphate group

Nitrogen-carrying base

Sugar molecule

Figure 12–4. A DNA molecule resembles a twisted ladder. Its sides are formed from long chains of sugars and phosphates. The 'rungs' are pairs of nitrogen-carrying bases.

The Watson-Crick Model By unifying the existing information on DNA, Watson and Crick concluded that the DNA molecule is shaped like a *double helix*. As Figure 12–4 shows, a double helix somewhat resembles a spiral staircase, or a twisted ladder. Furthermore, Watson and Crick determined that the sides of the "ladder" are composed of alternating phosphate groups and sugar molecules. The "rungs" on the staircase consist of pairs of nitrogen-carrying bases. The two bases that make up each rung are joined to one another by weak chemical bonds.

A close look at the rungs of the DNA ladder shows that the nitrogen-carrying bases always pair up in a specific pattern. Based on Chargaff's chemical analysis of DNA, Watson and Crick reasoned that a purine and a pyrimidine must pair with each other to make a rung that is the right width. Two purines would produce a rung that is too wide. Two pyrimidines would produce a rung that is not wide enough to connect the sides of the ladder. Adenine (A) pairs only with thymine (T). Likewise, guanine (G) pairs only with cytosine (C).

Notice in Figure 12–4 that each base, or half rung, is attached to a sugar molecule and a phosphate group. A single DNA molecule may be composed of many thousands of such nucleotides. The DNA molecule in the smallest known virus contains about 5,000 nucleotides. Together, all 46 chromosomes in human cells contain more than 5 billion nucleotides.

The pairs of nucleotides forming the DNA ladder can appear in any order. *The sequence of the nucleotides is the code that controls the production of all the proteins of an organism. A gene is a sequence of nucleotides that controls the production of a polypeptide or an RNA molecule.* You will study genes in more detail later in this chapter. However, you may already realize that the number of genes, and thus the amount of information carried in DNA is staggering. Scientists estimate that information stored in DNA from one human cell equals the amount of information in one thousand 500-page books.

12.3 Replication of DNA

How would you like to copy all of the information in 1,000 books, each 500 pages long? Could you do it in one evening? Of course not. The DNA molecules in your cells, however, can make copies of themselves—and therefore of all the information they contain—in about six hours. The process by which DNA copies itself is called **replication** (rehp luh KAY shuhn).

DNA replicates itself so that every new cell receives a complete copy of the genetic code. Thus DNA replicates before mitosis, when new cells are produced for growth and repair.

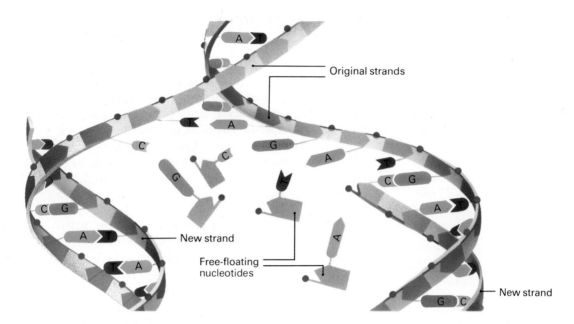

Original strands

New strand

Free-floating nucleotides

New strand

DNA also replicates before the first division of meiosis so that each gamete receives a copy of the genetic material present in the somatic cells of the organism.

The Watson-Crick model made clear how DNA copies itself exactly. Figure 12–5 shows what happens during DNA replication. First, the chemical bonds connecting the bases break in several places and the molecule separates down the middle. As the molecule splits into separate strands, special enzymes cause the proper nucleotides to pair with complementary nucleotides on each single strand. Other enzymes then link the new nucleotides into one long strand. Each original strand serves as a *template*, or pattern, for the creation of the new strand. Every T (thymine) nucleotide pairs with a nucleotide containing an A (adenine). Likewise, every G (guanine) nucleotide pairs with a nucleotide containing a C (cytosine). Each completed DNA molecule contains one old and one new strand. The entire process is powered by energy from ATP and the action of enzymes.

Figure 12–5. During replication, the two strands of the DNA molecule separate. The bases on each strand attract complementary bases that are carried on free-floating nucleotides. As the nucleotide units move into place, two identical molecules of DNA form. The base sequences of the two resulting DNA molecules are thus identical to each other. The base sequences are also identical to that of the original DNA molecule.

Reading Critically

Analyzing Information If all organisms contain DNA, how can they be different?

Section Review

1. **Identifying Ideas** What led Avery and his associates to conclude that DNA is the hereditary substance?
2. **Communicating Ideas** Describe the shape of DNA.
3. **Summarizing Ideas** Name the parts of a nucleotide.
4. **Formulating Conclusions** Why is DNA replication necessary to life?

Thinking Critically

Once scientists understood the structure of DNA, they were able to understand better how DNA works. Scientists discovered that DNA controls **protein synthesis,** the process by which proteins are made from amino acids. Some proteins are part of the structure of each organism, and other proteins are *enzymes* that control most chemical reactions. The characteristics of any organism are determined by its proteins and, ultimately, by its DNA.

12.4 DNA and RNA

DNA, with its blueprint for protein synthesis, is located in the cell nucleus. Yet the manufacture of protein molecules takes place in the cytoplasm of the cell on structures called *ribosomes*. DNA molecules do not leave the nucleus to control the production of protein. Instead, another type of nucleic acid acts as a messenger between DNA and ribosomes and carries out protein synthesis. This nucleic acid is called **RNA,** or **ribonucleic** (ry boh noo KLEE ihk) **acid.**

DNA and RNA are similar in many ways. For example, both are nucleic acids and are made up of nucleotides arranged in a certain sequence. However, RNA differs from DNA in three important ways. First, RNA nucleotides contain the sugar **ribose** instead of deoxyribose. Second, the pyrimidine base **uracil** (YOOR uh sihl) substitutes for thymine. Like thymine, uracil (U) pairs only with adenine. Third, RNA is primarily a single-stranded molecule, while DNA is usually double-stranded.

There are three kinds of RNA. One kind, called **messenger RNA,** or **mRNA,** carries sequences of nucleotides that code for protein from the nucleus to the ribosomes. A second kind of RNA, called **transfer RNA,** or **tRNA,** picks up individual amino acids in the cytoplasm and carries them to the ribosomes. There the amino acids are joined together in proper order to make a protein. Ribosomes contain the third kind of RNA, called **ribosomal RNA,** or **rRNA.** Ribosomal RNA helps bind mRNA and tRNA together during one step of protein synthesis.

12.5 Transcription

The process by which mRNA is copied from DNA molecules is called **transcription.** In this process, the genetic code of DNA is transferred to molecules of mRNA. First a segment of DNA separates, thereby exposing the two strands. One of these

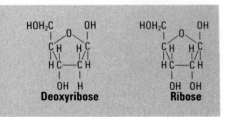

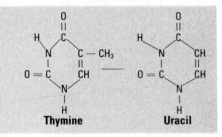

Figure 12–6. In RNA, the sugar is ribose and not the deoxyribose found in DNA. In addition, the base uracil substitutes for thymine in RNA. How does the chemical structure of uracil differ from that of thymine?

strands serves as a template, or pattern, to make a molecule of mRNA. This strand and the molecule of mRNA it produces may be 1,000 to 10,000 nucleotides long. The other strand of DNA does not take part in transcription.

Next mRNA nucleotides in the nucleus bind to their complementary nucleotides on the active strand of DNA. Thus the sequence of bases in mRNA is determined by the order of bases in DNA. For instance, if DNA has the base sequence AGCTGA, the complementary bases in mRNA would then be UCGACU. Recall that in RNA uracil is the complement of adenine. The sequence of bases in mRNA is a code that enables the mRNA to collect the right amino acids and assemble them in the correct sequence to synthesize a particular protein. The mRNA code is a series of three-letter "words," with each base standing for one "letter." Every combination of three "letters," or bases, is called a **codon** (КОН dahn).

How do scientists know that a codon is made up of three bases? Because 20 different amino acids are used to produce proteins, mRNA needs at least 20 codons, one for each amino acid. If a codon consisted of one base, the total number of codons in mRNA would be four—A, C, G, and U. Thus mRNA would be able to collect and assemble only four of the 20 amino acids. With codons two bases long, mRNA could assemble 16 amino acids, because four bases can be arranged in 16 different pairs. Codons with three bases, however, can be arranged in 64 different combinations, more than enough to code for all 20 amino acids. Experiments have confirmed that amino acids are coded by three-base codons, or *triplet codons*.

Figure 12–8 shows the triplet codon for each amino acid. As you can see, several different codons can stand for the same

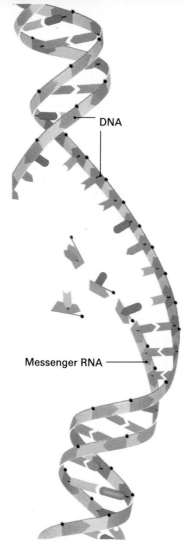

Figure 12–7. During transcription a single strand of DNA serves as a template for the assembly of messenger RNA from free nucleotides. Once formed, mRNA leaves the nucleus and enters the cytoplasm.

Figure 12–8. Each amino acid is coded for by three bases arranged in a specific sequence. According to the chart on the left, what are the triplet codons for alanine? for proline?

Second Base in Codon

		U	C	A	G	
		Phenylalanine	Serine	Tyrosine	Cysteine	U
	U	Phenylalanine	Serine	Tyrosine	Cysteine	C
		Leucine	Serine	Stop Codon	Stop Codon	A
		Leucine	Serine	Stop Codon	Tryptophan	G
		Leucine	Proline	Histidine	Arginine	U
	C	Leucine	Proline	Histidine	Arginine	C
		Leucine	Proline	Glutamine	Arginine	A
		Leucine	Proline	Glutamine	Arginine	G
		Isoleucine	Threonine	Asparagine	Serine	U
	A	Isoleucine	Threonine	Asparagine	Serine	C
		Isoleucine	Threonine	Lysine	Arginine	A
		Methionine	Threonine	Lysine	Arginine	G
		Valine	Alanine	Aspartic Acid	Glycine	U
	G	Valine	Alanine	Aspartic Acid	Glycine	C
		Valine	Alanine	Glutamic Acid	Glycine	A
		Valine	Alanine	Glutamic Acid	Glycine	G

First Base in Codon (vertical label, left)

Third Base in Codon (vertical label, right)

Reading Critically

Inferring Conclusions What would happen if the first codon translated by RNA was UGA? Explain.

For information about a career in cell biology, see pages 926–927.

Figure 12–9. During translation a codon on mRNA links up with an anticodon on tRNA while both are on a ribosome. Amino acids are thus assembled one after another to form a functional protein. The nucleus and the ribosomes are not drawn to scale.

amino acid. Other codons do not stand for any amino acid; they are *stop*, or *terminator, codons* that tell RNA to stop synthesizing proteins. The codon AUG, which specifies the amino acid methionine, is the start signal. All protein synthesis begins at an AUG codon.

12.6 Translation

As each section of the genetic code on DNA is transcribed to mRNA, the two strands of DNA rejoin. Then the mRNA moves into the cytoplasm through a pore in the nuclear membrane. In the cytoplasm, ribosomes attach to the mRNA to carry out the formation of a protein in a process called **translation.** This process translates the RNA base sequence into the amino acid sequence of protein. Several ribosomes are involved in translation, thus enabling the cell to use a single mRNA molecule to repeatedly produce a specific protein molecule.

As Figure 12–9 shows, a ribosome is made up of two parts. The smaller part attaches to the mRNA. The larger part contains an enzyme that helps link the amino acids to form a protein. Figure 12–9 also shows that mRNA and rRNA do not carry out translation by themselves. They rely on tRNA, the small molecules that pick up specific amino acids and carry them to the

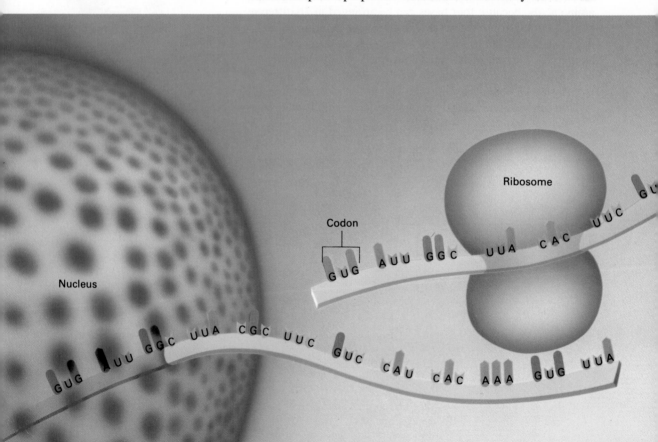

mRNA. The cytoplasm contains more than 20 kinds of tRNA, at least one for each of the 20 amino acids needed to synthesize proteins.

Each tRNA molecule is about 80 nucleotides long. The three loops of the tRNA molecule give it a shape somewhat like a cloverleaf. One end of tRNA attaches to its amino acid with the help of an enzyme and ATP. The other end of tRNA contains a sequence of three bases that complement the triplet code on mRNA. The sequence of three bases on tRNA is called an **anticodon** (AN tee koh dahn). Since there is at least one codon for each of the 20 amino acids, there are at least 20 different anticodons.

Translation begins at an AUG codon. The ribosomes move along the strand of mRNA and indicate each codon to approaching molecules of tRNA carrying their amino acids. As each codon is indicated, the tRNA with the complementary anticodon binds to the mRNA. In this way amino acids are placed in the proper sequence to make a certain protein. Once the tRNA has bound to the mRNA, an enzyme in the ribosome links the new amino acid to the neighboring amino acid by means of a *peptide bond*. After the amino acids are linked, the tRNA is released and returns to the cytoplasm to collect another amino acid. As each ribosome moves along the mRNA, a chain of amino acids

Biofact

Q: *How does tRNA recognize its specific amino acid?*

A: Transfer RNA recognizes its specific amino acids with the help of activating enzymes in the cytoplasm. Each of the 20 amino acids has a corresponding activating enzyme. With energy provided by ATP, an activating enzyme attaches its amino acid to the correct tRNA molecule.

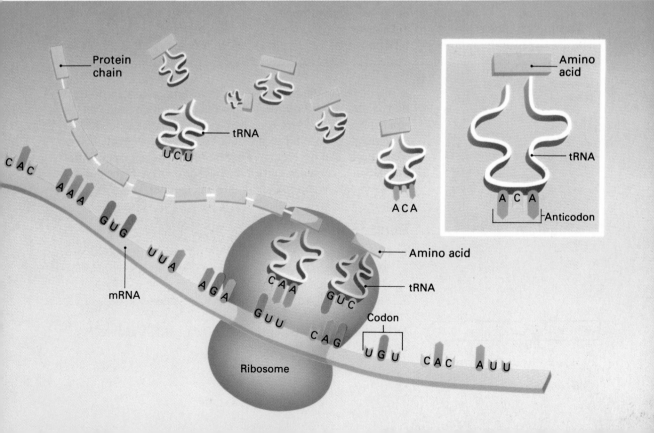

Scientists have learned a great deal about genes since the work of Watson and Crick and Franklin. They now know that a gene is a sequence of nucleotides on a strand of DNA that codes for a certain protein. The code of each gene is transcribed to a molecule of RNA. This RNA molecule travels into the cytoplasm and provides a blueprint for linking amino acids into a chain called a *polypeptide.* Some proteins consist of a single polypeptide, but others consist of two or more chains.

Though scientists understand how protein synthesis works, questions remain about the relationship between genes and the traits they determine. In only a few cases have scientists been able to understand how a gene-produced protein causes a trait to appear. Scientists do know that in humans a change in one nucleotide causes a change in an amino acid of *hemoglobin,* a protein in red blood cells that combines with oxygen. The change in the amino acid causes the shape of the red blood cells to change from round to bent, or sickle-shaped.

Another unsolved mystery concerns nucleotide sequences that may determine when a gene will become active. Except for the sex cells, every cell in the human body contains exactly the same genes. How is it then that brain cells are so different from the cells that make up blood or skin? The answer lies in the fact that different genes are active in different cells. Just how genes are turned on and off is the subject of much current research.

■ **Predicting Outcomes**
What kinds of future research might answer questions about how genes become active and inactive?

is assembled in the proper sequence to form a certain protein. Eventually, each ribosome reaches the termination codon on the strand of mRNA. There is no tRNA specifying an anticodon for the termination codon, so no amino acid is added. Protein synthesis stops, and the protein is released from the ribosome. After translation is complete and all the ribosomes have come off, the mRNA breaks down into individual nucleotides.

Section Review

1. **Comparing Ideas**   How is RNA different from DNA?
2. **Analyzing Conclusions**   How do scientists know that the DNA code is a triplet?
3. **Summarizing Ideas**   How is RNA manufactured from DNA?

Thinking Critically

4. **Synthesizing Relationships**   Why are tRNA and mRNA needed for protein synthesis?

Changes in the Genetic Code

Each time a cell divides, its DNA replicates so that the genetic code is passed on to the new cell. Usually the DNA copies itself exactly. ***Occasionally, replication mistakes or environmental factors cause a change in the genetic code.*** A change in a gene or chromosome is called a **mutation.** An organism in which a mutation is expressed is called a **mutant.**

Many mutations have little or no apparent effect on an organism or its offspring. However, some mutations have harmful effects. Mutations that cause death in offspring are called *lethal mutations.*

12.7 Gene Mutations

The most common type of mutation involves a change in a single gene. Such a mutation is called a **gene mutation,** or **point mutation.** In this type of change, one nitrogen-carrying base may be substituted for another. In other cases, a base may be lost or added.

A change in a single nucleotide may seem minor. However, when you consider the importance of the triplet code in DNA, you realize that changing even one base in the genetic code can have major consequences. You can compare a change in the triplet code to the change of one digit in the area code of a phone number. By dialing 213 instead of 212, for example, you reach Los Angeles instead of New York City. Likewise, changing one base in the DNA triplet code may mean that a different amino acid is placed in the protein chain. As a result, the protein itself is different from the one originally called for by the code.

The condition called *albinism* is caused by a gene mutation. Because of the change in a nucleotide base, organisms with this condition cannot produce the enzyme responsible for pigment synthesis. The changed base sequence produces a protein that cannot function as an enzyme, so no pigment is produced. Animals with this condition have white hair and pinkish eyes and skin. Some plants with albinism have no chlorophyll and cannot carry out photosynthesis.

12.8 Chromosome Mutations

Chromosome mutations involve changes in many genes. In some cases several genes may be lost, added, or moved to different chromosomes. In other cases, entire chromosomes may be lost or gained. Because so many genes are involved, many

Figure 12–10. Albinism occurs both in animals and in plants. The koala and the corn plants above are white because a gene mutation has resulted in an inability to produce normal pigments.

X Rays and Your Future

If you have ever been X-rayed in a dentist's or doctor's office, you may have noticed the technician step behind a shield before throwing the switch. There is good reason for protecting yourself from X-ray overexposure, too. One consumer advocate estimates that cancers and genetic damage from X rays kill as many as 1,000 people a year in the U.S.

X rays are potentially so harmful because they bombard the body with ionizing radiation. The rays excite electrons in the body's cells and cause them to break off in ion pairs. Repeated doses of radiation can alter the chemical structure of the genes in the cell nucleus, causing genetic mutation. Non-ionizing radiation from microwave ovens and sonogram machines has no harmful effects.

Ionizing radiation poses a special threat to the reproductive organs if it rearranges the genetic information contained in egg and sperm cells. These genetic codes are passed to offspring, and radiation-induced mutations can cause genetic disorders in children.

The harmful effects of X rays are cumulative, increasing with the total radiation dose over a lifetime. The degree of risk depends, in part, on past exposures and the part of the body being X-rayed. Patients can protect themselves during an X-ray procedure by

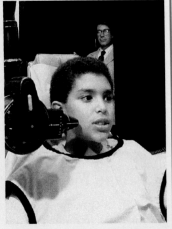

requesting that a lead shield be used to protect their reproductive organs and thyroid gland.

Experts are still debating how much radiation exposure can be considered safe over a lifetime. Most agree, however, that although X rays are valuable diagnostic tools, precautions should be taken by people who are exposed to them.

chromosome mutations are harmful or even lethal to organisms that inherit them.

Figure 12–11 shows three major kinds of chromosome mutations. One type of mutation involves a single chromosome. During mitosis or meiosis, a chromosome may break, and part of it may be lost. The loss of a chromosome segment is called a *deletion*. Its effect in animals is usually lethal. Occasionally, the middle section of a chromosome may break away, turn over, and recombine with the same chromosome in reverse order. This type of mutation is called an *inversion*. Inversions may not harm organisms since all the same genes are present on the chromosome.

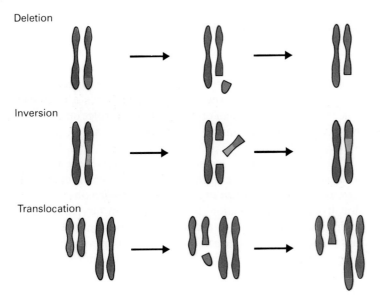

Deletion

Inversion

Translocation

Figure 12–11. Deletions, inversions, and translocations are mutations involving parts of chromosomes. A deletion occurs when part of a chromosome is lost. An inversion results when a segment of DNA is turned around within the chromosome. Translocation occurs when a segment of one chromosome becomes attached to a nonhomologous chromosome in which a break has occurred.

Another type of chromosome mutation involves changes in two chromosomes. For example, in *translocation,* a fragment of one chromosome may become attached to a nonhomologous chromosome. Translocation involving certain chromosomes may produce serious abnormalities in humans.

12.9 Somatic and Germ Mutations

Changes in the makeup of genes and chromosomes are the two major kinds of mutations. Mutations can also be categorized according to the type of cell in which they occur.

Germ cell mutations are those mutations that occur in reproductive cells. These mutations can occur during meiosis or the may occur after the gamete is already mature. Although germ cell mutations do not affect the individual in which they occur, they can be transmitted to offspring. Some germ cell mutations may not be expressed for several generations. Because any sort of mutation may occur within a reproductive cell, the effects of germ cell mutations may range from harmless to lethal.

Mutations that occur in body cells are called **somatic mutations.** Somatic mutations are not passed on to offspring. Yet cells produced by a mutant cell will also contain the mutation. Thus a somatic mutation may affect the individual in which it occurs. Scientists have found evidence that somatic mutations can change genes that control cell reproduction. If such a mutation occurs, cells may reproduce uncontrollably, resulting in a cancerous growth.

12.10 Effects and Frequencies of Mutations

Many mutations produce genes that are recessive, and so these mutations go undetected. In order for a mutated recessive allele to express itself, it must combine with a similarly mutated allele. Occasionally, however, a mutation produces a dominant gene that is expressed in an organism. For example, one form of dwarfism that occurs among human beings is the result of a dominant mutation.

Nearly all chromosome mutations in animals are harmful because they result in deformities and other traits that make it difficult for the organism to survive in its environment. Occasionally, however, mutations help an organism survive when its environment changes. For example, mutations enabled certain mosquitoes to resist insecticides after these poisons were introduced into their environment. The mutant mosquitoes thus survived and reproduced, creating more insects with resistance to insecticides.

Because many mutations are recessive and thus do not appear in organisms, it is difficult to calculate the exact rate of mutation. Based on studies of dominant and codominant mutations, however, scientists believe the rate of mutation is very low. An estimated rate for spontaneous mutations is only one or two in every 100,000 genes per generation.

Although the rate of spontaneous mutation is low, environmental factors can influence mutation rates. Anything that causes a mutation in cells is called a **mutagen.** Ultraviolet light, for instance, is known to increase mutation rates in bacteria. Scientists believe that ultraviolet rays from the sun may cause skin cancer. X rays and other forms of radiation are also known to be mutagens.

Other mutagens include tars in tobacco smoke, smog, certain viruses, and various chemicals and drugs. The chemical mustard gas, for example, removes guanine from DNA. Nitrous acid, another chemical, removes nitrogen from DNA bases. Both chemicals produce a variety of harmful results.

Section Review

1. **Comparing Structures**   Compare DNA and RNA.
2. **Summarizing Ideas**   Describe what happens in the chromosome when the following occur: deletion, inversion, translocation, and point mutation.
3. **Organizing Ideas**   Name some well-known mutagens.
4. **Inferring Relationships**   Why are mutations in somatic cells not transmitted to offspring?

Thinking Critically

INVESTIGATION 12:
How Is Nucleic Acid Extracted from Cells?

Objectives
- To *extract* DNA from a cell
- To *summarize* lab procedures

Materials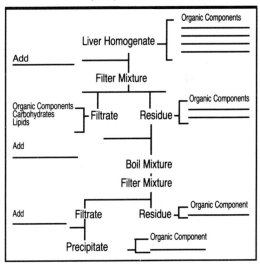
fresh liver homogenate, graduated cylinder, two 100-mL beakers, 150-mL beaker, 15 percent trichloracetic acid, stirring rod, filter paper, two 50-mL beakers, 10 percent sodium chloride solution, hot plate, water, tongs, refrigerated 95 percent ethyl alcohol, lens paper, glass slide, coverslip, compound microscope

Prelab Preparation

1. Where are DNA and RNA located in a cell?
2. What categories of organic compounds will be present in a liver homogenate?
3. Copy the extraction flow chart that appears at the bottom of the page.

Inquiry:

4. **CAUTION: Put on safety goggles, a laboratory apron, and rubber gloves and leave them on through step 5 to protect eyes, skin, and clothing from chemicals.** Pour 10 mL of liver homogenate into a graduated cylinder. Pour the homogenate into a 100-mL beaker.
5. Add 10mL of 15 percent trichloracetic acid to the beaker and mix well with a stirring rod.
6. Filter the contents of the beaker, collecting the liquid fraction in a 100-mL beaker. Transfer the residue on the filter paper to a clean 50-mL beaker.
7. Add 15 mL of 10 percent sodium chloride solution to the beaker and mix well.
8. **CAUTION: The hot plate and hot chemicals can be injurious.** Pour 75 mL of water into the 150-mL beaker. Heat the water to boiling on a hot plate.
9. Use tongs to place the 50-mL beaker into the 150-mL beaker water bath. Heat the smaller beaker for 10 minutes.
10. Use tongs to remove the 50-mL beaker from the boiling water bath. Allow the solution to cool.
11. Filter the mixture into a clean 150-mL beaker.
12. While tilting the beaker, slowly pour refrigerated 95 percent ethyl alcohol down the side into the filtrate.
13. The milky precipitate that forms is nucleic acid.
14. Place a stirring rod into the liquid. Gently roll the rod between your fingers. Transfer the strands that collect on the rod to a clean glass slide and add a coverslip.
15. Use low power to observe the slide. Switch to high power and record your observations.
16. Clean your area as directed by your teacher. Then, thoroughly wash your hands with soap and water.
17. Complete the flow chart.

Analysis

1. **Evaluating Methods** Why was a homogenate used in this Investigation?
2. **Summarizing Observations** Describe the nucleic acids as they appeared to the naked eye and at high power.
3. **Analyzing Results** How did trichloracetic acid affect the homogenate?
4. **Analyzing Methods** How were nucleic acids finally separated from proteins?

Chapter 12 Review

Summary

Since the 1940s, geneticists have focused on understanding what genes are and how they work. In 1944, Oswald Avery showed that DNA is the genetic material in chromosomes. Later, the work of James Watson, Francis Crick, and Rosalind Franklin led to knowledge about the structure of DNA. During replication, the DNA molecule splits into two strands. Free nucleotides bind with complementary nucleotides on each strand of DNA to produce two molecules.

Genes are segments of DNA that control protein synthesis. Through transcription, the DNA code is transferred to messenger RNA, which carries the code to the ribosomes. During translation, transfer RNA molecules carry amino acids to mRNA where they are linked in the proper sequence to produce a specific protein.

Mutations, or changes in the genetic code, involve genes or chromosomes. Most mutations are harmful. Mistakes in replication and environmental factors may produce mutations.

BioTerms

adenine (192)
anticodon (199)
chromosome
   mutation (201)
codon (197)
cytosine (192)
deoxyribonucleic
   acid (DNA) (191)
deoxyribose (193)
gene
   mutation (201)
germ cell
   mutation (203)

guanine (192)
messenger RNA
   (mRNA) (196)
mutagen (204)
mutant (201)
mutation (201)
nucleotide (193)
point mutation (201)
protein
   synthesis (196)
replication (194)
ribonucleic
   acid (RNA) (196)

ribose (196)
ribosomal RNA
   (rRNA) (196)
somatic mutation (203)
thymine (192)

transcription (196)
transfer RNA
   (tRNA) (196)
translation (198)
uracil (196)

For each pair of terms, explain the differences in their meanings.

1. transcription, translation
2. chromosome mutation, somatic mutation
3. deoxyribonucleic acid (DNA), ribonucleic acid (RNA)
4. uracil, thymine

BioQuiz   (Write all answers on a separate sheet of paper.)

Completion

1. Anything that increases the rate of mutation in cells is a _____ .
2. Mutations that occur in reproductive cells are called _____ mutations.
3. The loss of a chromosome segment is called a _____ .
4. Albinism is a _____ mutation.
5. The _____ in DNA consists of 64 three-base sequences.

Multiple Choice

6. _____ controls protein synthesis.
   a) tRNA   b) DNA   c) mRNA   d) rRN
7. In RNA, the base _____ pairs only with the base adenine.   a) guanine
   b) uracil   c) thymine   d) ribose
8. The process by which DNA copies itself is called   a) translocation.   b) translation.
   c) replication.   d) transcription.
9. _____ bonds link amino acids together.

a) Covalent   b) Phosphate   c) Peptide
d) Protein

10. The sequence of three bases on tRNA is called   a) translocation.   b) an anti-codon.   c) a translation.   d) a mutation.

11. If a base sequence in DNA is CCT, the complementary sequence in mRNA is
a) GGA.   b) GGU.   c) UUA.   d) UUC.

12. Uracil joins only with   a) adenine.
b) cytosine.   c) thymine.
d) guanine.

13. The double helix shape of DNA was discovered by   a) Wilkins and Franklin.
b) Morgan.   c) Watson and Crick.
d) Avery.

14. Which of the following is not a chromosome mutation?   a) deletion   b) inver-

sion   c) translocation   d) replication

15. A DNA molecule does not contain
a) adenine.   b) ribose.   c) phosphate.
d) cytosine.

Writing Critically

16. How did Oswald Avery and his associates determine that DNA was the genetic material in cells?

17. What evidence did Watson and Crick use to construct their model of DNA?

18. When does DNA replication occur in cells? Explain why this must be so.

19. Why are DNA codons made up of three bases?

20. How do cells manufacture proteins?

Application/Critical Thinking

1. **Analyzing Conclusions** Phebus A. Levene studied the chemical makeup of DNA and reached an incorrect hypothesis about its structure. Do library research to learn Levene's hypothesis and how Erwin Chargaff corrected his error.

2. **Identifying Relationships** Messenger RNA is broken down after it has synthesized the necessary protein(s). What might occur if the mRNA was not broken down?

3. **Interpreting Ideas** Oxytocin is a hor-

mone that causes a female mammal to secrete milk for her young. The following set of triplet codons specifies part of the sequence of amino acids that make up oxytocin: UGU UAC AUC CAA AAC UGC CCA CUA GCA. Translate this code into a sequence of amino acids.

4. **Evaluating Relationships** Researchers have found genes linked to human cancer. Do library research to learn how translocation of these genes may produce cancer.

Cross-Discipline Connection

Biology and Reading   Read *The Double Helix* (New York: Atheneum, 1968) by James Watson. This fascinating book gives the scientist's account of the events surrounding breakthroughs in understanding DNA. What convinced Watson and Crick that DNA was helical?

Discovery Through Reading

The article, "Scanning the Winding Coils of Naked DNA," *Science News* (January 28, 1989): 53, describes the first direct observation of chemically unaltered, uncoated, pure DNA. What type of microscope was used?

"Backward Genetics: Knocking Some 'Antisense' into Wayward Genes," *Science News* (June 10, 1989): 360–362, tells how "antisense" genetics is used to fight cancers and viral diseases. What does "antisense" strategy involve?

Human Genetics

Outline

Identical twins photographed in Austin, Texas

Focus

Geneticists have identified many human genes including several genes that are linked to inherited diseases. However, questions still remain about what controls the expression of genes and how the environment affects the actions of genes. Answers to these questions may result in the detection and cure of many human diseases and disorders.

- *Identical twins are formed from the same fertilized egg. What can be said about the genetic makeup of these twins?*

- *How can identical twin studies help scientists gain knowledge about the effects of the environment on DNA?*

The Study of Human Genetics

Section Objectives

- *List* three problems geneticists face in studying human genetics.
- *Name* the kinds of information revealed by the analysis of genealogies.
- *List* two goals of population sampling.
- *Explain* the process called twinning.

Geneticists cannot study people in the same way in which they study bacteria or fruit flies. Since humans choose their own mates, geneticists cannot conduct breeding experiments to determine how human traits are inherited. In addition, humans have a long life span. As a result, it takes many years, not just days or weeks, to produce several generations. Finally, most human families have small numbers of offspring—too few to verify the outcomes of crosses predicted by probability.

To overcome these problems, geneticists use special techniques to study human heredity. Three of the most common methods used to study human genetics are pedigree analysis, population sampling, and twin studies. Each method reveals a different kind of information about human genetics.

13.1 Pedigree Analysis

Geneticists study family trees by observing the occurrence of a trait over several generations. This study helps them understand dominance, sex-linkage, and other facts about genes in humans. Knowing the genetic background of a person is often medically useful, as will be discussed later in this chapter.

One study involved people with a streak of white hair near the crown. This trait is called the white forelock trait, or *piebaldness*. Researchers studying people with this trait made a **pedigree**, which is a record that shows how a trait is inherited over several generations. The pedigree in Figure 13–1 shows that piebaldness is inherited in a pattern typical of a dominant trait, controlled by a single dominant-recessive gene pair. Notice in the second generation that some children had white forelocks (W) and some had normal hair (w). This pattern indicates that the parent with the trait is heterozygous (Ww). If the parent were homozygous dominant, all the children would have white forelocks. In addition, the children of heterozygous individuals (Ww) married to homozygous recessive individuals (ww) were about half piebald and half normal. This is the pattern you would predict using probability.

13.2 Population Sampling

Another important way of learning about human genetics is to study the traits that appear in a certain *population,* or an interbreeding group living in a certain area. Obviously, it is impossible to study every person in a population as large as that of the

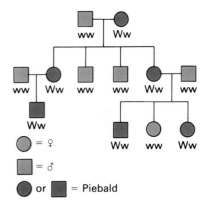

Figure 13–1. This pedigree traces the appearance of the trait of piebaldness through three generations of a single family.

| **Reading Critically** |

Interpreting Ideas What would be the phenotypic ratio of offspring of two individuals heterozygous dominant for piebaldness?

To calculate the percentage of certain traits among your classmates, see page 221.

United States. Instead, geneticists use **population sampling,** which involves determining how often a trait appears in a small, randomly selected group and then projecting the results to the population as a whole. To measure the frequency of certain traits, geneticists use questionnaires or tests. Information that scientists collect in this way reveals how frequently certain genes appear in a population or what the rates of mutation are.

Table 13–1: Some Human Characteristics Determined by a Single Gene

Some Dominant Traits	Some Recessive Traits
Webbed fingers or toes	Abnormally small head
Very short fingers or toes	Dry, thick skin on palms
Extra fingers or toes	Some forms of deafness
Drooping eyelids	Abnormal fat metabolism
Some kinds of dwarfism	

Two eggs are fertilized by two sperm and divide

Two masses of cells develop separately and each has a fetal sac

Figure 13–2. Fraternal twins develop when two eggs are fertilized by different sperm (above). Identical twins develop from a single, fertilized egg that splits (below).

Fertilized egg divides into two cells

Two cell masses develop nearly identically in one fetal sac

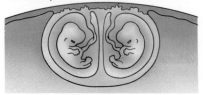

13.3   Twin Studies

Genes control the traits people possess, but factors in the environment may influence the expression of human traits. For example, genes play an important part in determining skin color, yet a person's skin may tan from exposure to the sun. Likewise, individuals who inherit musical or athletic ability may differ in performance due partly to the training they receive. Scientists do not fully understand how heredity and environment affect human traits, but the study of twins has provided some insights into the relationship of their effects.

Like many other organisms, humans can produce two types of twins. **Fraternal twins** develop from two eggs in the mother that are fertilized by two different sperm. These twins are as genetically different as any brothers and sisters. Geneticists are more interested in **identical twins,** who develop from a single fertilized egg that separates into two halves early in development. Barring mutations, identical twins have exactly the same genes and therefore are very similar in most of their traits. Identical twins are always the same sex. Their appearances are so similar that these twins are often difficult to tell apart. Because identical twins have the same genetic makeup, geneticists can attribute differences between them to the environment. Geneticists study identical twins raised apart and by different families to determine how heredity and environment influence human traits. The results are far from conclusive but have yielded some insight into the genetic influence on human traits.

The study of identical twins raised apart has revealed some amazing things. When the twins in the photograph were reunited after 39 years, they found they both were named Jim and had sons named James Allan. Both enjoyed woodworking, disliked baseball, and drove the same model of car.

It might seem that the twins' identical genes determined all these similarities. But scientists who study twins know the answer is not that simple, especially when trying to explain similarities in behavior.

Consider the fact that identical twins raised apart are often more alike than those raised together. You might predict just the opposite—that twins with the same genes and the same environment are the ones most alike. Scientists have learned, however, that a process called *twinning* takes place between twins raised together. Part of the time, the twins enjoy being alike. At other times, the twins attempt to be different so that they will stand out as individuals.

The process of twinning is just one of the problems scientists must take into account when studying twins. For example, although it is assumed that identical twins are genetically alike, a mutation may alter one twin's genetic code, making him or her

different from the other.

No one can explain similarities such as the Jims' choice of car or child's name. It is still impossible to determine whether such similarities are inherited or are merely coincidental.

■ **Synthesizing Information** In what way might dressing twins alike affect the twinning process?

By studying identical twins, geneticists have learned that genes seem to have a greater influence than the environment on such traits as height, weight, blood pressure, speech patterns, and gestures. They have also discovered that genes play a role in some medical problems once thought to be caused only by environmental factors. For instance, genes can cause a susceptibility to diseases such as diabetes and certain types of cancer.

Section Review

1. **Summarizing Ideas** What information can be learned by studying pedigrees?
2. **Identifying Relationships** What can population sampling reveal about human genetics?
3. **Interpreting Information** Why are identical twins used to study human genetics?

⟨ **Thinking Critically** ⟩

- *Identify* some human traits determined by single pairs of genes.
- *Distinguish* between polygenic traits and traits determined by multiple alleles.
- *Compare* sex-linked and sex-influenced traits.
- *List* several consequences of nondisjunction.
- *Describe* what is meant by a karyotype and how such a device is useful.

Inheritance of Human Traits

At the present time, scientists have identified the genetic basis for just a fraction of all human traits, most of them abnormalities. Scientists study abnormalities because most are easy to identify in the population and because many require medical treatment. ***Today scientists know that single genes, groups of genes, sex-linked genes, hormones, and chromosome abnormalities all influence human traits.*** Although many of the traits described here are disorders, they illustrate the way in which normal traits are inherited. Molecular biologists are now probing the mechanism of action of specific genes to determine how they cause disease. The recognition of dominant and recessive traits in humans is an important step in curing genetic disorders.

13.4 Traits Determined by Single Genes

Scientists have discovered hundreds of human traits determined by single dominant alleles. Some familiar ones are cleft chins, freckles, and free earlobes. Other traits produced by dominant alleles are less familiar. Individuals with **polydactyly** (pahl ih DAK tih lee), for example, have extra fingers or toes. Persons with **Huntington disease** develop a serious nervous system disorder after the age of 30. Huntington disease begins with a loss of muscle control, then progresses to mental deterioration and death. No cure or treatment for Huntington disease has yet been found.

More than 2,000 traits, many of them genetic disorders, are known to occur when an individual inherits two recessive alleles for a trait. **PKU,** or **phenylketonuria** (fehn ihl keet uh NYOOR ee uh), is a biochemical disorder produced by two recessive alleles. Individuals with PKU are unable to synthesize the enzyme that breaks down the amino acid phenylalanine. Gradually, phenylalanine accumulates in the body and destroys brain cells. Children who inherit PKU develop severe mental retardation. Fortunately, testing the blood of newborns reveals the presence of this abnormality. Most states, in fact, require PKU testing of newborn babies. If PKU is present, children are placed on a diet low in phenylalanine for the first six years of life. This usually prevents brain damage.

Another homozygous recessive condition causes a biochemical disorder called **sickle-cell disease.** In this disease red blood cells become sickle-shaped. Red blood cells contain a protein called *hemoglobin* that carries oxygen to body tissues. In sickle-cell disease, recessive alleles cause the substitution of

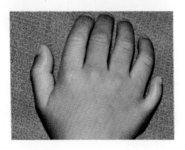

Figure 13–3 Red hair and freckles (above) and a six-fingered hand (below) are traits determined by single genes.

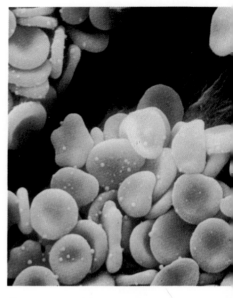

one amino acid in hemoglobin. *Valine* is substituted for *glutamic acid*. When the concentration of oxygen in the blood is low, the abnormal hemoglobin molecules stick together and cause the red blood cells to bend into a sickle shape. These sickle-shaped cells clog small blood vessels, thus depriving tissues of needed oxygen and causing severe pain. Gradually, vital organs are destroyed, and death sometimes occurs within the first 20 years of life. Sickle-cell disease occurs mostly in persons of African descent.

Figure 13–4. The scanning electron microscope image (right) shows normal red blood cells magnified 2,000 times. Sickle-shaped blood cells are shown magnified 5,555 times (left).

13.5 Traits Determined by Multiple Alleles

Several human traits are determined by genes with **multiple alleles,** which are three or more alleles of a gene rather than only two. Blood type for example, is a trait determined by three different alleles. Of course, each individual carries only two of the three alleles, one from each parent. The two alleles determine a person's blood type. In the whole population, however, there are three alleles. The frequency of those alleles varies from one population to another.

Blood types were discovered in 1900 by Karl Landsteiner, an Austrian scientist. Landsteiner found that when red blood cells from different persons are mixed, some intermingle and others clump together, or *agglutinate*. Through further research, Landsteiner determined that special proteins called *antigens* on the cell membranes of red blood cells cause the clumping. The presence or absence of these antigens determines four different types of red blood cells, which Landsteiner labeled A, B, AB, and O. Type A blood cells have an A antigen on their membranes. Similarly, type B blood cells have a B antigen. Type AB blood cells have both A and B antigens, while type O blood cells have neither A nor B antigens. The type of antigen on a person's blood cells affects the type of blood he or she can receive in a

Reading Critically

Evaluating Ideas Why can't the blood type of an individual be ABO?

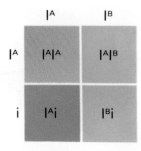

	I^A	I^B
I^A	$I^A I^A$	$I^A I^B$
i	$I^A i$	$I^B i$

Figure 13–5. A Punnett square shows that children with any of four different blood genotypes can be born to a mother with an $I^A i$ genotype and a father with an $I^A I^B$ genotype. How many phenotypes are possible?

transfusion. For example, a person with type A blood can safely receive type A blood. A transfusion of type B blood, however, will produce clumping, causing the blood to clot in the blood vessels.

The alleles for these four blood types are represented with three symbols. The letter I represents the dominant alleles, while the letter i stands for the recessive alleles. Because the alleles that determine blood types A and B are both dominant, they are written I^A and I^B. The allele that determines type O blood is recessive and is written i. A person with type A blood, then, may possess the genotype $I^A I^A$ or $I^A i$. Similarly, a person with type B blood may have the genotype $I^B I^B$ or $I^B i$. The alleles for types A and B show codominance, so when both are present they both have an effect. The genotype for AB blood, then, is written $I^A I^B$. Since the allele for type O blood is recessive, the genotype for type O blood is ii. Figure 13–5 shows the possible blood types in offspring produced by a mother with an $I^A i$ genotype and a father with an $I^A I^B$ genotype.

13.6 Polygenic Traits

Some traits are **polygenic,** or determined by several genes. In this method of inheritance, none of the genes are dominant. Instead, each gene consists of an *active allele* that has a small additive effect on the phenotype and an *inactive allele* that has no effect. Since each of the genes involved may add something to the phenotype, a continuous range of phenotypes is possible. Skin color, eye color, and height are all polygenic traits.

Figure 13–6. These members of a high school class exhibit a wide range of skin colors. Skin tone is determined by several genes, each of which has only a small effect on the overall color.

13.7 Sex-Linked Traits

Sex in humans, as in many other organisms, is determined by X and Y chromosomes. Females have two X chromosomes while males have an X and a Y chromosome. Sex-linked traits in humans are determined by genes carried only on the X chromosome with no alleles on the Y chromosome. Recessive sex-linked traits rarely appear in females because a dominant allele on one X chromosome will mask the effect of a recessive allele on the other X chromosome. Since males have only one X chromosome, however, recessive genes on that chromosome are always expressed.

Colorblindness   In humans the gene for color vision is carried on the X chromosome. The recessive allele of the normal gene may produce **colorblindness,** or the inability to distinguish certain colors. Persons with red-green colorblindness, for example, cannot distinguish between red and green.

Since the gene for color vision is located only on the X chromosome, the normal allele is designated X^C. The recessive allele that determines colorblindness is designated X^c. Homozygous ($X^C X^C$) and heterozygous ($X^C X^c$) females have normal color vision. A female who is heterozygous for a trait is said to be a **carrier** because she carries the recessive allele but does not express it. Only homozygous recessive females ($X^c X^c$) are colorblind. Since males have only one X chromosome, they are either colorblind ($X^c Y$) or have normal color vision ($X^C Y$).

Hemophilia   A recessive gene on the X chromosome produces a disorder called **hemophilia** (hee muh FIHL ee uh). People with hemophilia cannot produce a protein needed for normal blood clotting. As a result, small cuts can cause severe bleeding. Hemophiliacs can bleed to death from internal bleeding.

Hemophilia appeared in European royal families in the nineteenth century, and a mutant allele in Queen Victoria is believed to have been the source. Since Queen Victoria was heterozygous for the condition, she did not have hemophilia. However, she passed the allele on to one son and two daughters. Through marriage these children carried the disease to royal families in Russia, Germany, and Spain.

13.8 Sex-Influenced Traits

Certain traits appear more often in one sex than the other, but they are not sex-linked. A trait that is generally associated with one sex but is produced by genes carried on autosomes is called

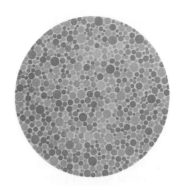

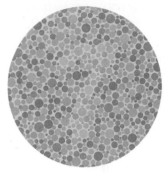

Figure 13–7. The photos above are used to test colorblindness. A person with red-green colorblindness will not be able to read the numbers. What numbers do you read?

Biofact

Q: *Are there other sex-linked traits besides colorblindness and hemophilia?*

A: Yes. There are many known sex-linked traits, and about 50 of them are common. Among these are gout, caused by high levels of uric acid in the blood, and Duchenne muscular dystrophy, a gradual deterioration of the muscles.

Karyotypes are pictures of paired human chromosomes arranged by size. They are used in identifying chromosome abnormalities in fetuses and in infants with abnormal features.

The first step in producing a karyotype is to take cells from a sample of the amniotic fluid surrounding a fetus or cells from a blood sample from a child. The cells are kept in a tissue culture that promotes their growth. When the cells begin to divide, *colchicine* is added to the culture. This chemical stops cell division during metaphase.

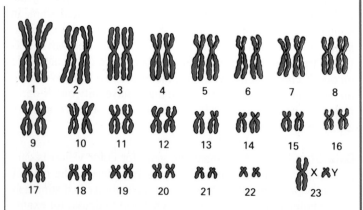

Next, the cells are placed in a solution that ruptures their membranes, freeing the chromosomes. The chromosomes are then stained and photographed. The photograph is enlarged and cut into pieces containing one chromosome

each. These pieces are arranged on a sheet of paper in numbered homologous pairs according to shape, size, and staining bands.

■ **Inferring Relationships** Why is colchicine important to karyotyping?

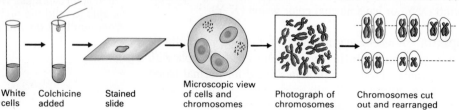

White cells   Colchicine added   Stained slide   Microscopic view of cells and chromosomes   Photograph of chromosomes   Chromosomes cut out and rearranged

a **sex-influenced trait.** Male and female hormones influence the expression of these genes.

Baldness is one example of a sex-influenced trait. In humans, the allele coding for baldness is H^B. This allele is dominant in males but recessive in females. The allele that codes for normal hair, H^N, is recessive in males but dominant in females. Both males and females with genotype $H^B H^B$ are likely to lose their hair. Neither males nor females with genotype $H^N H^N$ are likely to go bald. However, men having $H^B H^N$ usually go bald, but females with this genotype do not. Baldness is affected by the presence of male and female hormones.

13.9 Chromosomal Abnormalities

Some human genetic disorders are determined by abnormal chromosomes. Several of these disorders result from **nondisjunction** (nahn dihs JUHNGK shuhn)—the failure of a chromosome pair to separate during meiosis. When nondisjunction occurs during the first division in meiosis, half of the gametes produced lack one chromosome. The other half have an extra chromosome. When a gamete with one less chromosome combines with a normal gamete, the resulting zygote has 45 chromosomes instead of 46. A gamete with an extra chromosome that combines with a normal gamete produces a zygote with 47 instead of 46 chromosomes. Individuals with 45 chromosomes have the condition called **monosomy** (MAHN uh soh mee). Those with 47 chromosomes have the condition called **trisomy** (try SOH mee). A zygote with more than 47 chromosomes usually does not survive to form an embryo.

A variety of serious problems result from monosomy and trisomy. Children with an extra chromosome 21, for example, have **Down syndrome.** Individuals with Down syndrome have a number of distinctive features, including almond-shaped eyes, short limbs, and thick tongues. They are also mentally retarded in varying degrees.

Males with an extra X chromosome suffer from **Klinefelter syndrome.** This condition results from nondisjunction in the female parent in which an egg carries two X chromosomes. Such an egg fertilized by a Y-carrying sperm results in a zygote with the chromosomes XXY. Most males with Klinefelter syndrome are sterile. Many show some degree of mental retardation. Some females who inherit an extra X chromosome develop normally. However, many of these females are sterile.

Individuals with **Turner syndrome** have only one X chromosome and no other sex chromosome. Although these individuals are females (XO), they do not develop normally and they are sterile. In addition, these females are short and have thick, webbed necks. Some are mildly retarded.

20 21 22 23

Figure 13–8. Persons with Down syndrome have distinctive facial characteristics and suffer from mental retardation. Through education such persons are able to make positive contributions to society and many live independently and are self-sufficient.

Issues surrounding genetic testing are discussed on page 234.

Section Review

1. **Listing Ideas**   What are four traits determined by single pairs of genes?
2. **Identifying Relationships**   What are the genetic mechanisms that determine blood types and skin color?
3. **Identifying Ideas**   What genetic disorders result from nondisjunction?
4. **Inferring Relationships**   How are karyotypes used?

Thinking Critically

- *Explain* the purpose of genetic counseling.
- *Name* three disorders that can be detected through amniocentesis.
- *Compare* the processes of ultrasound testing and fetoscopy.
- *List* the steps in chorionic villi sampling.

Detecting Genetic Disorders

Every year about 250,000 babies in the United States are born with some sort of genetic disorder. ***Physicians and other specialists have developed a variety of tests to identify genetic disorders.*** Since these disorders are produced by abnormal genes or chromosomes, the ultimate cure involves replacing those genes and chromosomes. Although modern techniques such as genetic engineering show promise along these lines, no such cures currently exist.

13.10 Genetic Counseling

A procedure used to inform couples about their chances of passing a harmful trait on to their children is called **genetic counseling.** To determine whether prospective parents carry genes for a disorder, sample cells are tested for certain proteins, and karyotypes are made of their chromosomes. These tests may reveal recessive alleles or abnormal chromosomes that may result in various disorders. Genetic counselors use this information as well as other data, such as pedigree analysis, to explain a couple's chances of transmitting genetic abnormalities to their offspring. As a result of counseling, couples may decide not to have children or to adopt children instead of having their own.

13.11 Tests During Pregnancy

Figure 13–9. Amniocentesis involves withdrawing some of the amniotic fluid that surrounds a fetus (left), and then analyzing the cells that have grown in a laboratory dish (right).

Nearly 200 genetic disorders can be discovered during pregnancy through the use of various tests. One of these tests, called **amniocentesis** (am nee oh sehn TEE sihs), involves the use of a long needle to withdraw fluid surrounding the fetus. This fluid contains skin cells shed by the fetus as well as fetal wastes

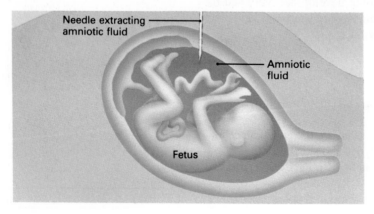
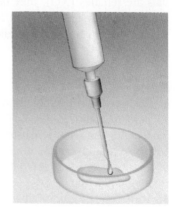

Needle extracting amniotic fluid

Amniotic fluid

Fetus

containing various proteins. Chemical tests of the cells and proteins can detect sickle-cell disease and other disorders. Karyotypes produced from fetal cells reveal such problems as Down syndrome and Turner syndrome. Although it is useful in many cases, amniocentesis is still regarded as controversial by some people.

Ultrasound testing is a technique that involves sending high frequency sound waves through the mother's abdomen. Some of the sound waves bounce off the tissues of the fetus and

Reading Critically

Interpreting Ideas How can fluid in the womb reveal anything about the fetus?

BIOLOGY AND YOU:

Genetic Counseling

Many married couples who are planning to have a family but fear that one or both members of the pair carry genes for an inherited disorder are aided by a genetic counselor. A genetic counselor works with a medical team, advising both married partners and a variety of other individuals about genetic disorders. Often, these counselors advise couples about their chances of having children with disorders. Counselors also work with many pregnant women over the age of 35. Such women are more likely than younger women to have babies with Down syndrome or other chromosomal abnormalities. Genetic counselors also advise individuals who think they may have inherited a genetic disorder.

Although individual cases may vary, genetic counselors follow a similar procedure with all of their clients. First they assemble a detailed personal history and construct a family pedigree. If necessary, they advise that the client have a blood sample taken so that chemical tests may be performed in the laboratory. Physicians use the pedigrees, clinical examinations, and laboratory results of blood tests to make a diagnosis. Then the genetic counselor explains the diagnosis, discusses the probable risks prospective parents face, and outlines the options for dealing with those risks. Genetic counselors also help individuals cope with their fears about genetic disorders. The services of a genetic counselor often lead to a person's discovery that they do not have the genes for the genetic disease they are concerned about. In many cases,

genetic counselors also help people who do have inherited disorders to understand that their conditions may be treated because of early detection.

The work of genetic counselors allows couples to become informed about the probability that they will pass on genes for a genetic disorder to their offspring. This information is valuable because it allows a couple to make an informed decision about whether or not to have children.

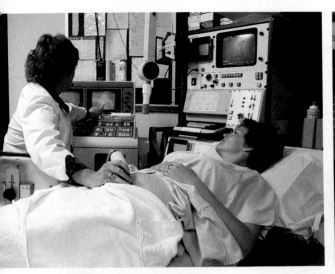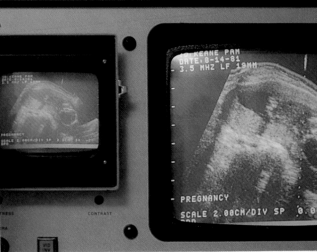

Figure 13–10. Ultrasound waves that penetrate the mother's abdomen (left) are reflected from fetal tissue. The reflected waves form an image of the fetus (right).

produce an image called a *sonogram*. The sonogram can be used to detect an abnormal fetus or one that has died. Ultrasound testing is routinely used to locate the fetus before performing amniocentesis. In this way, the needle can be inserted with less chance of harming the fetus.

A technique called **fetoscopy** (fee TAH skuh pee) allows a physician to actually view the developing fetus. This technique is performed by inserting a slender, hollow needle into the womb through a small incision in the mother's abdomen. The needle is connected to a special microscope. The physician can view the fetus through the needle and determine whether any physical defects exist.

Chorionic villi sampling is one of the newest means of discovering problems in unborn children. This technique involves the insertion of a thin, hollow tube into the womb with the help of ultrasound equipment. Then a sample is taken of *chorionic villi*, tiny protrusions from a membrane called the *chorion* that surrounds the fetus. These tissues have the same makeup as the fetus and can reveal PKU, sickle-cell disease, and Down syndrome. Chorionic villi sampling can be done earlier in pregnancy than amniocentesis and provides faster results.

Biofact

Q: *Can amniocentesis detect any other information about the fetus?*

A: Yes. Karyotypes made from fetal cells show whether the fetus has two X chromosomes or an X and a Y, and thus whether it is a girl or a boy. The test is not used solely for this purpose.

Thinking Critically

Section Review

1. **Summarizing Ideas**   What is genetic counseling?
2. **Identifying Relationships**   What disorders can be detected through amniocentesis, ultrasound testing, and fetoscopy?
3. **Synthesizing Conclusions**   What birth defects would not be detected by chorionic villi sampling?

INVESTIGATION 13:
What Is Your Genetic Profile?

Objectives
- To *observe* a variety of human traits
- To *determine* possible genotypes

Materials
paper, pencil

Prelab Preparation
1. Explain the value of pedigrees when studying human hereditary traits.
2. Explain how males, females, parents, and offspring are shown on a pedigree.
3. Make a table with five columns and ten rows. Use the following titles for the columns: Trait, Phenotype, Dominant/Recessive, Genotype, and Percent of Group. In the first column, list the nine traits described below.

Inquiry: Observation
4. Work with your laboratory partner to check whether or not you have each trait described below. Record your observations in the table.
   a. **Mid-digital Hair** *Is hair present above the knuckle on any of your fingers?*
   b. **Tongue Rolling** *When you stick out your tongue, can you roll up the edges?*
   c. **Dimples** *Are there small indentations in your cheeks when you smile?*
   d. **Chin Cleft** *Do you have an indentation in the middle of your chin?*
   e. **Attached Earlobes** Examine your own earlobes. *Are your earlobes completely attached to the side of your head or are they partially hanging free?*
   f. **Freckles** *Do you have small reddish-brown spots on your skin?*
   g. **Pointed Hairline** Push your hair away from your forehead. *Does the hairline form a point in the center or does it go straight across?*
   h. **Five Fingers** *Were you born with five fingers on each hand, rather than six?*
5. Pool your data with that of your group. Calculate the percentage of students in the group that shows each trait.

Analysis
1. **Analyzing Data** Does the evidence indicate that dominant traits are always the most common? Explain.
2. **Analyzing Data** Look at the pedigree for attached earlobes. Shaded shapes represent individuals that show the trait. Why do individual IV-8 and her parents provide evidence that this trait is recessive?
3. **Analyzing Data** Analyze the pedigrees for tongue rolling and five fingers. Explain whether each trait is dominant or recessive. Each of the other traits is dominant.

Pedigree for attached earlobes

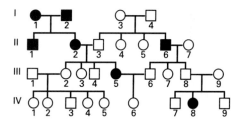

Pedigree for tongue rolling

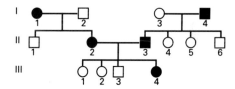

Pedigree for five fingers

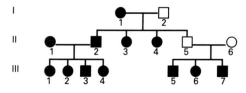

Chapter 13 Review

Summary

Geneticists cannot experiment and breed humans as they do other organisms. Also, humans produce few offspring and take years to produce several generations. As a result, geneticists use pedigrees to study facts about genes, and they use population sampling to measure the frequency of genes in a population. They study identical twins raised apart to understand the influences of heredity and environment.

Through their studies geneticists have learned that cleft chins and polydactyly are each produced by one dominant allele, while PKU and sickle-cell disease each result from two recessive alleles. Multiple alleles determine blood type, and several genes determine skin color. Other traits, such as color blindness, result from genes on the X chromosome. Nondisjunction of chromosomes can result in Down, Turner, and Klinefelter syndromes.

Genetic counselors advise couples of their chance of having a child with a genetic disorder. Amniocentesis, ultrasound testing, fetoscopy, and chorionic villi sampling may detect disorders in the unborn.

BioTerms

amniocentesis (218)
carrier (215)
colorblindness (215)
chorionic villi
   sampling (220)
Down
   syndrome (217)
fetoscopy (220)
fraternal twins (210)
genetic
   counseling (218)
hemophilia (215)
Huntington

disease (212)
identical twins (210)
karyotype (216)
Klinefelter
   syndrome (217)
monosomy (217)
multiple
   alleles (213)
nondisjunction (217)
pedigree (209)
phenylketonuria
   (PKU) (212)
polydactyly (212)

polygenic trait (214)
population
   sampling (210)
sex-influenced
   trait (216)
sickle-cell

disease (212)
trisomy (217)
Turner
   syndrome (217)
ultrasound
   testing (219)

For each pair of terms, explain the differences in their meanings.

1. fraternal twins, identical twins
2. sex-linked trait, sex-influenced trait
3. monosomy, trisomy
4. amniocentesis, chorionic villi sampling

BioQuiz   (Write all answers on a separate sheet of paper.)

Completion

1. Monosomy results from _____ .
2. Recessive _____ traits appear more often in males than in females.
3. Twins produced by two eggs fertilized by two sperm are _____ twins.
4. Sickle-cell disease is a result of an incorrect amino acid in _____ .
5. A female who is heterozygous for a sex-linked trait is a _____ .

Multiple Choice

6. A person with blood type AB has the genotype   a) ii.   b) $I^B i$.   c) $I^A I^B$.   d) $I^A i$.
7. A picture of chromosomes arranged in numbered pairs is called   a) a karyotype.   b) a polygenic trait.   c) an ultrasound test.   d) a pedigree analysis.
8. Down syndrome is an example of   a) monosomy.   b) trisomy.   c) a sex-influenced trait.   d) a polygenic trait.

9. A chart tracing genetic inheritance over several generations is a   a) Punnett square.   b) population sample.   c) pedigree.   d) karyotype.

10. Height is believed to be a   a) polygenic trait.   b) sex-linked trait.   c) karyotype.   d) polydactylic trait.

11. Turner syndrome is a disorder that results from   a) multiple alleles.   b) trisomy.   c) monosomy.   d) antigens.

12. An inherited disease in which hemoglobin becomes misshapen is   a) PKU.   b) sickle-cell disease.   c) Down syndrome.   d) Turner syndrome.

13. Klinefelter syndrome, Turner syndrome, and Down syndrome are all examples of   a) nondisjunction.   b) multiple alleles.   c) trisomy.   d) monosomy.

14. Individuals called carriers are   a) homozygous dominant.   b) heterozygous.   c) homozygous recessive.   d) mutant.

15. Fluid surrounding a fetus is withdrawn in a process called   a) fetoscopy.   b) ultrasound.   c) karyotyping.   d) amniocentesis.

Writing Critically

16. Why do geneticists use different techniques for studying human heredity than they do for studying the heredity of other organisms?

17. Why do scientists study identical twins to learn about the influences of heredity and environment?

18. Explain the differences between polygenic inheritance and inheritance by multiple alleles.

19. Why are there fewer colorblind females than there are colorblind males?

20. What technique can be used to detect monosomy in a fetus?

Application/Critical Thinking

1. **Synthesizing Ideas**   A couple's daughter is colorblind. Does the father have normal color vision, or is he colorblind? Explain your answer. Draw pedigrees that show the possible phenotypes of parents and colorblind daughters.

2. **Evaluating Experiments**   Suppose scientists develop techniques for letting parents choose their child's sex. How might such techniques help prevent some genetic disorders?

Cross-Discipline Connection

Biology and Social Studies   Identify and report on the agencies in your own community and state that provide assistance in the diagnosis and treatment of genetic disorders.

Discovery Through Reading

"The Eerie World of Reunited Twins," *Discover* (September, 1987): 36–46, describes ongoing research into the surprising similarities in behavior that exist between twins who have been separated at birth or very early in life. What does "heritable" mean?

Read the article "The Causes of Down Syndrome," *Scientific American* 257 (August 1987): 52. This article presents a summary of the causes of Down syndrome. What are some of the new areas of research described in this article?

Mapping the Human Genome

Computer-generated models of DNA

Scientists are working to identify the coded base sequence of every human gene and record each of their positions on the 23 pairs of human chromosomes. This complete set of genes is called the *human genome*. These genes are sets of instructions that occur in the nucleus of every human body cell. The complete set represents the coded directions for all the cellular activities that are required to produce a human organism and maintain his or her life. Scientists plan to complete their map of the human genome early in the twenty-first century. To complete this project, geneticists have established an international organization, based in Switzerland, called the *Human Genome Organization (HUGO)*.

The enormous task of isolating and cataloging the human genome can be understood by making a comparison. If each codon were a six-letter word, the approximately 100,000 genes in the human genome would fill 500 books, each with 1,000 pages. One thousand words would appear on each page. HUGO coordinates international work being done by private companies, universities, and governments. HUGO's aim is to unravel the sequence of

Computers assist in analyzing data about genes.

James Watson, associate director of the National Institutes of Health Human Genome Project

the 3 billion bits of information in the 100,000 human genes. Once complete, that basic information must be interpreted, which may take many more years.

Magazines and newspapers have compared this task to the effort that occurred in the 1960s of placing an astronaut on the moon. Putting together the genome puzzle will be an important achievement for humankind. Once completed, the genome map will permit most genetic disorders to be detected and eventually treated.

About 3,000 human disorders are known to be caused by single inherited defective genes. Research data supports the hypothesis that numerous other disorders such as cancer and heart disease are influenced by genes.

With the help of a genome map, scientists will be able to identify defective genes. Analysis of the genes of diabetics, for example, may enable researchers to predict who will be most likely to develop the disease.

As the technology develops, geneticists may be able to treat genetic disorders by replacing defective genes. For example, the gene for Duchenne's muscular dystrophy has been found and researchers now believe that a treatment for this crippling and fatal disease is finally possible. The Human Genome Project may provide insights into how defective genes result in inborn errors of metabolism, and how genetic disorders may be controlled or eliminated.

> ### *Putting together the genome puzzle will be an important achievement for humankind.*

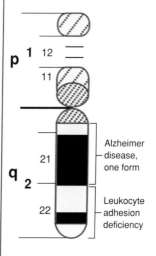

A genetic disorder map of human chromosome 21

225

14

Applied Genetics

Outline

Controlled Breeding

Other Genetic Techniques

Morgan horses, products of special breeding

Focus

Scientists today are rapidly adding to what is known about how genes work and how genes can be manipulated. Their work provides opportunities in **applied genetics,** a field that focuses on the practical use of genetic knowledge. Knowledge about genetics and new technology allow humans to develop varieties of organisms that can serve many purposes—from making substances that fight human diseases to producing new, less expensive sources of energy.

- *How might applied genetics be used by the animal breeder who bred the Morgan horses in the photograph?*

- *How might gene manipulation be used to improve crops?*

Controlled Breeding

Section Objectives

- *List* several ways in which breeders have adapted plants and animals to human needs.
- *Describe* the process of mass selection.
- *Compare* inbreeding and hybridization.

The effort to improve plants and animals is much older than the science of genetics. In fact, the earliest attempts at breeding probably occurred about 11,000 years ago when people first domesticated plants and animals. At that time, people must have noticed that some of the offspring of strong or productive animals had the same desirable traits as their parents. Breeders picked the animals with the traits they wanted and mated them. Using the same reasoning, farmers saved seeds from the hardiest and most productive plants and planted them for the next year's crop.

The process of selecting individuals with desirable traits to produce the next generation is called **controlled breeding.** In recent decades breeders have applied the knowledge of genetics to controlled breeding. In this way, they have been able to adapt plants and animals to many human needs in a much shorter period of time than was previously possible.

To apply genetic principles to dog breeding, see page 235.

14.1 Goals of Breeders

People who breed plants and animals have many goals. For example, breeders working to increase the food supply have developed animals that produce more offspring. Plant varieties have been developed that produce more seeds and can better withstand disease and harsh weather. These breeders have also developed more nutritious plants, such as corn that contains more protein.

Other breeders have bred plants that are better suited to the mechanized methods of modern farming. One such plant is a variety of tomato that has a thick skin to resist bruising by harvesting machines. This fruit is also uniform in shape so that more of the product will fit into a packing crate. Other breeders develop plants and animals that are bred for qualities that have nothing to do with food. These include fast racehorses, purebred dogs, and new strains of ornamental plants.

14.2 Techniques of Controlled Breeding

Modern breeders use combinations of several methods to develop plants and animals with desired traits. *The most important methods of controlled breeding are mass selection, hybridization, and inbreeding.* Each of these traditional methods has been made more effective through the application of genetic principles.

Figure 14–1. This wheat was developed from wild wheat through the process of controlled breeding.

Figure 14–2. Luther Burbank became famous for his success in breeding new plant varieties by mass selection. The Shasta daisy is one of his best-known accomplishments.

Mass Selection The process of raising a great many plants and animals and selecting the best in each generation for further breeding is called **mass selection.** Luther Burbank, an American plant breeder of the late 1800s and early 1900s, used mass selection to develop more than 800 new or improved fruits, vegetables, flowers, and grains. Among his famous plant varieties are the Shasta daisy and the Burbank potato. Today large corporations and government agencies fund enormous breeding stations so that mass selection is carried out efficiently.

Inbreeding Frequently breeders want to establish pure lines, or populations of plants or animals made up of genetically similar individuals. Such lines usually *breed true* for certain traits, which means that offspring are almost identical to their parents in these traits. By developing pure lines, breeders preserve desirable traits. The pure lines also serve as known quantities in breeding experiments.

Pure lines are established by following mass selection with **inbreeding,** a method that involves mating genetically similar individuals. With animals, close relatives such as brothers or

---

BIOLOGY AND YOU:

The Profit in Genes

Biotechnology companies are looking for profits in genetically engineered products to produce everything from cleaner jeans to tastier corn on the cob.

A Japanese company, for example, is marketing a "compact" laundry detergent with a genetically engineered enzyme, called *alkaline cellulase,* that dislodges dirt from clothes fibers. To produce new enzymes, researchers begin with a DNA sequence from an existing enzyme and then rearrange its structure using 3-dimensional models on supercomputers. A

machine then manufactures this altered DNA that codes for the new enzyme. The altered DNA is transplanted into bacteria, which mass-produce the new enzyme.

Genetic engineering can also make a farmer's corn grow higher. One agricultural lab has learned to vaccinate corn seed against the European corn borer, which costs U.S. farmers $400 million a year. Researchers spliced a single gene of the toxic bacterium, *Bacillus thuringiensis,* onto a harmless carrier. The carrier was then injected

into corn seed. Armed with the bacterial gene, the corn plant grows its own pesticide, eliminating the need to cover a whole field with chemical sprays. Agricultural researchers hope to be able to add genes for pest-resistance and herbicide-resistance directly to the crop plant itself.

sisters are mated over several generations. With plants, inbred varieties are produced by self-pollination. After many generations, inbreeding produces individuals that are homozygous for most traits. Some of these traits are desirable. However, others may be undesirable, caused by homozygous recessive genes that are not expressed in a heterozygous individual. For instance, a gene causing deafness has become common in Dalmatians—an inbred pure-line variety of dog.

Inferring Conclusions Why would a breeder want to breed animals that are homozygous for traits?

Hybridization

Hybridization is a method of crossing two different species, breeds, varieties, or pure lines. When inbred varieties are crossed, the resulting hybrids may show every possible combination of traits of the parent species. Thus, some hybrid offspring inherit the best traits of each parent and are larger, hardier, and more productive than either parent. When the offspring is superior to both parents for a specific trait, this improvement is known as **hybrid vigor.**

Over the years some of the greatest breeding advances have come about through hybridization. Santa Gertrudis cattle were developed by mating shorthorn beef cattle with heat- and insect-resistant Brahman cattle from India. The Santa Gertrudis displays the best traits of each parent. Hybridization has also produced new crops such as *triticale,* a cross between wheat and rye. Triticale is more resistant to drought and more nutritious than either wheat or rye.

Figure 14–3. Santa Gertrudis cattle are the result of successful hybridization. They are resistant to heat and insects and also produce high quality beef.

Hybridization has its drawbacks, however. In some cases offspring inherit the worst traits of each parent. Other hybrids, such as mules, are sterile. Even in hybrids that can reproduce, hybrid vigor may disappear if hybrids are crossed over many generations.

Breeders may combine hybridization with inbreeding and mass selection to produce new true-breeding varieties. On the other hand, hybrid plants can be reproduced asexually. Roses and orchard fruits, for example, are sometimes propagated by *grafting,* or joining a branch of a new variety to the stem and roots of an existing plant. All growth from this branch has the traits of the new variety. In other instances, such as hybrid corn, the original crosses are repeated to produce new hybrid seeds for each year's crop.

Section Review

1. **Analyzing Ideas** How have breeders improved plants?
2. **Summarizing Ideas** What is mass selection?
3. **Comparing Ideas** How do inbreeding and hybridization differ?

Thinking Critically

Controlled breeding is just one means of developing organisms adapted to human needs. Biologists have also learned to produce identical copies of desirable organisms. *In the last 30 years, biologists have found new ways to change the genetic makeup of an organism or its offspring by artificial means.* Among these techniques is a process of transferring genes from one organism to another, a revolutionary technology promising major changes in many fields.

14.3   Cloning

Biologists can now duplicate certain organisms by means of **cloning,** which is the production of organisms with identical genes. Some methods of cloning are simple. Just cutting leaves from a plant, rooting them in water, and planting them results in **clones**—organisms that are developed from one parent and genetically identical to one another. Grafting is another form of cloning.

A more complex kind of cloning involves growing a complete plant from one *somatic* cell. This is any cell not normally involved in sexual reproduction. First tissues from a parent plant are kept alive in a nutrient solution. Then a single cell is removed and treated with substances that cause it to grow and divide. Eventually, a new plant identical to the parent develops.

Scientists have also cloned a few animals. Frogs have been cloned by replacing the nuclei of frog eggs with nuclei from tadpoles of another kind of frog. Rabbits and mice have also been cloned. Such experiments suggest that cloning many vertebrates may be possible. However, that development is not expected soon, in part because scientists still do not fully understand embryonic development.

Figure 14–4. In one type of cloning, new banana plants are produced by culturing tissue from a single banana plant.

14.4   Polyploidy

Artificially changing the quantity of DNA is another way to improve organisms. One such change is called **polyploidy** (PAHL ih ploy dee), a condition in which an organism has more than two complete sets of chromosomes. A diploid organism has two sets of chromosomes—one set from each parent. A polyploid organism may have three, four, or more sets. For example, diploid strains of wheat have two sets of 7 chromosomes, or a total of 14 chromosomes. Durum wheat, which is used to make pasta, has four sets, or a total of 28 chromosomes.

A method of manipulating genes may make it possible to develop hybrids from plants that are distantly related. This process, called **cell fusion,** joins cells from two very different kinds of plants.

First, the cell walls are removed from the cells that will be fused. The cell parts that remain are called *protoplasts.* The proto-plasts from two species of plants, such as potatoes and tomatoes, are then combined. Next, the fused cells are treated with chemicals that cause a new cell wall to develop. Finally, the cell is treated with substances that stimulate growth. The cells of the new plant contain two complete sets of chromosomes from each parent, making it a hybrid polyploid.

Laboratories perform similar experiments that may result in better plants. For instance, the fusion of protoplasts of a potato and a tomato may result in a potato plant with the tomato's natural resistance to disease.

■ **Identifying Relationships** What are some other plants that might be suitable for cell fusion?

Polyploidy does not usually occur in animals since most changes in the number of chromosomes are fatal. However, polyploidy is common in plants and often produces varieties that are larger, hardier, and sometimes more productive than diploid varieties of the same species.

Polyploid plants develop when duplicated chromosomes fail to separate during meiosis. One daughter cell then receives two sets of chromosomes. If this cell is fertilized by another diploid gamete, the fertilized cell will have four sets of chromosomes instead of the normal two.

Biologists produce polyploidy by using *colchicine,* a chemical that prevents cells from dividing after the chromosomes duplicate. The result is a cell with twice the diploid number of chromosomes. Today, breeders use colchicine to grow polyploid cabbages, blueberries, and other plants.

14.5 Recombinant DNA

The most revolutionary means of changing DNA is through **genetic engineering,** the process of transferring DNA segments from one organism into the DNA of another species. The new molecule of DNA containing DNA from both species is called **recombinant DNA.** Bacteria containing recombinant DNA

Figure 14–5. The large apple in the photograph is an example of fruit produced by a polyploid plant.

have already produced medicines to combat certain human diseases. In the future, recombinant DNA may dramatically change agriculture, food processing, and energy production.

Reading Critically

Inferring Conclusions Why would horses be poor choices for studying recombinant DNA technology?

Producing Recombinant DNA The organism most often used in recombinant DNA technology is *Escherichia coli,* or *E. coli,* a bacterium normally found in the human intestine. Because this bacterium divides about once every 20 minutes, many new bacteria containing recombinant DNA can be produced quickly. These bacteria will then produce the protein coded for by the transplanted DNA. In this way, *E. coli* can be made to generate proteins normally produced by other organisms.

As Figure 14–6 shows, the first step in producing recombinant DNA is to extract DNA from a donor organism. Then enzymes called *restriction endonucleases* are used to remove a gene from the DNA. These enzymes cut the DNA molecule only at certain points and leave a few unpaired bases at one end of each DNA strand. These unpaired bases are called "sticky ends" because they will bond to complementary unpaired bases at the end of another DNA molecule.

Next, small circles of DNA called **plasmids** (PLAZ mihdz) are extracted from the *E. coli* cells. The plasmids are broken open with the same enzymes used to remove the gene from the donor DNA. Consequently, the ends of the plasmid DNA and

Figure 14–6. This illustration shows the major steps involved in recombinant DNA technology. The small triangles indicate the points at which enzymes are used to cut the strands of DNA.

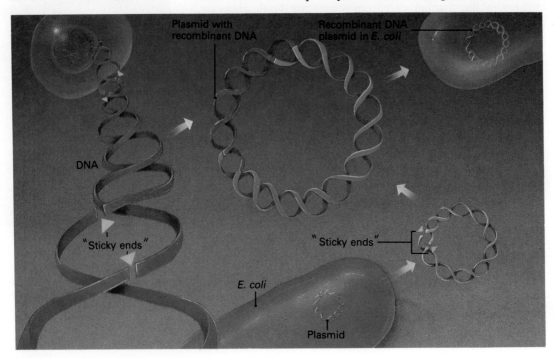

Plasmid with recombinant DNA

Recombinant DNA plasmid in *E. coli*

DNA

"Sticky ends"

"Sticky ends"

E. coli

Plasmid

the donor DNA are complementary. For example, the sequence adenine-cytosine-thymine on the DNA segment will bond to the sequence thymine-guanine-adenine on the plasmid. Recombination occurs when the pieces of donor DNA bond to the ends of the plasmid strands. With the addition of another kind of enzyme, the plasmids with new sections of DNA inserted are made to seal themselves into rings.

Finally, the plasmids are mixed with *E. coli* cells, which are chemically treated so the plasmids travel through their cell membranes. Not every bacterium picks up a plasmid containing recombinant DNA, but only those that have picked up recombinant DNA are allowed to multiply. When the bacteria divide, their plasmids are passed on to daughter cells. Soon a large colony of bacteria with recombinant DNA results. The new genes produce proteins coded for by the new section of DNA.

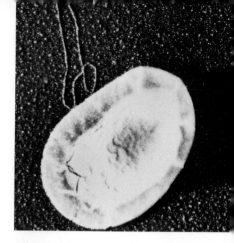

Figure 14–7. This photograph shows a plasmid entering an *E. coli* bacterium magnified 100,000 times.

The Importance of Recombinant DNA
When recombinant DNA experiments began in the early 1970s, several scientists asked that such experiments stop until the potential dangers of this technique were evaluated. These scientists feared that cells containing harmful genes might escape from laboratories and cause widespread disease. In 1976 the United States government issued safety guidelines for laboratories developing recombinant DNA. These guidelines required special equipment and methods to prevent problems from occurring.

Since 1976 scientists have made remarkable advances in recombinant DNA technology. In 1978 they first used bacteria to make human *insulin*, a hormone that controls the level of sugar in the blood. Insulin is used to treat individuals with *diabetes mellitus*, a disease in which not enough insulin is produced so the blood sugar rises to dangerous levels. In 1980 scientists produced a bacterium that made human *interferon*, a protein that prevents the multiplication of viruses. Experiments indicate that interferon stops the growth of some cancerous tumors.

In the future, bacteria containing recombinant DNA may produce many substances. This technology may provide other amazing results, such as wheat plants that produce their own nitrogen fertilizer and cures for genetic diseases.

Biofact

Q: *How do experimenters know which bacteria contain recombinant DNA so they can allow only those bacteria to multiply?*

A: Along with segments of DNA, the experimenters attach marker genes to the plasmids. These genes provide resistance to *streptomycin,* an antibiotic that kills certain bacteria. If the recipient bacteria are grown on a medium containing streptomycin, the colonies that survive must contain marker genes and therefore recombinant DNA.

Section Review

1. **Summarizing Ideas** Explain how a tree can be grown from a single somatic cell.
2. **Summarizing Ideas** What is polyploidy?
3. **Comparing Ideas** In what way is cell fusion similar to genetic engineering?

> **Thinking Critically**

Genetic Testing

Scientists are working to locate *genetic markers,* points along the cell's DNA that identify the positions of specific genes. A set of markers is unique for each individual and is, therefore, often called a *DNA fingerprint.* Genetic markers may also identify the presence of specific genes that are associated with inborn errors of metabolism such as leukemia, Huntington disease, and sickle-cell anemia.

Researchers have already identified more than 400 genetic markers. These markers can be used to help predict whether or not a person will develop a genetic disorder. The use of genetic markers can allow early treatment of a disorder, alert prospective parents about the possibility of having children with inherited disorders, and even allow for prevention of the onset of the disorder in some cases.

The ability of researchers to determine whether or not a person carries genes that are associated with genetic disorders has raised legal and ethical questions.

For example, some people are concerned that information about their genetic makeup will be used to deny them employment. A similar dilemma resulted when large numbers of people were tested for the genetic disorder sickle-cell anemia. During the 1970s, many African Americans were screened for the sickle-cell gene so that they could be treated for the condition. The tests, however, also identified carriers of the disease who usually suffer no ill effects although they can pass the gene to their offspring. As a result of the tests, some carriers applying for airline pilot positions were denied employment.

Laws were passed to prevent discrimination based on sickle-cell testing. However, if genetic screening becomes widespread, it may become difficult to keep genetic information private.

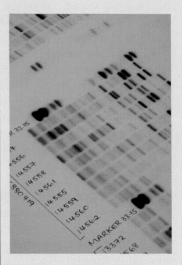

Analyze the Issue

1. What are genetic markers and how can they be used for both legal and medical benefits?

2. What forms of discrimination might result from tests that show a genetic predisposition to a disease such as leukemia, paranoid schizophrenia, or hemophilia?

3. Discuss some ways in which people with known genetic disorders could be protected from discrimination.

4. Who do you think should make decisions about genetic testing— the individual, a committee of individuals who are concerned with ethical questions, doctors, courts, or some other individual or group? Support your opinion.

INVESTIGATION 14:
How Are Dogs Bred for Desired Traits?

Objectives
- To *apply* genetic principles to a breeding problem
- To *evaluate* breeding methods

Materials
paper and pencil

Prelab Preparation
1. Describe traits that dog breeders might want to select when breeding dogs.
2. Explain why mass selection is more difficult for breeding dogs than it is for breeding plants.
3. Explain the possible drawbacks of inbreeding.

Inquiry: Exploration
4. Red coat color and pointing ability are dominant traits. Size is controlled by a pair of incompletely dominant alleles. As a breeder, you wish to produce a breed that is small and red with pointing ability. Study the information in the table shown at the bottom of this page.
5. Use a Punnett square to find the genotypes that result from crossing Dog A and Dog B for the three traits shown in the table. *What are the genotype and phenotype of the F₁ offspring?*
6. Use a Punnett square to cross two of the F₁ generation dogs. *What are the possible genotypes and phenotypes in the F₂ generation?*

Analysis
1. **Analyzing Data**   How do the F_1 dogs compare to their parents?
2. **Analyzing Data**   What fraction of the F_2 generation is expected to be small with a red coat and pointing ability?
3. **Analyzing Data**   Will all the small-sized, red pointers in the F_2 generation breed true? Explain your answer.
4. **Inferring Ideas**   Why can developing a new breed of dog require large amounts of time and money?
5. **Analyzing Data**   Given enough time, would it be possible to develop a true-breeding, medium-sized, red pointer?

Characteristic	Phenotype	Genotype
Dog A		
Coat color	Red	RR
Hunting instinct	Does not point at birds	hh
Size	Large	$S^T S^T$
Dog B		
Coat color	White	rr
Hunting instinct	Points at birds	HH
Size	Small	$S^S S^S$

Chapter 14 Review

Summary

Progress in the science of genetics has produced not only new knowledge but also applications that benefit people. Plant and animal breeders now apply genetic information to methods of controlled breeding that have long been used. Mass selection involves raising large numbers of plants or animals and mating the best in each generation. Inbreeding is the mating of genetically similar individuals to produce organisms that are homozygous for desirable traits. In hybridization, two different species or varieties are crossed to produce heterozygous offspring with the best traits of each parent. By using genetic information, breeders can now more quickly achieve results from these methods.

Biologists have also learned to produce identical copies of organisms and to make artificial changes in DNA. Use of the chemical colchicine, for example, which prevents cells from dividing after the chromosomes duplicate, produces polyploid plants that have more chromosomes than the normal diploid number. These plants are often larger, hardier, and more productive than diploid varieties. Through genetic engineering, scientists have also created recombinant DNA, which contains DNA from two species. Bacteria containing recombinant DNA have already produced human insulin and human interferon. One day recombinant DNA may be used to manufacture other drugs as well as to provide new sources of food.

BioTerms

applied
  genetics (226)
cell fusion (231)
clone (230)
cloning (230)
controlled breeding
  (227)
genetic

engineering (231)
hybridization (229)
hybrid
  vigor (229)
inbreeding (228)
mass
  selection (228)
plasmid (232)

polyploidy (230)

recombinant
  DNA (231)

For each pair of terms, explain the differences in their meanings.

1. mass selection, inbreeding
2. cloning, polyploidy
3. controlled breeding, genetic engineering

BioQuiz   (Write all answers on a separate sheet of paper.)

Completion

1. Individuals that are genetically identical to their parents are _____ .
2. Luther Burbank's Shasta daisies are the result of _____ .
3. Small circles of DNA extracted from cells are called _____ .
4. Crossing two different species of cattle is an example of _____ .
5. Enzymes called _____ are used to remove a gene from DNA.

Multiple Choice

6. Interferon prevents the multiplication of
   a) bacteria. b) viruses. c) clones.
   d) unicellular organisms.
7. Hybrid polyploids are created by means
   of a) mass selection. b) cloning.
   c) inbreeding. d) cell fusion.
8. Hybridization can be combined with
   _____ to produce new true-breeding
   varieties. a) plasmids b) inbreeding
   c) recombinant DNA d) polyploidy

9. A method that involves the mating of genetically similar individuals is called a) cloning. b) mass selection. c) hybridization. d) inbreeding.
10. Plants with more than the usual number of sets of chromosomes are a) cloned. b) somatic. c) haploid. d) polyploid.
11. Cells stripped of their cell walls are called a) mutants. b) cloned. c) protoplasts. d) polyploid.
12. Scientists have used recombinant DNA to manufacture human insulin and a) cells. b) interferon. c) triticale. d) clones.
13. A section of DNA with the unpaired base ATC would bond with the plasmid base sequence a) TAG. b) TAC. c) GCT. d) CGA.

14. The existence of triticale is due to a) mass selection. b) inbreeding. c) hybrid vigor. d) hybridization.
15. Genetically identical organisms result from a) inbreeding. b) cloning. c) colchicine. d) hybridization.

Writing Critically

16. What is the purpose of inbreeding?
17. What are two of the drawbacks of hybridization?
18. How is polyploidy induced in plants?
19. What enables a section of DNA to bond with a broken plasmid?
20. Why is recombinant DNA technology considered revolutionary?

Application/Critical Thinking

1. **Expressing Viewpoints** Imagine that you are a plant breeder who has been asked to develop the ideal plant for space missions. Name some traits that this ideal plant might be engineered to have.
2. **Synthesizing Information** Seedless grapes, oranges, and watermelons have an odd number of sets of chromosomes. Do library research to learn how plant breeders produce fruits that have no seeds. Describe this process to the class.
3. **Developing Experiments** Citrus growers are at the mercy of cold spells that sometimes severely damage crops. Imagine that you are a breeder searching for a tree that can withstand the cold and still produce large, flavorful oranges. You have some seeds from a hardy species that produces small, bitter fruit. Explain how you could develop a tree with desirable features using the methods of controlled breeding and recombinant DNA technology. List any problems or benefits associated with each model.

Cross-Discipline Connection

Biology and Economics Investigate the potential economic impact of recombinant DNA technology. One approach is to review the growth of companies using such technology.

Discovery Through Reading

"Doling out DNA," *Science News* (February 4, 1989): 72–74, describes how proper management of the gene pool ensures the survival of endangered species in zoos. How is DNA fingerprinting used in captive breeding programs?

"The Making of a Monster," *U.S. News and World Report (August 31, 1987):* 103, discusses government control of some genetic experiments. What argument do some scientists give against elaborate regulation?

Summary

Genetics, the scientific study of heredity, was pioneered by Gregor Mendel. Mendel's mathematical analyses of inheritance patterns in garden peas in the mid-1800s allowed him to establish three basic principles. These are the principle of dominance, the principle of segregation, and the principle of independent assortment. These principles conform to the laws of probability.

In 1903, Walter Sutton proposed that chromosomes carry hereditary information. Thomas Hunt Morgan first showed that genes can occur on specific chromosomes when he discovered that sex-linked traits were determined by alleles carried only on the X chromosome of the fruit fly. The experiments of Morgan and others showed that other genes can be linked to specific chromosomes and that sometimes linkage groups cross over between members of a chromosome pair.

The work of James Watson, Francis Crick, Rosalind Franklin and others revealed the structure of DNA, the genetic material of the cell. Genes, made of DNA, act as blueprints for the proteins that can be made by cells. DNA replicates and transcribes genetic codes to RNA, which directs the synthesis of proteins on ribosomes. Changes in a genetic code may be environmentally produced mutations or spontaneous errors. Most changes in DNA are harmful or lethal.

Geneticists use pedigrees to study inheritance patterns and population sampling to measure the gene frequencies in populations. Some human traits are determined by single genes, some by multiple alleles, and some are polygenic. Some human traits are sex-linked, governed by genes that occur on the X chromosome. Nondisjunction can result in inborn errors of metabolism that are expressed as genetic disorders. These disorders can often be predicted through genetic counseling.

Methods of genetically based controlled breeding such as mass selection and hybridization produce plants and animals with desirable traits. Genetic techniques such as cloning and recombining DNA are used in a rapidly advancing technology. The application of this technology sometimes raises legal and ethical questions in today's society.

Synthesis

Synthesis Statement

The application of a scientific method to the study of inheritance has had tremendous impact on society in this century. In addition, advances in microscope technology allowed scientists to understand how genetic material is passed from one generation to the next. X-ray crystallography and advances in chemistry provided information that finally led to the understanding of the genetic code and how this code controls many of the activities of life that go on within organisms. Increasing knowledge about genetics will have continued impact on society in the future.

Synthesis Questions

Apply your understanding of this unit to the following questions.

1. How does testing a hypothesis about inheritance patterns in garden peas differ from testing a hypothesis about inheritance in humans?

2. What did animal breeders know about the inheritance of traits prior to Mendel's discoveries?

3. Why might the knowledge of an individual's genome be beneficial? Describe some ways in which this information might be used to the detriment of certain individuals.

4. The traits that Mendel selected for study in the garden pea were either dominant or recessive and easy to see. Why would Mendel have found it difficult to explain the phenomena of gene linkage and crossing over?

5. What must a husband and wife know in order to determine the chances that their child will inherit a disease? How would the inheritance of the disease be affected if it were a sex-linked disease?

6. How might your diet be affected if genetically engineered *E. coli* bacteria cells that could produce certain amino acids became established in your intestine?

7. Offer suggestions for ways in which our society might weigh the benefits of recombinant DNA technology against the potential dangers.

8. Could techniques of cloning enable the development of human clones in the laboratory? Describe some of the ethical questions that would be raised by research in human cloning.

9. Use a separate piece of paper to draw a concept map like the one below. Place each of the following terms inside the appropriate figure: protein synthesis, enzyme, gene, biochemical reaction, trait.

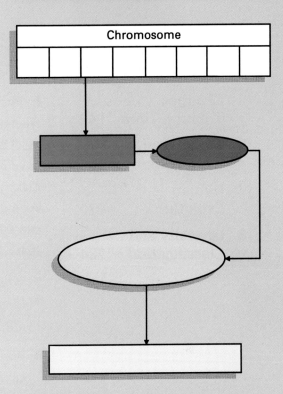

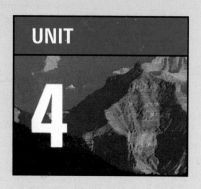

UNIT

4

HISTORY AND DIVERSITY OF LIFE

Unit Outline

Unit Focus

Evidence shows that life forms on Earth have changed over vast amounts of time. Some of this evidence is recorded in the form of organisms that have been preserved in the stratified layers that make up the Earth's surface. Other evidence has been gathered from the similarities in chemistry and embryological development that life forms share.

■ *What features of the Grand Canyon shown in the photograph suggest that the canyon is very old?*

■ *Why would walking down into the canyon be similar to going backwards in time?*

The Colorado River began shaping the walls of the Grand Canyon about 6 million years ago.

Changes Through Time

Outline

A region of the Milky Way Spiral Galaxy

Focus

Evidence suggests that the Earth was formed about 4.6 billion years ago and has undergone many changes since then. Evidence also indicates that living things have changed during the approximately 3.5 billion years they have inhabited Earth. This chapter examines current knowledge gained from scientific inquiry about the origin of the universe, Earth, and life on Earth. This chapter also presents evidence that indicates that living things have changed over time, a process called **evolution.**

■ *What parts of organisms might be preserved over vast amounts of time?*

■ *What part of the cell theory does not take into account the origin of life on Earth?*

The Beginning of Life

Section Objectives

- *Summarize* the big-bang theory.
- *List* the steps in the formation of life on Earth, according to the Haldane–Oparin model.
- *Describe* Miller and Urey's experiment and their results.

A basic principle of biology states that cells arise only from existing cells. But where did the first cell come from? It is not possible to travel back in time to learn the answer. So scientists have developed theories concerning the beginning of life—and the universe—based on evidence gained from observation and laboratory work.

15.1 Origin of the Universe

Several theories exist to explain the origin of the universe. However, most scientists today favor the big-bang theory proposed in 1927 by Belgian astronomer Georges Lemaitre. The big-bang theory states that the universe began about 15 billion years ago as a dense concentration of matter smaller than a speck of dust. For reasons that today's physicists do not completely understand, this concentration of matter exploded violently. Energy and new forms of matter created by this explosion spread into space. Eventually, gravitational attraction drew these bits and pieces of matter together, forming stars and planets.

15.2 Origin of Earth

Billions of years ago, clouds of molecules, mostly composed of hydrogen gas, began to condense to form stars. One of these stars was the Sun. Earth and the other planets of this solar system developed about 4.6 billion years ago out of gases and dust orbiting the Sun. At first the dust cloud was very cool and gaseous. Soon gravity caused local accumulations of dust to form planets. This solid matter was layered according to density. Heavy elements, such as iron, collected into a dense core. Lighter elements formed a solid crust at the Earth's surface. Radioactive decay deep in the Earth raised the temperature of the core, and molten rock called *magma* rose to the Earth's surface. Volcanic eruptions forced the hot gases such as nitrogen and water vapor out of the magma. These gases, in which there was no free oxygen, then formed an atmosphere.

15.3 Origin of Life

Although scientists will never know exactly how life began, they have gathered general evidence and developed some models of how it could have happened. Scientists agree that the Earth of 4.6 billion years ago was far different from the Earth of today.

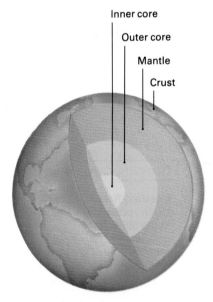

Inner core

Outer core

Mantle

Crust

Figure 15–1. The cross section above shows the layers of the earth. The inner core is hot, solid metal; the outer core is molten metal; the mantle is solid rock; and the outer layer, the crust, is also rock.

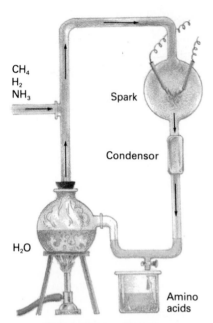

CH₄
H₂
NH₃

Spark

Condensor

H₂O

Amino
acids

Figure 15–2. The diagram above shows how Miller and Urey demonstrated that common organic compounds could be formed from inorganic materials.

Reading Critically

Inferring Relationships Why did the presence of amino acids in the Miller-Urey experiment strongly support the idea that life could have begun from ammonia, water vapor methane, and hydrogen?

Thinking Critically

They think much of the surface was covered with hot seas, kept hot by the molten Earth. Steam from these seas rose into the atmospheres and formed huge clouds. The water vapor in these heavy clouds slowly cooled, condensed, and fell to Earth in violent rainstorms, accompanied by lightning. On land, active volcanoes spouted gas, steam, and magma.

In the 1920s, the Russian scientist, Alexander Oparin, and the British scientist, J.B.S. Haldane, began to develop similar models that might be used to explain how life arose on Earth. Oparin presented his model in 1936. According to Oparin's hypothesis, the early atmosphere and oceans probably contained ammonia, water vapor, methane, and hydrogen. Lightning, the heat from Earth, and ultraviolet light from the sun provided energy to split these molecules into atoms. The atoms bonded together to form small *organic* compounds, carbon-containing molecules characteristic of living things. These molecules accumulated in the oceans and formed a kind of "organic soup." After a great length of time, they combined into globules of molecules that could reproduce themselves. These molecules were the first life on Earth.

In 1953 American chemists Stanley Miller and Harold Urey tested Oparin's hypothesis. They filled the apparatus shown in Figure 15–2 with water vapor, methane, and ammonia and passed an electric spark through the mixture. A liquid trap collected any molecules that might have formed in the apparatus. After seven days, they analyzed the liquid and found amino acids, the building blocks of proteins. Their experiments showed that amino acids could have formed on the ancient Earth. But life is more than just amino acids. It took hundreds of millions of years after the origin of Earth for cells to form.

The first cells probably resembled anaerobic bacteria, since no free oxygen existed in the atmosphere. They probably lived off organic compounds in their environments. Cells capable of photosynthesis, such as cyanobacteria and other bacteria, developed later, about 3 billion years ago. These organisms not only made their own food but also gave off oxygen. This oxygen gradually accumulated in the atmosphere and paved the way for more complex forms of life that were capable of utilizing oxygen for their energy needs.

Section Review

1. **Summarizing Ideas**   What is the big-bang theory?
2. **Interpreting Ideas**   According to the Haldane-Oparin model, how did the first life forms arise?
3. **Inferring Relationships**   Explain why the first cells could not have been aerobic bacteria.

Evidence of Evolution

Organisms have changed dramatically since they appeared on Earth about 3.5 billion years ago. The first simple cells gave rise to more varied and complex organisms, changing in size and structure in response to changing conditions. Scientists have found evidence of such changes in fossils and in the characteristics of today's living things.

15.4 The Fossil Record

A **fossil** is any preserved part or trace of an organism that once lived. You have probably seen fossils, such as dinosaur skeletons, in museums. Fossils are important sources of evidence that organisms have changed over time.

Fossil Evidence A fossil is formed when all or part of an organism is buried before it can be eaten or before it decays. Most fossils are found in **sedimentary** rock. Sedimentary rocks are formed from *sediments* such as mud, silt, and sand that have been deposited in layers on top of one another. Particles deep in these sediments are subjected to great pressure. They become cemented together to form sandstone, limestone, shale, and other types of sedimentary rocks.

Organisms buried in sediments may become fossilized. Soft body structures, such as feathers or leaves, may form **imprints**—that is, impressions in the developing rock. Teeth, shells, bones, and other hard body parts may form **molds,** which are depressions in the rock shaped like the organism's

Section Objectives

- *Describe* how fossils are formed.
- *Explain* how carbon-14 is used to date fossils.
- *List* the major divisions of the geologic time scale.
- *Compare* and *contrast* homologous, analogous, and vestigial structures.
- *Explain* how comparative embryology and biochemistry support the theory of evolution.

To read about the study of ancient climates, see pages 282–283.

Figure 15–3. The photographs below show three types of fossils: a fly in amber (left), a cast of a trilobite (center), and an imprint of a leaf (right).

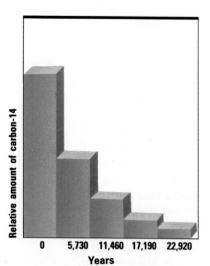

Figure 15–4. The bar graph above shows the rate of decay of carbon-14. What percentage of the atoms has become stable after 11,460 years?

parts. Sometimes the original material decomposes and the resulting molds are filled in with another material, forming **casts.** Other times, hard parts of an organism are gradually replaced by minerals, creating fossils called **petrified fossils.**

Occasionally entire organisms are preserved intact. Many small organisms have been trapped in *amber,* the sap of trees that hardens into a transparent covering. Other, larger organisms have been trapped in tar, which prevented their decay.

Determining the Age of Fossils   Fossils tell us what kinds of life existed in the past. But we must know the age of fossils to understand the sequence in which organisms appeared and how they changed over time.

The age of fossils can be determined by their positions in sedimentary rock. Sediments are built up in layers, the newer layers on top of the older layers. In undisturbed sedimentary rock, the most recent fossils are found in upper layers, and older fossils in lower layers. By comparing the sediment position of fossils, scientists can determine their relative ages.

Scientists can determine the age of fossils more exactly by using *isotopes*. Isotopes are those atoms of an element that have different *atomic masses*. For example, a nucleus of carbon with six protons and six neutrons is the isotope called carbon-12, or ^{12}C. Carbon-13 has six protons and seven neutrons; ^{14}C has six protons and eight neutrons. The isotopes of most value to scientists are **radioactive isotopes.** These isotopes have unstable nuclei that gradually break down into stable elements called **decay elements.** For example, uranium-238 decays into lead-206. Carbon-14 decays into nitrogen-14. Radioactive isotopes are useful because they decay at a constant, known rate. The time it takes for one-half of the isotopes in radioactive material to decay is called the **half-life** of the isotope. The half-life of ^{14}C is 5,730 years.

Carbon-14 is often used to date fossils because it is incorporated into the molecules of the organisms while they are alive. When organisms die, they stop taking in both ^{14}C and ^{12}C. The ^{14}C in their bodies decays over time, but the ^{12}C remains stable. As a result, scientists can determine the age of a fossil by comparing the ^{14}C and ^{12}C in it. The ratio of ^{14}C to ^{12}C in living tissue of today and in living tissue of the past is assumed to be the same. Therefore, a fossil containing half the amount of ^{14}C of the organism's living tissue would be 5,730 years old. A fossil with one-fourth the ^{14}C of living tissue would be 11,460 years old (5,730 plus 5,730). Carbon-14 is used to date relatively young fossils. Uranium-238, with a half-life of 4.5 billion years, is used to date rocks in which older fossils are found.

Structures Without Functions?

The functions of most of the structures in the human body are obvious, if not to most people, at least to the experts who study them. There are, however, some structures that do not have an obvious function. For example, if you look closely at the inner corner of your eye in a mirror, you will see a small, crescent-shaped piece of tissue. It does not have an apparent function. However, everyone has this structure in each of their eyes. Structures like this one are called *vestigial structures.* They often have a counterpart in some other related organism in which they do have an apparent function. The vestigial flap of thin tissue in the corner of the human eye, for example, is homologous to the membrane that functions to completely cover over the eye of a frog as a "third eyelid." In frogs, this membrane protects the eye while allowing the animal to see—frogs have an eyelid that they can see through.

The human appendix is another example of a human body structure that does not have an apparent function that is related to its shape. This structure is a wormlike tube that extends from the intestine.

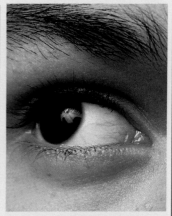

People sometimes become aware of their own appendix when it becomes infected. This painful situation can be life-threatening if the infected appendix is not surgically removed.

Besides humans, only the wombat monkey and the great apes have an appendix.

Interpreting the Fossil Record Scientists in various fields interpret the fossil record. **Paleontologists** (pay lee ahn TAHL uh jihsts) look for and study fossils. **Geologists** use fossils to explain the history of Earth. **Physical anthropologists** (an thruh PAHL uh jihsts) study human fossils.

The work of these scientists has revealed many changes in Earth during its long history. For example, fossils of palm trees have been found in the Antarctic, suggesting that the climate there was once warm. Fossils have also revealed tremendous changes in organisms.

Based on the information collected by dating fossils, geologists have developed a geologic time scale of the Earth's history (Table 15–1 on page 248). This scale allows scientists to communicate about events that have occurred since Earth was formed. The geologic time scale is divided into four **eras,** vast spans of time millions of years long. An era may be subdivided into time spans called *periods*, which may be further subdivided into smaller *epochs*.

Reading Critically

Synthesizing Relationships
What would the discovery of fossils reveal about the area in which they were found?

Table 15–1: Geologic Time Scale

Era	Period	Epoch	Began (millions of years ago)	Significant Events
Cenozoic	Quaternary	Recent	0.025	Complex human societies arise.
		Pleistocene	2	The Ice Age begins.
	Tertiary	Pliocene	5	Modern mammals, birds, and sea life appear. Early hominids appear. Apes present.
		Miocene	24	Grasslands spread.
		Oligocene	37	Primitive elephants, horses, and camels develop.
		Eocene	58	Large mammals appear. Primates present. Fruit-bearing trees become common.
		Paleocene	65	Small mammals become plentiful and spread rapidly.
Mesozoic	Cretaceous		144	Flowering plants and trees appear. Dinosaurs die out at end.
	Jurassic		208	Dinosaurs abundant. First feathered birds and mammals appear.
	Triassic		245	Insects and cone-bearing trees plentiful. Dinosaurs appear.
Paleozoic	Permian		286	Fish, reptiles, and amphibians are plentiful.
	Carboniferous	Pennsylvanian	320	Age of amphibians. First seed plants appear. Large ferns, swampy forests; reptiles appear.
		Mississippian	360	Coral reefs formed. Extensive land forests develop.
	Devonian		408	Fish are common. First swampy forests grow. Amphibians and insects appear.
	Silurian		438	First land plants develop. Fish and shell-forming sea animals appear.
	Ordovician		505	Algae and shelled animals are common. First vertebrates appear in sea.
	Cambrian		570	Clams and snails appear. Algae are common.
Precambrian			4.5 (billion years)	Few fossils. Bacteria and algae predominate.

History of Life on Earth The earliest traces of life suggest the presence of microorganisms about 3.5 billion years ago during the earliest era, the Precambrian. The first cells with nuclei appeared about 1.5 billion years ago. These evolved into simple forms of life that gave rise to more complex forms. Land plants, amphibians, and insects came into existence between 435 million and 225 million years ago, during the Paleozoic era. Dinosaurs dominated the Mesozoic era, which began about 225 million years ago. The most recent era—the Cenozoic—began about 65 million years ago. It was not until the last several million years of this era that human beings appeared on Earth.

To investigate the conditions under which the first cells may have evolved, see page 251.

15.5 Other Evidence of Evolution

Fossils are one major source of evidence supporting evolution. However, the study of living organisms has also revealed important evidence of relationships among organisms.

THINKING ABOUT BIOLOGY: Biochemical Evidence of Evolution

The most recent evidence of evolution has come from **comparative biochemistry,** the study of molecules that make up different living things. Biochemists have found that all living things share certain substances made of proteins. These proteins are composed of various combinations of smaller substances called amino acids. The order in which amino acids are assembled into proteins is determined by DNA.

Cytochrome c, a protein used in aerobic respiration, is one of the proteins researchers studied in many different organisms. The computer-generated image above shows cyto-

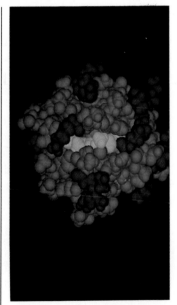

chrome c. Researchers paid special attention to the sequences of amino acids in cytochrome c from differ-

ent organisms. They were able to calculate the number of DNA segments, called nucleotides, needed to account for the differing sequences. They found that in human beings and monkeys only 1 nucleotide differed. In human beings and turtles, 19 nucleotides were different. Such information suggests that organisms with few differences in DNA nucleotides, and therefore in cytochrome c, have a close evolutionary relationship.

■ **Analyzing Relationships** What does the fact that there were 19 different nucleotides in humans and turtles suggest about their evolutionary relationship?

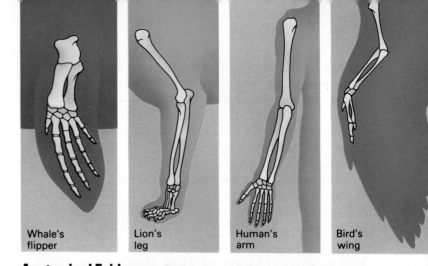

Figure 15–5. Vertebrate limbs are homologous structures. The flipper of a whale, leg of a lion, arm of a human, and wing of a bird differ in size and shape, but are alike in the arrangement of bones.

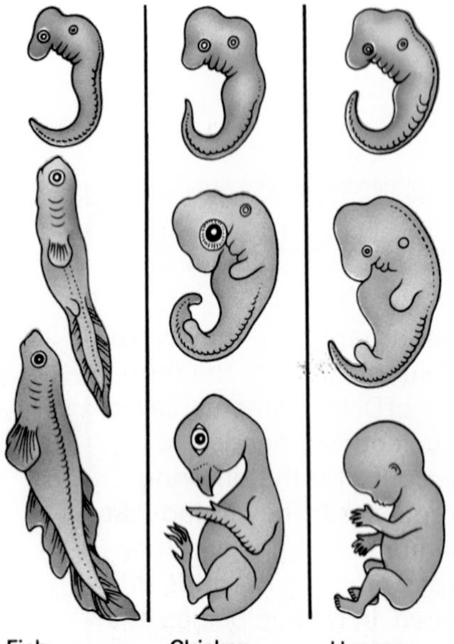

Whale's flipper | Lion's leg | Human's arm | Bird's wing

Anatomical Evidence Body parts with the same basic structure are called **homologous** (hoh MAHL uh guhs) **structures.** *Homologous structures found in different organisms suggest that these organisms have a common ancestry.* In homologous structures, the size and shape of each structure is different, but the number and arrangement of bones is similar.

Body parts that are similar in function but not in basic structure, such as the wings of birds and the wings of insects, are called **analogous** (uh NAL uh guhs) **structures.** These body parts do not indicate an evolutionary relationship.

Other body structures that provide evidence of evolution are **vestigial** (vehs TIHJ ee uhl) **structures.** These are structures that have been reduced in size because they no longer serve an important function. The tiny hip bones in some snakes have no apparent purpose, but they suggest that snakes evolved from ancestors with hips.

Embryological Evidence Organisms in the early stages of development are called *embryos.* The study of **comparative embryology,** which compares embryos of different species, has found similarities that support the theory of evolution. Biologists believe that these vertebrates share common genetic instructions for embryo development and, therefore, share a common ancestor.

Fish | Chicken | Human

Figure 15–6. Similarities in the development of fish, chicken, and human embryos suggest an evolutionary relationship.

Section Review

1. **Summarizing Ideas** How are most fossils formed?
2. **Identifying Relationships** How is carbon-14 used to date fossils?
3. **Organizing Ideas** What are the major divisions of the geologic time scale?
4. **Inferring Conclusions** How do homologous structures and similarities in embryology and biochemistry among different animals support evolution?

Thinking Critically

INVESTIGATION 15:
What Are Coacervates?

Objectives
- To *examine* coacervates
- To *relate* lab observations to conditions under which first cells may have evolved

Materials 📱 👓 🧤 🧪
gelatin solution, test tube, three medicine droppers, gum arabic solution, pH paper, glass slides, coverslips, compound light microscope, hydrochloric acid (HCl)

Prelab Preparation
1. Describe the conditions thought to be present on Earth when life first evolved.
2. Explain the Oparin–Haldane hypothesis about the beginning of life on Earth.
3. Summarize Stanley Miller and Harold Urey's experiment.
4. Review the microscope procedures on pages 908–909.

Inquiry: Observation
5. Pour 5 mL of gelatin solution into a clean test tube.
6. Add 3 mL of gum arabic solution and mix gently.
7. Test the pH of the gelatin-gum arabic mixture. *What is the pH value?*
8. Make a wet mount of the gelatin-gum arabic mixture. Using low power, observe the slide. Then switch to high power and sketch the mixture. *What is the appearance of this mixture as seen at high power?*
9. **CAUTION: Put on safety goggles, a laboratory apron, and rubber gloves. Hydrochloric acid burns the skin and can damage clothing. If you get HCl on your skin or clothing, immediately wash with a large amount of water and notify your teacher.** Add a drop of HCl to the test tube containing the gelatin-gum arabic mixture. Gently roll the test tube between your palms to mix the contents. Determine the pH of the mixture and record the results.
10. Make a wet mount of the mixture treated with hydrochloric acid and examine this slide using low power. Switch to high power and sketch the mixture. *What is the appearance of this mixture as seen at high power?*
11. Repeat steps 9 and 10 until you are able to observe coacervates. The coacervates should appear similar to the illustration shown. *At what pH did the coacervates first appear?*
12. Repeat steps 9 and 10, until no coacervates can be observed.

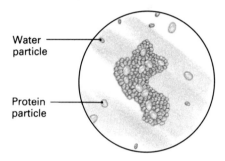

Water particle

Protein particle

Analysis
1. **Summarizing Observations** Summarize your observations.
2. **Analyzing Observations** How does pH affect the formation of coacervates?
3. **Comparing Ideas** Gelatin is a protein; gum arabic is a carbohydrate. Explain the possible similarities and differences between these organic substances and the ones thought to have been present on early Earth.

Chapter 15 Review

Summary

In the last 200 years, scientists have developed several theories explaining the formation of the universe and Earth and the beginning of life. The big-bang theory states that a huge explosion formed the universe about 15 billion years ago. Gases and dust from this explosion eventually formed stars and planets.

Alexander Oparin and J.B.S. Haldane suggested that life arose spontaneously from the compounds ammonia, water vapor, methane, and hydrogen. According to Oparin, these compounds bonded together to form the organic compounds from which life arose.

Scientists have also found evidence that life forms have evolved, or changed, since they appeared on Earth. Fossils, or traces of organisms that lived in the past, are one such source of evidence. Carbon-14 and other radioactive isotopes are used to establish an approximate date for these fossils. Other evidence of change is derived from the study of homologous structures and from embryology. Homologous and vestigial body structures as well as similarities in embryos and body chemicals of different organisms reveal evolutionary relationships.

BioTerms

analogous
  structures (250)
cast (246)
comparative
  biochemistry (249)
comparative
  embryology (250)
decay element (246)
era (247)
evolution (242)
fossil (245)
geologist (247)

half-life (246)
homologous
  structure (250)
imprint (245)
mold (245)
paleontologist (247)
petrified
  fossil (246)
physical anthro-
  pologist (247)
radioactive
  isotope (246)

sedimentary
  (245)

vestigial
  structures (250)

For each pair of terms, explain the differences in their meanings.

1. analogous structures, homologous structures
2. imprint, cast
3. paleontologist, physical anthropologist
4. comparative biochemistry, comparative embryology

BioQuiz   (Write all answers on a separate sheet of paper.)

Completion

1. The longest time spans on the geologic time scale are _____ .
2. The wings of bats and the wings of butterflies are _____ structures.
3. A footprint preserved in rock is an example of a _____ .
4. Unicellular life arose in the _____ era.
5. Hard parts of organisms that are replaced by minerals form _____ .

Multiple Choice

6. The era during which the earliest traces of life appeared was the   a) Precambrian. b) Paleozoic. c) Mesozoic. d) Cenozoic.
7. Decay elements come from   a) radioactive isotopes.   b) petrified fossils. c) sedimentary rock.   d) molds.
8. The Cenozoic era began how many years ago?   a) 56 million   b) 76 million c) 65 million   d) 100 million

9. Complex human societies arose during the _____ era. a) Mesozoic b) Cenozoic c) Precambrian d) Paleozoic
10. Which of the following is an example of a vestigial structure? a) bird's wing b) snake's hip bones c) whale's flipper d) butterfly's wing
11. _____ structures are reduced in size and seem to have no function.
    a) Homologous b) Analogous
    c) Embryological d) Vestigial
12. The process by which living things change over time is called a) half-life. b) evolution. c) the big-bang theory. d) comparative biochemistry.
13. Fossils produced by soft body parts are called a) molds. b) casts. c) imprints. d) decay elements.
14. A scientist who looks for and studies fossils is a) a paleontologist.
b) a biochemist. c) an embryologist. d) a geologist.
15. Uranium-238 is used to date fossils that are a) more than 700 million years old. b) less than 50,000 years old. c) only in sedimentary rock. d) only volcanic in origin.

Writing Critically

16. How do scientists think stars and planets were formed?
17. What conditions probably existed just before life appeared on Earth?
18. How is a mold fossil different from a cast fossil?
19. Why do scientists think that organisms have changed since life began?
20. What evidence in living things suggests that many organisms have a common ancestor?

Application/Critical Thinking

1. **Organizing Ideas** Fossils of horses have been found in different forms. Do library research to learn about these early horses. Create a chart and include the name of each epoch in which a particular form of the horse existed, along with a drawing of each type of horse, its name, and details about its size and characteristics.
2. **Synthesizing Conclusions** A fossil is analyzed through carbon-14 dating and found to contain about one-third as much carbon-14 as a comparable amount of living tissue. What is the approximate age of this fossil?
3. **Analyzing Information** The American scientist, Sidney Fox, extensively studied structures called *proteinoid microspheres*. Do library research to learn more about these structures. What is the importance of proteinoid microspheres in relation to the scientific explanation of how life began? Present your findings to the class.

Cross-Discipline Connection

Biology and Mathematics Uranium-235 has a half-life of 1.25 billion years. What is the age of a fossil that has 1/8 of the amount of uranium-235 that it originally had?

Discovery Through Reading

The article "Closing in on Creation," *Smithsonian* (May 1983): 32–51, describes the big-bang theory of the creation of the universe. The article is illustrated with a fold-out timeline chart. According to the theory, when did the big bang occur?

Theories of Evolution

Outline

Giraffes on an African plain

Focus

The most important contribution to scientific knowledge about how organisms *evolve*, or change over time, was made by the British naturalist Charles Darwin in 1859. Darwin's theory of evolution explains how the environment selects the kinds of adaptations in organisms that help them survive. Darwin's theory and the mechanisms and patterns of evolution are the topics of this chapter.

■ *What adaptations do the giraffes show that make them successful at feeding on the leaves of acacia trees?*

■ *What might happen to a giraffe that was born with a short neck?*

Theories of Evolution

By the early 1800s, scientists had begun to speculate that organisms changed over time, and that new groups of organisms were being formed continuously. Scientists believed this change affected groups of organisms called species. A **species** is a biological group whose members resemble one another and have the capacity to mate and produce fertile offspring. If it was true that species changed, then there had to exist a natural process that caused the origin and change of species. But what was this process? Some scientists, such as Lamarck and Darwin, developed theories to explain how new species arose.

16.1 Lamarck's Theory

In 1809 a French biologist named Jean Baptiste de Lamarck presented an explanation of the origin of species in his work *Zoological Philosophy*. Lamarck developed a theory of evolution based on his belief in two biological processes:

- *The use and disuse of organs*. According to Lamarck, organisms respond to changes in their environment by developing new organs or changing the structure and function of old organs. Use is actually an adaptation to the environment; the new organ is an *acquired trait*. Disuse is the response to environmental change by which an organ disappears because it is no longer needed.
- *Inheritance of acquired traits*. Lamarck believed that acquired characteristics were passed on to the organism's offspring. He called this phenomenon the inheritance of acquired traits. In this way, he said, new generations benefit from useful structures developed by their parents.

Lamarck's theory can be illustrated by explaining how his ideas account for the long necks of giraffes. According to Lamarck's thinking, the earliest giraffes might have had short necks suitable for reaching grass. If grass became scarce, the giraffes would have had to stretch their necks to reach leaves in the trees. The more they stretched, the longer their necks became. Giraffes that acquired the useful trait of long necks then passed the change in neck length on to their offspring. In this way, organisms change as the environment changes.

Lamarck was a respected biologist and philosopher in his day, and his ideas were, at first, widely accepted. However, he could not support his theory of evolution with actual data, and it is no longer accepted.

- *State* Lamarck's theory of evolution.
- *Summarize* Darwin's theory of evolution.
- *Tell* how Darwin's observation of finches of the Galapagos Islands influenced his thinking.
- *Explain* the significance of variation within a species.

Figure 16–1. Fifty years separated the theories of evolution presented by Jean Baptiste de Lamarck (top) and Charles Darwin (bottom).

Figure 16–2. The similar yet different South American rhea (top) and the Australian emu (bottom) are examples of unrelated species that adapted in similar ways to like environments.

16.2 Darwin's Theory

Fifty years after Lamarck presented his theory of evolution, Charles Darwin, a British naturalist, published the *Origin of Species*. In this landmark work, Darwin presented evidence that demonstrated that all living things on Earth evolved from other living things.

The Voyage of the *Beagle* In 1831 Darwin was a young man studying to become a minister. He was not a serious student, preferring to ride horses and collect beetles rather than study. By the time he was 20, he had learned much about nature. When he was offered a position on the *H.M.S. Beagle* to go on a voyage of exploration around the world, he accepted. Thus, he became the ship's naturalist.

At the time the voyage began, Darwin did not accept the idea that species change. He accepted instead two of the prevailing ideas of his time. The first was that the earth was 6,000 years old and had remained unchanged except for the effects of floods and other catastrophes. The second was that organisms were designed especially for certain habitats and appeared on the earth in their present forms.

Early in the voyage, after having read the works of a noted geologist, Darwin began to change his ideas. He saw evidence that the earth was very old. In South America he witnessed an earthquake that lifted the land level several feet. He realized that mountains could be built by the action of earthquakes over millions of years. He found fossils of marine animals in high mountains, and realized that the rocks must have been lifted out of the ocean.

Darwin also studied animals and plants. On the Galapagos Islands he found animals that were like those of the South American continent, but not exactly alike. He realized that they must have come to the islands from the mainland, and then changed into new species. He also observed the animals and plants of South America, oceanic islands, and the Far East. He saw many examples that indicated that animals in similar environments did not always look exactly alike. For example, the emus of Australia and the rheas of South America are two distinct species, yet occupy the same kind of habitat. If animals were formed for a specific habitat, why would different species be found in similar habitats?

By the time Darwin returned to England, he was convinced that all living things arose by evolution. Over the next 20 years, he gathered evidence for his new theory. His masterful book was published in 1859.

The Galapagos Islands straddle the equator 950 km (600 mi.) west of South America. On his famous journey, Darwin saw unique life forms there, including marine lizards and birds called *flightless cormorants.* He also saw giant land tortoises, called *galapagos* in Spanish. The islands were named for these tortoises.

Darwin also observed 13 species of finches. The finches Darwin saw resembled their counterparts on the mainland in general appearance and behavior, but Darwin noticed that each species had a distinctive beak. Moreover, each type of beak was well suited for obtaining a certain kind of food. The finch in the left

photograph, for example, uses its large, heavy beak to break open seeds. The finch at the right has a small, sharp beak for hunting insects.

Darwin saw the finches as evidence of the process of evolution. He speculated that the different species evolved from a few mainland finches that had come to the islands. The beaks of some finches allowed them to feed more effec-

tively than others in their new environment. Those birds were more likely to survive and to reproduce successfully. Because their offspring would tend to have beaks like those of their parents, the finch populations slowly adapted on each island.

■ **Synthesizing Information** How does the variation in beak size and shape relate to the variety of finches found on the islands?

Darwin's Theory of Evolution by Natural Selection

Based on his observations and studies, Darwin developed a new theory of evolution. Darwin's ideas, though modified by new knowledge, form the cornerstone of modern evolutionary thought.

- *Variation exists within species.* Traits vary among individuals of the same species. For example, some gorillas have longer arms than others; some red-tailed hawks have sharper claws than other red-tailed hawks.
- *All organisms compete for limited natural resources.* Organisms compete for food and other necessities of life. These resources are limited. As a result, some organisms will get more of the resources; others will get less.
- *Organisms produce more offspring than can survive.* The number of young that parents can produce is greater than the resources available to support these individuals.

Biofact

Q: *Did other scientists of Darwin's time believe the earth was older than 6,000 years?*

A: Yes. Primary among them was Charles Lyell, a British geologist. Darwin read Lyell's book *Principles of Geology* aboard the *Beagle* and was profoundly influenced by its contention that the earth was millions of years old.

• *The environment selects organisms with beneficial traits.* Darwin believed that organisms with traits well suited to the environment survive and reproduce at a greater rate than organisms less suited to the environment. They thus pass desirable traits to their offspring. He called this process **natural selection** since the environment acts to preserve, or select, "fit" individuals. "Fitness" is measured by the number of fertile offspring produced. Some people call natural selection *survival of the fittest,* but "replacement by the most fit" is more accurate.

According to Darwin, a natural force such as bitter cold would favor animals with thick fur. Animals with thick fur would survive the cold temperatures and reproduce in greater numbers to pass on the trait of thick fur. Thick fur is an **adaptation,** an inherited trait that gives the organism an advantage in its particular environment.

16.3 The Origins of Variations

If natural selection is always weeding out the less fit, why is it that individuals in a species vary and do not all look alike? A key to the solution of the origins of variations came from the work of the German biologist August Weismann. Weismann showed that two kinds of variations exist. One is variation produced by the environment and the other is variation produced by changes in what biologists would later call *genes.* Weismann showed that variations caused by the environment—acquired traits—could not be passed to offspring. *Only genetic variations are passed on from generation to generation.*

Biologists now know that two fundamental sources of genetic variations exist in species. The first is *mutation,* a change in the chemical structure of a gene. The second source of genetic variation is *genetic recombination,* which occurs when an individual's genes are intermingled during meiosis. Mutation and genetic recombination provide variations acted upon by natural selection.

Figure 16–3. Genetic variation in coat color is exhibited by this litter of kittens.

Section Review

1. **Identifying Relationships** Compare Lamarck's theory of evolution with that of Darwin.
2. **Summarizing Ideas** Describe the process of natural selection.
3. **Inferring Conclusions** How did Darwin's observations of the Galapagos Islands finches influence his thinking?

Mechanisms of Evolution

The modern concept of evolution is broader than that first proposed by Darwin. Since the rediscovery of Mendel's ideas about genetics in the early 1900s, genetic principles have been added to Darwin's ideas to form the modern theory of evolution.

16.4 Species and Populations

Recall that a species is a group of similar individuals that have the capacity to produce fertile offspring. Stated simply, members of a species usually look alike and have offspring that can reproduce in nature. All redwood trees are members of the same species. All blue whales are members of the same species. You will learn more about species and the way in which living things are classified in Chapter 18.

Members of a species that live in the same area are members of a **population.** All the bluebells in a field, for example, are in the same population. All the rabbits in a forest also make up a population.

Evolution occurs when there is a change in the genetic makeup of a population. To understand how populations change, biologists study the kinds and number of genes in a population. This field of study is called **population genetics.** Population geneticists study a population's **gene pool**—that is, all the alleles of all the genes in all of the individuals in a population.

16.5 The Hardy-Weinberg Principle

Consider a population of wild fruit flies living on an island. If you could list all the alleles of all the genes in every fruit fly, you would know many facts about the population's gene pool. You would know, for example, the frequency of every allele in the population. Suppose you found that the allele for normal-sized wings occurred 750 times and the allele for undeveloped wings occurred 250 times. Since the wing-size gene has only two alleles, you could determine that the frequency—the percentage of occurrence expressed as a decimal—of the normal-wing allele is 0.75 and that of the undeveloped-wing allele is 0.25. In doing so you would have determined what biologists call the **gene frequency** of the wing-size alleles. Gene frequency is a measure of the relative occurrence of alleles in a population.

In 1908 a British mathematician named Godfrey Hardy and a German physician named Wilhelm Weinberg were independently studying gene frequencies in populations. Through their

Section Objectives

- *State* the main point of the Hardy-Weinberg principle.
- *List* the five ways in which genetic equilibrium may be disrupted.
- *Describe* the process of genetic drift.
- *Contrast* the three main types of natural selection.
- *Summarize* the effects of migration and isolation.

Figure 16–4. The purple lupines in the field shown above all belong to the same biological population.

studies Hardy and Weinberg arrived at the same conclusion, which came to be known as the **Hardy-Weinberg principle.** The Hardy-Weinberg principle states that the frequency of alleles in a population stays the same generation after generation unless it is altered by some external factor. In other words, the genetic makeup of a population will remain relatively stable unless something happens to make it change. This stability is called **genetic equilibrium,** also known as the *Hardy-Weinberg equilibrium.*

16.6 Changes in Genetic Equilibrium

A population in genetic equilibrium does not evolve. Genes determine the traits of a population. If the kinds of genes in a population never change, the traits of the population can never change, either. *For evolution to take place, something must upset the genetic equilibrium of a population.* In fact, evolution occurs when any of the following processes upset a population's genetic equilibrium: natural selection, migration, genetic drift, isolation, and mutation.

Natural Selection   Natural selection disrupts a population's genetic equilibrium by allowing fit individuals to survive and reproduce at a greater rate than less fit individuals. To see how natural selection works, reconsider the question of how giraffes acquired long necks. Imagine a population of an ancestral species of giraffe living on an African plain hundreds of thousands of years ago. Assume that variation in this species is such that neck length ranges from very short to very long. The numbers of individuals and the length of their necks are graphed in Figure 16–5. The graph of neck length versus number of individuals is shaped like a bell, and so is called a *bell curve.* Most individuals have average-length necks, but some individuals have very short necks and some have very long necks.

Assume that this population of ancestral giraffes has been at genetic equilibrium for centuries. Now what would happen if another species, such as leaf-eating deer, entered the area? These deer would be able to compete effectively with shorter-necked giraffes for leaves on the lower parts of trees. Soon the leaves would become scarce. The shorter-necked giraffes would be in danger of starvation because they are less fit to acquire food in this competitive environment. Their reproductive rates would be lower, and their genes would be slowly selected out of the gene pool. Longer-necked giraffes, however, would survive in greater numbers and thus have greater reproductive advantage. Over many years, the average neck length would increase.

Biofact

Q: *How quickly does the development of a species occur?*

A: It depends on the species and the environmental force. Some species evolve rapidly, others very slowly.

To simulate the process of natural selection, see page 267.

The shift is graphed in Figure 16–5. The new distribution is still a bell curve, but it has shifted to the right. After thousands of years of natural selection, modern giraffes exist.

Three fundamental kinds of natural selection exist. The example above is called **directional selection** because evolution has proceeded in the direction of longer necks. Figure 16–5 shows two other kinds: stabilizing and disruptive selection.

Stabilizing selection eliminates the extremes of a trait, causing a reduction of variation in species. For example, imagine a population of rabbits with varying leg lengths. In an environment with coyotes, rabbits with long legs are eliminated because they cannot crawl into small holes to escape coyotes. Rabbits with short legs are eliminated because they cannot run fast enough to evade coyotes. The result is a rabbit population with "average-length" legs. Variation has been reduced and the population has been stabilized.

Disruptive selection selects against the average and favors the extremes of a trait. Consider the size of acorns in a population of oak trees. Acorn sizes range from small to large. Suppose a species of acorn-eating squirrel now invades the oak forest. The squirrels do not eat small acorns, however, because they are too difficult to locate. The squirrels cannot eat large acorns because they are too large to carry. After many years, the average-sized acorns would be eliminated, but the small and large acorns would survive and germinate. The oak forest would soon have trees with two different sizes of acorns.

Reading Critically

Relating Ideas If giraffes had undergone stabilizing selection, what kind of necks would they have?

Figure 16–5. The graphs below illustrate the three main types of natural selection: directional selection (bottom left), stabilizing selection (top right), and disruptive selection (bottom right).

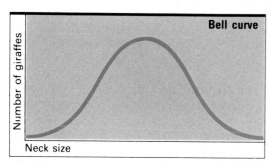

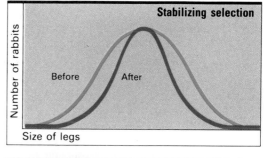

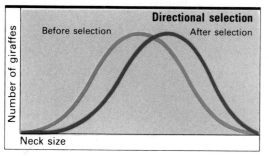

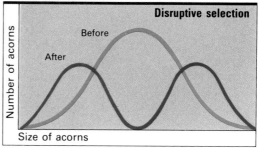

Spread of the Fire Ants

Red fire ants have been steadily increasing in number in the southern United States after these ants first appeared in Alabama in the 1940s. The ants probably arrived as "stowaways" on a cargo ship.

Red fire ants are more aggressive than native species, but like all 8,000 of the world's ant species, these ants originally lived in individual mounds, each of which had a single queen. Pest control agents could control the ants by killing the queen.

Since 1972, however, entomologists have seen a change in the red fire ants' behavior. The ants are now building multiple-queen colonies containing up to 500 egg-laying queens. These super-colonies consist of connected mounds that may stretch for hundreds of feet. The colonies contain as many as 8 million ants per acre—about 180 ants per square foot.

Scientists think that the lack of competition and predators in the ants' new environment may be res-

ponsible for the success of the red fire ant in the southern part of the United States. These factors, in addition to the development of the ants' ability to form multi-queen colonies, make red fire ants extremely difficult to control.

Migration   A population's genetic equilibrium may also be upset by **migration,** the movement of organisms into or out of a population. Organisms that leave a population take their genes out of the gene pool. Organisms that enter a population add their genes to the gene pool.

Consider a herd of caribou in northern Alaska. The herd is a population with a characteristic gene pool. Suppose another herd of caribou, one from northern Canada, migrates and becomes part of the Alaskan herd. The frequencies of genes will change because a whole new set of genes has been added from outside the population. The genetic equilibrium is thus disrupted. This is an example of *immigration*, the movement of new individuals into a population. Gene frequencies also change when individuals leave, a process called *emigration*.

Genetic Drift   A process called genetic drift can also change the genetic equilibrium in small populations. **Genetic drift** is the change in gene frequency of a very small population due to chance. Consider an isolated population of 15 long-horned beetles. Suppose one of these beetles is red and all the others are black. If random mating occurs, it is probable that the one red beetle will not mate and the genes for redness would not be transferred to offspring. The gene frequency would change. Genetic drift is thus a result of the laws of probability or chance.

Isolation The equilibrium of a gene pool can also be upset by isolation—the separation of populations into groups that no longer interact. *Geographic isolation* occurs when a physical barrier separates populations. Barriers can include rivers, mountains, and canyons. Geographic isolation may change a population's gene frequency because the gene frequency of one resulting population may be different from that of the combined group. Geographic isolation often results in the two populations being unable to interbreed. This phenomenon is called **genetic isolation.**

Isolation often results in the evolution of a new species. For example, fossil evidence indicates that the camel originated in the western United States. Scientists believe that the camel population spread north and south, crossing land bridges into both Asia and South America. The disappearance of the northern land bridge geographically isolated the Old World and American populations. Different environmental pressures acted on these two populations. Over millions of years, the modern camel evolved in the Old World, and the llama evolved in South America.

Mutation Mutations also upset a population's genetic equilibrium. Most mutations are harmful. An organism with a harmful mutation may be less fit than a normal organism. If the organism fails to reproduce, the mutant gene is removed from the gene pool. Some mutations, however, make an individual better adapted to its environment. An individual with such a mutation is more likely to live to reproductive age and pass the gene to its offspring. Therefore, the frequency of alleles in a population changes. Though most mutations do not have an immediate evolutionary effect, they provide a source of variation that can be influenced by natural selection.

Figure 16–6. The South American llama (top) and the Old-World camel (bottom) are examples of two species that evolved from a common ancestor as a result of genetic isolation.

Section Review

1. **Listing Ideas** What five processes upset genetic equilibrium?
2. **Summarizing Information** What are the three types of natural selection?
3. **Inferring Relationships** What are the evolutionary effects of isolation and migration?

> **Thinking Critically**

- *Explain* how divergent evolution occurs.
- *Define* the term *convergent evolution*.
- *Distinguish* between microevolution and macroevolution.

Reading Critically

Comprehending Ideas What factors cause divergent evolution?

Patterns of Evolution

Many of the processes that disrupt genetic equilibrium contribute to the general phenomenon of evolution. Evolution has produced many interesting similarities and differences in organisms. In some cases, organisms that are only distantly related resemble one another. In other cases, organisms that are closely related look very different.

16.7 Divergent Evolution

The process by which related organisms become less alike is called **divergent evolution.** Divergent evolution leads to **speciation**—the formation of a new species. The two new species at first are quite similar, but they may undergo divergent evolution if natural selection exerts a strong effect on one or both of the species. For example, consider the case of a group of brown bears that became geographically isolated in northern regions from the main group of bears. In time, the small group was genetically isolated and became a new species. Acted upon by natural selection, this group diverged into polar bears. These bears have many traits not found in their relatives. For example, their coats are white, and they have heads and necks modified for swimming. They diverged from their ancestors.

Divergent evolution also results in **adaptive radiation,** the process by which members of a species adapt to a variety of habitats. The finches Darwin saw on the Galapagos Islands are examples of adaptive radiation. A number of species of finches

Figure 16–7. The brown bear (left) differs from the arctic polar bear (right) as a result of divergent evolution. The polar bear's white coat is an adaptation to hunting sea mammals on ice floes.

exist on the islands. While each species is adapted to a different habitat, the finches share enough features to show that they evolved from a common ancestor. Adaptative radiation occurs when species with suitable adaptations move into a new habitat. There they encounter less competition and have greater reproductive success.

16.8 Convergent Evolution

The process by which distantly related organisms develop similar characteristics is called **convergent evolution.** This pattern of evolution occurs when different species share the same environment and are therefore subject to the same pressures.

For example, whales and dolphins were once land mammals that adapted to an aquatic environment. As a result, their front limbs evolved into flippers for swimming. Today, the limbs of whales and dolphins resemble those of fish because they were shaped by the same environment. Yet the two groups of organisms—marine mammals and fish—are not closely related. If two organisms possess similar-looking organs, this does not necessarily mean that they are closely related. It indicates only that they were subject to the same kinds of environmental pressures that led to the formation of similar structures.

Convergent evolution can often lead to cases of **mimicry**—the evolution of one organism so it comes to resemble another. Mimicry often occurs in cases where one species is poisonous or distasteful. A nonpoisonous insect, for example, that looks like

Figure 16–8. The similarities of dolphins (top left), salmon (top right), and whales (bottom) are the result of convergent evolution. The two species of mammals and the fish all share a marine environment.

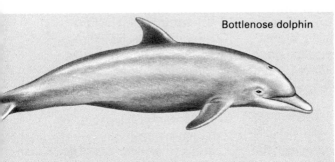
Bottlenose dolphin

Atlantic salmon

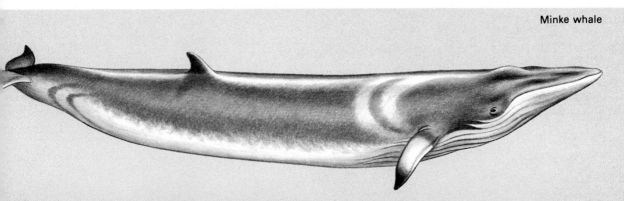
Minke whale

THINKING ABOUT BIOLOGY: Evolutionary Theory Today

Scientists know that environmental conditions cause changes in the gene pool of a population over successive generations, a process called **microevolution**. This slow, gradual change that eventually leads to the formation of a new group is called *gradualism.* Scientists think that the changes produced by microevolution can lead to changes on a grand scale—called **macroevolution**—such as the appearance of feathers. When influenced by natural selection and changes in the environment, microevolution can result in new trends in the evolution of a species, or sudden mass extinction. Fossils present some evidence about how major groups evolved. For

example, *Archaeopteryx,* the animal in the picture, shows how birds might have arisen. *Archaeopteryx* lived 140 million years ago and shows characteristics of two different groups: the heavy skeleton and claws of a reptile and the feathers of a bird, which provides evidence that birds evolved from reptiles.

However, the fossil record often shows that species appeared rather suddenly. This has led some scientists to propose a view called *punctuated equilibrium*—new

species evolve rather rapidly, then undergo a long period of relative stability. The rate of evolution may differ depending on the species and the conditions that the environment presents.

Some scientists suggest that new species sometimes evolve on the edges of a larger group's territory, then adapt quickly and replace the older group. Others think that whole groups might have been extinguished by the effects of meteors and other cataclysmic events. Still others suggest that if two groups exist at once, only the one that is more fit will survive.

■ **Inferring Conclusions**
How does fossil evidence support the process of macroevolution?

a poisonous insect will appear to predators to be poisonous, and hence will be left alone. Sometimes animals evolve to look like plants, and in doing so blend into their surroundings. These animals have a *selective advantage* in being able to avoid being eaten because they are well hidden.

Section Review

1. **Contrasting Ideas**   Contrast convergent and divergent evolution.
2. **Inferring Relationships**   What conditions might result in very rapid evolution?

Thinking Critically

INVESTIGATION 16:
How Does Antibiotic Concentration Affect Bacterial Growth?

Objectives
- To *simulate* the process of evolution
- To *evaluate* the effect of antibiotic concentration on bacteria

Materials
sterile petri plates containing nutrient agar, cotton swab, disinfectant, inoculating loop, stock culture of *Escherichia coli,* forceps, disks with varying dilutions of antibiotic, incubator, Bunsen burner, marking pencil

Prelab Preparation
1. Name the source of variations in a population. Describe the role of the environment in natural selection.
2. Discuss the problem that is the title of this Investigation with your partner and state your hypothesis.
3. Identify the independent and dependent variables suggested by your hypothesis.

Inquiry: Experimentation
CAUTION: **Although the bacteria used in this Investigation are not pathogenic, all bacteria may become dangerous. Use care and follow your teacher's instructions for proper handling and disposal of bacteria.**

4. Mark the bottom of the petri dish as shown in the illustration.

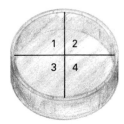

5. CAUTION: **Put on safety goggles, a laboratory apron, and rubber gloves.** Moisten a sterile cotton swab with *E. coli* culture. Inoculate the agar by gently rubbing the swab over the entire surface. Place the used swab into disinfectant.

6. Use sterile forceps to place the disk containing the weakest concentration of diluted antibiotic into quadrant 1. Place disks with other antibiotic concentrations in quadrants 2 and 3 and cover the dish. *Why is no disk placed in quadrant 4?*
7. Use tape to seal the dish. Invert the dish and incubate it for 24 hours at 37°C.
8. Do not remove the cover after incubation. *What signs of bacterial growth can be observed in each quadrant?*
9. Look for a clear area called a *zone of inhibition* around any of the disks. *What does this clear area indicate?*
10. Check each zone of inhibition for bacterial growth very near the disk. *What is the antibiotic concentration of each disk where such a colony is found? Why can a bacteria colony grow in this zone?*
11. Mark a fresh petri dish as you did before.
12. CAUTION: **Put on safety goggles, a laboratory apron, and rubber gloves.** Sterilize an inoculating loop in the flame of a Bunsen burner. Transfer bacteria from a zone of inhibition to the fresh agar plate. Gently spread the bacteria over the surface and sterilize the inoculating loop. Mark the petri dish with the letter of the quadrant from which bacteria were taken.
13. Use sterile forceps to place disks of differing antibiotic concentrations in each quadrant. Identify the origin of the bacteria transferred to the plate. Repeat steps 6 through 10. Record your observations.
14. Follow your teacher's instructions for the disposal of your petri dishes.

Analysis
1. **Analyzing Data** Explain whether or not your data support your hypothesis.
2. **Identifying Relationships** Would it be correct to say that the bacteria developed resistance to the antibiotic after one generation? Explain.
3. **Identifying Relationships** How does this Investigation simulate the process of natural selection?

Chapter 16 Review

Summary

In 1809, Jean Baptiste de Lamarck suggested that organisms acquire traits, maintain them with use, and transmit them to their offspring.

In 1859 Charles Darwin presented the ideas that are the basis of modern evolutionary theory. According to this theory, variations exist in species. Those members with variations suited to the environments pass their traits on to their offspring; those less suited are less likely to reproduce successfully. Darwin called this process natural selection.

The Hardy-Weinberg principle, presented in 1908, states that gene frequencies do not change unless acted upon by something external. The processes that disrupt genetic equilibrium are natural selection, migration, isolation, genetic drift, and mutation.

Together, these forces of evolution operate in two major patterns. Through divergent evolution, related organisms become less alike. Through convergent evolution, distantly related organisms develop similar traits.

BioTerms

adaptation (258)
adaptive
    radiation (264)
convergent
    evolution (265)
directional
    selection (261)
disruptive
    selection (261)
divergent
    evolution (264)

gene frequency (259)
gene pool (259)
genetic drift (262)
genetic
    equilibrium (260)
genetic isolation (263)
Hardy-Weinberg
    Principle (260)
macroevolution (266)
microevolution (266)
migration (262)

mimicry (265)
natural
    selection (258)
population (259)
population

genetics (259)
speciation (264)
species (255)
stabilizing
    selection (261)

For each pair of terms, explain the differences in their meanings.

1. convergent evolution, divergent evolution
2. genetic drift, genetic equilibrium
3. microevolution, macroevolution

BioQuiz   (Write all answers on a separate sheet of paper.)

Completion

1. _____ are beneficial inherited traits.
2. A _____ is a biological group whose members resemble one another and have the capacity to produce fertile offspring.
3. The 13 species of finches Darwin found on the Galapagos Islands supported his hypothesis that organisms adapt to their_____ .
4. The measure of the relative occurrence of alleles in a population is _____ .
5. The movement of organisms into or out of a population is _____ .

Multiple Choice

6. Birds and bats illustrate the pattern of   a) macroevolution.   b) microevolution.   c) divergent evolution.   d) convergent evolution.
7. The change in gene frequency of a very small population due to chance is called a) migration.   b) genetic drift.   c) genetic equilibrium.   d) genetic isolation.
8. All squirrels in a forest form a a) genus.   b) species.   c) gene pool.   d) population.

9. The evolution of one species so it resembles another species is called a) adaptive radiation. b) speciation. c) mimicry. d) mutation.
10. The evolution of long necks in giraffes is an example of a) stabilizing selection. b) genetic drift. c) directional selection. d) All choices are correct.
11. Evolution occurs when there is a change in the genetic makeup of a) a population. b) an individual. c) an adaptation. d) the stabilizing selection.
12. The condition in which selection favors the extremes of a certain trait is _____ selection. a) disruptive b) directional c) stabilizing d) All are correct.
13. Adaptive radiation is a form of a) convergent evolution. b) disruptive selection. c) divergent evolution. d) stabilizing selection.

14. The frequency of alleles in a population stays the same when the population is in a a) genetic equilibrium. b) genetic drift. c) microevolution. d) macroevolution.
15. The two fundamental sources of genetic variation are mutation and a) adaptation. b) genetic drift. c) genetic equilibrium. d) genetic recombination.

Writing Critically

16. How does stabilizing selection work?
17. What is geographical isolation?
18. What role does the environment play in natural selection?
19. Why is it impossible for convergent evolution to result in identical organisms?
20. How can the two fundamental sources of genetic variation be described?

Application/Critical Thinking

1. **Inferring Conclusions** The shark has changed so little over thousands of years that it is referred to as a living fossil. What type of selection is acting on sharks?
2. **Synthesizing Information** According to the Hardy-Weinberg principle, all possible genotypes in a population can be represented by the formula $p^2 + 2pq + q^2 = 1$. Do library research to learn how this formula works. Then use it to answer the following questions. What are the frequencies of the dominant and recessive alleles in a population of 100 cattle, of which 36 have the recessive trait? How many of the cattle are heterozygous? If natural selection eliminated all the cattle with the recessive phenotype, what would the gene frequencies be in the next generation?

Cross-Discipline Connection

Biology and Reading   Report orally or in writing on Charles Darwin's theory after reading his book *On the Origin of Species*. The book is available in most school and public libraries.

Discovery Through Reading

Read the article "Galapagos Wildlife Under Pressure," *National Geographic* (January 1988): 122–145. This beautifully illustrated article describes the continuing process of evolution evident in the wildlife on the Galapagos Islands. Where are the Galapagos Islands? Name two introduced predators that threaten the existence of the Galapagos tortoises. Identify the six species of mammals that are native to the islands.

Human Evolution

Outline

An archaeologist clears an ancient human burial site

Focus

Evidence suggests that the order Primates to which humans belong began to evolve in the Cenozoic era, which began about 65 million years ago. Evidence also shows that the process of evolution eventually led to the divergence of human ancestors within the last 5 to 10 million years. Clues to human beginnings exist as partial fossils of a few hundred individuals and other evidence, such as 3.75 million-year-old footprints in East Africa.

- *Why might ancient human burial sites provide clues to how early humans lived?*

- *In what ways might human footprints be preserved from prehistoric times?*

Early Human Evolution

One of the most fascinating areas in paleontology is the history of the **hominids**—that is, human beings and their ancestors. Humans are among the more than 200 living species that belong to the order Primates. Evidence shows that primates began to evolve early in the Cenozoic era, which began about 65 million years ago. Eventually, the ancestors of *Homo sapiens* branched off from the ancestors of living chimpanzees and gorillas, probably between 10 million and 5 million years ago.

17.1 *Australopithecus afarensis*

Most scientists agree that the oldest known hominid species is *Australopithecus afarensis*. **Australopithecus** is a genus of primitive hominid whose name means "southern ape." The first *A. afarensis* fossils were discovered in Ethiopia in 1973 by American anthropologist Donald Johanson. Other *A. afarensis* fossils, determined to be about 3.75 million years old, were later found in Tanzania. The most important record of this species is a 3 million-year-old skeleton of an erect-walking female, which Johanson nicknamed Lucy.

Lucy's skeleton reveals a combination of apelike and human characteristics. She stood about 1 m (3.5 ft.) tall and weighed about 25 kg (55 lb.). She had long arms, a thrusting jaw, receding forehead, and no chin. Her brain was only slightly larger than that of apes living today, and there is no evidence that her species used tools. Lucy's pelvis and leg bones, however, indicate that she was **bipedal**—that is, she walked on two legs.

Further evidence that *A. afarensis* was bipedal was found by Mary Leakey, member of a famous family of British anthropologists. She discovered fossil footprints that were made by an erect-walking hominid. Since the footprints are dated at 3.75 million years old, the same age as the oldest *A. afarensis* fossils, most scientists agree that they were made by *A. afarensis*.

Johanson and his associate Timothy White propose that *A. afarensis* is the earliest ancestor of human beings. Other scientists disagree. Mary Leakey and her son Richard, for example, contend that *A. afarensis* was part of a line of *Australopithecus* that later became extinct.

Though unanswered questions about early human ancestors remain, the discovery of *A. afarensis* has clarified an important point. The brain size of early hominids did not increase until after they developed the ability to stand upright. This is known because *A. afarensis* walked bipedally and yet had a relatively small brain.

Section Objectives

- *Explain* the significance of *Australopithecus afarensis*.
- *Contrast Australopithecus africanus* and *Australopithecus robustus*.
- *Explain* why *Homo habilis* is considered the first representative of the genus *Homo*.
- *Explain* the significance of *Homo erectus*.

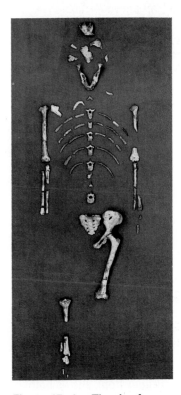

Figure 17–1. The *A. afarensis* skeleton called Lucy represents the oldest known hominid. The pelvis shape indicates a female.

17.2 Later Species of *Australopithecus*

According to the existing fossil record, two other species of *Australopithecus* appeared thousands of years after *A. afarensis*. Both species lived in Africa. The first one discovered was *Australopithecus africanus*, which lived between 3 million and 2.5 million years ago. The first *A. africanus* fossil found was the skull of a five-year-old child. Raymond Dart, a South African anthropologist, studied the skull in 1924. Dart called the fossil "the *Taung baby*," named after the South African cave in which it was discovered.

Based on the Taung skull and other fossils, scientists have found that *A. africanus* had a rounded skull and a larger brain capacity than *A. afarensis*. In *A. africanus*, the cranial capacity, or the space available for the brain, averaged about 500 cm³ (31 cu. in.). The cranial capacity of modern human beings is 1,000 to 2,000 cm³ (61 to 122 cu. in.).

Fossils also indicate that *A. africanus* stood about 1.5 m (5 ft.) tall and weighed about 35 to 45 kg (77 to 99 lb.). *A. africanus* also walked on two legs and had the broad, flat thumb that is common to human beings. The back teeth had thick enamel for grinding, and the small front teeth were used for slicing. Animal bones found near the fossil remains of *A. africanus* indicate that the early hominids occasionally ate meat. There is no evidence, however, that they hunted. The meat may have been scavenged from the carcasses of animals killed by carnivores.

A third species of *Australopithecus*—*A. robustus*—lived later, about 2.2 million to 1.4 million years ago. *A. robustus* was larger than *A. africanus*. Individuals of this species weighed 70 kg (154 lb.) or more and had large back teeth set in thick jaws. Evidence leads most scientists to agree that *A. robustus* was not in the line that was ancestral to modern humans. Since *A. robustus* lived at the same time as the earliest human beings, competition between the two groups may have led to the extinction of *A. robustus*.

17.3 *Homo habilis*

Beginning in the early 1960s, the Leakey family found fossils in East Africa of a species they named *Homo habilis*. The fossils are the first representatives of *Homo*, the genus to which our own species belongs. *Homo habilis* lived between 2.2 million and 1.5 million years ago.

Like *Australopithecus africanus* before it, *Homo habilis* probably stood no taller than 1.5 m (5 ft.). However, certain

Figure 17–2. The skull of *A. africanus* (top), shows both human and nonhuman primate characteristics. The drawing (bottom) of the erect figure is based on the skull and other fossils.

characteristics set *Homo habilis* apart from earlier hominids and justify its classification in the genus *Homo*. First, its brain size averaged 650 cm³ (40 cu. in.), a substantial increase over the cranial capacities of members of the genus *Australopithecus*. Second, the facial structure of *Homo habilis* was different from previous hominids. Its face did not project as much as that of *Australopithecus*, and its jaws were not as large.

Homo habilis was different from *Australopithecus* and similar to later members of the genus *Homo* in a third important respect. *Homo habilis* individuals probably made the first stone tools. In fact, the Leakeys chose the name *Homo habilis* because it means "handy-human." Simple implements, probably used for scraping and chopping, have been found along with the fossil remains. Numerous bones of game animals have also been found, indicating that the species ate meat and may have hunted.

Fossils are grouped into species such as Homo habilis *on the basis of similarities among individuals. To investigate differences among members of the same species, see page 279.*

Reading Critically

Analyzing Relationships
Why did the Leakeys name their fossil "handy human"?

THINKING ABOUT BIOLOGY: Ape or Human?

How can a paleontologist tell an ape from a human when only a skull is available? Comparing the skull of a modern human with that of an ape reveals some of the differences.

One important difference is the location of the *foramen magnum,* the hole in the skull through which the spinal cord passes. As you see in the drawing, the foramen magnum is located near the rear of the ape's skull. In human beings, however, the foramen magnum is located at the bottom of the skull and the head sits atop the spinal column.

The angle at which the spinal cord enters the skull is one clue. The angle of the face in relation to the

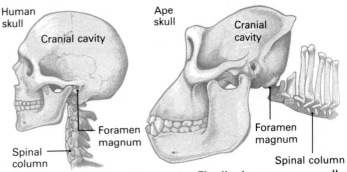

spine is another. In apes, the face slopes outward from the skull. In humans, however, the face does not angle outwards. Instead, it is vertical and parallels the spinal column, as you see in the drawing.

A third major clue is the size of the cranial cavity, the space inside the skull that houses the brain. The cranial cavity of humans is about three times larger.

Finally, humans generally have a higher, vertical forehead in place of the short, slanting one found in apes. Furthermore, the thick ridges above the eyes in apes have virtually disappeared in present-day humans.

■ **Relating Ideas** How are differences in posture between apes and humans related to the structure of the skull?

17.4 *Homo erectus*

The position of *Homo erectus* in human evolution is clear: *Homo erectus* was almost certainly ancestral to our own species, *Homo sapiens*. The species *Homo erectus* appeared about 1.5 million years ago and survived until about 500,000 years ago. It probably originated in Africa and later migrated to Asia and Europe. *Homo erectus* means "upright human." The species was named before earlier hominids were discovered. At the time, scientists did not know that *Homo erectus* was not the first hominid species to walk upright.

The skeleton of a 12-year-old male *Homo erectus* found in East Africa suggests that some adult *Homo erectus* individuals could have been 1.8 m (6 ft.) tall. The bones of *Homo erectus* individuals were thicker and heavier than those of modern human beings. The skull had a forehead that sloped backward and massive ridges above the eyes. *Homo erectus* teeth were similar to modern human teeth, though slightly larger. The brain capacity of *Homo erectus* was 700 to 1,200 cm^3 (43 to 73 cu. in.), which approaches that of modern human beings.

The larger-brained *Homo erectus* made a variety of tools. At first this species used simple stone tools to prepare food and fashion other implements. Eventually they made large hand axes. Hand axes were probably used for many purposes, including digging up edible roots and cutting the meat of game animals.

Judging by the bones of bears, rhinoceroses, and elephants found at their campsites, *Homo erectus* groups hunted large game. Evidence exists that *Homo erectus* groups ran large animals over cliffs. Then these early humans could cut the meat with their stone tools.

Homo erectus was the first hominid species known to use fire. Hearth fires probably provided warmth in cold climates and kept predators away at night. Charred bones at *Homo erectus* campsites indicate that they also used fires to cook meat.

Figure 17–3. The skull of *Homo erectus* above (top) was found in Kenya. The drawing (bottom) shows the sloping forehead and heavy brow ridges of the species.

Thinking Critically

Section Review

1. **Summarizing Ideas** Describe the hypothesis of Johanson and White regarding *A. afarensis*.
2. **Contrasting Ideas** What were the differences between *A. africanus* and *A. robustus*?
3. **Contrasting Ideas** Name three ways in which *Homo habilis* was different from previous hominids.
4. **Drawing Conclusions** What conclusion can be drawn about *Homo erectus* social organization from the evidence that they hunted large animals?

Modern Human Evolution

Homo sapiens, which means "wise human," is the species in which Neandertals and modern humans are classified. Among the earliest *Homo sapiens* fossils are those from Swanscombe, England, and Steinheim, Germany. Anthropologists have determined that these fossils are between 400,000 and 200,000 years old. Since the appearance of *Homo sapiens,* the history of the hominids has been one of few anatomical changes, but many cultural innovations.

17.5 The Neandertals

In 1856, human bones were found in a cave in the Neander Valley in Germany. These fossils and those of similar people became known as **Neandertals.** These humans lived in Europe and Asia between 35,000 and 130,000 years ago, during the Ice Age. Most scientists consider Neandertals to be members of our own species and classify them as *Homo sapiens neandertalensis.*

Neandertals were stocky and had relatively short limbs and large trunks. They stood about 1.5 m (5 ft.) tall. They had large, protruding faces and heavy ridges above the eyes. Their brain capacities averaged slightly greater than those of contemporary human beings.

Neandertals were more culturally advanced than their predecessors. They made more complex stone tools and shelters. For example, one Neandertal group built a shelter of mammoth bones and animal hides that measured 540 cm (18 ft.) across. The remains of the shelter were found at a site in what is now the Soviet Union. Neandertals were also the first to bury their dead. Evidence near burial sites suggests that group ceremonies may have been part of Neandertal life.

Section Objectives

- *Describe* the physical and cultural characteristics of the Neandertals.
- *Compare* the Neandertals and anatomically modern humans.
- *Summarize* one hypothesis for the cause of the agricultural revolution.

Reading Critically

Comparing Information
How does the illustration of the Neandertal below differ from the drawing of the *Homo erectus* on the opposite page?

Figure 17–4. The Neandertal skull (below left) was excavated at La Ferrassie in France. The drawing (below right) shows that Neandertals were robust, stocky people.

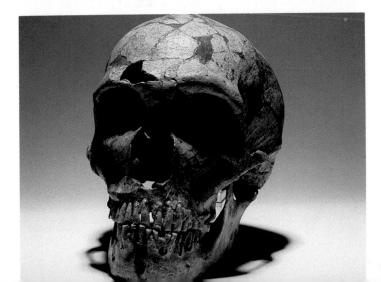

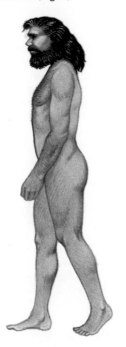

Figure 17–5. *Homo sapiens sapiens* produced the earliest known cave paintings. These often depicted animals of the hunt, such as the bison and goat above. Below is a drawing of how the first modern humans might have looked (left), based on fossils such as the skull (right).

17.6 *Homo sapiens sapiens*

Anatomically modern humans, *Homo sapiens sapiens*, emerged before the disappearance of the Neandertals. Fossil evidence for the appearance of *Homo sapiens sapiens* was first found in 1868 by French railroad workers. It consisted of five skeletons found at the rear of the Cro-Magnon Cave near Les Eyzies, France. Because of the location of the discovery, early modern humans are sometimes called Cro-Magnons.

Fossils show that in physical terms, early *Homo sapiens sapiens* were identical to contemporary humans. They had large brains; small, even teeth; and rounded skulls. They also had high foreheads. Their chins protruded in much the same way as those of contemporary humans.

Evidence suggests that these early modern *Homo sapiens* lived in groups of 30 to 100 individuals and developed varied and complex cultures. Their cultures included large-scale cooperative hunting, art, and shared rituals. They made elaborate tools and weapons. The sites of many well-established camps have been discovered. Engravings and cave paintings have also been found at these sites.

Early *Homo sapiens sapiens* were efficient hunters who had highly developed social structures. The Neandertals disappeared after *Homo sapiens sapiens* came into being, perhaps as a result of competition between the two groups.

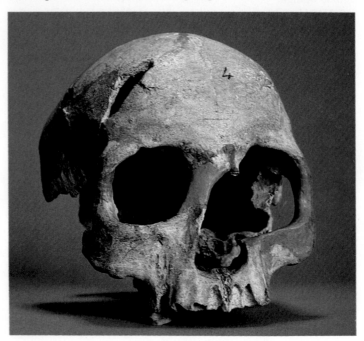

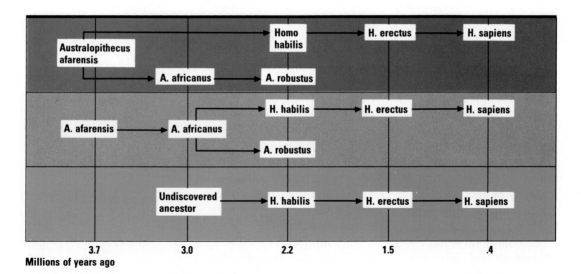

| | 3.7 | 3.0 | 2.2 | 1.5 | .4 |

Millions of years ago

17.7 The Agricultural Revolution

Until about 11,000 years ago, all people practiced a way of life called *hunting and gathering*. Hunter-gatherers subsist on hunting, fishing, and gathering of wild vegetable food. With the beginning of agriculture, most human societies gave up a way of life that their ancestors had followed for millions of years.

What caused such a widespread change from the hunting-gathering way of life? According to one explanation, the world climate began to grow warmer about 15,000 years ago and the glaciers made their final retreat. The grasslands were replaced by forests. The level of the sea rose, and much of the coastal plain disappeared.

Some scientists believe that these changes significantly reduced populations of mammoths, bears, and other large animals that were the major source of food for early human beings. As hunting became difficult, human groups turned to agriculture to maintain their food supplies.

The settled agricultural life caused widespread social changes. Because people no longer had to be on the move constantly hunting and gathering, they were able to set up more complex economic systems than they had before. A constant and abundant food supply supported an increasing population. As the new social systems developed, they accommodated more people than could a hunting society.

As a consequence of the agricultural revolution, the size of the human population began a steady increase that eventually became an explosion. Scientists estimate that 25,000 years ago the human population numbered 3 million. By 1650, 500

Figure 17–6. The illustration above shows three of the possible lines of human evolution that have been proposed by various scientists.

Biofact

Q: *Where did agriculture begin?*

A: The earliest evidence of farming has been found in the Middle East, in the modern countries of Turkey, Iraq, and Iran. Scientists think that the first crops were wheat and barley.

Early Diets

Evidence suggests that early humans probably consumed more cholesterol than most Americans do. Early hunters and gatherers had available to them a variety of wild game. These animals, most likely, supplied much of their diet. Since animal fat is high in cholesterol and saturated fats, ancient diets probably contained these lipids. However, even though their intake of fat was high, the percentage of protein that early humans consumed was much higher when compared with the diet of humans who are alive today.

The fruits and vegetables that hunters and gatherers ate provided them with an abundance of vitamins and minerals. These plants contributed a high level of nonnutrient fiber to the diet. Early humans had far less sugar in their diet than is consumed by the average American today. Instead, early diets were higher in bulk.

Early humans were undoubtedly familiar with wild grains and lived in areas where these grains were available. However, for grains to become a substantial part of any diet, they must be collected, threshed from the stalks on which they grow, stored, and processed. Because grains require so much work, early humans probably preferred animal meat and plants other than grains in

their diet, even when wild grains were abundant around them. Today's humans eat more grains than their ancestors. However, overall, the hunter and gatherer's diet probably provided five to ten times the level of nonnutrient fiber as contemporary diets. This fiber came from the fruits and vegetables that gatherers consumed.

million people lived on the Earth. Today, the human species numbers about 5 billion. In terms of numbers, *Homo sapiens* has been highly successful. Whether or not *Homo sapiens* will surpass the one-million-year span of *Homo erectus*, a primitive ancestor, remains a question. Only the passing of time will supply the answer.

Section Review

1. **Summarizing Ideas**   Describe the size and appearance of Neandertals.
2. **Comparing Ideas**   In what ways were anatomically modern humans more advanced than the Neandertals?

Thinking Critically

3. **Inferring Relationships**   How could the agricultural revolution have caused an increase in the human population?

INVESTIGATION 17:
How Are Variations Distributed Through a Population?

Objectives
- To *measure* the frequency of certain variations in a group
- To *determine* the pattern of distribution of certain variations in a group

Materials
metric ruler or tape measure, calculator

Prelab Preparation
1. Explain the relationship between natural selection and variation.
2. List human characteristics that show variation. Describe the variations associated with each trait.
3. Make a table for recording your height, the length of your left index finger, and the length of your left forearm from the wrist to the elbow.

Inquiry: Exploration
4. Work with your laboratory partner to make your measurements. Record your measurements in centimeters.
5. Pool your data from step 4 with the others in your group. For each characteristic list the measurements in descending order. Make a bar graph for each trait similar to the one shown.

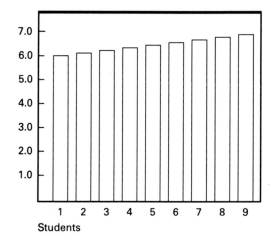

Students

6. Use the calculator and the example below to find the average height for the members of your group.
   a. Enter the data for height for each student in your group:
   152.4 ⊞ 153.6 ⊞ 161.2 ⊞ 170.0 ⊞ 180.9 ⊟ 818.1 ►Total
   b. Divide the total that you obtained in step 6a by the number of students in your group:
   818.1 ⊟ 5 ⊟ 163.62 ►Average height (cm)
7. Use the calculator to find the group averages for finger length and for forearm length.
8. Use the bar graph that represents height of students to draw a line representing the average height of students. *How many students are above average or below the group average?*
9. Draw lines on the bar graph that shows finger length and on the bar graph that shows forearm length to represent the group averages. *How many students are above or below the group average for each of these measurements?*

Analysis
1. **Summarizing Data** Describe the data for each trait.
2. **Analyzing Data** What similarities and differences do you observe in all the graphs?
3. **Making Inferences** How might you account for variation in the measurements?
4. **Making Inferences** The Pygmies are nomadic hunters and gatherers in equatorial Africa. The average adult male height is 1.5 m. Although variation exists in this population, the average height has remained the same for hundreds of years. Explain why this is true.

Chapter 17 Review

Summary

Modern human beings and their ancestors are called hominids. The earliest known hominid is *Australopithecus afarensis*, determined to be about 3.75 million years old. *A. afarensis* stood upright. The discovery of *A. afarensis* fossils show hominid brain size did not increase until after they walked bipedally. Two other bipedal species of *Australopithecus*, *A. africanus* and *A. robustus*, appeared later than *A. afarensis*.

Homo habilis, the earliest known member of the genus *Homo*, appeared about 2.2 million years ago and was the first species known to make tools. *Homo erectus* appeared about 1.5 million years ago and survived for about 1 million years. This hominid had a brain capacity almost as large as modern humans, hunted game in groups, and used fire.

Neandertals and modern humans are classified as *Homo sapiens*. The Neandertals lived between 130,000 and 35,000 years ago. They were the first hominids to bury their dead and leave evidence of group rituals. Neandertals disappeared after anatomically modern humans appeared.

About 11,000 years ago, humans began to farm and to domesticate animals. As a result, human populations began to grow rapidly.

BioTerms

Australopithecus (271)
bipedal (271)
hominid (271)
Homo erectus (274)
Homo habilis (272)
Homo sapiens (275)
Neandertal (275)

For each pair of terms, explain the differences in their meanings.

1. *Homo erectus*, *Homo sapiens*
2. *Australopithecus*, *Homo habilis*

BioQuiz   (Write all answers on a separate sheet of paper.)

Completion

1. The oldest known hominid species is _____ .
2. Lucy's skeleton indicates that early hominids developed _____ before they developed large brains.
3. Two species of the genus *Australopithecus* that appeared later than *Australopithecus afarensis* are *Australopithecus africanus* and _____ .
4. _____ were Ice-Age hominids who had cranial capacities that averaged slightly greater than modern humans.
5. An era of time that began about 65 million years ago and in which primates began to evolve is the _____ .

Multiple Choice

6. The earliest known cave paintings were produced by   a) Neandertals.
   b) *Homo sapiens sapiens*.   c) *Homo habilis*.   d) *Australopithecus*.
7. The first hominids known to bury their dead were   a) *Homo erectus*.
   b) Neandertals.   c) *A. africanus*.
   d) *Homo habilis*.
8. Which hominid belongs to the same species as modern humans?   a) *Homo erectus*   b) Neandertal   c) *Australopithecus robustus*   d) *Homo habilis*
9. The _____ is a hole in the skull through which the spinal cord passes.
   a) foramen magnum   b) bipedal

c) cranial capacity   d) pelvis
10. What is the age in millions of years of the earliest hominid fosil?
    a) 17   b) 3.75 c) 12   d) 1.5
11. Paleontologists can tell an ape skull from a human skull by the size of the
    a) foreman magnum.   b) spinal cord.
    c) cranial cavity.   d) teeth.
12. The first hominid to make and use fire was   a) Neandertal.   b) *Homo habilis.*
    c) *Homo erectus.*   d) *Australopithecus.*
13. The size of the human population began a steady increase due to   a) the Ice Age.
    b) the controlled use of fire.   c) the agricultural revolution.   d) interbreeding.
14. The oldest known hominid is thought to be   a) Neandertal.   b) *A. africanus.*
    c) *Homo habilis.*   d) *A. afarensis.*

15. The cranial capacity of modern humans is
    a) 1,000 to 2,000 cm^3.   b) 500 to 1,000 cm^3.   c) 500 cm^3.   d) 700 to 1,200 cm^3.

Writing Critically

16. According to Johanson and the Leakeys, what evolutionary role does *A. afarensis* play?
17. Why do scientists consider *H. erectus* an ancient human?
18. How are Neandertals and *Homo sapiens sapiens* different from each other?
19. What is the importance of the agricultural revolution?
20. What evidence leads you to conclude that *Homo erectus* lived after *Homo habilis?*

Application/Critical Thinking

1. **Summarizing Information** Assemble a bulletin board comparing Neandertals and anatomically modern humans, including drawings or photographs of their tools, clothing, and art.
2. **Analyzing Information** In 1912 a British paleontologist and student of early humans announced the discovery of an early human fossil in Britain. This fossil, called *Piltdown Man,* was later found to be a fake. How was the hoax detected?
3. **Synthesizing Conclusions** Human beings are the result of millions of years of evolution and have characteristics that make them fit to live in many different environments. Suggest how each of the following characteristics helps humans cope with their environments: a fully opposable thumb, bipedalism, a large brain, and language.

Cross-Discipline Connection

Biology and Geography Use library references to mark on a world map the locations of primate fossil finds. Note the person who found the fossil and the date of discovery. Note the countries in which most of these fossils were found. Present your findings to the class.

Discovery Through Reading

The article "The Search for Modern Humans," *National Geographic* (October 1988): 438–481, focuses on archaeologists' continuing search for clues about the emergence of *Homo sapiens.* Where did modern humans evolve?

The article "Neandertals Get an Evolutionary Face-Lift," *Science News* (April 15, 1989): 229, discusses the history of Neandertals. What new evidence suggests that Neandertals are closely related to modern humans?

Mapping Ancient Climates

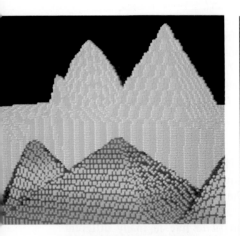

Computer-generated map of the topography of a climate using fractal geometry

Traces of ancient human settlements have been found in the Sahara. How could people have survived in such a dry, barren place? The answer is that the climate of the Sahara, now hot and arid, was once far more hospitable. Over time, the climate of a region changes. As a result of scientific advances, the nature of these changes in past climates can be studied in detail.

The prevailing weather patterns result from complex interactions of the atmosphere with the Earth's oceans, ice cover, and land masses. Scientists called *paleoclimatologists* study the climates of the Earth's past. In many cases, they can provide a description of the climate of a particular place at a particular time in history, such as the ancient climate of the Sahara.

One major source of information about ancient climates lies in layers of sediment deep beneath the floors of oceans and lakes. By examining the size and composition of these layers with *magnetic resonance imaging* (MRI), scientists can determine the surface conditions that existed on the continents thousands of years ago. The intensity of the winds that blew over

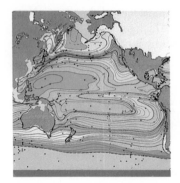
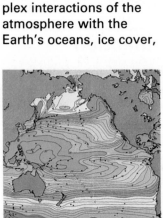

Computer-generated maps of sea surface temperature from 18,000 years ago (left) and from the present (right)

Microfossils provide clues to the climatic conditions under which the organisms that produced them must have lived.

once arid lands, for instance, can be determined from the size of the dust particles found in the sediment.

Another method scientists use to determine ancient climates is fractal geometry. Using fractal geometry, scientists can create computer-generated maps of the irregular shapes and fragmented patterns that occur in nature. Mountain ranges, cloud formations, and coastlines have all been drawn in great detail. What is more astounding, however, is that fractal geometry allows scientists to make mathematical calculations of processes such as the turbulent flow of air or fluids, the spread of a plant species over a

region, or the movements of a lightning bolt, and then show these processes as three-dimensional images.

To create a three-dimensional fractal image of a landscape, the researcher assigns numbers between whole numbers to the various features in the landscape. These numbers indicate the fractal dimensions and the geometric shapes of those features. The computer then interprets the correlations among the shapes and numbers and displays the pattern that they create as a picture on the screen. Eventually, fractal drawings will assist scientists in re-creating the long and complex history of the Earth's climate.

Scientists called paleoclimatologists study the climates of the Earth's past.

Ocean Core

Age of core segment in millions of years
Temperature of surface

Present
5°C

1 million
10°C

5 million
15°C

15 million
20°C

25 million
25°C

283

Diversity and Classification

Outline

Mollusk shells on a beach in Valdes, Argentina

Focus

The millions of different kinds of organisms on Earth share varying degrees of structural and chemical similarities. They also show varying degrees of similarity in their development. These similarities form the basis of a classification system that allows scientists to group organisms. Similarities and differences among organisms also show whether organisms are closely or distantly related.

■ *How would you group the shells in the photograph?*

■ *What suggests that the animals who once lived in these shells are more closely related to each other than they are to crabs and lobsters?*

The History of Classification

Section Objectives
- *Define* the term *taxonomy*.
- *Compare* Aristotle's system of classification with that of Linnaeus.
- *List* the problems associated with the use of common names.
- *Explain* the system of binomial nomenclature.

The need to classify living things gave rise to **taxonomy**—the science of grouping organisms on the basis of their similarities. One of the first taxonomic systems was proposed by the Greek philosopher Aristotle around 350 B.C. He divided living things into two groups, animals and plants. Aristotle subdivided animals on the basis of habitat and behavior and plants on their size and structure. He said, for example, that herbs, shrubs, and trees are the three major divisions of the plant kingdom. Although Aristotle's system contained many errors, it was used for more than 2,000 years.

18.1 The System of Linnaeus

During the mid-1700s, biologists began to explore the world to search for previously unknown forms of life. As a result, thousands of newly discovered organisms were collected and described yearly. Although biologists used Aristotle's system of taxonomy to classify these organisms, most recognized that this system did not sufficiently explain the relationships between the organisms. For example, two plants might have the same kind of flowers and leaves. However, because one was a shrub and the other a tree, the scientists were forced to place them in different groups. In addition, the methods naturalists used to name these newly discovered organisms varied greatly. The use of many ineffective, competing, and often contradictory systems made communication between biologists very difficult.

A way out of these difficulties was provided by a Swedish botanist named Carolus Linnaeus. *Linnaeus developed a new classification system that revolutionized taxonomy.* He suggested that organisms with similar structures should be placed in the same taxonomic group and suggested that this group be called a *species.* As you will recall from Chapter 16, two organisms of the same species will produce fertile offspring when they breed. Linnaeus further suggested that similar species be grouped into a larger category called a **genus.** For example, dogs, wolves, and jackals—each a different species—are similar enough to be considered members of the same genus.

18.2 The Scientific Name

An organism is often known primarily by its **common name**—that is, the name given it by the people of an area. This practice may cause a great deal of confusion because one kind of organ-

Figure 18–1. Many small seed-eating birds are commonly called sparrows. The house sparrow shown above, *Passer domesticus,* is related more to weaver-finches than to other sparrows. Sometimes called the English sparrow, *Passer domesticus* is actually found worldwide.

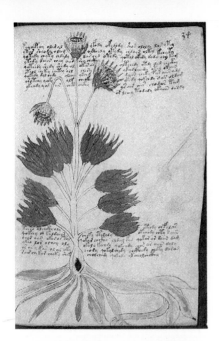

Figure 18–2. The sunflowers above are part of an herbal listing in a manuscript dating from the 1400s or the 1500s.

Reading Critically

Relating Ideas Why is the designation *Felis* much less specific than *Felis concolor*?

ism may have many different names. For example, in one region the mountain lion is called a puma, in another a cougar, in others a catamount or panther. Many organisms have also been misnamed, implying misleading relationships. Prairie dogs may yelp and bark, but they are more like squirrels than dogs. Starfish, silverfish, and jellyfish differ greatly from one another—and not one of them is a fish.

To avoid such problems, early taxonomists introduced the idea that each organism be given a **scientific name**—that is, a short, standard name that is accepted by all scientists. Linnaeus suggested that the scientific name of an organism consist of its genus name followed by its specific name. This system of naming is known as **binomial nomenclature.** *Binomial* means two names, and *nomenclature* means the naming of things. Linnaeus continued the practice of using Latin, which was considered the "language of science" and was understood by all scientists of the time. The practice of writing scientific names in Latin is still followed today.

An organism's scientific name is written in a precise way. The genus name begins with a capital letter; the specific name with a lower-case letter. A scientific name is written in italic type or underlined. *Felis concolor,* or *F. concolor* for short, is the scientific name of the puma or mountain lion. This name is recognized and accepted by scientists throughout the world.

Many scientific names are descriptive. For example, the red maple is *Acer rubrum,* which means "red maple" in Latin. Sometimes a scientist names an organism after a scientist he or she admires. The genus *Linnea,* an herb of cold areas, was named in honor of Linnaeus. In many cases, a specific name describes where the organism lives, such as *Darlingtonia californica,* the carnivorous cobra lily of California.

Taxonomists may also cite the name of the person who first described the organism. For example, the scientific name of the cobra lily is often written *Darlingtonia californica* Torr. to indicate that is was given its scientific name by John Torrey, a famous American botanist.

Section Review

1. **Summarizing Ideas** What is taxonomy?
2. **Identifying Relationships** On what did Linnaeus base his system of classification?
3. **Synthesizing Ideas** Why does the use of common names lead to confusion?
4. **Inferring Conclusions** What information does an organism's scientific name provide?

Thinking Critically

Modern Taxonomy

Section Objectives

- *Tell* what factors are considered by taxonomists in classifying organisms.
- *List* the classification levels in order, from general to specific.
- *Name* each kingdom in the five-kingdom system.
- *Explain* what is meant by *biosystematics*.

Linnaeus's system, published in 1753, remains the starting point for all modern taxonomy. Since the publication of Charles Darwin's *Origin of Species* in 1859, the theory of evolution has influenced classification. As a result, taxonomists now base classification on evolutionary relationships.

18.3 Bases of Modern Classification

Though similarity of structure still remains the basis for grouping organisms, biologists also use other kinds of evidence in classification. *Modern taxonomists study chromosome structure, DNA base sequences, reproduction, biochemical similarities, and embryology to determine relationships among organisms.*

Comparing one organism's chromosome makeup, or **karyotype,** with that of another organism helps biologists determine relationships. Taxonomists know that similarity of karyotypes usually indicates a close taxonomic relationship.

Taxonomists also study the reproduction of organisms to determine relationships. Botanists, for example, perform many experimental crosses with related plants to see which will produce fertile offspring. Those that do are said to belong to the same species.

An organism's biochemical makeup also provides evidence of its relationships. Similar sequences in the amino acids of proteins from two organisms may indicate that they are closely related. For example, the horseshoe crab was given its common name and classified according to its external appearance. Examination of blood proteins, however, revealed that these so-called crabs more closely resemble spiders. As a result, taxonomists reclassified them.

Scientists also study the embryological development to determine whether or not organisms show *homologous structures*. For example, a taxonomist might note that the wing of a bat and the flipper of a whale originate from the same embryonic tissues and initially develop in a similar manner. The similarities might then suggest to the taxonomist that the two animals had a common ancestor.

Figure 18–3. These images produced by electrophoresis show a comparison of blood proteins from (top to bottom) a rat, a cat, and a dog.

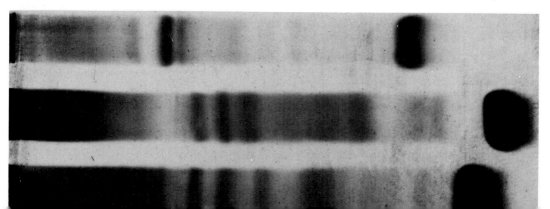

Everyday Classification

Take some time to think about how classification schemes that are not associated with biology may be reflected in a classroom. For example, items found in a classroom are usually organized in a certain way. Books and supplies that are used by a teacher may be found in a certain place. Supplies that are used by the students may be found in another place. By separating the items used by a teacher from those used by the students, two groups of items have been identified. The groups of items may be subdivided into smaller groups of items. For example, one group may include things that are used for writing. Another group may include things that are used for doing art work. A third group of items may include those that are used frequently throughout the day. This group may include hall passes, staplers, and tape.

Each classroom has its own unique classification scheme. Each may be similar to that of other classrooms in some ways. However, different classrooms are usually very different in the way some

items in them are grouped. Observing how things are grouped in these different classrooms often provides a clue to how the person who did the grouping thinks and what kinds of activities take place in a particular classroom.

18.4 Categories of Classification

Taxonomists use several categories in addition to the genus and species when classifying organisms. When taken in order from the largest, most generalized category to the smallest, most specific one, they are *kingdom, phylum, class, order, family, genus,* and *species.*

Each organism has a place in this taxonomic system. For example, a tiger is a member of the kingdom Animalia, the animal kingdom. It is also a member of the phylum Chordata, a group composed mostly of animals with backbones. Because it has hair and nurses its young with milk, it is placed in the class Mammalia with animals that share these traits, such as whales and monkeys. Like all meat eaters with enlarged canine teeth, the tiger is a member of the order Carnivora. Tigers and other cats are members of the family Felidae. Tigers, lions, and Old World panthers are members of the genus *Panthera;* tigers are put in the species *tigris.* The scientific name of the tigers, therefore, is *Panthera tigris.* An African or Asian lion belongs to all

Biofact

Q: *How many species can one genus contain?*

A: There is no limit. Some genera contain only a single species. The genus of fruit-flies, *Drosophila,* however, contains over 1,000 species.

the same higher taxonomic categories as a tiger, but is a different species, *Panthera leo*.

Members of the same species that differ in some important way—such as flower size or ear shape—are said to be members of different **varieties,** or subdivisions of a species. The variety of a species is often listed as a part of the scientific name. It is written after the species name. When two varieties are separated geographically from each other, many taxonomists prefer to call them *subspecies*.

Reading Critically

Comparing Ideas How is a variety different from a sub-species?

18.5 Systems of Classification

When Linnaeus developed his new system of classification, he retained the idea of two kingdoms. All **autotrophs,** or organisms that produce their own food, were placed in the plant kingdom. All **heterotrophs,** which are organisms dependent on others for food, were placed in the animal kingdom. As scientists learned more, they realized that the two-kingdom system was inadequate. Some organisms, such as the single-celled *Euglena,* share important features with both plants and animals. It is incorrect to call *Euglena* an animal and equally incorrect to call it a plant. Some taxonomists suggested that a third kingdom, Protista, be established for organisms like *Euglena.*

The development of the light microscope enabled scientists to see that bacteria, blue-green bacteria, and some other kinds of microorganisms do not have nuclei. Certainly, said some taxonomists, these organisms cannot be considered members of any of the three kingdoms. Therefore, a fourth kingdom, Monera,

Table 18–1: Comparison of Classification Systems

Number of Kingdoms				
Kingdom	Two	Three	Four	Five
Animalia	Animals, protozoa	All multicellular animals	All multicellular animals	All multicellular animals
Plantae	Plants, algae, fungi, slime molds	Plants, algae, fungi, slime molds	All multicellular plants and all fungi	All multicellular plants
Protista		Unicellular organisms and colonial protozoa	Most unicellular organisms	Most unicellular organisms
Monera			Cyanobacteria, bacteria, and other organisms that lack nuclei	Cyanobacteria, bacteria, and other microorganisms that lack nuclei
Fungi				All fungi

was established and organisms without nuclei were assigned there. Many taxonomists, however, were still troubled by mushrooms and molds, which have nuclei but are not plants or animals or similar to protists. A fifth kingdom, Fungi, was established to accommodate these organisms. Today some scientists favor the three-kingdom system; some prefer four kingdoms; and most favor five. Biologists continue to debate which classification system is most accurate and how best to categorize organisms. In this textbook, the five-kingdom system of classification is used. The kingdoms, their characteristics, and their major groups are shown in Table 18–2.

Table 18–2: The Five-Kingdom System of Classification

Kingdom	Characteristics	Major Groups	
Monera	Simple organisms without nuclei	Schizophyta Cyanophyta Prochlorophyta	
Protista	A varied group of organisms with nuclei; many unicellular; both autotrophic and heterotrophic forms, includes protozoa and algae	Mastigophora Sarcodina Ciliophora Sporozoa Euglenophyta Acrasiomycota Myxomycota Oomycota	Pyrrophyta Chrysophyta Phaeophyta Rhodophyta Chlorophyta
Fungi	Multicellular heterotrophs with nuclei, absorb food through cell wall	Zygomycota Ascomycota Basidiomycota Deuteromycota	
Plantae	Multicellular, nucleated autotrophs with photosynthesis in chloroplasts	Bryophyta Psilophyta Sphenophyta Lycophyta Pterophyta	Cycadophyta Ginkophyta Gnetophyta Coniferophyta Anthophyta
Animalia	Multicellular heterotrophs with nuclei	Porifera Coelenterata (Cnidaria) Platyhelminthes Nematoda Mollusca	Annelida Arthropoda Echinodermata Chordata

Some taxonomists study details of the evolution of species. These taxonomists are called *biosystematists.* Their field of study is **biosystematics.**

Biosystematists document the differences in traits between populations of the same species. For each population they may record data on size, color, shape, and other characteristics of individual members. The biosystematists develop a population profile that shows variation of traits. A biosystematist studying lilies might determine variation in length of leaves, time of blooming, number of flowers, and width of seeds.

These data are then analyzed. Graphs showing the range of variation of individual traits within one lily population are then compared with variations of those traits in a hundred lily populations.

By noting differences and similarities in the populations, the biosystematists develop hypotheses regarding how the species is changing. The systematists may find, for example, that some lily populations bloom in August, whereas others bloom only in May. This may indicate that the two populations are becoming *genetically isolated* and two subspecies are in the process of evolving into two species.

■ **Interpreting Ideas** What effect might climate have on genetic isolation?

18.6 The Ongoing Science of Taxonomy

Since the time of Aristotle, taxonomists have continued to classify organisms. Today, taxonomists often use computers that can analyze much more data on species than was possible in the past. With the help of computers, modern taxonomists determine relationships quickly and accurately.

Most of today's taxonomists work in museums or herbariums where they have access to large numbers of organisms collected from all over the world. Many, however, are adventurers who travel to uncharted regions of the world in search of undiscovered forms of life.

Section Review

1. **Listing Information** Name five features that are used in modern classification.
2. **Organizing Information** List the levels of classification from least specific to most specific.
3. **Comprehending Ideas** What are the five biological kingdoms?
4. **Inferring Conclusions** How do biosystematists go about determining relationships?

Thinking Critically

Extinction: Dinosaurs and Other Species

In 1974, scientists discovered that the Earth's crust contained a thin layer of *iridium*—a chemical element that is rare on Earth but common in asteroids. The impact of a large asteroid could have spread iridium-rich dust across the Earth's surface.

If a large asteroid had struck the ocean, it may have created a global "steam bath" of hot water vapor. If this event had been followed by acid rainfall, the shells and skins of many marine creatures could have been destroyed, leaving no fossil evidence of their existence. If the asteroid had struck land it could have exploded in an immense fireball, filling the skies with dense clouds of dust and blocking the sun's warming rays. Widespread fires might have produced gases that destroyed many species including the dinosaurs.

Some researchers think that a sudden catastrophe best accounts for the disappearance of large numbers of species in a short time period. Others hypothesize that more gradual changes, such as the floating apart of large land masses and gradual changes in temperature would have had similar results.

Some researchers hypothesize that many human activities may accelerate irreversible changes in the environment to which many species, including the human species, cannot adapt.

Geological evidence may supply insight into the consequences of human activity on species that are alive today. Some scientists, for example, are concerned that the destruction of rain forests may contribute to a rise in global temperatures. This rise in temperature may cause a rise in sea levels if the polar ice caps melt. The release of *chlorofluorocarbons,* chemicals that are released from many manufacturing processes and that are used as coolants in air conditioners and refrigerators, may be depleting parts of the ozone layer that help filter harmful ultraviolet rays. Increased radiation may result in more cancers in the human population. The large-scale dumping of wastes into the Earth's oceans may be

destroying populations of organisms that are important in food chains and in oxygen production.

Analyze the Issue

1. What global events might have resulted in the extinction of the dinosaurs?

2. What effects would a rise of 5 degrees C (41 degrees F.) in the temperature of the region in which you live affect life forms in the region?

3. Should measures be taken to limit both activities and production of materials that may cause widespread changes in the Earth's environment? If so, how should these limits be determined and imposed? Support your views.

INVESTIGATION 18:
How Do You Make a Key for Classifying Organisms?

Objectives
- To *observe* the structural characteristics of a variety of living things
- To *construct* a key for classifying specimens

Materials
a variety of living and preserved specimens

Prelab Preparation
1. State the bases of taxonomic schemes.
2. Explain how modern schemes of classification help in identifying organisms.
3. Your teacher will tell you how many specimens will be observed in this Investigation. Make a table for recording each specimen's name or identification code and its observable characteristics. Also, make a diagram similar to the one shown.

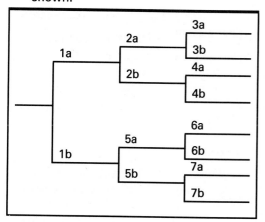

Inquiry: Lab Technique
4. Work with a partner and observe each specimen. Record the name or identification code and the characteristics that you observe for each specimen.
5. Divide the specimens into two groups based only on contrasting characteristics that you observed. State the characteristic used to form the two groups on lines 1a and 1b of the diagram.
6. On the basis of another observed characteristic, subdivide each group into two groups. Then, record this characteristic on lines 2a and 2b, or lines 5a and 5b, as appropriate.
7. Continue to subdivide each group, using two contrasting characteristics. Record each characteristic, adding lines to your diagram as needed. Label all new lines with an appropriate number-letter combination.
8. When a specimen has been separated from the others, record its name or identification code at the end of the line.
9. Using the illustration as an example, convert your diagram into a classification key.

1a.	gills present _____	go to 5
b.	gills absent _____	go to 2
2a.	six legs _____	*insect*
b.	more than six legs _____	go to 3
3a.	eight legs _____	*spider*
b.	more than eight legs _____	go to 4
4a.	one leg per segment _____	*centipede*
b.	two legs per segment _____	*millipede*
5a.	large claws _____	*crayfish*
b.	claws absent _____	go to 6

10. Exchange keys with another student. Test their key by identifying each specimen. Discuss any areas of confusion or disagreement.

Analysis
1. **Evaluating Methods** What is the advantage of working as a team during this Investigation?
2. **Evaluating Methods** Why is a taxonomy based on physical characteristics more accurate than one based on habitat or behavior?

Chapter 18 Review

Summary

Taxonomy is the science of grouping organisms on the basis of their similarities. Aristotle, one of the first to develop a taxonomic system, generally considered all organisms either animals or plants. In the mid-1700s, Carolus Linnaeus developed a system based on similarities of structure organisms in which similar organisms were placed in the same species.

Each organism is assigned a scientific name composed of its genus and species names. This two-part naming system is called binomial nomenclature.

Today's systems of classification show evolutionary relationships among organisms and use such characteristics as structure of chromosomes, reproductive potential, biochemical makeup, and embryology. The seven levels of classification are kingdom, phylum, class, order, family, genus, and species.

Taxonomic systems have been repeatedly modified to reflect advances in biological knowledge, including the discovery of new species. Many scientists use the five-kingdom system of classification, which has the following kingdoms: Monera, Protista, Fungi, Plantae, and Animalia. Biological classification will continue to change as new information is collected.

BioTerms

autotroph (289)
binomial
   nomenclature (286)
biosystematics (291)
common name (285)
genus (285)
heterotroph (289)
karyotype (287)
scientific
   name (286)
taxonomy (285)
variety (289)

For each pair of terms, explain the differences in their meanings.

1. common name, scientific name
2. autotroph, heterotroph
3. binomial nomenclature, biosystematics

BioQuiz   (Write all answers on a separate sheet of paper.)

Completion

1. Binomial nomenclature is the system of giving an organism a two-word scientific name in _____ .
2. In the five-kingdom system, most unicellular organisms with _____ are placed in the kingdom Protista.
3. Two varieties that are geographically separated are known as _____ .
4. The discovery that bacteria had no nuclei led to the establishment of the kingdom _____ .
5. The examination of homologous structures in the _____ often gives clues to an organism's relationships.

Multiple Choice

6. Which of the following is not studied to determine relationships among organisms?   a) biochemical similarities   b) reproductive potential   c) homologous structures   d) life span
7. Aristotle's classification system contained   a) two kingdoms.   b) three kingdoms.   c) four kingdoms.   d) five kingdoms.
8. The next smaller division after class in the classification system is   a) family.   b) order.   c) genus.   d) phylum.
9. Organisms without nuclei are part of the kingdom   a) Protista.   b) Fungi.   c) Monera.   d) Plantae.

10. Multicellular heterotrophs with nuclei that absorb food through a cell wall belong to the kingdom   a) Monera. b) Protista.   c) Fungi.   d) Plantae.
11. The most general of all classification groups is the   a) order.   b) genus. c) family.   d) kingdom.
12. The next largest division after class is   a) order.   b) phylum.   c) kingdom. d) family.
13. The current system of classification consists of _____ kingdoms.   a) two b) three   c) four   d) five
14. The study of the details of the evolution of a species is called   a) taxonomy. b) macrobiology.   c) biosystematics. d) paleontology.
15. All plants are   a) autotrophs. b) heterotrophs.   c) karyotypes. d) Protista.

16. What determines whether two individuals are the same species?
17. What characteristics distinguish bio-systematics from classical taxonomy?
18. Why is Aristotle's two-kingdom approach no longer used?
19. What types of information can be communicated by a taxonomist when picking the species name of an organism?
20. What are two contributions of Linnaeus to the science of taxonomy?

Application/Critical Thinking

1. **Identifying Relationships**   Two kinds of daisies both belong to the genus *Aster*. Although they look exactly alike and produce fertile hybrids in the laboratory, they never cross in nature because one kind flowers only in May and the other only in October. Are they the same species? State your reasons for saying yes or no. What criteria could be used to determine the answer?
2. **Summarizing Ideas**   Use your knowledge of evolution from Chapter 16 to write a paragraph telling how one species gradually becomes two subspecies and, ultimately, two separate species.
3. **Analyzing Viewpoints**   Two species of oak tree, the burr oak and the white oak, are common in many parts of the United States. Some scientists argue that they are the same species because hybridization produces individuals that are fertile and show a blend of traits between the two parents. Other scientists say the two kinds of oak look so different, they must be considered two separate species. How can such a disagreement be resolved? Can it be resolved at all?

Cross-Discipline Connection

Biology and Reading   Read the book *Life on Earth: A Natural History,* by David Attenborough. Write a paper about the diversity of life on Earth that uses examples from this book.

Discovery Through Reading

The article "Taxonomic Tangles," *Natural History* (March 1987): 54–55, discusses some difficulties of classifying organisms. How did classifying the South American dog-like mammals called canids present a problem?

Read the article "Meet the New Bug on the Block," *Science 83* (December 1983): 6. What new phylum of animals is described in this article?

Summary

Scientists have proposed theories about the origin of the universe, the Earth, and life. Alexander Oparin hypothesized that life may have begun spontaneously under conditions that were present on Earth several billion years ago. Fossil evidence suggests that life forms have evolved or changed over time since they first appeared. Homologous structures, comparative embryology, and chemical and genetic similarities among organisms support the idea of evolution.

A theory of evolution proposed by Charles Darwin in 1859 identifies natural selection as a process through which organisms evolve. Natural selection acts on changes in gene frequencies that result from migration, isolation, genetic drift, and mutation. Divergent evolution results in organisms becoming less similar. Convergent evolution results in similarities among distantly related organisms.

Studies of the evolution of humans involve primates called hominids. About 2.2 million years ago *Homo habilis,* the first representative of the genus to which present-day humans belong, appeared.

The earliest *Homo sapiens,* the species to which present-day humans belong, appeared about 400,000 years ago. Neandertals and anatomically modern humans are members of this species.

The classification of living things is based on structure, biochemical makeup, and embryology. The science of classifying organisms is called taxonomy. There are five kingdoms in modern taxonomic systems: Monera, Protista, Fungi, Plantae, and Animalia. These kingdoms are subdivided into groups in which organisms share an increasing number of similarities. The major groups are phyla, classes, orders, families, genera, and species.

Synthesis

Synthesis Statement

Many explanations have been proposed about the origins of the universe, Earth, and life on Earth. Although many questions still remain unanswered, scientists agree that the conditions that were present when Earth first formed no longer exist. Life forms could have originated under the conditions that existed early in the Earth's history.

Charles Darwin's theory about how natural selection can cause organisms to change over time helps explain how new species arise and how organisms are related. This theory also explains how organisms can share characteristics and be diverse at the same time. The degree of similarity in biochemistry, structure, and development show the degree of relatedness among organisms.

Synthesis Questions

Apply your understanding of this unit to the following questions.

1. How are fossils useful to biologists who wish to reconstruct evolutionary relationships among extinct organisms and their modern descendants? What are the limitations of fossil evidence in establishing these relationships?

2. Explain why variations persist in a species that is successful in its environment. How does genetic variation make natural selection possible?

3. Discuss ways in which natural selection may result in new species. Describe how a migration might produce changes in a species.

4. Describe how a mutation may alter the gene pool of a species. Could a new species arise by mutation alone?

5. Why is Aristotle's system of classifying plants on the basis of their size and structure considered inaccurate today? How can an understanding of the evolutionary relationships among a group of organisms help biologists to classify them?

6. Would a species be benefited if an adaptive trait was not encoded in the genome of an individual exhibiting it? Discuss the evolutionary value of genes and chromosomes.

7. Describe how the environmental pressures that faced *Homo erectus* differed from those facing humans in modern society. What human characteristics would you consider to be of value in modern society? Discuss some ways that your list might change in the next century.

8. Use a separate piece of paper to draw a concept map like the one below. Place each of the following terms inside the appropriate figure: natural selection, new species.

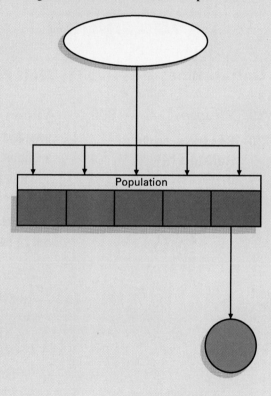

Population

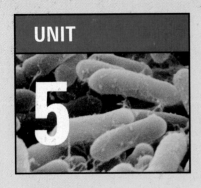

UNIT

5

VIRUSES AND MONERA

Unit Outline

Unit Focus

Viruses and bacteria cannot be seen with the unaided eye. Both play important roles that affect humans. Bacteria, for example, include some species that are beneficial to humans and some that are harmful. Viruses do not share the characteristics of living things and can reproduce only after they have invaded living cells.

- *What advantages and disadvantages do both bacteria and viruses have that are related to their small size?*

- *If viruses do not show the characteristics of living things, why are they included in a biology textbook?*

Salmonella **bacteria,** × **12,000**

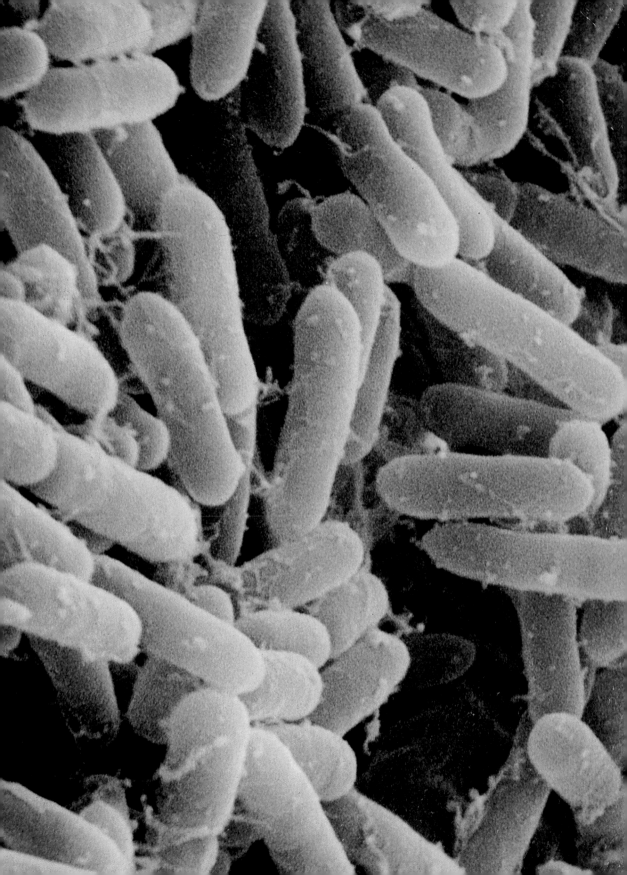

Viruses

Outline

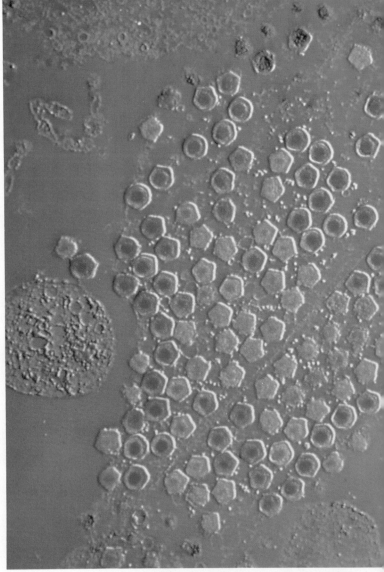

Transmission electron micrograph (TEM) of virions of African swine fever

Focus

A **virus** is a microscopic form that can reproduce only inside a living cell called a *host cell*. Viruses invade the cells of most organisms. In humans, viruses cause diseases that include the common cold, flu, poliomyelitis, and smallpox. The incurable disease AIDS, which threatens to reach epidemic proportions that are unknown in recent history, is caused by a virus.

■ *Why are viruses not considered living things?*

■ *Why do you think that the understanding of viruses has progressed rapidly over the past 25 years?*

Characteristics of Viruses

Viruses do not easily fit into the classification systems used for living things. Some biologists even question whether viruses should be considered alive at all. *Viruses exhibit some but not all of the characteristics of living things.* Viruses, like all living things, contain protein and nucleic acid. Yet, unlike cells, viruses can be solidified into crystals. When placed in a solution, they become active again. Viruses can reproduce only within a living cell, called a **host cell.** Unlike cellular organisms, viruses do not respire, grow, or respond to stimuli.

19.1 Size of Viruses

Viruses differ greatly in size. They range in length from 0.01 micrometer (μm) to over 0.3 μm. The virus that causes influenza is of medium size, about 0.1 μm; yet over 500 of them can fit on the point of a pin.

19.2 Structure and Shape of Viruses

A typical virus consists of two parts, an inner core of nucleic acid and a protective outer coat of protein. The nucleic-acid core may consist of either DNA or RNA, the chemicals that contain coded genetic information. Unlike cells, which contain both DNA and RNA, each virus has only one type of nucleic acid. The DNA or RNA enables a virus to reproduce new viruses

Section Objectives

- *State* similarities and differences between viruses and living things.
- *Identify* the main parts of a typical virus.
- *Contrast* viruses and viroids.
- *Describe* viral reproduction.
- *Explain* how viruses can transmit genetic information from one cell to another.

For information about making models of viruses, see the Investigation on page 309.

THINKING ABOUT BIOLOGY: Viroids

Viruses are not the smallest known disease-causing agents. In 1967 biologists discovered that the potato tuber disease is caused by a tiny agent that consists entirely of a short strand of RNA. Scientists gave the name **viroid** (VY royd) to this disease-causing agent.

Viroids have been identified as the cause of disease in at least seven kinds of plants, including cucumbers and tomatoes, and they may cause some diseases in animals and humans.

A viroid lacks the protective protein coat of a virus. A viroid reproduces itself only inside a host cell and causes disease by interfering with the normal functioning of the host cell.

Scientists still do not understand how viroids replicate. It appears that reproduction takes place inside the nucleus of the host cell rather than in the cytoplasm.

■ **Inferring Relationships** Why must a viroid be in a host cell to reproduce?

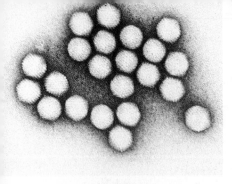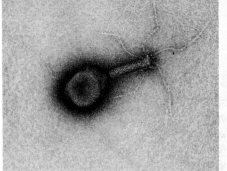

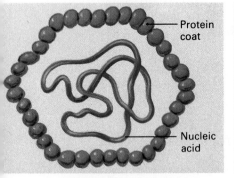

Protein coat

Nucleic acid

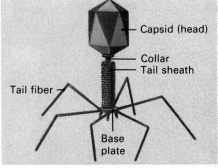

Capsid (head)

Collar
Tail sheath

Tail fiber

Base plate

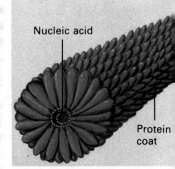

Nucleic acid

Protein coat

Figure 19–1. Polyhedral viruses (left), bacteriophages (center), and rod-shaped viruses (right) each have a protein coat that surrounds a central core of RNA or DNA.

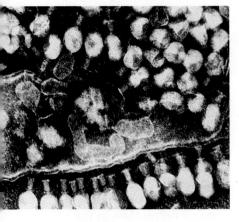

Figure 19–2. Bacteriophages attack a bacterium by first adhering to the cell wall. They then inject viral nucleic acids that alter the cell's genetic code.

exactly like itself. In cells, the DNA is double-stranded and the RNA is single-stranded. A virus, on the other hand, may have a nucleic-acid strand that is single or double, linear or circular.

The outer protein coat, called the **capsid,** makes up 95 percent of the body of the virus. Some of the proteins of the capsid are enzymes. The arrangement of the proteins in the outer coat determines the shape of a virus. Figure 19–1 shows that some viruses are polyhedral, having many sides, or facets. Others are rod-shaped viruses made up of repeating units of protein in a spiral arrangement. Viruses that invade bacteria, called **bacteriophages** (bak TIHR ee uh fayj uhz), have a polyhedral head and a hollow tail, usually with several fibers at the tip. Some viruses also have a membrane that surrounds the capsid. This membrane consists of proteins, lipids, and carbohydrates.

19.3 Reproductive Cycles of Viruses

Viruses cannot reproduce themselves unless they have invaded a host cell. Each type of virus attaches itself to specific plant, animal, or bacterial cells.

Lytic Cycle   During reproduction, many viruses kill the host cell. Such a process is called a **lytic** (LIHT ihk) **cycle.** Most knowledge of the lytic cycle comes from the study of bacteriophages, also known as *phages* (FAYJ uhz). The cycle begins when the phage comes into contact with a host cell. As Figure 19–3 (page 304) shows, the cycle has five main stages.

Strategies for Conquering the Common Cold

Each time a person catches a cold, his or her immune system develops specific antibodies against the variety of virus responsible for the runny nose, sneezing, and aching feeling that accompany the cold. Unfortunately, there are at least 100 varieties of the common cold virus. Since antibodies are specific, producing them against one variety of the cold virus does not protect a person from the other varieties. For this reason, the person does not become immune to the common cold.

The virus that causes the common cold is called *rhinovirus* (*rhino* is derived from the Greek word for nose). Until recently, scientists understood little about the rhinovirus's structure. Now, scientists working with highly advanced X-ray crystallography have mapped the protein coat of the rhinovirus. Armed with this knowledge, researchers are working to develop drugs that may destroy the cold virus and vaccines that will make a person immune to cold viruses.

Researchers have found that sites on the surface of the cold virus that allow the virus to penetrate a human cell are located in deep "canyons" in the protein coat. Because human antibody molecules cannot penetrate the "canyons", the antibodies are not effective in preventing cold viruses from entering cells.

Researchers are trying to apply this knowledge to find cures for the common cold. One experimental cold drug is made of

molecules small enough to invade the "canyons" in the virus's protein coat, enter the virus, and destroy its nucleic acid. Because the nucleic acid of all rhinoviruses is similar, drugs like this one may be effective against many varieties of rhinoviruses.

Other researchers are working to develop a vaccine that would block sites, called *receptor sites,* on the surfaces of human cells where the virus enters, thus preventing the virus from invading the cells.

1. *Adsorption.* The phage attaches itself to the cell wall. A chemical bond forms between specific molecular sites on the tail of the virus and corresponding sites on the cell wall, called **receptor sites.** The match between virus and receptor site is like that between a lock and key.
2. *Entry.* The phage releases an enzyme that breaks down the cell wall. The outer covering of the phage tail contracts, forcing the tail through the weakened cell wall. The nucleic acid of the phage passes through the hollow tail into the host cell, leaving the empty capsid outside.

Reading Critically

Inferring Relationships What site on the cell wall supports the idea that viruses are specific to certain cells? Explain.

3. *Replication.* Once viral nucleic acid enters the cell, it begins to replicate new virus parts. In a DNA virus, the viral DNA enters the host cell's chromosome and acts as a template for the formation of messenger RNA. Some viral DNA replicates to form more viral DNA. The messenger RNA then migrates to the cytoplasm and causes the synthesis of viral proteins and viral RNA. Most RNA viruses contain an enzyme called *RNA transcriptase.* This enzyme causes the replication of viral RNA, which then acts as messenger RNA. Some viruses use an enzyme to make viral DNA from viral RNA. The viral DNA then migrates to the nucleus and directs the synthesis of new viruses.

4. *Assembly.* The viral nucleic acid and proteins are assembled into new, complete virus particles, called **virions** (VY ree ahnz).

5. *Release.* The new phages release an enzyme that weakens the cell wall. The host cell breaks open, or *lyses* (LY suhz), and releases the newly created viruses. Up to 300 new viruses can be produced in one cell.

The lytic cycle is similar for all viruses, though animal and plant viruses differ from bacteriophages in the way they enter

Figure 19–3. Viruses reproduce by both lytic and lysogenic cycles. In a lytic cycle, viruses invade, reproduce, and exit immediately. In a lysogenic cycle, viral genes are initially inactive.

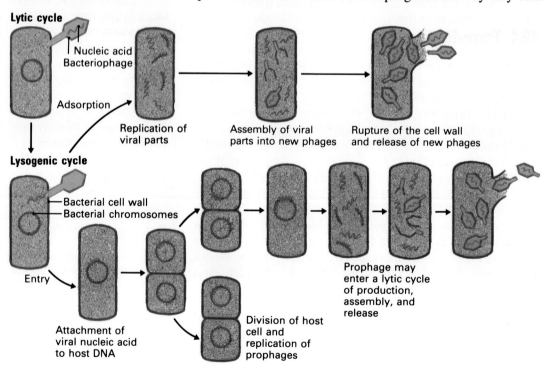

Lytic cycle

Nucleic acid
Bacteriophage

Adsorption

Replication of viral parts

Assembly of viral parts into new phages

Rupture of the cell wall and release of new phages

Lysogenic cycle

Bacterial cell wall
Bacterial chromosomes

Entry

Attachment of viral nucleic acid to host DNA

Division of host cell and replication of prophages

Prophage may enter a lytic cycle of production, assembly, and release cells. The whole animal virus passes through the cell membrane by *phagocytosis,* the same process by which large food particles enter the cell. Once inside the cell, the protein outer coat is destroyed by enzymes. Most plant viruses are injected through cell walls by insects.

Lysogenic Cycle   After entering a host cell, some phages remain inactive for many generations. Then suddenly the phages may become active and enter a lytic cycle of destruction. Scientists do not yet understand how inactive phages are activated. These phages are known as **temperate phages,** and the inactive cycle they undergo is called a **lysogenic** (ly suh JEHN ihk) **cycle.** This cycle goes through the following stages:

1. *Attachment.* The nucleic acid of the invading phage attaches itself to the DNA of the host cell. Such viral nucleic acid is called **prophage** (PROH fayj).
2. *Replication.* The prophage is replicated along with the DNA of the host cell during cell division.
3. *Activation.* The prophage enters a lytic cycle and orders the assembly of new viral parts. This process usually leads to the release of new phages and the destruction of the cell.

19.4 Transduction

Viruses have the ability to transfer genetic information from one host cell to another. This process is called **transduction** (trans DUHK shuhn). Two types of transduction have been identified. One, called *general transduction,* transfers random fragments of the host's DNA to the receiving cell. A second type, called *special transduction,* involves the transfer of specific genes from one cell to another. In each case, the gene fragments are packed into the virus just prior to lysis, and then transferred to a receiving cell during subsequent infection. ***Through transduction, a virus can alter the hereditary code of a cell.***

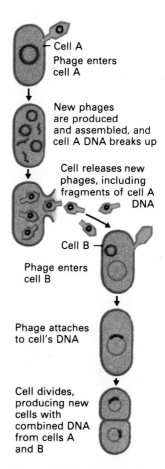

Figure 19–4. Transduction occurs when viruses carry genetic information from one host cell to another.

Section Review

1. **Comparing Ideas**   Compare viruses to living things.
2. **Summarizing Ideas**   How do viruses and viroids reproduce?
3. **Identifying Structures**   Identify the parts of a virus.
4. **Inferring Conclusions**   What role may viruses play in spreading genetic information that governs certain hereditary traits to other members of the species they infect?

⟨ **Thinking Critically** ⟩

- *Summarize* the early research that led to the discovery of viruses.
- *Explain* how some inactive viral infections recur.
- *List* three ways in which the body defends itself against viral infections.

Viruses and Disease

Viruses cause disease in plants and animals by destroying or altering the cells they inhabit. Disease-causing viruses, as well as certain bacteria and other microscopic parasites, are called **pathogens.**

19.5 Discovery of Viruses

A disease of tobacco plants known as tobacco mosaic first led to the identification of a virus as a pathogen. This disease causes the leaves of tobacco plants to become mottled with a yellow and green mosaic pattern. In 1892 the Russian biologist Dimitri Iwanowski squeezed the fluid from a diseased plant and passed it through a filter designed to hold back the smallest bacteria. He examined the fluid and the remains left on the filter under a light microscope. In both instances he found nothing. Yet rubbing the fluid on a healthy plant caused the plant to become diseased.

In 1898 the Dutch botanist Martinus Beijerinck repeated Iwanowski's work. Beijerinck concluded that the fluid contained an unknown factor, smaller than bacteria. He called this factor a *virus,* the Latin word for "poison."

An American biologist, Wendell Stanley, finally isolated the tobacco mosaic virus in 1935. Stanley extracted and crystallized the virus from the fluid of thousands of diseased plants. From a ton of diseased tobacco leaves Stanley produced a teaspoonful of crystals. In their crystallized form, the viruses did not appear to be alive. However, when the virus crystals were put back into solution and rubbed on a healthy plant, the plant contracted the disease.

19.6 Kinds of Viral Infections

Diseases caused by viruses range from minor infections that may go unnoticed to serious diseases, such as hepatitis and AIDS. Some viruses cause major disturbances in a cell's growth and reproduction, resulting in tumors or cancer.

Viruses tend to attack a particular species of animal or plant and a specific type of cell within that organism. A cold virus, for example, attacks cells of the respiratory system, and a polio virus invades nerve cells. Many viruses attack more than one species, however. Rabies, for example, can be transmitted from dogs, raccoons, foxes, and bats to other mammals, including humans. Cowpox can be transmitted to humans handling diseased herds. The virus responsible for a pneumonialike disease

Figure 19–5. When healthy tobacco plants (above) are attacked by the tobacco mosaic virus, their leaves become mottled yellow (inset). Tobacco mosaic is just one of many viral diseases.

called *psittacosis* (siht uh KOH sihs) can travel to humans from parrots and other birds infected with the disease.

Infections produced by viruses that undergo a lysogenic cycle may remain latent, or inactive, for a long period, then become active again. One example is the recurring infection caused by the *herpes simplex* virus. One type of herpes causes cold sores, and another type causes genital sores. These sores disappear during the inactive, lysogenic cycle and reappear during the virulent lytic cycle.

The ability of a virus to cause disease is called **virulence.** Several factors determine the virulence of a virus. One factor is the presence and activity of receptor sites on the surface of the cell, which enable the virus to become attached. Another factor is the speed with which the virus multiplies once it penetrates a host cell. A third factor is the response of the host organism to the invading viruses. For example, the cell may die immediately, it may divide abnormally, or it may produce defenses against the viruses.

Reading Critically

Analyzing Conclusions
Explain how you could be infected by a virus and not know it.

For information about virus research, see the BioTech on pages 312–313.

19.7 Defenses Against Viral Infections

Many drugs used to treat other infections cannot be used on viruses. Those drugs that can inactivate the viruses would also harm the host cells. *The body provides its own best natural defense against viral disease.* This natural resistance to disease is called **immunity.**

The skin and the mucous membranes are the body's first line of defense. Viruses usually cannot penetrate the skin except through an existing cut or the bite of an animal such as a rabid dog. Cilia and mucus in body linings inhibit the entry of some pathogens. Nevertheless, most viruses enter the body through the nose and mouth.

Once viruses enter, the body attacks them directly. White blood cells called *phagocytes* (FAG uh syts) engulf and destroy invading viruses. A second method of defense involves the production of certain protein molecules. The foreign protein of the virus is called an **antigen** (AN tuh juhn). When the antigen enters the body, it triggers the production of **antibodies.** The antibodies are highly specific and attack only the antigen that triggered their production. Then, attaching themselves to the antigen, antibodies destroy the viruses completely or make it easier for the phagocytes to engulf and destroy the viruses.

Figure 19–6. Vaccination is an important method of providing individuals with active immunity to many viral diseases.

Active and Passive Immunity Immunity to disease resulting from the production of antibodies is called **active immunity.** Antibodies can be produced in response to exposure to a

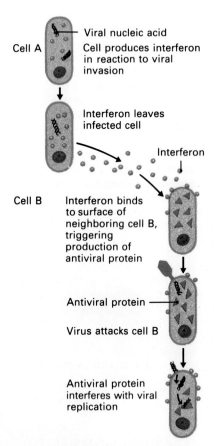

Cell A — Viral nucleic acid
Cell produces interferon in reaction to viral invasion

Interferon leaves infected cell

Interferon

Cell B — Interferon binds to surface of neighboring cell B, triggering production of antiviral protein

Antiviral protein

Virus attacks cell B

Antiviral protein interferes with viral replication

Figure 19–7. Production of interferon is triggered when a human body cell is invaded by a virus. This interferon then induces other cells to produce protective proteins. These proteins defend against subsequent viral attacks.

Thinking Critically

pathogen or in response to injection of a vaccine. A **vaccine** is a solution of weakened or killed pathogens. A vaccine serves as an antigen to stimulate the production of specific antibodies. Active immunity is usually lifelong. One attack of measles or one measles vaccination, for example, usually provides permanent resistance. An example of the effectiveness of a vaccine against a viral disease is the polio vaccine that was developed by the American physician Dr. Jonas Salk and administered to school children in 1954. Salk developed this vaccine against the poliomyletis virus after over a decade of study and experimentation. Soon afterward, Albert Sabin, another American physician, developed an oral vaccine against polio. The polio vaccine resulted in about a 90 percent reduction of polio cases in the United States between 1954 and 1962. **Passive immunity** occurs when a person receives antibodies produced in another person or in an animal that has developed immunity to the disease. One example of passive immunity is that received by an unborn child from its mother through antibodies passed in the blood. *Gamma globulin* is a blood protein often used to provide passive immunity to certain diseases. Passive immunity is always temporary.

Interferon   The body's third method of defense is the production of the protein **interferon** (ihn tuhr FIHR ahn). Interferon "interferes" with viral replication. Unlike antibodies, it will affect any type of virus that invades the body. Interferon produced by cells under viral attack triggers other cells to produce protective proteins. *Interferon triggers the production of an enzyme that enables a cell to recognize a virus as a foreign invader.* The enzyme inhibits the reproduction of viruses.

Interferon is *species specific*—that is, interferon produced in one species will work only in that species. For example, interferon produced by a mouse will not be effective in a rabbit or in humans.

Recombinant DNA technology is providing ways to produce large amounts of interferon. If the gene containing the codes for interferon production is spliced into the DNA of a bacterium, the bacterium and its offspring will produce interferon. Human interferon that has been produced using recombinant DNA techniques has been used with some success in patients with some forms of cancer.

Section Review

1. **Comprehending Ideas**   How were viruses discovered?
2. **Identifying Information**   Name three ways in which the body attacks invading viruses.
3. **Inferring Relationships**   Why do symptoms of some viral infections recur after having disappeared?

INVESTIGATION 19:
How Are Models of Viruses Constructed?

Objectives
- To *construct* models of viruses
- To *recognize* size relationships among different viruses

Materials
toothpicks, clay, plastic foam in different shapes, construction paper, pipe cleaners, wooden dowels, wire hangers, insulated electrical wire, tape, cork

Prelab Preparation
1. Describe the size and structure of a typical virus.
2. Make a table similar to the one shown to record information about your models.

Virus	Actual size	Scale factor	Scale size
Mumps	0.2 μm		
Potato X	0.01 × 0.5 μm		
Tobacco mosaic	0.018 × 0.3 μm		
Polio	0.028 μm		
Influenza	0.1 μm		

Inquiry: Exploration
3. Study the illustrations of viruses. These illustrations are not drawn to scale. The actual size of each virus is shown in the table.
4. Use the illustrations and the table to build a three-dimensional model of each virus. Each model must represent the actual size of each virus in relation to the size of the other models. Use the information that follows as a guide.

5. Find the range of sizes in the viruses shown. The smallest value is 0.01 μm, the diameter of the potato virus. The length of the potato virus is the largest value, 0.5 μm. Dividing the largest value by the smallest indicates that the largest model dimension will be 50 times greater than the smallest, that is, the *range factor* for these viruses is 50.
6. Next, decide on a practical *scale factor.* This factor is similar to the magnification of a microscope. It indicates how many times larger than actual size you plan to make your models. To make this decision, you should consider the materials you plan to use and the range factor. For example, since a virus is very small, you might decide to make your models 10,000 times larger than actual size. At this scale factor, 0.01 μm becomes 1 cm, but with a range factor of 50, the largest dimension becomes 50 cm. This might be a much larger model than you wish to build. *What is the scale factor for your models?*
7. Multiply the dimensions of each virus by your scale factor. Record the result.
8. Construct and display your models. Include your scale factor.

Analysis
1. **Analyzing Data** How many times larger is the mumps virus than the influenza virus?
2. **Evaluating Methods** In what ways might models be more useful than drawings or photographs?
3. **Applying Methods** A virus is 0.005 μm in diameter and 0.6 μm in length. Based on your scale factor, what dimensions would a model of the virus have?

Influenza virus

Mumps virus

Polio virus

Tobacco mosaic virus

Potato X virus

Chapter 19 Review

Summary

Viruses consist of a nucleic-acid core surrounded by a protein outer coat. Viruses can reproduce themselves, but only within a living host cell. The lytic cycle of viral reproduction results in the production of many new viruses and the destruction of the host cell. In the lysogenic cycle, viral nucleic acid fuses with the host DNA and is replicated during cell division. Such viruses may lie dormant for some time, then begin a lytic cycle. Scientists do not know how they are activated.

Transduction occurs when a virus carries a bit of the DNA from one host cell to another.

This process may alter the traits of the second host cell.

By interfering with the operation of the host cells, viruses can cause diseases in bacteria, plants, and animals. In humans, the body's own immune system is the best defense. Phagocytes produced by the body directly attack and destroy invading viruses. Antibodies combine with specific viral antigens, resulting in destruction of viruses. Immunity against diseases is either active or passive. Vaccines stimulate the production of antibodies. Interferon stimulates the body's defenses.

BioTerms

active
   immunity (**307**)
antibody (**307**)
antigen (**307**)
bacteriophage
   (**302**)
capsid (**302**)
host cell (**301**)
immunity (**307**)
interferon (**308**)

lysogenic
   cycle (**305**)
lytic cycle (**302**)
passive
   immunity (**308**)
pathogen (**306**)
prophage (**305**)
receptor site (**303**)
temperate phage (**305**)
transduction (**305**)

vaccine (**308**)
virion (**304**)
viroid (**301**)

virulence (**307**)
virus (**300**)

For each pair of terms, explain the differences in their meanings.

1. lytic cycle, lysogenic cycle
2. antigen, antibody
3. active immunity, passive immunity
4. prophage, temperate phage

BioQuiz   (Write all answers on a separate sheet of paper.)

Completion

1. An invading virus attaches itself to a _____ site prior to injecting its nucleic acid.
2. The _____ cycle results in the rapid destruction of the host cell.
3. A _____ is a solution of weakened or killed pathogens that can increase the body's immunity against disease.
4. A tiny agent that consists entirely of a short strand of RNA is a _____ .
5. The enzyme that causes the replication of viral RNA in the host cell is called _____ .

Multiple Choice

6. Viral nucleic acid that attaches to the DNA of the host cell is a   a) phagocyte.
   b) prophage.   c) capsid.
   d) viroid.
7. The process of transferring DNA from one host cell to another by a virus is called   a) replication.   b) assembly.
   c) transduction.   d) absorption.
8. Unlike living things, viruses have the ability to   a) dehydrate.   b) crystallize.
   c) replicate.   d) transduce.

9. A virus that may remain inactive within a host cell is   a) temperate.
   b) lytic.   c) a capsid.   d) a viroid.
10. The outer coat of a virus is made of
   a) prophages.   b) DNA.   c) fats.
   d) protein.
11. Gamma globulin is a blood protein that can confer   a) active immunity.
   b) passive immunity.   c) virulence.
   d) transduction.
12. The tail of a virus attaches to areas on the cell wall called   a) receptor sites.   b) capsids.   c) bacteriophages.   d) virions.
13. A virus is able to alter the hereditary code of a cell by   a) mitosis.
   b) reproduction.   c) prophage.
   d) transduction.
14. The term lysis means   a) to break open.

b) to infect.   c) to reproduce.   d) to grow.
15. The body's protein that interferes with viral replication is   a) gamma globulin.
   b) interferon.   c) lysogen.   d) a capsid.

16. What characteristics of living things do viruses show?
17. How can a virus introduce new traits into the cell it attacks?
18. How did Wendell Stanley first isolate a virus?
19. What is the difference between active immunity and passive immunity?
20. How does a bacteriophage enter a host cell?

Application/Critical Thinking

1. **Organizing Information**   Research the various folk remedies used to treat the common cold. Based on what you have learned about viruses, which remedies do you think are apt to be most helpful?
2. **Interpreting Graphics**   Draw a series of diagrams showing how a bacteriophage penetrates the bacterial cell wall. Label receptor sites, release of enzymes, contraction of tail, penetration, and passage of nucleic acid.
3. **Inferring Relationships**   Most animal viruses pass through the cell membrane whole. Use your knowledge of cellular transport to explain how this might take place.
4. **Analyzing Information**   Report on a viral disease that attacks economically important animals or plants, such as Newcastle disease or potato spindle tuber disease. Tell about the symptoms, transmittal, and control of the disease.
5. **Researching Information**   Prepare a report comparing viruses, viroids, and prions. Discuss the structure of each life form.

Cross-Discipline Connection

Biology and Health   Contact a public health official to find out how viral outbreaks or epidemics are controlled in your community. Share your findings with the rest of the class.

Discovery Through Reading

The article "As If the Flu Weren't Bad Enough," *Discover* (July 1988): 14, explains how major changes in flu-causing viruses are increasing at an alarming rate and why this is dangerous to human health. What changes are occurring in flu viruses?

Knowledge from AIDS Research

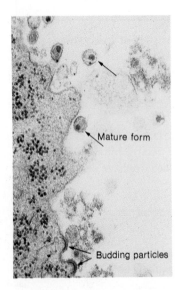

The AIDS virus escaping from a T lymphocyte

When AIDS was first identified in 1981, an effort began to find its cause. AIDS was quickly linked to a type of virus known as a *retrovirus.* A retrovirus codes for an enzyme that transcribes RNA into DNA. The techniques that were developed to isolate the AIDS retrovirus also helped researchers to isolate other retroviruses. Some of these retroviruses are now suspected of causing different forms of leukemia and other cancers.

The international effort to detect and treat HIV infection has led to many other medical discoveries. AIDS research has also increased scientists' understanding of the body's immune system, especially of the white blood cells, called *T lymphocytes,* that help fight infection. The virus that causes AIDS, *human immunodeficiency virus (HIV),* destroys the body's immune system by attacking the T lymphocytes. The exact location on the T lymphocyte where HIV binds to the T lymphocyte before the virus gains entry has now been identified. This location, called the *CD4 receptor,* is a protein on the surface of the lymphocyte that recognizes and binds to foreign antigens. Researchers have recently developed a method to mass produce

The blue dots are AIDS viruses attacking a T lymphocyte.

Lennart Nilsson/Boehringer Ingelheim International GmbH

the receptor protein using recombinant DNA technology. When injected into the body, the protein binds to the virus before the virus can bind to T lymphocytes. Now that receptor proteins can be mass produced, they may be used to treat many other diseases in which a virus binds to a receptor.

Other ways to fight viral infections have been developed as a result of AIDS research. Treatment with the protein *alpha interferon,* for example, has shown promise in fighting the AIDS virus. Alpha interferon is produced by the body's lymphocytes as a defense against viral infection. Recombinant DNA techniques may allow researchers to produce large amounts of this protein, which might then be used to treat AIDS and other viral infections, including influenza, shingles, and perhaps even the common cold.

The laboratory methods that were used to detect the AIDS virus also contribute to other areas of research. One example is a procedure called *polymerase chain reaction.* An early application of PCR was to find HIV even when there were only small amounts of the virus in the blood. In this procedure, many copies of DNA fragments are produced from a sample, thereby increasing the chances that the HIV virus will be detected in the sample. Polymerase chain reaction is now used to identify criminals through traces of DNA left by suspects in a blood stain or a hair.

Some genetic disorders may one day be cured as an indirect result of AIDS research. HIV excels at invading cells and inserting its own genes into the nucleus. Researchers may engineer a similar but harmless virus that can replace harmful genes with normal ones.

The international effort to detect and treat HIV infections has led to many other medical discoveries.

Precautions have been instituted to prevent AIDS researchers from contracting the virus.

Bacteria and Related Micro-organisms

Outline

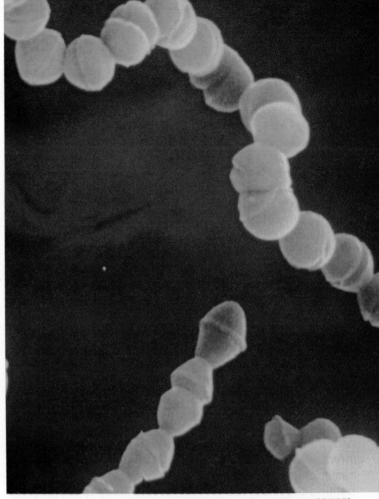

**Scanning electron micrograph (SEM)
of streptococcus bacteria, × 34,000**

Focus

Simple, one-celled organisms called **bacteria** and related microorganisms may have been among the earliest forms of life to appear on Earth. Bacteria play important roles as decomposers. In this way, they make essential atoms in the bodies of dead organisms available to living organisms. Scientists study bacteria such as *Escherichia coli* to learn about the structure and function of more complex cells. Some bacteria cause diseases. However, many bacteria are economically important to humans.

■ *Why does the small size of bacteria make these organisms valuable in scientific research?*

■ *What would result from the destruction of all bacteria on Earth?*

The Kingdom Monera

Bacteria and other members of the kingdom Monera live almost everywhere, including places in which few other organisms can survive. Some thrive in hot springs where the temperature is about 95°C (203°F.). Others have been found in Antarctica growing slowly at −7°C (22°F.). Monerans also live on and in every living thing. Human skin, even after a thorough cleansing, is home to millions of monerans.

Section Objectives

- *Name* the distinguishing characteristics of monerans.
- *Distinguish* the three phyla of monerans.

20.1 Characteristics

All monerans are prokaryotes. That is, their cells lack a true nucleus and membrane-bound organelles such as chloroplasts and mitochondria. The genetic material of monerans is a single, continuous loop of nucleic acid in direct contact with the cytoplasm. The ribosomes of monerans are smaller than those in eukaryotes.

Like plant cells, moneran cells have cell walls. However, almost all moneran cell walls contain acids and sugars instead of the cellulose found in plant cell walls.

20.2 Classification

The kingdom Monera consists of three phyla. Bacteria are classified in the phylum Schizophyta (skihz AHF uh tuh). Photosynthetic cyanobacteria make up the phylum Cyanophyta (sy uh NAHF uh tuh). The members of the third phylum, Prochlorophyta (proh klawr AHF uh tuh), also carry out photosynthesis but differ from the Cyanophyta mainly in the pigments used in the process.

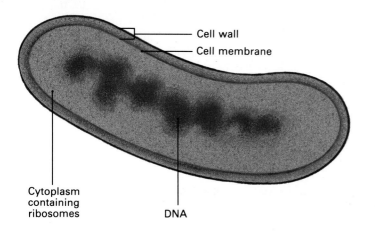

Cell wall
Cell membrane
Cytoplasm containing ribosomes
DNA

Figure 20–1. This illustration shows the features that are found in a bacterium, a typical moneran cell. A protective cell wall surrounds a selectively permeable cell membrane. The cytoplasm within the membrane contains both ribosomes and DNA.

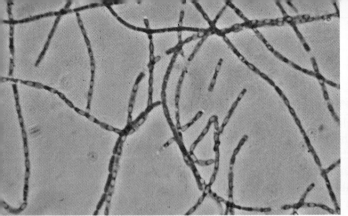
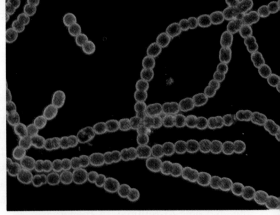

Figure 20–2. Representative organisms from two phyla of the kingdom Monera are shown above. Bacteria (left) are members of the phylum Schizophyta. Cyanobacteria (right) belong to the phylum Cyanophyta.

The classification of the kingdom Monera appears on page 914.

Reading Critically

Summarizing Ideas Why has the electron microscope allowed scientists to classify monerans better?

Biologists at one time classified monerans mainly on the basis of appearance, such as size, shape, and movement. Modern tools, such as the electron microscope and chemical analyses, have enabled scientists to develop a better understanding of the biochemical characteristics of monerans.

Today biologists group the members of the phylum Schizophyta into 19 classes based on their biochemical characteristics. All of the members of this phylum are generally called bacteria. The term *eubacteria,* or true bacteria, is sometimes used to refer to 12 of the classes. Other Schizophyta organisms include **rickettsias** (rih KEHT see uhz), **mycoplasmas** (my koh PLAZ muhz), and **spirochetes** (SPY ruh keets). Rickettsias, unlike eubacteria, can live only inside other cells. Mycoplasmas are the only monerans that lack a cell wall. Spirochetes differ from other bacteria mainly in their relatively large size.

As scientists have learned more about the biochemistry of monerans, they have continued to revise their classification scheme. Cyanobacteria, for example, were once classified with algae because both groups carry out photosynthesis with the resulting production of oxygen. As scientists learned about the prokaryotic structure of cyanobacteria, they began to classify them with the monerans. Prochlorophytes were not classified as a phylum separate from cyanobacteria until 1976. More recently, some scientists have proposed that one group of monerans, the *archaebacteria,* be placed in a separate kingdom entirely. These bacteria live in environments unsuitable for other organisms, such as the bottom of swamps or water habitats seven times as salty as sea water. Some archaebacteria live in volcanic vents deep in the ocean where the pressure is great and the temperature is 306°C (581°F.).

Thinking Critically

Section Review

1. **Classifying Data**   Name the major moneran characteristics.
2. **Contrasting Ideas**   What features distinguish the three phyla of monerans?

Bacteria

Bacteria show a wide diversity of structure and function and carry out all the biological activities required for life. They play many important roles in the biosphere. Bacteria decompose and recycle the remains of dead organisms and thus return essential elements and compounds to the soil. Although some bacteria cause serious diseases, most are beneficial. Many are used to produce food and life-saving drugs.

20.3 Size and Shape

Bacteria vary widely in size, although all bacteria are microscopic. An average-sized bacterium measures about 1 μm in length. It would take about 300,000 such bacteria to cover the period at the end of this sentence. Spirochetes range in length from 5 to 500 μm. At the other extreme, rickettsias average about 0.5 to 1 μm. Mycoplasmas are the smallest free-living cells, measuring about 0.1 μm in length.

Bacteria can be characterized by their shape and by the way they group together. Bacteria have three basic shapes. Sphere-shaped bacteria are called **cocci** (KAHK sy), rod-shaped bacteria are called **bacilli** (buh SIHL eye), and corkscrew-shaped bacteria are called **spirilla** (spy RIHL uh). Cocci that form pairs are called *diplococci*, those that form clusters are called *staphylococci*, and those that form chains are called *streptococci*. Most bacilli separate after dividing. Those that stick together tend to form filaments, or threads. Spirilla do not group together but separate after division.

Section Objectives

- *Name* the parts of a bacterial cell and describe the function of each part.
- *Describe* and *name* three different kinds of bacterial shapes.
- *Describe* the methods by which bacteria obtain or produce food.
- *List* some useful and harmful bacteria.
- *Explain* the major methods used to defend the body against bacterial invasion.
- *Describe* how and why Gram stains are used.

cocci (singular, *coccus*)
bacilli (singular, *bacillus*)
spirilla (singular, *spirillum*)

Figure 20–3. The photographs show the three basic shapes of bacteria. Bacilli (left) are rod-shaped. Cocci (center) are sphere-shaped. Spirilla (right) are corkscrew-shaped.

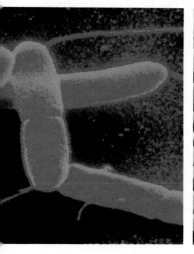
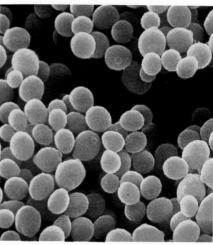
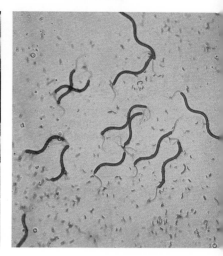

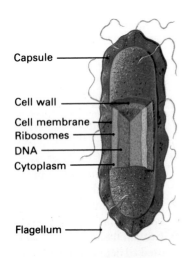

Capsule

Cell wall

Cell membrane
Ribosomes
DNA
Cytoplasm

Flagellum

Figure 20–4. Bacteria are well-protected organisms. A slimy capsule covers and protects the entire cell. The cell wall and cell membrane also protect the cytoplasm, ribosomes, and DNA.

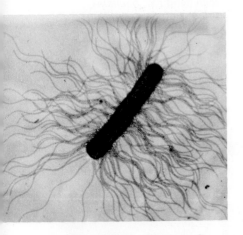

Figure 20–5. The long flagella that help this bacterium move are visible here, magnified 16,000 times.

flagella (singular, *flagellum*)

pili (singular, *pilus*)

20.4 Structure

Some bacteria have rigid cell walls and others have flexible walls. Some infectious bacteria produce a layer of slime that surrounds the outer surface of the cell wall, forming a protective **capsule.** The capsule may protect the bacteria from attack by a host's immune system. A thin cell membrane lies just inside the cell wall. Mycoplasmas, although they have no cell wall, do have a cell membrane and all the other major characteristics of bacteria.

The cytoplasm of a bacterial cell contains many ribosomes. Most of the cell's DNA forms a single, circular chromosome. In addition, some DNA may exist as smaller separate segments called **plasmids.** Like the other bacterial DNA, plasmids are circular and self-reproducing. One bacterium may have as many as a dozen different plasmids. These play a role in certain kinds of genetic transfers.

Some bacteria have long thin extensions called **flagella.** A bacterium may have a single flagellum or numerous flagella, all over its cell surface. **Pili** (PIHL ee) are extensions similar to flagella, but are shorter, thinner, and more numerous. Bacteria use pili to attach themselves to a source of food or oxygen or to another bacterium.

20.5 Movement

Not all bacterial cells are capable of movement. Those that move are called *motile,* and those that do not move are called *nonmotile.* Some motile bacteria move by gliding over a layer of slime. Other bacteria, such as the spirochetes, move by twisting or turning in a corkscrew fashion through water or other fluids. Still other bacteria propel themselves by using their flagella, which move in a rotating fashion.

20.6 Nutrition

Some bacteria are *autotrophic*—that is, they produce their own food. Others are *heterotrophic,* depending on autotrophs for food. Some autotrophic bacteria derive their energy from sunlight. Others derive their energy from the breakdown of inorganic chemicals—a process called **chemosynthesis.** Most heterotrophic bacteria have specialized enzyme systems that allow them to digest certain foods. Some species digest cellulose, while others digest only starch. Because of these various specializations, many types of bacteria can coexist in a single area with little or no competition among them for food.

Expensive Bacteria

Automobiles, bridges, and stainless steel sinks are things that are a part of most people's everyday lives. Unfortunately, these items can rust and corrode. The corrosion of metals is not only a nuisance, but it can also cause much expense and can even be dangerous.

Most metals deteriorate when they are exposed to certain environmental conditions. Some metals, however, corrode as a result of the action of certain bacteria. Some bacteria can break down metals such as stainless steel and aluminum that are ordinarily resistant to corrosion.

"Metal-eating" bacteria are resilient and adaptable. They thrive in a variety of environments that have different acidities and temperatures. Corrosive bacteria may be either aerobic or anaerobic. The most destructive are those that produce potentially corrosive byproducts. For example, some bacteria produce hydrogen sulfide gas, which is highly corrosive to steel.

Corrosive bacteria are a serious problem in industries that rely on the durability of high-technology metal alloys. These bacteria can concentrate and reproduce in places inside the machinery made of these

metals. They can then damage or destroy metal parts that are not harmed by ordinary, everyday use.

"Metal-eating" bacteria can be found in places as familiar as a stainless steel kitchen sink. One metallurgist estimates that, under optimal conditions, bacteria that cause corrosion could eat through a steel sink in a matter of weeks.

Photosynthetic Bacteria   Bacteria that perform photosynthesis use different pigments than plants do. The purple sulfur bacteria and purple nonsulfur bacteria contain a chlorophyll chemically different from plant chlorophyll. Purple sulfur and purple nonsulfur bacteria also have red and yellow pigments called carotenes. Green sulfur bacteria contain a chlorophyll similar to the chlorophyll *a* in plants.

Another way photosynthetic bacteria differ from plants is that the bacteria do not use water and do not produce oxygen as a byproduct. Sulfur bacteria produce carbohydrates by combining carbon dioxide and hydrogen sulfide, using the energy of sunlight. Sulfur is produced as a byproduct. The reaction is:

$$CO_2 + 2H_2S \xrightarrow{\text{light, pigments}} (CH_2O) + H_2O + 2S$$

Purple nonsulfur bacteria use a variety of organic substances as raw materials instead of water.

Reading Critically

Relating Ideas   Why is sulfur bacteria considered autotrophic?

Figure 20-6. The food preservation industry controls bacterial growth in a variety of ways. The photos above show a worker drying fish in the Philippines (top) and others curing Virginia hams with salt (bottom).

Chemosynthetic Bacteria Various types of chemosynthetic bacteria use different energy sources. These sources include nitrogen and sulfur compounds. *Methanogens* convert CO_2 and H_2 to methane gas (CH_4), and in doing so create usable chemical energy for the cell. This conversion of CO_2 and H_2 to CH_4 usually takes place in the mud at the bottom of swamps or marshes.

Heterotrophic Bacteria Most bacteria feed on dead organisms. Such bacteria are called **saprophytes** (SAP ruh fyts). These bacteria of decay break down organic matter and recycle it for use by other organisms. Some saprophytic bacteria live in the soil, others live on rotting bread or fruit. Still other saprophytes break down organic matter inside the intestines of humans and other animals.

20.7 Respiration

Some bacteria require oxygen to carry out respiration. Others use oxygen when it is available. Still others do not require oxygen at all, and in fact die in the presence of oxygen.

Bacteria that require oxygen to live are called **obligate aerobes.** Obligate aerobes generally live where there is an ample supply of oxygen, such as in the air or in loose soil. *Mycobacterium tuberculosis,* the bacterium that causes tuberculosis, is an obligate aerobe that can live in the lungs of human beings.

Bacteria that cannot live in the presence of oxygen are called **obligate anaerobes.** These organisms are found where there is little or no oxygen, such as deep in the soil or in mud at the bottom of lakes. Methanogens are obligate anaerobes. An obligate anaerobe called *Clostridium botulinum* causes a rare but extremely dangerous type of food poisoning known as *botulism*. If food is improperly prepared during canning, botulism bacteria may multiply in the almost oxygen-free environment inside the can or jar.

A third type of bacteria, called **facultative anaerobes,** can grow and reproduce with or without oxygen. The most common bacterium in the human digestive tract, *E. coli*, is a facultative anaerobe.

20.8 Growth

Bacterial growth usually refers to an increase in the number of bacteria, rather than to an increase in the size of an individual cell. A **colony** is a large group of bacteria, such as that grown on a nutrient plate in a laboratory. All the members of a colony are descendants of a single bacterium.

All bacteria need food and water and many need oxygen. Other factors that influence growth are temperature, sunlight, and chemicals. Limiting these growth factors helps prevent food spoilage due to bacterial action. Figure 20–6 shows how bacterial growth is controlled in food.

Some bacteria, particularly certain bacilli, survive harsh conditions such as high or low temperatures, lack of nutrients, or lack of water by forming special cells called **endospores.** The process typically begins when a colony of bacteria has begun to use up its food supply. The DNA replicates and a cell membrane forms around one strand of DNA and a bit of cytoplasm, creating a cell within a cell. A coat then develops around the smaller cell, forming the endospore. Once the endospore is developed, the rest of the cell may die. The endospore can lie dormant for hours or even years. When conditions in the environment

For information about distinguishing types of bacteria using the Gram stain, see the Investigation on page 329.

THINKING ABOUT BIOLOGY: The Gram Stain

Most bacteria are colorless. This feature makes them difficult to view under a microscope. In 1894 the Danish scientist Christian Gram developed a method to stain bacteria. The Gram stain is a differential stain—that is, a stain used to distinguish among types of bacteria.

To perform a Gram stain, a drop of bacteria culture is placed on a slide and dried. The bacterial smear is stained with *crystal violet* stain for one minute. The slide is then washed with water, and iodine is added for one minute. After another wash with water, the slide is washed in a decolorizing agent such as alcohol. If the bacteria have taken up the crystal violet stain, the decolorizing agent will have no effect. If the bacteria have not been stained by crystal violet, then another stain must be used. A pink counterstain called *safranin* is added for 15 seconds. The slide is then washed and blotted dry. Cells that have been stained violet are *Gram-positive.* Those that have stained pink are *Gram-negative.*

The chemical makeup of the cell wall determines how bacteria react to the Gram stain. Since many antibiotics work by attacking the cell wall, the Gram stain also helps researchers identify the types of bacteria likely to be affected by antibiotics. Researchers have found that antibiotics are more likely to be effective against Gram-positive bacteria than against Gram-negative bacteria.

■ **Identifying Relationships** How does the cell wall determine how bacteria react to the Gram stain?

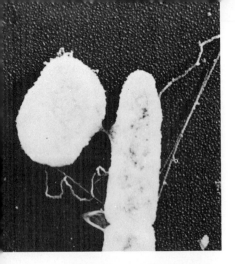

Figure 20–7. When bacteria conjugate, DNA from one bacterium passes through a long conjugation tube into another bacterium.

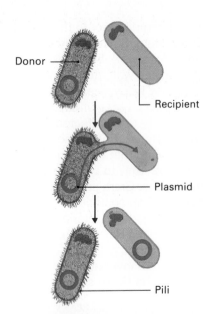

Donor

Recipient

Plasmid

Pili

Figure 20–8. During conjugation, a DNA plasmid is transferred from a donor to an acceptor bacterium.

are again favorable for growth, such as an increase in the supply of nutrients, the spore coat dissolves. The endospore then develops into a normal bacterial cell.

20.9 Reproduction and Genetic Transfer

Under ideal conditions, some bacteria can reproduce every 20 to 30 minutes. *Bacteria usually reproduce through binary fission, or splitting in two. Except for occasional mutations, each new cell is exactly like the parent cell.* Mutations, the result of errors or changes in the genetic code, account in part for the extraordinary ability of bacteria to adjust to differing conditions.

Genetic material in some cases is transferred from one bacterium to another, resulting in *genetic recombination.* When the bacterium later divides, it passes on its new genes to the daughter cells. In this way, resistance to antibiotics can be transferred from one strain, or genetic type, of bacteria to another.

In a process called **conjugation,** a donor bacterium transfers genetic material to an acceptor bacterium through direct contact. Conjugation occurs between two bacteria of the same species when one bacterium has a plasmid that the other lacks. Some of the genetic material of the donor passes to the recipient through a connective pilus. Conjugation occurs rarely and only in some species of bacteria.

As explained in Chapter 19, viruses can transfer genetic material from one bacterium to another through a process called *transduction.* Yet another process, called **transformation,** transfers genetic material from a dead strain of bacteria to a live strain. An example of transformation is provided by experiments of the British bacteriologist Frank Griffith, described in Chapter 12.

20.10 Beneficial and Harmful Bacteria

Some bacteria live independently. Others live in a close, permanent association with organisms of other species. When at least one of two organisms in close association with one another benefits from the relationship, the condition is called **symbiosis.** Three forms of symbiosis occur. In *mutualism* both organisms— the bacterium and its host—benefit. In *commensalism* one organism benefits and the other is neither helped nor harmed. In *parasitism* one organism benefits and the other is harmed. Bacteria that are **parasites,** or harmful to the host, are pathogens. These bacteria cause disease.

Under various circumstances, one type of bacteria may exist in a condition of commensalism, mutualism, or parasitism with its hosts. Consider as an example the *E. coli* that inhabits the digestive tract of humans and certain other mammals. In a commensal relationship, the *E. coli* absorbs nutrients from its host but does not help or harm the host. When producing enzymes, the *E. coli* benefits its host and is in a mutual association. If the *E. coli* enters the bloodstream, however, it may cause disease and is considered a pathogen.

Beneficial Bacteria The majority of bacteria that live on and in the human body are harmless and many are even helpful. The inside of the human intestinal tract, for example, is lined with millions of bacteria, some of which make vitamin K. Many of these bacteria aid digestion by breaking down proteins, starches, and fats. Skin is covered with bacteria. Although some bacteria are harmful and cause skin irritations, most do not.

Many types of bacteria are used in food production. The genus *Lactobacillus,* for instance, is noted for its effect on milk products, producing buttermilk, yogurt, sour cream, and cheese. Lactobacilli are also used in the commercial production of sauerkraut and pickles.

The most important role of bacteria is ecological. Bacteria break down and decompose organic matter. Large, complex organic molecules are consumed and changed into simple chemicals that are then available for use by other organisms.

Nitrogen, an essential element of all proteins, makes up 78 percent of the atmosphere. However, most organisms cannot convert atmospheric nitrogen for their own use. Some bacteria, particularly the *Rhizobium,* take nitrogen from the atmosphere and incorporate it into nitrogen compounds. This process is called **nitrogen fixation.** The *Rhizobium* bacteria live in symbiosis with legumes, which are members of the pea family. The bacteria form *nodules,* or swellings, on the legume roots. The bacteria release "fixed" nitrogen into the plant's cytoplasm, and also release surplus nitrogen into the soil. Animals acquire usable nitrogen by eating the plants that have received nitrogen from the bacteria or from the soil.

Bacterial Infection Not all bacteria are harmless. Many bacteria are pathogens. These bacteria cause minor skin infections as well as such serious diseases as diphtheria, typhoid, tuberculosis, pneumonia, cholera, and leprosy. *Yersinia pestis,* for example, is the bacterium responsible for a disease called *plague* or *black death,* which killed one out of every four people in Europe between 1348 and 1350.

Pathogens damage the body by direct attack and also by the production of *toxins,* or poisons. Diphtheria, for example, is a

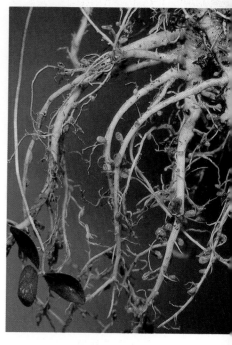

Figure 20–9. Nodules on the roots of this plant are home to millions of *Rhizobium* bacteria. The bacteria fix nitrogen and thus provide compounds that the plant needs.

Q: *What is Rocky Mountain spotted fever?*

A: Rocky Mountain spotted fever is a serious disease caused by rickettsias that live in the salivary glands of ticks. The organisms are transmitted to humans when a person is bitten by an infected tick. Although the disease was first discovered in the Rocky Mountains, it occurs in wooded areas throughout the United States.

disease caused by *Corynebacterium diphtheriae*. The bacteria invade the respiratory tract. The toxin produced by the bacteria enters the bloodstream. It is then absorbed by body cells and interferes with the functioning of the cells, sometimes resulting in the death of the victim.

Protection Against Bacterial Infection   The human body defends against bacterial invaders much as it does against viral infections. Attack by white blood cells and the production of antibodies are part of the body's own immune system. Another defense against bacterial infection has come through the use of antibiotics. **Antibiotics** are chemicals capable of inhibiting the growth of some bacteria.

The first antibiotic was discovered in 1928 by Alexander Fleming, a British bacteriologist. While growing a *Staphylococci* culture, he noticed that a mold had contaminated the bacterial culture. At first Fleming was annoyed that the mold had ruined his experiment. Before throwing out his cultures, however, Fleming noticed that the bacteria were not growing in the area around the mold. Apparently the mold secreted a substance that inhibited bacterial growth. Fleming later named the substance **penicillin,** after the mold, which was *Penicillium notatum*. Penicillin acts by inhibiting the growth of bacterial cell walls. Penicillin is effective against several pathogens including *Streptococcus*. The discovery of penicillin is one of the greatest scientific advances of this century. Hundreds of thousands of lives have been saved through use of this antibiotic since methods were developed to produce it in large quantities. It is particularly effective when used for common infections.

Since Fleming's discovery, many other antibiotics have been identified. *Tetracycline* and *streptomycin* are common antibiotics that interfere with the protein synthesis of some pathogenic bacteria.

Section Review

1. **Classifying Data**   Name and describe the three basic shapes of bacterial cells.
2. **Summarizing Ideas**   Name all the major structural features of a cell of bacteria.
3. **Comparing Ideas**   How does photosynthesis in bacteria differ from photosynthesis in plants?
4. **Identifying Relationships**   What is the ecological importance of bacteria.
5. **Synthesizing Information**   What are the relationships among the Gram stain, antibiotics, and disease?

Thinking Critically

Cyanobacteria

The blue-green bacteria, or **cyanobacteria,** are an extremely hardy group of monerans that live throughout the world. Some live in moist soil; others are found in the desert. Most are aquatic, living in fresh water or salt water.

20.11 Characteristics

Most of the 200 distinct species of cyanobacteria form filaments, or long threads of attached cells. The others are unicellular, shaped like rods or spheres. The cell walls usually have a thick outer covering or sheath. Some, such as *Anabaena,* form single filaments. Others, such as *Nostoc,* cluster together in colonies of filaments organized in a gelatinous ball. The cells of cyanobacteria filaments have interconnecting cytoplasm, and some cells may even have specialized functions. For this reason, some scientists consider them to be a simple type of multicellular organism.

Cyanobacteria are photosynthetic. They contain chlorophyll *a,* the pigment found in plants, rather than the chlorophyll found in bacteria. Cyanobacteria have xanthophyll and carotenes, also found in plants, plus additional accessory pigments called

Section Objectives

- *List* the major characteristics of cyanobacteria.
- *Describe* how cyanobacteria reproduce.
- *Explain* what causes algal blooms.
- *Compare* cyanobacteria and prochlorophyta.

Figure 20–10. Cyanobacteria have diverse shapes and sizes. *Trichodesmium* (top left), *Anabaena* (bottom left), and *Oscillatoria* (below) are examples of this phylum of monerans.

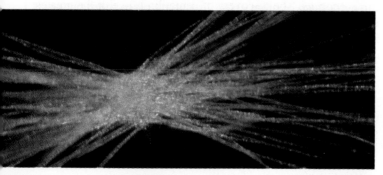

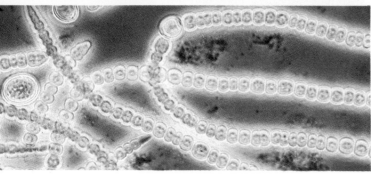

In 1976 a new group was discovered by Roger Lewin of the Scripps Institute in La Jolla, California. This phylum, called Prochlorophyta, has characteristics of both cyanobacteria and higher green algae. The prochlorophytes consist of prokaryotic organisms that are photosynthetic. These organisms almost always live in close association with certain small marine animals.

Prochlorophytes contain both chlorophyll *a* and *b,* the same photosynthetic pigments used by more complex eukaryotic algae and plants. Cyanobacteria contain only chlorophyll *a.* Prochlorophytes and cyanobacteria also differ in the accessory pigments. Prochlorophytes have the standard xanthophylls and carotenes of plants. However, they lack the red and blue phycobilins possessed by cyanobacteria.

News of the discovery of prochlorophytes aroused considerable interest among scientists because the existence of these organisms helped to explain the origin of chloroplasts in eukaryotic cells. Biologists had earlier speculated that chloroplasts in plant cells came about as the result of an invasion of the cytoplasm of other cells by cyanobacteria billions of years ago. This theory did not account, however, for the differences in the pigments of cyanobacteria and the pigments found in plants.

The close similarity between prochlorophytes and plants suggests that the earlier hypothesis may be substantially correct but may need some revision. Some scientists now suggest that prochlorophytes, not cyanobacteria, may be the living descendants of the organism that first gave rise to chloroplasts through invading other cells.

■ **Classifying Ideas** What characteristics of prochlorophyta place them between eukaryotes and cyanobacteria?

phycobilins (FY koh by luhnz). The chlorophyll and other pigments are not enclosed in chloroplasts as they are in plants. Instead the pigments are located on sheets of membrane found in the cytoplasm. Like plants, and unlike photosynthetic bacteria, cyanobacteria use water as a raw material of photosynthesis. They also produce oxygen as a byproduct of the process of photosynthesis.

Not all cyanobacteria are blue-green in color. The presence of the accessory pigments causes these organisms to have a wide range of colors. Various species of cyanobacteria are bright green, golden yellow, blue-black, violet, and many other colors.

Like some forms of bacteria, some cyanobacteria carry out nitrogen fixation. For example, in Southeast Asia nitrogen-fixation by cyanobacteria in rice paddies enables farmers to grow rice on the same land year after year without adding fertilizers.

Reading Critically

Evaluating Ideas Why is cyanobacteria an unusual form of bacteria?

Figure 20–11. Unrestricted growth of cyanobacteria can lead to an algal bloom like this one.

20.12 Reproduction and Growth

Cyanobacteria reproduce by binary fission. Colonies of these organisms also reproduce through **fragmentation,** a process in which the colony breaks into pieces and each piece forms a new organism or colony. Like bacteria, some cyanobacteria can also produce resistant spores that survive in harsh conditions.

The growth of cyanobacteria depends in part on the chemical content of the water in which they live. Dumping phosphates and certain other chemicals into lake water can result in rapid growth of cyanobacteria and algae called an **algal bloom.** The water takes on the color of the cyanobacteria and algae living in it. The decay of overabundant organisms reduces the amount of oxygen in the water. This process in turn causes fishes to die and makes the treatment of the water more difficult. For this reason, the use of phosphate in detergents has been reduced in recent years so that fewer of these chemicals are added to water.

Biofact

Q: *How did the Red Sea get its name?*

A: The waters of the Red Sea are not red, but occasionally a bloom will cause the water to have a red tint. The bacteria responsible for the bloom is a species of cyanobacteria that has a very high content of red phycobilin.

Section Review

1. **Contrasting Data**   Contrast the pigments in cyanobacteria and prochlorophyta.
2. **Summarizing Information**   Describe fragmentation.
3. **Analyzing Relationships**   Explain how algal blooms affect freshwater lakes and the animals that live in them.

Thinking Critically

Testing for AIDS

There are many benefits to AIDS testing. A person who is infected with HIV can seek medical and psychological counseling that may help delay the onset of symptoms and provide ways of dealing with the problems that may arise when symptoms become apparent. People with positive test results can also practice behaviors that will prevent them from spreading the virus to others.

Many people think that testing for the AIDS virus should be mandatory and widespread because of the benefits. Other people are opposed to mandatory testing. They fear that people who are known to be infected with HIV may face problems from prospective employers, may not be able to obtain insurance, and in the case of young people of school age, may encounter opposition that may make it difficult for them to attend school. In response to these fears, health agencies are being asked to guard the privacy of those who are tested for HIV or to give anonymous tests.

Proponents of mandatory AIDS testing insist that the threat of AIDS to the public health overshadows the individual's right to privacy. HIV testing, they argue, benefits the public because every case of HIV infection that can be prevented now could prevent two to five cases by the year 2000.

The interest in privacy surrounding AIDS testing has sparked interest in home HIV tests. Some companies sell kits that allow individuals to collect their own blood sample, mail it to a laboratory for testing, and receive the results by telephone. Other companies are interested in marketing home tests that are similar to those for pregnancy and diabetes. Advocates argue that home tests could increase the number of individuals who know that they carry the virus and that these kinds of tests would insure confidentiality. Many health officials, however, question the reliability of home tests and are concerned about the adequacy of medical and psychological counseling to people who test positive in home tests. These officials encourage public

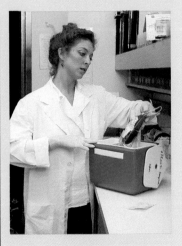

education and stricter confidentiality of records, rather than self-testing for HIV infection.

Analyze the Issue

1. Describe the possible advantages and disadvantages of both mandatory and voluntary widespread AIDS testing.

2. What issues are raised by home testing rather than clinic testing?

3. If you were a student member of a commission on AIDS, what policies would you recommend concerning a student who tested positive for HIV antibodies? Support your view.

INVESTIGATION 20:
How Are Bacteria Identified?

Objectives
- To *prepare* bacteria for examination using the Gram staining technique
- To *distinguish* between types of bacteria

Materials
E. coli culture, inoculating loop, Bunsen burner, three medicine droppers, two glass slides, forceps, crystal violet, Gram's iodine, safranin, 95 percent ethanol, beaker, water, paper towels, immersion oil, compound light microscope with oil immersion objective, *Sarcina lutea* culture, cleaning solvent

Prelab Preparation
1. List the characteristics of bacteria.
2. Read Thinking About Biology: The Gram Stain on page 321.
3. Explain why using the Gram stain is useful when studying bacteria.

Inquiry: Lab Technique
4. **CAUTION: Put on safety goggles, a laboratory apron, and rubber gloves. Follow your teacher's instructions for proper handling and disposal of bacteria.**
5. Obtain a stock culture of *E. coli.* Heat an inoculating loop in the Bunsen burner flame. *Why is the loop flamed?* Remove the stopper from the culture tube, flame the mouth of the tube, and use the loop to transfer a drop of culture to a glass slide. Flame the loop and the mouth of the culture tube, then seal the tube with the stopper. *Why are the loop and tube flamed a second time?*
6. Smear the drop of culture on a clean glass slide and allow it to dry. Use forceps to hold the slide with the smear side up, pass the slide quickly through the flame three times. Allow the slide to cool. *Why is the slide flamed?*
7. Flood the slide with crystal violet stain and allow it to stand for one minute. Pour off the excess stain and gently rinse the slide in a beaker of water.
8. Remove the slide from the water and flood the smear with Gram's iodine. Let it stand for one minute. Gently rinse the slide in a beaker of water.
9. While holding the slide at an angle over the beaker, rinse the smear with ethanol until no stain rinses off.
10. Rinse the slide in clean water and flood the smear with safranin stain. Allow the slide to stand for 15 seconds.
11. Rinse the slide in the water and carefully blot it dry with a paper towel.
12. Add a drop of immersion oil to the smear. Use low power to focus, then switch to high power and locate an area that shows stain. Switch the oil immersion objective into place. The objective will be immersed in the oil but it should not be touching the slide.
13. Draw the bacteria as they appear under the oil immersion objective. *Are they Gram-positive or Gram-negative?*
14. Repeat steps 1 through 10 using the *S. lutea* culture.
15. When you have finished, use cleaning solvent to carefully clean the immersion oil objective.

Analysis
1. **Analyzing Relationships** Why is the Gram stain useful in classifying bacteria?
2. **Analyzing Methods** Explain why some bacteria test Gram-positive and others test Gram-negative?
3. **Making Inferences** Why might other stains also be used to study bacteria?

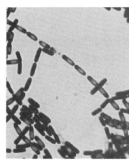
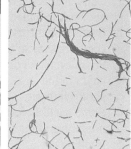

Gram-positive   Gram-negative

Chapter 20 Review

Summary

Monerans, which are all prokaryotes, are found in nearly every habitat on Earth. The three phyla of the kingdom Monera are the Schizophyta, which includes the bacteria; the Cyanophyta, also known as cyanobacteria; and the Prochlorophyta, monerans that use chlorophylls *a* and *b* for photosynthesis.

Most bacteria are heterotrophic, although some are autotrophic. Some autotrophic bacteria are photosynthetic, and others are chemosynthetic. Obligate aerobes need oxygen to grow; obligate anaerobes die in the presence of oxygen. Although some bacteria live independently, others form symbiotic relationships.

Bacteria are important ecologically because they help break down dead organisms into useful organic nutrients. Bacteria convert nitrogen into forms usable by plants. Some bacteria cause disease.

Cyanobacteria are photosynthetic. They have many pigments found in eukaryotic algae and plants plus phycobilins.

BioTerms

algal bloom (327)
antibiotic (324)
bacillus (317)
bacterium (314)
capsule (318)
chemosynthesis (318)
coccus (317)
colony (320)
conjugation (322)
cyanobacteria (325)
endospore (321)

facultative anaerobe (320)
flagella (318)
fragmentation (327)
mycoplasma (316)
nitrogen fixation (323)
obligate aerobe (320)
obligate anaerobe (320)
parasite (322)
penicillin (324)

pilus (318)
plasmid (318)
rickettsia (316)
saprophyte (320)

spirillum (317)
spirochete (316)
symbiosis (322)
transformation (322)

For each pair of terms, explain the differences in their meanings.

1. obligate aerobe, obligate anaerobe
2. conjugation, transformation
3. bacillus, coccus
4. fragmentation, algal bloom

BioQuiz   (Write all answers on a separate sheet of paper.)

Completion

1. Cells that lack a membrane-bound nucleus are called _____ .
2. Bacteria that survive harsh environmental conditions do so by forming _____ .
3. Prochlorophyta differ from Cyanophyta in the _____ used to carry out photosynthesis.
4. Some bacteria form a protective _____ by producing slime.
5. Bacteria use _____ to attach themselves to a source of food or oxygen.

Multiple Choice

6. _____ bacteria are light pink in color after a Gram stain.   a) Gram-positive b) Gram-neutral   c) Gram-negative d) Parasitic
7. Organisms that obtain nutrition from dead organisms are called   a) parasitic. b) obligate anaerobes. c) chemosynthetic.   d) saprophytic.
8. Smaller segments of DNA that exist in the cytoplasm are called   a) plasmids. b) pili. c) mycoplasmas. d) spirochetes.

9. Dumping phosphates into lake water can result in   a) nitrogen-fixation.   b) algal blooms.   c) fragmentation.   d) transformation.
10. Cyanobacteria are   a) saprophytic.   b) heterotrophic.   c) chemosynthetic.   d) photosynthetic.
11. Bacteria that live underground are probably   a) obligate aerobes. b) obligate anaerobes.   c) prochlorophytes.   d) cyanobacteria.
12. Bacteria transmit genetic information through transformation or   a) conjugation.   b) fragmentation.   c) chemosynthesis.   d) symbiosis.
13. *Yersinia pestis* is a bacterium that is   a) an antibiotic.   b) a rickettsia.   c) a saprophyte.   d) a parasite.
14. Cyanobacteria contain an accessory pigment called   a) phycobilin.   b) carotene.   c) xanthophyll.   d) chlorophyll *a*.
15. Which of the following is not a form of symbiosis among bacteria?   a) mutualism   b) commensalism   c) parasitism   d) All are forms of symbiosis.

Writing Critically

16. How do motile bacteria move about?
17. How did new technology lead to changes in moneran classification?
18. How is the growth of bacteria controlled in food products?
19. Why is it possible for many different bacteria to coexist in a small area of space?
20. How do bacteria benefit humans?

Application/Critical Thinking

1. **Inferring Relationships**   Scientists think that the atmosphere of the ancient Earth contained little or no free atmospheric oxygen gas. In that case, which types of bacteria probably were the first to appear? Explain.
2. **Synthesizing Data**   Use your school library or public library to research penicillin. Write a paragraph about how this antibiotic kills bacterial cells.
3. **Recognizing Relationships**   The bacterium *Streptococcus mutans* lives on teeth and produces an acid that can cause tooth enamel to decay. Use this information to explain why people who eat a lot of food containing sugar generally have more cavities than those who do not.
4. **Inferring Conclusions**   Tetanus is a disease caused by an anaerobic bacterium that lives in the soil. Anyone who has stepped on a nail or received any other deep puncture wound must usually get an injection to prevent tetanus. Since bacteria could enter through any break in the skin, why is tetanus more likely to result from a puncture wound than from a scratch or a cut?

Cross-Discipline Connection

Biology and Social Studies   Invite a career counselor to speak at your school. What occupations rely on knowledge of bacterial growth and reproduction?

Discovery Through Reading

Read "Microbes to the Rescue," *Newsweek* (June 19, 1989): 56–57. How are bacteria being used to clean up aquifers, toxic dumps, and oil spills? What is bioremediation?

Summary

Viruses are microscopic forms that consist of a nucleic acid core surrounded by a protein coat. Biologists do not consider viruses to be alive. Viruses cannot reproduce unless they invade a living cell. Some viruses undergo an inactive, or dormant, lysogenic cycle after they invade a cell. The active lytic cycle of viral reproduction results in the production of many new viruses and the destruction of the host cell.

Viruses can transfer genetic information from one cell to another through the process of transduction, which alters the genetic code of a cell. Viruses cause diseases in many organisms. The human immune system produces phagocytes, antibodies, and interferon that protect the body against viruses. Vaccines containing weakened pathogens confer active immunity by stimulating antibody production. Active immunity is the production of antibodies that result from exposure to a pathogen.

Monerans are prokaryotes found in nearly every habitat on the Earth. The kingdom Monera includes bacteria and cyanobacteria. Bacteria generally have one of three shapes—spherical (coccus), rod (bacillus), or corkscrew (spirilum). Most bacteria are beneficial. Many are decomposers that release essential atoms from dead organisms. Others fix nitrogen in compounds that plants can use. Although microscopic, bacteria vary from 0.1 μm to 500 μm in length. Some bacteria are autotrophic, although most are heterotrophic. Only some autotrophic bacteria are photosynthetic, and others are chemosynthetic.

Bacteria reproduce through binary fission. Obligate aerobes require oxygen; obligate anaerobes cannot reproduce in the presence of oxygen. Although some bacteria are free-living, others form symbiotic relationships.

Cyanobacteria are photosynthetic. They contain phycobilins in addition to many pigments found in eukaryotic algae.

Synthesis

Synthesis Statement

Viruses cannot grow, respire, or respond to stimuli. They are not able to reproduce outside the cells of a host organism. For these reasons, biologists do not consider viruses to be alive. However, the requirement of viruses for a living host, in addition to the nucleic acid and protein makeup of viruses, makes viruses a target for biological study.

Bacteria show adaptations that allow them to survive in most environments. These organisms also show adaptations that allow them to survive under unfavorable conditions. Their method of asexual reproduction and their ability to live in air, water, on most surfaces, and even between soil particles, have contributed to their success.

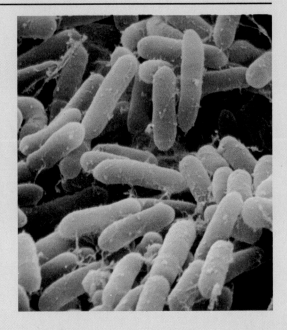

Synthesis Questions

Apply your understanding of this unit to the following questions.

1. Most bacteria and viruses have very specific habitat requirements yet are extremely successful. Describe some reasons for the evolutionary success of bacteria and viruses.

2. Why were monerans once grouped with plants in the classification of living things? Describe ways in which monerans resemble plants. Why do modern biologists place the monerans in their own kingdom?

3. Should a sixth kingdom be created for the viruses? Offer arguments for and against the formation of a new kingdom for the viruses.

4. The different species of bacterial and other members of the kingdom Monera have a wide variety of nutritional sources. How might humans benefit from genetically engineered bacteria that feed on unusual substances?

5. Antibiotics control some bacteria diseases. Discuss the drawbacks to the widespread use of antibiotics among humans and livestock.

6. How do species of pathogenic bacteria survive when a host dies and a new host is not immediately available? Name viral adaptations that solve the same problem.

7. Describe some ways in which unicellularity is advantageous to bacteria.

8. Discuss the differences between pathogenic viruses and pathogenic bacteria.

9. List some reasons why the geographic movements of viral and bacterial diseases might have changed during the last century.

10. Use a separate piece of paper to draw a concept map like the one below. Place each of the following terms or phrases inside the appropriate figure: bacteria, protein coat, nucleic acid, nuclear area, microscopic, all require a host, autotrophic, heterotrophic, photosynthesis, and chemosynthetic. More than one term or phrase may be placed in the two large circles and in the area where they overlap.

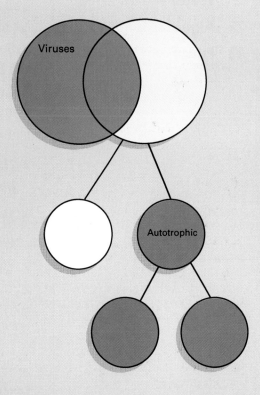

UNIT

6

PROTISTA AND FUNGI

Unit Outline

Unit Focus

Protists include heterotrophic forms such as the protozoa, slime molds, and water molds, as well as the autotrophic algae. All fungi are heterotrophs.

Some members of both the kingdoms Protista and Fungi are of economic importance to humans, some play important roles in the cycling of materials in the environment, and some cause human diseases.

■ *How do you think the slime mold in the photograph obtains food?*

■ *Protozoa are often heterotrophs. Why do you think taxonomists formerly classified these organisms as animals?*

Lavender slime molds

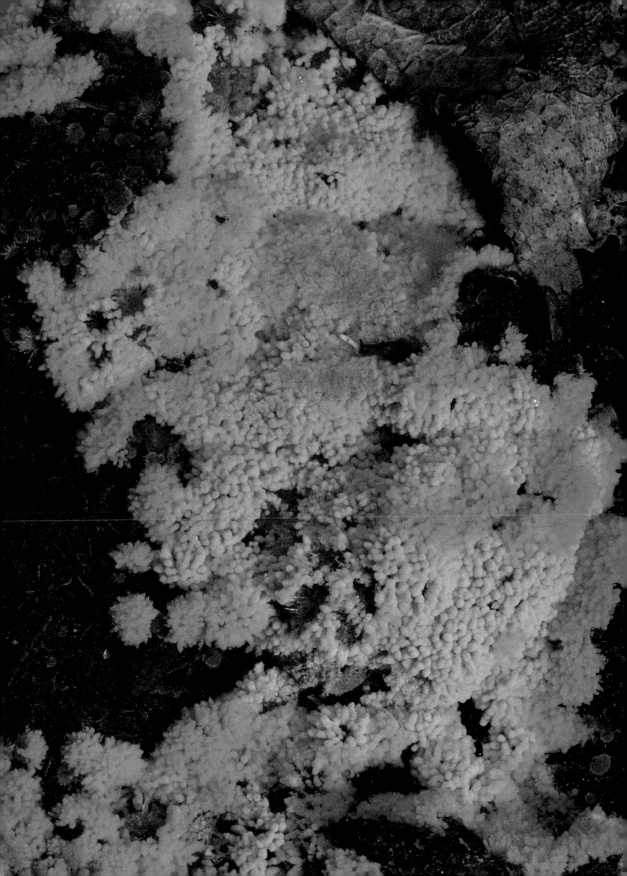

Protozoa, Slime Molds, and Water Molds

Outline

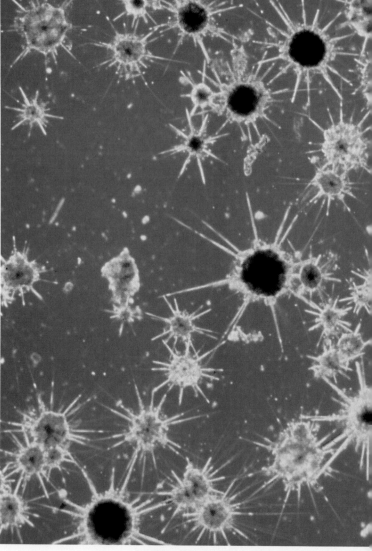

Live radiolarians, marine protozoa

Focus

Protozoa are a diverse group of unicellular eukaryotes that belong to the kingdom Protista. The word protozoa means "first animal." Even though they are single-celled, protozoa are complex heterotrophs that perform all the basic activities of life. Water molds and slime molds are also heterotrophic protists. All protists ingest food, excrete wastes, respire, and reproduce. They also respond to stimuli in the environment.

- *What adaptation shown by the radiolarians in the photograph allows them to trap plankton as they float beneath the surface of the water?*

- *Why do you think protozoa were once classified as animals?*

Protozoa

Protozoa include a diverse group of unicellular organisms that are members of the kingdom Protista. Like other protists, protozoa are eukaryotes that have a membrane-bound nucleus. Unlike many other protists, however, protozoa are heterotrophic—that is, they obtain energy by feeding on other organisms. Although a few of the approximately 27,000 species of protozoa can be up to 5 cm (2 in.) in length, most protozoan species are microscopic.

Most protozoa are aquatic. *Protozoa are usually classified according to their method of movement, which is related to their structure.* Three of the major phyla of protozoa are motile—that is, they use energy to move about freely. One phylum includes nonmotile protozoa. Marine protozoa and other microscopic heterotrophs drifting in the ocean are collectively called **zooplankton** (zoh uh PLANK tuhn).

Protozoa live independently or in **symbiosis**—that is, in close association with another species of organism. Symbiotic relationships take one of three forms. In **parasitism,** one species is helped and the other is harmed. The species that benefits is called a *parasite.* The species that is harmed is called a *host.* Most protozoa that live in symbiosis are parasites. Other protozoa are found in two other forms of symbiosis. In *mutualism,* both species benefit from the association. In *commensalism,* one species benefits and the other is unaffected by the relationship.

Section Objectives

- *Identify* the characteristics of protozoa.
- *Name* the basis for classifying protozoa.
- *Contrast* the ways in which amoebas and paramecia capture and digest food.
- *Explain* how paramecia reproduce sexually.
- *Describe* the life cycle of a typical sporozoan.
- Compare the features of protozoa and *Euglena.*

21.1 Flagellates

Protozoa that belong to the phylum Mastigophora are called *flagellates* because they move by means of one or more flagella. About 2,500 species of protozoa are flagellates.

Many materials diffuse through the cell membrane of a flagellate cell. Oxygen, potassium, and other dissolved substances pass into the cell by diffusion. Carbon dioxide, ammonia, and other molecular wastes leave the cell by diffusion. Like most other motile protozoa, flagellates are almost constantly moving. A few species of flagellates are free-living, but most are parasites or commensals. Some parasitic flagellates have complex life cycles involving two or more hosts. Parasitic flagellates live in the body tissues and fluids of both plants and animals.

Figure 21–1 shows flagellates that belong to the genus *Trypanosoma.* Members of this species are parasites that move by means of a single flagellum and the wavelike motion of a thin membrane that runs along one side of the cell. Trypanosomes cause African sleeping sickness in humans and cattle.

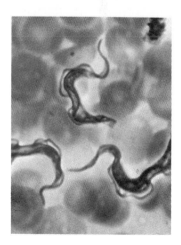

Figure 21–1. These protozoa of the genus *Trypanosoma* cause African sleeping sickness in humans and cattle.

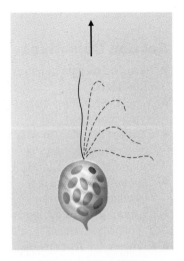

Figure 21–2. Flagellates are pulled through the water by the action of the flagellum.

The life cycle of trypanosomes begins not in humans or cattle, however, but in the tsetse fly. Here the trypanosomes reproduce but cause no harm to their hosts. When the tsetse fly bites humans or cattle, trypanosomes enter the bloodstream of their new host in the fly's saliva. There the trypanosomes reproduce again and secrete poisons that cause fever and the common symptom of extreme sleepiness that gives the disease its name. In general, however, they do not kill their hosts. A tsetse fly that bites an infected host ingests trypanosomes and continues to spread the disease.

Members of the genus *Trichonympha* live in the digestive system of termites. Termites feed on cellulose fibers in wood. However, they lack the enzyme that can digest tough fibers. The flagellates produce an enzyme that breaks down the wood fibers into a carbohydrate that both they and the termite can use. These flagellates show a symbiotic relationship in which both organisms benefit.

THINKING ABOUT BIOLOGY: *Euglena*

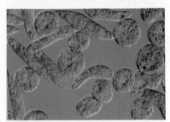

Euglena is a genus of freshwater, unicellular organism. Members of this group have features of both protozoa and of plantlike protists called *algae.* Like mastigophorans, *Euglena* move by using flagella. Like algae, these organisms carry on photosynthesis. *Euglena* is sometimes classified as a separate phylum because of this unique combination of characteristics.

When in the presence of light, *Euglena* is autotrophic. These unicellular forms have features that enhance their ability to produce food. If a population of *Euglena* is left in a glass by a window, a green cloud forms on the sunny side of the glass. This shows that the organisms move toward light, a characteristic called **positive phototropism.** A red-pigment **eyespot** that is sensitive to light allows the organism to sense a light source that provides a maximum opportunity for photosynthesis to take place.

If *Euglena* cells are kept in the dark for a long

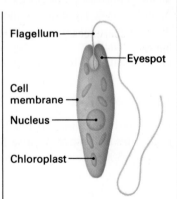

period, they become heterotrophs. They lose their chloroplasts and engulf and digest decaying materials in the water in which they live.

■ **Analyzing Relationships** What characteristic of Euglena most strongly suggests that it is a protist?

21.2 Sarcodines

About 11,500 species of protozoa belong to the phylum Sarcodina, commonly called *sarcodines*. Sarcodines move by extending parts of their cytoplasm and cell membrane to form footlike projections. These projections, called **pseudopodia** (soo duh POH dee uh), are pushed out by cytoplasm flowing in the cell. The word *pseudopodia* means "false feet."

Many sarcodines have shells. Members of the marine genus *Foraminifera* secrete hard outer shells of calcium carbonate. *Foraminifera* extend pseudopodia through spaces in their shells. Members of the genus *Radiolaria* have internal shells made of silica. Radiolaria have pointed pseudopodia, which are coated with a sticky substance that traps food.

Other species of sarcodines have no shells. The most familiar of these belong to the genus *Amoeba* (uh MEE buh). Amoebas are soft, jellylike organisms. They live in muddy lake bottoms, the ocean floor, and on the surface of water plants.

Structure of Amoebas   Amoebas look like shapeless, irregular masses of cytoplasm, yet they are highly organized cells. Each amoeba contains at least one nucleus and other organelles. It also has a specialized organelle called the *contractile vacuole* that collects excess water and pumps it out of the cell. This regulation of water in the cell keeps the amoeba from bursting.

Most of an amoeba is filled with **endoplasm,** a thick, grainy kind of cytoplasm. Between the endoplasm and the cell membrane is a clear, thin layer of cytoplasm called **ectoplasm.** When amoebas move, the endoplasm pushes forward to form new pseudopodia while existing pseudopodia are drawn up from behind. This characteristic creeping motion is called **amoeboid movement.** The pseudopodia give amoebas their ever-changing shape. Pseudopodia can form anywhere on the cell surface and are used both for locomotion and for capturing food.

Capturing Food   Amoebas absorb water and dissolved nutrients through their cell membrane, but they also actively seek food. Amoebas use pseudopodia to capture unicellular organisms and other bits of food in a process called *phagocytosis.* When an amoeba comes into contact with a food particle, one or more pseudopodia engulf the food. The cell membrane that surrounds the particle then pinches together and separates from the outer membrane, forming a *food vacuole.* Enzymes diffuse into the vacuole and digest the food. Undigested food is excreted by the opposite process of *exocytosis.* In exocytosis a vacuole forms around the waste, moves toward the outside of the cell,

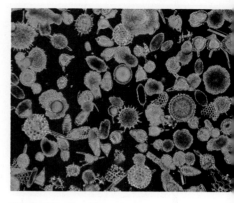

Figure 21–3.   Many sarcodines secrete shells that protect their soft bodies. This radiolarian shell is made of silica compounds.

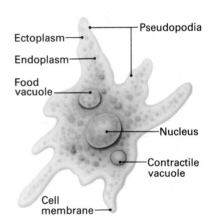

Ectoplasm
Endoplasm
Food vacuole
Pseudopodia
Nucleus
Contractile vacuole
Cell membrane

Figure 21–4.   Amoebas are the most familiar sarcodines. Although irregular in shape, amoebas are highly organized cells. Amoebas move by extending parts of their cytoplasm as pseudopodia.

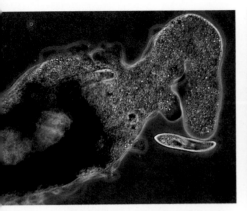
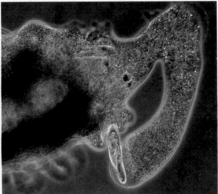
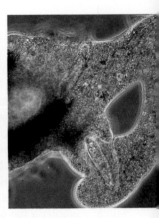

Figure 21–5. Amoebas engulf food through phagocytosis. An amoeba first encircles the food with pseudopodia (left). The pseudopodia then close around the food and draw it close to the cell (center). Later the amoeba engulfs the food and digests it (right).

Reading Critically

Analyzing Ideas What two characteristics help the amoeba survive and reproduce?

Protists will be observed in the Investigation on page 346.

fuses with the cell membrane, and expels its contents through a temporary opening. The vacuole then remains fused with the cell membrane.

Reproduction Amoebas reproduce asexually by **binary fission,** a process in which two identical daughter cells form from one parent cell. The nucleus of the parent cell replicates and the cell membrane pinches in half, dividing the cytoplasm between the two new cells. Binary fission occurs about every 24 hours unless conditions are unfavorable for survival. Then the amoeba's cell membrane thickens into a protective outer structure called a **cyst** (sihst). Within the cyst, the organism's nucleus may divide many times in a process called **multiple fission.** Many new amoebas are released from the cyst when conditions again become favorable for their survival.

Response Like all organisms, amoebas are sensitive to their environment. In a response called **negative phototropism,** amoebas move away from light. Amoebas feed on the nutrient-rich bodies of dead organisms, called *detritus,* that collect on the dark floors of lakes and the oceans. Negative phototropism helps amoebas survive by leading them into regions where they are most likely to find food.

Amoebas show sensitivity to chemicals in their environment by moving toward those they sense as food and away from those they sense as harmful. Amoebas also move around objects that block their paths.

21.3 Ciliates

The phylum Ciliophora, called *ciliates,* includes about 7,200 species. Ciliates are the most complex protozoa. Instead of one or two flagella, ciliate cells have hundreds of cilia. Each cilium looks like a fine eyelash. The cilia may cover the entire surface of the cell or they may grow only from a specific part of the cell. Cilia beat continuously and rapidly, sometimes as fast as 60 times per second. Their movements are highly synchronized.

Most ciliates are free-living and use their cilia to propel themselves through water in pursuit of prey. However, some types of ciliates become permanently attached to a rock or other surface. Organisms that remain anchored in one place for most of their lives are said to be **sessile.** Sessile ciliates are not free to move through the water and pursue prey. Instead, the beating of their cilia creates a whorl of water that sucks food particles into the cell.

Structure of *Paramecium*

The genus *Paramecium* is a familiar representative of the ciliates. Paramecia live in fresh water and are easy to collect. These organisms have distinct anterior and posterior ends, as shown in Figure 21–8 on page 322. The shape of a paramecium is maintained by a sheath of protein called the pellicle that surrounds the cell membrane. Rows of beating cilia move the cell forward in a spiral path.

Like most ciliates, paramecia contain two nuclei. The smaller nucleus, called the **micronucleus,** controls reproduction. The larger nucleus, called the **macronucleus,** directs the

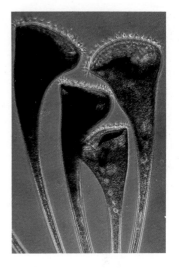

Figure 21–6. This funnel-shaped ciliate called *Stentor* collects food by creating a whirlpool with cilia located around its mouth. As organisms swim by, they are swept into the funnel.

BIOLOGY AND YOU:

A Killer Amoeba

Lurking at the bottom of swimming holes and lakes is an amoeba that can kill in a matter of hours. The killer amoeba emerges from a protective cyst when water temperature in fresh water ponds and lakes reaches about 29° C (85° F). The organism usually enters the body when water from the bottom of a lake, river, or pond forcibly enters the nose. This can happen, for example, when diving, water-skiing, or swimming around the mucky bottom where the amoeba lives.

The amoeba migrates to the brain where it causes a disease called *primary amoebic meningoencephalitis (PAM).* Headache and fever appear almost immediately, followed in 24 hours by a coma, and in 48 hours by death.

Fortunately, killer amoeba deaths are rare. Only one case of PAM appears for every 2.2 million freshwater swimmers.

The best ways to prevent becoming infected by this amoeba are to wear a nose clip that prevents water from entering the nose and to avoid diving and swimming near the bottom.

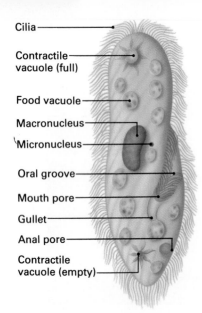

Cilia

Contractile vacuole (full)

Food vacuole

Macronucleus

Micronucleus

Oral groove

Mouth pore

Gullet

Anal pore

Contractile vacuole (empty)

Figure 21–7. A paramecium gathers food into an oral groove and gullet, digests it in food vacuoles, and excretes wastes through an anal pore. Water balance is regulated by a contractile vacuole.

Figure 21–8. The process of conjugation, illustrated below, allows the transfer of genes from one paramecium to another.

other metabolic functions in the cell. A paramecium cell has endoplasm, ectoplasm, and the organelles found in amoebas. In paramecia, however, the contractile vacuole is more specialized. Structures called **radiating canals** surround the vacuole. The radiating canals function like drainpipes by collecting excess water from a wide area around the contractile vacuole.

Capturing Food Paramecia have more complex means of capturing and digesting food than do amoebas. Figure 21–7 shows the food passageway in a paramecium. Cilia sweep food particles into a channel known as the **oral groove.** From there the food travels to an opening called the **mouth pore,** where food enters the endoplasm. The food is then stored in a chamber beneath the mouth pore called the **gullet.** At the end of the gullet, a food vacuole forms. As in amoebas, enzymes diffuse into the vacuole and digest the food. Undigested wastes are carried to the **anal pore,** where the vacuole expels the wastes through exocytosis.

Reproduction Paramecia may undergo a process called *conjugation,* a series of events during which two cells exchange genetic material. In some species of paramecia, one of the two donor cells dies after conjugation. This type of conjugation resembles bacterial conjugation.

Conjugation begins when two paramecia join at their oral grooves. The micronucleus in each paramecium then undergoes meiosis, producing two haploid micronuclei in each organism. One of these micronuclei and the macronucleus of each cell disappear. Then the remaining micronuclei move to the oral groove, where they undergo mitosis. As figure 21–8 shows, the oral groove now contains four haploid micronuclei, one matching pair from each cell.

 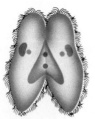 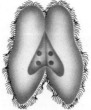 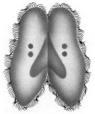 

Paramecia join at oral groove; micronuclei divide

One new micronucleus in each moves to oral groove; macronuclei disintegrate

Micronuclei divide by mitosis, leaving two matching pairs (four micronuclei in groove)

One from each pair transfers to the other paramecium

New pairs fuse; paramecia separate; new macronuclei develop

Next, the paramecia exchange genetic material. Each cell keeps one micronucleus and donates the second one to the other cell. The new pairs of haploid micronuclei in each paramecium fuse, forming diploid micronuclei with a new combination of genetic material. As the two paramecia separate, a macronucleus containing the new combination of genetic material forms in each organism.

Like amoebas, paramecia also reproduce asexually by binary fission. However, this process is somewhat different in paramecia. The micronucleus divides by mitosis, and the resulting micronuclei move to opposite ends of the cell. A new set of organelles forms so that each daughter cell has a complete set. The genetic material in the macronucleus is divided between the daughter cells. The cytoplasm also divides, forming two separate paramecia.

Response When a paramecium bumps into an object, it stops, reverses direction, and then continues forward at a different angle. It repeats this *avoidance reaction* as often as necessary to get past the obstacle. When attacked by another organism, a paramecium shows a *defense reaction* by discharging tiny threads of material called **trichocysts** (TRIKH uh sihsts), which harden upon contact with water. Trichocysts can drive away attacking organisms or paralyze organisms that the paramecium then consumes.

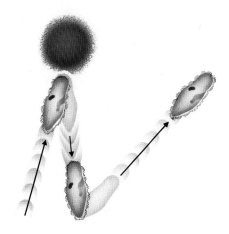

Figure 21–9. When a paramecium encounters an obstacle, such as a drop of ink, it backs off, alters its course slightly, and proceeds forward. Scientists call this behavior an *avoidance reaction.*

21.4 Sporozoans

The phylum Sporozoa contains about 6,000 species, all of which are nonmotile parasites. These protozoa do not have flagella, cilia, pseudopodia, or any structures that produce independent movement. They are carried along by currents in the blood or other body fluids of their hosts.

As parasites, sporozoans cause a wide variety of serious diseases. *Plasmodium,* shown in Figure 21–10 on page 346, is the genus that causes *malaria.* **The disease cycle of Plasmodium illustrates the life cycle of a typical sporozoan.**

Plasmodium has a complex life cycle that involves more than one host. The cycle begins when a female *Anopheles* mosquito bites an infected person and ingests the *Plasmodium* parasites along with the person's blood. Male mosquitoes are not responsible for transmitting the disease because males do not feed as adults. The parasites reproduce sexually inside the female mosquito's body and then form cysts in the mosquito's digestive tract. The nucleus in each cyst divides repeatedly until the cyst bursts, releasing the next stage

Biofact

Q: *How serious is malaria?*

A: Malaria has killed more people than any other infectious disease in history. Due to shortages of quinine, more people died from malaria in World War II than were killed in battle.

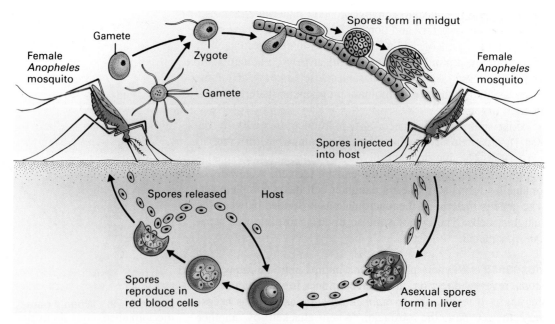

Gamete

Zygote

Gamete

Female Anopheles mosquito

Spores form in midgut

Female Anopheles mosquito

Spores injected into host

Spores released   Host

Spores reproduce in red blood cells

Asexual spores form in liver

Figure 21–10. *Plasmodium,* the cause of malaria, is carried from host to host by mosquitoes. Sexual reproduction takes place in the mosquito's gut. The formation of asexual spores takes place in the host's liver and red blood cells.

Problems associated with malaria control are discussed on page 372.

into the mosquito's body. Some parasites reach the mosquito's salivary glands. The parasites are transmitted to a human host when the female takes another human blood meal. Once inside a person's blood stream, the parasite invades the red blood cells where it reproduces asexually at regular intervals of from 5 to 12 days. The cycle of reproduction in the human results in the regular recurrence of symptoms that include chills and fever. Although *Plasmodium* can be killed with antibiotics, the organism has become resistant to these drugs in many areas. Scientists are working to develop a vaccine against malaria. Sporozoans appear to have lost many complex adaptations as they became parasites. Thus, their very simplicity is considered to be an advanced adaptation.

Section Review

1. **Analyzing Ideas**   What characteristic distinguishes protozoa from other members of the kingdom Protista?
2. **Inferring Relationships**   How do amoebas and paramecia capture food?
3. **Summarizing Ideas**   Describe the life cycle of the malaria parasite.
4. **Comparing Ideas**   Distinguish between fission and conjugation in paramecium.
5. **Analyzing Relationships**   What characteristics does *Euglena* share with protozoans?

> **Thinking Critically**

Funguslike Protists

The funguslike protists include the water molds and the slime molds. The water molds and the slime molds are not true molds. Because they resemble fungi, the water molds and the slime molds have sometimes been placed in the kingdom Fungi. However, the water molds and the slime molds share structural and reproductive features that distinguish them as protists.

21.5 Slime Molds

The slime molds are difficult to classify. In body form, slime molds resemble protozoa, but their method of reproduction somewhat resembles that of a fungus. They are classified as protists because of their resemblance to amoebas.

There are two main groups of slime molds, plasmodial slime molds and cellular slime molds. A plasmodial slime mold consists of a brightly colored, streaming mass of cytoplasm called a **plasmodium,** which contains many nuclei. It creeps by amoeboid movement over the ground and dead organic material. Like an amoeba, the plasmodium engulfs microscopic prey and digests the food in food vacuoles.

When its food supply runs short, the plasmodium separates into tiny mounds of cytoplasm that develop into funguslike sporangia. The brightly-colored pigmented species of plasmodial slime molds require light to begin spore production. The spores produced in these sporangia may be scattered to new areas where food is more plentiful. Slime mold spores grow into either flagellated or amoebalike cells. A new plasmodium develops when two flagellated cells fuse or when a mass of the amoebalike cells join and form the larger organism.

Cellular slime molds also form a slimelike mass, which consists of individual cells separated by cell membranes.

Section Objectives

- *List* the characteristics that slime molds share with fungi and those they share with protozoa.
- *Summarize* the methods of feeding and reproduction in the slime molds.
- *Describe* the basis for classifying the water molds as protists.

Reading Critically

Evaluating Relationships
How could you encourage the formation of sporangia in a slime mold grown in the laboratory?

Figure 21–11. A plasmodium (left) is the vegetative portion of a slime mold life cycle. Dramatic changes convert a jellylike plasmodium into numerous sporangia (right) that produce spores.

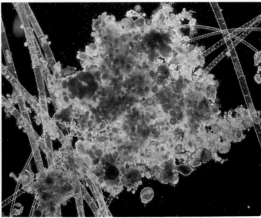

Figure 21–12. Water molds may be animal parasites (left) or saprophytes that grow on aquatic debris (right).

21.6 Water Molds

Most water molds are water-dwelling organisms that live upon dead organisms. *Unlike fungi, water molds produce distinctly male and female gametes.* The differentiation of gametes into distinctly male (sperm) and female (egg) forms is called **oogamy** (oh AHG uh mee). The water molds also produce motile zoospores, another characteristic that sets them apart from the fungi. Each zoospore swims by means of two flagella. Terrestrial water molds require a film of water to complete their life cycle.

Some species of water molds are plant parasites. A water mold called *Phytophthora infestans* ruined potato crops in Ireland between 1845 and 1847. Potatoes were Ireland's main crop, and the resulting famine caused the death of more than 2 million people. The loss of the potato crop helped trigger a massive wave of Irish immigration to the United States and elsewhere.

Other water molds cause disease in fishes and their eggs, a common problem in home aquariums.

Section Review

1. **Comparing Ideas**   In what ways do the slime molds resemble protozoa?
2. **Analyzing Information**   Why have the water molds sometimes been placed in the kingdom Fungi?
3. **Inferring Relationships**   What is the relationship between food supply and reproduction in plasmodial slime molds?
4. **Inferring Relationships**   Why are the water molds classified as protists?

Thinking Critically

INVESTIGATION 21:
What Do Protists Look Like?

Objectives
- To *observe* various protists
- To *compare* structural characteristics, methods of locomotion, and feeding response among protists

Materials
paramecium culture, three other protist cultures, medicine droppers, glass slides, coverslips, compound light microscope, yeast-Congo red solution, methyl cellulose

Prelab Preparation

1. State differences among protists, monera, plants, and animals.
2. Make a table, similar to the one shown below, to record your observations of characteristics of at least three protists. In addition to paramecium, other protists will be provided by your teacher.
3. Review the procedure for making a wet mount described on page 909.

6. Make a labeled drawing of this organism. Include the organism's name and the magnification which the drawing represents. Write a brief description of your observations on your drawing.
7. Place a drop of paramecium culture on a clean slide. Add a drop of yeast-Congo red solution to the slide. Complete the wet mount and use both low power and high power to observe the slide. Record your observations in your table.
8. Using a clean dropper for each culture, repeat steps 4 through 6 for cultures other than paramecium culture. Record your observations in your table.

Analysis

1. **Analyzing Observations** What characteristics are common to all the organisms that you observed?
2. **Analyzing Observations** What evidence did you observe that suggests that these organisms are eukaryotes?

Protist Name	Sketch	General Description (Size/Shape/Color)	Type of Movement	Feeding Mechanism

Inquiry: Observation

4. Place a drop of methyl cellulose on a glass slide. This material slows the movement of protists. Place a drop of paramecium culture on the methyl cellulose and add a coverslip.
5. Use low power to locate the organisms on the slide. Switch to high power and focus on one paramecium for several minutes. Record your observations in your table.

3. **Analyzing Observations** What evidence do you have that some protists might be capable of photosynthesis?
4. **Inferring Conclusions** How does a protist's ability to move relate to its method of obtaining nutrition?
5. **Identifying Relationships** Based on observable characteristics, make a simple taxonomic key which could be used to identify three organisms that you observed.

Chapter 21 Review

Summary

Protozoa are unicellular, eukaryotic, heterotrophic organisms. Most of them live in water. Protozoa live independently or in a form of symbiosis such as parasitism, mutualism, or commensalism.

Protozoa are classified according to their method of movement. Flagellates move by flagella. *Euglena* may be classified in its own phylum.

Sarcodines use footlike extensions called pseudopodia both to move and to capture food. Amoebas feed by engulfing food, and they reproduce by binary fission. Like other protozoa, sarcodines respond to light, chemicals, and food in the environment.

Ciliates move by the synchronized beating of cilia. The complex cells of paramecia contain food vacuoles, radiating canals, and an oral groove leading to a mouth pore and gullet.

Sporozoans are nonmotile, parasitic protozoa. They are represented by *Plasmodium,* the parasite that causes malaria.

Funguslike protists include the slime molds and the water molds.

BioTerms

amoeboid movement (**339**)	multiple fission (**340**)	sessile (**341**)	trichocyst (**343**)
anal pore (**342**)	negative phototropism (**340**)	symbiosis (**337**)	zooplankton (**337**)
binary fission (**340**)	oogamy (**346**)		
cyst (**340**)	oral groove (**342**)		
ectoplasm (**339**)	parasitism (**337**)	For each pair of terms, explain the differences in their meanings.	
endoplasm (**339**)	plasmodium (**345**)		
eyespot (**338**)	positive phototropism (**338**)	1. symbiosis, parasitism	
gullet (**342**)	protozoa (**336**)	2. ectoplasm, endoplasm	
macronucleus (**341**)	pseudopodia (**339**)	3. macronucleus, micronucleus	
micronucleus (**341**)	radiating canal (**342**)	4. negative phototropism, positive phototropism	
mouth pore (**342**)			

BioQuiz (Write all answers on a separate sheet of paper.)

Completion

1. Paramecia respond to attack by discharging _____ .
2. Marine protozoa and other microscopic heterotrophs of the ocean are called _____ .
3. The disease caused by parasitic flagellates of the genus *Trypanosoma* is _____ .
4. A thick, grainy type of cytoplasm that fills an amoeba is called _____ .
5. An amoeba undergoes multiple fission in a _____ .

Multiple Choice

6. Amoebas take in solids by
   a) exocytosis.   b) endocytosis.
   c) phagocytosis.   d) active transport.
7. _____ directs amoebas away from sources of light.   a) Negative phototropism
   b) Positive phototropism   c) Negative geotropism   d) Negative thigmotropism
8. Protozoa such as *Foraminifera* belong to the phylum   a) Mastigophora.   b) Sarcodina.   c) Ciliophora.   d) Sporozoa.

9. The part of the paramecium that directs the metabolic functions is the   a) micronucleus.   b) oral groove.   c) contractile vacuole.   d) macronucleus.
10. Protozoa that move by pseudopodia are called   a) ciliates.   b) flagellates.   c) sarcodines.   d) sporozoans.
11. When a paramecium encounters an obstacle, it reverses and alters course, a process called   a) defense reaction.   b) avoidance reaction.   c) pseudopodia.   d) amoeboid movement.
12. Differentiation of gametes into male and female forms is   a) binary fission.   b) oogamy.   c) mutualism.   d) conjugation.
13. Organisms anchored in one place for most of their life are   a) parasites.   b) symbiotic.   c) sessile.   d) zooplankton.
14. Protozoa are   a) autotrophic.   b) parasitic.   c) motile.   d) unicellular.
15. A plasmodium is found in   a) water molds.   b) ciliates.   c) sarcodines.   d) slime molds.

Writing Critically

16. What role does diffusion play in the nutrition of protozoa?
17. What traits of a euglenoid cell make it autotrophic?
18. How do amoebas and *Euglena* cells respond to light? Why is it adaptive for these organisms to respond as they do?
19. How do water molds carry out the process of sexual reproduction?
20. How do *Plasmodium* cells reproduce?

Application/Critical Thinking

1. **Inferring Relationships**   Many people suffer from African sleeping sickness, but not all of them die from the disease. Write a paragraph explaining what would happen to parasitic species, such as the trypanosomes, if they killed every member of the host species in which they live.
2. **Synthesizing Information**   One of the most common diseases caused by amoebas is amoebic dysentery. Use your school or public library to research amoebic dysentery. Summarize the life cycle of *Entamoeba histolytica* and explain how the disease can be prevented.
3. **Analyzing Information**   *Foraminifera* secrete hard shells of calcium carbonate, or limestone. Amoebas, on the other hand, have no protective covering outside the cell membrane. What are the advantages of each cell structure for the survival of the organism? What are the disadvantages?

Cross-Discipline Connection

Biology and Geology   Use the library to find out what the accumulation of foraminifera and radiolarian shells reveals about the geologic history of different areas of Earth.

Discovery Through Reading

Read the article "How the Trypanosome Changes Its Coat," *Scientific American* (February 1985): 44–51. Why is it difficult for the human immune system to combat some trypanosomes?

A valuable discussion of the biology of protozoa is covered in J. Lee and others' *Illustrated Guide to Protozoa* (New York, 1985). Use this guide to help you identify common species of pond protozoa in your area.

Algae

Outline

Kelp, *Laminaria digitata*, with holdfasts for attachment

Focus

Among the organisms that contain chlorophyll and produce food on Earth, no group is more important than the **algae** (AL jee). Algae are the autotrophic members of the Kingdom Protista. Like marine and freshwater protozoa, algae provide food for countless species of water-dwelling heterotrophs. In addition, photosynthetic activity that takes place in algae is responsible for 90 percent of the oxygen in Earth's atmosphere.

- *What would happen to marine animals if all marine algae were destroyed?*

- *What would happen to land animals if all marine algae were destroyed?*

Overview of Algae

Algae are simple, water-dwelling organisms that are more like plants than animals. *Unlike most other protists, algae are autotrophic organisms.* Most algae float or swim near the water's surface, where sunlight is most direct and the photosynthetic cells can produce a maximum amount of food. Algae absorb nutrients by diffusion across the cell membrane.

22.1 Characteristics

Algae vary greatly in size and shape, from microscopic, hard-shelled forms to rubbery kelps that grow as long as 70 m (230 ft.). Like those of all protists, the cells of algae are eukaryotic. Most algal cells are supported by an inner wall of cellulose. Cells are held together by a jellylike substance called **pectin.**

Some algae are unicellular; others are multicellular. Many unicellular algae move by means of flagella. Kelps and many other multicellular algae are nonmotile. The bodies of multicellular algae consist of filaments that become meshed together into a solid mass. An unspecialized, multicellular body is called a **thallus.**

22.2 Habitats

Algae are common in freshwater lakes, streams, and the oceans. There they may form a layer of green scum on the water's surface or hang in strands from rocks or logs. Along with protozoa and other small organisms, algae make up **plankton** (PLANK tuhn). *Plankton is the food source for most of the world's water-dwelling organisms.* Billions of tiny, drifting algae are called *phytoplankton* (fy tuh PLANK tuhn).

Algae also live on land in the thin films of water found on rocks and soil particles. Some species of algae thrive in snowfields, deserts, cold springs, or the almost boiling water of hot springs. Air samples from 15,000 m (49,000 ft.) above sea level have contained algal cysts, which are much like protozoan cysts.

22.3 Classification

Algae are classified into five groups according to the pigments they contain. These five groups are golden algae, fire algae, green algae, brown algae, and red algae. The pigments give the

Section Objectives

- *Name* three characteristics found in all algae.
- *Contrast* the features of algae and protozoa.
- *Name* the main characteristic used to classify algae.
- *Summarize* the importance of algae to land animals and to humans.

thallus (plural, *thalli* or *thalluses*)

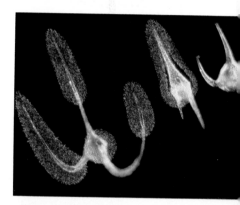

Figure 22–1. Algae range in size from microscopic unicellular dinoflagellates (top) to giant kelps (bottom).

Algae and products made from algae have a long history of usefulness. Dulse, a red alga, has been used as food for people and domestic animals for centuries. The alga now most widely used for food is *nori,* grown chiefly by coastal villagers in Japan. Nori is dried into sheets that are used in soups and biscuits, and as a flavoring in many foods.

Although most algae are low in protein, they contain concentrated minerals and some starch. In many countries, dried algae are ground into a powder and added to animal feed as a mineral supplement.

Algae yield valuable extracts. Agar, an extract taken from red algae, is a jellylike substance that is used for laboratory cultures in which bacteria are grown.

Carrageenin is another extract from red algae that is used to keep small particles in suspension in many foods. For example, carrageenin prevents chocolate from separating out in chocolate milk. Carrageenin is a common ingredient in jams and jellies, instant coffee, honey, wine, and ice cream.

■ **Comparing Ideas** In what way is agar similar to carrageenin?

Reading Critically

Evaluating Relationships
Why is it not disadvantageous for algae of one color to exist near algae of another color?

algae in each phylum their characteristic color. Regardless of their color, all algae contain a green pigment called chlorophyll *a*. Most also contain a second type of chlorophyll. In some algae, the dominant colors of other pigments mask the chlorophyll's green. These other pigments not only change the color of the alga but also enhance photosynthesis by capturing the energy from other colors of light and transferring it to the chlorophyll. Algae are also commonly classified by the form in which they store food and by their means of reproduction.

Section Review

1. **Identifying Information**   What are three characteristics found in all algae?
2. **Comparing Information**   What is the main difference between algae and protozoa?
3. **Evaluating Conclusions**   How are algae important?
4. **Relating Information**   Why must all algae contain chlorophyll *a*?

Thinking Critically

Kinds of Algae

The five phyla of algae, listed in Table 22–1, are Chrysophyta (kruh SAHF uh tuh), the golden algae; Pyrrophyta (puh RAHF uh tuh), the fire algae; Chlorophyta (klaw RAHF uh tuh), the green algae; Phaeophyta (fay AHF uh tuh), the brown algae; and Rhodophyta (roh DAHF uh tuh), the red algae. Most species of algae are free-living. Some species, however, live on or in other organisms. For example, one species of alga lives on the fur of South American sloths. The green of the algae matches the color of surrounding trees, helping to conceal the tree-climbing sloth from its enemies.

Section Objectives

- *Distinguish* between diatoms and dinoflagellates.
- *Describe* how *Spirogyra* reproduces asexually and sexually.
- *Summarize* the alternation of generations in *Ulva*.
- *Contrast* the structure and habitat of a typical brown alga with those of a typical red alga.

22.4 Golden Algae

The phylum Chrysophyta, the golden algae, includes about 12,000 species of algae that live in fresh water or in the sea. Golden algae contain chlorophylls *a* and *c*. The characteristic golden color of the algae comes from three accessory pigments: orange *carotenes*, yellow *xanthophylls* (ZAN thuh fihlz), and brown *fucoxanthins* (FYOO koh zan thuhnz).

The five phyla of algae are described on page 914.

Table 22–1: Characteristics of Algae

Phylum	Species	Pigments	Food Storage	Reproduction
Chrysophyta (golden algae)	12,000	Chlorophylls *a* and *c*, carotenes, xanthophylls, fucoxanthins	Usually oils	Asexual by binary fission, sexual by fusion of gametes in zygote
Pyrrophyta (fire algae)	1,100	Chlorophylls *a* and *c*, xanthophyll	Starch and oils	Usually asexual by binary fission
Chlorophyta (green algae)	7,000	Chlorophylls *a* and *b*, carotene	Starch	Various sexual means; sexual by alternation of generations
Phaeophyta (brown algae)	1,500	Chlorophylls *a* and *c*, fucoxanthin	Laminarin and oils	Sexual by alternation of generations
Rhodophyta (red algae)	4,000	Chlorophylls *a* and *d*, carotenes, phycobilins	Starch	Sexual by alternation of generations

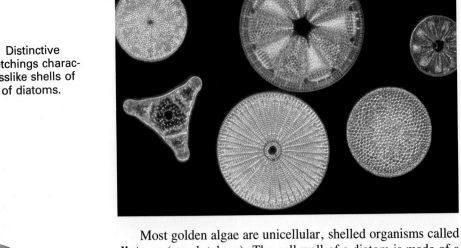

Figure 22–2. Distinctive shapes and etchings characterize the glasslike shells of each species of diatoms.

Complete shell

Shell halves separating

New shell halves added; two new shells formed

Figure 22–3. When a diatom reproduces asexually, its shell first splits into an upper and a lower half. The cell inside divides, and each new cell associates with one half of the original shell. A new half-shell then forms for each new diatom.

Reading Critically

Inferring Relationships
What might indicate that a red tide has occurred in a certain area of the ocean?

Algal blooms are discussed on pages 362–363.

Most golden algae are unicellular, shelled organisms called **diatoms** (DY uh tahmz). The cell wall of a diatom is made of a hard, glasslike substance called *silica*. The two halves of the diatom's shell fit together like the sides of a petri dish. In asexual reproduction, the halves separate and each forms a new shell, as shown in Figure 22–3. Diatoms also reproduce sexually by forming gametes.

Diatoms store food in the form of oils. The oils give an unpleasant taste to fish that eat diatoms. When diatoms die, their cytoplasm and cell walls decay while the outer shell of silica remains intact. The shells accumulate on the ocean floor, creating deposits called *diatomaceous earth*. Diatomaceous earth is used as a filtering material and in abrasives.

22.5 Fire Algae

The phylum Pyrrophyta, with just 1,100 species, accounts for a large part of the sea's phytoplankton. Fire algae get their red color from chlorophylls *a* and *c* and xanthophyll. They are called "fire algae" because they sometimes look like a fire smoldering in the water. When passing ships or dolphins stir up the water, disturbed fire algae glow like a neon light. The production of light by living things is called **bioluminescence.** It also occurs in land organisms such as fireflies.

The largest group of fire algae is the **dinoflagellates,** unicellular algae with stiff, armorlike cell walls and two flagella. One flagellum pulls the cell forward while the other flagellum wraps around the cell, making it spin. Dinoflagellates store food as starch or oil. They usually reproduce asexually by binary fission. Certain chemicals or changes in water temperature may cause an uncontrolled growth of algae called an **algal bloom.** Blooms of dinoflagellates, or **red tides,** may release poisons that kill thousands of fish. Red tides also make algae-eating shellfish dangerous for humans to eat.

22.6 Green Algae

Green algae make up the phylum Chlorophyta, the most diverse of all algal phyla. The 7,000 species of green algae range from microscopic single cells to multicellular organisms over 8 m (25 ft.) long. Green algae, unlike any other group of algae, contain the same three pigments found in land plants: chlorophyll *a*, chlorophyll *b*, and a type of carotene. Like many land plants, green algae store food as starch. *The similarities between plants and green algae have led scientists to agree that plants evolved from green algae ages ago.*

Protococcus The unicellular green algae *Protococcus* is common in damp forests, where it forms a slippery green film on moist rocks or a green dust on tree trunks. *Protococcus* reproduces asexually. The oval cell divides by binary fission, producing two genetically identical daughter cells.

Volvox The order *Volvocales* includes examples of **colonial algae,** organisms made of individual cells held together by a jellylike substance or strands of cytoplasm. Colonial algae differ from multicellular organisms because their cells do not have

Biofact

Q: *How do algae survive the low temperatures of winter?*

A: Many species form cold-resistant spores or cysts, or they break into fragments. These fragments sink to deeper levels where the water does not freeze.

To observe variety among algae, see the Investigation on page 359.

BIOLOGY AND YOU:

Seaweed Beauty Treatments

Extracts from algae find their way into many familiar products. A substance called *algin* is used often in salad dressings, ice cream, and other food products to keep the ingredients from separating.

Algae have also made an appearance in the "beauty" industry. For example, a trendy treatment called *thallassotherapy* is a modern version of a treatment that was first used in France at the turn of the century. In thallasso-therapy, the body is smeared with a seaweed wrap that is the consistency of creamed spinach. The desired result is to make the surface of the skin appear moist.

Algae are also used in a variety of cosmetics, including creams and astringents. Extracts from some brown algae have antibacterial properties. Manufacturers of creams and lotions containing these extracts advertise the antiseptic nature of their products.

Most of the algae used in thallassotherapy are harvested off the northern coast of France. Other algae used in cosmetics are gathered from underground springs.

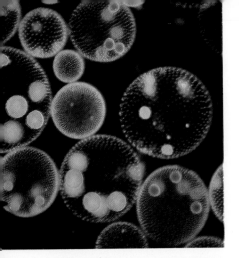

Figure 22–4. *Volvox* is a colonial green alga that rolls through the water, propelled by hundreds of flagella.

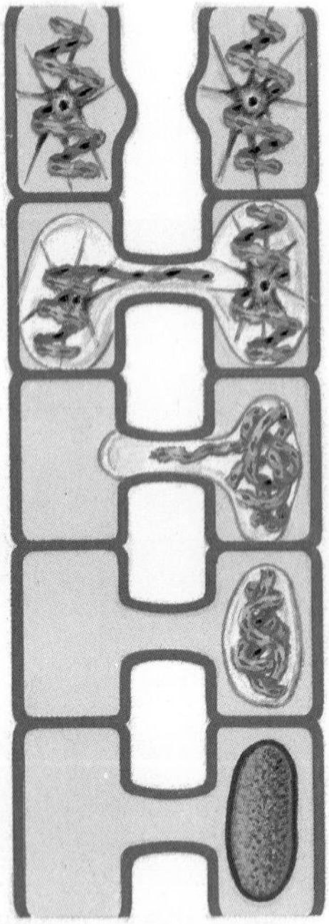

Connecting tube forms

Cells begin to fuse

Contents combine in one cell

Zygote forms

Zygospore develops

Figure 22–5. *Spirogyra* reproduces sexually through the process of conjugation illustrated above.

specialized functions. Cells in a colony can reproduce sexually more readily than single cells because mating cells are always nearby. The size of the colony protects the members from organisms such as protozoa that feed on single cells.

One of the most beautiful colonial algae is *Volvox*. A *Volvox* colony is a hollow ball formed by hundreds or thousands of bright green cells. The entire colony spins slowly through the water by the synchronized beating of the cells' flagella.

Spirogyra *Spirogyra* (spy ruh JY ruh) is a multicellular green alga that grows in shallow freshwater pools. Its cells lengthen and divide without separating, forming long, slender filaments that look like transparent green ribbons. Each chloroplast contains a small protein body called a **pyrenoid** (py REE noyd), which stores starch.

Spirogyra reproduces asexually in two ways. The cells may undergo binary fission, which lengthens the filament. If the filament is broken, each fragment continues to grow on its own. This process is called **fragmentation.** Fragmentation does not harm the individual cells, and it helps disperse the algae.

Sexual reproduction in *Spirogyra* involves a process of *conjugation* that differs from conjugation in paramecia. The process begins when two neighboring *Spirogyra* filaments form connecting tubes, as shown in step 1 of Figure 22–5. The contents of one cell flow through the tube into the adjacent cell. A diploid zygote forms when the contents of the two cells join together. The wall of the receiving cell then thickens around the zygote, forming a durable **zygospore** that can survive harsh conditions. When conditions become favorable for growth, the zygospore becomes active once again. It then undergoes meiosis and develops into a new *Spirogyra* filament.

Ulva *Ulva*, the sea lettuce, is a genus of multicellular green alga whose life cycle involves two distinct forms of the organism. Although the two forms of *Ulva* look alike, they are genetically different. In one of the forms, *Ulva* cells are haploid—that is, they have (n) chromosomes. In the other form, the cells are diploid—that is, they have (2n) chromosomes. To see how these two life forms alternate, examine Figure 22–6. The haploid form of the organism is called the **gametophyte** (guh MEET uh fyt) because it produces gametes. When gametes from two *Ulva* fuse, they form a diploid zygote. All the cells that develop from the zygote are diploid. The resulting diploid form of the alga is called the **sporophyte** (SPAWR uh fyt), because its cells undergo meiosis and produce spores. Each haploid spore then develops into a haploid gametophyte.

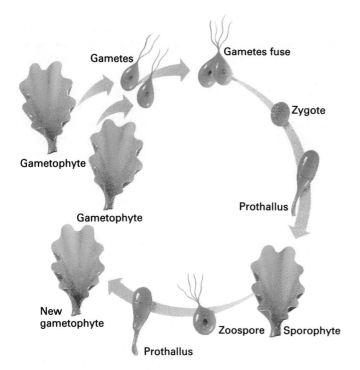

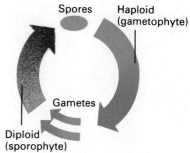

Figure 22-6. The life cycle of the green alga *Ulva* (left) involves an alternation of generations. The diagram above shows the alternation of haploid and diploid phases in this life cycle.

The alternation between sporophyte and gametophyte stages in a life cycle is called **alternation of generations.** *Many species of algae and all plants go through an alternation of generations.* This life cycle is widespread because it has great survival value. The species benefits from the recombination of parents' traits through the fusion of gametes. The species also benefits from the opportunity to reproduce by the less risky process of forming spores. In *Ulva*, the gametophyte and sporophyte forms look identical. In other algae and in plants, the two forms may look very different.

22.7 Brown Algae

The world's rocky coasts and colder oceans abound with tough seaweeds and kelps. These are the brown algae, members of the phylum Phaeophyta. About 1,500 species of brown algae have been identified, including the largest forms of algae. Brown algae commonly form extensive underwater forests, creating a relatively sheltered habitat for other organisms. Members of the phylum Phaeophyta contain chlorophylls *a* and *c* and the accessory pigment fucoxanthin. Brown algae may store food either as oil or as an unusual carbohydrate called *laminarin*. The life cycle of most species of brown algae exhibits an alternation of generations.

Biofact

Q: *How do algae in tidal areas survive exposure to the air and wind?*

A: Algae that have developed structures to retain water, such as water bladders and thick cell walls, can survive several hours of exposure during low tide. Even these algae, however, show slower rates of photosynthesis and respiration during exposure.

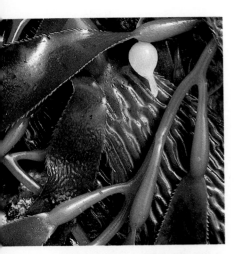

Figure 22–7. This kelp is an example of a marine brown alga.

Figure 22–8. Some red algae live in very deep water. Their red phycobilin pigments capture blue light that penetrates the oceans to 265 m (884 ft.).

Thinking Critically >

Many brown algae have tissues that resemble the roots, stems, and leaves of plants. Algae in the genus *Laminaria,* including the most familiar kelps, are firmly anchored by a root-like structure called a **holdfast.** The long, stemlike portion of *Laminaria* ends in a broad, leaflike structure that carries on photosynthesis. Despite its outward resemblance to plants, however, *Laminaria* is a true alga. Its cells are not highly specialized. Unlike roots, the holdfast does not absorb minerals from the soil. Instead, the kelp thallus absorbs minerals directly from sea water.

Both anchored and free-floating brown algae have a leathery, highly flexible thallus that sways freely and can withstand the motion of waves. Many brown algae that grow from the sea floor have air-filled structures called **air bladders.** The buoyant air bladders help keep the photosynthetic parts of the algae near the water's surface.

22.8 Red Algae

In warm tropical oceans, algae in the phylum Rhodophyta are the predominant form of seaweed. Species of red algae have been found in most climates, however, as well as in fresh water. The 4,000 species of red algae contain chlorophylls *a* and *d,* carotenes, and red or blue accessory pigments, which are known as *phycobilins.*

The red phycobilins absorb blue light, which penetrates into water more deeply than any other color of light. This trait enables red algae to grow in deeper water than any other algae. Red algae are found as far down as 150 m (490 ft.) below sea level. Wave motion at this depth is minimal. The thallus of a typical red alga is a delicate network of filaments that fan out in the water. This fragile kind of thallus would not survive well in the more turbulent water along exposed, rocky shores where brown algae live.

Red algae store food as starch. They are usually sessile, or stationary. Most species of red algae undergo an alternation of generations.

Section Review

1. **Contrasting Ideas**   Describe four ways in which dinoflagellates are different from diatoms.
2. **Identifying Relationships**   How are the gametophyte and sporophyte generations different in *Ulva?*
3. **Inferring Relationships**   Why can red algae live in deeper water than brown algae?

INVESTIGATION 22:
How Do Algae Differ?

Objectives
- To *observe* various kinds of algae
- To *compare* characteristics

Materials
cultures of four different species of algae, stereomicroscope, compound light microscope, four medicine droppers, four glass slides, four coverslips

Prelab Preparation
1. Name environments where algae live.
2. Review the groups of algae.
3. Make a table similar to the one shown below to record your observations of four different algae. Leave space in your table for the name of each specimen, its macroscopic features, its microscopic features, and its relative size. Your teacher will provide the names of the specimens that you will study.

the compound light microscope. Describe additional features that you observe.
7. Repeat steps 4 through 6 for each specimen. Record your observations in your table.

Fucus
(brown alga)

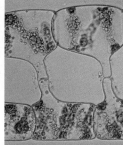

Spirogyra
(green algae)

Name of Species	Drawing	Relative Size	Macroscopic Features	Microscopic Features

Inquiry: Observation
4. Observe one of the specimens macroscopically, that is, without magnifying the specimen. Make a drawing of the specimen and record the specimen's distinctive features in your table.
5. Observe the specimen under the stereomicroscope. Record the features that you observe in your table.
6. Tear off a small piece of algal tissue and make a wet mount. View the specimen with low power. Switch to high power and observe the tissue. Make a drawing of the specimen as it appears at high power of

Analysis
1. **Analyzing Observations** How do the specimens differ in color?
2. **Analyzing Observations** Compare both the macroscopic and microscopic features of your specimens.
3. **Identifying Relationships** What characteristics appear to be common to all the algae you observed?
4. **Analyzing Observations** How can chloroplasts be identified other than by color?
5. **Inferring Ideas** If all algae have chloroplasts, why do algae differ in color?

Chapter 22 Review

Summary

Algae are autotrophic members of the kingdom Protista. They produce most of the world's atmospheric oxygen and provide the basis for much of its food supply. Most algae are aquatic. Asexual reproduction occurs by binary fission, fragmentation, or the production of spores. Many species also reproduce sexually.

Almost all golden algae and fire algae are unicellular organisms. Diatoms are tiny golden algae with silica shells. Dinoflagellates, the most common fire algae, move by two flagella. Dinoflagellates show bioluminescence when disturbed and cause dangerous algal blooms called red tides.

Most green, brown, and red algae are multicellular organisms. The green algae have the most diverse forms, including the colonial *Volvox* and filamentous *Spirogyra*. The life cycle of *Ulva* typifies the pattern of alternating haploid gametophyte and diploid sporophyte generations. This pattern is called alternation of generations.

Most brown algae live primarily in colder oceans. They include many seaweeds and kelps. Red algae grow primarily in tropical oceans. They grow at greater depths than other algae and typically have a delicate, fan-shaped thallus.

BioTerms

air bladder (358)
algae (350)
algal bloom (354)
alternation of
  generations (357)
bioluminescence
  (354)
colonial
  algae (355)

diatom (354)
dinoflagellate (354)
fragmentation
  (356)
gametophyte (356)
holdfast (358)
pectin (351)
plankton (351)
pyrenoid (356)

red tide (354)
sporophyte (356)

thallus (351)
zygospore (356)

For each pair of terms, explain the differences in their meanings.

1. algal bloom, red tide
2. gametophyte, sporophyte
3. pectin, thallus
4. diatom, dinoflagellate

BioQuiz   (Write all answers on a separate sheet of paper.)

Completion

1. Unicellular, free-floating algae are called _____ .
2. A delicate, fan-shaped thallus is the typical body form of _____ algae.
3. Red tides are a dangerous kind of algal bloom caused by a sudden growth of _____ .
4. Alternation of generations involves two forms: a diploid _____ and a haploid gametophyte.
5. When _____ reproduce asexually, their shells separate into two parts.

Multiple Choice

6. Kelps are one kind of _____ algae.
   a) red   b) green   c) brown   d) golden
7. Algae are classified into five groups based on their   a) pigments.
   b) habitats.   c) food sources.
   d) growth rates.
8. Layers of algae cells are held together by a jellylike substance called   a) holdfast.
   b) pectin.   c) silica.   d) thallus.
9. The cell walls of diatoms are made of a glasslike substance called   a) silica.

b) pectin. c) calcium. d) potassium.

10. The production of light by living things is
    called a) algal bloom. b) red tide.
    c) alternation of generations. d) bio-
    luminescence.

11. Which pigment is not found in golden
    algae? a) chlorophyll *a* b) xanthophylls
    c) carotenes d) chlorophyll *b*

12. Structures that allow brown algae to stay
    near the water's surface are called
    a) holdfasts. b) air bladders.
    c) planktons. d) thalli.

13. All algae are a) green. b) autotrophic.
    c) unicellular. d) multicellular.

14. The unspecialized body of multicellular
    algae is called the a) air bladder.
    b) holdfast. c) thallus. d) filament.

15. A brown alga is anchored by a) a holdfast.

b) a thallus. c) an air bladder. d) a
pyrenoid.

Writing Critically

16. Why is the life cycle shared by *Ulva* and
    many other kinds of algae known as
    alternation of generations?

17. In what ways is the holdfast of a kelp
    similar to the root of a plant? In what
    ways is it different?

18. How does the arrangement of flagella in
    a dinoflagellate affect the organism's
    movement?

19. How is diatomaceous earth formed, and
    for what is it used?

20. How does the process of asexual reproduc-
    tion in *Ulva* differ from that in *Spirogyra*?

Application/Critical Thinking

1. **Reporting Research** Research the Sargasso Sea and write a paragraph explaining
   how *Sargassum* influences its environment.

2. **Synthesizing Relationships** Algal blooms
   can cause oxygen depletion in lakes.
   Research desmids and other algae that
   bloom in polluted water. Report on the
   impact and prevention of algal blooms.

3. **Analyzing Information** Some scientists
   consider algae one way to help the world's
   growing population. Research alga farm-

ing and report how algae might be used
more extensively in the future to augment
the production and distribution of the
world's available food energy.

4. **Inferring Relationships** Fireflies produce light signals that attract mates. Some
   algae, including some poisonous dinoflagellates, bioluminesce when disturbed by
   would-be predators. How might bioluminescence help promote the survival of a
   species of algae?

Cross-Discipline Connection

Biology and Economics   After researching in
the library, create a chart on the positive and

negative impact of algae on the economics of
seaside communities and entire countries.

Discovery Through Reading

"Enlisting the Lowly Algae in a High Tech
Scheme," *Business Week* (April 11, 1988):
123, focuses on the new technological uses
for algae. What is one proposed future use of

algae? What species of alga is suggested for
this purpose? Describe a current problem with
using these algae to split water molecules.

Controlling Algal Blooms

Algae are present in all bodies of water. When conditions are favorable, algae multiply rapidly and form colored patches called *blooms* on the surface of the water. These algal blooms pose a variety of problems. They are a threat to aquatic plants and animals, to certain industries that depend on marine life, and to supplies of drinking water.

When fresh water is enriched with nutrients such as those that come from treated sewage or runoff of fertilized farm soil, algae reproduce rapidly. When the algae die and decompose, they cause an oxygen shortage in the water. This condition is called *eutrophication.*

Algal blooms also limit the amount of sunlight that can reach the bottom of a lake or river. As a result, photosynthetic plants die, and the ecosystem of the water where the blooms take hold is further damaged.

Toxic ocean blooms, commonly called *red tides* because they give the water a red cast, are a recurrent phenomenon. **Dinoflagellates**, a type of alga, cause red tides. Dinoflagellate toxin becomes concentrated in marine animals such as clams and mussels. If the

Draining a pond is one way to combat algal blooms.

These algal blooms are caused by the dumping of phosphates into the water.

contaminated shellfish are eaten, the toxin can cause a fatal type of paralytic poisoning. In humans, ocean spray that contains red tide dinoflagellates can cause respiratory problems.

Control of algal blooms in bodies of fresh water is possible but expensive. Cleaning up affected water requires the removal of the algae and of the bottom sediment. If the discharge of sewage cannot be stopped, silica must be added to the sewage before it empties into the fresh water. Silica encourages the growth of diatoms, a type of algae that does not bloom. Instead, diatoms inhibit plankton growth and increase the food supply of fish.

The problem of red tide in the oceans is not as easily solved. None of the strategies used so far has been effective.

Today scientists are researching possible beneficial effects of red tide on the ecosystem. Reports of larger-than-usual catches of shrimp have been reported in years following a major red tide, and scientists believe that dinoflagellate blooms are responsible for oil deposits in the North Sea.

Researchers are now turning their attention to developing models for predicting the occurrence of red tides. Prediction rather than control may prove to be the more feasible and beneficial solution.

Algal blooms seem to have both beneficial and detrimental effects on aquatic ecosystems.

Bloom-causing dinoflagellates (far left) have been offset by the addition of diatoms to the water (left and above).

Massive numbers of fish die when red tides form in oceans.

363

Fungi

Outline

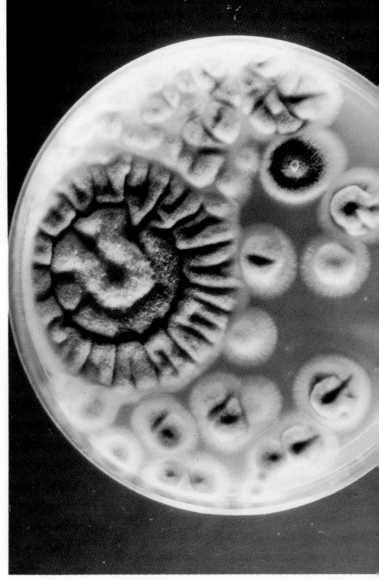

Penicillin mold growing in a petri dish

Focus

Organisms in the kingdom Fungi play an important ecological role as decomposers. Fungal decay of organic matter returns nutrients to the soil where living organisms can use them for new growth. Some antibiotics, such as penicillin, are produced from fungi. In addition, some fungi, such as mushrooms, are used as food. Other fungi are parasites that destroy crops and cause diseases in other plants, animals, and humans.

■ *Why do you think that fungi were once classified as plants?*

■ *Why is the decomposition of organic matter necessary?*

Overview of Fungi

Fungi are nonmotile organisms that obtain food by decomposing organic matter. Fungi were once considered plants, but studies later revealed that fungi have none of the characteristics that plants possess. Unlike most plants, fungi lack chloroplasts and cannot carry out photosynthesis. Neither do fungi have many animal characteristics. Because of their unusual combination of traits, fungi are classified in a separate kingdom.

23.1 Characteristics

Fungi are eukaryotic organisms; most species are multicellular. The cell walls of most fungi contain a hard substance called **chitin** (KYT uhn). Chitin is found only in fungi and in the hard outer skeletons of insects.

The body of a typical fungus consists of many individual filaments called **hyphae** (HY fee). Hyphae contain cytoplasm and one or more nuclei. Hyphae secrete enzymes that digest food. The fungus then absorbs the nutrients from the food through its cell walls.

Intertwined hyphae form the body of the fungus, or **mycelium** (my SEE lee uhm). Most of a fungus lives under the *substrate,* or material in which the fungus is growing. The visible part contains the spore-producing structures and is called the **fruiting body.** *Saprophytic* fungi feed on dead matter. *Parasitic* fungi feed on living organisms.

23.2 Habitats

Fungi have adapted to almost every environment where organic material and moisture are available. They flourish in forests, grasslands, and other areas where dead wood and leaves are abundant. Some species of fungi live in deserts. Others live high atop mountains. Certain marine fungi live on the remains of dead bacteria and plankton trapped in polar icecaps. You may have seen molds—small, fuzzy growths of fungi on fruit, bread, or other foods.

Though nonmotile, fungi can reach these diverse environments by means of spores that drift in the wind. A single fungus may produce millions or even trillions of spores at a time. Many of these spores land in unsuitable environments and perish. However, many others will survive and germinate. Most kinds of fungi rely on their spores to disperse the species and to find new food sources.

Section Objectives

- *List* the characteristics that fungi have in common.
- *Describe* the structure of a typical fungus.
- *Explain* how fungi obtain food.
- *Explain* how lichens show a mutualistic relationship.
- *Summarize* the harmful and the beneficial effects of fungi.

Reading Critically

Relating Ideas Why are fungi considered heterotrophic?

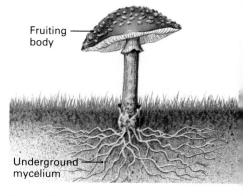

Fruiting body

Underground mycelium

Figure 23–1. A mushroom is the reproductive organ of one class of fungi. The mycelium is an underground saprophyte that gathers food by feeding on decaying organisms.

The next time you are strolling in the woods, look for rocks with orange or green patches. The patches are **lichens** (LY kuhnz), organisms that consist of a fungus and an alga. The fungus and the alga live in a symbiotic relationship. Fungal hyphae give the lichen its internal structure and characteristic shape. Algal cells are embedded in the mycelium, as the photograph shows.

Most lichens are mutualistic. In a lichen, the fungus shields the alga from excessive sunlight and retains water that the alga

 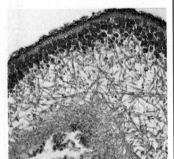

needs for photosynthesis. The alga secretes carbohydrates that the fungus absorbs as food. The alga allows the lichen to survive on bare rocks where the fungus alone cannot grow. Lichens are among the first organisms to suffer from air pollution. Because

lichens absorb water directly, they absorb more dissolved toxic substances than do plants that use water that has first been filtered through the ground.

■ **Comparing Information** What would happen to a lichen deprived of sunlight?

Biofact

Q: *Why do mushrooms sometimes grow in circles called "fairy rings"?*

A: In popular legend, a fairy ring marks the spot where fairies danced in the night. The mushrooms actually mark the outer edge of a large underground mycelium.

Thinking Critically

23.3 Ecological and Economic Roles

Fungi help perform the important ecological function of decomposing dead organic matter. This process not only helps clear dead plants and animals from the environment but also returns nitrogen, phosphorus, and other nutrients to the soil. Fungi are also economically important. They are used directly as food or in making such foods as bread and cheese. Fungi also produce medically valuable antibiotics, such as penicillin and streptomycin. However, fungi can be extremely destructive when they attack crops. Saprophytic fungi destroy millions of dollars worth of food crops each year. Some fungi also cause certain diseases in animals, including humans.

Section Review

1. **Identifying Relationships**   What characteristics are shared by all fungi?
2. **Summarizing Ideas**   How are fungi economically important?

Kinds of Fungi

The fungi include about 81,500 species. Two groups, the slime molds and water molds, were formerly considered fungi, but are now classified in the kingdom Protista. The fungi are divided among four classes distinguished by differences in their structure and methods of reproduction.

23.4 Terrestrial Molds

About 600 species of terrestrial molds make up the class Zygomycetes. The fuzzy part of the mold actually consists of the specialized hyphae that produce tiny spores in structures called **sporangia.** These stalklike hyphae are called **sporangiophores.**

The common black bread mold, *Rhizopus stolonifer,* shows the development of a typical terrestrial mold. An airborne spore that lands on a piece of bread forms hyphae, which branch out over the bread's surface. These surface hyphae, called **stolons,** form short extensions that penetrate into the bread. These extensions are called **rhizoids.** Rhizoids anchor the mold to its food supply, secrete digestive enzymes, and absorb the nutrients.

Sexual reproduction occurs in terrestrial molds when contact occurs between hyphae from two genetically different molds, called **mating strains.** The mating strains are called *plus* (+) and *minus* (−) rather than male and female, because they have identical shapes and functions. The tip of each mating hypha contains nuclei that fuse and form a diploid zygote. In unfavorable conditions the zygote may become a durable zygospore. In favorable conditions the zygote undergoes meiosis and produces spores that form new hyphae. Terrestrial molds and other fungi do not go through alternation of generations.

Section Objectives

- *Summarize* the methods of feeding and reproduction in terrestrial molds.
- *Identify* the basic parts of a club fungus.
- *Name* three kinds of fungal plant diseases and the fungi that cause them.
- *Discuss* the traits of yeasts.

Different kinds of fungi are examined in the Investigation on page 373.

Figure 23–2. The common black bread mold, *Rhizopus stolonifer,* has a mycelium composed of both rhizoids and stolons. When nutrients are depleted, the fungus produces spores in sporangia held up by sporangiophores.

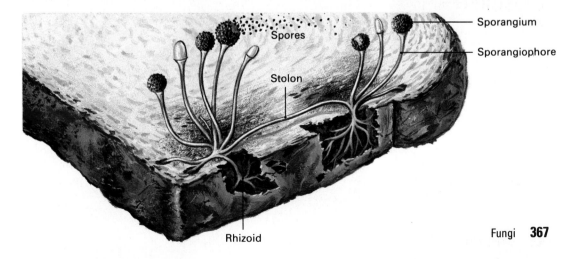

Spores

Sporangium

Sporangiophore

Stolon

Rhizoid

23.5 Club Fungi

The class Basidiomycetes contains about 25,000 species, including mushrooms, shelf fungi, puffballs, rusts, and smuts. Basidiomycetes are called *club fungi* because they produce spores on club-shaped, microscopic structures called **basidia.** The basidia develop within the fruiting body. Most of the fungi that you will see growing in the forest or on a damp lawn are fruiting bodies of basidiomycetes.

Mushrooms The most common club fungi are mushrooms. What is called a mushroom is actually the spore-producing structure of an underground mycelium. Mushrooms are able to appear as quickly as overnight because the underground mycelium is already extensively developed before mushrooms appear. The mushroom first develops as a tight mass of hyphae called a **button.** A stemlike structure known as the **stipe** pushes the button above ground. There the button opens into a **cap,** the fruiting portion of the mushroom. The underside of the cap contains thin sheets of tissue, or **gills,** to which the basidia are attached. Within each basidium are two haploid nuclei that fuse to form a diploid nucleus. This nucleus undergoes meiosis, and the resulting haploid nuclei produce four **basidiospores.** Each basidiospore is capable of developing into a new mushroom.

Some kinds of mushrooms are edible. The mushrooms that are sold in the grocery store are commercially grown basidiomycetes. Other kinds of mushrooms are poisonous. Because some poisonous mushrooms resemble harmless ones, you should never eat wild mushrooms. For example, even a small portion of the "destroying angel," *Amanita bisporigera,* can be lethal. A

Reading Critically

Identifying Characteristics
What are two main distinctions between mushrooms and rusts?

Figure 23–3. The fruiting bodies of club fungi vary. Mushrooms (left) form spores under a cap. Bracket fungi (top right) form spores under a shelflike fruiting body. Puffballs (bottom right) have a ball-like fruiting body.

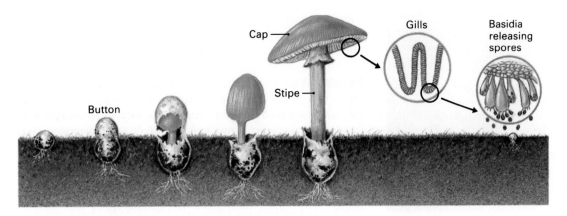

Cap

Stipe

Button

Gills

Basidia releasing spores

toxin in this mushroom damages the liver so severely that death results.

Figure 23–4. A mushroom starts to form when a button breaks through the soil. A stipe then lifts the cap above the ground. Later, basidia form on gills under the cap.

Rusts and Smuts Rusts and smuts are parasitic club fungi that cause severe damage to cereal and vegetable crops. Rusts and smuts produce basidiospores, but not in mushroomlike fruiting bodies. The mycelia spread throughout the host plant, destroying the plant's cells while producing billions of basidiospores. In rusts, the basidiospores are visible as a reddish-brown powder on the leaves of an infected plant. The basidiospores of smuts resemble black dust.

The life cycle of wheat rust involves two alternate hosts. In the spring, the fungal spores infect young wheat plants. In the summer, a second cycle of spore production infects barberry plants. The disease can be controlled by destroying all barberry bushes growing near wheat fields.

Corn smut produces large deformed growths on ears of corn. The growths eventually break open, releasing millions of dusty black spores. The life cycle of corn smut involves only one host. Corn smut can be eliminated by burying or burning the infected plants before the fungi produce spores. Farmers may also control or eliminate rusts and smuts by using *fungicides*. Fungicides are chemicals that kill fungi.

23.6 Sac Fungi

About 30,000 species belong to the class Ascomycetes. Members of this class include the gourmet delicacies morels and truffles, as well as the single-celled yeast used in making bread. Ascomycetes are called *sac fungi* because sexually produced spores form in an **ascus,** or "little sac." An ascus begins to develop when two gametes or two mating strains fuse. Nuclei divide as the hypha grows, resulting in a row of haploid

Biofact

Q: *Do any serious fungal diseases affect humans?*

A: Yes. One is ergotism, a disease caused by eating fungus-infected rye. The fungus causes severe abdominal pain, hallucinations, gangrene, and even death. The fungus is also a source of lysergic acid diethylamide, also known as LSD.

Figure 23–5. The fruiting bodies of this ascomycete resemble small cups. Hyphae on the outside of the cup help protect it from predators.

ascospores within the ascus. In sac fungi and club fungi, hyphae are divided by cross walls. Nuclei and cytoplasm flow through pores in these cross walls as the hyphae grow.

Yeasts   Yeasts are unusual sac fungi. They contain chitin and reproduce sexually by forming ascospores, but they are unicellular and do not form hyphae. Yeasts also reproduce asexually by budding. Many yeasts grow most rapidly in an environment with a high sugar content. In bread dough, yeast cells feed on carbohydrates. As yeast cells grow, they produce carbon dioxide gas by respiration. The carbon dioxide gas causes bread to rise. When yeast cells are deprived of oxygen, they carry out fermentation and produce ethyl alcohol. The process of fermentation releases carbon dioxide as a byproduct and creates the bubbles in beer. Yeasts are also used in the making of wine.

Yeasts have many other commercial uses in addition to their role in baking and brewing. Dried yeasts are a rich source of

BIOLOGY AND YOU:

Yeast Cells

A yeast called *Saccharomyces cerevisiae* is used commercially to make bread, brew beer, and produce wine. This yeast is becoming important to researchers who wish to find out more about how all cells, including human cells, make proteins, communicate with each other, and divide.

There are many advantages to studying yeast cells. Yeast cells are eukaryotic cells with a nucleus that is separate from the cytoplasm and surrounded by a membrane, unlike the prokaryotic bacterial cells which have been used extensively in cell research.

Yeast cells have 17 pairs of chromosomes that behave in much the same way that human chromosomes behave. Some of the genes on these chromosomes direct the synthesis of some of the same enzymes that are found in the cells of vertebrate animals. However, the common yeast that is used commercially has only about 10,000 genes—a number that allows researchers the hope of mapping and analyzing the yeast genome in detail. Human cells contain about 97 percent more genes than yeast cells do.

Yeast cells are easy to cul-

ture. Also, by exposing the cells to a variety of chemicals and to radiation, researchers can generate many different mutations in yeast cells and study their effects. This research may provide clues to human genetic disorders, including inborn errors of metabolism and cancer.

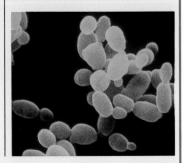

protein and are used as a nourishing food additive for livestock. Yeasts also play an important role in genetic research.

Parasitic Sac Fungi   The powdery mildews are among the most destructive of the parasitic sac fungi. The mycelia of these fungi form a white powder on the leaves of apples, roses, grapes, and other economically important plants. The growth of powdery mildew destroys the tissues of the host plant. This process interferes with the plant's abililty to carry out photosynthesis, and further damages the plant.

Dutch elm disease is caused by another sac fungus. The hyphae of the fungus grow into the wood of an elm tree and clog the tissues that carry water and nutrients from the soil up to the leaves. The ascomycete that causes Dutch elm disease is carried by two different species of beetles. The fungus grows rapidly throughout an infected tree, which may die in as little as four weeks. The spread of Dutch elm disease can be slowed by the cutting and burning of diseased trees. The disease can also be treated with fungicides. Dutch elm disease threatens to wipe out all American elms. Chestnut blight, caused by a related fungus, poses a similar threat.

Figure 23–6.   The mycelium of this powdery mildew (above) forms a dusty white powder on infected plants. Imperfect fungi such as *Penicillium* (below) reproduce by means of asexual spores.

23.7 Imperfect Fungi

The class Deuteromycetes includes about 25,000 species. Fungi in this class are called "imperfect" because they do not reproduce sexually or because their sexual life cycles have not been observed. The most familiar imperfect fungi belong to the genus *Penicillium*. These fungi are used to produce the antibiotic penicillin. Other imperfect fungi cause skin diseases such as athlete's foot and ringworm in humans. Another imperfect fungus causes thrush, an infection of the mucous membranes. Imperfect fungi are responsible for the flavors of Camembert and Roquefort cheeses. Cyclosporine, a drug that suppresses the body's rejection of transplanted organs, is made by an imperfect fungus.

The different kinds of fungi are described on pages 914–915.

Section Review

1. **Summarizing Ideas**   How does mold grow on a piece of bread?
2. **Identifying Relationships**   Why are basidiomycetes called club fungi?
3. **Identifying Characteristics**   How do rusts and smuts obtain nutrition?
4. **Identifying Relationships**   In what ways are yeasts unusual fungi?

> **Thinking Critically**

Malaria

Health officials once thought they had conquered *malaria,* a disease caused by the protozoan *Plasmodium* and transmitted through the bite of the *Anopheles* mosquito. However, this disease still claims the lives of one million children a year in Africa alone.

The solution seemed in sight in the 1950s, when the World Health Organization undertook a worldwide anti-malaria campaign. Health officials hoped to exterminate the *Anopheles* mosquito with the pesticide *DDT,* and malaria patients were treated with the drug *chloroquine,* a synthetic version of the traditional quinine treatment. However, *Anopheles* mosquito populations became resistant to DDT, and some *Plasmodium* populations developed an immunity to chloroquine.

Biomedical researchers are now working to develop an anti-malarial vaccine. Since most successful vaccines have been against viruses and bacteria, it would be a major breakthrough to develop a vaccine against a disease-causing protozoan. Unfortunately, research is hampered by the complex life cycle of the *Plasmodium* organism, and by the quickness with which this organism develops resistance to drugs. Development and testing of drugs also involves laboratory and field tests and is, therefore, excruciatingly slow.

In addition, development of land for agriculture in countries where malaria is found often makes the area more hospitable to *Anopheles* mosquitoes. Irrigation

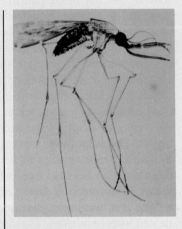

ditches and artificial ponds created by new construction create new breeding areas for *Anopheles* mosquitoes.

Analyze the Issue

1. Use a world map to identify countries that probably have a malaria problem. Describe their climate and geography.

2. What problems must be solved before malaria is eradicated?

3. Is it practical to continue trying to eradicate certain diseases, considering the persistence of disease organisms and their increased resistance to each new remedy? Support your view.

INVESTIGATION 23:
How Do Molds Differ?

Objectives
- To *observe* several kinds of fungi
- To *compare* characteristics of fungi

Materials
three mold cultures, prepared slides of various molds, hand lens or stereomicroscope, compound light microscope

Prelab Preparation
1. Name the characteristics common to all fungi.
2. List habitats where fungi are found.
3. List characteristics that are used to distinguish among fungi.
4. Name the conditions under which you would try to grow fungi.
5. Make a table similar to the one below to record your observations of fungi. Include space in your table for sketching and describing both macroscopic and microscopic features, as well as stating the food source on which the fungus is growing.

Describe the macroscopic appearance of the mold and identify the food source. Record this data in your table.
8. Use a hand lens or stereomicroscope to observe a sample of the mold. Make a sketch and describe the mold's appearance.
9. Use low power and then high power to observe prepared slides of three different molds. Sketch and describe each specimen in your data table.

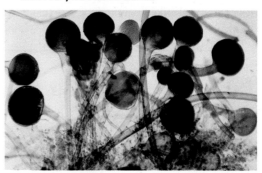
Black bread mold

Name of Species	Drawing	Macroscopic Features	Microscopic Features	Food Source

6. Review the procedures on pages 908–909 for using the microscope and making a wet mount.

Inquiry: Exploration
7. **CAUTION: Do not open the containers or remove the plastic wrap from the containers. Some people are allergic to the spores that may be released.** Obtain a sample of mold growing on food.

Analysis
1. **Analyzing Observations** What macroscopic features can be used to distinguish between different species of molds?
2. **Inferring Ideas** Why might most food sources have only one kind of mold present?
3. **Inferring Ideas** What is the origin of the mold in each sample?

Chapter 23 Review

Summary

The cell walls of most fungi contain chitin. Fungi feed by decomposing organic matter. Hyphae secrete digestive enzymes and absorb food through cell walls. Many intertwined hyphae form the mycelium.

The fungi are divided among four classes distinguished by differences in their structure and methods of reproduction. Fungi include terrestrial molds, club fungi, sac fungi, and imperfect fungi.

Terrestrial molds reproduce asexually by forming spores and sexually when two mating strains come into contact. Club fungi produce spores in basidia, club-shaped structures. Mushrooms are the most common club fungi. Rusts and smuts are parasitic club fungi that do severe damage to crops.

Sac fungi produce spores in an ascus. Imperfect fungi are called "imperfect" because they do not reproduce sexually or because their sexual life cycles have not been observed by scientists. The medicine penicillin is produced by the imperfect fungus, *Penicillium*.

BioTerms

ascospore (370)	fungus (365)
ascus (369)	gill (368)
basidiospore (368)	hypha (365)
basidium (368)	lichen (366)
button (368)	mating strain (367)
cap (368)	mycelium (365)
chitin (365)	rhizoid (367)
fruiting body (365)	sporangiophore (367)

sporangium (367)

stipe (368)
stolon (367)

For each pair of terms, explain the differences in their meanings.

1. ascus, ascospore
2. basidium, basidiospore
3. stolon, rhizoid
4. hypha, mycelium

BioQuiz (Write all answers on a separate sheet of paper.)

Completion

1. Fungi feed by secreting _____ and by absorbing nutrients from the digested food.
2. Unicellular sac fungi that do not form hyphae are called _____ .
3. The spore-producing sheets of tissue beneath the cap of a mushroom are called _____ .
4. Terrestrial molds reproduce sexually when hyphae from two _____ strains come into contact.
5. Extensions of stolons that penetrate into the surface of bread are called _____ .

Multiple Choice

6. Fungal spores are usually formed in structures called a) mycelia. b) sporangia. c) basidia. d) rhizoids.
7. The body of a typical fungus consists of many individual filaments called a) basidiospores. b) plasmodiums. c) hyphae. d) fruiting bodies.
8. The cap is part of a mushroom's a) basidium. b) ascus. c) stolon. d) fruiting body.
9. A lichen consists of a fungus and a) a bacterium. b) a protozoan. c) an alga. d) a virus.

10. Fungi reproduce by forming   a) spores.
    b) gametes.   c) zygotes.   d) All of
    the above.
11. Saprophytic fungi feed on   a) living
    organisms.   b) dead matter.   c) chitin.
    d) cellulose.
12. Fungi   a) are nonmotile.   b) lack
    chloroplasts.   c) are neither animals nor
    plants.   d) All choices are correct.
13. Which class of fungi has the most species?
    a) Deuteromycetes   b) Ascomycetes
    c) Basidiomycetes   d) Zygomycetes
14. The spores for sac fungi are formed in
    a) a fruiting body.   b) a gill.   c) an
    ascospore.   d) an ascus.

15. The cell walls of most fungi contain a
    hard substance called   a) chitin.
    b) cellulose.   c) cytoplasm.   d) hyphae.

Writing Critically

16. How do parasitic fungi injure their host
    organisms?
17. Why are fungi ecologically important?
18. In what way does a lichen demonstrate
    mutualism?
19. What kinds of fungi are economically
    beneficial?
20. Why are slime molds considered a link
    between fungi and protozoa?

Application/Critical Thinking

1. **Analyzing Information** Powdery mildews attack hundreds of different species
   of flowering plants, including many valuable fruits such as peaches and grapes.
   Write a brief report explaining how powdery mildews grow, why they are so
   destructive, and how plants can be protected against them.
2. **Solving Problems** Farmers and agricultural researchers have developed various
   ways to prevent fungi from spoiling fresh
   food in storage. Use your school or public
   library to research food preservation and
   fungicides. Then write a paragraph explain-

ing one method of keeping fresh fruits or
vegetables safe from fungal infections.
3. **Relating Ideas** Mycorrhiza is the association of a fungus and the roots of a plant.
   Research mycorrhizal associations in citrus
   trees or orchids and write a report on how
   the plant is helped by the fungus.
4. **Synthesizing Information** Basidiomycetes are considered the most advanced
   group of fungi. How do the structure and
   life cycle of a typical club fungus support
   this idea? Compare the class Basidiomycetes with other classes of fungi in your
   answer.

Cross-Discipline Connection

Biology and History Write a report on the
discovery of penicillin by Dr. Alexander Fleming. What research was Dr. Fleming performing when he discovered penicillin? What event
led to his discovery? Pay special attention to
the importance of luck in this discovery.

Discovery Through Reading

Read the article "Mushrooms Made Easy,"
Organic Gardening (October 1988): 54–59.
This article describes how to grow mushrooms
by organic methods. Name four types of
mushrooms that can be easily grown at home.
   Read the article "Yeasts at Work," *Science
'85* 6 (July/August 1985): 30–36. What are the
uses of yeasts in industry and in medicine?

Summary

The kingdom Protista includes eukaryotes such as protozoa, water molds, slime molds, and algae. The protozoa are unicellular, heterotrophic organisms that are classified by their mode of locomotion. Flagellates have flagella that pull them through the water. Sarcodines have pseudopodia, and ciliates have numerous eyelash-like cilia.

Sporozoans are nonmotile and parasitic. Protozoa reproduce by binary fission. Some protozoa are free-living and others cause diseases such as dysentery and malaria.

Slime molds and water molds are heterotrophic protists. The often brightly colored plasmodium creeps over a surface in an amoeboid manner. Water molds are often parasitic.

Algae contain chlorophyll in addition to some other pigment. These protists provide food for aquatic animals and produce much of the oxygen found in the atmosphere.

Fungi include mushrooms, puffballs, bracket fungi, rusts, and smuts. Many fungi are decomposers. Some fungi are animal parasites; some cause diseases that destroy food crops.

The bodies of fungi are made of hyphae which may be modified for different functions. In black bread mold for example, hyphae that are modified as stolons branch along the surface of the bread. Rhizoids penetrate the bread and digest and absorb food. Sporangiophores bear capsules in which spores are produced. The hyphae of mushrooms form a compact fruiting body. Basidiospores are produced in gills under the mushroom cap. Some mushrooms are edible and some can be lethal if eaten. The cell walls of most fungi contain chitin. Most fungi have sexual and asexual reproductive stages and form spores.

Rusts and smuts are parasitic fungi that can cause severe damage to cereal and vegetable crops. Sac fungi produce sexual spores in an ascus. Members of this group include truffles and morels. Yeasts are unicellular fungi that carry out fermentation and are important in baking and brewing.

Synthesis

Synthesis Statement

The protozoa perform all the activities that are associated with living things within a single eukaryotic cell. Except for one exclusively parasitic group, protozoa have organelles that function in locomotion. Some of these same organelles are also found in the bodies of multicellular organisms.

Unlike the protozoa, algae are major producers. They are found mostly in water environments where they are important as a food source for aquatic organisms. Many fungi, through their activities of decomposition and decay, make life on Earth possible by returning essential atoms to the biosphere.

Synthesis Questions

Apply your understanding of this unit to the following questions.

1. Early biologists classified the heterotrophic protists as animals and the autotrophic protists as plants. What have modern biologists learned about the protists that justifies placing these organisms into one kingdom?

2. Compare and contrast the methods of obtaining nutrition among the protists, algae, and fungi. Describe some nutritional characteristics that are common among these organisms.

3. Most protists are aquatic. Discuss the benefits and the shortcomings of an aquatic habitat.

4. What advantages do multicellular protists have over unicellular protists?

5. Compare the reproduction of protozoans, algae, and fungi.

6. Compare a life cycle that includes alternation of sexually and asexually reproducing generations to a life cycle that includes only asexual reproduction by cell division.

7. How are humans similar to fungi? Explain why biologists would consider humans to have more in common with fungi than with photosynthetic protists.

8. Discuss the relationship between the structure of various protists and fungi and the manner in which each obtains its food.

9. Discuss the reasons why protozoans and algae are able to successfully live together in similar environments.

10. Use a separate piece of paper to draw a concept map like the one shown. Place each of the following terms inside the appropriate figure: algae, terrestrial, autotrophs, and heterotrophs. Add lines that connect the shapes to show relationships that complete the concept map.

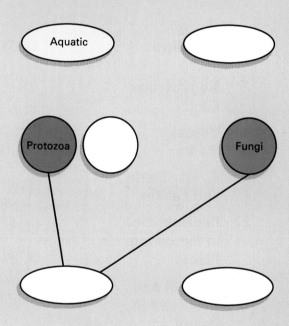

UNIT

7

PLANTS

Unit Outline

Unit Focus

The energy required to sustain all life on Earth comes from the sun. Green plants trap some of this sunlight energy and, in doing so, make it available to other forms of life on this planet.

■ *What structural adaptations are seen in the green plants in the photograph that enable them to trap sunlight energy?*

■ *What would happen if suddenly all green plants disappeared from the surface of the Earth?*

Redwoods in California

Nonvascular Plants

Outline

A star moss of the genus *Polytrichum*

Focus

The green algae that first invaded a land environment about 400 million years ago are probably the ancestors of today's land plants. The group of plants that are described in this chapter do not have organized tissues to transport water and other materials throughout their bodies. This group of plants includes the mosses and other plants that show many of the same adaptations that originally allowed some green algae to survive on land.

■ *Why would you expect to find mosses only in moist areas?*

■ *Why would you expect nonvascular plants to be small in size?*

Origin of Land Plants

Modern land plants share certain characteristics with algae. For example, the life cycle of plants resembles that of some algae. Like most kinds of algae, the cell wall of plants is made primarily of cellulose. Land plants and some groups of algae store food as starch. Only green algae contain the two types of chlorophyll, *a* and *b*, found in modern land plants. Because of these chemical similarities, scientists claim that modern land plants evolved from forms of the green algae, Chlorophyta.

24.1 Adaptations to Life on Land

Adaptation is the process by which a species gradually becomes better able to survive in a given environment. *The specialized structures of land plants are adaptations that allowed the aquatic green algae that gave rise to plants to overcome the problems of living on land and to best use land resources.*

Most of the problems of a land habitat result from the lack of surrounding water. Algae absorb water and minerals directly by diffusion across the cell membrane. In some land plants, pores evolved. Pores absorb moisture from the environment. Other plants developed specialized structures that draw water and minerals from the soil.

In the open air, plants are in danger of losing moisture because of evaporation. A protective outer coating called a **cuticle** (KYOOT ih kuhl) is an adaptation that helps prevent evaporation. The cuticle also protects the plant from the relatively wide and abrupt temperature changes encountered on land.

Unfortunately, the cuticle also prevents the exchange of oxygen and carbon dioxide with the air. Small pores evolved on some of the aboveground portions of the plant. These pores, called **stomata** (stoh MAH tah), allow the necessary exchange of gases. In some plants, *guard cells* regulate the opening and closing of stomata in response to various environmental conditions.

Surrounding water supports algal cells. Multicellular land plants produce a complex compound called **lignin** (LIHG nihn). Lignin, combined with cellulose, forms an extremely tough material that supports soft plant tissues. By keeping plants exposed to the direct sunlight available on land, this support allows land plants to maximize opportunities for photosynthesis.

For aquatic plants, surrounding water allows flagellated sperm to swim to egg cells. In order to reproduce sexually, some land plants still need water for sperm movement. Other

Section Objectives
- *List* the evidence that indicates land plants probably developed from green algae.
- *Describe* the adaptations that enabled plants to survive on land.
- *Distinguish* between the two major groups of land plants.

stomata (singular, *stoma*)

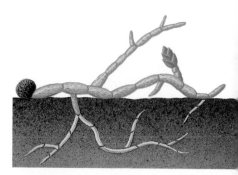

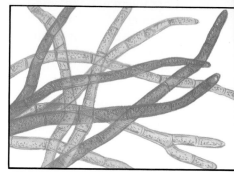

Figure 24–1. Land plants, such as mosses (top), have adaptations that enable them to live on land. Most algae (bottom) live only in water.

plants evolved structures that produce sperm that can travel through the air, in the wind, or on the bodies of insects or animals. Many plants developed multicellular reproductive structures to protect the developing zygote and to keep it from drying.

About 400 million years ago, green algae-like organisms evolved those structures necessary to survive on land—cuticles, stomata, lignified cells, and multicellular reproductive organs. Plants then colonized the land and exploited a habitat where they had no competitors.

BIOLOGY AND YOU:

Peat Moss

Most ecosystems show a balance of photosynthetic producers, animals that consume the producers, and decomposing bacteria. A peat bog is an unusual ecosystem. The major producer in a peat bog is a moss that belongs to the genus *Sphagnum* called *sphagnum moss.* A combination of the chemistry of this organism and the environmental conditions under which it lives prevents the dead bodies of sphagnum moss from decaying completely. These dead bodies accumulate over hundreds and even thousands of years. Depending on the conditions and the length of time over which the accumulation occurs, peat bogs yield fuel and a variety of commercial products.

Peat bogs that formed

during the Carboniferous period were the sites of the first step in the formation of coal. The plants that lived in swampy areas died and fell into the boggy waters where there was little oxygen and few decomposing bacteria. As the sea advanced and withdrew, leaving sediments behind, these partially decomposed plants and peat mosses were subjected to pressure, hardened, and became coal.

Peat, however, is often farmed long before it becomes coal. Large chunks of peat are removed from the bog, allowed to dry, and burned. In addition, because sphagnum moss can absorb about 20 times its weight in water, it is often used to keep plants and aquatic animals moist when they are transported from place to place. Sphagnum moss is also used in gardening to improve the ability of soil to hold water.

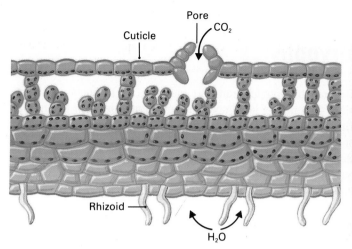

Cuticle — Pore CO$_2$

Rhizoid — H$_2$O

24.2 Vascular and Nonvascular Plants

Not all plants adapted to life on land in the same ways. One of the major distinctions between groups of plants is the way they transport water and nutrients throughout the plant body. The majority of land plant species have an internal system of interconnected tubes and vessels called **vascular tissues.** These plants, grouped as **vascular plants,** will be discussed in the next chapter. Most of the plants you are familiar with—oak trees, roses, grasses, and house plants—are vascular plants and have vascular tissue. The other main group of plants, the **bryophytes** (BRY uh fyts), lack vascular tissues. These **nonvascular plants** transport water and nutrients by osmosis and diffusion, much as algae do.

The earliest fossils of vascular plants are about 400 million years old, but the earliest fossils of bryophytes are only about 350 million years old. For this reason, some scientists claim that bryophytes developed from vascular plants that gradually lost their vascular tissues. However, other scientists claim that bryophytes evolved independently. If many early bryophytes decomposed before they were fossilized, perhaps bryophytes developed earlier than the fossil record indicates.

Figure 24–2. A protective cuticle enables land plants to have leafy surfaces for photosynthesis (right). Plants such as common mosses have pores (left) for gas exchange in those areas covered with a cuticle.

Biofact

Q: *Do any bryophytes live in water?*

A: Yes. The brook moss, *Fontinalis,* grows long streamers that are supported on the surface of flowing water.

Section Review

1. **Comparing Information** In what ways are green algae and modern land plants similar?
2. **Identifying Relationships** Why is lignin important for the survival of modern land plants?
3. **Synthesizing Relationships** What limitations do bryophytes have due to the fact that the structure of the plant has no vascular tissue?

⟨**Thinking Critically**⟩

- *List* the major characteristics of bryophytes.
- *Diagram* the life cycle of mosses.
- *Name* the two ways in which liverworts reproduce asexually.
- *Distinguish* the characteristics of the liverwort sporophyte from those of the hornwort sporophyte.
- *Name* a kind of moss that is commercially important.

Bryophytes

Because bryophytes transport materials by osmosis and diffusion, they need a large and constant supply of water to survive. Bryophytes also need water for sexual reproduction. Like algal sperm, bryophyte sperm must swim to the egg to fertilize it. For these reasons, most bryophytes grow in moist environments such as forests, low-lying areas where water tends to collect, and shady areas where it is cool.

24.3 Characteristics of Bryophytes

Almost all bryophytes are small plants, ranging in height from 1 to 20 cm (0.3 to 8 in.). Because they lack vascular tissues, nonvascular plants grow close to the ground. Bryophytes also lack the rigid tissues that vascular plants have to support vertical growth. Some bryophytes, however, grow to a large size. Most large bryophytes are aquatic species that live in rivers and streams. Supported by the buoyancy of water, these aquatic bryophytes can grow larger than terrestrial species.

Because they do not have vascular tissue, bryophytes do not possess true roots, leaves, or stems. What appear to be "roots" and "leaves" in bryophytes are not specialized structures like those of vascular plants, but mere elongations of the "stem." The *roots* of vascular plants anchor the plant body and absorb water from the soil. Rootlike **rhizoids** in bryophytes perform the same functions but do not channel water to other parts of the plant. The upper parts of bryophytes obtain moisture through their leaves, which absorb water through pores. Bryophyte leaves are usually only two cells thick.

The life cycles of bryophytes exhibit alternation of generations. The **gametophyte** (n) produces gametes (n) by mitosis. During fertilization, the gametes fuse. The resulting zygote grows into the **sporophyte** (2n), which produces spores (n) by meiosis. When these spores germinate, they develop into the new gametophyte (n) generation. *In all bryophytes, the gametophyte is the dominant form.* In other words, the gametophyte is the green leafy plant that makes up the major portion of the organism's life cycle.

The phylum Bryophyta is grouped into three classes. Over 9,500 species are included in the class Muscopsida, the mosses. About 6,000 species of liverworts belong to the class Hepaticopsida. The smallest class, Antherocerotopsida, has about 100 species. Members of this class are commonly called hornworts.

Figure 24–3. Mosses have small stems that cannot conduct water. Bryophyte stems (inset) lack the vascular tissues characteristic of other land plants.

24.4 Mosses

Mosses are small, soft plants that grow in clumps close together. They grow in a wide variety of moist, shaded habitats— on the sides of trees, in sidewalk cracks, on rocks and logs. Some mosses form a dense carpet on the floor of coniferous forests. The greatest number of mosses grow in areas of high humidity, such as the Olympic and Great Smoky mountains, the rain forests of the tropics, and in colder regions as well.

The body of a moss is composed of "leaves" arranged in a spiral around a central stem. Moss plants range in size from 1 or 2 cm (0.4 to 0.8 in.) to more than a meter (39 in.) long. Moss plants may stand erect or trail along the ground.

Life Cycle of Mosses As in all bryophytes, the dominant generation in the moss life cycle is the haploid gametophyte. This form is the familiar green, leaflike moss plant. The sporophyte generation of mosses, which appears as a stalk tipped with a spore-bearing capsule, does not photosynthesize. Because it is dependent on the dominant generation for nutrition, the sporophyte remains physically attached to the gametophyte throughout its life.

Figure 24–5 on page 386 illustrates the alternation of generation in the life cycle of a moss. This cycle begins when the sporophyte (2n) releases spores. When the environment is suitably warm and moist, a spore (n) will germinate and produce a horizontal filament called the **protonema** (proht uh NEE muh). Protonema cells contain chloroplasts and carry out photosynthesis. As the protonema grows, it periodically produces buds that develop into additional gametophytes.

Biofact

Q: *Are all plants that are called "moss" really mosses?*

A: No. Only members of the class Muscopsida are "true" mosses; other plants called "moss" are not. For example, Reindeer moss is a lichen; Spanish moss is a flowering vascular plant; and Irish moss is a red alga.

The relationship of structure and function in mosses is explored on page 389.

Reading Critically

Inferring Conclusions What do you think would happen to the spores of a moss if the environment was not warm and moist.

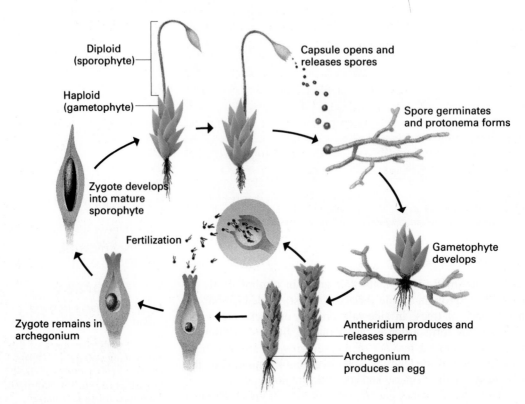

Diploid (sporophyte)

Haploid (gametophyte)

Capsule opens and releases spores

Spore germinates and protonema forms

Zygote develops into mature sporophyte

Gametophyte develops

Fertilization

Zygote remains in archegonium

Antheridium produces and releases sperm

Archegonium produces an egg

Figure 24–5. The moss life cycle (above) involves an alternation of generations in which the gametophyte is the dominant phase. A simplified cycle is diagramed below.

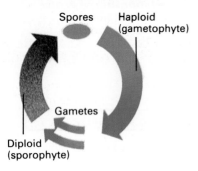

Spores

Haploid (gametophyte)

Gametes

Diploid (sporophyte)

antheridium (plural, *antheridia*)
archegonium (plural, *archegonia*)

Gametophytes produce gametes through mitosis. Sperm are produced in the male reproductive structures, called **antheridia** (an thuh RIHD ee uh). Female reproductive structures, or **archegonia** (ahr kuh GOH nee uh), each contain an egg cell. In some species of moss, both antheridia and archegonia are found on the same plant, but other species have separate male and female plants.

In the gametophyte generation of mosses, fertilization can only take place in a moist environment. Sperm, which must swim to reach the egg cells, are not released from the antheridia unless the moss is covered with moisture such as heavy dew, fog, or rain.

The sporophyte generation begins with the fertilized egg (2n). As the zygote develops into a mature sporophyte, it grows up through the neck of the archegonium. Inside the spore capsule of the sporophyte, layers of diploid cells undergo meiosis and form spores. When the sporophyte is fully mature, the end of the spore capsule drops off. The wind can then shake the spores from the capsule and scatter them, thus beginning the cycle again.

Importance of Mosses Mosses are among the first plants to grow in otherwise barren areas. Mosses help to create new soil and help prevent erosion by anchoring existing soil. After mosses start to grow, other plants soon become established.

One kind of moss, sphagnum moss, is commercially important. Sphagnum is the main component in peat moss, an organic fuel used in homes in Ireland, Canada, the Soviet Union, and other northern countries. Peat is cut from areas called *bogs* that are made up largely of the decomposing bodies of bryophytes. At one time, peat bogs were also the source of some coals that formed millions of years ago.

24.5 Liverworts

Liverworts get their name from the flat, liverlike shape of the main body of the plant. There are two kinds of liverworts. Liverworts that have a flattened or straplike body are *thallose* liverworts. Liverworts that have "leaves" that resemble those of mosses are *leafy* liverworts. Most liverworts are much smaller than mosses.

The upper surface of the liverwort plant is covered with many small pores through which gases are exchanged. The pores are continuously open. Because the pores cannot close, liverworts are restricted to warm, moist habitats.

Liverworts have a sexual life cycle similar to that of mosses. The major difference between the two cycles is the way the plants produce archegonia and antheridia. As shown in Figure 24–6, liverworts send up stalks that bear the reproductive structures.

Liverworts also reproduce asexually. Small pieces that break off will form new plants by *fragmentation*. In some liverworts, special pieces of tissue called **gemmae** (JEHM ee) are produced in small, cupped structures that form on the upper part of the plant. When rain hits the cup, the gemmae splash out and begin to grow into new plants.

24.6 Hornworts

Hornworts are the smallest group of bryophytes. Only one genus, *Anthoceros* of the class Antherocerotopsida, now exists. Most hornworts grow in damp areas such as ditches, along the edges of streams, or near the shores of lakes.

Hornworts look like liverworts. The gametophyte generation is flat and circular, with lobed leaves. Hornworts take their name from the sporophyte, which resembles a long animal horn.

Figure 24–6. Liverworts (top) are bryophytes whose stems often grow pressed to the soil surface. Liverworts reproduce asexually through the production of gemmae in gemmae cups (bottom).

Almost all mosses are small and insignificant in appearance. Yet these tiny plants can play a major role in the establishment of new plant communities.

The first plants to grow in barren areas are known as *pioneer plants.* Mosses and other bryophytes often act as pioneer plants because they can grow in places where there is little or no soil. Because their spores are carried by wind, mosses can become established in areas far away from parent plants. Mosses are often the first plants to appear after disturbances such as heavy

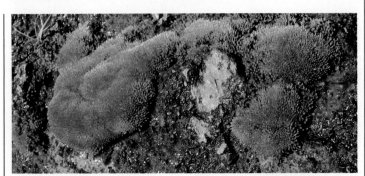

rainfall, flooding, or landslides. Mosses can grow in such inhospitable settings as rocky hillsides and cliff faces. As mosses become established, the growth of rhizoids splits off tiny pieces of rock. This process helps to slowly create new soil. When the bryophytes die, their bodies add organic matter to the soil. With

time, additional plants begin to grow.

Surprisingly, many mosses thrive in exposed settings where it is often hot and dry. Members of the genus *Andreaea* grow on rock faces and outcrops.

■ **Inferring Conclusions** How do bryophytes benefit from being pioneer plants?

Unlike that of liverworts, the sporophyte generation of hornworts conducts photosynthesis. Nevertheless, in hornworts as well as in liverworts, the sporophyte remains physically attached to the gametophyte. The sporangium of a hornwort splits open longitudinally to release its spores.

Section Review

1. **Identifying Information**   Why are bryophytes said not to have true roots, leaves, and stems?
2. **Comprehending Ideas**   What event in the life cycle of bryophytes requires a film of water?
3. **Comprehending Ideas**   In what two ways do liverworts carry out asexual reproduction?
4. **Contrasting Ideas**   How are the hornwort and liverwort sporophytes different?
5. **Evaluating Relationships**   Why is peat moss economically important?

Thinking Critically

INVESTIGATION 24:
How Is Structure Related to Function in Mosses?

Objectives
- To *observe* a moss plant
- To *relate* moss structure to function

Materials
prepared slide of moss protonema, live moss gametophyte and sporophyte, sphagnum moss, forceps, centimeter ruler, hand lens or stereomicroscope, compound light microscope, water, lens paper, two glass slides, coverslip, medicine dropper, triple-beam balance, 150-mL beaker, 100-mL graduated cylinder

Prelab Preparation
1. Review bryophyte characteristics.
2. Explain why mosses are found only in moist habitats.
3. Review the stages of the moss life cycle.
4. Explain why rhizoids are not considered true roots.

Sphagnum moss with spore capsules

Inquiry: Observation
5. Use first low power and then high power to observe a prepared slide of a moss protonema. Make a labeled drawing at each magnification. *What evidence shows that a gametophyte might develop from the protonema?*
6. Describe the structure of the protonema. *Considering the function of the rhizoids, how might they be distinguished from the rest of the protonema?*
7. Obtain a moss plant and identify the rhizoids, gametophyte, sporophyte, and

the spore-bearing capsule. Make a labeled drawing of the moss.
8. Use forceps to remove a leaf-like structure from the moss and make a wet mount of this specimen. Use low power to observe the specimen. Switch to high power and make a labeled drawing of the structure. *How many cells thick is this structure?*
9. Use the forceps to remove the sporophyte. Place the spore capsule on a glass slide and add a drop of water. Place a second slide on top of the first. Crush the spore capsule by gently pressing on the slide. Remove the top slide and add a coverslip. Use first low power and then high power to observe the crushed spore capsule. Describe the capsule's contents.
10. Place 8 g of dry sphagnum moss into a 150-mL beaker. Add 100-mL of water.
11. Wait two minutes and then pour any water that has not absorbed by the moss into the graduated cylinder. Measure the volume of the water in the cylinder and record your data.
12. *Calculate the absorption capacity using the following formula.*

$$\text{Absorption} = \frac{\text{Volume of water absorbed (in mL)}}{\text{Mass of moss (in g)}}$$

Analysis
1. **Identifying Relationships** Based on your observations of the protonema, what evidence indicates that moss is a plant?
2. **Comparing Structures** Compare the structure and color of sporophyte and gametophyte.
3. **Inferring Relationships** Why does the position of the spore capsule suggest that spores are dispersed by wind rather than by water?
4. **Inferring Ideas** Why might wind dispersal of spores be more advantageous to a moss plant than dispersal by water?

Chapter 24 Review

Summary

Modern land plants are probably descendants of green algalike organisms that adapted to life on land. Modern plants are divided into two groups. Vascular plants have special tissues that transport water and nutrients throughout the plant. Nonvascular plants, such as bryophytes, lack vascular tissue. Bryophytes transport materials by osmosis and diffusion. The life cycle of bryophytes exhibits an alternation of generations in which the haploid gametophyte is the dominant form. Bryophytes do not have true roots, leaves, or stems.

Bryophytes are divided into three classes: mosses, liverworts, and hornworts. The sporophyte phase (2n) of the moss life cycle occurs when gametes fuse. The zygote develops into a sporophyte, which in turn produces haploid spores by meiosis. When the spores germinate, they give rise to the protonema. The new gametophyte produces archegonia and antheridia. Egg and sperm are formed. When they unite, a new zygote is established.

The gametophytes of most liverworts and hornworts are flat-bodied. Both of these groups have a life cycle similar to that of mosses. Liverworts also reproduce asexually by fragmentation and by the production of gemmae usually formed in special gemmae cups.

BioTerms

antheridia (386)
archegonia (386)
bryophytes (383)
cuticle (381)
gametophyte (384)
gemmae (387)
lignin (381)

nonvascular plants (383)
protonema (385)
rhizoid (384)
sporophyte (384)
stomata (383)
vascular plants (383)
vascular tissue (383)

For each pair of terms, explain the differences in their meanings.

1. nonvascular plants, vascular plants
2. antheridia, archegonia
3. gametophyte, sporophyte
4. stomata, cuticle

BioQuiz   (Write all answers on a separate sheet of paper.)

Completion

1. The _____ is the dominant generation in all bryophytes.
2. The egg cell of a moss plant is fertilized in the _____ .
3. In land plants, water loss due to _____ is prevented by the cuticle.
4. Due to the structural support of the substance _____ , plants are able to maximize their opportunities for photosynthesis.
5. Because bryophytes do not have true roots, _____ perform the function of absorbing water.

Multiple Choice

6. _____ is/are the main component of peat bogs.   a) Sphagnum moss
   b) Liverworts   c) Hornworts
   d) Spanish moss
7. The establishment of mosses in a barren area helps create   a) peat bogs.
   b) vascular plants.   c) top soil.
   d) fertilizer.
8. Stomata allow land plants to carry out
   a) water uptake.   b) reproduction.
   c) osmosis.   d) gas exchange.
9. In mosses, the process of nuclear division called meiosis produces   a) gametes.

b) spores. c) gametophytes.
d) sporophytes.
10. In mosses, sperm are produced in the
    a) cuticle. b) stoma. c) antheridium.
    d) archegonium.
11. Which class of bryophytes has the fewest
    species? a) mosses b) hornworts
    c) liverworts d) algae
12. Which structure allows for gas exchange
    through the cuticle? a) stoma
    b) lignin c) rhizoid d) gemmae
13. Moss spores produce filaments called
    a) gemmae. b) protonema cells.
    c) stomata. d) rhizoids.
14. Some liverworts produce special cupped
    structures for spores called a) rhizoids.
    b) antheridium. c) gemmae.
    d) archegonium.

15. Which class of bryophytes can reproduce
    by fragmentation? a) hornworts
    b) mosses c) liverworts d) algae

Writing Critically

16. Why do scientists think that plants such
    as mosses and vascular plants evolved
    from green algae?
17. What are the advantages of multicellular
    reproductive structures over the unicellu-
    lar type found in algae?
18. Why are mosses and other bryophytes
    generally small?
19. What role does dew play in the repro-
    duction of mosses?
20. Did bryophytes evolve from vascular
    plants? Explain your answer by citing
    evidence from bryophyte structure.

Application/Critical Thinking

1. **Diagramming Information** Use your
   library to research asexual reproduction in
   liverworts that produce gemmae. Diagram
   the steps of the process. Include captions
   and labels in your diagram. The labels
   should name each part of the liverwort and
   indicate whether they are haploid (n) or
   diploid (2n). The captions should explain
   what happens during each stage of the
   process.
2. **Analyzing Relationships** The spores of
   some mosses can remain dormant in conditions that are unfavorable for survival.

Explain in writing how this characteristic
of moss spores might be beneficial to
mosses in their role as pioneer plants.
3. **Inferring Relationships** Explain how
   conditions in a terrestrial environment
   made the presence of stomata an effective
   adaptation to life on land.
4. **Evaluating Information** Bryophytes produce gametes through mitosis rather than
   meiosis, the method of gamete formation in animals. Explain why bryophyte
   gametes are nevertheless haploid, just as
   animal gametes are.

Cross-Discipline Connection

Biology and Engineering Bryophytes are
adapted to hostile environments. How can
some bryophyte adaptations serve as models

for engineers who develop equipment, materials, and strategies suitable for use in space and
on ocean bottoms?

Discovery Through Reading

Read the article "Don't Look Down on the
Humble Moss," *Audubon* (September 1988):

46–55. What are some unique growth habits
found in mosses?

Vascular Plants

Deciduous angiosperm trees in fall coloration at Mount Rainier National Park in Washington

Focus

The more than 250,000 species of grasses, trees, ferns, shrubs, and wildflowers that cover the Earth are vascular plants. These plants have specialized tissue cells that allow them to transport water and other materials throughout their bodies. This and other adaptations have made vascular plants the most successful land-dwelling plants. Vascular plants supply food and shelter to many species of animals.

- *What importance do vascular plants have to humans?*

- *How do you think having specialized tissues for transporting water relates to the success of vascular plants?*

Development of Vascular Plants

Section Objectives
- *List* the basic plant structures that vascular and nonvascular plants have in common.
- *Describe* the vascular system of plants.
- *Name* the dominant generation in the life cycle of vascular plants.
- *Explain* how vascular plants show adaptations to life on land.

Like nonvascular plants, vascular plants are thought to have developed from water-dwelling green algae approximately 400 million years ago. The **tracheophytes** (TRAY kee uh fyts), or vascular plants, share some basic adaptations to life on land with the bryophytes. Both groups have a waxy outer *cuticle* that retains water, and stomata in the cuticle that allow an exchange of gases. Multicellular reproductive structures that protect delicate zygotes evolved in both vascular and nonvascular plants.

Unlike bryophytes, tracheophytes have an internal network of tubes known as the **vascular system.** The tubes carry water, nutrients, and the products of photosynthesis throughout the plant. The vascular system can transport fluids over long distances, from roots buried deep in the soil to treetops perhaps hundreds of meters above the ground. The cell walls of tracheophytes contain *lignin,* a substance that helps support the plant body.

The effects of crowding on vascular plant growth are explored on page 405.

25.1 The Vascular System

The body of a vascular plant is made up of three types of structures. The *roots* absorb moisture and nutrients from the soil and anchor the plant. *Leaves* have chloroplasts and produce food by photosynthesis. The *stem* contains vascular tissues that transport substances between the roots and leaves and support the leaves. Because they contain vascular tissue, tracheophytes are said to have true roots, stems, and leaves.

The vascular system includes two distinct kinds of vascular tissues. The **xylem** (ZY luhm) transports water and minerals absorbed by the roots up to those parts of the plant that are above the ground. The **phloem** (FLOH ehm) carries sugar and other soluble organic materials produced by photosynthesis from the leaves to the rest of the plant.

25.2 Reproduction in Vascular Plants

The life cycles of vascular plants are different from those of nonvascular plants. ***In vascular plants, the sporophyte is the dominant generation.*** The sporophyte is physically larger, shows more complex development, and produces more varied types of cells than the gametophyte.

Tracheophytes are traditionally divided into two groups, seedless plants and seed plants. Seedless plants developed first and still have traits that show their watery origin. Most seedless plants require water for sexual reproduction.

Figure 25–1. Vascular plants have tissues that conduct water and nutrients. The inset shows a cross section of the plant's stem with xylem in orange and phloem in green.

Figure 25–2. About 300 million years ago, vascular plants dominated the earth. Giant club mosses and giant horsetails were common in the great hot swamps of the Carboniferous period.

Seed plants developed an important adaptation; they reproduce sexually by forming seeds. The details of the life cycles of specific vascular plants will be covered later in this chapter.

25.3 Adaptations in Vascular Plants

Certain adaptations in tracheophytes gave them important evolutionary advantages over nonvascular plants. Consider, for example, the problems bryophytes and vascular plants face in a dry environment. To survive in such an environment, a plant must have mechanisms to overcome the lack of available water. Nonvascular plants cannot easily tolerate dry conditions. Bryophytes need an abundant supply of water to transport materials by osmosis and diffusion and to reproduce sexually. However, tracheophytes are able to obtain the water they need from roots growing beneath the dry surface. The sperm of seed plants, protected in pollen, can reach egg cells through the air. Seeds from seed plants can remain dormant until conditions are favorable for their germination. These adaptations enabled tracheophytes to survive in dry conditions and contributed to the worldwide proliferation of vascular plants.

Reading Critically

Evaluating Relationships
Which type of plant would be more likely to survive in the desert: a bryophyte or a tracheophyte? Explain your answer.

Thinking Critically

Section Review

1. **Comparing Information**   What are three traits that are shared by vascular and nonvascular plants?
2. **Interpreting Information**   What functions do xylem and phloem perform?
3. **Inferring Relationships**   How did the development of the vascular system help plants survive on land?

Seedless Vascular Plants

The seedless vascular plants include living representatives from four phyla: Psilophyta (sy LAHF uh tuh), the wisk ferns; Sphenophyta (sfee NAHF uh tuh), the horsetails; Lycophyta (ly KAHF uh tuh), the club mosses and their relatives; and Pterophyta (tehr AHF uh tuh), the ferns. *Seedless vascular plants reproduce sexually by means of flagellated sperm that need water to swim to the egg cells.* The sporophyte generation produces haploid spores that develop into small, independent gametophytes.

25.4 Whisk Ferns

The few surviving species of whisk ferns are the simplest vascular plants living today. Whisk ferns are unique among vascular plants because they lack roots and leaves. Most of the whisk fern body consists of an unspecialized, branching stem that contains vascular tissues. The green portion of the stem above the ground carries out photosynthesis. The underground stem, called a **rhizome,** anchors the plant and produces rhizoids that absorb water and nutrients from the soil. Whisk ferns grow from 10 to 40 cm (4 to 16 in.) tall.

25.5 Horsetails

The 15 living species of horsetails all belongs to the genus *Equisetum,* Latin for "horsetail." Perhaps their ribbed stems and whorls of branches suggested the name. Horsetails are the only seedless vascular plants that have hollow stems. *Silica,* a sandlike substance, gives the stem a coarse texture. The ancestors of horsetails were treelike swamp plants that lived over 300 million years ago. Horsetails today live primarily in warm, moist environments.

The seedless vascular plants are described on page 915.

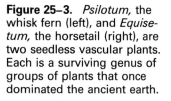

Biofact

Q: *Why are horsetails also called "scouring rushes"?*

A: Pioneers used the plants' tough stems to scour dirty pots and pans.

Figure 25–3. *Psilotum,* the whisk fern (left), and *Equisetum,* the horsetail (right), are two seedless vascular plants. Each is a surviving genus of groups of plants that once dominated the ancient earth.

25.6 Club Mosses and Their Relatives

Club mosses and their relatives date back to the Devonian period, 345–395 million years ago. About 1,000 species survive today. Of the five genera of club mosses, the two most important are *Lycopodium* and *Selaginella*. Both of these genera have many representatives in both temperate and tropical areas.

Lycopodium   There are about 200 species of club mosses in the genus *Lycopodium*. Most club mosses live in shady, moist places like the floor of a forest. *Lycopodium* is called a club moss because it produces spores on narrow, clublike cones. These cones have many small leaves called **sporophylls.** At the base of each sporophyll is a *sporangium*, in which spores are formed by meiosis. In club mosses, the sporophyte is clearly the dominant generation. The gametophyte is so small it is difficult to see. Its only function is to produce male and female reproductive structures, *antheridia* and *archegonia*, which are often present on the same plant. Some gametophytes lie dormant underground for almost 10 years.

Figure 25–4. The club moss, *Lycopodium*, produces spores in distinct reproductive structures that resemble cones. The leaves of these cones are called sporophylls.

THINKING ABOUT BIOLOGY: Fossil Fuel

Most coal was formed from the remains of plants that lived on Earth long ago. During the Carboniferous period, which occurred about 250 million to 350 million years ago, much of the Earth was covered by dense forests and swamps of giant horsetails, club mosses, and ferns. As these plants died, they formed thick layers of partially decomposed organic material called *peat.* In time, the peat was buried under minerals and sand. The weight of these overlying layers put tremendous pressure on the peat, causing it to transform into a form of coal called *lignite.*

As more and more organic matter accumulated, the lignite was further compressed. It was gradually transformed into *subbituminous coal, bituminous coal,* and finally *anthracite,* the hardest of all types of coal. Geologists estimate that it takes a layer of compressed plant material 2.1 m (7 ft.) thick to make 0.4 m (1 ft.) of anthracite.

The plant species that were formed into coal are now almost all extinct. However, coal formation is still occurring. Under proper conditions, plants growing in today' swamps may one day become coal. However, the process of coal formation is very slow and coal reserves in the United States and in the world are being rapidly depleted. Some large deposits of anthracite are still found in Pennsylvania and Virginia, but coal and other fossil fuels such as petroleum will soon be used up.

■ **Inferring Conclusions** If coal formation is still occurring, why will fossil fuels soon run out?

Selaginella   *Selaginella* grows in tropical regions and desert environments. Over 700 species have been identified. These plants are characteristically small. Their trailing stems branch frequently and produce many small leaves.

Selaginella produces two kinds of spores. The smaller spores are called *microspores*. They develop into male gametophytes that produce only antheridia. The larger spores, called *megaspores*, develop into female gametophytes that produce only archegonia.

25.7 Ferns

Approximately 12,000 species of ferns have been identified, more than any other group of seedless vascular plants. Most ferns prefer moist, fertile soil and live in the tropics, but ferns have adapted to almost every climate. Certain types of ferns are even found in very cold areas north of the Arctic Circle or high atop mountains.

Ferns have a wide range of sizes as well. Some are very small plants, but others grow as tall as trees.

Figure 25–5. This species of *Selaginella* lies flat on the ground. *Selaginella* differs from most seedless vascular plants in producing male and female spores and male and female gametophytes.

Figure 25–6. Ferns range in size from small species (far left) to large tree ferns (left).

Physical Structure   Some ferns are delicate plants scarcely 3 mm (0.12 in.) tall. In contrast, huge tree ferns can reach 28 m (92 ft.). Few plant phyla show such wide variation.

Generally ferns are supported by underground rhizomes that produce roots. Each fern leaf, called a **frond,** has two parts. The *stipe* is the stemlike structure that attaches the leaf to the rhizome. The *blade* is the broad, green part of the leaf that carries on photosynthesis. Fronds spread out over a wide area. In this way they catch the dim light that reaches the forest floor.

Reading Critically

Inferring Relationships
What structural feature provides ferns with the ability to exist and grow in areas that receive small amounts of light?

Cultured Ferns

Ferns are popular decorative plants and, for this reason, are commonly grown in commercial plant nurseries. In the past, fern growers raised ferns from spores. Nurseries provided the ideal environment in which the fern's normal life cycle could take place. However, growing ferns from spores often resulted in inconsistent yields. In addition, growing ferns from spores was quite slow. It may take many months for a spore to grow into a fern that is ready for sale in the marketplace.

Many nurseries now use a method of growing several species of ferns that involves growing new plants from small bits of tissue from a mature fern. This method produces identical ferns with all the characteristics of the original fern from which the tissue was taken. First, a small piece is cut from the fern, usually from the rhizome. This piece of tissue, called an *explant,* is sterilized and placed in a flask containing a special nutrient agar. If the laboratory conditions are properly controlled, the explant begins producing shoots within a short time.

Later, the shoots are separated from the explant and transferred to other flasks. Here they are treated with special plant hormones that promote the growth of roots. When these plantlets reach a certain size, they are transferred to sterilized soil. The ferns then continue their development and become mature plants.

Contamination with disease-causing organisms is a key problem when using this method to grow new plants. Extreme caution must be taken to prevent microorganisms from entering the growth flasks. However, if contamination is avoided, the process of separating and transplanting shoots from the explant can produce hundreds of identical plants from one original plant.

Thus far, only a few species of ferns, including the Boston fern, are grown commercially using this method. Researchers are working to find the precise conditions and nutrients required to grow other species of ferns in this way. This knowledge will enable them to grow several hundred identical fern offspring from one parent plant simultaneously in other species of ferns.

Life Cycle of Ferns The fern life cycle is typical of seedless vascular plants. Gametes from the gametophyte generation fuse to form zygotes. The sporophyte generation grows from the zygote. As the sporophyte matures, it forms a tightly curled leaf called a *fiddlehead.* When the fiddlehead is exposed to sunlight, it gradually opens into a new frond. Haploid fern spores develop in sporangia on the underside of fronds. Sporangia usually occur in clusters called **sori.** Mature spores are released from the sporangia and dispersed by the wind.

sori (singular, *sorus*)

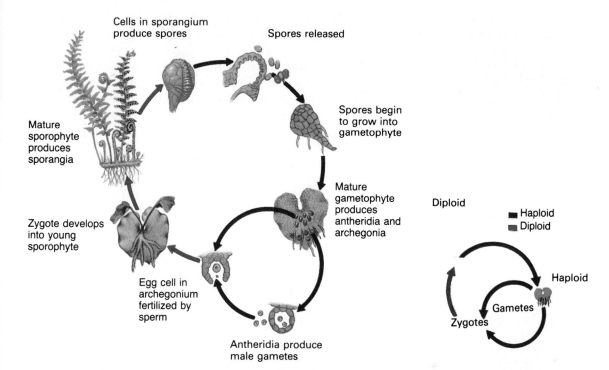

Cells in sporangium produce spores

Spores released

Spores begin to grow into gametophyte

Mature sporophyte produces sporangia

Mature gametophyte produces antheridia and archegonia

Zygote develops into young sporophyte

Egg cell in archegonium fertilized by sperm

Antheridia produce male gametes

Diploid

■ Haploid
■ Diploid

Haploid

Gametes

Zygotes

Fern spores develop into the gametophyte generation, called the **prothallus.** The prothallus is a green organism, often heart-shaped, that attaches itself to soil, rocks, or tree bark by rhizoids. The typical prothallus is only 1 cm (0.4 in.) wide. Archegonia and antheridia develop on the underside of the prothallus, where a film of rain or dew collects and enables sperm to swim to the archegonia. The fertilized egg cell produces a diploid zygote that in time develops into a new fern sporophyte.

Ferns can be cloned by cutting a section containing rhizome from a mature fern and replanting it in soil. Cloned ferns are genetically identical to the parent plant.

Figure 25–7. The life cycle of ferns (above) involves an alternation of generations in which the sporophyte is the dominant phase. The inset shows a simplified diagram of this life cycle.

Section Review

1. **Identifying Ideas** What unique characteristics distinguish whisk ferns from other vascular plants?
2. **Inferring Relationships** Why is a film of water necessary for sexual reproduction in club mosses?
3. **Analyzing Ideas** What stages of fern reproduction involve the prothallus?

⟨ **Thinking Critically** ⟩

Section Objectives

- *Identify* the parts of a seed.
- *Name* three ways in which seeds increased the adaptability of vascular plants.
- *List* the similarities and differences between gymnosperms and angiosperms.
- *Distinguish* between monocots and dicots.
- *Summarize* the economic and ecological importance of angiosperms.

Seed Plants

Seed plants reproduce chiefly by forming seeds. Every seed contains a plant **embryo,** or partially developed plant that is capable of growing into a mature plant. A seed also contains one or two leaflike structures called **cotyledons** (kaht uhl EED uhnz). Cotyledons may be used as a food supply when the seed sprouts and begins to grow. A hard covering called the **seed coat** encases the embryo and cotyledons and protects them from physical injury and drought.

The development of seeds greatly increased the ability of tracheophytes to survive in unfavorable environments. Seeds protect plant embryos from harsh conditions. As a result, embryos can lie dormant for years and still produce healthy plants when conditions allow. Some seed-bearing structures, including stickers, burrs, and thistledown, travel long distances on animals or in the wind. In this way, seeds substitute for mobility, allowing vascular plant species to spread to new areas.

Two groups of seed plants developed from early vascular plants. **Gymnosperms** (JIHM nuh spuhrmz) produce their seeds in cones and generally keep their leaves throughout the year. **Angiosperms** (AN jee uh spuhrmz) produce flowers, bear their seeds in fruit, and in general lose their leaves annually. Like all tracheophytes, the dominant generation in gymnosperms and angiosperms is the sporophyte. The roots, stems, and leaves of the sporophyte make up the plant's **vegetative body.** The leaves and stems carry out photosynthesis and normal growth.

25.8 Gymnosperms

The seeds of most gymnosperms develop uncovered on *cone scales*. Four groups of gymnosperms have living representatives. Most of the 550 species of gymnosperms are conifers. Cycads (SY kadz) have about 100 species, and the order Gnetales (NEHT ah lehs) has approximately 70. Ginkgoes, the rarest of gymnosperms, have only one species.

Conifers *Conifer* means "cone-bearer." Pines, spruces, firs, and other conifers are characterized by their stiff cones and needlelike leaves. Coniferous forests were once common in temperate zones. Now, forests of conifers are found mostly in northern areas and other regions with sandy soil, cold winters, and moderate rainfall.

Conifers can thrive in harsh conditions because of special adaptations. Their needles are sheathed in a hard, waxy cuticle

Figure 25–8. Conifers like this pine have stiff cones and needlelike leaves.

and have recessed stomata. As a result, needles retain moisture through hot, dry summers and the coldest of winters. Needles are shed and replaced throughout the year, rather than being lost every autumn and replaced every spring. Conifers send roots out over a wide area rather than deep into the soil. This shallow root system holds the tree stable even where soil is scarce.

Sexual reproduction in most conifers involves separate male and female cones that grow on the same tree. The male *pollen cones* produce microspores that develop into pollen grains. Each pollen grain is a male gametophyte. Within the female *seed cones*, megaspores develop into female gametophytes that contain egg cells. When the egg cells begin to form, the female cones secrete a sticky sap that traps pollen drifting in the wind. As the sap dries, it draws the pollen toward the egg cells. The pollen grains then produce male gametes, or sperm, which fertilize the egg cells. The resulting diploid zygote develops into a conifer embryo, contained within the seed.

Conifers do not need a film of water to carry out sexual reproduction because pollen grains containing the sperm are dispersed by the wind. Conifers can therefore reproduce in areas where nonvascular plants and seedless vascular plants cannot.

Other Gymnosperms
Forests of cycads were once common. Now, these gymnosperms live mainly in the tropics. Cycads

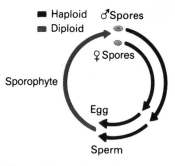

Figure 25–9. The life cycle of a conifer (below) involves an alternation of generations. Male cones produce pollen that travels to the female cone. A simplified life cycle diagram is shown above.

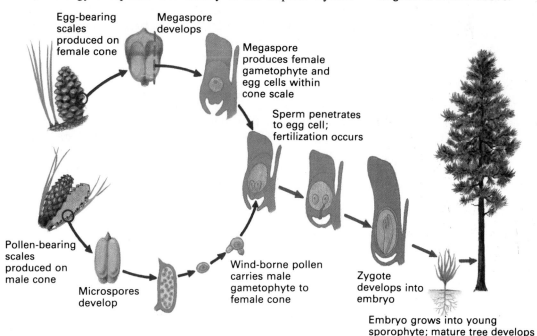

Figure 25–10. Gymnosperms are a diverse group of seed plants. *Welwitschia* (left) grows only in the deserts of southern Africa. Cycads (center) are palmlike plants from the tropics. Ginkgo trees (right) are native to China.

resemble palms but are unrelated to them. The cycad reproductive cycle is similar to that of conifers, but most cycad trees are either male or female.

The order Gnetales includes trees and woody vines that have traits of gymnosperms, but some species have reproductive structures like those found in angiosperms. One species produces an edible plumlike fruit. Another, *Welwitschia*, grows only in the deserts of southern Africa.

The ginkgo is the last species of a once widespread family of trees. They are called "living fossils" because they have remained essentially unchanged from earlier geologic times. Ginkgoes have unique fan-shaped leaves. Pollen is produced in small conelike structures that dangle from the tree branches of male ginkgoes. After fertilization, female trees produce fleshy seeds that look like pale berries.

25.9 Angiosperms

Angiosperms are flowering plants. They produce seeds enclosed in fruits, as opposed to the uncovered seeds of the gymnosperms. To botanists, the history of angiosperms is still a mystery, because the flowering plants appeared so suddenly in the fossil record about 130 million years ago. Without a doubt, however, the angiosperms have been extremely successful. Of the more than 250,000 species of vascular plants, about 235,000 are angiosperms. They include most green plants. Oaks, birches, vegetables, and grasses are all angiosperms.

Physical Structure   Angiosperms are classified according to the number of cotyledons in their seeds. Plants with one cotyledon are called **monocots;** those with two are called **dicots.** Monocots include about 65,000 species; dicots have about

170,000. Monocots and dicots can also be identified by the characteristics illustrated in Figure 25–11. For example, the flower petals of monocots usually occur in threes or multiples of three, while the petals of dicots usually occur in fours, fives, or multiples of four or five. Monocots usually have leaves with parallel veins. Dicots usually have netlike veins.

Angiosperms are also commonly classified by the characteristics of their stem tissues. In **woody plants,** the xylem and phloem produce cumulative layers of new plant tissue that increase the width of the stem and make it strong and hard. This cumulative growth is called **secondary growth.** Woody plants often live for many years and tend to produce relatively few seeds. Most woody plants are dicots, such as maple, walnut, and chestnut trees.

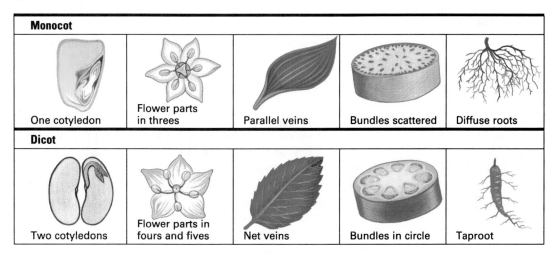

Monocot				
One cotyledon	Flower parts in threes	Parallel veins	Bundles scattered	Diffuse roots
Dicot				
Two cotyledons	Flower parts in fours and fives	Net veins	Bundles in circle	Taproot

Almost all monocots are **herbaceous plants.** Their stems are usually green and lack secondary growth. Herbaceous plants typically have shorter lives and produce more seeds than woody plants. Grasses and orchids are examples of herbaceous monocot plants. Tomatoes and spinach are herbaceous dicots.

Figure 25–11. The differences between the two groups of angiosperms, dicots and monocots, are shown in the diagrams. Each group represents a distinct line of angiosperm evolution.

25.10 Flowers and Fruits in Reproduction

All angiosperms produce reproductive structures called *flowers.* In some species, the flower contains both male and female reproductive organs. After the male sperm fertilize the female eggs, the flower petals usually die and the remaining flower structures develop into a *fruit.* Fruits protect seeds and help disperse them in various ways. When an animal eats fruit, for example, it may scatter the seeds or deposit them unharmed in a new area.

Table 25–1: Summary of Characteristics of Nonvascular and Vascular Plants

Common Name	Vascular System	Structure	Life Cycle and Reproduction	Habitats
Mosses Liverworts Hornworts	None	Relatively simple; no true roots, stems, or leaves	Require water for sexual reproduction; gametophyte dominant	Moist areas
Club mosses Horsetails Whisk ferns	Relatively simple	True roots, stems, and leaves	Require water for sexual reproduction; sporophyte dominant	Areas with at least periodic moisture
Ferns	Relatively simple	True roots, stems, and leaves	Require water for sexual reproduction; sporophyte dominant; asexual reproduction from rhizome	Areas with at least periodic moisture
Conifers	Complex	True roots, stems, and leaves	Do not require water for sexual reproduction; naked seeds; gametophyte reduced to a few cells	Wide range of land environments
Flowering plants	Complex	True roots, stems, and leaves	Do not require water for sexual reproduction; enclosed seeds; gametophyte reduced to a few cells	Almost all land environments

The development of seeds provided animals with a high-energy food source. Prehistoric people gathered seeds and fleshy fruits for food. About 11,000 years ago, people began to cultivate wild grains and to herd livestock on grassy pastures. People have depended on angiosperms ever since for food, lumber, fibers, clothing, and medicines. The grains used most often are corn, rice, wheat, and sorghum. All of these are the seeds of grasses—a highly evolved group of angiosperms.

Section Review

1. **Listing Information**   What are the main parts of a seed?
2. **Identifying Relationships**   How do seeds increase a plant's ability to survive?
3. **Inferring Relationships**   What features help conifers to grow in cold, dry climates?
4. **Relating Information**   What are some monocots that you eat?
5. **Analyzing Information**   What characteristics of angiosperms allow them great success on land?

Thinking Critically

INVESTIGATION 25:
How Does Crowding Affect Plant Growth?

Objectives
- To *design* a controlled experiment
- To *evaluate* the effect of crowding on plant growth

Materials
potting soil, three 15-cm pots, centimeter ruler, 20 lima bean seeds, calipers, scissors, triple-beam balance

Prelab Preparation
1. Explain how a seed differs from a spore.
2. State the role that soil plays in seed germination and plant growth.
3. What plant structures might be measured to indicate plant growth?
4. Discuss the question that is the topic of this Investigation with your laboratory partner and construct a hypothesis. Explain why you chose your hypothesis.

Inquiry: Experimentation
5. Use the following information to design a controlled experiment that tests your hypothesis.
   a. Work with your laboratory partner. Each team will have a complete set of materials and conduct the experiment separately.
   b. Fill three pots with soil up to 2.5 cm from the rim. Plant the seeds just below the surface of the soil.
   c. Allow the plants to grow for one week after germination before you begin to record measurements.
   d. Collect measurements for those plant structures that show growth. Share the data with the other teams in your group. Calculate the average measurement for each structure and use this average to answer the analysis questions.
6. Describe the design of your experiment, including both dependent and independent variables. Explain why your design represents a controlled experiment.
7. *What factors will you hold constant for all the pots?*

8. After having your experimental design approved by your teacher, conduct your experiment.
9. Make bar graphs similar to the one shown below, that compare the average measurements of the plants in each pot.

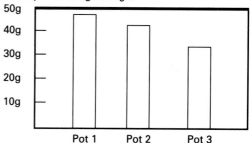

Bar Graph—Average Weight

Analysis
1. **Summarizing Data** Summarize the data collected throughout your experiment.
2. **Evaluating Methods** How is a graph of the data more useful than is a table?
3. **Analyzing Data** Do you observe the same pattern between the different pots for each characteristic of growth?
4. **Inferring Conclusions** What conclusion can you draw about your hypothesis? Explain how the data support or do not support your conclusion.
5. **Evaluating Methods** What sources of error might have affected your data? What could be done to improve the design of the experiment?
6. **Evaluating Methods** Some seeds that were used in the experiment may not have been viable. These seeds would not germinate under any conditions. How does this fact affect the validity of your conclusions?
7. **Making Inferences** Speculate on a possible explanation for the relationship you observed between crowding and plant growth.

Chapter 25 Review

Summary

Both vascular and nonvascular plants adapted to life on land. The vascular plants, however, developed specialized vascular tissues as well as roots, stems, and leaves. These structures enabled vascular plants to grow taller, disperse their reproductive cells more widely, and withstand harsher climates than nonvascular plants can.

Seedless vascular plants require a film of water for sexual reproduction. Whisk ferns, horsetails, club mosses, and ferns are living relatives of the early seedless vascular plants. Club mosses and ferns have similar life cycles, involving sporangia and spores that develop into the gametophyte generation. Ferns, the most varied seedless nonvascular plants, also commonly reproduce asexually.

Seed plants include gymnosperms and angiosperms, the flowering plants. Both produce seeds that consist of an embryo, one or two cotyledons, and a seed coat. Conifers have adapted well to life in cold, arid regions. They do not require a film of water for reproduction. Angiosperms are the dominant plants on Earth. They are classified as monocots or dicots. Angiosperms produce flowers and fruits that provide much of the food essential for animal life.

BioTerms

angiosperm (**400**)
cotyledon (**400**)
dicot (**402**)
embryo (**400**)
frond (**397**)
gymnosperm (**400**)
herbaceous
  plant (**403**)
monocot (**402**)

phloem (**393**)
prothallus (**399**)
rhizome (**395**)
secondary
  growth (**403**)
seed coat (**400**)
sori (**398**)
sporophyll (**396**)
tracheophyte (**393**)

vascular system (**393**)   woody plant (**403**)
vegetative body (**400**)   xylem (**393**)

For each pair of terms, explain the differences in their meanings.

1. xylem, phloem
2. monocot, dicot
3. gymnosperm, angiosperm
4. herbaceous plant, woody plant

BioQuiz   (Write all answers on a separate sheet of paper.)

Completion

1. The sporangia of ferns are attached to the _____ .

2. In ginkgoes, small conelike structures on the branches of male trees produce _____ .

3. The vascular system in tracheophytes consists of xylem and _____ .

4. In ferns, the gametophyte generation is called the _____ .

5. The underground stem in whisk ferns that anchors the plant and produces rhizoids is the _____ .

Multiple Choice

6. The most widespread tracheophytes are the a) monocots. b) dicots.
  c) angiosperms. d) gymnosperms.

7. Dicot leaves usually have a) parallel veins. b) net veins. c) bundles in circles. d) parts in fours or fives.

8. Food reserves in seeds may be stored in a) the seed coat. b) the cotyledons.
  c) a diffuse root. d) phloem.

9. The only seedless vascular plants with hollow stems are a) horsetails. b) club mosses. c) ginkgoes. d) ferns.

10. The leaves found on cones produced by club mosses are called a) pollen-bearing scales. b) sporophylls. c) egg-bearing scales. d) cotyledons.
11. The hardest coal is a) anthracite. b) carboniferous. c) peat. d) organic.
12. The green part of the fern leaf that carries on photosynthesis is the a) blade. b) stripe. c) sorus. d) seed coat.
13. Which of the following is not part of a seed? a) seed coat b) sorus c) embryo d) cotyledon
14. When subjected to intense pressure, peat first formed a) anthracite. b) sub-bituminous coal. c) bituminous coal. d) lignite.
15. Leaflike structures in seeds are a) sori b) cotyledons. c) fiddleheads. d) fronds.

16. How are angiosperms important to humans and other animals?
17. What is the advantage of a shallow root system to a conifer?
18. Why do seedless vascular plants such as horsetails grow primarily in warm, moist habitats?
19. What are three basic differences between monocots and dicots?
20. What is the basic difference between the two major groups of seed plants, gymnosperms and angiosperms?

Application/Critical Thinking

1. **Inferring Relationships** Florists sometimes dye carnations bright colors by putting dye in the flowers' water. What parts of the flowers' internal structure make this method effective?
2. **Designing Experiments** Herbaceous plants are more sensitive to a lack of soil moisture than are woody plants. What characteristics of herbaceous plants might account for this? Write directions for a class experiment that will test your answer.
3. **Contrasting Ideas** What aspects of the fern life cycle are similar to aspects of the life cycle of typical nonvascular plants? Make a list of their similarities and differences.
4. **Evaluating Conclusions** After researching coniferous forests, explain why pine forests tend to have less undergrowth than do hardwood forests.
5. **Inferring Conclusions** Grasses are highly specialized angiosperms. It is easy to overlook their flowers because they are generally small and pale. What might the size and color of these flowers indicate about the way grasses are pollinated?

Cross-Discipline Connection

Biology and Art Use library references to find art of plants and flowers by artists from both western and eastern cultures. Report on the differences in style.

Discovery Through Reading

"Unfinished Redwood," *Audubon* (September 1988): 56–77, describes the formation of Redwood National Park in California and the importance of saving giant redwood trees. Describe how saving these trees will benefit humans.

Roots, Stems, and Leaves

Outline

A bald cypress swamp

Focus

The roots of a vascular plant anchor the plant in the soil and absorb water and minerals. Stems support the plant; transport water, minerals, and food; and display the leaves to light. Leaves produce food which the plant may convert to energy immediately, or store for later use. Like a well-designed building, the body of a vascular plant is sturdy and functions efficiently.

■ *In what way is the trunk of a tree like a skeleton?*

■ *Why is it important that leaves receive a constant supply of water?*

Kinds of Plant Tissue

Section Objectives

- *State* the function of meristems.
- *Name* three kinds of tissue found in plants.
- *Contrast* vessel members and sieve-tube members in terms of their structures and functions.

One of the chief differences between plants and animals is the location of cell division in the organism. Many kinds of cells in an animal's body may undergo division. In plants, cells divide only in specific areas called **meristems** (MEHR uh stehmz). The meristems located near the tips of roots and stems are called *apical meristems*. *The apical meristems produce the most rapid growth.*

As the apical meristem produces new cells, the root or stem grows longer. The lengthening of roots and stems is called **primary growth.** Young plants show primary growth as they send up green shoots. Mature plants also show primary growth in the lengthening of their roots and stems.

The cells produced by meristems elongate and then become specialized to carry out particular plant functions. **Differentiation** is the name for this specialization. *Plant cells differentiate into three basic kinds of tissue: the epidermis, vascular tissue, and ground tissue.*

26.1 Epidermis

The outermost layer of plant cells develops into protective tissue called the **epidermis.** The epidermis of stems and leaves helps retain moisture in several ways. It secretes a waxy layer of *cutin,* which not only slows evaporation from the plant's surface but also protects the plant against the invasion of parasites. Cells in the epidermis may develop hairlike structures that trap water vapor next to the plant surface.

26.2 Vascular Tissue

Vascular tissue consists primarily of tubelike xylem and phloem. These tissues transport water, dissolved minerals, and food throughout the plant.

Two kinds of conducting cells develop in the xylem. **Tracheids** (TRAY kee ihdz) are long, tapered cells. Water and minerals pass from one tracheid to another through small pits in the cell end walls. Tracheids are the only xylem cells found in most gymnosperms. The xylem in most angiosperms consists mostly of **vessel members,** which are short, open tubes that are more efficient conducting tubes than tracheids. The cytoplasm in both tracheids and vessel members dissolves at maturity, and the cells die. The remaining parts of the cell are hollow tubes through which water and minerals pass easily.

Apical meristem

Root meristems

Figure 26–1. A seedling grows when cells in its meristems divide and enlarge. Cell divisions in the apical meristem establish the stem. Divisions in the root meristem form the root, which gathers water and nutrients.

Figure 26–2. A cross section of angiosperm wood (left, ×500) shows that it is composed of small, thick-walled tracheids and a few large, thin-walled vessels. Vessels are composed of vessel members, which are connected to each other by perforated, overlapping cell walls (right, ×1200).

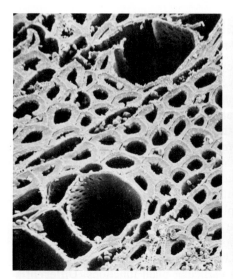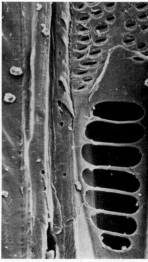

Reading Critically

Inferring Conclusions
What do you think would happen to a vascular plant if it did not have sieve-tube members?

Phloem cells are called **sieve-tube members** because their end walls look and act something like sieves. Food passes freely from one cell to another through small holes in the end walls. *Unlike xylem cells, sieve-tube members are living cells.* Although they are living, sieve-tube members have no nuclei. A *companion cell* is attached to each sieve-tube member and supplies energy to the sieve-tube members.

26.3 Ground Tissue

Ground tissue is relatively unspecialized tissue that supports vascular tissues and protects them from physical injury. It usually consists of two concentric regions. The ground tissue in the center of roots and stems is generally called **pith.** Pith contains soft, spongy cells called **parenchyma** (puh REHN kih muh). Pith is surrounded by an outer layer of more rigid cells that make up the **cortex.** Generally, ground tissue stores food and water and supports the vascular tissue. The specific makeup and function of ground tissue varies in each organ of the plant.

Section Review

1. **Identifying Ideas**   What areas of the plant produce primary growth?
2. **Summarizing Information**   Where are the two main regions of ground tissue located in a plant?
3. **Evaluating Conclusions**   Describe what would happen to a plant if the vessel members and sieve-tube members were switched.

Thinking Critically

Roots

Through variations in their roots, plants are able to grow in many different kinds of soil. Some roots split rocks as they grow through cracks in the rock. Others push through dense clay, or anchor plants in sifting sand. In any environment, roots carry out three basic functions. *Roots anchor the plant, absorb water and minerals from the soil, and store food produced in leaves and the green stem.*

26.4 Root Systems

The first root produced by a young plant is called the **primary root.** The primary root develops into one of two types of root systems. In many dicots, such as carrots and oak trees, the primary root matures into a large, thick root, called a **taproot,** that reaches deep into the soil. As a taproot grows, it produces smaller roots called *secondary roots*. In most monocots, such as grasses, the primary root shrivels and dies as the plant matures. It is replaced by secondary roots that grow from the base of the stem. These roots grow out over a wide area, forming a **fibrous root** system. A fibrous root system often extends farther underground than the visible parts of the plant extend above ground.

26.5 Root Structure

Both taproot systems and fibrous root systems consist of individual roots with a similar internal structure. The roots of most angiosperms and gymnosperms contain three concentric layers of tissue: the epidermis, the cortex, and the vascular cylinder.

Epidermis The root epidermis forms a protective outer layer around internal root tissues. Some of the epidermal cells have tiny outgrowths called **root hairs,** which absorb water and minerals from the soil.

Water enters the root hairs by osmosis. Recall that osmosis is the movement of water across a membrane into a region of lower water concentration. Because root hairs contain higher concentrations of solutes than the soil does, water moves into the hairs. The cell membranes of the root hair cells allow water and minerals to pass into the cells. However, these cell membranes prevent the escape of the larger molecules of sugar and starch that are stored in root cells.

Root hairs greatly increase the surface area of the root system and so increase the plant's capacity to absorb water.

Section Objectives

- *List* the three main functions of roots.
- *Label* the three basic layers of tissue in a diagram of a root.
- *Contrast* primary growth and secondary growth in roots.
- *Give* examples of two kinds of root adaptations and explain the survival value of each.

Figure 26–3. Most monocots (top) have fibrous root systems. Many dicots (bottom) have a taproot that develops directly from the primary root.

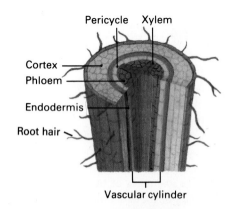

Cortex
Phloem
Endodermis
Root hair
Pericycle Xylem

Vascular cylinder

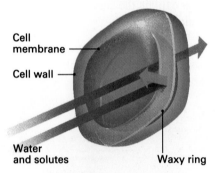

Cell membrane
Cell wall

Water and solutes
Waxy ring

Figure 26–4. A root (top) is composed of distinct tissues and cells. Each cell of the endodermis (bottom) has a waxy ring that prevents water from flowing around the cell. Water and solutes (arrows) must pass through the cell.

Root hairs are very numerous. One rye plant, for example, may have 14 billion root hairs. The surface area of the plant's root system greatly exceeds that of its aboveground portions.

Cortex In a young plant, the cortex forms the bulk of root tissue. The root cortex primarily consists of loosely packed cells that may store food. Water moves easily around and through these cells. The innermost layer of cells in the root cortex, however, is tightly packed. This single layer of cells is called the **endodermis.** Each endodermis cell has a waxy ring that prevents water from flowing around it. Hence, water must flow through the endodermis cells. When the endodermal cells absorb minerals, a low concentration of water inside the endodermal cells results. Water rushes into the cells, creating root pressure.

Vascular Cylinder The endodermis forms a sheath around the tissues in the center of the root. These central tissues, which form the **vascular cylinder,** consist of xylem, phloem, and special layers of meristematic cells. One of the layers of meristematic cells, called the **pericycle,** forms the outer layer of the vascular cylinder. The pericycle produces secondary roots. The other layer of meristematic cells develops between the xylem and phloem. This layer, called the **vascular cambium,** produces new xylem and phloem cells.

26.6 Root Growth

Roots grow in both length and width. The lengthwise growth occurs at the tip, or apical meristem. The cells in the apical meristem divide and then elongate. The new cells may elongate up to 10 times their original length. Either during or after elongation, the root cells differentiate and form the epidermis, cortex, and vascular cylinder.

The sequence of cell development in the growing root tip is visible in three regions of growth, which are shown in Figure 26–5. New cells result from division of cells in the region of the apical meristem. The new cells gradually lengthen in the region of elongation. Farther up is the region of differentiation, where all the various tissues of the root mature.

The elongation of cells pushes the apical meristem through the soil. The fragile meristem would be torn and crushed if it were not protected by an outer layer of cells called the **root cap.** The cells in the root cap are continuously scraped away and replaced by new cells formed in the apical meristem.

As the root matures, the meristematic cells in the vascular cambium and pericycle become active. Cell divisions in the vascular cambium produce new xylem and phloem, resulting in *secondary growth*, which increases the plant's diameter rather than its length or height. ***In both roots and stems, all secondary growth is produced by the vascular cambium.*** Roots with secondary growth can become very large. Often these woody roots are used to help prop up the tree by forming a strong, stable base that will support a solid, tall trunk.

Secondary roots that grow out from a mature root are produced by cell divisions in the pericycle. A new root develops a root cap and vascular tissue while it grows through the cortex of the mature root. By the time the secondary root reaches the soil, it is fully protected against abrasion and ready to absorb water and minerals for the plant.

Older roots with many layers of secondary growth often develop a tough outer tissue called *bark*. Bark replaces the epidermis and much of the cortex. It consists of phloem and *cork* cells, which are produced by a meristem called the **cork cambium.** As you will see later in this chapter, the cork cambium is especially important in stems.

26.7 Adaptations

Roots that arise from unusual places on the plant are called *adventitious* (ad vuhn TIHSH uhs) roots. The stems of corn and some other monocots develop adventitious roots that help brace and support the plant. Tropical orchids grow on tree trunks, with their roots exposed to the air. These *aerial* roots absorb water and minerals directly from the air.

Mangroves have especially unusual root systems. These large trees grow in or near warm coastal waters in the tropics. They often grow in soil that is muddy and that contains little oxygen. Mangrove stems produce adventitious roots that hold

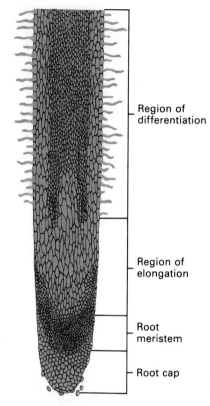

Figure 26–5. A longitudinal section of a root shows that it is composed of three growth regions: the meristem, the region of elongation, and the region of differentiation. A root cap protects the meristematic tissue.

Region of differentiation

Region of elongation

Root meristem

Root cap

Figure 26–6. Many roots are modified in ways that help plants survive. The prop roots of corn (left) support the narrow, slender base of the stem. Adventitious roots of a mangrove (right) stabilize the plant in the shifting soil and changing tides.

Roots, Stems, and Leaves   **413**

The Roots, Stems, and Leaves You Eat

There are thousands of species of edible plants. However, only a few dozen are widely cultivated. The roots, stems, and leaves of some of these are brought to market as vegetables. Two plants that are grown for their roots are beets and carrots. Lettuce and Swiss chard are raised for their leaves. A turnip is an example of a vegetable raised for both its root and its leaves.

Vegetables that are stems are a minority among commonly available produce. This is not surprising considering the stem's primary function—

to transport nutrients between the root and the leaves and to act as a physical support for the plant. Some plants do store food reserves in the stem, however, and there are a few commercially important stem crops.

Perhaps the most important stem vegetable is the white potato, a crop now grown around the world. White potatoes are storage stems that grow underground. We also eat the rhizomes, which are stems, of a few plants such as the Jerusalem artichoke, arrowroot, and ginger. Water chestnuts

and taro are examples of corms, another type of stem vegetable.

Only a few stem vegetables grow above the ground. Asparagus, bamboo shoots, and sugarcane are the main examples. In many regions of the world, stem vegetables are vital staples that are consumed in the diet daily.

The soil-anchoring abilities of root systems are explored on page 423.

the plant steady in shifting tides. Some mangrove roots grow up into the air. From the air, the exposed root tips absorb oxygen that the mangrove needs for cellular respiration. Mangrove seedlings germinate while still on the tree. The primary root is pointed. When the seed falls, the root sticks into the mud.

Section Review

1. **Listing Information**   What are the three main layers of root tissue?
2. **Identifying Information**   Where is the vascular cylinder located in the root?
3. **Identifying Information**   Which layer of root cells and stem cells produces secondary growth?
4. **Relating Information**   What kinds of plants have adventitious roots? Explain your answer.

Thinking Critically

Stems

A plant's roots need food from the leaves to carry out their functions. At the same time, the leaves need water and minerals absorbed by the roots to carry out photosynthesis. Stems contain vessels through which these materials flow. ***Stems transport food, water, and minerals between the roots and leaves, and support plant growth above the ground.*** The thin stem of a four-leaf clover and the mammoth stem of a redwood tree both perform these tasks.

26.8 Structure of Stems

Like young root cells, stem cells differentiate into the epidermis, vascular tissues, and ground tissues. The tissues of xylem and phloem that occur in the root extend up through the stem. In some stems, the vascular tissues are arranged in groupings called **vascular bundles.** The pattern of vascular bundles in a monocot differs from the pattern in a dicot, as Figure 26–7 shows. In monocots, bundles are scattered through the ground tissues. In dicots, bundles are arranged in a ring that separates the inner core of pith from the outer ring of cortex cells.

Herbaceous Stems   Most herbaceous monocots and dicots have soft, fleshy stems that produce little or no secondary growth. For this reason, the structure of a young herbaceous stem does not change significantly as the plant matures, though some of the stem tissues may become slightly lignified.

Figure 26–7.   In monocots (left), the vascular bundles are distributed throughout the stem. In dicots (right), the bundles are arranged in a ring and form a boundary between the cortex and pith.

Monocot flower and stem   Dicot flower and stem

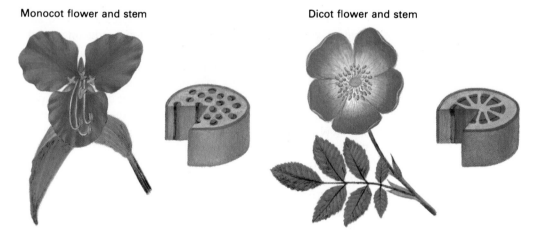

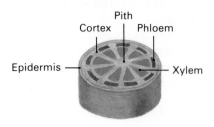

Figure 26–8. As a young dicot stem matures, a vascular cambium begins to form between the xylem and phloem of each vascular bundle (top). The cells of the vascular cambium eventually form a solid cylinder (bottom left). In a woody stem (bottom right), older xylem cells become wood.

Pith
Cortex | Phloem

Epidermis ———— Xylem

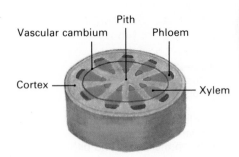

Pith
Vascular cambium | Phloem

Cortex ———— Xylem

Herbaceous stems are partially supported by the water that fills their cells. The water in each cell presses against the cell wall. This creates a force called *turgor pressure,* which makes the cell rigid. How might the loss of water from its cells affect the stem of a herbaceous plant?

Woody Stems Many dicots and most gymnosperms produce woody stems. As a woody plant matures and produces secondary growth, the structure of its stem changes. A young dicot stem contains vascular bundles arranged in a ring. As the stem matures, the vascular cambium produces xylem toward the center of the stem and phloem toward the outside. In cold temperate climates, woody dicots add another ring of xylem each year. This increasingly wider column of wood supports the plant's vertical growth.

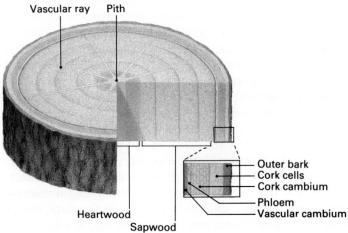

Vascular ray   Pith

Outer bark
Cork cells
Cork cambium
Phloem
Vascular cambium
Heartwood
Sapwood

In time, the conducting xylem cells, called *sapwood,* surround a core of older xylem cells that stop conducting water. This nonfunctioning xylem, called *heartwood,* becomes plugged with substances that make the wood hard and dry. Heartwood forms the bulk of a mature woody stem.

At the same time, the increasing diameter of the stem splits the epidermis and triggers cell divisions in the cork cambium. The new cork cells produced by this cell division gradually replace the cortex. Together with phloem, cork forms a layer of bark around the stem. Bark protects stems from physical injury and insects. The hollow, air-filled cork cells insulate the stem from extremes in temperature. They also contain a waxy substance that helps retain water in the stem. These traits are important to the survival of trees and other woody plants that must endure harsh winters. Bark is not airtight, however. Tiny openings in the bark, called *lenticels,* permit air to pass through the

In cold temperate climates, a tree's annual growth is permanently recorded inside the tree in *growth rings*. The vascular cambium produces new growth mainly during the spring and summer. Each growth ring shows the amount of secondary xylem produced during one growing season. You can determine the age of a tree by counting its rings.

Scientists use tree-ring dating to piece together the history of weather on Earth. In years when rainfall is plentiful, rapid growth is shown by broad rings. In dry years, the rings are narrow, showing that little growth took place. By comparing rings from many trees in an area, a scientist can determine which years were wet and which were dry. Correlating these data with the tree's age and other information,

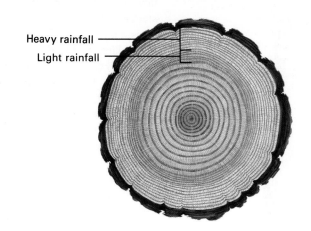

Heavy rainfall

Light rainfall

the researcher can reconstruct the environmental conditions of the past.

Recent research has found evidence of volcanic eruptions recorded in ancient bristlecone pines. The natural air pollution of erupting volcanoes causes periods of cool, dry weather, which are recorded in the pines' growth rings as periods of slow growth.

Tree-ring dating is also useful to archaeologists. By matching the tree rings in firewood found in an ancient village to those in living trees, archaeologists can determine the age of the settlement where the firewood was found.

■ **Inferring Conclusions** What other natural phenomena might cause slow growth in a tree?

---

epidermis to underlying cells. You can see bumps on the outside of small twigs. They appear where lenticels were on twigs when they were green and herbaceous.

26.9 Buds

Like roots, stems continue to produce primary growth at the tip, or apical meristem. A **bud** is a structure that holds and protects an embryonic shoot along a stem. Unlike the root tip, buds do not need a protective covering, such as a root cap, because they grow into the open air. However, if

Reading Critically

Evaluating Information
What do you think would happen to a tree if it lost all its bark? Explain your answer.

The career of urban forester is described on pages 928–929.

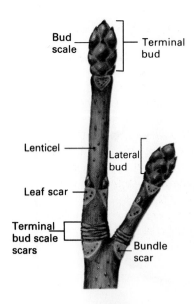

Bud scale

Terminal bud

Lenticel

Lateral bud

Leaf scar

Terminal bud scale scars

Bundle scar

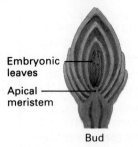

Embryonic leaves

Apical meristem

Bud

Figure 26–9. Buds allow woody plants of temperate climates to survive the winter. Terminal buds occur at stem tips; lateral buds occur on the side of the stem (top). The meristem in each bud is protected and insulated by bud scales (bottom).

Thinking Critically

they remained exposed during the winter, the sensitive meristematic cells would freeze and dry out.

In woody plants of cold temperate regions, buds usually develop during the fall. They consist of three basic parts: meristematic cells; embryonic, or partially developed, plant structures; and *bud scales*. Bud scales are modified leaves that wrap tightly around the meristem and become hard, sealing in moisture and keeping out cold and protecting the apical meristem. In the spring, the embryonic structures inside the bud absorb moisture, swell, and force the scales to open. *Terminal buds* will lengthen the stem in the spring. Buds along the side of the stem, called *lateral buds,* may produce leaves, flowers, or a new branch. The place on the stem where a new structure arises is called a *node*. The gap between each node is called an *internode*. Wherever bud scales drop off to make way for new growth, they leave a *bud scale scar*.

26.10 Adaptations

Many plants have stems adapted to perform special functions. In such climbing plants as the grape and morning glory, stems form long, thin structures called *tendrils*. These specialized stems support the plant by winding tightly around posts, trees, and other objects. Some modified stems function as storage units. Potatoes are underground stems that store starch. The giant saguaro cactus stores water in its stem.

Many stems also carry out asexual reproduction. The stem of a strawberry plant, for example, sends out shoots called *runners* that grow out over the ground. These shoots take root and produce new plants. Another stem adaptation is that of the jumping cholla cactus. The lateral branches are loosely held to the stem. They are dispersed by wind or by attaching themselves to passing animals.

Section Review

1. **Inferring Relationships**   Describe the functions of the stem.
2. **Comparing Ideas**   Compare the structure of stems in herbaceous and woody plants.
3. **Summarizing Ideas**   How do woody stems increase in thickness?
4. **Evaluating Relationships**   How do buds help a woody plant survive a cold winter?
5. **Summarizing Ideas**   Describe the appearance of tree rings formed during drought years.

Leaves

Young, growing stems often carry out a small amount of photosynthesis. In most plants, however, food production takes place mainly in the leaves. The broad part of the leaf, called the **blade,** contains most of the plant's photosynthetic cells. The **petiole** (PEHT ee ohl), or leaf stalk, supports the blade. The petiole is attached to the stem at the **leaf base.** A leaf that has a single, undivided blade is called a **simple leaf.** If the blade is divided into several separate parts that are attached to an extension of the petiole, the leaf is called a **compound leaf.** These and other traits, such as leaf arrangement, used to classify leaves are illustrated in Figure 26–10.

Section Objectives
- *State* the chief function that leaves perform.
- *List* some leaf adaptations found in carnivorous plants.
- *Describe* the internal structure of a typical leaf.
- *Summarize* how water and food are transported through plants.
- *Explain* the survival value of abscission.

26.11 Structure of Leaves

Leaves use sunlight, water, and carbon dioxide to carry out photosynthesis. They also transport the food they produce to the rest of the plant in a process called **translocation.** In addition, leaves exchange gases with the atmosphere and release water vapor. The structure of the leaf is well suited to performing these and other functions.

Epidermis   The epidermis in most leaves is a single layer of nonphotosynthetic cells. Sunlight passes directly through these cells to the photosynthetic cells below. The epidermis is covered with a layer of *cutin*, which minimizes water loss.

Figure 26–10.   A leaf has a blade, a petiole, and a leaf base (right). Monocot leaves have parallel veins; dicot leaves have net veins and can be simple or compound (left). Leaf arrangement is alternate, opposite, or whorled.

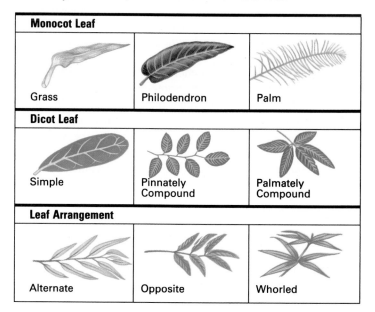

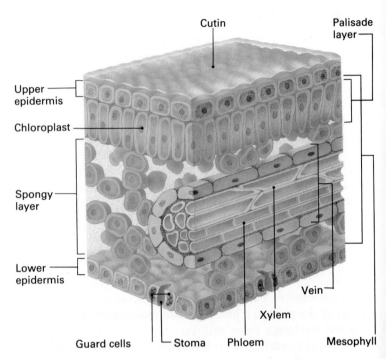

Upper epidermis

Chloroplast

Spongy layer

Lower epidermis

Cutin

Palisade layer

Guard cells   Stoma   Phloem   Mesophyll

Xylem

Vein

Figure 26–11. The two types of mesophyll cells (×500) as they actually appear (above) are clearly shown in the drawing (right) to lie between two epidermal layers.

Figure 26–12. Stomata occur primarily on the lower epidermis of leaves.

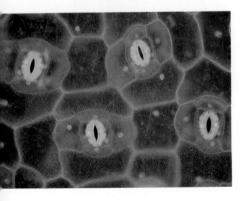

Carbon dioxide, oxygen, and water vapor enter and exit the leaf through openings in the epidermis called *stomata*. Each stoma is flanked by two kidney-shaped **guard cells.** Guard cells change shape to allow the entry and exit of gases. For example, when the plant must retain water, the guard cells change shape, causing the stomata to close. Most guard cells are located on the underside of the leaf, where the surface is shaded and the rate of evaporation is lower than on the upper leaf surface.

Mesophyll   The epidermis encloses the middle portion of the leaf, called the **mesophyll.** The parenchyma cells in the mesophyll contain chlorophyll and other pigments. Cells in the upper layer of the mesophyll are arranged in close-fitting columns that expose a maximum number of chloroplasts to the sun. This layer is called the *palisade layer*. The layer below, called the *spongy layer*, consists of loosely bunched, irregularly shaped cells surrounded by air spaces. Gases and water vapor accumulate in these spaces.

Vascular bundles extend through the spongy layer. Vascular bundles are seen in the blade of the leaves as veins. The main vein extends through the petiole and is called the *midrib*. The veins transport water and minerals into the leaf and carry organic materials from the leaf.

26.12 Leaves and Water Loss

Over ninety percent of the water that enters the roots is lost as water vapor, most of it through open stomata in the leaves. The process by which plants lose water is called **transpiration.** How can plants survive losing so much of their moisture? The answer is that the water lost through the top of the plant is continuously replenished from the roots below.

Several forces are involved in the movement of water in plants. Water enters the cells of the root epidermis by osmosis and moves through the cortex and into the xylem. Xylem cells form long, narrow tubes, and the water in these tubes is attracted to the xylem cell walls. This attraction tends to pull the water up the walls. The force of attraction that causes water to move up narrow tubes is called *capillary action.* However, the major force behind the movement of water in plants is the attraction of water molecules for one another. The upward movement of one molecule tugs on the molecules below. Each water molecule that evaporates from a leaf exerts a pull all the way down to the roots. The loss of water from the leaves thus helps maintain water flow throughout the plant.

Plants benefit from transpiration in many ways. It provides all parts of the plant with a steady supply of water and inorganic ions from the soil. The evaporation of water from the leaves cools the plant. Transpiration also prevents the accumulation of excess water in the plant body.

26.13 Adaptations

Plants have developed several adaptations to climates in which there are cold winters. During cold winters, less water is available for absorption by a plant's roots, partly because the soil may freeze.

One of the most valuable adaptations in plants that endure cold winters is **abscission,** the shedding of leaves. Abscission reduces water loss due to transpiration. Seasonal changes trigger abscission. As the air cools and the days grow shorter, a row of cells called the *abscission layer* develops in the leaf base. These cells are weak and cause the vascular bundles and connecting tissue between the leaf base and the stem to degenerate. The leaf then drops off. Trees that shed their leaves every year, such as maple and oak trees, are said to be *deciduous.*

Conifers, which also grow in climates with cold winters, have continual leaf cover. Conifer leaves have a thick epidermis and their stomata are sunken below the leaf surface. These features make the leaves less vulnerable to evaporation.

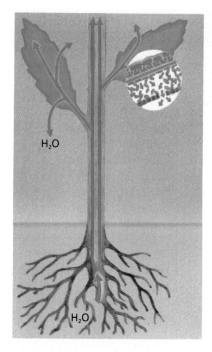

H_2O

H_2O

Figure 26–13. This illustration shows that water is pulled upwards through the xylem during transpiration. The inset shows that water vapor is lost through stomata on the lower surface of leaves.

Reading Critically

Evaluating Relationships
Why is it an advantage for deciduous trees to lose all their leaves during the winter?

Carnivorous plants have remarkable leaf modifications. The leaves are specialized to capture insects and other small invertebrates. Because the ingested animals contain nitrogen, the carnivorous plants can live in nitrogen-poor soil where most other plants cannot survive.

Pitcher plants catch animals in leaves that are modified into tubes. The tube is lined with downward-pointing hairs and filled with water. An insect is lured to the tube by sweet-smelling nectar. Once inside the tube, the insect cannot crawl back out against the slanting hairs. It eventually falls into the water and is digested by enzymes.

The sundew has another type of insect trap. The leaf of the sundew is covered with epidermal hairs that secrete a sticky substance. An unsuspecting insect that wanders onto the leaf will become stuck. The leaf folds like a closing fist, and enzymes digest the insect.

The Venus's flytrap captures its prey in a different way. The blade of the leaf is modified into two halves, which have special trigger hairs. If an insect trips these hairs, the entire leaf closes rapidly on the insect.

■ **Inferring Conclusions** How do carnivorous plants benefit from living in nitrogen-poor soil?

Aquatic plants and desert plants show highly specialized adaptations. Some aquatic plants have narrow leaves that ride easily over waves. In contrast, cactus leaves are hard, nonphotosynthetic spines. The spines transpire almost no water.

Section Review

1. **Analyzing Functions** What functions do guard cells perform?
2. **Summarizing Ideas** How does food exit the leaf?
3. **Inferring Relationships** How does osmosis help plants transport water?

Thinking Critically

INVESTIGATION 26:
What Type of Root System Can Hold the Most Soil?

Objectives
- To *interpret* data
- To *compare* the soil-anchoring ability of different root systems

Materials
three lima bean seeds, three corn seeds, six 7-cm pots, potting soil, centimeter ruler, adhesive tape, scissors, cord, hand-held spring scale, paper, triple-beam balance, water

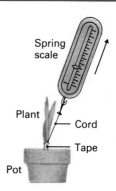

Spring scale

Plant

Cord

Tape

Pot

Prelab Preparation
1. Describe differences among primary root systems, tap root systems, and fibrous root systems.
2. Discuss what you think the differences in anchoring ability would be among different types of root systems.

Inquiry: Observation
3. Fill each pot with potting soil up to 2.5 cm from the rim. Place one lima bean seed 1 cm below the soil surface in each of three pots. Plant one corn seed in each of the other three pots. Moderately water the soil in each pot.
4. Place the plants in a moderately lighted area. Water the plants sparingly, but do not let the soil become too dry. *How will a reduced water supply affect root growth in these plants?*
5. When the plants become 5 cm high, place a small piece of adhesive tape around each stem at the soil level.
6. Attach one end of a cord to the tape and the other end to a spring scale.
7. Carefully pull the scale upward and slightly away from the plant while reading the force on the calibrated indicator.
8. As the plant is uprooted, note the force on the indicator. Without shaking the soil from the roots, place the plant on a piece of paper. Record your results. Using separate pieces of paper, repeat the process for each plant.
9. Allow the plants to dry overnight.

10. Shake the roots of each plant over the paper. Remove as much soil as possible. Record the mass of the loose soil collected from each plant.
11. Measure the length and diameter of each root system and record your results.
12. Combine your data with the data collected by the other teams in your group. *What is the advantage of pooling the data?*
13. Make a table that summarizes the data collected by each team in your group. Find the group average for each measurement made during this Investigation.
14. Using the group averages, make bar graphs that compare the two kinds of plants for each measurement.

Analysis
1. **Summarizing Data** Summarize the data in your graphs.
2. **Identifying Relationships** Is there evidence of a relationship between the force required to pull the plant out of the soil and any of the other measurements? Explain your answer.
3. **Inferring Relationships** What can you infer about the relative effectiveness of the two root systems in anchoring soil to the plant?
4. **Analyzing Ideas** Which root system would be most effective in an area where wind erosion could be a problem? Explain your answer.

Chapter 26 Review

Summary

Plants consist of three kinds of tissue: epidermal, vascular, and ground. New plant cells are produced in specific areas called meristems. Roots anchor the plant, absorb water and minerals, and store food. Roots may develop as taproots or fibrous roots.

Stems support plant growth above ground and transport water and food between roots and leaves. Herbaceous stems are partially supported by turgor pressure. Woody stems are supported by the wood produced by secondary growth.

Most of a plant's photosynthetic cells are contained in the leaf blade. Leaves exchange gases and release water by the opening and closing of their stomata. Water movement in plants results from capillary action and the pull created by transpiration.

BioTerms

abscission (**421**)
blade (**419**)
bud (**417**)
compound leaf (**419**)
cork cambium (**413**)
cortex (**410**)
differentiation (**409**)
endodermis (**412**)
epidermis (**409**)
fibrous root (**411**)
ground tissue (**410**)
guard cell (**420**)
leaf base (**419**)

meristem (**409**)
mesophyll (**420**)
parenchyma (**410**)
pericycle (**412**)
petiole (**419**)
pith (**410**)
primary growth (**409**)
primary root (**411**)
root cap (**412**)
root hair (**411**)
sieve-tube
  member (**410**)
simple leaf (**419**)

taproot (**411**)
tracheid (**409**)
translocation (**419**)
transpiration (**421**)
vascular bundle (**415**)

vascular
  cambium (**412**)
vascular
  cylinder (**412**)
vessel member (**409**)

For each pair of terms, explain the differences in their meanings.

1. simple leaf, compound leaf
2. tracheid, vessel member
3. pith, cortex
4. vascular cylinder, vascular cambium

BioQuiz   (Write all answers on a separate sheet of paper.)

Completion

1. The _____ system of oak trees goes deep into soil and produces smaller roots.
2. Woody plants protect apical _____ during winter by enclosing them in buds.
3. Food produced by photosynthesis conducted in the leaves moves through the plant by the process known as _____ .
4. The _____ added each year to the stems of woody plants supports the plants' vertical growth.
5. Secondary roots are produced by cell divisions in the _____ .

Multiple Choice

6. Stomatal opening is controlled by
   a) guard cells.   b) tracheids.
   c) veins.   d) cutin.
7. The primary function of meristems in plants is   a) translocation.   b) cell division.   c) differentiation.
   d) transpiration.
8. The stems of some Monocots are braced by   a) adventitious roots.   b) root caps.
   c) taproots.   d) aerial roots.
9. Because sieve-tube members have no nuclei, metabolism is performed by

a) cork cambium. b) root hairs.
c) companion cells. d) guard cells.
10. Photosynthesis takes place in the leaf
a) epidermis. b) veins. c) cutin.
d) mesophyll.
11. The bulk of root tissue in young plants
is a) cortex. b) cork cambium.
c) endodermis. d) pith.
12. The apical meristem in roots is protected
by a) ground tissue. b) root caps.
c) taproots. d) petioles.
13. All secondary growth in both roots and
stems is produced by the   a) vascular
cylinder. b) endodermis.
c) epidermis. d) vascular cambium.
14. If a plant wilts in very hot, dry weather,
then it is probably   a) a woody plant.

b) an adventitious plant.   c) a herba-
cious plant.   d) a carnivorous plant.
15. Plants lose water through a) root
pressure. b) transpiration.
c) translocation. d) primary growth.

Writing Critically

16. What are the functions of vessel members
and sieve-tube members?
17. How are carnivorous plants adapted to
living in nitrogen-poor soil?
18. How is water transported from a plant's
roots to its leaves?
19. How do the tissues in a woody stem
change as the stem matures?
20. What do growth rings show?

Application/Critical Thinking

1. **Diagramming Conclusions** Furniture
makers use heartwood rather than sapwood
to make furniture. What characteristics of
heartwood and sapwood might explain this
preference? Illustrate your answer.
2. **Inferring Conclusions** If you drove a
nail into the trunk of a young tree, the nail
would remain at that height regardless of
how tall the tree grew over the years. Explain which characteristics of plant growth
could account for this phenomenon.

3. **Evaluating Relationships** Pines have
needlelike leaves and sunken stomata similar to those in cacti. Why might both
kinds of plants benefit from these traits,
given that pines live in regions of adequate
rainfall while cacti live in deserts?
4. **Synthesizing Information** Bonsai plants
are usually dwarfed by trimming away
some of their roots. Considering that food
is produced in the leaves, explain why
trimming the roots produces dwarf plants.

Cross-Discipline Connection

Biology and Industrial Arts   The woody stems
of plants can be made into many useful substances such as lumber, plywood, paper, and
cardboard. Use references in your library to
prepare a class report on how each of these
items is manufactured.

Discovery Through Reading

"Dead Trees Tell Tales," *National Wildlife*
(August–September 1987): 40, describes how
analyzing the growth rings of trees helps scientists make predictions and read the past. What
information is recorded in the rings of trees?

Read the beautifully illustrated article "A
World of Leaves," *Smithsonian* 16 (April
1985): 150–155. What are some common leaf
structures and unusual variations in several different plants?

Reproduction in Flowering Plants

Outline

Orchids growing in a garden in the Philippines

Focus

Flowers are adaptations involved in sexual reproduction of some plants. Flowers that are showy and fragrant attract insects and other animals that aid in the plant's reproductive process. The flowers of some plants are inconspicuous. The products of some of these inconspicuous flowers are carried through the air by wind currents and can cause uncomfortable allergic reactions in some people.

■ *In what way do flowers contribute to a plant's success in a land environment?*

■ *How do insects detect the fragrance of flowers?*

Sexual Reproduction

Most people think of flowers only as beautiful decorations. For insects and some other animals, however, flowers produce important kinds of food. *In the plants that produce them, flowers function in sexual reproduction.* The brilliant colors of flowers, as well as their varied scents and shapes, all help plants reproduce sexually.

27.1 Structure of the Flower

The various flower parts evolved from leaves that bore reproductive structures along their edges, as shown in Figure 27–1. Over time, the leaves curled inward and provided greater protection for the developing gametes. These leaves gradually became closed structures. Today flowers consist of several kinds of highly modified leaves, each of which is classified as either essential or nonessential.

Essential Flower Parts The parts of the flower that produce the gametes and carry out sexual reproduction are called the *essential flower parts*. These include the male parts, called **stamens,** and the female parts, called **pistils.**

Most flowers have three, four, or five stamens. The thin, stemlike portion of a stamen is called the **filament. Pollen** is produced at the tip of the filament, generally in an oblong structure called the **anther.**

Section Objectives

- *State* the function of flowers in the life of a plant.
- *Name* two essential flower parts and three nonessential flower parts.
- *Summarize* the processes of pollination and fertilization in a typical flowering plant.
- *Explain* the survival value of double fertilization.
- *Describe* some adaptations of flowers that help to ensure pollination.

Figure 27–1. A flower is the result of a series of evolutionary changes by which an entire fertile branch became a compressed reproductive organ. The ovary and stamens evolved from the top two whorls of leaves. The petals and sepals arose from the two lowest whorls.

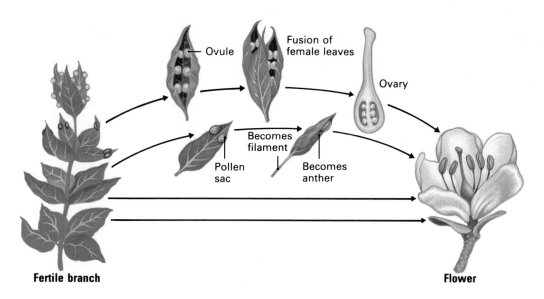

Ovule

Fusion of female leaves

Ovary

Pollen sac

Becomes filament

Becomes anther

Fertile branch

Flower

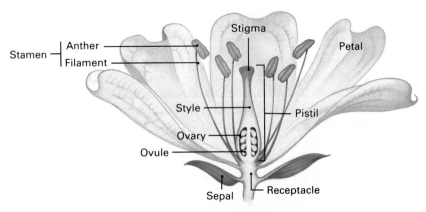

Stamen {
Anther
Filament

Stigma

Petal

Style

Pistil

Ovary

Ovule

Sepal

Receptacle

Figure 27–2. A perfect, complete flower is composed of both essential and nonessential parts. The pistil and the stamens are essential parts. The sepals and petals are nonessential parts.

Most flowers contain only a single pistil. The pistil contains three main parts. The swollen base of the pistil is called the **ovary.** Within the ovary, one or more **ovules** produce the egg cells. The slender middle part of the pistil is called the **style.** At the tip of the style is the **stigma.** The stigma produces a sticky substance to which pollen grains become attached.

Nonessential Flower Parts   The delicate essential flower parts are protected and adorned by the *nonessential flower parts.* Nonessential flower parts contain neither male nor female parts.

The base of the flower is called the **receptacle.** The **sepals** grow out from the receptacle and enclose the flower bud before it blooms. Sepals look much like tiny leaves and in many species are green. The sepals collectively form a structure called the *calyx,* which protects the ovary.

Petals grow between the sepals and the essential flower parts. They protect the pistil and stamens, and are often fragrant and brightly colored. Collectively, the petals form the *corolla.*

27.2 Kinds of Flowers

Flowers differ in the number and kinds of parts they possess. **Complete flowers** contain all the essential and nonessential parts. Roses, violets, and mustard blossoms, for example, are complete flowers. **Incomplete flowers** lack one or more of the essential or nonessential parts. The flowers of most grasses lack developed petals and sepals, and so are incomplete.

The flower in Figure 27–2 is a **perfect flower** because it contains both stamens and a pistil. In many other species, however, the male and female structures develop on separate flowers. Flowers that contain the reproductive structures of only one sex are called **imperfect flowers.** Corn is a plant with imperfect flowers. The tassel of corn is made of many male flowers. The

Figure 27–3. The male flowers of corn are located on the tassels. The female flowers are located on the ear. Each corn flower is thus an imperfect flower.

ear of corn developed from a structure that had many female flowers. A corn plant is also an example of a plant that has male and female flowers on the same individual. Other plants, like spinach, have male and female flowers on separate plants.

27.3 Formation of Gametes

Stamens and pistils are part of the diploid, sporophyte generation of the plant's life cycle. The male gametes formed in the anthers and the female gametes formed in the ovules are parts of the plant's haploid, gametophyte generation. Both male and female parts are needed to complete the life cycle.

Pollen Grain Formation Most anthers have four pollen sacs, each of which contains hundreds of cells called *microspore mother cells*. Each of these cells undergoes meiosis and produces four haploid *microspores*. The nucleus of each microspore then divides by mitosis, but the new cell wall forms internally. The result is a *pollen grain,* which is made up of two cells of unequal size located inside a hard, outer wall. The larger internal cell is called the **tube cell.** The smaller cell is called the **generative cell.** The pollen grain is the male gametophyte.

Egg Cell Formation The development of the female gametophyte occurs in the ovule, located inside the ovary. A *megaspore mother cell* in each ovule undergoes meiosis and forms four haploid *megaspores*. Three of the four megaspores die, leaving one megaspore in the ovule.

The surviving megaspore enlarges to several times its original size, filling up most of the ovule. The nucleus of the

Biofact

Q: *Why do certain kinds of pollen make people sneeze?*

A: Spiny pollen grains, such as ragweed pollen, irritate the sensitive tissues of the eyes and nasal passages. The body responds to this irritation by producing a sneeze.

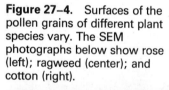

The parts of the flower are investigated on page 439.

Figure 27–4. Surfaces of the pollen grains of different plant species vary. The SEM photographs below show rose (left); ragweed (center); and cotton (right).

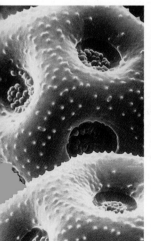
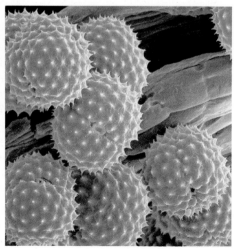

megaspore then undergoes mitotic divisions and produces eight haploid nuclei. As Figure 27–5 shows, three of these nuclei migrate to one end of the cell, three migrate to the other end, and two migrate to the center. The two central nuclei are called **polar nuclei.** The two polar nuclei remain together in the middle of the cell.

Cell walls form around each of the three nuclei at each end of the cell and around the polar nuclei in the center. The result is a large structure which, in most species, contains eight nuclei enclosed in seven cells. This structure, called the **embryo sac,** is the female gametophyte. The cell located nearest the ovule opening is the egg cell.

Figure 27–5. The life cycle of flowering plants is shown below. In the male part of the cycle, microspores form pollen grains. In the female part, a megaspore forms an embryo sac. Pollen grains are dispersed, land on the stigma, and form sperm that fertilize the egg.

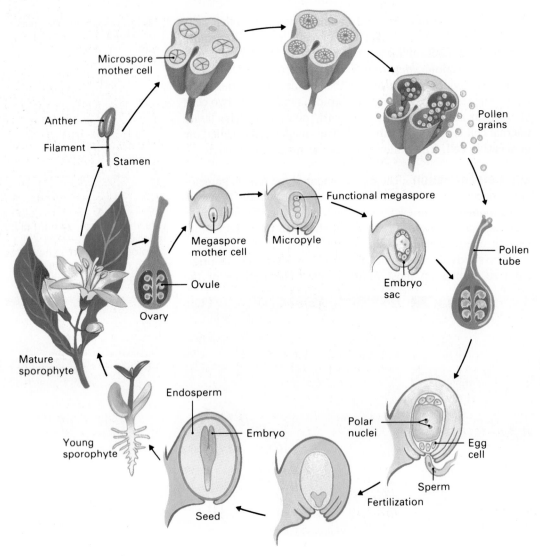

27.4 Pollination and Fertilization

For sexual reproduction to occur, pollen must first reach the stigma. The process of transferring ripe pollen from the anther to the stigma is called **pollination.** *Self-pollination* occurs when pollen falls from an anther onto the stigma of a flower on the same plant. A flower is *cross-pollinated* when its stigma traps pollen from another plant. Because cross-pollination mixes gametes from two different plants, it tends to produce offspring with more varied genes.

Pollination   Animals, wind, and water all transport pollen from flower to flower. *The nonessential flower parts reflect the specific type of pollination a plant undergoes.* In flowers that are pollinated by animals, for example, the stem and receptacle hold the flower out where its colors and scent are most obvious. Insects and birds attracted by the petals feed on pollen or the sweet liquid called *nectar* that some flowers produce. As it feeds, an animal accumulates pollen on its body. This pollen is then transferred to a stigma when the animal goes to another flower.

In contrast, flowers pollinated by wind-blown pollen grains are not showy. The nonessential parts are not modified to attract animals. Similarly, plants with pollen that floats on water do not have attractive petals or scents.

Fertilization   The landing of a pollen grain on a stigma starts the process of *fertilization,* the union of male and female gametes. Sugars and enzymes in the stigma cause the tube cell inside the pollen grain to grow. The tube cell breaks out of the pollen grain and forms a tube, called a **pollen tube,** that grows through the stigma. Meanwhile the generative cell divides mitotically into two sperm cells, the male gametes. These sperm cells move down through the pollen tube towards the ovule. When they reach the embryo sac, one sperm cell enters and fertilizes the egg cell, producing a diploid *zygote.* The other sperm cell joins with the two polar nuclei, producing a triploid (3n) nucleus that divides to form a special nutritive tissue called **endosperm.** The white part of a piece of popcorn is an example of endosperm.

Flowering plants are the only organisms that undergo two kinds of fertilization, one that forms the zygote and one that forms the endosperm. This process is called **double fertilization.** Double fertilization has great survival value for the plant because each new generation carries its own temporary source of nutrition.

Figure 27–6. Wind transports the pollen released by cockfoot grass. The pollen then lands on other grass flowers and completes the process of pollination.

Reading Critically

Inferring Relationships   Why is the pollen tube an essential part of fertilization?

Many adaptations in both flowers and insects ensure that when insects seek food, they also transfer pollen from one flower to another. For example, butterfly mouthparts form a long tube used to suck nectar from deep within the cuplike structures of some flowers.

Insects, especially bees, are the most important animal pollinators. Flowers attract a distant bee with their red, yellow, or purple petals. Close by, the bee is attracted by fragrant oils the petals produce. Plants such as violets and pansies provide landing platforms in the form of a broad, sturdy petal. Color patterns

called *nectar guides* lead the bee to the place the nectar is found inside the flower.

One of the most remarkable of all flower modifica- tions is that of the orchid genus *Orchis.* This flower has evolved to resemble the female of one certain species of wasp. Male wasps, while attempting

to mate with what they believe to be females of the species, pick up pollen from the orchid and carry it to the next orchid.

■ **Analyzing Ideas** Why would some flowers not need any of these modifications?

While the endosperm divides and grows, the zygote itself develops to form the *embryo.* At the same time, the outer layer of the ovule loses moisture and develops a hard *seed coat.* The seed coat surrounds and protects the embryo and its nutritive endosperm.

Section Review

1. **Identifying Ideas** What kind of cell forms the embryo sac? Where is the egg cell located?
2. **Inferring Relationships** How do male gametes from one flower reach the female gametes in another flower?
3. **Inferring Relationships** Why is double fertilization so important to the plant?
4. **Synthesizing Ideas** What special adaptations of flowers ensure pollination?

Thinking Critically

Fruits and Seeds

Once an egg has been fertilized, the ovule undergoes changes to become a seed. All of the seeds are located inside the ovary. As the seeds mature, the ovary ripens. The ripened ovary is called a **fruit.** A fruit, therefore, usually contains seeds. Tomatoes, squash, cucumbers, pumpkins, and eggplants are all fruits because they all contain seeds. Whole peanuts are also fruits; the edible portions are seeds.

27.5 Fruit Formation

Fruit formation begins when the ovary begins to swell and ripen. It soon changes color and may become either fleshy or dry. Many fleshy fruits become sweet as sugars translocated from the leaves accumulate in the fruit. Peaches, apples, and berries are examples of such fruits. Nuts, burrs, and the winged fruit of maple trees are examples of dry fruits. The paperlike "wings" of the maple protect the seed from being eaten and help disperse the seed in the wind.

All fruits, both fleshy and dry, can be classified into one of three groups. Beans, peaches, tomatoes, and other fruits that form from a single ovary are called *simple fruits. Aggregate fruits* form from flowers that have many pistils on the same flower. Blackberries, raspberries, and strawberries are aggregate fruits. Pineapples and figs are *multiple fruits.* A multiple fruit consists of the fruits formed by many flowers that have grown so close together that they form a single structure.

27.6 Seed Dispersal

Seeds are dispersed with or without their surrounding fruits. Both seeds and fruits are modified to ensure successful dispersal of the young plant. *Because flowering plants are nonmotile, they rely primarily on the dispersal of their seeds to prevent overcrowding, as well as to carry new plant generations to more favorable environments.*

Dispersal by Animals Sweet, fleshy fruits attract animals of all kinds. Birds eat fruit and transport the seeds in their digestive tracts. The seeds are eliminated, unharmed, in the feces some distance from the parent plant. Squirrels bury dry fruits, such as acorns, before the onset of winter. Some of the seeds are never retrieved and later grow into new plants. Some dry fruits have natural hooks or claws that catch on animals' fur or people's

Figure 27–7. Three kinds of fruits are shown above. A cherry (top) is a simple fruit. A strawberry (middle) is an aggregate fruit formed from many ovaries on a single flower. A fig (bottom) is a multiple fruit.

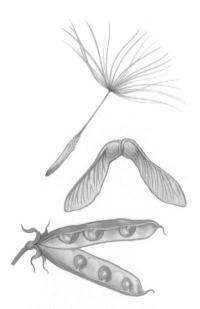

Figure 27–8. Plants disperse fruits and seeds in many ways. A dandelion fruit (top) floats on the air. Winged maple fruits (middle) twirl like the blades of a helicopter as they blow in the wind. Peas (bottom) are dispersed when animals searching for food open the pod.

clothing. You may have transported small fruits yourself while hiking through a forest or prairie.

Dispersal by Wind and Water Most fruits and seeds dispersed by wind have special adaptations for traveling by air. The wind carries winged maple seeds far from the parent tree. Tiny dandelion fruits have feathery plumes that act like parachutes. The thousands of tiny seeds produced by an orchid plant have no special structures, but they are so tiny and light that the wind can blow them for miles.

Seeds dispersed by water can float. The best-known fruits dispersed by water are those of the coconut palm. Ocean currents carry these fruits from one island to another, often over great distances. Air trapped inside the coconut keeps it afloat, and a waxy coating prevents salt water from entering and rotting the seed.

Self-Dispersal Many dry fruits disperse their seeds by propelling them away from the parent plant. The dwarf mistletoe fruit absorbs water until the pressure within the tissues finally bursts the fruit open, throwing the seeds as far as 14.5 m (16 yd.). Seed pods of the Scotch gorse, an evergreen shrub, become warped and dry in the summer. On a particularly hot day, the pods will suddenly explode with a force that scatters the seeds in all directions.

The seeds of some grasses produce long bristles. As the bristles coil and uncoil in response to air moisture, the seeds creep along the ground. Similar structures in a species of wall ivy help bury the ivy seeds in small crevices in rocks or bricks.

27.7 Seed Germination

After a seed is dispersed from the parent plant, the enclosed embryo does not begin to grow immediately. The seed usually undergoes *dormancy,* a period of rest in which metabolic activity is low. For the seed to **germinate,** or resume its growth, the seed coat must first undergo modifications that allow water and oxygen to penetrate the seed. In some cases the modifications are stimulated by internal chemical changes. In other cases environmental influences, such as animals or changes in weather, cause the modifications. After water and oxygen enter the seed, the embryo swells, grows, and cracks through the seed coat. The young plant is a *seedling.*

The embryo of flowering plants possesses all the basic plant organs in embryonic form. The embryonic leaves are called *cotyledons.* The embryonic root of a plant is called the

Reading Critically

Synthesizing Relationships
What is the purpose of dormancy before germination in seeds?

radicle. The embryonic stem consists of two parts. The part above the radicle and below the cotyledons is called the **hypocotyl.** The part of the stem above the cotyledons is called the **epicotyl.**

Dicot and monocot embryos differ in structure. Dicots have two cotyledons; monocots have one. In monocots the long, thin epicotyl is called a *plumule.* The plumule is surrounded by a protective sheath called a *coleoptile.*

Dicot and monocot seedlings develop in different ways. In dicots, such as the bean shown in Figure 27–9, the endosperm transfers its food reserves to the cotyledons, which become thick. As the seed germinates, the cotyledons serve as a food supply. The radicle grows downward and becomes the *primary root.* The first leaves form from the apical meristem located atop the epicotyl. These leaves then begin the process of photo-

Biofact

Q: *What are the seed and fruit in a corn plant?*

A: The corn kernel contains both the fruit and seed. The ovary wall fuses with the seed and a single structure develops on the cob.

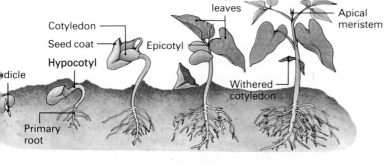

Figure 27–9. When a dicot seed such as a bean (left) germinates, the expanding hypocotyl lifts the cotyledons out of the ground. Later, leaves form at the apical meristem and the cotyledons wither. In a monocot such as corn (below), the cotyledon remains underground as the plumule pierces the soil.

synthesis and in doing so produce food for the seedling's further growth.

In many monocots the endosperm retains the seed's food reserves. In most monocots the cotyledon remains below the ground as the plumule grows upward and forms leaves. At the same time, the radicle grows to become the primary root, which immediately begins to form lateral roots. In both monocots and dicots, the cotyledons shrink or fall off the stem as the young plant grows.

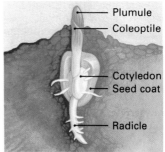

Section Review

1. **Inferring Relationships**   Describe fruit ripening.
2. **Contrasting Ideas**   What is the difference between a simple and an aggregate fruit?
3. **Organizing Information**   Name three methods by which seeds are dispersed with or without their fruit.
4. **Synthesizing Information**   What organs are formed by the radicle and epicotyl?

Thinking Critically

Asexual Reproduction

Section Objectives

- *Explain* the advantages plants obtain from vegetative propagation.
- *Name* four types of modified stems that are used in vegetative propagation.
- *Describe* two kinds of artificial propagation.

Many species of flowering plants produce new plants without the aid of fertilization. Asexual reproduction is common in strawberries, potatoes, irises, spider plants, and grasses and many other species. ***Any plant produced asexually has the same genes as its parent plant.*** Since identical offspring are often desirable, plant cultivators use artificial propagation to ensure that offspring have certain traits.

27.8 Natural Propagation

Producing new individuals from roots, stems, or leaves of existing plants is called **vegetative propagation.** Vegetative propagation occurs naturally in any of six kinds of plant structures: runners, rhizomes, tubers, bulbs, food-storing roots, and leaves.

Runners, also called stolons, are modified stems produced by low-growing plants such as strawberries. Lateral stems grow along the top of the ground and send adventitious roots into the ground at nodes. Once a root is anchored in the soil, the node produces leaves. The runner then breaks off from the parent plant and forms a new plant.

Rhizomes are long, modified stems that grow under the soil. Like runners, rhizomes produce new plants at nodes along the stem. Some grasses and irises reproduce by rhizomes. *Tubers* are also modified storage stems. They are shorter and thicker than rhizomes. Potatoes and yams are familiar tubers. Each potato "eye" is a bud capable of producing a new plant. *Corms* are similar to tubers but are smaller and usually round.

Bulbs are slightly different organs of propagation. A bulb, such as an onion, consists of a short stem surrounded by layers

Figure 27–10. Three forms of vegetative propagation are shown below. A strawberry plant (left) sends out runners. Grasses (center) produce underground stems called rhizomes. A potato (right), a tuber, can sprout new plants.

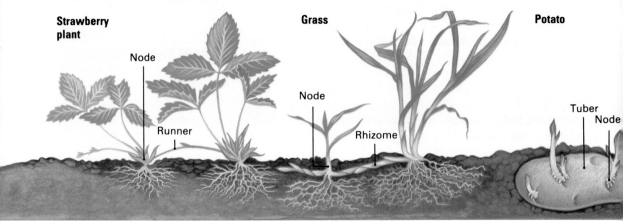

Strawberry plant

Node

Runner

Grass

Node

Rhizome

Potato

Tuber

Node

of modified leaves. The leaves protect the stem and produce food. The food nourishes the young plant that grows up from the buds of the stem.

Some plants propagate with *food-storing roots*. Carrots and beets are food-storing roots capable of producing a new stem and leaves.

An unusual plant called *Kalanchoe* reproduces asexually by growing tiny plants along the edges of its leaves. These plants drop off the "mother" plant and root in the soil. Because it produces so many offspring, *Kalanchoe* is called the "maternity plant."

27.9 Artificial Propagation

A few kinds of economically important plants reproduce by natural vegetative propagation. Commercial plant growers, however, use methods of artificial propagation such as cuttings, grafting, and tissue culturing. These methods are generally faster and easier to control than natural methods.

Cuttings *Cuttings* are pieces of stem that are cut from the parent plant and kept in water, moist soil or sand, or some other medium. Adventitious roots develop at the base of the stem. When the roots are sufficiently developed, the stem is planted. Stem cuttings are used to propagate many garden plants. Cuttings can also be made from leaves. In this method, used with such plants as African violets, cut leaves are placed in water or soil until roots and stems form.

Grafting *Grafting* is a method used to propagate fruit trees, roses, and grapes. Buds or sections of a stem, called *scions* (SY uhnz), are cut from the top of one plant and attached to another plant, called a *stock,* that is already rooted in soil. The scion produces flowers, fruits, and seeds. Because it provides the root system, the stock furnishes the plant with nourishment as well as support.

Tissue Culture and Layering Some commercial crops are often propagated by *tissue culture*. Pieces of *pith,* the center portion of stems, are removed from the plant and placed in flasks. The flasks contain a growth medium. Whole plants develop from the pith tissue. When plants develop, they are removed from the flasks and planted. Factors such as nutrient supply and invasions by disease-causing organisms can be better controlled in the laboratory than if the seedlings were grown in the field.

Figure 27–11. Tiny plants form along the edge of leaves of the genus *Kalanchoe.* These plants later drop off the leaf, root in the ground, and form new individuals.

Reading Critically

Evaluating Ideas What are some advantages of cuttings as a form of cloning?

The career of ornamental horticulturist is described on pages 922–923.

Biofact

Q: *Why do dandelions grow back if you cut them off at ground level?*

A: Dandelion roots produce adventitious buds that are capable of growing new stems. Also, they have roots that contract and pull the apical meristem to safety under the soil.

Hearts and Flowers

Exotic perfumes with equally exotic names often cost hundreds of dollars an ounce. In the United States alone, users of perfume spend almost $4 billion a year on perfume, and there are signs that the number of perfume buyers is growing. What makes expensive perfumes cost so much?

Making a perfume that uses flower petals can be time-consuming and costly. Many of the flower petals that are suitable for making perfume must be collected by hand. Machines often cannot be used to harvest flowers because machines can bruise or destroy the delicate petals. Today, as in the past, jasmine and rose petals prized for their fragrances are handpicked at dawn before the flowers become moist with morning dews.

Most perfumes depend upon the essential oils of flowers for their aroma. The extraction of these flower oils involves time-consuming and expensive processes. Traditionally, flower petals are placed between plates of glass that are coated with special fats. Over time, the flower oils slowly dissolve into the fats. After the maximum amount of

the flower's essential oil has been absorbed, the petals must be carefully removed from the plates by hand.

Chemists try to synthesize the oils of certain flowers in the laboratory so that perfumes may be produced that are not expensive. Their efforts result in a wider selection of scents on the market.

Layering is another type of artificial vegetative propagation. A branch of the plant is folded down and covered with soil. Roots are produced at nodes and new plants form. The new growth is then cut off and planted. Commercial crops such as blackberries are produced by layering.

Section Review

1. **Identifying Ideas**   Why do plants reproduced asexually look identical to the parent plant?
2. **Relating Ideas**   Why do runners produce new plants at their growth nodes?
3. **Relating Ideas**   When growing potatoes from pieces of a tuber, why do you have to make sure each piece has an "eye"?

Thinking Critically

4. **Evaluating Conclusions**   Why is it advantageous to tissue-culture plants?

INVESTIGATION 27:
How Is Flower Structure Related to Function?

Objectives
- To *identify* the parts of a flower
- To *relate* the structure of floral parts to their function

Materials
a complete flower, hand lens or stereomicroscope, white paper, scissors, forceps, scalpel or single edge razor blade, glue, medicine dropper, glass slide, coverslip, compound light microscope

Prelab Preparation
1. State the function of a flower.
2. Define each of the following: essential flower part, nonessential flower part, complete flower, incomplete flower, perfect flower, and imperfect flower.
3. Make a table to record your observations. Include space in your table for the name of each flower structure observed, a description of its location and appearance, and its function.

Inquiry: Observation
4. Review Figure 27–2 on page 428.
5. Carefully examine the flower. Identify the sepals at the base of your flower. *Where are the sepals located in relation to the petals? What color are the sepals and how many are present?*
6. Locate and describe the petals, stamens, and pistil of your flower. Record your observations.
7. Use the hand lens or a stereomicroscope to examine the flower. *What additional details do you see?*
8. Use the forceps to carefully remove the sepals. Arrange these structures in a row on a sheet of plain paper. *What name is given to the entire whorl of sepals?*
9. Carefully remove the petals. If the petals are fused together, remove them in one piece. Arrange the petals above the sepals in a row on the paper. *What name is given to all the petals collectively? Once the sepals and petals are removed, what additional structures can you see?*

10. Count and remove the stamens. Identify the anther. *What is the relationship between the number of sepals, petals, and stamens in your flower? Based on these numbers, in which group should this flower be classified?*
11. Examine the pistil. Record your description of the pistil in your table.

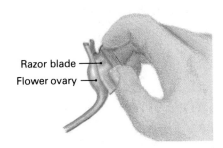

Razor blade
Flower ovary

12. **CAUTION: Use extreme care when working with sharp instruments.** With a scalpel or razor blade, make a longitudinal cut through the pistil. Examine the cut ovary under the hand lens or stereomicroscope. *What structures can be identified inside the ovary and what are their functions?*
13. Except for one stamen, glue each flower part to the paper. Label each part.
14. Place a drop of water on a glass slide. While holding an anther over the water, strike it with a fingernail. Add a coverslip to the slide. Using low power of a compound light microscope, observe the specimen. Switch to high power and sketch what you see. Glue the last stamen to the paper.

Analysis
1. **Analyzing Observations** Is the flower that you observed complete or incomplete? Explain your answer.
2. **Analyzing Observations** Is the flower perfect or imperfect? Explain your answer.
3. **Inferring Ideas** What evidence suggests that this flower is insect-pollinated?

Chapter 27 Review

Summary

Flowers consist of specialized leaves that carry out sexual reproduction. Essential flower parts include the pollen-producing stamen and the pistil, which contains the ovary. Nonessential flower parts protect the reproductive structures and aid in pollen dispersal.

Pollination is the process of transferring ripe pollen from an anther to a stigma. Each pollen grain contains a generative cell and a tube cell. The generative cell produces two sperm cells. In double fertilization, one sperm cell fuses with the egg cell while the other fuses with the polar nuclei. This forms a diploid zygote and endosperm, which nourishes the developing embryo.

A fruit develops from the ovary of a flower. Fleshy fruits are attractive to animals, which eat them and then disperse their seeds. Dry fruits may have structures that help carry their seeds in wind and water currents.

Plants produced asexually have the same genes as the parent plant. Plant cultivators use methods of artificial propagation such as cutting, grafting, tissue culture, and layering.

BioTerms

anther (**427**)
complete flower (**428**)
double fertilization (**431**)
embryo sac (**430**)
endosperm (**431**)
epicotyl (**435**)
filament (**427**)
fruit (**433**)
generative cell (**429**)
germinate (**434**)
hypocotyl (**435**)

imperfect flower (**428**)
incomplete flower (**428**)
ovary (**428**)
ovule (**428**)
perfect flower (**428**)
petal (**428**)
pistil (**427**)
polar nuclei (**430**)
pollen (**427**)
pollen tube (**431**)

pollination (**431**)
radicle (**435**)
receptacle (**428**)
sepal (**428**)
stamen (**427**)

stigma (**428**)
style (**428**)
tube cell (**429**)
vegetative propagation (**436**)

For each pair of terms, explain the differences in their meanings.

1. complete flower, incomplete flower
2. perfect flower, imperfect flower
3. pistil, stamen
4. petal, sepal

BioQuiz   (Write all answers on a separate sheet of paper.)

Completion

1. In pollination, bees deposit pollen on the _____ of the flower.
2. Before reaching the egg, the generative cell divides into _____ .
3. The formation of endosperm and a zygote in flowering plants is known as _____ .
4. Runners are stems that grow along the ground and produce new plants at _____ .
5. The male gametophyte of flowering plants is the _____ .

Multiple Choice

6. The _____ provides food for the developing embryo.   a) radicle   b) endosperm   c) embryo sac   d) pollen grain
7. The structure of the seedling that grows to become the stem is the   a) hypocotyl.   b) radicle.   c) cotyledon.   d) epicotyl.
8. The sperm cell is produced by the   a) endosperm.   b) polar nuclei.   c) pollen grain.   d) megaspore.

9. Which of the following is a nonessential flower part? a) stamen b) pistil c) sepal d) stigma
10. Nonessential flower parts aid in a) pollination. b) fertilization. c) propagation. d) reproduction.
11. Flowering plants cannot disperse their seeds because they are a) imperfect flowers. b) perfect flowers. c) motile. d) nonmotile.
12. Offspring that are identical to the parents result from a) cuttings. b) grafting. c) tissue culture. d) All choices are correct.
13. A strawberry is a) a seed. b) a simple fruit. c) a multiple fruit. d) an aggregate fruit.
14. A flower that contains both essential and nonessential parts is a) a complete flower. b) an incomplete flower. c) a perfect flower. d) an imperfect flower.
15. Which of the following is not a means by which plants undergo natural vegetative propagation? a) runners b) rhizomes c) bulbs d) cuttings

Writing Critically

16. What role do a flower's petals play in the reproductive process of the plant?
17. How does the embryo of a monocot differ from the embryo of a dicot?
18. How do fleshy fruits aid seed dispersal?
19. What is the difference between a tuber and a bulb?
20. Why do plant cultivators use artificial propagation rather than sexual propagation to produce fruit trees and other special crops?

Application/Critical Thinking

1. **Inferring Conclusions** Groups of flowers that are in clusters, such as sunflowers, are called *inflorescences*. What advantage might a plant have in producing an inflorescence instead of a single flower?
2. **Researching Information** Do library research on bees. Then write a brief report about the special structures bees possess that trap pollen. What characteristics of bees' vision help explain why they are attracted to brightly colored flowers? What flower colors attract bees most effectively?
3. **Synthesizing Relationships** Seeds ordinarily reach maturity before the fruit is fully ripe. How might the lag in fruit development increase a plant's chances for survival?
4. **Inferring Conclusions** Explain why it is not possible to produce hybrid roses from seeds.

Cross-Discipline Connection

Biology and Art Design a new animal whose task is pollinating one specific type of flower. Make a drawing of the animal and write a short paragraph explaining your design.

Discovery Through Reading

The article "The Mysterious Magic of Pollination," *National Wildlife* (August–September 1987): 14–17, describes plant pollination. Write a paragraph that describes three different adaptations that aid in pollination.

"A Bit of Wilderness in Your Own Backyard," *National Wildlife* (April–May 1987): 22–28 describes how to grow a wildflower meadow. What five basic steps would you follow in planting such a meadow?

Growth and Response in Plants

Outline

Daffodils, from bud to fully expanded flower

Focus

Special internal chemicals in plants regulate growth, seed germination, and differentiation of root, stem, and leaf tissues. Although plants lack nervous tissue, plants respond to external stimuli. For example, stems grow toward light and roots grow down in response to gravity.

■ *What are the advantages of producing chemicals that control activities in response to environmental conditions?*

■ *Why is the lack of nervous tissue of no significance to plant survival?*

Factors Affecting Plant Growth

Plant growth is best understood as the result of interactions between the plant and its environment. In your study of plants thus far, you have focused on individual plant tissues and functions. In this section, you will see how the development of the entire organism is influenced by various factors, both external and internal.

28.1 Influences from the Environment

Light, moisture, and temperature are some of the important external factors that influence plant growth. Every kind of plant has certain requirements for light, moisture, and temperature. Changes in these external factors trigger some of the basic phases in the plant's life cycle, such as growth, flowering, and movement.

Light Light supplies the energy that plants use to carry out photosynthesis. Without light, plants cannot produce the glucose that they need to grow. The duration of light also affects plant growth. There are more hours of daylight in the summer than there are in the winter. Strawberry plants and apple trees are examples of plants that monitor the length of day. They contain a pigment called *phytochrome* (FYT oh krohm). As light gives way to darkness, and darkness to light, phytochrome changes from one chemical form to another. By detecting the type and amount of phytochrome present, plants determine

Section Objectives

- *Define* the term *photoperiodism.*
- *Distinguish* among short-day, long-day, and day-neutral plants.
- *Explain* the survival value of vernalization.
- *State* the functions of three kinds of plant hormones.

To compare the growth rates of different kinds of plants, see page 451.

Figure 28–1. These two flowers bloom in response to changing day length. The poinsettia (left) is a short-day plant. The blackberry (right) is a long-day plant.

the length of darkness and light each day. The response that plants show to changing light and dark periods is called **photo-periodism** (foht oh PIHR ee uhd ihz uhm).

When photoperiodic plants are in the dark for specific amounts of time, they begin to flower. This amount of darkness is called the **critical dark period.** Plants are classified according to their critical dark periods. A **short-day plant** begins to produce flowers during the short days of spring or fall, when the nights are the same length as or longer than the plant's critical dark period. A **long-day plant** produces flowers during the long days of summer, when the nights are shorter than the plant's critical dark period. Plants that do not flower in response to the duration of light are called **day-neutral plants.**

One of the effects of photoperiodism is that plants bear fruit at different times. Strawberry and blueberry plants are short-day plants that produce ripe fruit by early summer. Pear and apple trees are long-day plants that produce fruit in the fall. Day-neutral plants such as tomatoes can produce fruit throughout the entire growing season.

Moisture   Plants need water for photosynthesis and other cellular functions. Water carries dissolved minerals throughout the plant. Water, which is stored in the enlarged central vacuole, makes up most of the volume of plant cells and gives the cells their internal pressure.

The amount of water a plant needs for proper growth varies greatly. Some plants, called *xerophytes* (ZIHR uh fyts), are adapted to dry conditions. Plants of the southern African genus *Xerophyllum* can survive with as little as 5 percent of their body weight as water. Some plants thrive in very wet conditions. These plants, such as water lilies and duckweeds, are *hydrophytes*. Most plants, however, maintain an amount of water in their cells intermediate between that of xerophytes and hydrophytes. These plants are called *mesophytes*. Most house plants are mesophytes.

Some plants may accumulate excess water after the stomata have been closed for several hours, such as during the night. *Guttation* is a process in which the plant secretes excess droplets of water from the tips of its leaves.

Temperature   Temperature is a crucial factor in plant growth. Most plants grow best in temperatures between 10°C and 38°C (50°F and 100°F). Temperatures colder than 10°C slow down chemical reactions in the cells. Temperatures above 38°C begin to destroy enzymes and other important molecules in most plants.

Figure 28–2. Drops of water extruded at the edges of this leaf are the plant's way of expelling excess water.

In temperate regions, as autumn days grow shorter and the nights colder, plant activity slows down dramatically. Woody plants stop producing secondary growth, and most plants stop producing new leaves. The plants gradually enter **dormancy,** a condition in which little growth occurs and metabolism proceeds at a very low rate. Dormant plants survive through the winter by using only the minimal amount of energy and food needed to keep their cells alive.

Many kinds of seeds are adapted to cold regions. In addition to becoming dormant, these seeds must go through a period of chilling called **vernalization** (vuhr nuhl eye ZAY shuhn) before they will germinate. If a seed germinated in autumn, the seedling would be killed by frost. Vernalization keeps the seed inside its protective coat until spring, when the seedling has a much better chance for survival. Seeds that need vernalization can be germinated by storing them first in a freezer. After a month or two of freezing, the seeds can be thawed and germinated.

28.2 Internal Factors

Because plants are sensitive to light, moisture, and temperature, they can respond to major environmental changes, such as winter or periods of drought. Most internal changes in plants, including normal cell growth, involve tiny amounts of powerful chemicals called **hormones.** Hormones are internally produced chemicals that regulate the functions of tissues and organs in an organism.

Hormones are produced in one part of a plant and transported to another part, where they cause specific changes in cellular activity. Hormones may stimulate or inhibit cell growth and development. The three major groups of plant hormones are *auxins* (AWK sihnz), *gibberellins* (jihb uh REHL ihnz), and *cytokinins* (sy tuh KY nihnz).

Auxins The term *auxin* comes from the Greek word meaning "to increase." **Auxins** are hormones that tend to stimulate the elongation of cells. Auxins produce their effects by breaking chemical bonds between the cellulose molecules in the cell wall. As a result, the cell becomes more flexible and grows longer as it absorbs water and synthesizes new proteins.

The amount of auxin necessary to cause the elongation and differentiation of cells varies for each plant organ. In growing plant stems, relatively high concentrations of the auxin *indole-acetic acid (IAA)* produce growth at the apical meristem. The IAA in the stem tip promotes growth in the terminal bud while inhibiting the growth of lateral buds. This characteristic pattern

The career of horticultural technician is described on pages 936–937.

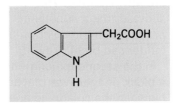

Figure 28–3. Indoleacetic acid (IAA) is an auxin that consists of a two-ring indole portion and an acetic acid group.

of growth is called *apical dominance* because growth at the tip controls growth elsewhere on the stem. The tall, pyramidal shape of spruce and fir trees is a result of the dominance of the central trunk over the lateral branches. The lower branches are large because they are far away from the apical meristem.

Auxins also inhibit the process of *abscission*—that is, the loss of plant parts such as leaves, flowers, and fruit. Fruit trees are often sprayed with auxin to prevent the fruit from dropping, so that it will accumulate as much sugar from the tree as possible. Artificially produced auxins are widely used commercially. Horticulturists use small amounts of auxins to stimulate root growth in cuttings. Auxins are also used to prevent stored potatoes from sprouting.

THINKING ABOUT BIOLOGY: Discovery of Auxin

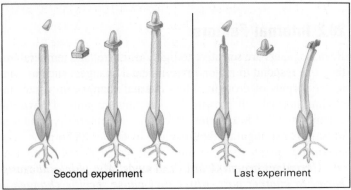

Second experiment   Last experiment

A Dutch plant physiologist named Frits W. Went conducted a series of four experiments with oat seedlings in 1926. In these experiments, Went identified auxin and showed how auxins regulate plant growth.

In the first experiment, Went removed the *coleoptile,* the sheath that covers the shoot tip. He observed that the shoot then stopped growing. When the coleoptile was replaced, normal growth resumed. This showed that a substance produced in the coleoptile influenced plant growth.

In the second experiment, a block of agar was placed between the coleoptile and the rest of the shoot. The shoot continued to grow. Based on this observation, Went concluded that the substance produced in the coleoptile was transported to the rest of the shoot.

In the third test, the coleoptile was placed cut side down on a block of agar and left there for one to four hours. When the agar block was placed on the cut shoot, the shoot grew. Growth was regulated by a particular substance, not the coleoptile itself.

In the last experiment, the coleoptile was removed and placed on a block of agar. A small piece of the agar was then placed on one side of the cut shoot. The shoot bent as it grew more rapidly on the side where the agar was placed. As a result, Went concluded that a chemical from the coleoptile caused the seedling to bend. He named the chemical *auxin.*

■ **Synthesizing Information** How does the third experiment differ from the last experiment?

Gibberellins Hormones called **gibberellins** stimulate rapid growth in some plants. Gibberellins were discovered in 1935 by Japanese researchers who were studying "foolish seedling disease" in rice. The diseased seedlings grew so tall in such a short period of time that they were unable to support themselves. The rice seedlings were infected with a fungus called *Gibberella fujikuroi*. This fungus produced the chemical that the researchers named *gibberellin*.

Gibberellin and its acidic form, gibberellic acid, begin the process of converting a seed's endosperm into sugars and amino acids that the seed can use to grow and develop. In some plants, gibberellins cause the stem to elongate suddenly just before the plant flowers and subsequently dies. The process, called *bolting*, produces a long stem that holds the flower up to pollinators and the wind. Most plants can be made to bolt artificially by applying gibberellin to the stem.

Cytokinins The group of hormones called **cytokinins** stimulate cell division in plants. These hormones are mostly concentrated in endosperm and young fruits. Cytokinins cause plant cells to divide many times without differentiating or specializing. When a balance of auxins and cytokinins work in combination, however, the hormones stimulate normal growth in the plant.

Other Hormones In addition to auxins, gibberellins, and cytokinins, plants produce three other kinds of hormones that affect the development of fruits and seeds. *Abscissic acid* causes dormancy in seeds and buds by inhibiting cellular activity. *Maleic hydrazine* works with abscissic acid to maintain dormancy. *Ethylene* is an unusual hormone because it is a gas. Ethylene ripens fruit by stimulating color change, softening fruit cell walls, and stimulating the conversion of starches and acids into sugar. Fruit is often picked while it is still green and then treated with ethylene on its way to market.

Figure 28–4. Gibberellic acid causes normal lettuce plants (top) to bolt. Bolting causes the stems to elongate and the leaves to spread apart (bottom).

Section Review

1. **Inferring Relationships** What role does phytochrome play in photoperiodism?
2. **Comparing Ideas** What is the difference between a short-day plant and a long-day plant?
3. **Evaluating Relationships** In what way does vernalization benefit seeds?
4. **Relating Ideas** What would happen if auxin were produced only in the roots of plants?

〈 **Thinking Critically** 〉

Section Objectives

- *Distinguish* between tropisms and nastic movements.
- *Explain* the survival value of phototropism.
- *Describe* how geotropism affects the growth of roots and stems.
- *List* three kinds of nastic movements.

Plant Movements

Photoperiodism, dormancy, and vernalization are all adaptations that enable plants to survive winter. Plants have other mechanisms that help them survive. These mechanisms allow plants to move in response to changes in their environment. New generations move through seed dispersal and vegetative propagation. Mature plants also move—stems twine around posts, flowers open and close, and leaves turn toward the sun. The stimuli for these limited but important movements come from the environment.

28.3 Tropisms

A plant may respond to a stimulus by growing toward or away from the stimulus. Such a movement is called a **tropism.** *Tropisms occur when one part of a plant organ grows faster than other parts, causing the organ to bend.* In a *positive tropism,* the plant moves toward the stimulus. In a *negative tropism,* the plant moves away from the stimulus.

Phototropism The response of a plant to the direction of its light source is called **phototropism.** The above-ground organs of a growing plant tend to bend toward light. You may be familiar with this type of phototropism in house plants. The sun shines directly on the side of a plant next to a window, while the other side is partially shaded. This uneven stimulus causes auxins in the plant's stem to move to the shady side of the stem. There they stimulate cell growth and so cause the dark side of the stem to expand more rapidly than the sunny side. As Figure 28–5 shows, this uneven growth causes the stem to bend toward the light. This positive phototropism exposes the plant's photosynthetic cells to as much light as possible.

Unlike stems and leaves, roots show negative phototropism by growing away from light. This response helps direct roots toward water and minerals deep in the soil.

Geotropism Roots are also directed down into the soil by a response to gravity called **geotropism.** Roots show *positive geotropism*—they grow toward the earth. Stems and leaves show *negative geotropism*—they grow upward against gravity. Scientists are not certain what causes geotropism, though the response appears to be stimulated in part by the movement of particles called *statoliths.* These tiny pellets of starch are located in the root cap. When a plant is placed on its side, the statoliths

Figure 28–5. The movement of a plant's stems and leaves towards a source of light is called positive phototropism.

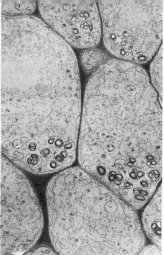

settle to the lower side of the cap. The root then curves downward and the stem curves upward, perhaps in response to the redistribution of hormones. As the root returns to a vertical position, the statoliths settle back in the cells of the root cap. Figure 28–6 shows an electron photomicrograph of statoliths.

Other Tropisms Two other kinds of tropic movements important to plant survival are **thigmotropism** and **hydrotropism.** Thigmotropism is a curving response to contact with a solid object. Grape and ivy plants have thigmotropic stems that coil tightly around posts, trees, rocks, or other supporting objects. Hydrotropism is the movement of a plant's roots toward water. Willow trees and other plants that need a great deal of water show positive hydrotropism.

28.4 Nastic Movements

A seedling bends toward light, but not all plant responses are related to the location of the stimulus. For example, morning glory flowers open and close in response to daylight and darkness. The direction of the petals' movement is independent of the direction of the light. Plant movements unrelated to the direction of an external stimulus are called **nastic movements.** Nastic movements occur rapidly and do not necessarily involve the growth of cells.

The most common kinds of nastic movements involve changes in the internal pressure of cells. For example, turgor pressure in the base of clover leaves decreases after sunset, causing the leaves to droop and fold. Such movements ir. leaves and flowers help plants conserve water, heat, and energy by exposing less surface area to the air. When the sun rises, the turgor pressure increases, and the leaves return to their upright, daytime positions.

Figure 28–6. The stem and leaves of an impatiens plant placed on its side for 16 hours exhibit negative geotropism (left), as statoliths resettle in the root cap. The electron photomicrograph (right) shows statoliths in a single root cell of a maize plant, magnified 5,000 times.

Reading Critically

Inferring Relationships How does the internal pressure of cells affect the appearance of plants?

Fruits Without Seeds

The fruits of some plants, such as bananas and pineapples, produce no seeds. Scientists describe the ability of these plants to develop fruits without the fertilization of eggs as *parthenocarpy.* Horticulturists are interested in finding out more about parthenocarpy so that commercially desirable seedless fruits can be developed.

Researchers have learned to induce parthenocarpy in some fruits by applying the plant hormone, auxin, to plants at certain stages in their development. A substantially higher auxin content is found in natu-

rally seedless varieties of grapes and citrus fruits than in seeded varieties. Seedless tomatoes can be experimentally grown by cutting off the anthers of the flowers to prevent pollination, and then spraying auxin on the base of the flower bud. The auxin stimulates development of a seedless fruit without pollination occurring.

Experimental treatment with auxin results in seedlessness in tomatoes and in melons, while the hormone gibberellin has a similar effect on peaches, cherries and apricots.

Perhaps further research will allow humans to bite into these fruits and others, such as watermelons, without worrying about the seeds.

Nastic movements are especially rapid in *Mimosa pudica*, the sensitive plant. The slightest touch causes the leaves to release a chemical that suddenly lessens the turgor pressure in special swellings at the bases of leaves and leaflets. The leaves close almost instantly.

Section Review

1. **Inferring Relationships**   What changes cause a stem to bend toward light?
2. **Evaluating Relationships**   How do plants benefit from phototropism?
3. **Relating Ideas**   Explain how positive geotropism can help a plant survive.
4. **Contrasting Ideas**   What is the major difference between a tropism and a nastic movement?

Thinking Critically

INVESTIGATION 28:
Do All Plants Grow at the Same Rate?

Objectives
- To *test* a hypothesis through controlled experimentation
- To *compare* growth rates among plants

Materials
seeds of four plant species, such as bean, corn, sunflower, and oat; four pots; potting soil; centimeter ruler, calipers

Prelab Preparation
1. State the environmental factors that affect plant growth. Do all plant species require the same environmental conditions for proper growth? Explain your answer.
2. Name the internal factors that affect plant growth.
3. List indicators of plant growth that could be measured regularly over four weeks.
4. After discussing the topic of this Investigation with your partner, form a hypothesis. Discuss your hypothesis with another team and form a hypothesis that represents the ideas of both teams. State reasons that support the hypothesis.

Inquiry: Experimentation
5. Use the following information to design a controlled experiment to test the hypothesis.
   a. Each team should have a complete set of materials and conduct the experiment separately.
   b. Data for your team will be collected at weekly intervals for four consecutive weeks.
   c. Prepare two tables similar to the example shown on this page. Each week, calculate the average height and stem diameter for the plants of each species in your group. Record these pooled data in the data table. Analyses and conclusions will be based on these pooled data. Title one table "Average Height" and the other "Average Diameter."

Plant Growth

Species of Plant	Height of Plant			
	Week 1	Week 2	Week 3	Week 4

6. Describe the design of your experiment.
   a. Identify the independent and dependent variables that will be used to test your hypothesis.
   b. State how many species of seeds and how many seeds will be planted in each pot.
   c. List the factors you will hold constant for all the pots in your experiment.
7. After having your experimental design approved by your teacher, conduct your experiment. Record your data in your table.
8. Make a line graph that compares the average height of each plant species over a four-week period. Make a similar line graph that compares the average diameter of each plant species.

Analysis
1. **Summarizing Data** Summarize the data collected throughout your experiment.
2. **Evaluating Ideas** Why were measurements made weekly rather than daily or only once after four weeks of growth?
3. **Evaluating Methods** What are the advantages and disadvantages of planting the seeds of only one plant species in each pot?
4. **Analyzing Data** Do all species in the experiment show the same growth pattern for both height and stem diameter?
5. **Analyzing Ideas** Explain whether or not the data support your hypothesis.
6. **Making Inferences** What factor best explains the growth rates observed in the plants that were studied?

Chapter 28 Review

Summary

Growth and response in plants result from interactions between plants and their environment. All plants need a certain amount of light and water to grow. The length of daily exposure to light also triggers flowering in some plants. This response is called photoperiodism. Day-neutral plants can produce flowers throughout the growing season. Dormancy and vernalization are responses to temperature that help plants survive winter in temperate regions.

A plant's hormones alter its internal chemistry. Auxins stimulate cell elongation while inhibiting the growth of buds and roots. Gibberellins stimulate rapid growth, and cytokinins stimulate cell division. Other hormones affect the development of fruits and seeds.

Plants also respond to external stimuli by moving. Tropisms such as phototropism result from growth toward or away from a stimulus. Nastic movements result chiefly from changes in turgor pressure and are independent of the direction of the stimulus. Typical nastic movements involve the opening and closing of leaves or flowers in response to daylight and darkness.

BioTerms

auxin (**445**)
critical dark period (**444**)
cytokinin (**447**)
day-neutral plant (**444**)
dormancy (**445**)
geotropism (**448**)
gibberellin (**447**)

hormone (**445**)
hydrotropism (**449**)
long-day plant (**444**)
nastic movement (**449**)
photoperiodism (**444**)
phototropism (**448**)
short-day plant (**444**)
thigmotropism (**449**)

tropism (**448**)

vernalization (**445**)

For each pair of terms, explain the differences in their meaning.

1. auxin, gibberellin
2. long-day plant, short-day plant
3. phototropism, thigmotropism
4. tropism, nastic movement

BioQuiz (Write all answers on a separate sheet of paper.)

Completion

1. In phototropism, auxin moves to the _____ side of the stem.
2. _____ prevents seeds in temperate climates from sprouting in autumn.
3. _____ movements are caused by changes in the turgor pressure of plant cells.
4. A _____ plant will flower when the daily period of darkness is shorter than its critical dark period.
5. Plants in temperate regions undergo a period of _____ when their metabolic rate slows down dramatically.

Multiple Choice

6. Apical dominance is caused by the hormone   a) gibberellin.   b) indoleacetic acid.   c) ethylene.   d) cytokinin.
7. Photoperiodism affects the production of   a) flowers.   b) stems.   c) roots.   d) leaves.
8. The response in which roots curve toward water is called   a) geotropism.   b) phototropism.   c) thigmotropism.   d) hydrotropism.
9. One way in which plants get rid of excess water is through   a) dormancy.   b) guttation.   c) vernalization.   d) thigmotropism.

10. Plants monitor the length of darkness and light each day by measuring levels of a) phytochrome. b) auxins. c) cytokinin. d) gibberellin.
11. If a plant moves away from a stimulus, it is demonstrating a) positive tropism. b) dormancy. c) negative tropism. d) vernalization.
12. Tiny pellets of starch located in the root cap associated with geotropism are a) phytochrome. b) xerophytes. c) mesophytes. d) statoliths.
13. If a hydrophyte were planted in the desert, it would a) thrive. b) flower immediately. c) die. d) undergo vernalization.
14. Horticulturists can affect the appearance of plants by changing the amount of a) auxin present. b) phytochrome present. c) ethylene present. d) All choices are correct.
15. Auxins are hormones that a) stimulate the elongation of cells. b) regulate photoperiodism. c) trigger abscission. d) stimulate seed production.

Writing Critically

16. Why do apple growers spray fruit trees with auxin as the apples mature?
17. What kinds of functions do nastic movements perform in plants?
18. What kind of growth do cytokinins tend to produce when they act alone on plant cells?
19. How does photoperiodism help flowering plants to survive?
20. How do tropisms affect root growth?

Application/Critical Thinking

1. **Evaluating Information** The leaves of trees and ivy often grow so that they barely overlap. How might phototropism account for this pattern of growth? Does this pattern have survival value for the plant? Explain your answer.
2. **Analyzing Experiments** Design an experiment to test the effects of applying various concentrations of the hormone IAA to plant stems. Conduct the experiment and summarize the results.
3. **Developing Conclusions** The flowering of photoperiodic plants can be controlled artificially. Do library research on photoperiodism and write a report explaining why short-day plants will never flower if a red light flashes once in the middle of every night. Note the role of the different chemical forms of phytochrome in your answer.

Cross-Discipline Connection

Biology and Horticulture Report on the commercial production that occurs at specific times of the year of large numbers of plants such as poinsettias, Easter lilies, tulips, and daffodils.

Discovery Through Reading

"Plant Eyes," *Omni* (September 1987): 30, describes photoreceptor cells in veins of leaves. What color of light determines the direction in which a plant moves? What color are the receptor cells?

Read the article "How Roots Respond to Gravity," *Scientific American* (December 1986): 112–119. Why does a root that is placed on its side grow downward in response to gravity?

Growing Plants in Space

©Walt Disney World

Scientists at The Land, EPCOT Center, are cooperating in the development of an accurate lunar soil simulant for studying plant growth. They carry out such studies to support a future moon base.

During the twenty-first century, people may spend months and even years in space. Orbiting space stations and bases on moons and planets must be designed with balanced, self-sustaining life-support systems. Technology must provide ways to supply air, water, food, and warmth and to dispose of or recycle wastes. Green plants could serve several functions as part of these complex technological systems.

An adequate food supply for extended missions would take up a large amount of storage space, and the additional mass would require extra fuel. Raising food crops while in space may help solve the problem of food supply. Fresh food would no doubt be a welcome change from prepackaged, freeze-dried fare.

Plants could also serve to recycle wastes, taking up carbon dioxide exhaled by human inhabitants and releasing oxygen back into the air. Digestive wastes could be used to fertilize the plants.

Finally, plants could provide a psychological benefit by surrounding people with living reminders of Earth. Plants could create a pleasant, natural oasis in the high-technology environment of a space station or lunar base.

To solve the problem of growing plants in the confined area of a space station, scientists are

Hydroponically grown lettuce and tomatoes

experimenting with water solution as a substitute for soil—a technology called *hydroponics.* The solution contains the 13 elements essential for plant growth.

Another problem in raising plants is the lack of gravity in space. Scientists are designing special devices that put plant roots in contact with the hydroponic solution without letting the solution escape into the surrounding air. One system currently being researched by NASA scientists isolates the hydroponic solution behind an artificial semipermeable membrane. The hydroponic solution is circulated on one side of the membrane. As the roots grow on the other side, they draw the solution through the membrane.

Lunar soil is composed of minerals that are similar to those on Earth, but that were formed under a different chemical environment. Lunar soil could supply plants with cal-

cium, magnesium, iron, and small quantities of potassium, phosphorus, and micronutrients. However, the two elements that plants require in the largest quantities— carbon from air and nitrogen from soil—are absent on the moon. Scientists must overcome such limitations to grow food away from the familiar soil of Earth.

Growing plants in space requires new propagation techniques.

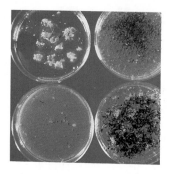

Carrot tissue culture

In the CELSS research facility at the Kennedy Space Center, plants grow under totally artificial, but optimal, conditions. Scientists experimentally feed the roots through artificial membranes. In the microgravity of space, the membranes would hold in the hydroponic solution.

Applied Plant Biology

Outline

Beans growing in irrigated farmland

Focus

Scientists apply knowledge about plant growth, development, reproduction, and genetics to develop ways of providing food and manufactured goods to a growing human population. Scientists continue to find ways to make agriculture more efficient, to develop plants that are resistant to disease, and to expand the areas where agriculture is possible.

- *What are the benefits to all humans of the development of food crops that are resistant to insect pests?*

- *How does the application of knowledge about plant biology affect the size of the human population?*

Plants for Food

Out of the approximately 275,000 species of plants, scarcely 100 are cultivated as major food crops. People began to cultivate crops from wild plants about 11,000 years ago. They favored plants that produced highly nutritious food in forms that could be stored over long periods. Today, farmers and agricultural scientists continue to refine many of the same crops. The major food crops fall into three main categories: cereal grains, legumes, and root crops.

29.1 Cereal Grains

Cereal grains are the small, one-seeded fruits of grasses. Wheat, rice, corn, barley, sorghum, oats, millet, and rye are all important cereal grains. Because grains are a dry form of fruit, they can be kept for months or years without spoiling if stored under the proper conditions.

Cereal grains form the basis of the human diet in many countries. The *endosperm* in each grain contains carbohydrates and protein. Endosperm is plant material that supplies food for the plant embryo. As food for humans, endosperm is the main component of flour. The embryo and seed coat contain vitamins as well as fibers that help move food through the digestive system.

Most cereal grains are grown in temperate environments with fertile soil and moderate rainfall. Wheat grows best in the sunny grasslands of the central plains in the United States and Canada and in similar areas of the Soviet Union. Corn, the only cereal grain that originated in the Americas, grows chiefly in

Section Objectives

- *List* three major food crops and *summarize* their nutritional value.
- *Explain* the advantage of rotating crops rather than growing the same crop every year.
- *List* three kinds of crop improvements that are made possible through genetic engineering.
- *Contrast* the benefits and problems introduced by the Green Revolution.
- *Discuss* three new crops or technologies that could provide food for the future.

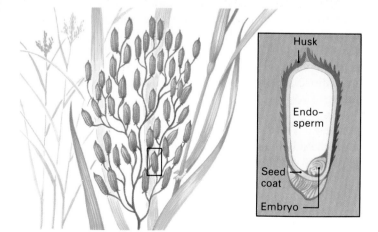

Husk

Endo-
sperm

Seed
coat

Embryo

Figure 29–1. Rice is the principal food in many parts of Asia. The rice grain is actually a fruit.

To learn how to grow plants without soil, see page 465.

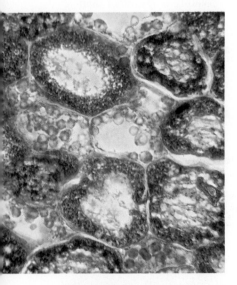

Figure 29-2. Nitrogen-fixing bacteria form nodules, or swellings, on legume roots. Root cells within these nodules contain many nitrogen-fixing bacteria.

areas that receive more than 50 cm (20 in.) of rain during the growing season. Rice, which requires even more rainfall, originated in the warm, humid tropics. Many tropical varieties of rice thrive in fields flooded by heavy rainfall.

29.2 Legumes

Plants that produce seeds in pods that open along both sides are called **legumes.** Peanuts, soybeans, peas, and beans are important legumes in the human diet. Alfalfa and clover are legumes that are grown primarily to feed animals.

Most legumes are grown in the same environment in which cereal crops are grown. Some legumes, including peanuts, also grow in the tropical areas of Africa and Asia. *Legumes have nutritional value comparable to cereal grains.* Soybeans, the most nutritious of all legumes, have more protein, minerals, and vitamins per gram than beef liver. Soybean oil is used widely to make margarine and cooking oil. Protein from soybeans is often added to animal feed.

29.3 Root Crops

Edible roots and underground stems are called **root crops.** Potatoes, sweet potatoes, and sugar beets are root crops with a high carbohydrate content. Cassava, a large, whitish root, is an important food in the tropics. *Root crops contain less protein and fewer vitamins than legumes and grains.* Potatoes, however, are a good source of vitamin C.

29.4 Improvements in Food Crops

As growing populations use up more and more farmland as places to live, farmers and agricultural scientists strive to make the remaining land produce food more efficiently. Efforts to increase the amount and quality of food production have focused on developing new varieties of crops, making plants more resistant to diseases and pests, and improving the nutritional value of crops.

Increased Yield Many food crops use up the available nutrients in the soil in just a few growing seasons. Farmers maximize the productivity of their crops by using fertilizers or by rotating crops to enrich the soil. **Crop rotation** is the alternating cultivation of two or more crops in the same field. After a season of growing corn, for example, a farmer may plant the field in soybeans. Soybeans and other legumes house a particular type of

Biofact

Q: Are potatoes native to Ireland or the United States?

A: Neither. Potatoes originated in the valleys of the Andes Mountains in South America. Spanish explorers introduced them to Europe in the 1500s.

bacteria in their roots. The bacteria in the roots then convert the nitrogen in the atmosphere to a form of nitrogen that the plant can absorb. This process is called *nitrogen fixation*. The nitrogen compounds that remain in the soil provide nutrients for the next crop of grain. Farmers in dry areas use **irrigation,** the artificial watering of crops, to ensure large crop yields.

The most dramatic improvements in crop yield have come from the development of new plant varieties. Scientists have used *cross-breeding* to produce high-yield crop species. In cross-breeding, two different varieties of plant are used as parents in order to combine the most desirable traits of each in the offspring. *Genetic engineering,* the process of transferring genes from one species to another, is also being used to create improved crops. Scientists are attempting to transfer the genes that make nitrogen fixation possible from legumes to grains. If these grains could be made to add nitrogen to the soil, farmers could use less fertilizer.

Reading Critically

Relating Ideas If you examined a field and found the soil contained a high percentage of nitrogen, what might the previous crop have been?

The career of plant breeder is described on pages 924–925.

THINKING ABOUT BIOLOGY: The Green Revolution

One of the most comprehensive efforts to introduce high-yield crops into poor agricultural regions is the **Green Revolution.** The Green Revolution began in Mexico and India in the 1950s. Intensive plant-breeding programs produced varieties of "miracle" wheat and rice that could yield two to five times as much grain per acre as ordinary varieties.

The miracle varieties produce large, heavy heads of seed. In ordinary wheat or rice, these heads would topple the long, slender stems before harvest, wasting the grain. The miracle varieties, however, have genes of dwarf varieties that grow

short, strong stalks that can support the extra weight.

Although these crops produced surplus food, they presented problems for poor farmers. The grains required expensive fertilizers, irrigation, and pesticides. Poor farmers could not afford to buy the materials and machinery needed to cultivate the grains prop-

erly. Some lost their crops to pests or disease. Others, unable to compete with mechanized farms, had to sell their land. The Green Revolution is still going on, but it is no longer viewed as entirely positive.

■ **Inferring Relationships** Why was the plan to introduce miracle varieties called the Green Revolution?

Increased Resistance   Both cross-breeding and genetic engineering have shown that it is possible to produce new crop species that resist drought, heat, and cold as well as certain diseases and parasites. Winter wheat, the result of years of breeding experiments, can survive cold Canadian winters.

Improved Nutritional Value   Although food crops are rich in carbohydrates, many are relatively poor sources of protein. The most common grains, legumes, and root crops provide *incomplete protein* because none of them alone provides all of the amino acids needed by human beings. Twenty amino acids make up the building blocks of protein. The eight amino acids that humans cannot produce themselves are called *essential amino acids*. To improve the protein content of crops, genetic engineers are attempting to transfer genes for essential amino acids to corn and other grains. This research could prove important in countries where people depend on a plant-based diet.

New research that explores the possibility of growing plants in space is discussed on pages 454–455.

29.5 Foods for the Future

In addition to improving existing crops, scientists are seeking new sources of food. One promising discovery is *grain amaranth,* once a staple food of the Aztec empire. Amaranth outranks other common grains in protein content and contains important amino acids that most grains lack. When eaten in combination with grains such as corn that are deficient in some amino acids, the protein in both grains can be more completely used by the human body. Some species of amaranth are also grown for their outer leaves, rich in essential nutrients.

Plant researchers are also looking for ways to enable some genetically engineered plant varieties to pass on their new, improved traits in their seeds. One solution is artificial seeds. In this technique plant embryos are produced from stems or leaves. The embryos are then encased in artificial seed coats. These seeds produce plants of unusually high quality. Technologists are also experimenting with new crop varieties that will grow in the desert with the help of irrigation and special fertilizers.

Figure 29–3. Artificial seeds like these are produced by encasing plant embryos in artificial seed coats.

Thinking Critically

Section Review

1. **Summarizing Ideas**   What are cereal grains? How do cereal grains differ from legumes?
2. **Summarizing Ideas**   What two new technological advances have most improved crop yield?
3. **Synthesizing Ideas**   How could the Green Revolution benefit from crop rotation?

Other Uses of Plants

Plants have many uses in addition to providing food. Trees provide fuel, lumber, and raw materials for manufactured products such as paper. Various parts of other plants are used as fibers, medicines, and food seasonings.

29.6 Forestry

Forestry is the business of cultivating trees to provide fuel, lumber, and wood products. Much of the wood cut from the world's forests each year is used as fuel. Wood has always been an important building material. Thousands of products are made from wood, including paper goods of all kinds. Waste liquids from paper pulp mills are used in cleaning compounds, insecticides, cosmetics, and medicines. Wood chips and sawdust are used to make particle board, soil mulches, and soil conditioners. Pine extracts yield turpentine and rosin, which are used in paints and varnishes.

A crop of trees may need 20 to 50 years to mature. *To ensure a steady production of wood over many years, forests must be carefully managed.* Forestry companies may use chemicals to prevent disease and fertilizers to stimulate growth. Most companies choose a limited number of areas with mature trees for cutting each year, replacing the cleared areas with seedlings. Enough mature trees are left standing to protect the animals that use them as shelter and as sources for food. The newly planted seedlings prevent the erosion of soil as well as the loss of nutrients the soil contains.

Section Objectives

- *List* three important wood products.
- *Explain* how forests are managed to produce a steady supply of wood.
- *Describe* the source of two kinds of natural fibers.
- *Name* two kinds of plants that are used in medicines and two that are used as herbs.
- *Discuss* the value of developing desert plants as substitutes for other natural resources.

Reading Critically

Relating Ideas What would happen to an area in which all the trees were cut down?

Figure 29–4. As an important part of forest management, foresters take core samples to monitor the health of trees.

Figure 29–5. The stem of the flax plant is the source of a strong, durable fiber that is used to make linen cloth.

Figure 29–6. The leaves of the foxglove contain digitalis, a powerful heart stimulant.

29.7 Fibers

Cotton is the world's most important plant fiber. Cotton thread is spun from the strong, fine fibers attached to cotton seeds. The stems of flax plants yield a soft, durable fiber that is used to make a cloth known as *linen.* Although synthetic fibers now make up more than 30 percent of the world's fibers, natural fibers are still prized for their strength and resilience.

29.8 Medicines and Seasonings

Long before the age of modern medicine, people used plants to cure illness and soothe discomfort. Some medicinal plants are still in use. Dried foxglove leaves yield a substance called *digitalis,* which is used to treat heart disease. Extracts from the opium poppy are used in the powerful pain relievers *morphine* and *codeine.* The bark of the cinchona tree contains *quinine,* a drug used to treat malaria.

Food seasonings may come from various parts of plants. The seasonings rosemary, chives, parsley, and basil are leaves. Dill, pepper, anise, nutmeg, and mustard are derived from seeds. Capers and cloves are flowers, horseradish is a root, and coriander, a fruit. Parts of stems may also provide seasonings. Cinnamon comes from the bark of certain trees, and ginger, from a rhizome.

29.9 New Uses for Desert Plants

Many substances produced by desert plants can be used as substitutes for scarce natural resources. Often these plants are easier to obtain than the scarce natural resource they replace. For example, the sperm whale, now an endangered species, once supplied oil used in cosmetics, lubricating oils, and floor wax. Scientists have found, however, that oil from the desert shrub

Where's the Bran?

Although research about the value of dietary bran is incomplete, many people are increasing the amount of bran in their diet. White toast is being replaced at many breakfast tables by bran cereals. The popularity of these cereals reflects an increased concern and interest that people have about the connection between diet and certain diseases, such as cancer and heart and blood vessel diseases.

Bran is found in the tough seed coat that covers the *endosperm*—material that is used as food by a plant embryo. The seed coat of a grain surrounds the endosperm in much the same manner that a peel surrounds the pulp of an orange. Composed primarily of cellulose fiber that does not contain calories, bran contains about 20 percent of a grain's protein and many of its B vitamins. The fiber adds bulk and roughage to the diet. When eaten, fiber passes through the intestine without being digested and absorbed into the body. In this way, the fiber in bran helps move other undigested waste and food through the intestinal tract.

Cereal grains are usually processed and refined before they are used in commercial products.

When a grain is processed, the bran is often removed and discarded. The flour that results is used to make many familiar bakery products, including white bread, pastries, and some breakfast cereal foods. Whole-grain breads and whole-grain cereal retain most of the bran.

jojoba (hoh HOH buh) has many of the same properties as sperm whale oil. Guayule (gwah YOO lee), another desert plant, produces a substitute for natural rubber. Discovering how desert plants survive their harsh conditions may some day make it possible to transfer those traits to other plants so that farming desert land would not require extensive irrigation.

Section Review

1. **Evaluating Ideas**   What are three important products made from wood?
2. **Identifying Information**   How are forests managed?
3. **Inferring Relationships**   In what new ways are desert plants useful?

> **Thinking Critically**

Forest Fires: Let Them Burn?

In the summer of 1988, a forest fire destroyed over one-fourth of Yellowstone National Park. Park officials had let the fire burn for several weeks before they took measures to put it out. By the time the first snows finally doused the flames, a controversy was blazing over the *let-burn* policy, a decision that allows a fire caused by lightning or other natural causes to burn itself out unless human life or property is threatened.

The let-burn policy is based on the idea that naturally occurring forest fires contribute to the overall long-term stability of the forest environment. Small forest fires destroy fallen trees and leaves on the forest floor before large amounts of this debris can accumulate and cause larger and more destructive fires. The earlier practice of suppressing all fires may have contributed to the intensity of the 1988 Yellowstone fire because large amounts of tinder had built up on the forest floor.

Foresters have set controlled fires to burn ground tinder in the Sequoia National Forest. Controlled burning allows rangers to choose optimal conditions of wind level, humidity, and time of day so that fires do not get out of control.

Forest fires also maintain the diversity of plant and animal life. Small fires destroy some tall trees and thus allow for the growth of low bushes and grasses that attract small animal wildlife.

However, many people criticized the let-burn policy after the Yellowstone fire. Local ranchers were concerned that elk and bison would be driven out of the park and compete with cattle herds for food. Others questioned the safety of allowing a fire during a drought. Many people were confused by a change in policy after a hundred years of anti-fire publicity. Some ecologists pointed out the difficulty of determining what is "natural" in a forest that has been sustained by human activity.

In the meantime, Yellowstone officials have announced a return to the no-burn policy that existed before 1970; at

least until experts agree that letting forest fires burn themselves out is justified.

Analyze the Issue

1. Explain the difference between a let-burn and a no-burn policy toward forest fires.

2. Analyze a forest fire's drawbacks and benefits. Which of these drawbacks and benefits primarily affect nature? Which ones mainly affect humans?

3. Should a fire started by natural causes be treated differently than one started by humans? Why or why not? Support your view.

INVESTIGATION 29:
Can Plants Be Grown Without Soil?

Objectives
- To *design* a controlled experiment
- To *compare* the growth of plants culti-vated using hydroponic methods with those grown in soil

Materials
bean seeds, two small clay pots, potting soil, glass wool wick, sand, beaker, commercial water-soluble fertilizer, centimeter ruler

Prelab Preparation
1. Explain how soil and fertilizer help a plant grow.
2. Growing plants using nutrient solutions instead of soil is called *hydroponics.* The hydroponic method in which plants are grown in sand that receives a regular supply of nutrient solution will be used in this Investigation. Another hydro-ponic method is one in which plants are grown with their roots directly in the nutrient solution.
3. After discussing the problem that is the topic of this Investigation with your part-ner, state your hypothesis. Explain why you chose this hypothesis.

Inquiry: Experimentation
4. Pull a glass wool wick through the hole in the bottom of a clay pot. Add sand to the pot until it is 2.5 cm from the top. Fill a second pot with soil until it is 2.5 cm from the top.

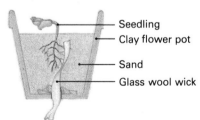

- Seedling
- Clay flower pot
- Sand
- Glass wool wick

5. Plant six bean seeds in each pot. Water both pots. Keep the planting medium moist but not wet and allow the seeds to germinate. Record the number of seeds that germinate in each pot.

6. Place the sand-filled pot in a beaker of nutrient solution as shown in the illus-tration. The soil-filled pot will be treated in a normal fashion. *What factors should be held constant for both pots during the experiment? What is the independent variable being tested in this experiment?*

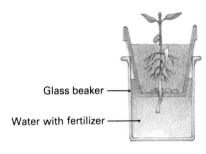

Glass beaker

Water with fertilizer

7. Measure and record the height of each plant and the number of leaves of each plant at weekly intervals for a period of weeks. Calculate the average height, average number of leaves, and average leaf width for the plants from each pot on the same days that height and leaf number are measured. Record the differ-ences between the seedlings in the two pots. Enter your data in a data table.
8. At the end of the observation period, make a bar graph that compares the ger-mination rates observed in the two pots. Make line graphs that compare average height, average number of leaves, and average leaf width of the seedlings in each pot at weekly intervals.

Analysis
1. **Summarizing Data** Summarize the data collected during the experiment.
2. **Analyzing Data** Do you observe a simi-lar pattern between the two pots for height, leaf number, and leaf width?
3. **Analyzing Data** Do the data support your hypothesis? Explain your answer.
4. **Making Inferences** State the relation-ships you observed between rates of growth and the method of cultivation of each of the plants in the pot.

Chapter 29 Review

Summary

Only about 100 species of plants are cultivated as food crops. Cereal grains, the small, one-seeded fruits of grasses, include wheat, rice, and corn. Grains form the basis of people's diet in much of the world. Legumes are seeds that are produced in pods that open along both sides. Peanuts, soybeans, and all other legumes permit nitrogen-fixing bacteria to convert nitrogen in the atmosphere to nitrogen compounds useful to plants. Rotating grain and legume crops thus helps replace lost nutrients by adding nitrogen compounds to the soil. Root crops, are generally less nutritious than grains and legumes.

Food crops have been greatly improved over the last century. By cross-breeding plants with desirable traits or transferring genes by genetic engineering, scientists have developed new varieties of crops with higher resistance, increased yield, and better nutritional value. Many foods lack essential amino acids. As a result, their proteins are incompletely utilized by humans. Amaranth is a grain high in both proteins and amino acids and is a promising new food source. Future needs for food will require further improvements in technology including new ways to develop and improve land for agricultural use.

Trees are cultivated to provide fuel, lumber, and thousands of manufactured products. Forests must be carefully managed to ensure continued production. Other plants are grown for fibers, medicinal effects, and flavors. Desert plants are being cultivated as substitute sources for whale oil, natural rubber, and other scarce resources.

BioTerms

cereal grain (**457**)
crop rotation (**458**)
forestry (**461**)
Green
   Revolution (**459**)
irrigation (**459**)
legume (**458**)
root crop (**458**)

For each pair of terms, explain the differences in their meanings.

1. legume, root crop
2. crop rotation, irrigation

BioQuiz   (Write all answers on a separate sheet of paper.)

Completion

1. The endosperm in cereal grains contains protein and _____ .
2. Guayule, a desert plant, produces a substitute for _____ .
3. The planting of legumes is useful in crop rotation because they supply _____ to the soil.
4. Animal feed is often prepared with protein added from _____ .
5. One source of food that has found renewed interest is _____ , which dates back to the time of the Aztecs.

Multiple Choice

6. Plants that produce seeds in pods are called   a) root crops.   b) cereal grains.   c) legumes.   d) None of the above is correct.
7. An herbal medicine that is used in the treatment of heart disease is a) quinine.   b) digitalis.   c) penicillin.   d) codeine.
8. Cereal grains are the small, one-seeded fruits of   a) grasses.   b) legumes.   c) root crops.   d) amaranth.

9. Endosperm is plant material that supplies food for the plant a) root. b) stem. c) fruit. d) embryo.

10. Alternating crops in the same field is a) irrigation. b) crop rotation. c) terracing. d) the Green Revolution.

11. Which of the following is not a legume? a) peas b) soybeans c) peanuts d) sorghum

12. Which of the following seasonings does not come from the leaves of the plant? a) dill b) chives c) basil d) parsley

13. Soybeans are used in crop rotation to a) increase crop yield. b) increase nitrogen content of the soil. c) increase amino acid content of the soil. d) decrease irrigation requirements.

14. What is the biggest use of forests? a) lumber b) paper c) fuel d) turpentine

15. Jojoba is a desert shrub that has properties similar to a) natural rubber. b) sperm whale oil. c) wood pulp. d) root crops.

Writing Critically

16. What was the major contribution provided to poor agricultural regions by the Green Revolution?

17. How might genetic engineering improve nutritional value of grains or legumes?

18. What advantage do the products of plants such as the jojoba have over the scarce resources that they replace?

19. What might happen to a forest if all its mature trees were cut for timber at the same time? How would the cutting affect forest animal life?

20. Why are root crops considered less nutritious than grains and legumes?

Application/Critical Thinking

1. **Applying Information** Plants may have uses other than as foods, fibers, and medicines. For example, landscapers and interior decorators use plants to add beauty to indoor and outdoor areas. Design a setting in which plants are used as decoration. Draw a diagram of the setting. Include instructions on the climate and care the plants would need.

2. **Inferring Relationships** What advantage would a grain plant gain if genetic engineers could introduce genes for nitrogen fixation?

3. **Synthesizing Ideas** Few countries have developed extensive desert agriculture. What problems are posed by desert cultivation? Discuss difficulties plants must overcome to survive in the desert.

Cross-Discipline Connection

Biology and History Research the historical importance and use of jojoba (*Simmondsia chinensis*), tepary bean (*Phaseolus acutifolius*), and amaranth (*Amaranthus hypochondriacus*).

Discovery Through Reading

The article "Cancer-Fighting Tobacco Plants?" *Science News* (April 15, 1989): 238, focuses on genetic engineering of tobacco plants. How might tobacco plants be genetically engineered to become mini-factories that produce anti-cancer drugs?

Summary

Bryophytes are nonvascular plants that include mosses, liverworts, and hornworts. Like the algae, bryophytes do not have specialized tissues for transporting water and materials. They lack true roots, leaves, and stems and require water for reproduction. Bryophytes live in moist areas.

Mosses have a life cycle that includes a dominant haploid gametophyte generation that alternates with a diploid sporophyte generation. The gametophyte produces haploid gametes and the sporophyte produces haploid spores. Mosses are important in the production of soil.

Tracheophytes are vascular plants that have tissues that transport water and nutrients. They have true roots, stems, and leaves. Leaves carry on photosynthesis. Roots anchor the plant and transport water, food, and other materials. Stems support the plant and display the leaves to sunlight. The sporophyte is dominant in vascular plants.

Seedless tracheophytes include horsetails, club mosses, and ferns. Gymnosperms and angiosperms are tracheophytes that produce seeds. Seeds can remain dormant under harsh environmental conditions and can be dispersed by wind or animals. Conifers are gymnosperms that bear cones where sex cells are produced. Angiosperms are the dominant land plants on Earth. Angiosperm flowers are modified leaves that produce sex cells. The ovary of the flower develops into a fruit that often aids in seed dispersal after the egg is fertilized. Plant growth is influenced by both environmental factors and hormones.

Knowledge about growth and reproduction in plants is often applied to the development of improved root crops, cereals, and legumes for human consumption.

Synthesis

Synthesis Statement

The first land plants were restricted to moist environments that prevented them from drying out and provided enough water so that reproduction could take place. The transition of plants from moist to dry environments is related to many adaptations. These adaptations prevent water loss from plant tissues, allow the transport of water around the plant body, provide support and anchorage, and free fertilization and dispersal of the offspring from a dependence on water.

The development of fruits in flowering plants allows for the wide dispersal of offspring by wind or animals. The adaptations shown by flowering plants make these plants the most successful of all land-dwelling plants that are alive today.

Synthesis Questions

Apply your understanding of this unit to the following questions.

1. What characteristics do plants share with algae? Give reasons why biologists have concluded that plants evolved from algae.

2. Explain why vascular plants are better suited for life on land than bryophytes.

3. Most animals move about to seek food and opportunities to mate. Plants, however, remain rooted in one place. Describe plant adaptations that compensate for their inability to change location.

4. List several plants that are found in the area in which you live. Give reasons why each plant is well-suited to its location. Describe some of the structures that make it possible for the plant to be successful.

5. Compare the ferns to the bryophytes and the seed plants. Suggest some reasons why the lush forests of giant club mosses, horsetails, and tree ferns that dominated North America during the Carboniferous period have vanished.

6. Why do gymnosperm tree species outnumber angiosperm tree species at far northern latitudes or at high elevations? Offer some reasons why extensive pine forests also occur in areas with poor, sandy soils at low elevations.

7. What adaptations allow angiosperms to be so successful on land?

8. Explain how different kinds of fruits aid in the dispersal of seeds.

9. Use a separate piece of paper to draw a concept map like the one shown. Place each of the following terms inside the appropriate figure: petals, pollen, fruit, style, anther, pollen tube, ovary, and stamen. Identify the arrow that represents pollination. Identify the structures that may be absent in wind-pollinated flowers and explain your answer.

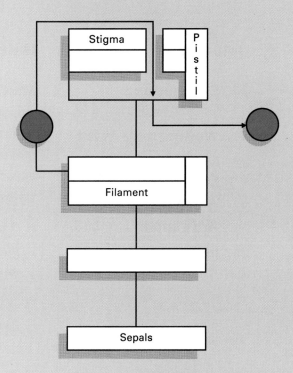

UNIT

8

INVERTEBRATES

Unit Outline

Unit Focus

Most of the animals in existence are invertebrates: animals without backbones. The many ways in which invertebrates have solved the problems of movement and support is reflected by the amazing diversity of forms, habitats, and "life styles" these animals show.

■ *What characteristics does the beetle in the photograph show that allow it to live in a land environment?*

■ *Why do you think so many of the invertebrates live in water?*

A beetle walks over dunes in the Sahara desert.

Sponges and Coelenterates

Outline

Corals and sponges on a reef

Focus

The sponges and coral in the photograph are **sessile**—that is, they attach themselves to an object and remain in that place all their lives. Sponges create water currents that flow through their bodies and trap microorganisms found in these currents for food. Corals capture prey that swim within their reach.

- ■ *What are the advantages of being a sessile animal?*

- ■ *Sponges were once classified as plants. Why do you think this was so?*

Introduction to Animals

An elephant, a hummingbird, and a jellyfish differ greatly in their size, shape, and behavior. Nevertheless, they are all animals. In distinguishing between types of organisms, the characteristics animals have in common far outweigh the differences among them. However, differences in body structure are useful in classifying animals. *The arrangement of body parts is related to how a particular animal species meets the challenges of living, which include gathering food, protecting itself, and reproducing.*

30.1 Symmetry and Body Plans

The arrangement of an animal's body parts determines its **symmetry.** Most animals are symmetrical in some way. Only a few animals can be described as *asymmetrical,* or having an arrangement of body parts that cannot be divided into corresponding sections. Many sponges are asymmetrical. They grow in varied and irregular shapes.

The symmetry of an animal generally provides a clue to its way of life. An organism with a round form—with no front or back, no right or left side—shows **spherical symmetry.** This form is well suited to certain protozoa that roll and float in water. Such organisms face all directions at once.

Animals whose body parts are arranged around a central axis, like spokes around the hub of a wheel, exhibit **radial symmetry.** Their sensory organs are located around the circumference of the body. Jellyfish and sea anemones show radial symmetry. Such animals do not move efficiently. Either they are sessile, or they float in the water or crawl along the bottom of the sea.

Figure 30–1. The body parts of the blue sea anemone (left) are organized around a central point. The asymmetrical sponge below has an irregular body plan.

Bilateral symmetry

Figure 30–2. The body plan of the swallowtail butterfly displays bilateral symmetry. The body can be divided into right and left halves that are mirror images of each other.

For a comparison between invertebrate and vertebrate systems, see pages 890–905.

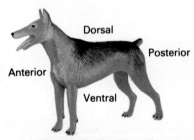

Figure 30–3. This diagram shows the location of the dorsal and ventral surfaces and the anterior and posterior ends of a dog, a bilaterally symmetrical animal.

> **Thinking Critically**

Most animal species have **bilateral symmetry**—that is, one-half of the body is a mirror image of the other half. A butterfly is a good example of bilateral symmetry. If a line were drawn lengthwise through the butterfly's body—the longitudinal axis—the right half would appear to be the exact opposite of the left half.

All bilaterally symmetrical animals have a distinct top and bottom, and a front and hind end. The abdominal surface is called the **ventral** surface, and the back surface, the **dorsal** surface. The front is the **anterior** end, and the hind, the **posterior** end. For example, the backbone of a dog is dorsal, and the stomach is ventral. The head is at the anterior end, and the tail is at the posterior end.

Animals that have a definite anterior end and move head first generally exhibit **cephalization** (sehf uh lih ZAY shuhn). Cephalization is an adaptation in which the neural and sensory organs are concentrated in the anterior end in animals. When such animals move, their sensory organs go first, providing information about the environment that lies ahead of the animals.

30.2 Vertebrates and Invertebrates

Scientists make a major distinction between **vertebrates,** animals with a backbone or a spine, and **invertebrates,** animals without a backbone. Humans and other mammals are vertebrates, as are fish, amphibians, reptiles, and birds. Vertebrates are included in the phylum Chordata. Although they are the most widely recognized and familiar of all animals, vertebrates make up only about 3 percent of the more than 1 million species of animals. Vertebrates are categorized by bilateral symmetry and cephalization.

About 97 percent of the animal kingdom are invertebrates. Invertebrates include sponges, jellyfish, starfish, worms, mollusks, insects, and crabs. Some species of invertebrates have radial symmetry, and some bilateral. Some, but not all, species are characterized by cephalization.

Section Review

1. **Identifying Relationships** Name the type of symmetry shown by a jellyfish, an eagle, and a human.
2. **Comparing Ideas** What characteristic distinguishes vertebrates from invertebrates?
3. **Inferring Relationships** How is the symmetry of an animal's body related to its movement?

Sponges

Sponges are so unlike other animals that they are sometimes put in their own subkingdom. *Sponges have the simplest body organization of any animal.* They have no head, no mouth, and no digestive, circulatory, or nervous system. Early naturalists classified sponges as plants, or as plant-animals, mainly because of their branchlike forms and their inability to move around. Sponges were not classified as animals until the mid-1800s, when scientists first began to closely study sponges and their method of feeding.

Most sponges live in shallow seas, though some have been found at depths of 8,500 m (27,800 ft.). A few species live in fresh water. In size, sponges range from less than 1 cm (0.4 in.) to more than 2 m (6.6 ft.). In color, they range from white and gray to brilliant shades of red, yellow, green, purple, and black. Sponges have many shapes—they may look like balls, discs, vases, goblets, branching shrubs, or small trees. The approximately 5,000 species of sponges make up the phylum Porifera (puh RIHF uhr uh). *Porifera* means "pore bearing." Sponges have been described as looking like sacks full of holes.

30.3 Characteristics of Sponges

Once a sponge attaches itself to a rock, shell, or other submerged object, it does not move. *Sponges feed by filtering food and nutrients out of the water.* The body wall of a sponge consists of two layers of cells, with a jellylike layer between them. The outer layer is called the **ectoderm,** and the inner layer the **endoderm.** The body wall surrounds a cavity through which water flows. Water is drawn in through the **incurrent pores** in the ectoderm and leaves through a larger opening called the **osculum** (AHS kyuh luhm). The water carries food and dissolved oxygen. Cells that digest the food, called **collar cells** or *choanocytes* (koh AN uh syts), are located in the endoderm. Each collar cell has a flagellum. The movement of the flagella sets up a current of water through filaments that make up the collar of the cells. The filaments catch and remove bacteria, unicellular algae, and other microorganisms from the water. This food is drawn into the collar cells and digested. Amoeba-like cells called **amoebocytes** (uh MEE buh syts) in the jellylike layer carry the nutrients to the other body cells and take away waste matter.

Without some kind of skeletal structure, sponges would collapse under their own weight. The composition of their skeletal

Section Objectives

- *List* the major characteristics of sponges.
- *Describe* how sponges obtain food.
- *Name* three ways in which sponges reproduce.
- *List* some common commercial uses of sponges.

For information about a career as a marine biologist, see pages 932–933.

Figure 30–4. Each of the large openings in the sponge above is an osculum, through which water leaves the body of a sponge.

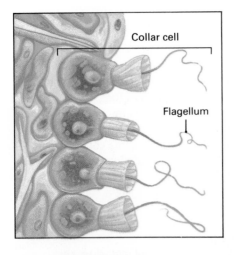

Collar cell

Flagellum

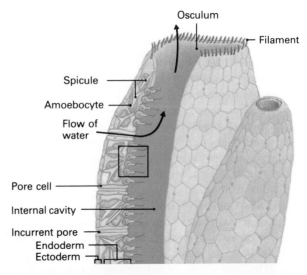

Osculum

Filament

Spicule

Amoebocyte

Flow of water

Pore cell

Internal cavity

Incurrent pore

Endoderm

Ectoderm

Figure 30–5. The large diagram shows the structures a sponge uses to draw in and expel water. The inset illustrates the collar cells that digest microorganisms trapped by filaments that make up the collar.

structure is the basis of classification of sponges. Some sponges have skeletons made of **spicules** (SPIHK yoolz), tough interlocking spikes of either calcium or silicon. Other sponges have skeletons made of a flexible protein called **spongin.** Bath sponges, for example, have skeletons composed of spongin, which makes them firm but soft. Some sponge skeletons are a mixture of both spicules and spongin.

Sponges may grow individually or in colonies. Some colonies are so dense that it is difficult to distinguish one sponge from its neighbor.

Sponges have a remarkable ability to **regenerate**—that is, to grow new parts to replace those that are lost. *A sponge not only can regenerate parts of its body, but can also regenerate the entire body from fragments.* A sponge can also reform if it has been separated into single cells by being pushed through a fine silk cloth. The cells will move around, form clumps, and then larger groups. Within a few days the group of cells will reform into several new sponges. If sponges of two different species are pushed through a screen and mixed together, the fragments will regroup into sponges of the original two species.

30.4 Reproduction of Sponges

Sponges reproduce both sexually and asexually. Most species are **hermaphrodites** (huhr MAF ruh dyts)—that is, an individual sponge can produce both eggs and sperm, though at different times. Sperm cells produced by one sponge are carried to another sponge by water currents. Once inside the sponge, sperm cells are captured by carrier cells, which are modified collar cells. The carrier cells take the sperm to the egg. The fertilized egg develops into a **larva** (LAHR vuh), an immature form. Sponge larvae have flagella and swim about. They soon attach themselves to objects in the water and develop into adult sponges.

Fragmentation is a common method of asexual reproduction among sponges. Even a small branch that breaks off from the parent sponge can develop into a full-grown animal. Sponges also reproduce asexually by producing **gemmules** (JEHM yoolz)— special food-filled balls of amoebocytes surrounded by protective coats. Generally only freshwater sponges produce gemmules. The gemmules can survive harsh conditions, such as extreme cold or periods of dry weather. When conditions are favorable for growth, sponge cells emerge through an opening in the gemmules and grow into new sponges.

larva (plural, *larvae)*

Reading Critically

Inferring Conclusions What is the advantage of sponges having so many methods of reproduction?

Section Review

1. **Summarizing Ideas** Where do sponges live?
2. **Identifying Relationships** What keeps sponges from collapsing under their own weight?
3. **Drawing Conclusions** How do sponges feed?
4. **Listing Ideas** Name two commercial uses of sponges.
5. **Inferring Relationships** During what part of their life cycle are sponges able to move about? How are they able to move?

Thinking Critically

Coelenterates

- *Name* four common coelenterates.
- *List* the major characteristics common to all coelenterates.
- *Distinguish* between a polyp and a medusa.
- *Describe* how hydras feed.
- *Name* the major organisms that inhabit a coral-reef community.

Coelenterates (sih LEHN tuh rayts) are animals with saclike bodies and long, flexible appendages called **tentacles.** Most coelenterates live in sea water. One group, the hydras, lives in fresh water. The 9,000 species of coelenterates also include jellyfish, sea anemones, and corals. Although corals are one of the simpler forms of animal life, they have had profound effects on the geography of continents and islands. Millions of tiny coral skeletons massed together over centuries have formed entire islands and offshore reefs. These islands and reefs are found primarily in the South Pacific Ocean, in the Caribbean Sea, and along the Florida coast.

30.5 Characteristics of Coelenterates

Coelenterates get their name from their *coelenteron,* or "hollow gut." The coelenteron is a digestive cavity with only one opening. Coelenterates also have special stinging cells called **cnidocytes** (NYD uh syts). For this reason, they are also known as *cnidarians* (ny DAIR ee uhnz).

medusae (singular, *medusa*)

Coelenterates generally exhibit radial symmetry. They have two body plans: vase-shaped and bell-shaped. Hydras and some other coelenterates develop only a vase-shaped body, called a **polyp.** Jellyfish and some other coelenterates go through a polyp stage but spend most of their lives as a bell-shaped **medusa** (muh DOO suh).

Coelenterates live singly or in colonies. Individual animals within a coelenterate colony may have specialized functions. The Portuguese man-of-war is an example of a colonial coelenterate. Some of the individual animals specialize in reproduction or feeding, others in gathering food.

The bodies of both polyps and medusae consist of two layers of cells, the endoderm and the ectoderm, separated by a jellylike substance called **mesoglea** (mehz uh GLEE uh). The mesoglea of a polyp is thin. In a medusa, however, the mesoglea often makes up the major part of the body substance.

The tentacles of most coelenterates circle the mouth of the animal, and the cnidocytes are in the tentacles. Inside each cnidocyte is a sac containing a coiled stinger, called a **nematocyst** (neh MAT uh sihst). When discharged, the stinger can paralyze or lasso small prey. New cnidocytes replace those whose nematocysts have been discharged. The tentacles draw the food up to the mouth. Enzymes inside the digestive cavity break down the food, and the food particles are absorbed by the

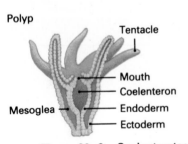

Medusa
— Mesoglea
— Endoderm
— Coelenteron
— Ectoderm
Tentacle   Mouth

Polyp
Tentacle
Mouth
Coelenteron
Mesoglea   Endoderm
Ectoderm

Figure 30–6. Coelenterates are either vase-shaped polyps (bottom) or bell-shaped medusae (top).

cells that line the cavity. Undigested waste products are expelled through the animal's mouth. Individual cells carry out respiration directly, taking in oxygen from the surrounding water by diffusion.

30.6 Hydras

Hydras and related animals make up the class Hydrozoa (hy druh ZOH uh). Hydras are the most extensively studied coelenterates, but they are not typical of hydrozoans in some ways. For example, hydras have only the polyp form, while most hydrozoans go through a medusa stage as well.

Hydras are only about 1 cm (0.4 in.) long. Most hydras are orange, brown, white, or gray in color, but some are green due to algae that grow in the cells of their endoderm. Hydras live in freshwater streams and ponds. They attach themselves to leaves and other debris in the water by means of a flattened adhesive base called the *basal disc*. Hydras move by floating, gliding, or somersaulting.

Although primitive animals, hydras show a great degree of specialization in their nematocysts. Four distinct types have been identified. One type of nematocyst anchors the tentacles when the animal moves, and another repels animals other than prey. A third holds the prey by winding around the animal, while a fourth nematocyst stings the prey, paralyzing it.

Like other coelenterates, hydras have no brain or central nervous system. A network of nerves, the *nerve net,* permits some coordination of responses and some simple movements. Hydras also have sensory cells that respond to chemical and mechanical stimuli. The animals have little control in their responses to stimuli. If touched with a probe on one part of the body, for example, the whole body will contract.

When a hydra catches a shrimp or a water flea in its tentacles, a feeding response begins. The tentacles move the prey towards the mouth, the mouth opens in response to a chemical given off by the prey, and the prey is pushed in whole. Enzymes are released that digest the food, and the undigested remains are expelled through the mouth.

Hydras reproduce asexually by forming small buds on the outside of their bodies. These buds grow, and within two or three days they fall off and begin life as independent animals. Hydras also reproduce sexually, usually in autumn. When the water temperature drops, individual hydras begin to develop either egg-producing **ovaries** or sperm-producing **testes.** The sperm swims to the egg, which remains attached to the body of the hydra. After fertilization has occurred, the egg begins to

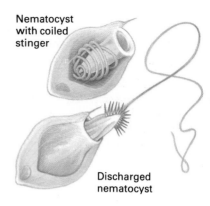

Nematocyst with coiled stinger

Discharged nematocyst

Figure 30–7. This diagram shows the nematocyst found in the tentacles of coelenterates. The coiled stinger inside the cnidocyte (top) can stun or kill small organisms when released (bottom).

An Investigation that compares two species of hydra is on page 483.

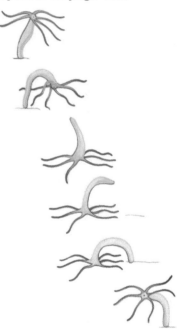

Figure 30–8. The nerve net of the hydra enables its muscles to produce a somersaulting motion, one way in which hydras travel.

divide and falls off the adult female. The young hydra emerges in the spring.

Hydras live individually and independently. Most other hydrozoans, however, live in colonies. Most hydrozoans also have both polyp and medusa forms at different times in their life cycle. Certain species, for example, spend most of their lives as colonial polyps. A single polyp multiplies by budding, forming a colony. Within the colony, the polyps become specialized. Some are feeding polyps, and some are reproductive polyps. Tiny medusae bud off the reproductive polyps. These medusae produce eggs or sperm. Thus, colonial polyps exhibit a division of function between feeding and reproductive forms. Other colonial coelenterates also show specialization of individuals.

30.7 Jellyfish

From a distance, jellyfish resemble inflated plastic bags. Observed more closely, jellyfish can be seen swimming by rhythmically contracting and relaxing their "bells." Jellyfish belong to the class Scyphozoa (sy fuh ZOH uh), which means "cup animals." The tentacles of jellyfish with their stingers may reach up to 70 m (230 ft.) in length. Their central discs may range from 4 cm (1.5 in.) to a meter (3.3 ft.) in diameter, though one observer has recorded a central disc 3.6 m (12 ft.) in diameter.

In the life cycle of a jellyfish, the medusa reproduces sexually, and the polyp reproduces asexually. Figure 30–10 shows the life cycle of one species of jellyfish. The male medusa releases sperm cells through its mouth, and the female releases eggs. The eggs lodge in pockets on the tentacles of the female

Figure 30–10. This diagram shows the sexual and asexual phases of the Aurelia jellyfish life cycle.

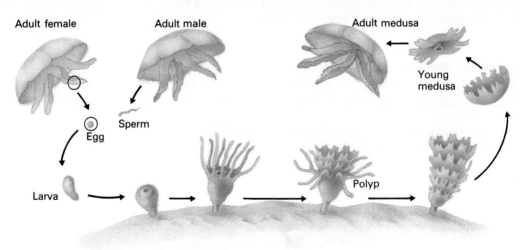

Adult female   Adult male   Adult medusa   Young medusa   Sperm   Egg   Larva   Polyp

A Sting Operation

Ocean swimmers some-times encounter an animal that looks like a jellyfish and can deliver a painful sting. This unusual "creature" is not a jelly-fish at all. It is a relative of hydra called the *Portuguese man-of-war.* Unlike hydra, however, this animal is a colony of hundreds of individual polyps that work together in the colony. Each polyp performs a special-ized function that contrib-utes to the survival of the colony. Some polyps digest food, others produce

eggs, and still others produce sperm. The polyps that swimmers fear are those that are modified for the colony's defense against predators. These polyps can sting humans.

The polyps that make up this colonial animal are suspended from a float, called a *pneumatophore.* The float contains nitrogen gas. When the float is filled it serves as a sail that allows the colony to be transported from place to place by wind currents. When the sail is deflated

the colony floats under the surface of the water, where it is protected in stormy weather and carried by water currents.

The "tentacles" of the Portuguese man-of-war are polyps that can be up to 5 meters (16.4 feet) long. Some of these polyps dis-charge poison that can paralyze or kill fishes.

and are fertilized. The eggs grow and develop into small, free-swimming larvae.

The larvae swim away and attach themselves to the sea floor. There they develop into a polyp stage that resembles the hydra. The jellyfish polyp grows and eventually produces buds. This development is the asexual phase of its reproductive cycle. The buds grow and eventually begin to form medusae, which, as they build up, resemble a stack of plates. These medusae bud off one by one and begin the cycle again. The polyp may repeat the process the following year.

30.8 Sea Anemones and Corals

The sea anemones (uh NEHM uh neez) and corals belong to the class Anthozoa (an thuh ZOH uh). *Anthozoa* means "flower ani-mals." These coelenterates are often beautifully colored and have varied forms.

Sea anemones are marine polyps that inhabit coastal areas. A sea anemone has a basal disc like that of the hydra, by which the anemone attaches itself to rocks or other objects. Sea anem-ones are solitary. They feed on fish and crabs that swim within

Figure 30–11. Sea anemo-nes look like flowers but are animals that use stinging cells in their tentacles to kill smaller organisms for food.

A coral reef is a crowded community. In spite of the vast size of the ocean, corals and sponges sometimes end up competing for the same underwater space. Other plants, animals, and algae benefit from one another's presence.

Coral reefs grow best in tropical waters, where the average temperature is 27°C (80°F). Corals can live in much colder waters. However, the warm waters and sunlight are necessary to ensure the presence of photosynthesizing algae that live in a *mutualistic*, or mutually helpful, relationship with coral. Some algae live inside coral tissues. They use the wastes from the coral and provide oxygen for the coral. The algae also speed up the production of calcium deposits by the coral. These deposits, which make up the coral's skeleton, form the reef.

The algae are a link in a vast food web in and around the coral branches. The corals and small fish eat the tiny marine organisms called *plankton,* and big fish eat the small fish.

Corals have enemies within the coral-reef community. The crown-of-thorns starfish consumes soft corals. Some borer sponges compete with corals for space. Humans take away corals as souvenirs and pollute the

waters. Drastic changes in one group of plants and animals can upset the precarious balance of undersea life.

■ **Making Predictions** What would happen to a coral reef community if all the algae were suddenly eliminated?

Reading Critically

Comparing Ideas How are corals and sea anemones similar?

reach of their tentacles. Sea anemones digest their food in much the same way as hydras do.

Corals resemble sea anemones but have skeletons and live in colonies. Soft coral species have flexible skeletons. The stony coral has an external skeleton that is almost pure limestone. The skeletons of some corals are used to make jewelry. The skeletons of dead corals accumulate and form the reefs often seen rising above the surface of tropical waters.

Section Review

1. **Summarizing Ideas** Name four characteristics of coelenterates.
2. **Comparing Ideas** Compare the manner of movement among hydras, jellyfish, and sea anemones.
3. **Inferring Relationships** How do algae and coral benefit each other?

Thinking Critically

INVESTIGATION 30:
What Stimulates a Hydra to Feed?

Objectives
- To *observe* feeding by a hydra
- To *identify* stimulus-response relationships

Materials
watch glass, hydra, *Daphnia,* dry yeast, mortar and pestle, spring or aquarium water, vinegar, methylene blue, two medicine droppers, stereomicroscope, forceps, filter paper, flashlight, glass depression slide, coverslip, paper towel, compound microscope, probes or toothpicks

Prelab Preparation
1. Describe the characteristics of a hydra.
2. Explain how hydras obtain food.
3. Name the stimuli that might cause a hydra to begin its feeding response.

Inquiry: Observation
4. Use a clean medicine dropper to gently transfer a hydra from the stock culture to a watch glass. Add enough culture medium to cover the animal.
5. Use the stereomicroscope to observe the hydra for a few minutes. Record a detailed description of the specimen.
6. While observing the hydra, gently touch its tentacles with the tip of a probe or toothpick. After the hydra recovers, touch the body stalk. Describe the hydra's response to touch. *Is there any evidence that hydra possess sense organs?*
7. Aim a flashlight on the hydra. Turn the light on for a minute; then turn it off. *Is there any evidence that the hydra is sensitive to light?*
8. Use a medicine dropper to transfer several *Daphnia* to the watch glass. Observe the responses of the hydra to the *Daphnia* for several minutes. Record your observations.
9. Place the hydra in the culture jar labeled "Recently Fed Hydra."
10. Transfer another unfed specimen from the stock culture to a watch glass as you did in step 4.

11. Use a mortar and pestle to crush a small amount of dry yeast. Add a small amount of water to the dry yeast and continue crushing it for a minute or two. Using a forceps, dip a tiny piece of filter paper into the yeast-water mixture. Then, place the filter paper near the hydra. Observe the animal for a few minutes and record your observations.
12. Use a medicine dropper to carefully transfer the animal and a drop of culture medium to a clean glass depression slide. Gently add a coverslip.
13. Place a drop of methylene blue stain along one edge of the coverslip. Use a small piece of paper towel to absorb water along the opposite edge of the coverslip. Observe the hydra under low power with the compound microscope, paying special attention to the tentacles. Record your observations.
14. While continuing to observe the specimen, place a drop of vinegar along one edge of the coverslip and use a paper towel to draw the liquid under the coverslip as was done in step 10. Record your observations. *What evidence indicates that the vinegar caused the discharge of nematocysts?*

Analysis
1. **Summarizing Observations** Describe the hydra's feeding response.
2. **Analyzing Observations** Is it likely that touch is the stimulus that triggers the feeding response in hydras? Explain.
3. **Analyzing Observations** What evidence indicates that chemicals trigger a hydra's feeding response?

Chapter 30 Review

Summary

Animals differ in their symmetry, the arrangement of their body parts around a center point or line. Most animals exhibit one of these forms of symmetry: spherical, radial, or bilateral. Some simple animals, such as sponges, have no symmetry. Another major division among animals is between vertebrates, which have a backbone, and invertebrates, which do not. All vertebrates are bilaterally symmetrical. Mammals, fishes, amphibians, reptiles, and birds are vertebrates.

The simplest type of invertebrate is the sponge. Sponges are sessile, chiefly marine animals that feed by filtering nutrients from water that circulates through their bodies. They reproduce sexually and asexually.

Coelenterates include hydras, jellyfish, sea anemones, and corals. Coelenterates feed by grasping their prey with tentacles and stinging the prey with nematocysts. Many coelenterates have a polyp form, which reproduces asexually, and a medusa form, which reproduces sexually. Coelenterate colonies exhibit specialization in the functions of individual animals. Coral reefs form from the accumulation of coral skeletons.

BioTerms

amoebocyte (**475**)
anterior (**474**)
bilateral
   symmetry (**474**)
cephalization (**474**)
cnidoctye (**478**)
coelenterate (**478**)
collar cell (**475**)
dorsal (**474**)
ectoderm (**475**)
endoderm (**475**)
gemmule (**477**)
hermaphrodite (**476**)

incurrent pore (**475**)
invertebrate (**474**)
larva (**477**)
medusa (**478**)
mesoglea (**478**)
nematocyst (**478**)
osculum (**475**)
ovary (**479**)
polyp (**478**)
posterior (**474**)
radial symmetry (**473**)
regenerate (**476**)
sessile (**472**)

spherical
   symmetry (**473**)
spicule (**476**)
spongin (**476**)
symmetry (**473**)

tentacle (**478**)
testes (**479**)
ventral (**474**)
vertebrate (**474**)

For each pair of terms, explain the differences in their meanings.

1. radial symmetry, spherical symmetry
2. dorsal, ventral
3. anterior, posterior
4. endoderm, ectoderm

BioQuiz   (Write all answers on a separate sheet of paper.)

Completion

1. Water enters the central cavity of a sponge through the _____ .
2. A sea anemone shows _____ symmetry.
3. An organism with reproductive organs of both sexes is called _____ .
4. Animals that have a definite anterior end and move headfirst exhibit _____ .
5. Jellyfish polyps develop from _____ .

Multiple Choice

6. Structures called _____ form the skeleton of many sponges.   a) nemocysts   b) spicules   c) silicon   d) mesoglea
7. _____ carry nutrients in the endoderm of a sponge's body.   a) Collar cells   b) Nematocysts   c) Amoebocytes   d) Spicules

8. The tail of an animal is found on the _____ surface. a) anterior b) posterior c) dorsal d) ventral
9. A freshwater coelenterate that moves by floating or somersaulting is a) a sponge. b) a hydra. c) a sea anemone. d) a coral.
10. Cells that digest food in sponges are a) amoebocytes. b) cnidocytes. c) collar cells. d) endoderms.
11. The fertilized egg from a sponge develops into a swimming a) larva. b) embryo. c) polyp. d) All choices are correct.
12. Vertebrates are characterized by cephalization and a) spherical symmetry. b) radial symmetry. c) mesoglea. d) bilateral symmetry.
13. Sponges can reproduce a) sexually. b) asexually. c) by fragmentation. d) All choices are correct.

14. A jellylike substance separating the endoderm and ectoderm in coelenterates is called a) mesoglea. b) spongin. c) nematocyst. d) amoebocyte.
15. An example of a stage that reproduces asexually is a a) medusa. b) jellyfish. c) polyp. d) nematocyst.

16. What is the advantage of cephalization?
17. How are the sensory structures arranged in radially symmetrical organisms?
18. Why do corals grow best in tropical waters?
19. How do the individuals in some coelenterate colonies show specialization of function?
20. How does water enter and leave a sponge?

Application/Critical Thinking

1. **Summarizing Ideas** Use a library to research how precious coral differs from other varieties of coral. Write a report describing how precious coral is harvested and polished. If possible, display color photographs showing some of the interesting shapes in which coral forms.
2. **Inferring Relationships** The life cycle of some animals resembles the alternation of generations exhibited in the life cycle of plants. Compare and contrast the life cycles of a jellyfish and a fern.
3. **Designing Experiments** Sexual reproduction in hydras usually occurs in the autumn. Design an experiment that would establish whether it is the change in temperature or the diminished light in autumn that prompts sexual development in hydras.

Cross-Discipline Connection

Biology and Art Use colored modeling clays to make cross-sectional models of a sponge and a jellyfish. Construct the models to show the relative thickness of the body layers.

Discovery Through Reading

The article, "Spiral Effect," *National Wildlife* (April–May 1989): 52–59, beautifully illustrates the variety of spiral shapes that are found in nature. What organisms show spiral shapes? Why is the spiral shape so commonly found in nature?

Worms

Outline

Tube worms on the ocean floor

Focus

The common grouping, worms, is used to describe several different phyla of animals. These phyla include flatworms, roundworms, and segmented worms. Taken together there are over 36,000 species of worms which range in size from microscopic to over 3.3 m (11 ft.) in length. Some worms are free-living and others are parasitic. Worms are found in soil and in fresh and marine waters.

■ *What structural characteristics do you associate with the word "worm"?*

■ *How do you think the sessile tube worms in the photograph obtain food?*

Flatworms

Section Objectives
- *List* the major characteristics of flatworms.
- *Describe* the feeding behavior of planarians.
- *Diagram* the life cycle of the liver fluke.
- *Describe* how tapeworms reproduce.
- *Explain* how the body plan of flatworms differs from that of the two other major worm phyla.

Flatworms make up the phylum Platyhelminthes (plat ee HEHL mihn theez). The phylum name is derived from two Greek words: *platy,* which means flat, and *helminthes,* which means worm. The 13,000 species of flatworms belong to three major classes. Members of the class Turbellaria are called *free-living* because they live independently of other animals. Members of the class Trematoda, the flukes, and the class Cestoda, the tapeworms, are parasites. They derive nutrition from living hosts.

Flatworms have a digestive cavity with only one opening for receiving food and expelling wastes. However, flatworms lack circulatory and respiratory systems. The flat shape of their bodies allows cells to obtain oxygen and food molecules through diffusion. Flatworms range in length from a fraction of a millimeter to over 15 m (17 yd.).

31.1 Planarians

The most common flatworm is the planarian (pluh NEHR ee uhn), which belongs to the class Turbellaria. Planarians live in both aquatic and terrestrial environments. Some kinds grow to be 30 cm (1 ft.) long, and many are brightly colored. The freshwater planarians that live in North America are gray, brown, or black and average 3 to 15 mm (0.1 to 0.6 in.) in length.

Planarians have a spade-shaped head and a body covered with cilia. The mouth is located in the middle of the ventral side. Planarians move by laying down a trail of slime from mucus-producing cells and using their cilia to propel themselves along the trail.

Nervous Control in Planarians A planarian will move away from light and toward food. These responses are made possible by the planarian's simple nervous system. A planarian has two light-sensitive areas on its head called *eyespots* that contain pigments. When light strikes the pigments, chemical reactions take place that stimulate special photoreceptor cells to carry electrical impulses. The head area also has cells sensitive to chemicals and to touch. Messages from these receptors travel to a concentration of nerve cells in the worm's head known as the **ganglion** (GAN glee uhn). From the ganglion two main nerve cords run the length of the planarian's body. Messages from the receptors cause nerves to stimulate action by the planarian's muscles. In this way, the planarian can respond to changes in light or chemical surroundings.

Biofact

Q: *Are planarians cross-eyed?*

A: No. Although planarians do not have image-forming eyes, their pigmented eyespots are sensitive to light. Because the eyespots are located close together, planarians have the appearance of being cross-eyed.

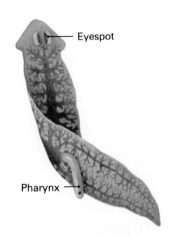

— Eyespot

Pharynx —

Figure 31–1. This diagram shows the major structures of a planarian.

Digestion in Planarians Planarians eat dead animals or slow-moving organisms, including smaller planarians. The animal feeds by extending a muscular organ called a **pharynx** out of its mouth. Enzymes released through the pharynx partially digest the food, which is then sucked into the digestive cavity. Nutrients travel through branches of the digestive cavity to all parts of the body. Solid wastes exit through the pharynx since there is only one opening to the digestive tract.

A network of fine tubules extending the entire length of the body of the animal allows for the removal of excess water. Some of the tubes end in cells called **flame cells.** Cilia in these cells beat back and forth, much like the flickering of a candle flame. The beating of the cilia moves water and liquid wastes along the tubules to surface pores where the wastes are excreted.

Reproduction in Planarians Planarians are hermaphrodites—that is, each animal has both male and female reproductive structures. Fertilization occurs as a result of the exchange of sperm between two planarians. Each animal sheds fertilized eggs in capsules containing up to 10 eggs. The capsules attach to objects in water until the eggs hatch.

Planarians have the ability to regenerate parts of their bodies. For example, an anterior piece of the body may regenerate a new posterior part. Because of this capacity for regeneration, a planarian that is accidentally or deliberately cut may regenerate new parts or sometimes grow into two new organisms.

31.2 Flukes

Flukes belong to the class Trematoda. Flukes are parasites and are a serious health hazard in many areas of the world. Many kinds of flukes cause serious and even fatal diseases. Suckers or hooks on the anterior end of the fluke attach the parasite to its host. Flukes usually live on the fluids of a host, such as blood and mucus. Many flukes may live for years off a single host.

Mature flukes do not have cilia. Instead their skin is covered with a thick protective coating called a **cuticle** (KYOOT ih kuhl), which prevents the host from digesting them.

Some flukes are *ectoparasites*—that is, they live on the outside of their host's body. Most flukes are *endoparasites* and live inside the body of their host. Flukes have a complex life cycle often involving two or more hosts. For example, the liver fluke spends most of its life in the digestive tract of a sheep or other vertebrate. There the fluke lays thousands of eggs, many of which are carried out of the sheep's body in its **feces,** or solid wastes.

Reading Critically

Analyzing Conclusions
How can flukes survive inside a host?

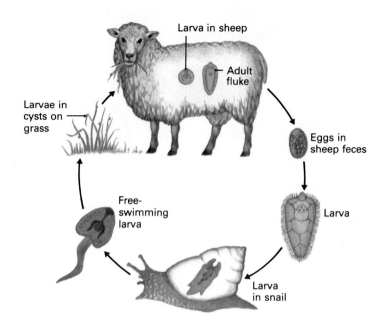

Larva in sheep

Adult fluke

Larvae in cysts on grass

Eggs in sheep feces

Free-swimming larva

Larva

Larva in snail

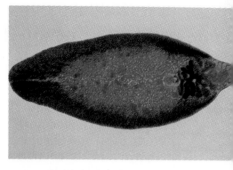

Figure 31–2. The adult liver fluke (above) lives in the digestive system of sheep and other vertebrates. It releases eggs that develop into adults through a complex life cycle involving two hosts (left).

If the eggs fall into water, immature flukes called larvae develop. The microscopic larvae must next enter the body of a certain species of snail. Fluke larvae die if they do not find the right type of snail soon enough. Once inside the host snail, the larvae remain only long enough to reproduce asexually. The many new parasites that result then leave the snail.

After swimming about, a larva attaches itself to a blade of grass near the water. It then forms a thick-walled structure around itself, called a **cyst.** The fluke remains inactive inside the cyst until it is taken into the digestive system of a sheep grazing on the grass. Inside the body of the sheep, the cyst dissolves and the larva develops into an adult fluke.

31.3 Tapeworms

Tapeworms, another group of common parasitic flatworms, belong to the class Cestoda. *Tapeworms live in the intestines of vertebrates where they feed by absorbing food that has already been digested by their host.*

The head of a tapeworm is called the **scolex** (SKOH lehks). Hooks and suckers on the scolex attach the tapeworm to the intestinal wall of the host. Tapeworms have no mouth or digestive system of their own.

Most tapeworms measure about 1 meter (3 ft.) in length, but some grow much longer. The tapeworm's long ribbonlike

Figure 31–3. The tapeworm (top) clings to the intestinal wall of its host by means of hooks and suckers on its head or scolex (bottom).

Sponges and coelenterates have two embryonic layers of cells—an ectoderm and an endoderm. Worms and other bilaterally symmetrical animals have a third layer in between, called the **mesoderm.** These three layers of cells are called the **germ layers.**

All worms have three germ layers, but various types of worms differ greatly in their general body plan. A major difference is the presence or absence of a **coelom** (SEE luhm), a body cavity in the mesoderm layer.

Of the three major types of worms, flatworms have

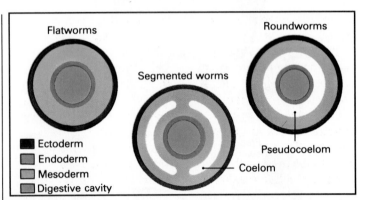

Ectoderm
Endoderm
Mesoderm
Digestive cavity

the simplest structure. A flatworm's mesoderm consists of a layer of densely packed cells. There is no coelom. Flatworms and other animals without a coelom are called *acoelomatic* (ay see luh MAT ihk).

Segmented worms have a true coelom. The stomach, heart, and other internal organs are suspended in the coelom by membranes.

Roundworms have a cavity called a **pseudocoelom** (SOO doh see luhm). The organs within a pseudocoelom are not suspended by membranes, and

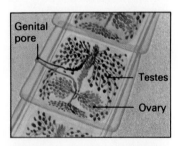

Genital pore

Testes

Ovary

Figure 31–4. The dark areas on a tapeworm's segments, or proglottids, are its reproductive structures.

body is divided into many sections called **proglottids** (proh GLAHT ihdz). Tapeworms grow by adding proglottids at the anterior end.

Each proglottid is a hermaphroditic reproductive unit in which the male structures usually develop first. As the proglottid matures, the female organs develop. When two or more tapeworms are present in a host, they may cross-fertilize. Tapeworms may also self-fertilize by folding in upon themselves. In this case sperm is usually transferred from a forward, sperm-producing segment to a more mature proglottid farther back. One tapeworm proglottid may contain as many as 100,000 eggs.

A person may become infested with a tapeworm by eating raw or undercooked meat that contains tapeworm larvae. When inside the meat, the tapeworm larva is surrounded by a saclike bladder and is called a *bladderworm.* Once inside the digestive tract of the host, the larva attaches to the wall of the host's intestine, matures, and begins to produce proglottids. Proglottids containing fertilized eggs the intestine lacks a lining.

The formation of germ layers and coelom occurs in an early stage of development. Development begins when the sperm penetrates and fertilizes the egg. The **zygote** divides into two cells in a process called **cleavage**. Repeated cleavage forms a ball of cells, the **blastula** (BLAS choo luh). This sphere has a fluid-filled cavity in the center. Because the cells do not grow as they divide, the blastula is about the same size as the original egg cell.

Next the blastula begins to indent and become a cup-shaped **gastrula** (GAS troo luh). This process, called *gastrulation,* can be compared to what happens when you press the surface of an underinflated balloon. The surface moves inward and forms a dent.

The illustration below shows that the mesoderm forms between the ectoderm and the endoderm. The coelom forms inside the mesoderm. Each germ layer gives rise to different organ structures in the fully developed animal.

■ **Inferring Conclusions** Rank the three types of worms according to complexity of body plan. Explain your answer.

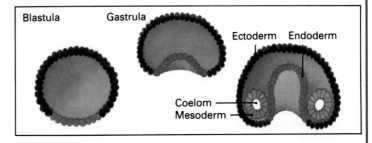

break off and pass out of the host in the feces. Cattle eat grass contaminated by feces and take in the eggs, which hatch in the intestines. The worms then travel through the blood to the muscles. There the bladderworms form cysts in the muscles, allowing the cycle to begin again. Other kinds of human tapeworms have fish and small crustaceans as intermediate hosts. Tapeworms of all kinds may compete with the host for nutrition, and the host is often fatigued. If a host harbors large numbers of tapeworms, death may occur.

Section Review

1. **Summarizing Ideas**   List major flatworm characteristics.
2. **Identifying Relationships**   How do planarians feed?
3. **Summarizing Ideas**   Describe the life cycles of the liver fluke and the tapeworm.
4. **Inferring Relationships**   Why is the presence of a coelom indicative of a complex worm?

> **Thinking Critically**

- *List* the major characteristics of roundworms.
- *Diagram* the life cycles of some common parasitic roundworms.
- *State* how some human diseases caused by roundworms can be prevented.

Roundworms

Roundworms make up the phylum Nematoda, so they are also called *nematodes*. Like flukes and tapeworms, most roundworms are parasites. Almost all species of plants and animals are affected by one of the 12,000 species of roundworms.

One shovelful of garden soil may contain over 1 million nematodes. Roundworms feed on plants by sucking the juices from them. Growers of fruit trees, strawberries, vegetables, and cotton suffer annual financial losses due to roundworms. Humans are hosts to about 50 species of roundworms. In fact, more than a third of the world's population suffers from diseases caused by roundworms. These diseases are most common in areas of Africa, Asia, and South America where sanitation is poor. Pinworms, hookworms, and intestinal roundworms are common human parasites.

Nematodes have tubular bodies covered by a tough cuticle and tapered at both ends. A fluid-filled *pseudocoelom* provides a structure against which the worm's longitudinal muscles can contract. The absence of circular muscles gives roundworms their characteristic thrashing or whipping motion in water.

The roundworm's digestive system consists of a tube called the *alimentary canal,* which is open at both ends. The anterior opening is the mouth. The posterior opening is the **anus,** through which solid wastes leave the body. Liquid wastes are collected by a system of tubes and are expelled through an *excretory pore* in the worm's posterior end.

Most roundworm species have separate male and female sexes. The females, which produce thousands of eggs, are usually larger than the males. The male guinea worm, for example, is about 2.5 cm (1 in.) long, while the female is 60 to 120 cm (24 to 48 in.) long. In the male reproductive system, sperm passes from the testis into the **cloaca** (kloh AY kuh), a common chamber into which digestive, reproductive, and excretory systems empty. During mating the sperm leaves the cloaca and enters the female's reproductive opening. Sperm is then stored in the female's body and used to fertilize eggs when they mature. Young roundworms develop in the body of the female or, in some species, outside of the female's body.

Reading Critically

Analyzing Relationships
How can a nematode move if it has no circular muscles?

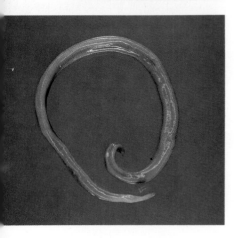

Figure 31–5. *Ascaris,* or intestinal roundworm, may infect more than 650 million people worldwide.

31.4 *Ascaris*

One of the largest nematodes that lives in humans is *Ascaris* (AS kuh rihs), or the intestinal roundworm. These worms grow to 30 cm (12 in.) in length. *Ascaris* also lives in the intestines of pigs and horses. Usually an intestinal roundworm does not cause serious health problems, but when many worms are present they may block the intestine and cause the death of the host.

The life cycle of *Ascaris* is typical of many roundworm species. The cycle begins when a human or other host eats vegetables grown in soil containing the eggs. The eggs hatch in the intestine of the host. The larvae bore through the intestinal wall, enter the bloodstream, and are carried to the lungs. The larvae are then coughed up into the mouth, swallowed, and returned to the small intestine. There they develop into mature adults and reproduce. The fertilized eggs leave the host's body in the feces and may be picked up by other hosts. *Ascaris* eggs are well protected by tough shells that allow them to survive outside a host for as long as five years.

31.5 Hookworms

The hookworm may get its name from the bent position of its anterior end. This worm attaches to the host's intestinal wall and sucks blood. Hookworms can cause much damage to their hosts because of their method of attachment. The host often loses blood and may suffer from anemia as a result of being infected.

The hookworm is a serious problem in warm, moist areas throughout the world, including some parts of the United States. The problem is most acute in areas where people walk barefoot in contaminated soil. Hookworm larvae develop in the soil and enter a human host through microscopic cracks in the soles of the feet. Like *Ascaris*, hookworms travel through the circulatory system to the lungs. There they are coughed up and swallowed, thus entering the digestive system where they complete their life cycle.

31.6 Trichina

The trichina (trih KY nuh) worm lives throughout the world and ranges from 1.5 to 4 mm (0.06 to .15 in.) in length. The trichina worm causes a serious disease called *trichinosis* (trihk uh NOH sihs) that is transmitted primarily through eating raw or undercooked pork.

The trichina life cycle begins with sexual reproduction in a host mammal such as a pig. The female trichina hatches the fertilized eggs in her body. The larvae are then deposited in the lining of the intestine of the host. The larvae work their way into the bloodstream where they travel to all parts of the body. The worms eventually lodge in muscle tissue where they develop cysts and cause cramps.

Figure 31–6. This light microscope image, enlarged 150 times, shows a trichina encysted in the muscle tissues of a pig.

Just a Fluke

Blood flukes have a long and established parasitic relationship with humans. Archeologists have found the eggs of these parasites in Egyptian mummies.

Blood flukes cause diseases known as *schistosomiasis,* which affect the intestine and bladder. Schistosomiasis affects a large number of people primarily in Africa and east Asia, although it is also found in South America and the West Indies. Many people suffer from infection in Egypt, where the fluke larvae breed in rivers, irrigation ditches, and canals. The blood fluke larvae causing schistosomiasis usually make their way into humans through the skin or mouth. No effective drug treatments exist for most forms of schistosomiasis.

Less harmful North American varieties of the blood fluke cause a malady known as "swimmer's itch" or "clam digger's itch." This parasite, carried by waterfowl, is found in bodies of fresh water. The fluke larvae may attempt to burrow into the skin of swimmers. Although they cannot penetrate the skin and get into the bloodstream, the flukes can cause red itchy bumps. Swimmer's itch may be treated with *antihistamines,* chemicals that

reduce inflammation, and lotions to soothe the itching skin.

Among the flukes, blood flukes are unique because the male and female travel together. The long, thin male has a groove along the length of its body into which the threadlike female fits. These traveling companions do not have a problem finding their mates.

The life cycle of the trichina worm continues if the muscle tissue containing the cysts is eaten. A single gram of raw pork meat may contain as many as 3,000 trichina cysts. The heat of cooking can kill the trichina larvae in their cysts. For this reason, pork should always be cooked thoroughly before the meat is tasted or eaten. Trichinosis is uncommon in the United States because farmers cook meat scraps before feeding them to hogs.

Section Review

1. **Analyzing Ideas**   What are two characteristics all roundworms share?
2. **Summarizing Ideas**   What are the stages of the life cycle of *Ascaris?*

Thinking Critically

3. **Inferring Conclusions**   What happens in the trichina life cycle after the worms form cysts in human muscle?

Segmented Worms

Section Objectives

- *List* the major characteristics of segmented worms.
- *Identify* the main structures of an earthworm.
- *Explain* why earthworms can live only in moist soil.
- *Compare* earthworms and leeches.

Worms that make up the phylum Annelida have bodies that are divided into a series of segments, which are often visible as rings on the outside of the body. These worms are also called *annelids,* which means "little rings." The 9,000 species of annelids include earthworms, leeches, and a variety of marine worms.

Annelids are the most complex of all worms. Like flatworms and roundworms, annelids have three tissue layers and a bilaterally symmetrical body plan. ***Annelids differ from the other worms in having a true coelom, giving them a "tube-within-a-tube" body plan.*** Two sets of muscles, circular and longitudinal, allow annelids to move more efficiently than other worms. Annelids also have more complex circulatory, respiratory, and nervous systems than other worms.

To compare the systems of the earthworm to those of other invertebrates, see pages 890–893.

31.7 Earthworms

Earthworms, which belong to the class Oligochaeta (ahl uh goh KEET uh), live in soils all over the world. Earthworms vary in size from a few centimeters to 3.3 m (11 ft.) long. A common North American species has a dark dorsal surface and light ventral surface. Most of the worm's 100 to 150 segments are identical, except for the pointed anterior and posterior ends. Between segments 35 and 37 lies a swelling called the **clitellum,** which plays an important role in reproduction.

setae (singular, *seta*)

Earthworms have pairs of bristles, called **setae** (SEET ee), on each body segment except the first and last. An earthworm moves by anchoring the setae on its posterior segments and then contracting the circular muscles in front of the anchored segments. These contractions extend the body forward.

Figure 31–7. This diagram illustrates the external structures of the earthworm.

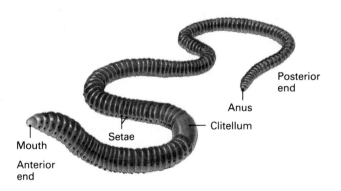

Posterior end

Anus

Clitellum

Setae

Mouth

Anterior end

Figure 31–8. Setae are clearly visible in this closeup view of a section of an earthworm.

The ecological role of earthworms is the topic of the Investigation on page 499.

Figure 31–9. The specialized organs of the earthworm's nervous, digestive, circulatory, and reproductive systems occupy the segments at its anterior end.

Digestion in Earthworms   An earthworm feeds by taking in soil with its muscular pharynx. The soil moves down a tube called the **esophagus** and then enters a storage chamber called the **crop.** From the crop, the soil moves to another chamber called the **gizzard.** Here, the grinding together of soil particles swallowed by the earthworm crushes pieces of organic matter. The food next moves into the intestine, which extends to the posterior end of the worm. Folds in the wall of the intestine increase the surface area where absorption of digested food into the bloodstream takes place. Solid wastes pass out of the body through the anus.

Earthworms are very valuable to gardeners and farmers. As the worms eat their way through the soil, they break up soil clumps, aerate the soil, and add nutrients. Earthworms break down organic material faster than normal bacterial decomposition does.

Circulation in Earthworms   Unlike flatworms and roundworms, earthworms have a *closed circulatory system,* as shown in Figure 31–9. In a closed circulatory system, the blood circulates through a series of vessels. Dorsal and ventral blood vessels run the length of the worm's body. The blood absorbs molecules and carries them through the dorsal vessel to five pairs of muscular pumping tubes, or "hearts." These "hearts" pump blood into the main ventral blood vessel. Smaller blood vessels carry the blood to all parts of the body.

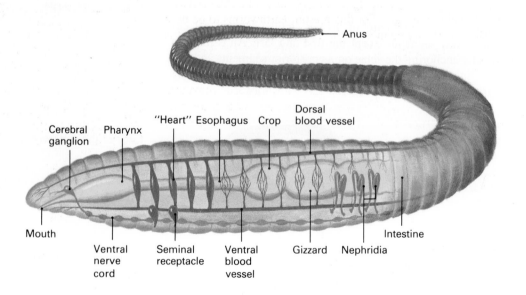

Respiration and Excretion in Earthworms Earthworms take in oxygen and give off carbon dioxide by diffusion through the skin. Because diffusion can occur only across a moist membrane, an earthworm must remain in an environment that is neither too wet nor too dry. Earthworms can drown in soil that is saturated with water because there is not enough oxygen. During dry periods, earthworms dig deep into the soil where there is more moisture.

Earthworms eliminate liquid wastes through ciliated tubes called **nephridia** (neh FRIHD ee uh). The beating of cilia draws fluid from the coelom into a funnel-shaped opening in the nephridia. As the fluid passes through the tubules, some water is reabsorbed by tiny blood vessels. Waste materials then pass out of the body through a pore in the skin. Each body segment has a pair of nephridia.

Nervous Control in Earthworms An earthworm can respond rapidly to changes in its environment because of a concentration of nerve cells called a *cerebral ganglion,* near the worm's anterior end. The cerebral ganglion is connected to the rest of the body by a ventral nerve cord that extends the entire length of the animal. A ganglion connects each body segment to the ventral nerve cord.

The earthworm has no external eyes or ears, but receptors in the skin enable the worm to react to light, sound, and chemicals. Earthworms are active mainly at night and will move away from bright light. However, the light-sensitive cells of earthworms do not respond to red light. For this reason, earthworms to be used as fishing bait may be most easily dug up at night if red light is used for illumination.

Reproduction in Earthworms Like planarians, earthworms are hermaphrodites. The female structures are located towards the anterior portion of the earthworm, and the male structures towards the posterior. Fertilization occurs when two worms exchange sperm. A mucous secretion from the clitellum holds the two earthworms together while they mate. The sperm each worm receives is stored in a *seminal receptacle* until just before the eggs are laid.

Two or three days after mating, the earthworm produces an external mucous case formed of sticky secretions from the clitellum. Muscular contractions push the case along the body. Mature eggs and sperm held in the seminal receptacle enter the case as it passes over the body of the worm. The case then seals, forming a coat that protects the fertilized eggs until they hatch.

Figure 31–10. After mating, earthworms produce a mucous case that is moved along the body to collect sperm and eggs. The case slips off the anterior end of the earthworm and seals to protect the developing eggs.

Polychaetes (PAHL ih keets) are a class of segmented worms that live mainly in salt water. Unlike earthworms, polychaetes have tentacles, antennae, and specialized mouth-parts. Each polychaete segment has a pair of appendages called **parapodia** (pa ruh POHD ee uh) that assist in move-ment. Some polychaetes live in elaborate tubes constructed from sand or mud on the ocean floor.

Giant tube worms that grow to be 1.5 to 3 m (5 to 10 ft.) in length were discovered in 1977. These strange worms, named *Riftia pachyptila,* have no eyes, mouths, or digestive tracts. The worms belong to their own phylum, the Pogonophora (poh guh NAHF uh ruh).

The giant tube worms live in an area called the Galapagos Rift. Here water is heated by volcanic rocks, which create a warm "oasis" in the near-freezing waters.

The Galapagos Rift is an unusual environment deep beneath the surface of the ocean where sunlight does not penetrate and photosynthesis cannot occur. *Riftia* get energy from bacteria that live inside their bodies. The bacteria produce energy through chemical reactions involving sulfur compounds that the worms absorb from sea water.

■ **Analyzing Relationships** What kind of relationship does *Riftia* have with the bacteria that live inside their bodies?

31.8 Leeches

Another common segmented worm is the leech, which belongs to the class Hirudinea (hihr yuh DIHN ee uh). Most leeches live in fresh water, although some may be found in salt water or in moist soil. Unlike other kinds of segmented worms, leeches do not have setae. The body of a leech, which is often flat and tapered, has a large sucker at each end.

Leeches feed on the blood of other animals. A leech can attach to its host by its anterior sucker. Three sharp jaws pierce the skin of the host and the leech extracts blood from the wound. The leech secretes a substance that prevents the host's blood from clotting while the leech feeds.

Reading Critically

Comparing Ideas How do leeches differ from most segmented worms?

Section Review

1. **Comparing Ideas** How does the body plan of earthworms differ from the body plans of flatworms and roundworms?
2. **Inferring Relationships** Why do earthworms come to the surface when it rains?
3. **Analyzing Conclusions** What structures of a leech are adaptations to a parasitic life style?

Thinking Critically

INVESTIGATION 31:
How Does Temperature Affect an Earthworm's Heart Rate?

Objectives
- To *observe* the effect of environmental temperature on an earthworm's heart rate
- To *test* a hypothesis and *interpret* data

Materials
live earthworm, ice, pan, paper towels, stopwatch, flashlight, hot plate, three 600-mL beakers, water, thermometer

Prelab Preparation
1. Describe earthworm circulation.
2. Define heart rate and explain how it might be measured.
3. Discuss the question that is the title of this Investigation with your partner. State your hypothesis, and explain your reasoning.
4. State the independent and dependent variables suggested by your hypothesis.
5. Make a table for recording heart rate at 8°C, 12°C, 16°C, 20°C, and 24°C. Allow space for data from three trials.

Inquiry: Experimentation
6. Label the beakers "Bath," "Cold," and "Hot," respectively. Fill each beaker three-quarters full with water. Place the "Hot" beaker on the hot plate, warming it to about 30°C. Fill the remainder of the "Cold" beaker with ice. Use the water in these beakers to adjust the temperature of the water in the "Bath" beaker.
7. Place six layers of moist paper towels in the bottom of the pan. Gently place the earthworm in the pan. Covering its anterior end with more moist paper towels

will help calm it. Touch the worm as little as possible. Allow a minute or two for the worm to become accustomed to the environment. *Why does covering the worm calm it? Why is it important to keep the worm moist?*
8. Shine a flashlight on the worm while observing its dorsal surface. You will see the dorsal blood vessel running along the length of the body, just below the skin. Watch the blood vessel expand and contract, as blood pulses through it.
9. Adjust the bath water temperature to 24°C.
10. Pour the bath water into the pan, covering the worm. Wait two minutes, then measure the worm's heart rate for one minute. Record your results.
11. If necessary, adjust the temperature of the bath by adding a small amount of warm or cold water. Then record the worm's heart rate for two more trials.
12. Return the water to the bath beaker. Then repeat steps 10 and 11 for the remaining temperatures, beginning with 20°C.
13. Return the earthworm to its storage container and clean your laboratory area.
14. Share your data with those of three other teams. Use the combined data to calculate the average heart rate for each temperature.
15. Construct a line graph that shows the relationship between heart rate and external temperature for earthworms.

Analysis
1. **Summarizing Data** Summarize the data collected during this Investigation.
2. **Analyzing Data** State your conclusion and explain how the data supports it.
3. **Making Inferences** What might be the adaptive value of the earthworm's response to changes in temperature?
4. **Making Predictions** Predict the outcome of a similar experiment that uses a rabbit. Explain the reasoning.

Chapter 31 Review

Summary

The three main worm phyla discussed in this chapter are all bilaterally symmetrical and have three tissue layers. However, they differ significantly in their body plans. Acoelomatic flatworms have a digestive cavity with one opening. Roundworms, or nematodes, have a pseudocoelom and a tubular digestive system that is open at both ends. Segmented worms have a true coelom and efficient digestive, circulatory, and respiratory systems.

Flatworms include planarians, which are free-living, and flukes and tapeworms, which are parasites. The life cycle of the liver fluke is typical of many parasitic worms. The adult develops and reproduces inside a host. The eggs hatch into larvae outside the host's body. They must be picked up by another host for the cycle to continue. After reproducing asexually, a larva leaves the host and forms a cyst, which may be picked up by a new host.

Common parasitic roundworms that infest humans and other mammals include the *Ascaris* worm and the hookworm. Transmission of parasites to human hosts can largely be prevented by improved sanitation and thorough cooking of certain foods.

Segmented worms include the common earthworms and blood-sucking leeches.

BioTerms

anus (492)
bladderworm (490)
blastula (491)
cleavage (491)
clitellum (495)
cloaca (492)
coelom (490)
crop (496)
cuticle (488)
cyst (489)

esophagus (496)
feces (488)
flame cell (488)
ganglion (487)
gastrula (491)
germ layer (490)
gizzard (496)
mesoderm (490)
nephridia (497)
parapodia (498)

pharynx (488)
proglottid (490)
pseudocoelom (490)

scolex (489)
setae (495)
zygote (491)

For each pair of terms, explain the differences in their meanings.

1. coelom, pseudocoelom
2. clitellum, setae
3. crop, gizzard
4. proglottid, scolex

BioQuiz   (Write all answers on a separate sheet of paper.)

Completion

1. Messages from receptors travel to a concentration of nerve cells in the planarian's head called a _____ .
2. The head of a tapeworm is the _____ .
3. Eating uncooked pork can lead to an illness called _____ .
4. Roundworms have a false body cavity called _____ .
5. An earthworm crushes particles of food in its _____ .

Multiple Choice

6. Planarians expel liquid wastes through a) proglottids. b) flame cells. c) ganglia. d) nephridia.
7. Roundworms are also called a) nematodes. b) leeches. c) annelids. d) flukes.
8. The secondary host in the life cycle of a liver fluke is a) a plant leaf. b) a snail. c) a human. d) a sheep.
9. Flukes that live on the outside of the

host's body are   a) endoparasites.
b) larvae.   c) ectoparasites.
d) bladderworms.
10. Animals without a coelom are
a) acoelomatic.   b) parapodia.
c) parasitic.   d) endoparasitic.
11. A ball of cells resulting from the repeated
cleavage of the zygote is called   a) a
gastrula.   b) a larva.   c) a coelom.
d) a blastula.
12. One common route of transmission of
worm eggs is through   a) water.
b) feces.   c) blood.   d) air.
13. Earthworms eliminate liquid wastes
through ciliated tubes called
a) clitella.   b) setae.   c) nephridia.
d) parapodia.
14. The bodies of flukes are covered with a
protective covering of   a) feces.

b) mesoderm.   c) cuticle.   d) setae.
15. A tapeworm is attached to the intestinal
wall of its host by   a) the cuticle.
b) nephridia.   c) the scolex.
d) parapodia.

Writing Critically

16. Why does the tapeworm not need an
extensive digestive system?
17. In what way are humans poor hosts for
trichina parasites?
18. Through which parts of the body does the
hookworm travel?
19. How are the body plans of flatworms,
roundworms, and segmented worms similar and how are they different?
20. Why must earthworms live in a moist
environment?

Application/Critical Thinking

1. **Inferring Relationships** The dietary
laws of some religious groups forbid
members to eat pork. What might you
expect to be the incidence of trichinosis among members of these groups who
uphold this dietary restriction?
2. **Synthesizing Conclusions** As a species
evolves over time, it becomes better
adapted. The species shows structures and
systems that help it thrive in the environments it inhabits. A tapeworm proglottid

develops male structures first and female
structures later. Why is this characteristic
of proglottids adaptive?
3. **Researching Ideas**   At one time "leech-
ing" was a common medical practice.
Write a brief report explaining when
leeches were used by doctors and why.
4. **Inferring Relationships**   People who are
infested by *Ascaris* worms frequently
develop pneumonia. Suggest an explanation for this fact.

Cross-Discipline Connection

Biology and Medicine   Do library research to
find out how leeches were used in the past to
treat diseases. For what purposes are leeches
used in modern medicine?

Discovery Through Reading

Read the article "Return of the Bloodsuckers,"
International Wildlife (September–October
1987): 44–46. What leech species is most
commonly used in medicine? Name three practical reasons why this leech, and not others, is
used. Name three diseases in which the anti-
coagulating chemicals in leeches are helpful in
treatment.

Mollusks and Echinoderms

Outline

A starfish opening a clam

Focus

The clam in the photograph is a member of the phylum Mollusca. Although a few mollusks live in fresh water or on land, most are found in salt water. Oysters, snails, slugs, scallops,˙ squid, and octopuses are also members of this phylum. The starfish belongs to the phylum Echinodermata, which includes animals that are found only in marine environments. Other echinoderms include sea urchins, sand dollars, and sea cucumbers.

- *What kind of symmetry does the starfish in the photograph show?*

- *How are many mollusks economically important to humans?*

Mollusks

The term *mollusk* means "soft." It describes the bodies of organisms in the phylum Mollusca. Besides being soft, however, the 47,000 species of mollusks differ greatly. They range in size from tiny snails 5 mm (0.2 in.) long to giant squid 20 m (66 ft.) long. Mollusks live on ocean bottoms and in fresh water, as well as on land.

Many species of mollusks are protected by one or more shells. Imprints in rock made by the shells of prehistoric mollusks remain millions of years after the animals themselves died. As a result, the fossil record of mollusks is particularly clear. The fossils indicate that some classes of mollusks existed 500 million years ago. For centuries people have used the bodies of mollusks as food, and their shells as currency, utensils, and ornaments.

32.1 Characteristics of Mollusks

Despite their diversity, all mollusks share certain characteristics that include bilateral symmetry and a true coelom. **Mollusks have three distinct body parts: the head, the foot, and the visceral mass. The soft body parts are covered by a sheet of tissue called a mantle.** The **head** contains the mouth and sensory organs. Some mollusks have a toothed organ called a **radula** (RAJ OO luh). A mollusk uses its radula to scrape off bits of plant or animal matter that the animal uses for food. The **foot** is a muscular structure that clams and some other mollusks use for burrowing into sand. In squid and related species, the head and foot become merged during development and parts of the foot appear in adults as a circle of armlike tentacles around the mouth. The **visceral mass** contains digestive, excretory, and reproductive organs. The **mantle** covers the visceral mass and secretes the shell. The space between the mantle and the visceral mass is called the *mantle cavity*. Gills that function in respiration are located in this mantle cavity in aquatic mollusks. Land forms usually have a mantle that is modified as a respiratory surface.

Many mollusks have a larva called a **trochophore** (TROK uh fawr) that has the appearance of two cones placed together at their bases with a band of cilia encircling the widest part. The free-swimming larva disperses the species, which is especially important if the adult mollusk is sessile or restricted in its movements by a heavy shell. Some annelids also have a trochophore stage. This and other similarities in development between mollusks and annelids support the hypothesis that these two groups are closely related.

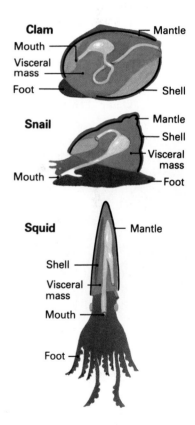

Figure 32–1. The diagram above compares the relationships among the mouth, foot, and visceral mass in three major groups of mollusks.

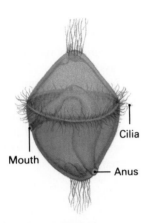

Cilia

Mouth

Anus

Figure 32–2. The larval stage of a mollusk, called a *trochophore,* is shaped like a top. The band of cilia that encircles the larva allows it to swim. This aids in the dispersal of the organism.

Figure 32–3. The siphons are clearly visible in this photograph of Florida coquinas, colorful clams that measure less than 2.5 cm (1 in.) in length.

Of the seven classes in the phylum Mollusca, the three major classes are two-shelled mollusks, such as clams, scallops, and oysters; one-shelled mollusks, such as snails; and head-footed mollusks, such as octopuses, squids, and cuttlefish.

32.2 Mollusks with Two Shells

Clams, oysters, and scallops belong to a class of mollusks that have two shells hinged together. These shells are called *valves.* The animals themselves are referred to as **bivalves.** Bivalves have a triangular, muscular foot. For this reason, the class is called *Pelecypoda* (peh luh SIHP uh duh), which means "hatchet-foot."

Clams Most clams live in the sand or mud at the sea bottom but some live in fresh water. Clams range in size from the tiny *Condylocardia* which measures 0.1 mm (0.004 in.) across to South Pacific giants that measure 1.2 m (4 ft.) across.

A clam's shells consist of three layers: a tough horny outer layer, a smooth shiny inner layer, and a middle prismatic layer made up of calcium carbonate crystals. The shells are secreted by the edges of the mantle and growth rings are often apparent on the shells. The shells are held together by ligaments. Two powerful adductor muscles function to close the shells.

Like all bivalves, clams can withdraw completely into their shells. Clams have no head and no radula. Like many slow-moving or sessile organisms, the sensory structures are poorly developed. Sensory structures along the edge of the mantle respond to light and touch. Masses of nerve cells called *ganglia* are located above the mouth and in the foot. The ganglia are connected by nerve cords.

Clams obtain both food and oxygen from the water that flows through their bodies. Clams usually remain buried in the sand with their two valves slightly open and two siphons, or tubes, projecting into the water. Water enters the clam through the **incurrent siphon.** Cilia move the water across respiratory organs, called **gills,** in the mantle cavity. Gills have a large surface area and an abundant supply of blood to allow for the exchange of gases. Water drawn into the clam by the incurrent siphon has more oxygen than the blood supply of the gills has. For this reason oxygen diffuses from the water to the blood, and carbon dioxide diffuses from the blood to the water. The clam then expels the water through the **excurrent siphon.**

Clams are *filter-feeders.* They live on microscopic organic matter carried in the water that flows through their siphons. Mucus on the gills traps the food matter, and cilia push the

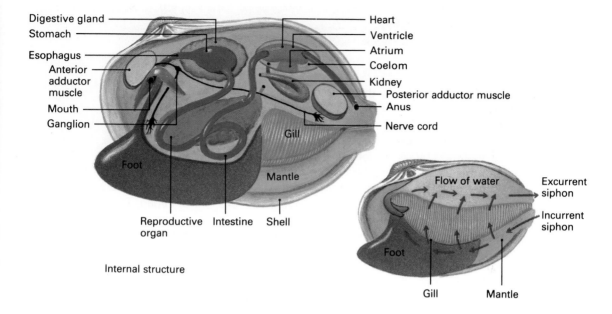

Internal structure

Digestive gland
Stomach
Esophagus
Anterior adductor muscle
Mouth
Ganglion
Foot
Reproductive organ
Intestine
Shell
Gill
Mantle

Heart
Ventricle
Atrium
Coelom
Kidney
Posterior adductor muscle
Anus
Nerve cord

Flow of water
Excurrent siphon
Incurrent siphon
Foot
Gill
Mantle

Figure 32–4. All the clam's organs are contained within its protective shell. Water is drawn across the gills (inset), which extract oxygen from the water.

food-laden mucus on to the clam's mouth. From there the food passes into the stomach. Undigested food particles leave the clam through the anus.

Clams have an *open circulatory system*. This means that the blood flows through large open spaces, or *sinuses,* rather than through a system of blood vessels. A three-chambered heart pumps the blood through the clam.

Most clam species have separate sexes. The sperm and eggs are shed into the water, where fertilization takes place. The fertilized egg becomes a trochophore larva that settles on the bottom and develops into an adult clam.

Other Bivalves   Scallops live in all oceans, mainly in shallow waters but also in ocean depths. Scallops range in diameter from 2.5 cm (1 in.) to 15 cm (6 in.). They have a fan-shaped shell that may be smooth or sculptured. Scallops may be purple, red, orange, yellow, or white. Scallops have a single large adductor muscle. When their valves are open, tentacles that rim the mantle can be seen. The scallop's eyes are also located along the edge of the mantle. One scallop may have as many as 100 eyes. Although the eyes cannot focus, they can distinguish between light and dark and can thus sense movement. Scallops propel themselves by opening and closing their valves and expelling water in bursts.

Unlike scallops, oysters cannot move about. Early in its life, an oyster permanently attaches its flat lower shell to a hard

Figure 32–5. Scallops have two rows of sightless blue eyes located at the edge of the mantle. Note the fringe of tentacles also located at the mantle's edge.

A Most Cultivated Gem

The history of pearls is filled with stories of romance and danger—stories of divers mauled by sharks and of lives shattered by the pursuit of this alluring "biological" gem. Obtaining a pearl today may be less dangerous. The cultivation of pearls allows more people to afford the gem's lustrous beauty.

Pearls suitable for commercial use grow in only a few varieties of fresh-water mollusks including some mollusks that are native to the Mississippi River. Pearls are also cultured in the commercial pearl oysters found in the warm seas of Japan, India, southeast Asia, and Mexico. These bivalves produce pearls that are suitable for commercial use.

All bivalve mollusks have the ability to secrete *nacre,* commonly called "mother-of-pearl," a material that is mostly composed of calcium carbonate. Pearls are formed when a foreign object accidentally enters a pearl-forming bivalve and lodges between the mantle and the shell. The nacre secretions gradually encapsule the object, coating it with 1,000 or more thin, lustrous layers.

The chances that a pearl will develop naturally are only about one in 40. Most pearls in today's jewelry shops are cultured pearls that have been cultivated in oysters in the South Sea

of Japan. There, technicians surgically implant a perfectly spherical piece of material, usually mollusk shell, along with a nacre-producing sac of mollusk tissue. The cultured pearl oysters are carefully stored in underwater baskets, where they are guarded against pollution, temperature changes, and thieves. After three years, about 20 percent of these oysters will have produced a cultured pearl that is virtually indistinguishable from its natural counterpart.

surface. The outer shell is rough in texture, while the inner surface of the shell is smooth and often iridescent. If an irritant such as a grain of sand enters an oyster shell, the oyster protects itself by covering the foreign matter with several layers of shell material. This process forms a pearl.

32.3 Mollusks with One Shell

The largest class of mollusks is the *Gastropoda* (gas TRAHP uh duh), a name that means "belly-footed." The 37,500 or more species include snails and slugs that live in water and on land. Most gastropods are **univalves**—that is, they have one shell. The snail's protective shell is usually coiled, which allows the long pointed visceral mass of the snail to be enclosed in a compact form. Slugs have no outer shell. Some slugs have an internal

---

Reading Critically

Inferring Relationships
What functions do shells serve in mollusks?

shell, which is actually an external shell that has been reduced and covered over by the mantle.

A characteristic of gastropods is **torsion,** or a twisting of the body, which occurs during larval development. Before torsion, the body plan of a snail is bilaterally symmetrical. One half of the body grows faster than the other, causing the anus to curve forward while the head and foot remain in place. The organs on one side of the visceral mass twist over to the other side. The mantle cavity, which originally opened to the back, now opens to the front. This arrangement of body parts allows the snail to draw its head into the shell, then plug the hole with its foot.

The nervous system of gastropods is more developed than that of bivalves. In gastropods, six pairs of ganglia are interconnected with nerve cords. Gastropods can detect light and shadows by means of eyes located at the tips of tentacles that extend from their heads. Like bivalves, gastropods have an open circulatory system. Unlike bivalves, fertilization of eggs occurs internally.

Snails

Most snails are less than 2.5 cm (1 in.) long. The Australian sea snail, however, sometimes grows a shell more than 60 cm (2 ft.) in length. On land, the largest is the giant African snail, which grows a shell 20 cm (8 in.) in length.

Snails that live in water have gills that function for oxygen exchange. They have one pair of tentacles. *Land snails respire through a network of blood vessels in the mantle.* To allow for the exchange of gases by diffusion, the mantle must be kept moist. Consequently, snails are most active at night or early morning when the air is moist. In dry weather, snails seal themselves inside their shells with a mucus plug in order to retain moisture. Some snails have a flat plate on the side of their foot called an **operculum** (oh PUHR kyoo luhm), which can be used like a trap door to close off the shell from the outside. Land snails have two pairs of tentacles.

Snails move by contracting their foot in a wavelike motion from back to front. They glide over a trail of mucus laid down by the leading edge of the foot.

Most land snails feed on plants. They scrape off bits of plant matter with their radula. Some snails feed on decaying material. Others can cause serious damage to garden plants because they feed on live plant tissues.

Slugs

Slugs can survive without shells because they live in moist environments. Like land snails, slugs that live on land respire through blood vessels in the mantle cavity. Most sea slugs respire through gills. However, some sea slugs, called

Figure 32–6. Land snails emerge from their shells only when the air is moist and warm. The eyes, located at the tips of the two tentacles, are pulled back into the tentacles when touched.

The relationship between stimulus and response in snails is the topic of the Investigation on page 513.

Biofact

Q: *How fast is a "snail's pace"?*

A: Many snails move at a speed of less than 8 cm (3 in.) per minute. This means that if a snail did not stop to rest or eat it could travel 4.8 m (0.003 mi.) per hour.

Figure 32–7. Like other nudibranchs, this golden dirona lives in shallow sea water and feeds on sea anemones.

nudibranchs (NOO duh branks), lack gills, shells, and mantle cavities. These slugs have frilly extensions on the surfaces of their bodies that may function as respiratory organs.

32.4 Head-Foot Mollusks

The class Cephalopoda (sehf uh LAHP uh duh) includes the most advanced of all mollusks—the squid, octopus, cuttlefish, and nautilus. Cephalopod means "head-foot" and reflects the fact that the head and foot of these mollusks is fused during development. The well-developed head bears a pair of complex eyes and the foot is divided into tentacles. Only the nautilus has an outer shell. In the squid and the cuttlefish, the shell is reduced in size and overgrown by the mantle. The octopus has no shell at all.

Cephalopods have a well-developed nervous system with many ganglia and a complex brain. The central mouth has jaws and a radula and is surrounded by arms or tentacles. The nautilus has over 90 tentacles, the octopus has eight, and the squid has eight tentacle-like arms and two long tentacles. Powerful suckers on the arms and tentacles of most cephalopods aid in grasping prey. Some cephalopods, such as the giant squid, have suckers that are armed with hooks.

All cephalopods are marine animals and live at all depths. Cephalopods are **predators**—that is, they kill and eat other animals, such as fishes, crabs, and bivalves.

Octopuses   The octopus is highly specialized for its predatory way of life. Because the octopus is not enclosed by an outer shell, it has great freedom to move about in search of prey. The octopus moves rapidly by jet propulsion. By forcibly contracting the muscles of its mantle and closing the mantle cavity, the octopus squirts out a jet of water through its siphon and speeds off in the opposite direction. The octopus also has special senses that help it locate prey. Its large eyes form images, but the octopus does not have stereoscopic vision. The suckers on its tentacles, more sensitive than human fingertips, contain special receptors that respond to chemicals in the water. The octopus uses its tentacles to reach into crevices for prey it cannot see.

The sexes are separate in the octopus, as they are in all cephalopods. The male octopus uses one of its tentacles, specialized for this function, to transfer sperm from its mantle cavity to the mantle cavity of the female. Later the female lays a mass of fertilized eggs encased in a gelatinous cover. The female **broods** the eggs—that is, she guards and cleans the eggs until they hatch.

Scientists have studied the behavior of the octopus extensively. By using a simple system of rewards and punishments,

Biofact

Q: *Does jet propulsion allow the octopus and the squid to move only backwards?*

A: No. The siphon with which the octopus and the squid eject water is flexible, and can be turned in any direction. This enables the animals to move quickly in any direction.

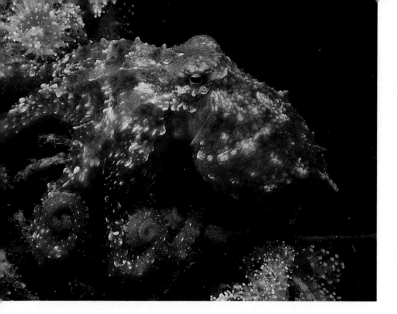

Figure 32–8. An octopus can change color in response to various stimuli.

See pages 916–917 for the classification of mollusks.

researchers have been able to condition these animals to pick up certain objects and to ignore others. An unusual aspect of the behavior of the octopus is its ability to change color. Octopuses have sacs of pink, blue, or purple pigment just below the surface of the skin. An octopus pales before a predator, making itself seem larger than it is. Against a mottled background, an octopus becomes dappled with color.

Other Cephalopods   Squid range in size from about 1.5 cm (0.6 in.) to the giant 20-meter (66 ft.) species that weighs 3,360 kg (7,410 lbs.). Squid do not use their tentacles for crawling. They move by jetting out streams of water through siphons and using two finlike extensions of the mantle cavity for steering. Squid have been studied much less than octopuses due to the difficulty of maintaining them in captivity.

The nautilus lives in the outermost chamber of a many-chambered coiled shell. A tube that runs from its visceral mass secretes a gas into all but the outermost chamber. By adjusting the amount of gas in the chambers, the nautilus can control the depth at which it floats. The cuttlefish can adjust its buoyancy in a similar fashion by controlling the amount of gas in its porous inner shell.

Figure 32–9.   Individual chambers are clearly visible in this cross-section of a chambered nautilus.

Section Review

1. **Comparing Ideas**   How is the structure of cephalopods different from other mollusks?
2. **Summarizing Functions**   How do clams feed?
3. **Inferring Relationships**   Name three features of the octopus that enable it to lead a predatory way of life.

> Thinking Critically

Section Objectives

- *List* the major characteristics of echinoderms.
- *Describe* the water-vascular system of the starfish.
- *Name* the features of the sea cucumber that are typical of echinoderms.

Echinoderms

The 6,000 living species of echinoderms (ih KY nuh durmz) include starfish, sea urchins, sand dollars, brittle stars, and sea cucumbers. Echinoderms live only in marine habitats. They are found in all oceans, both along coastal regions and at considerable depths.

The term *echinoderm* means "spiny-skinned" and refers to the spines of calcium found in these invertebrates. The spines are projections from an interior skeleton, or **endoskeleton,** that is covered by a thin layer of skin.

In their embryonic development, echinoderms more closely resemble vertebrates than they do most other invertebrates. Echinoderms are thus classified closest to the vertebrates.

Echinoderms begin life as bilaterally symmetrical creatures. However, the larva undergoes changes that result in an adult body plan that is radially symmetrical. A mature echinoderm frequently has five or more separate extensions, called arms, that are arranged around a central disc.

32.5 Starfish

Starfish range from 1 to 65 cm (0.4 to 25 in.) in diameter. Starfish, also known as sea stars, are in many ways typical echinoderms. Most species have five hollow arms, which extend from a central disc, but some species have up to 50 arms. The lower side of the arms are covered with rows of **tube feet,** which are hollow cylinders tipped with suckers. Each arm contains a pair of digestive glands and a pair of gonads.

The underside of the central disc is called the oral surface. The mouth of the starfish is located in the center of the oral surface and the stomach lies above the mouth. Starfish feed on mollusks, such as clams. The starfish first positions its body over the clam so that the mouth is over the place where the clam's shells open.

Figure 32–10. Three examples of echinoderms are (left to right) the starfish, the sea urchin, and the sand dollar.

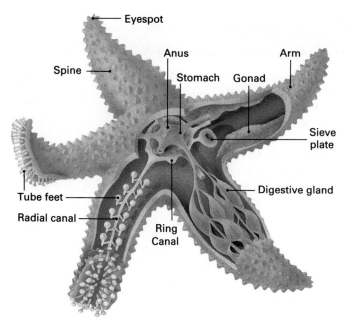

Eyespot

Anus — Arm

Spine — Stomach — Gonad

Sieve plate

Tube feet —

Radial canal —

Ring Canal

Digestive gland

Figure 32–11. The internal structures of the starfish (left) include paired digestive glands and gonads in each arm in addition to the structures of the water vascular system. The relationships of the structures in the starfish arm are shown in the cross-section (below).

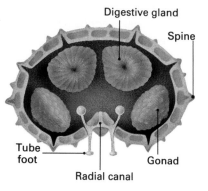

Digestive gland

Spine

Tube foot

Radial canal

Gonad

Suction from the tube feet of the starfish applies outward pressure on the two shells. Eventually, the clam's adductor muscles become tired and the clam opens. The starfish then turns its stomach inside-out and slips it into the opening. Digestive enzymes from the starfish break down the clam's soft body inside its own shell. When finished feeding, the starfish withdraws its stomach back into its own body. Starfish also feed on coral polyps and on other echinoderms.

The starfish has no brain. Its movements are coordinated by means of a nerve ring that surrounds the mouth and extends down each arm. Light-sensitive eyespots are found at the end of each arm. The starfish respires through skin gills that are protected by spines.

Starfish and other echinoderms have a unique method of locomotion. Their **water-vascular system** uses water pressure to create a "skeleton" for muscles to contract against. Water in the system flows through a *ring canal* and into *radial canals* that extend from each arm to rows of hollow tube feet. One end of each tube foot is a sucker, and the other end is a muscular sac. When the starfish contracts its sac muscles, water is forced into a tube foot. The sucker of the extended foot attaches to a surface, forcing water back into the sac at the base of the tube foot. This pulls the animal forward.

Most starfish reproduce sexually, depositing the sperm and eggs into the water. Sexes are usually separate, but a few species are hermaphroditic. The starfish may release as many as 2,500,000 eggs at one time. The females of some species brood their eggs and the young larvae.

Biofact

Q: *Are any echinoderms edible?*

A: Yes. The sea cucumber is dried and used in Chinese cooking. The sex organs of sea urchins are considered a delicacy in many parts of the world, eaten either raw or cooked.

Reading Critically

Summarizing Ideas What are two functions of the arms in starfish?

The sea cucumber has a soft cylindrical body with warty skin. This animal resembles a cucumber more than it does an echinoderm. The sea cucumber's endoskeleton is reduced to microscopic spicules. Five rows of tube feet extend from the mouth at one end to the anus at the other. The animal uses short tentacle-like tube feet around the mouth for feeding and for burrowing.

The sea cucumber has an unusual defense mecha-nism. It can expel sticky threads from its anus to entrap its enemies. When irritated, some species can even eject their internal organs and then regenerate new ones.

The pearlfish has a peculiar relationship with the sea cucumber. This fish lives inside the body of the sea cucumber, leaving only at night to feed. When it returns, it first pokes its head into the anus of the sea cucumber. Then it quickly turns so that it can

be drawn tail first into the body of the sea cucumber.

■ **Analyzing Concepts**
What kind of relationship do the pearlfish and the sea cucumber share?

Some starfish also reproduce asexually, by splitting in half and growing new parts. *The starfish has a remarkable ability to regenerate new body parts.* Most species can regenerate parts from a fragment that remains attached to a portion of the central disc. One species can grow a new body from a single arm.

For a comparison of the starfish systems to those of other invertebrates, see pages 890–893.

32.6 Other Echinoderms

Not all echinoderms have five arms, but they all show some radial characteristics. Sand dollars and sea urchins have no arms but do have five rows of tube feet. Both animals have strong jaws and the spines that are characteristic of echinoderms.

The brittle star, or serpent star has five arms that it uses to move in a snakelike manner. This animal has the ability to escape from a predator by shedding an arm.

Section Review

1. **Organizing Ideas** What structural features characterize echinoderms?
2. **Classifying Ideas** Why are sea cucumbers classified as echinoderms?
3. **Inferring Relationships** How is the water-vascular system of the starfish related to its ability to move?

Thinking Critically

INVESTIGATION 32:
How Do Snails Respond to Stimuli?

Objectives
- To *observe* snails
- To *relate* stimulus to response

Materials
land snail, flashlight, cotton swabs, filter paper, ammonium hydroxide, water, bristles from a paintbrush, forceps, pan, textbooks

Prelab Preparation
1. State characteristics that all mollusks share.
2. Explain how gastropods differ from other mollusks.
3. Predict where a snail's sense organs might be located.
4. In this Investigation, you will observe a snail's response to touch, moisture, gravity, ammonium hydroxide, and light. Make a table for recording your observations of the snail's response to each stimulus.

Inquiry: Exploration
5. **CAUTION: A land snail can be easily injured. Handle it gently and do not touch its tentacles.** Place the snail in the center of the pan. Allow a few minutes for the snail to become accustomed to the new environment.
6. Observe the snail. Describe its behavior. Identify the shell, muscular foot, tentacles, and eyes. Make a labeled drawing of the snail. After applying each stimulus described in this Investigation, allow

time for the snail to respond and then to return to its original behavior.
7. Using one clean bristle from a paintbrush, touch the shell. Then, touch the soft body parts of the foot and the area behind the tentacles. Being careful to avoid the tip where the eye is located, touch the base and middle section of a tentacle. Record your observations.
8. Consider the pan to be divided into four quadrants by imaginary lines running north–south and east–west. Place a disk of wet filter paper in the center of the northwest quadrant. Position the snail facing north in the center of the pan and observe its movements over several minutes. Return the snail to the center of the pan and repeat the test for each of the remaining quadrants. Record your observations.
9. Rest the north end of the pan on a stack of two textbooks, creating an incline. Position the snail facing north in the center of the pan. Observe the response for a few minutes. Repeat the test with the snail facing south, east, and west.
10. **CAUTION: Ammonium hydroxide can injure the skin, eyes, and nasal passages. Avoid inhaling the fumes. Wear safety goggles and rubber gloves. Avoid touching the snail with the cotton swab.** Dip a cotton swab in water and hold it near the snail's head. Dip the swab in ammonium hydroxide and hold it near the snail. Record your observations.
11. Use a flashlight to test the snail's response to light. Record your results.

Analysis
1. **Analyzing Observations** Is the snail's response to touch the same regardless of where the animal is touched? Why might this response have evolved?
2. **Analyzing Observations** How might a snail's response to moisture and gravity be of adaptive value?
3. **Making Inferences** What might be the adaptive advantage of a snail's response to light?

Chapter 32 Review

Summary

The three major classes of mollusks include the bivalves, or pelecypods; univalves, or gastropods; and head-footed mollusks, or cephalopods. Bilateral symmetry has undergone extreme modification in the body plans of snails, squids, and related species. Mollusks have three body parts: the head, the foot, and the visceral mass. A mantle secretes the shell. Most mollusks breathe by using gills.

Clams and other bivalves are filter-feeders. They take both food and oxygen out of the water that circulates through their bodies.

Gastropods include snails and slugs. Snails retreat into a coiled shell to protect themselves

and to conserve moisture. Land snails breathe by using blood vessels in their mantle cavities. Slugs have no shell or only an internal shell.

Cephalopods are predators with well-developed nervous systems. The absence or reduction of a shell contributes to the great mobility of the octopus and the squid.

Unlike mollusks, echinoderms are never found on land or in fresh water. The phylum includes starfish, sea urchins, sand dollars, and sea cucumbers. Echinoderms have an endoskeleton and a radially symmetrical body. They move by using a water-vascular system in which water pressure is controlled by muscular action.

BioTerms

bivalve (**504**)	incurrent	univalve (**506**)	water-vascular
brood (**508**)	siphon (**504**)	visceral mass (**503**)	system (**511**)
endoskeleton	mantle (**503**)		
(**510**)	operculum (**507**)		
excurrent	predator (**508**)		
siphon (**504**)	radula (**503**)		
foot (**503**)	torsion (**507**)		
gill (**504**)	trochophore (**503**)		
head (**503**)	tube foot (**510**)		

For each pair of terms, explain the differences in their meanings.

1. excurrent siphon, incurrent siphon
2. foot, tube foot
3. univalve, bivalve
4. radula, mantle

BioQuiz   (Write all answers on a separate sheet of paper.)

Completion

1. Snails excrete _____ from the front of the foot, which makes movement easier.
2. The _____ can eject its internal organs and grow new ones.
3. Clams move by burrowing into the mud with a muscular _____ .
4. Unlike other mollusks, _____ have no radula for feeding.
5. The visceral mass contains the _____ , excretory, and reproductive organs of the mollusk.

Multiple Choice

6. The _____ is the larval form of many mollusks. a) operculum b) radula c) trochophore d) mantle
7. Cuttlefish have an internal a) skeleton. b) mantle. c) shell. d) foot.
8. Squids move by a) jet propulsion. b) opening and closing their shells. c) moving their tails. d) squirting water through their tentacles.
9. The nautilus adjusts the gas in its shell chambers as a means of a) respiration.

b) movement. c) excretion.
d) reproduction.
10. _____ occurs in the larval development of gastropods. a) Torsion b) Operculation c) Gastrulation d) Radulation
11. All cephalopods are a) predators.
b) bivalves. c) broods. d) All choices are correct.
12. Starfish movements are coordinated by a) the radula. b) the mantle. c) the nerve ring. d) the tube foot.
13. Slugs survive without shells because of a) a lack of enemies. b) a powerful radula. c) a moist environment.
d) well-developed gills.
14. The respiratory organs of aquatic mollusks are in the a) foot. b) mantle cavity. c) radula. d) operculum.

15. Species of which of the following may be hermaphrodites? a) squid b) starfish c) octopus d) scallop

Writing Critically

16. What evidence is there that annelids and mollusks are closely related?
17. In what way do oysters benefit from forming pearls?
18. How is the bilaterally symmetrical body of a snail altered during its embryonic development?
19. How does a starfish feed?
20. How do land snails function without gills?

Application/Critical Thinking

1. **Identifying Relationships** Starfish are especially abundant around coral reefs. Propose an explanation for this.
2. **Inferring Conclusions** Oyster farmers once made a practice of taking all the starfish predators out of their oyster beds and chopping them into pieces. The farmers then threw the starfish pieces back into the water. Why do you think this practice was abandoned?

3. **Recognizing Relationships** How do the feeding habits of clams and other bivalves increase the risk of contamination to seagulls and humans who eat bivalves from polluted waters?
4. **Synthesizing Conclusions** At one time, slugs were found only in areas such as rain-drenched mountainsides, but now slugs have migrated into lowland gardens. What must the gardens provide to make it possible for slugs to survive there?

Cross-Discipline Connection

Biology and Economics Research the economic importance of mollusks. Focus on how mollusks can damage plants. Report on the economic impact that damage caused by mollusks could have on a small farming community?

Discovery Through Reading

Read the article "Ancient Survivor," *National Wildlife* (August–September 1988):36–39. This article describes the behavior of the chambered nautilus. For what is the nautilus named? How long has the nautilus survived on Earth? How does the nautilus swim? Where is the best place to find nautiluses? What is the average life span of a nautilus?

Thermal Vents

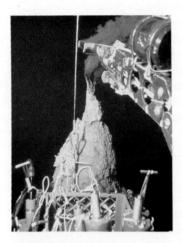

A "black smoker" releases hot water onto the ocean floor.

Imagine geysers on the ocean floor spewing hot, black "smoke" into the surrounding water. Imagine mounds formed by deposits of silica, where slender tube worms, clams, and a host of other organisms form an ecosystem in the darkness of the ocean. This science-fiction landscape actually exists as *hydrothermal vents* and the areas around them on the ocean floor. Such an incredible undersea environment provides homes for unusual organisms, some of them extinct on the rest of the planet since the Mesozoic and even the Paleozoic eras.

Hydrothermal vents occur at midoceanic ridges. These ridges are the source of much of the Earth's crust, three-quarters of which forms the deep ocean floors. These ridges mark spreading centers on the ocean floor that are the result of volcanic activity far below. Deep beneath the ridges lie magma chambers of molten, volcanic rock. Sea water seeping through the porous new crust to the volcanic rock below becomes heated and picks up abundant minerals along the way. Thermal vents, or "hot springs" in the shape of plumes, form when the heated water escapes onto the ocean floor.

Thermal vents include very hot (350° to 400° C), mineral-laden "black smokers" and cooler "white smokers." Areas

These tube worms thrive near thermal vents.

of diffuse venting, where the hot water escapes through fissures and faults in the sea floor, are found near the smokers.

The existence at these sites of organisms that were thought to be extinct may help scientists reconstruct the evolution of life on Earth. The astonishing creatures at the vents thrive in the dark, 3.2 km (2 mi.) below the surface. They survive on sulfur-oxidizing bacteria and are independent of photosynthesis. These

Marine researchers can now study life in unusual environments.

remarkable animals include types of clams, crabs, shrimps, mussels, and worms that existed at least 200 million years ago.

Scientists are studying how these animals tolerate the extreme heat and the toxic effects of chemicals that are found in large quantities around the vents. In addition, researchers are looking at the adaptations of these animals by comparing them to their deep-sea and shallow-water relatives.

The task of probing the faults near the vents (above) is aided by diving equipment such as Alvin (below).

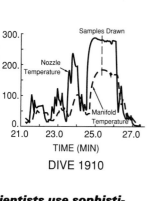

Scientists use sophisticated equipment that allows them to chart water temperatures near the thermal vents.

517

Overview of Arthropods

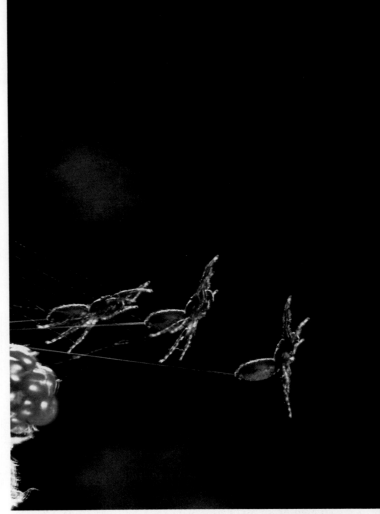

A male jumping spider leaping from a bramble berry

Focus

Arthropods are one of the Earth's most successful groups in terms of numbers of species and adaptability. Arthropods include such members as spiders, insects, lobsters, crabs, and centipedes. Some arthropods live in water environments and others live on land. More than 85 percent of all known animal species are arthropods. Some fossil arthropods are over 550 million years old.

- *Most animals have not adapted to life in urban areas. Which arthropods have adapted well to urban life?*

- *What connection is there between the word arthropod and the word arthritis?*

The Phylum Arthropoda

About 1 million species of arthropods have been identified. Scientists estimate, however, that as many as 10 million species of arthropods may live on Earth. The great success of arthropods is due in part to their body structure. Their large population is also due to their extreme diversity in form, feeding habits, and patterns of behavior.

Section Objectives

- *Name* three major characteristics of arthropods.
- *State* the advantages and disadvantages of the exoskeleton.
- *Name* the five major classes of arthropods and give an example of each.

33.1 Characteristics

The phylum name *Arthropoda* (ahr THRAHP uh duh) means "jointed leg." Legs or other movable extensions of the body are called **appendages.** *Arthropods are characterized by having jointed appendages, a segmented body, and an outer skeleton.*

Most of the jointed appendages of arthropods function for movement. Some, however, are specially modified for other functions, such as grabbing prey or injecting poison.

The number of body regions of arthropods varies. Insects, for example, have three body regions; spiders have two. The arthropod's body is covered by a skeleton that is external to the body. This type of skeleton is called an **exoskeleton.** The exoskeleton is secreted by the outer layer of cells and is made of protein and a carbohydrate called **chitin** (KYT uhn). The exoskeleton is composed of three layers. The waxy outer layer is waterproof; it keeps out water while retaining body fluids. The hard middle layer protects the organism. The inner layer, flexible at the joints, allows the animal to move freely.

Though an exoskeleton provides a flexible armorlike protection, it has two major disadvantages. First, the exoskeleton does not grow with the animal, but must be shed and replaced periodically. This process is called **molting.** During a molt the animal faces two dangers—attack from predators and drying out before the new skeleton forms. Many arthropods hide in cool places during molting.

A second disadvantage of an exoskeleton is its weight. On a large land animal, an exoskeleton would be very heavy. Most arthropods, therefore, are small and move with ease. Arthropods move by contracting muscles that are attached to the inside of the exoskeleton. In spite of the hard exoskeleton, arthropods are capable of a wide variety of movements.

Arthropods have well-developed circulatory and nervous systems. The arthropod's heart is a long dorsal tube. The circulatory system is open—that is, blood bathes the animal's cells and tissues and is not always contained in vessels. The nervous

Figure 33–1. A cricket sheds its old skeleton in a process called molting. A special layer of cells secretes a new exoskeleton.

system consists of two chains of nerves that run along the ventral side of the organism. A ganglion located above the esophagus serves as the brain.

33.2 Classification

The five major classes of arthropods are Insecta, Arachnida (uh RAK nihd uh), Crustacea (kruhs TAY shee uh), Diplopoda (dih PLAHP uh duh), and Chilopoda (ky LAHP uh duh). The largest of these classes is Insecta, the insects. This important group is discussed separately in Chapter 34.

The class Arachnida consists of spiders, scorpions, ticks, and mites. Class Crustacea is made up of crayfish, lobsters, crabs, and related organisms. Millipedes form the class Diplopoda, and centipedes, Chilopoda. Millipedes and centipedes are often collectively called **myriapods** (MIHR ee uh pahdz).

Section Review

1. **Listing Ideas**   What are three characteristics of arthropods?
2. **Classifying Ideas**   What are the five major classes of arthropods?
3. **Evaluating Function**   What is the function of the exoskeleton?

Arachnids

Section Objectives

- *Name* the major body parts of arachnids.
- *Describe* how spiders hunt and feed.
- *Describe* how spiders make and use web silk.
- *Name* the distinguishing characteristics of scorpions, ticks, and mites.

The 57,000 species of arachnids include spiders, scorpions, ticks, and mites. These organisms are found in most land areas of the world. Arachnids range in size from mites 0.1 mm (0.004 in.) long to a species of African scorpion 18 cm (7 in.) long.

Arachnids typically have two body regions and eight legs. The head and the *thorax,* the chest area, are fused to form the **cephalothorax** (sehf uh luh THAWR aks). The second region, the **abdomen,** contains most of the organs. The arachnids' eight legs are attached to the cephalothorax.

Arachnids also have two other pairs of appendages that are attached to the cephalothorax called the **chelicerae** (kuh LIHS uh ree), which bear clawlike fangs with poison glands at their base. The chelicerae are used to inject poison into prey. The other pair of appendages, called **pedipalps,** (PEHD ih palps), aid in feeding and also serve as sensory organs. Arachnids may have up to 12 **simple eyes.** These eyes can detect light but are not structured to form images. The jumping spider can detect motion at 10 to 20 cm (4 to 8 in.).

33.3 Spiders

Spiders, the most familiar arachnids, are among the world's most fascinating animals. Although some people shy away from spiders, few of the 30,000 species are harmful to humans. Spiders actually contribute to human welfare by eating insect pests.

The largest known land spider is the "bird-eating" spider from South America; it is 8.75 cm (3.5 in.) long and has a leg span of 25 cm (10 in.). The smallest type of spider lives in Samoa and measures only 0.04 cm (0.02 in.) long.

Respiration and Senses Oxygen is carried through the spider's body in two unusual ways. One way is through tubes called **tracheae** (TRAY kee ee), which carry air directly to the cells. The tubes receive air through slits in the exoskeleton called **spiracles** (SPY ruh kulz). The opening and closing of the spiracles regulates air flow.

In the second method of respiration, blood circulates through structures called **book lungs,** so named because they contain sheets of tissue that resemble the pages of a book. Book lungs are located near the front of the abdomen. Oxygen in the air that enters through the spiracles diffuses through the book lungs.

Some spiders have either tracheae or book lungs, but most species have both. These structures are unique to arthropods.

Figure 33–2. Spiders are the best known arachnids. They have four pairs of legs, unlike insects which have only three pairs.

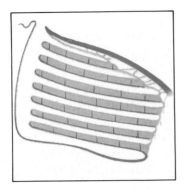

Figure 33–3. The diagram on the right shows the major body parts of the spider. The detail (above) is of the spider's book lungs.

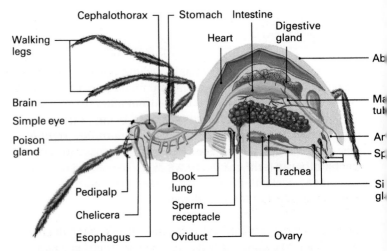

Cephalothorax — Stomach   Intestine
                                    Digestive
Walking   Heart   gland
legs
                                                        Ab
Brain   Ma
                                                        tul
Simple eye
                                                        Ar
Poison   Sp
gland
                         Book   Trachea
                         lung   Si
          Pedipalp   gl
                         Sperm
          Chelicera   receptacle
          Esophagus   Oviduct   Ovary

Reading Critically

Inferring Conclusions
Why do you think a spider would react before it is touched by an enemy?

Biofact

Q: *Why don't spiders get trapped in their own webs?*

A: Spiders can spin different kinds of threads. Dry threads are used to form the radial framework of the web. The sticky threads that trap victims are arranged in a spiral formation around the radial threads. Spiders walk only on the nonsticky threads.

However, the structures serve the same purpose as gills and other respiratory structures—they provide a large surface area over which oxygen can diffuse into cells.

Most spiders have eight eyes arranged in two rows at the top of the cephalothorax. Spiders also have hairs called **sensory setae** all over their bodies, but especially on the legs. The setae detect pressure and movement.

Feeding and Reproduction   All spiders are skillful hunters. Some catch prey by chasing and catching it or jumping on it. Many others trap prey with "trap doors" built into the ground or catch it in webs.

Webs are formed when short, fingerlike organs called **spinnerets** release a substance formed in *silk glands*. This substance is a strong, elastic protein that hardens on contact with air. Once the prey lands in a web, a spider captures it by wrapping the prey with silk.

Not all spiders make webs for trapping prey. Web silk is also used to build nurseries for the young, to line nests, and to hold sperm or eggs during reproduction. Baby spiders may even leave the nest by letting out a tiny strand of silk that acts like a parachute. The wind blows the baby spiders away by the hundreds. This form of travel is called *ballooning.*

Spiders feed by injecting enzymes into their prey to dissolve the body substances. The spiders then suck out and swallow the liquified remains. **Malpighian** (mal PIHG ee uhn) **tubules** found near the base of the abdomen form the excretory system of the spider. The Malpighian tubules remove excess nitrogen, a by-product of metabolism, from the blood. Spiders also have waste-removing organs on the first and third pairs of legs.

Like most arthropods, spiders are either male or female. A male spider approaches a female with caution. Since spiders are habitually solitary animals, a female might mistake a male suitor for potential prey. For this reason many species engage in complex courtship rituals, such as tapping on the web or stroking the female.

Having captured the attention of the female, the male puts sperm on his pedipalps and places it into her genital opening on the underside of the abdomen. Eggs, laid in special webs or cocoons, hatch in about two weeks.

Figure 33–4. A scorpion uses its huge pedipalps like pincers to capture and hold prey. It then injects the prey with poison from its long stinger.

33.4 Scorpions

Scorpions have two distinctive features. Their greatly enlarged pedipalps are held in a forward position, and they have an abdomen that ends in a tapered stinger. Scorpions are most common in tropical areas and deserts. The 800 known species range in length from 1.3 to 17.6 cm (0.5 to 7 in.).

Scorpions hide under rocks and in crevices by day and are active mainly at night. They feed on insects and spiders. A scorpion catches and holds its prey in its pedipalps. Then it curls its stinging abdomen over the top of its body and injects poison into the prey.

33.5 Ticks and Mites

Ticks and mites are tiny animals, usually less than 1 mm (0.04 in.) long. Scientists have identified over 30,000 species, but they estimate that there may be as many as 500,000. *Ticks and mites differ from other arachnids in that the cephalothorax and abdomen are fused to form a single body part.*

Although many ticks and mites are free-living, most are parasites. Ticks attach themselves to an animal's skin and suck blood. Many ticks carry disease-causing organisms that are transmitted to other animals through the tick's bite. Many humans have mites living in their hair follicles. The mites feed on bacteria and are so small that they often go unnoticed.

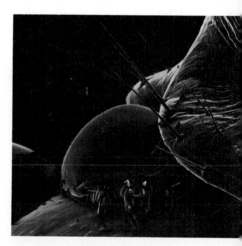

Figure 33–5. This scanning electron micrograph shows a mite that lives on a termite magnified 1,750 times.

Section Review

1. **Analyzing Data** What characteristics distinguish arachnids from other arthropods?
2. **Summarizing Ideas** How do spiders feed?
3. **Comparing Ideas** How do scorpions and ticks differ from spiders?
4. **Evaluating Function** What is the function of silk in spiders?

> **Thinking Critically**

Section Objectives

- *State* how crustaceans differ from arachnids.
- *List* the functions of the crayfish's appendages.
- *Describe* the compound eye and its advantages over the simple eye.
- *Summarize* the process of molting.

Crustaceans

The 25,000 species that make up the class Crustacea include crayfish, lobsters, crabs, shrimps, pill bugs, sow bugs, water fleas, and barnacles. Most crustaceans are small—one type of water flea measures only 0.25 mm (0.01 in.) long. The Japanese spider crab, on the other hand, has limbs that extend 3.6 m (12 ft.) or more. Almost all crustaceans live in the sea, although a few species live in fresh water or on land.

Crustaceans have chewing jaws. The jaws, called **mandibles,** are absent in arachnids. The crayfish, sometimes called a crawdad, is representative of a group of crustaceans that also includes lobsters, crabs, and shrimps.

33.6 Crayfish

Crayfish are freshwater animals that live at the bottoms of lakes and streams. Crayfish and related saltwater crustaceans are important sources of food in many areas.

As Figure 33–7 shows, the body of a crayfish is divided into two main parts—a cephalothorax and an abdomen. The cephalothorax consists of thirteen segments and is covered by a protective shield of exoskeleton called a **carapace.** The abdomen is made up of six segments.

Each crayfish segment has a pair of appendages. The first segment has two small, antenna-like structures called **antennules** that maintain balance and are sensitive to taste and touch. Behind the antennules are another pair of sense organs called **antennae,** which may be as long as the body of the crayfish. Behind the antennae lie the mandibles, which chew and crush food. Behind the mandibles are two pairs of **maxillae.** The first pair holds food. The other pair, which look like flat shovels, scoop water over the gills. These are the *gill bailers*.

The first pair of appendages on the thorax part of the cephalothorax are the **maxillipeds,** or jaw feet. The maxillipeds taste and hold food while it is being chewed. The next pair of appendages, the **chelipeds** (KEE luh pehdz), are large claws. They grab food and also protect the crayfish against enemies. Each of the last four segments of the cephalothorax has a pair of **walking legs** that are used for locomotion.

Five pairs of **swimmerets** located on the first five segments of the abdomen are used in swimming. The next pair of appendages has become fused and is used as a flipper, called a **uropod** (YOOR uh pahd). The **telson** is the middle part of the tail. By flipping the telson forward, the crayfish can move backwards.

Figure 33–6. Bottom-dwelling crayfish are most active at night or early morning. They feed on other freshwater animals, such as snails, tadpoles, and small insects.

Reading Critically

Analyzing Conclusions
How do crayfish protect themselves against enemies?

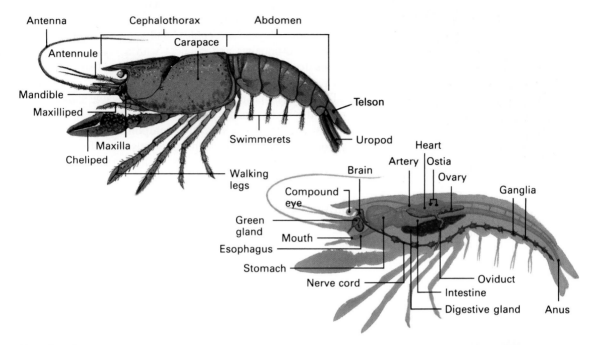

Antenna, Cephalothorax, Abdomen, Carapace, Antennule, Mandible, Maxilliped, Maxilla, Cheliped, Walking legs, Swimmerets, Telson, Uropod, Compound eye, Green gland, Mouth, Esophagus, Stomach, Brain, Nerve cord, Artery, Heart, Ostia, Ovary, Ganglia, Oviduct, Intestine, Digestive gland, Anus

Figure 33–7. This diagram shows the external and internal structures of a crayfish.

Respiration   The crayfish removes oxygen from the water by means of its gills. The featherlike gills contain a high concentration of blood vessels. The gills are attached to the walking legs, between the thorax and the carapace. As the animal walks, water flows over the gills. When the crayfish is not moving, the gill bailers move water over the gills.

Circulation   Crayfish, like spiders, have an open circulatory system. Blood enters the heart through three pairs of pores called **ostia.** Valves seal off the ostia, the heart contracts, and blood is forced into seven large arteries. These arteries then discharge blood into the spaces surrounding the organs. The blood drains out of these spaces and collects in a cavity called the *sternal sinus.* From there, blood travels through other vessels to the gills. Blood returning from the gills enters the *pericardial sinus* and then returns to the heart through the ostia.

Digestion and Excretion   Crayfish eat living and dead plants, worms, larvae, and tadpoles. Food moves from the mouth down the esophagus to the stomach, where it is ground by teeth of chitin. Undigested wastes move through the intestine and leave the body through the anus. Excretory organs called **green glands** are located at the base of the antennae. The green glands remove liquid wastes from the blood.

Biofact

Q: *Can crustaceans climb trees?*

A: Not most crustaceans. But *Bingus latro,* also known as the "robber crab," can. This crab lives on South Pacific islands and climbs coconut palms in search of food. It uses its pincers to cut the nut from the tree and to open the husk.

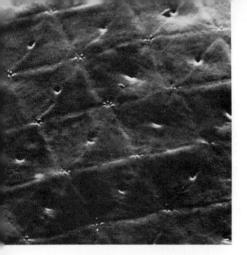

Figure 33–8. The scanning electron micrograph magnifies a part of the compound eye of a lobster 550 times. The eye is made up of over 2,500 lenses.

Figure 33–9. The Sally Lightfoot crab lives along the rocky shores of the Galapagos Islands off the coast of Ecuador.

Thinking Critically

Nervous System   The nervous system of crayfish consists of a dorsal brain formed from a pair of ganglia. Branches from the brain run to the eyes, antennules, and antennae. Other nerves encircle the esophagus and connect with a ventral nerve cord that runs the length of the body. Each of the crayfish's segments has a pair of ganglia.

The crayfish has two eyes located on movable stalks on the front of the body. Each eye has over 2,500 lenses. Eyes that have more than one lens are called **compound eyes.** Compound eyes form images by combining the sensations from multiple lenses. Such eyes respond rapidly to light and readily detect motion. Arthropods are the only animals with compound eyes.

Reproduction and Growth   Crayfish mate in the spring or fall. The male deposits sperm into the female, who stores it. About two weeks later, the female produces 200 to 300 eggs. They are then fertilized by the stored sperm and hatch in six weeks. The fertilized eggs are attached to the last three pairs of swimmerets of the female until they hatch.

Crayfish molt twice a year. Molting begins when the outer layer of body cells digests the inner layer of the exoskeleton, weakening it. The crayfish swells by absorbing water and taking in excess air. This causes the exoskeleton to crack, and the crayfish backs out. The outer body cell layer secretes salts that harden the new, developing exoskeleton.

33.7 Other Crustaceans

Lobsters, crabs, and shrimp closely resemble crayfish. Lobsters are much larger than crayfish. Crabs have a short, wide body. The abdomen is curled under the thorax, and the carapace forms a single, large shell over all the body segments. Shrimp typically have semitransparent bodies and long, whiplike antennae.

Pill bugs and sow bugs, called *isopods,* are common in gardens. Their exoskeletons are segmented, allowing them to roll into a tight ball when threatened. Water fleas are tiny organisms often seen twisting and turning in a drop of pond water.

Section Review

1. **Comparing Data**   Compare crustaceans and arachnids.
2. **Analyzing Information**   Describe a compound eye and state its advantages over a simple eye.
3. **Evaluating Function**   What is the function of maxillipeds and mandibles?
4. **Evaluating Ideas**   Why are crabs classified as crustaceans?

Myriapods

About 11,000 myriapod species have been identified. The name *myriapod* means "many feet." Both centipedes and millipedes have numerous legs with which they scurry over the ground. All myriapods have a head and numerous body segments. The head and thorax are not fused as in arachnids and some crustaceans. Like crustaceans, myriapods have mandibles.

Myriapods respire by means of tracheae. The openings to these tracheae do not close, which can result in loss of body fluids. In addition, the body of myriapods lacks a waxy outer layer that retains moisture. For these reasons, myriapods must live in moist environments.

33.8 Centipedes

Although the name *centipede* means "100 legs," not all centipedes have that many. Some, like the common house centipede, have only about 15 pairs of legs. On the other hand, *Himantarum gabrelis* of southern Europe has 177 pairs of legs. Some centipedes are as long as 33 cm (13 in.). Others, however, measure as little as 0.47 cm (0.18 in.) in length.

Centipedes have flattened bodies and one pair of legs per body segment. Every segment of the body has a pair of legs except the first segment, which has poisonous claws. These claws inject poison to kill prey, mainly insects and worms. Most centipedes have simple eyes, one pair of antennae, one pair of mandibles, and two pairs of maxillae. Liquid wastes are excreted through Malpighian tubules.

Centipedes live in such moist places as forest floors or tropical jungles. During mating centipedes undergo an elaborate courtship ritual that involves mutual caressing of the antennae. In most species the young have fewer segments than the adults and pass through several growth stages.

33.9 Millipedes

Like centipedes, millipedes have a pair of simple eyes, a pair of antennae, mandibles, and maxillae. *Millipedes differ from centipedes by having a rounded body and two pairs of legs per body segment.* The word *millipede* means "1,000 legs." The most legs ever recorded for a millipede, however, is 710. The largest millipede measures about 27.5 cm (11 in.) in length.

Millipedes feed mainly on decayed plants. These myriapods live in the tropics or in temperate areas under cool and wet

Figure 33–10. A centipede (top) has one pair of legs per body segment; a millipede (bottom) has two pairs per segment.

Spider Attack

Spiders will attack small prey but usually flee from larger animals such as humans. Even when they attack humans, the venom of most spiders is not fatal.

A spider delivers venom through two spinelike fangs connected to venom sacs in the spider's head. When the fangs puncture the victim's shell or skin, venom is squeezed through the fangs into the wound. The puncture wounds of many spiders are scarcely noticeable. However, the large fangs of spiders like the North American wolf spiders and tarantulas can cause pain similar to a bee sting.

The most dangerous spiders in North America are the brown recluse and the black widow spiders. The brown recluse is native to the midwestern United States and, as its name suggests, lives in dark corners. Most recluse spider attacks occur when a person puts on clothing in which the spider is hiding. The venom causes a black, gangrenous wound that is difficult to treat.

The black widow spider causes about eight deaths in the United States annually, usually among chil-dren. This spider is commonly shiny and black, with a red-orange spot that looks like an hourglass on the underside of the abdomen. Only the females are dangerous to humans. They will attack when provoked.

conditions. Millipedes avoid bright sun, and many dig burrows in which they escape high temperatures and dry conditions.

Millipedes defend themselves by rolling into a ball. Many millipedes also excrete a foul-smelling and often toxic substance from *stink glands*.

Section Review

1. **Comparing Ideas** Compare myriapod and arachnid body structures.
2. **Analyzing Ideas** Compare the bodies of millipedes and centipedes.
3. **Identifying Relationships** How do the feeding habits of millipedes and centipedes differ?

Thinking Critically

4. **Inferring Conclusions** How does a millipede defend itself when attacked?

INVESTIGATION 33:
Can Sow Bugs Detect Differences in Moisture and pH?

Objectives
- To *observe* a crustacean
- To *identify* a sow bug's response to pH differences in the environment

Materials

pan, sow bugs, ruler, dilute sodium hydroxide solution, vinegar, paper towels, three filter paper disks, pH test paper and color analysis scale

Prelab Preparation
1. Name the class of arthropods to which sow bugs belong.
2. Compare sow bugs with other arthropods.
3. List major arthropod sense organs and tell where they are located.
4. Define pH and state the pH values that represent acidic, alkaline, and neutral solutions.
5. Make a table similar to the one shown.

Time	Sow Bugs per Quadrant			
	A	B	C	D
0.5 min				
1.0 min				
1.5 min				
2.0 min				
2.5 min				
3.0 min				
3.5 min				
4.0 min				

Inquiry: Observation
6. Use a ruler and a pencil to mark a paper towel into four equal quadrants. Label the quadrants A, B, C, and D. Then in the center of the paper towel, draw a circle about 8 cm in diameter. Place the paper towel on top of five paper towels and place the stack in a clean pan.

7. Place 10 sow bugs in the center of the circle. Observe their responses over a period of four minutes, recording the number of sow bugs present in each quadrant after each 30-second interval. Repeat the test for two more trials.
8. **CAUTION: Acidic and alkaline solutions can injure the skin and eyes. Use goggles and rubber gloves. Thoroughly wash any area that has been contaminated by these solutions.** Use small strips of pH paper and the color analysis scale to find the pH of the water, the vinegar, and the sodium hydroxide solution. Record your results.
9. Soak a disk of filter paper with water, place it in the middle of one quadrant, and repeat step 7.
10. Soak a fresh disk of filter paper with vinegar and another with dilute sodium hydroxide. Place each disk in a separate quadrant of the paper towel.
11. Repeat step 7.
12. Return the sow bugs to the storage container and carefully clean your area.

Analysis
1. **Comparing Observations** Compare the behavior of sow bugs when placed on clean dry paper with the behavior of sow bugs when a water-soaked disk was placed in one quadrant.
2. **Analyzing Observations** Are sow bugs attracted directly to moisture, or do they move randomly until moisture is encountered? Explain how your observations support your answer.
3. **Evaluating Methods** Why was it necessary to first observe the sow bugs on a dry paper towel?
4. **Analyzing Observations** How did the sow bugs respond to differences in pH?
5. **Making Inferences** How does a sow bug's response to moisture and pH increase its chance of survival?
6. **Making Predictions** Predict a sow bug's response to light. Explain the reasons for your prediction.

Chapter 33 Review

Summary

Arthropods are invertebrates that have jointed appendages, segmented bodies, and exoskeletons. They shed and regenerate the exoskeleton by molting. The five principal classes of arthropods are Insecta, Arachnida, Crustacea, Chilopoda, and Diplopoda.

Arachnids include spiders, scorpions, ticks, and mites. Arachnids typically have two body segments, a cephalothorax and an abdomen. Spiders have four pairs of legs. They also have two clawlike chelicerae and two chewing pedipalps. Scorpions have an abdomen that ends in a stinger. Ticks and mites are small.

Crustaceans are mostly saltwater arthropods and have mandibles for chewing. Each body segment of the freshwater crayfish has a pair of specialized appendages.

Centipedes and millipedes are myriapods. Centipedes are characterized by one pair of legs per body segment; millipedes have two pairs. Centipedes are meat eaters; millipedes mostly eat decayed plants.

BioTerms

abdomen (521)	exoskeleton (519)	simple eye (521)	telson (524)
antenna (524)	green gland (525)	spinneret (522)	trachea (521)
antennule (524)	Malpighian	spiracle (521)	uropod (524)
appendage (519)	tubule (522)	swimmeret (524)	walking leg (524)
book lung (521)	mandible (524)		
carapace (524)	maxilla (524)		
cephalothorax (521)	maxilliped (524)		
chelicera (521)	molting (519)		
cheliped (524)	myriapod (520)		
chitin (519)	ostia (525)		
compound	pedipalp (521)		
eye (526)	sensory seta (522)		

For each pair of terms, explain the differences in their meanings.

1. trachea, spiracle
2. cephalothorax, abdomen
3. chelicera, pedipalp
4. maxilla, maxilliped

BioQuiz   (Write all answers on a separate sheet of paper.)

Completion

1. The _____ of spiders release protein from which the spiders spin their webs.
2. Air enters the trachea of a spider through slits in the exoskeleton called _____ .
3. Crustaceans differ from arachnids in that they have _____ .
4. Mites and ticks are both characterized by the fusion of the _____ and the cephalothorax.
5. Millipedes have _____ pairs of legs per body segment.

Multiple Choice

6. The _____ covers the cephalothorax in crustaceans. a) uropod b) carapace c) myriapod d) cheliped
7. _____ remove wastes from a spider's blood. a) Malpighian tubules b) Trachea c) Mandibles d) Chelicera
8. Crayfish are able to move backwards with the aid of a) walking legs. b) the telson. c) the uropod. d) the pedipalps.

9. Which of the following is a characteristic of arthropods? a) jointed appendages b) segmented body c) an outer skeleton d) All choices are correct.

10. Why is a crayfish not an arachnid? a) It has more than eight legs. b) Each segment has a pair of appendages. c) It has antennae.   d) All choices are correct.

11. Blood enters the heart of a crayfish through the a) ostia. b) book lungs. c) spinnerets. d) spiracles.

12. How are ticks and mites different from other arachnids?   a) They are larger. b) They are hermaphroditic.   c) The abdomen and cephalothorax are fused. d) They have no eyes.

13. Millipedes defend themselves by using their a) stink glands.   b) spinnerets.

c) green glands. d) maxilla.

14. The shedding of the exoskeleton is called a) excretion. b) molting. c) reproduction. d) digestion.

15. Unlike arachnids, crustaceans have a) tracheae. b) chitin. c) abdomens. d) mandibles.

Writing Critically

16. What is the function of each layer of the exoskeleton?
17. How is an exoskeleton an adaptation for arthropod survival?
18. For what functions do spiders spin silk?
19. How do tracheae differ from lungs and gills in oxygen distribution?
20. How does molting occur in the crayfish?

Application/Critical Thinking

1. **Collecting Data** Keep a record for a week of all spiders or evidences of spiders in your home or neighborhood. Research and identify if possible the species observed. If you fail to observe any spiders, write a report suggesting why that was so.

2. **Inferring Relationships** Krill are tiny marine crustaceans that are an important source of food for some of the largest animals on Earth. Use your school or public library to prepare a short report on krill. Explain how a reduction in their population would affect other animal life.

3. **Reporting Information** Write and illustrate a report on the hunting methods of spiders. Include the wolf spider, the trap door spider, and the bird-eating spider.

4. **Inferring Conclusions** What advantage might a compound eye have over a simple eye for animals such as crayfish?

Cross-Discipline Connection

Biology and Language Arts   Look up definitions for the prefixes *pod–/pode–, ped–/* *pedi–/pede–, di–/diplo–/, myria–, cent–*, and *milli–*. Write two words with each prefix.

Discovery Through Reading

The article "Lobster Love," *National Wildlife* (April–May 1987):18–21, describes mating behavior in lobsters. How does a lobster detect scents? Where are the chemoreceptors located? Name two characteristics of lobster behavior.

In lobsters, females are the aggressors when it comes to mating. What kind of male lobster does a female usually pursue? What must happen to the shell of a female lobster before mating can occur?

Insects

Honeybees on a hive

Focus

There are more than 750,000 species of insects. Insects can be considered the most successful of all animal groups in the ways in which they have adapted. Insects also play roles that are of tremendous economic and medical importance to humans. For example, honeybees and other insects pollinate plants; chewing insects destroy food, clothing, and housing; ladybugs feed on aphids that destroy garden plants; and some mosquitoes carry pathogens.

■ *What kinds of plants might disappear if pollinating species of insects disappeared?*

■ *What characteristics of insects makes some of them well suited for transmitting pathogens to humans?*

Overview of Insects

Almost three-quarters of all animal species on Earth are insects. Although insects are not found in salt water, they live in almost every freshwater and land habitat. The great diversity of insects extends also to size. Insects range from the fairy fly, only 0.2 mm (0.008 in.) long, to the African Goliath beetle, over 10 cm (4 in.) long. Insects are the only invertebrates that can fly.

The evolutionary success of insects is due in part to the characteristic structure they share with other arthropods—exoskeletons, segmented bodies, and jointed appendages. A key to their success is that most insects are small and have adapted to specific habitats. In many cases this allows multiple species of insects to exist in a small area without competing with one another for scarce resources. Their ability to fly has also added to their evolutionary success.

Insects are both harmful and beneficial to human society. Only about 1 percent of insect species are destructive to crops and property. Nevertheless, this small group causes several billion dollars of damage each year in the United States alone. Harmful insects include household pests, such as termites; crop and livestock pests, such as boll weevils; and hosts of disease-causing organisms, such as mosquitoes infected with parasitic protozoa.

Many insects, on the other hand, are beneficial to human society. Insects pollinate fruit trees, flowers, and many field crops. Bees produce honey and beeswax, silkworms form cocoons from which silk is spun, and lac insects provide the raw material for commercial shellac. Some kinds of insects are natural enemies of destructive insects. For example, the larvae of certain wasps feed on caterpillars that destroy plants.

34.1 Characteristics

All insects share certain characteristics. *Unlike other arthropods, insects have three distinct body regions and three pairs of legs.* The three body regions of an insect are a head, a thorax, and an abdomen.

On the head are antennae, compound eyes, and mouthparts. An insect's mouthparts are modified for different methods of feeding. Butterflies have mouthparts shaped like coiled tubes, which they uncoil and use to suck nectar from deep within flowers. A praying mantis tears its food apart with mandibles. Flies have no mandibles and therefore lap up food with a tonguelike lower lip.

Section Objectives

- *State* reasons for the evolutionary success of insects.
- *Discuss* the importance of insects to human society.
- *Distinguish* insects from other arthropods.
- *Identify* three feeding methods of insects and the modified mouthpart used.
- *Identify* eight insect orders and give an example of each order.

Chewing

Sucking

Lapping

Figure 34–1. Modified mouthparts of insects allow different feeding methods. A grasshopper (top) chews its food; a butterfly (center) sucks nectar from flowers; a fly (bottom) laps up food.

Condo-Eating Termites

A hard-to-control termite is spreading throughout the southeastern United States. Originally from China, the termite is called *Captotermes formosus* and is commonly called the Formosan termite. The pest is also found in Hawaii and parts of Asia. In these native habitats, these termites often form giant subterranean colonies that may occupy an entire acre of land.

Members of this species have become known as "condo eaters" because they have become pests in areas where condo-

miniums have been built in the last few years. The Formosan termite, however, does not restrict its activities to condominiums. They also invade older buildings. More than half of the older high-rise buildings along Waikiki Beach are infested with these termites. In China and Japan, Formosan termites have demolished numerous buildings that had historic significance.

Once established in an area, Formosan termites are almost impossible to eradicate. Conventional pest control methods are

often ineffective.

Fortunately, Formosan termites do not spread easily from area to area. The insect is a poor flyer and isolated groups are easy prey for predators such as fire ants. The termites are commonly transported from one location to another in loads of infested wood or soil.

Reading Critically

Analyzing Information How can you tell at a glance if an arthropod is an insect?

Three pairs of legs and any wings the insect has are attached to the thorax. The legs are usually adapted for jumping, walking, or running.

The abdomen may have as many as eleven segments. The abdomen houses the heart, the respiratory and excretory organs, and the spiracles through which the insect breathes. In respiration, tracheae carry air to body cells. All insects have an open circulatory system, through which blood flows into large open spaces surrounding the organs.

34.2 Classification

Scientists who study insects are called **entomologists.** Entomologists have grouped insects into more than 30 orders. Classification is based primarily on the number and type of wings the insect has. Eight important orders are shown in Table 34–1. Others are listed on pages 871–872.

Table 34–1: Insect Orders and Characteristics

Order		Examples	Characteristics
Orthoptera ("straight-winged")		Grasshoppers, crickets	Two pairs of straight wings; legs modified for jumping
Isoptera ("equal-winged")		Termites	Two pairs of similar wings that are shed after mating
Hemiptera ("half-winged")		True bugs, squash bugs	Two pairs of membranous wings overlap to form a "V" over abdomen
Homoptera ("uniformly winged")		Cicadas, aphids, scale insects	One or two pairs of membranous wings roof over the body when at rest (some species are wingless); mouthparts adapted for piercing-sucking; feed on plants
Diptera ("two-winged")		Flies, gnats, mosquitoes	One pair of membranous wings; mouthparts adapted for lapping or piercing-sucking
Lepidoptera ("scale-winged")		Butterflies, moths	Two pairs of wings; body and wings covered with scales
Coleoptera ("shield-winged")		Beetles (includes fireflies, ladybugs)	Two pairs of wings; hard forewings join to form a straight line down the back
Hymenoptera ("membrane-winged")		Ants, bees, wasps	Two pairs of membranous wings; chewing mouthparts; social insect

Section Review

1. **Analyzing Ideas**   How do insects benefit humans?
2. **Analyzing Ideas**   How do insect orders differ from each other and from other arthropod classes?
3. **Evaluating Function**   How are a butterfly's mouthparts adapted to feeding?
4. **Synthesizing Ideas**   Based on the information in Table 34–1, what characteristic appears to determine classification?

⟨ **Thinking Critically** ⟩

Grasshoppers are familiar insects found in almost all parts of the world. Because grasshoppers share many features with other species, they are often studied as representative insects.

Grasshoppers belong to the order Orthoptera. Most are large insects, averaging 7.5 cm (3 in.) in length. Common North American species range in color from green to olive or brown, making them hard to see amidst the grasses and plants on which they feed. Some orthopteran species are known as locusts. Locusts often move in large masses called **swarms** that migrate from place to place, destroying crops along their way.

34.3 External Structure

Like all insects, a grasshopper has three main body parts—the head, thorax, and abdomen. The grasshopper's mouthparts are modified for chewing. A grasshopper feeds by holding a blade of grass in its upper lip, called the **labrum.** The mandibles, or primary jaws, chew the food. The maxillae, or secondary jaws, help hold and tear the food. The lower lip, called the **labium,** is located behind the maxillae. The function of the labium is to press food against the jaws.

Figure 34–2. The external structure of the grasshopper shows the three-part division characteristic of all insects. Less typical are the strong back legs that propel the grasshopper into the air for long distances.

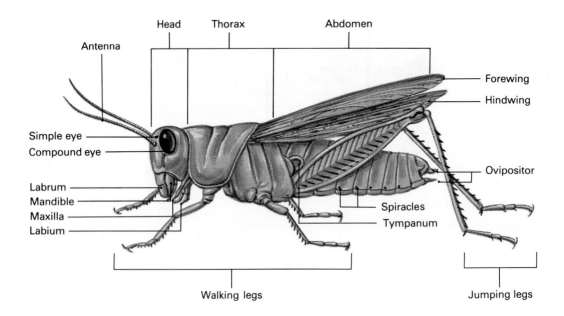

The grasshopper has two large compound eyes and three simple eyes. Between the compound eyes are a pair of antennae, which have highly sensitive receptors for smell.

The grasshopper's thorax is divided into three segments. A protective shield covers the first segment, the **prothorax.** The *forewings* are attached to the second segment, the **mesothorax.** The *hindwings* are attached to the third segment, the **metathorax.** Both pairs of wings are used in flight. The narrow, stiff forewings cover and protect the transparent, membranous hindwings. Hindwings fold up when they are not in use.

Each segment of the thorax has a pair of legs attached. The first and second pairs are modified for walking, and the hindlegs, for jumping. Each leg has five segments. The *coxa* attaches the leg to the thorax. The short *trochanter* connects the coxa to the *femur,* which houses the large leg muscles. The *tibia* is the lower part of the leg, which ends in a segmented, grasping foot called the *tarsus.*

The grasshopper's abdomen consists of 10 segments. The eardrums, thin flexible membranes called **tympanums,** are located near the front of the abdomen. In some species the tympanums are found at the posterior end of the thorax.

Figure 34–3. The grasshopper's mouthparts are derived from ancestral legs. The segmented character of legs is most clearly evident in the maxillae and labium, which hold and tear food.

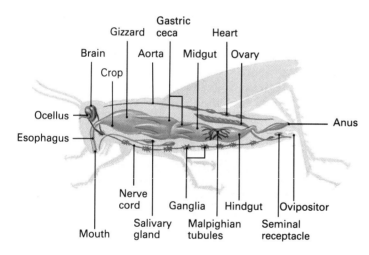

Figure 34–4. This diagram of the internal structure of a grasshopper shows its reproductive, digestive, and nervous systems. Activity increases the flow of blood through the insect's circulatory system.

34.4 Internal Structure

An insect's organ systems differ in some significant ways from the systems of other animals. As you read about the internal structure of a grasshopper, locate its major organs in Figure 34–4. Pairs of spiracles are found on the second and third segments of the thorax and on the first eight segments of the grasshopper's abdomen. As the flexible abdomen expands, air enters the spiracles and moves into the tracheae. The tracheae then

Reading Critically

Evaluating Information Why do grasshoppers excrete nitrogenous wastes as dry uric acid crystals?

transport air throughout the body, allowing the oxygen to diffuse directly into the tissues. When the grasshopper's abdomen contracts, the waste gases are forced out of the insect's body through the spiracles.

Food passes from the mouth to the crop. There the food is stored and moistened with saliva from **salivary glands.** Moistened food moves to the gizzard, where it is ground by teeth of chitin. Food then enters the insect's stomach, called the **midgut.** It is digested by enzymes secreted by pockets of the stomach called **gastric ceca** (SEE cah). Undigested food enters the intestine, called the **hindgut,** and leaves through the anus.

The grasshopper's heart is found in the dorsal part of the abdomen. The heart pumps blood through a large vessel, called an **aorta,** into the body cavity. There the blood bathes the organs, then reenters the heart through large pores called *ostia.*

Wastes are removed from blood by Malpighian tubules attached to the hindgut. These organs send nitrogenous wastes into the hindgut. From there, the wastes leave the body through the anus. Grasshoppers have an important adaptation that helps conserve the insect's bodily fluids; nitrogenous wastes are excreted as nearly dry uric acid crystals.

Like all arthropods, the grasshopper has a brain that consists of two ganglia located in the head. Two nerve cords run from the brain down the ventral side of the body. These cords connect a pair of ganglia in every segment. Nerve branches run from the ganglia to all parts of the body. Because grasshoppers have ganglia in every segment, a grasshopper can continue functioning for some time if its head is cut off.

Grasshoppers are either male or female. The reproductive organs of both sexes are located in the upper adbomen. During the mating season in early summer or fall, the male deposits sperm into a storage pouch in the female, called a *seminal receptacle.* When eggs are produced, they are fertilized by the stored sperm. The female then uses a pair of pointed organs called **ovipositors** to dig a hole in the ground and to deposit the eggs. The eggs hatch the next spring.

Section Review

1. **Comprehending Ideas** Name the structures attached to each thorax part of the grasshopper.
2. **Evaluating Conclusions** Describe grasshopper respiration.
3. **Inferring Conclusions** What is the advantage of the female grasshopper burying her eggs in the ground?

Thinking Critically

Insect Development

Only a few wingless insects, such as silverfish, emerge from the egg as miniature versions of their parents. *Most young insects differ in appearance, movement, and feeding habits from the adult insects they become.* The series of molts and profound changes that transform the immature form into the adult insect is termed a **metamorphosis.** Metamorphosis is governed by the action of *hormones,* or chemicals secreted by the insect's body.

34.5 Incomplete Metamorphosis

Some insects, such as grasshoppers and lice, go through a gradual transition from egg to adult called *incomplete metamorphosis.* In this type of development, the insect that emerges from the egg is called a *nymph.* The nymph is a smaller version of the adult insect of its species, similar in structure but without wings or mature reproductive organs.

34.6 Complete Metamorphosis

Most insects, including butterflies, beetles, ants, bees, and flies, go through a *complete metamorphosis.* This kind of development involves four stages: egg, larva, pupa, and adult.

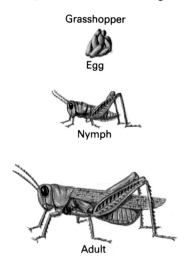

Silverfish

Butterfly
Egg
Larva
Pupa
Adult

Figure 34–5. Insects differ in their development. The grasshopper exhibits incomplete metamorphosis. The butterfly, as most insects, exhibits complete metamorphosis. Others such as silverfish do not change in form after hatching.

Grasshopper
Egg
Nymph
Adult

Adult

Dramatic changes transform a caterpillar into a butterfly. These changes result from the interaction of three hormones: brain hormone; molting hormone, also called *ecdysone;* and juvenile hormone.

Eating and growing are the major activities of a caterpillar. As the caterpillar grows, cells in the brain periodically secrete brain hormone into the blood. This hormone triggers the release of ecdysone from a gland in the thorax. The ecdysone

in turn causes the caterpillar to molt, or shed its outer covering to accommodate its larger size. A caterpillar may molt many times as it progresses through the larval stage.

Metamorphosis is actually a molt that produces not a larger larval form but an adult insect. Ecdysone controls this molt also, but its action is regulated by the presence of juvenile hormone. As long as juvenile hormone is present in sufficient quantity, ecdysone does

not trigger metamorphosis.

The insect reduces its production of juvenile hormone as it nears the end of the larval stage of development. When the amount of juvenile hormone is sufficiently reduced, ecdysone triggers the start of the pupal stage. The pupa forms a protective covering, the **chrysalis,** from which it will emerge as a butterfly.

■ **Inferring Conclusions** If the level of juvenile hormone remains high, what will happen to the caterpillar?

Biofact

Q: *Do any insects ever develop from unfertilized eggs?*

A: Yes. Aphids and gall wasps are two insects that can produce young without the benefit of fertilization by a process called *parthenogenesis.* In this process, the aphid produces a great number of eggs that develop even though they have not been fertilized.

When the egg of an insect hatches, an immature form called a *larva* emerges. The larva looks nothing like the adult. Larvae, like nymphs, cannot yet fly. Some larvae feed on different kinds of food than the adults do. The fact that adults and their young do not compete with each other for food is a key advantage of complete metamorphosis.

When the larval stage is complete, the insect enters an inactive stage called the **pupa.** Many pupae form a covering around themselves called a **cocoon.** For a period of several months, the pupa lies still and does not feed while larval tissues and organs are replaced with new tissues and organs. At the end of the pupal stage, a fully formed, sexually mature adult insect emerges.

Section Review

1. **Summarizing Ideas**   What is metamorphosis and of what advantage is it?
2. **Organizing Information**   What are the developmental stages of a grasshopper?
3. **Comparing Ideas**   Compare a nymph and a larva.
4. **Inferring Relationships**   What causes a caterpillar to begin the pupal stage?

Thinking Critically

Insect Behavior

All insects, whether they live singly or in groups, need to communicate and to defend themselves. Different kinds of insects accomplish these tasks in different ways. Part of the job of an entomologist, then, is to learn about the individual and collective behavior of insects.

34.7 Social Insects

Social insects live in communities and engage in a *division of labor*. In other words, individuals perform different tasks necessary for the survival of the group. Termites, ants, and some bees and wasps are social insects. Insect societies are probably the most complex of all nonhuman societies.

A termite colony may have over a million individuals. The most numerous kind are the workers, which collect food and build and repair the nest. Soldiers defend the colony against attack. They have large heads and powerful jaws. The only duty of the queen and king is to produce young.

All ant colonies have one or more queens, reproductive males, and female workers. Army ants that live above ground form an unusual society. When the food supply dwindles, the entire colony swarms out in search of a new home, chewing down everything in its way.

The most widely studied insect society is that of the honeybee. One of the 30,000 to 40,000 bees is the queen. A few are males, or drones. The vast majority are female workers. The queen is the only reproductive female in the hive. She flies from the hive only once. During this flight she collects enough sperm from drones of nearby hives to last throughout her five- to seven-year life of laying eggs. The sperm are stored in a special organ and released one at a time. In the springtime the queen lays unfertilized eggs, which develop into drones.

The only function of a drone is to inseminate the queen. In the fall, when the food supply dwindles, the workers usually drive the drones out of the hive or sting them to death.

The workers develop from fertilized eggs deposited in the waxy cells of the hive. Adult workers feed the developing bees until the larvae pupate and emerge as new adults. The first job of the worker is to feed the queen, drones, and larvae. After about a week of this work, she begins to excrete wax, which is used to build and repair the hive. In the final stage of her life, the worker helps forage for food. Her entire life cycle lasts about six weeks.

Section Objectives

- *Describe* the social structure in a honeybee hive.
- *List* three ways in which insects communicate.
- *Name* the major defense methods used by insects.
- *Compare* chemical control and biological control of insects.

Biofact

Q: *Are any bees solitary?*

A: Yes. Over 85 percent of all bees are solitary; they do not live in hives. Many crops, like alfalfa, are pollinated entirely by solitary bees.

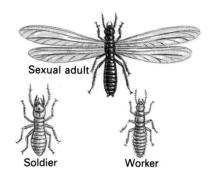

Sexual adult

Soldier   Worker

Fig. 34–6. Termite classes can be identified by their body structures. The king and queen shed their wings after mating. Workers and soldiers are wingless.

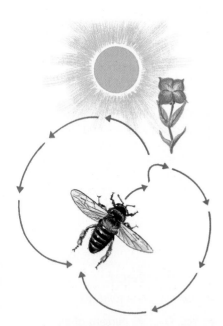

34.8 Communication

Both social and solitary insects need to communicate about food sources, predators, and possible mates. *Insects communicate through chemicals, visual signals, and motions.*

The most common means of communication is chemical. **Pheromones** are chemicals that influence the behavior of other insects. For example, the queen bee, on her flight from the hive, secretes a pheromone that attracts drones. Ants secrete pheromones that mark a trail from the nest to a food source. Only other members of the ant's own colony recognize the trail.

Fireflies communicate during the mating season by flashing a light. The female of each species emits a special series of flashes that males of her species recognize. Other insects communicate by tapping, rubbing, or stroking each other. Sometimes these are part of an elaborate courtship ritual.

Perhaps the most complex of all forms of insect communication is the dance of the honeybee. When a forager bee finds a source of nectar, she returns to the hive and does a "waggle dance." The dance lets other bees know where the food is.

Does all of this mean that insects "talk" to each other, using chemicals and light and signals instead of words? Research has shown that insects do not communicate as people do. For example, when an ant dies, it excretes a certain chemical that tells other ants to carry it out of the nest. If a live ant is painted with this chemical, its fellow ants will drag it out of the nest as it struggles. The ant will be dragged out of the nest again and again even though it is obviously not dead.

Fig. 34–7. A scout bee indicates the location of food by waggling her abdomen while running forward, then circling. The orientation of the run to the vertical hive symbolizes the direction to the food source. The number of turns indicates the distance from the hive.

34.9 Defense

Almost all insects will flee when threatened. Many insects, however, have more specialized means of defense. Roaches and stink-bugs, for example, secrete foul-smelling chemicals that deter aggressors. Bees, wasps, and some ants have poisonous stings that can kill smaller predators and cause pain for larger ones. The larvae of some insects have hairs filled with poison. If a predator eats one of these larvae, it may suffer a toxic reaction. Insects that defend themselves by unpleasant or dangerous chemicals gain two advantages. On one hand, they often deter a predator from eating them. On the other, predators learn not to bother them in the first place.

Other insects gain protection by **mimicry,** or similarity of appearance. In one kind of mimicry, insects with similar defense mechanisms look alike, and predators learn to avoid them all. Bees and wasps mimic each other in this way. In another

Fig. 34–8. The yellow jacket wasp (left) stings its foes. Similar color patterns protect its mimic, the stingless syrphid fly (right).

Because some insects can be destructive, the growth of their population must be controlled. **Insecticides,** chemicals that kill insects, are effective, but they have several drawbacks. One important consideration is that these deadly chemicals accumulate in the environment where they may harm other organisms.

For this reason, scientists have developed *biological controls,* or ways of controlling insect populations without the use of insecticides. These include such methods as controlling the entry of insect pests into an area, developing plants that are resistant to insect pests, and using the natural enemies of these pests.

For example, ladybugs were imported from Australia in 1888 to control the cottony scale insect that was devastating the California citrus groves. Pheromones are often used to lure insects into a trap. A small amount will attract insects from several kilometers away.

Sterilizing male insects is another way of eliminating insect pests. The screw-worm fly, for example, causes great financial losses to ranchers by laying its eggs in the open sores of livestock. The maggots that hatch then feed on the wounds, enlarging them.

Scientists raise screw-worm flies and subject the pupae to radiation. The sterile flies that emerge are then "dumped" into an area to mate with the local flies. The resulting eggs do not hatch, and in time the fertile flies die out.

■ **Comparing Ideas** How does biological control of insects differ from insecticides?

kind of mimicry, insects with no defenses of their own mimic the appearance of stinging or bad-tasting insects. Predators avoid the mimic as well as the insect with the unpleasant taste or sting. For example, syrphid flies look like bees but do not sting.

Another kind of defense based on appearance is **camouflage,** or the ability to blend into surroundings. Many kinds of insects and animals have distinctive color markings that make them difficult to see. Predators have trouble locating prey that looks like its background. An insect is more likely to survive and produce offspring if it is camouflaged than if it is not.

Reading Critically

Relating Ideas Name some examples of insects that use camouflage as a defense.

Section Review

1. **Analyzing Ideas** What is the role of the queen bee?
2. **Listing Ideas** Give examples of insect communication.
3. **Identifying Relationships** How does mimicry help mimic insects survive?
4. **Inferring Conclusions** What drawback of chemical insecticides is eliminated by the use of phermones for insect control?

Thinking Critically

Pesticides: Weighing the Options

Since World War II, farmers have depended on chemical pesticides to protect their crops from destruction by insect pests. The result has been an increase in crop yields and unblemished fruits and vegetables. However, widespread use of pesticides has exposed farmers and farm animals to high concentrations of chemicals. In addition, some pesticides may be ingested by humans when they eat produce. Exposure and ingestion of these chemicals may increase health risks.

Consumers in the United States depend on federally controlled inspection to insure safety of their food supply. However, inspection methods can detect only about 40 of the 500 pesticides that are likely to leave residues on fruits and vegetables.

In addition to possible health risks, the use of chemical pesticides puts farmers on a treadmill of increased use, rising costs, and reduced effectiveness. Initially, pesticides can be extremely effective in destroying pests. However, the pests that survive contact with a pesticide will pass this genetic resistance to new generations. New poisons must then be developed, and the cycle repeats itself. There are currently more than 17 known pest species that are immune to all known pesticides, and scientists warn that by the year 2000, all existing pesticides may be ineffective.

Alternatives to chemical pesticide use include biological controls. One method of biological control involves introducing insects and microorganisms that destroy pests into areas where crops are grown. Other alternatives include growing genetically engineered crops that are hardy and can resist insect pests.

Farmers are confronted with numerous problems when making decisions about the use of pesticides and other methods of pest control. For example, the use of biological controls often requires time-consuming training in new technologies. Furthermore, the produce may not have the unblemished appearance often seen in crops on which pesticides have been used

and thus may not be readily accepted by consumers.

Analyze the Issue

1. What are the risks and benefits of using chemicals in farming?

2. How do insect pest populations become resistant to chemical pesticides?

3. What problems would a farmer who decided to use biological controls be likely to confront?

4. How might consumers encourage the use of fewer chemicals to control insect pests?

INVESTIGATION 34:
Do Plants Produce Natural Insecticides?

Objectives
- To *evaluate* the effectiveness of a naturally occurring insecticide
- To *analyze* data

Materials
four culture vials; 0.01 percent, 0.1 percent, and 1.0 percent caffeine solutions; nonether anesthesia; *Drosophila melanogaster* (fruit flies); stereomicroscope; instant *Drosophila* medium; four test tubes; wax marking pencil

Prelab Preparation
1. Define the term insecticide.
2. Explain how the study of natural insecticides might help scientists develop synthetic insecticides that are environmentally safe.
3. Coffee, tea, and cacao plants are extremely resistant to insects. What substance found in these three plants might account for this resistance?
4. List the stages of insect development.
5. Do you think that an insecticide affects all stages of development equally? Explain your reasoning.
6. In this Investigation, you will evaluate the effectiveness of caffeine as an insecticide. After discussing the problem with your partner, state a hypothesis that relates to this problem and explain your reasoning.
7. Make a data table similar to the one shown below.

Day	Percent Caffeine			
	0	0.01	0.1	1.0
0				
1				
2				
3				
5				
9				
15				
20				

Inquiry: Experimentation
8. Prepare one culture vial of instant *Drosophila* medium according to the instructions on the package. Label this vial "0."
9. Prepare a second culture vial of instant *Drosophila* medium, substituting the 0.01 percent caffeine solution for water. Label this vial "0.01."
10. Repeat step 9 to produce two more culture vials using 0.1 percent and 1.0 percent caffeine solutions. Label the vials "0.1" and "1.0," respectively.
11. Allow the vials to stand until all the excess liquid has been absorbed.
12. Name the dependent and independent variables in this experiment. *Why are several different concentrations of caffeine used?*
13. Add six male and six female fruit flies to each of the four vials, following your teacher's directions. Record the number of live flies present in each vial on day 0.
14. Observe the vials on day 1 and record the number of live flies in each vial. Describe any evidence of the presence of larvae in the vials.
15. Repeat step 14 on days 2, 3, 5, and 9.
16. At least 10 days are required for the development of adults from newly laid eggs. After making your observations on Day 9, anesthetize any remaining adults according to your teacher's instructions and remove the adults from the vials.
17. Repeat step 14 for day 15 and day 20.

Analysis
1. **Evaluating Methods** Did you test your hypothesis through controlled experimentation? Explain your reasoning.
2. **Summarizing Data** Summarize the data collected in this experiment.
3. **Analyzing Data** Does caffeine affect adults and larvae equally? Explain your answer.
4. **Analyzing Data** Do the data support your hypothesis? Explain your answer.

Chapter 34 Review

Summary

There are over 750,000 different species of insects. They differ from other arthropods in having three pairs of legs and three main body parts—a head, a thorax, and an abdomen. Insects are the only arthropods that fly.

The grasshopper, a representative insect, has legs modified for jumping and two pairs of wings. It uses spiracles and tracheae to breathe. The female uses an ovipositor at the end of her abdomen to deposit her eggs.

Most insects go through complete metamorphosis—a four-stage development from egg to larva to pupa to adult. The immature insects do not resemble the adults. Species that

go through incomplete metamorphosis emerge from the egg as juveniles that resemble the adult.

Termites, ants, and some bees are social insects that live in large groups and engage in a division of labor. Honeybee hives consist of workers, drones, and a queen.

Many kinds of insects communicate with each other using flashes of light, motions, or chemicals called pheromones. Honeybees do a complex "waggle dance." Insects defend themselves by stinging or poisoning aggressors, mimicking other insects, and camouflaging themselves.

BioTerms

aorta (538)
camouflage (543)
chrysalis (540)
cocoon (540)
entomologist (534)
gastric ceca (538)
hindgut (538)
insecticide (543)
labium (536)

labrum (536)
mesothorax (537)
metamorphosis (539)
metathorax (537)
midgut (538)
mimicry (542)
ovipositor (538)
pheromone (542)
prothorax (537)

pupa (540)
salivary gland (538)

swarm (536)
tympanum (537)

For each pair of terms, explain the differences in their meanings.

1. labrum, labium
2. prothorax, metathorax
3. midgut, hindgut
4. pupa, cocoon

BioQuiz   (Write all answers on a separate sheet of paper.)

Completion

1. The female grasshopper deposits fertilized eggs with an _____ .
2. Food is ground up by chitinous teeth in an insect's _____ .
3. A grasshopper uses its _____ to hold food it is feeding on.
4. Undigested food enters the _____ of the grasshopper and leaves through the anus.
5. Metamorphosis is controlled by _____ that are secreted by the insect during development.

Multiple Choice

6. The _____ is a wingless, immature version of the adult grasshopper. a) larva b) pupa c) nymph d) chrysalis
7. Insects have _____ pairs of legs. a) two b) three c) four d) six
8. Entomologists study a) crustaceans. b) insects. c) metamorphosis. d) cephalapods.
9. Each of the grasshopper legs has _____ parts. a) two b) three c) four d) five

10. Enzymes from the grasshopper's _____ digest food. a) gastric cecae b) midgut c) ovipositor d) prothorax
11. Worker bees indicate the location of food by a) crawling. b) spitting. c) emitting a foul odor. d) dancing.
12. Male grasshoppers deposit sperm into the female's a) ovipositors. b) midgut. c) seminal receptacle. d) labium.
13. A fly that resembles a stinging wasp is an example of a) mimicry. b) a swarm. c) pheromones. d) metamorphosis.
14. Which of the following is not located on the head of a grasshopper? a) maxilla b) spiracles c) labrum d) simple eye

15. Which of the following does not undergo any metamorphosis? a) grasshopper b) butterfly c) silverfish d) bees

16. Why are bees said to engage in a division of labor?
17. How do chemical control and biological control of insects differ?
18. Is insect communication like human communication? Explain.
19. Is it beneficial for a bee to have a mimic? Why or why not?
20. How can the idea of natural selection help explain camouflage?

Application/Critical Thinking

1. **Summarizing Information** Report to the class on the variety of sounds that insects make. Explain how flies and bees hum, crickets chirp, cicadas sing, and June beetles buzz.
2. **Inferring Relationships** Many beekeepers have threatened to close their hives if "killer bees" arrive in the United States. Beekeepers do not wish to deal with these aggressive bees. In addition to raising the cost of honey and beeswax, what other effects do you think the closing of the hives might have?
3. **Synthesizing Ideas** The flashing of fire flies is a complex form of communication. Its primary function is to allow the insects to find mates of their own species. In some female fireflies, flashing has additional functions. Research the flashing patterns of *Photuris versicolor* and write a report explaining how females of this species use their flashing other than to attract mates.
4. **Analyzing Information** The exoskeleton of insects restricts the size of these animals. In addition, the manner in which insects respire through tracheal tubes may restrict size. Explain why the system of tracheae may not be effective in a large animal.

Cross-Discipline Connection

Biology and Economics Do library research to find information about three industries that make use of products that are produced by insects.

Discovery Through Reading

"The Hidden Strength of Gossamer Wings," *National Wildlife* (Aug–Sep 1988):4–11, describes some of the incredible adaptations of butterflies. What is the range of size of butterflies?

Read the article "Life as a Leaf," *International Wildlife* (March–April 1989):18–21. This illustrated article describes insect mimicry. Describe two types of katydid mimicry.

Summary

Animals may be asymmetrical or show spherical, radial, or bilateral symmetry. They can also develop from two or three embryonic layers and be grouped on the basis of whether they are invertebrates or vertebrates. Sponges are filter feeders with a simple, two-layered body plan. Coelenterates are radially symmetrical and include hydras, jellyfish, and corals. Both sponges and coelenterates include solitary and colonial forms.

Members of the phylum Platyhelminthes, flatworms, are bilateral organisms that develop from three embryonic layers. Flatworms include both free-living hydras and parasitic flukes and tapeworms. Roundworms also include both free-living and parasitic forms, such as the trichina worm and *Ascaris*. Segmented worms, such as the earthworm, have a true coelom and their body systems are more complex than those of other worms. Segmented worms also include forms that live in salt water.

In addition to having bilateral symmetry and a true coelom, all mollusks have a head, a foot, and a visceral mass that is covered with a mantle that secretes the shell. Mollusks are two-shelled, such as clams; one-shelled, such as snails; and shell-less, such as squids and octopuses.

The Echinoderms are the most advanced invertebrates and include starfish, sand dollars, and sea cucumbers. Most adult echinoderms show a five-part radial symmetry. Some have a water vascular system that functions in locomotion and feeding.

Arthropods are animals that have jointed appendages, a segmented body, and an outer skeleton. Most arthropods live in water. Insects, the most successful terrestrial arthropods, have six legs, a three-part body, and many have wings. Many insects carry human diseases; some destroy food crops and wood and thus compete with humans for food and shelter. Arachnids have eight legs and include spiders, mites, and ticks. Crustaceans have mandibles and most live in salt water. Many crustaceans provide humans with food. Centipedes have one pair of legs on each segment and millepedes have two pairs of legs on each segment.

Synthesis

Synthesis Statement

The diversity of organisms reflects the amazing number of ways in which different groups of organisms have adapted. Each kind of animal has changed over time in response to its requirements for food and space. The adaptations and body plans that different animals show have each been successful for those groups of animals that have avoided extinction. In addition, the different groups of living things show dynamic relationships to each other. These relationships result in an ever-changing web of life.

Synthesis Questions

Apply your understanding of this unit to the following questions.

1. What adaptations do insects show that make them the most successful of all land-dwelling invertebrates?

2. List the ways that invertebrates solve the problem of support without a backbone. List some ways in which the absence of a backbone limits invertebrates.

3. What is the advantage of cephalization and how is cephalization related to an animal's symmetry?

4. What kind of lifestyle is associated with the radial symmetry of coelentrates?

5. Unlike photosynthetic plants, animals are heterotrophs and must gather food from their surrounding environment. Describe the ways in which the need to obtain food has influenced body plan design among the invertebrates.

6. Discuss the structures and behaviors that invertebrates show that allow them to avoid being eaten by predators. Compare the defensive mechanisms of sessile invertebrates to those of mobile invertebrates.

7. Discuss the advantages of a closed circulatory system. What are some limits imposed by an open circulatory system?

8. Annelids, mollusks, echinoderms, and arthropods have true coeloms. Explain why the coelom allows these invertebrates to be larger and more complex than acoelomate invertebrates.

9. Compare the methods of respiration and excretion found among each invertebrate group and relate these methods to the environments in which each group is found.

10. Compare the nerve net of the hydra to the nervous system of an insect. Discuss the ways in which the organization of nervous tissue affects the way each organism responds to its environment.

11. Use a separate piece of paper to draw a concept map like the one below. Place each of the following terms in the appropriate figure: unsegmented, mollusks, arthropods, segmented, roundworms, coelenterates, and sponges.

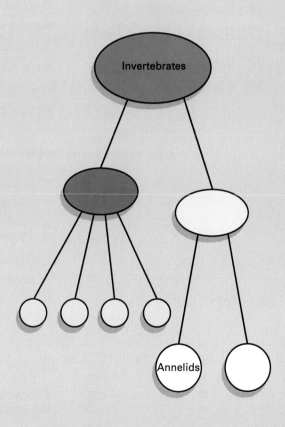

UNIT

9

VERTEBRATES

Unit Focus

Fishes spend all of their lives in water. Amphibians must return to the water to reproduce. The other vertebrates — reptiles, birds, and mammals — show adaptations that have allowed them to successfully inhabit land environments. Land vertebrates can be found almost everywhere including deserts, forests, and fields. The vertebrate group includes the only animals, except insects, that can fly.

■ *What adaptations allow vertebrates their tremendous success in land environments?*

■ *What advantages and disadvantages does living on land, and not in water, have for an animal?*

Penguins are adapted to a life both in and out of the water.

550

Fishes

Outline

Surgeonfish swimming near a coral reef

Focus

All fishes belong to the phylum Chordata. Like reptiles, amphibians, birds, and mammals, fishes have backbones. There are three classes of fishes. One class contains jawless fishes. A second class contains jawed fishes that have cartilage skeletons. Members of the third class have jaws and a bony skeleton.

■ *How would your life be different if there were no fishes in the world?*

■ *Some species of fishes travel in schools. How do fishes benefit from this kind of behavior?*

Chordates and Vertebrates

The 43,000 chordate species are the most recent products of evolution and the most complex of all animals. The chordates are amazingly diverse. They have adapted to life on land, in water, and in the air. They range in size from the tiny humming-bird to the giant blue whale, which is the largest animal ever to have lived on earth.

The vertebrates, animals with backbones, make up the largest subphylum within the phylum Chordata. The majority of the animals most familiar to you—sparrows and elephants, goldfish and human beings—are vertebrates.

Section Objectives

- *List* four characteristics of chordates.
- *Name* the seven living classes of vertebrates and give an example of each.
- *State* the major characteristics of vertebrates.
- *Name* the 10 organ systems of vertebrates and give the function of each.

35.1 Characteristics of Chordates

Despite their variety, all chordates share certain traits. *At some time during their life cycles, all chordates possess four distinctive structures: a notochord, a nerve cord, gill slits, and a tail.* The **notochord** is a long, firm rod that extends along the back of the animal's body. In vertebrates the notochord is present in the embryo and is later replaced by a backbone. The hollow, tubular **nerve cord** runs the dorsal length of the animal, just above the notochord. In most chordates the anterior end of this nerve cord becomes a brain. Paired openings in the throat region are called **gill slits.** In fish the gill slits serve a respiratory function. In more complex vertebrates, the gill slits have become modified for other uses. Finally, most adult chordates possess a **tail**, which is made of blocks of muscle tissue surrounding the posterior end of the animal's skeleton.

35.2 Classification of Chordates

In addition to the vertebrates, the phylum Chordata includes two other minor subphyla. Members of the subphylum Urochordata (YOOR uh kawr DAHD uh) are called *tunicates,* or *sea squirts.* Except for their gill slits, tunicates show little resemblance to other chordates. These cylinder-shaped animals attach themselves to underwater rocks, reefs, and ocean floors. The third subphylum, the Cephalochordata (SEF uh loh kawr DAHD uh), includes the lancelet, a thin, fishlike animal that lives in warm, shallow ocean waters. As Figure 35–1 shows, the lancelet retains all four chordate characteristics throughout its life. Members of the subphyla Urochordata and Cephalochordata are known as the *lower chordates.* The more complex species of the subphylum Vertebrata are called the *higher chordates.*

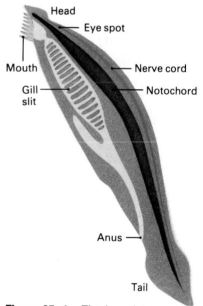

Figure 35–1. The lancelet exhibits all four chordate characteristics: notochord, nerve cord, gill slits, and tail.

Head — Eye spot — Nerve cord — Notochord — Mouth — Gill slit — Anus — Tail

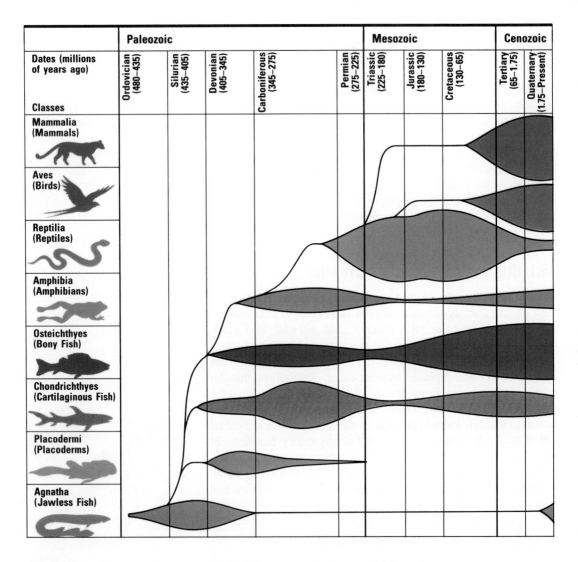

The table in the figure shows the following structure:

Dates (millions of years ago) / Classes	Paleozoic					Mesozoic			Cenozoic	
	Ordovician (480–435)	Silurian (435–405)	Devonian (405–345)	Carboniferous (345–275)	Permian (275–225)	Triassic (225–180)	Jurassic (180–130)	Cretaceous (130–65)	Tertiary (65–1.75)	Quaternary (1.75–Present)
Mammalia (Mammals)										
Aves (Birds)										
Reptilia (Reptiles)										
Amphibia (Amphibians)										
Osteichthyes (Bony Fish)										
Chondrichthyes (Cartilaginous Fish)										
Placodermi (Placoderms)										
Agnatha (Jawless Fish)										

Figure 35–2. A comparison of the changing populations of vertebrate classes over the last 500 million years shows only one extinct class. Placoderms died out by the end of the Paleozoic era.

Reading Critically

Identifying Relationships In what class would you expect humans to be? Why?

35.3 Characteristics of Vertebrates

A strong, flexible backbone and complex body systems have enabled the vertebrates to inhabit many environments. Three of the seven living vertebrate classes—the jawless fishes, cartilaginous fishes, and bony fishes—live entirely in water. The four other living vertebrate classes are amphibians, reptiles, birds, and mammals. Amphibians are adapted to life both on land and in the water, while reptiles and mammals are primarily land dwellers. All but a few birds, such as penguins, can fly.

All vertebrates share a number of physical characteristics that set them apart from the other chordates and all invertebrates. Vertebrates are bilaterally symmetrical with two pairs of

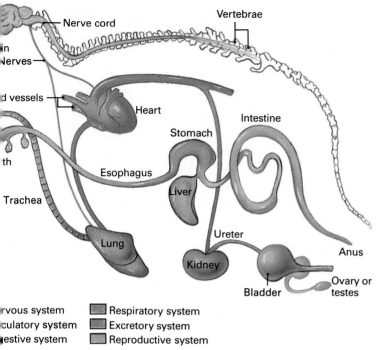

Nerve cord
Vertebrae
in
Nerves
d vessels
Heart
Intestine
Stomach
th
Esophagus
Liver
Trachea
Ureter
Anus
Lung
Kidney
Bladder
Ovary or
testes

rvous system   Respiratory system
culatory system   Excretory system
estive system   Reproductive system

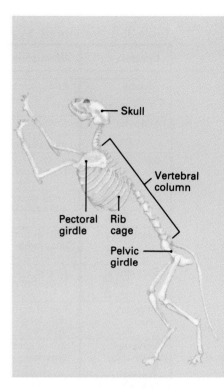

Skull
Vertebral
column
Pectoral Rib
girdle cage
Pelvic
girdle

Figure 35–3. The major body systems (left) and skeletal system (right) of the domestic cat are representative of all vertebrates. Note the locations of the pectoral and pelvic girdles.

appendages such as limbs, fins, or wings. They exhibit cephalization—that is, their main sense organs are located in their heads. All vertebrates also have a closed circulatory system and a **coelom,** which is a large central body cavity that contains vital organs. Finally, all vertebrates have an internal support system called an **endoskeleton.** The endoskeleton is made of bone or cartilage or a combination of both.

Figure 35–3 shows the skeletal system and most other major systems of a representative vertebrate, the domestic cat. A major part of the endoskeleton, and the feature that distinguishes vertebrates from all other animals, is the **vertebral column,** or backbone. The backbone is composed of bony parts called **vertebrae** cushioned by cartilage. Together, the backbone, the bones of the skull, and the rib cage make up the **axial** (AK see uhl) **skeleton.**

The endoskeleton of most vertebrates also includes two structures called *girdles*. The girdles are wide, flattened surfaces that connect the limbs—arms, legs, fins, wings, or flippers—to the axial skeleton. The **pectoral** (PEHK tuhr uhl) **girdle** is located toward the top or front of the animal. The **pelvic girdle** is found near the bottom or back of the animal. The girdles and their associated limbs make up the **appendicular** (ap uhn DIHK yuh luhr) **skeleton.**

Biofact

Q: *Do humans ever have tails?*

A: Yes. Tails form in human embryos and reach their greatest length during the second month of embryonic life. Afterwards, the tails usually disappear. In a few cases, however, infants are born with short tails. These are usually surgically removed soon after birth.

Table 35-1: Vertebrate Systems

System	Description	Function
Skeletal	Endoskeleton of bone and/or cartilage	Provides support and protection
Muscular	Contractile tissue attached to bone or cartilage; some is part of internal organ walls	Together with the skeleton, enables animals to move; protects some organs
Integumentary	Body coverings of skin, hair, scales, or feathers	Provides support and protection; also involved in excretion, respiration, and perception
Digestive	Tube extending from mouth to anus, and associated organs	Prepares food for use by the animal's cells; removes solid wastes from the body
Respiratory	Gills or lungs and associated structures	Exchanges gases between the animal and its environment
Circulatory	Closed system of blood vessels, with two-, three-, or four-chambered heart	Carries blood from the heart to the rest of the body
Excretory	Pair of kidneys and associated tubes; skin, lungs, and gills also may be involved	Removes cellular wastes from the body
Nervous	Spinal cord, brain, nerves, and sense organs	Monitors the environment; controls and coordinates many body functions
Reproductive	Male or female reproductive organs	Produces and carries eggs or sperm; in some vertebrates, allows for internal fertilization and development of offspring
Endocrine	Glands	Secretes chemicals that regulate body growth, reproduction, and development

35.4 Vertebrate Systems

For a comparison of vertebrate systems, see pages 894–905.

Both invertebrates and vertebrates have body tissues that are organized into organs that perform specific body functions. Look at Figure 35–3 on page 555. You can see that the mouth, esophagus, and stomach, for example, form one integrated system, the digestive system. On the whole, the organs of vertebrates are more highly developed than those of invertebrates and form 10 complex systems, shown in Table 35–1.

Section Review

1. **Comparing Systems**   What four characteristics do chordates have in common?
2. **Comparing Ideas**   In what ways does the appendicular skeleton differ from the axial skeleton?
3. **Organizing Ideas**   What systems do all seven living classes of vertebrates share?

> **Thinking Critically**

Jawless Fishes

Lampreys and hagfishes are the only existing members of the class Agnatha (AG nuh thuh). *Agnatha* means "without jaws." The 60 living species of agnathans all feed by latching onto their prey with suckerlike, jawless mouths. These fishes are the only parasitic vertebrates.

Agnathans have smooth, cylinder-like bodies with flexible skeletons formed of cartilage. They have a notochord at all stages of their life cycle. Like all fishes, agnathans have a heart with two chambers. The *ventricle* pumps blood to the body, and the *atrium* receives the blood as it returns from the body.

Section Objectives

- *Name* the major characteristics of the class Agnatha.
- *Describe* the feeding habits of lampreys and hagfishes.
- *Summarize* the life cycle of the lamprey.

35.5 Lampreys

Lampreys live in cool, fresh and coastal waters. Their long, thin bodies measure 40 to 80 cm (16 to 32 in.) in length. Lampreys have one or two fins that extend along their dorsal surface and a tail fin. They have seven circular gill slits on each side of their bodies. **Gills** are the respiratory organs of fish. Lampreys have a single nostril on the top of the head and well-developed eyes. The lamprey's mouth, a round sucking organ called an **oral disc,** has sharp, rasping teeth.

Figure 35–4. A toothed oral disc is used during feeding by a lamprey (left). This fish, which is jawless, attaches the oral disc to other fish and sucks out blood and body fluids (below).

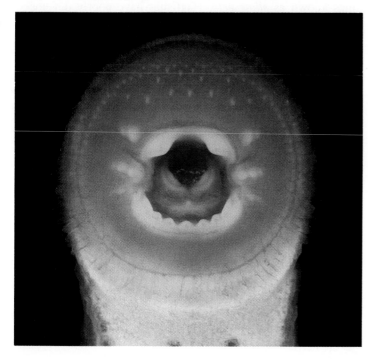

Reading Critically

Evaluating Information Why are lampreys called parasites?

Figure 35–5. The jawless hagfish often attacks fish caught in fishing nets. The hagfish bores inside its prey and eats the inside of the fish, leaving the skin intact.

Most species of lampreys are parasites. The lamprey uses its oral disc to fasten itself onto a fish. It then scrapes a hole in the side of the fish with its teeth and sucks out the blood and tissues. This usually results in the death of the host fish. Because of their feeding methods, lampreys can cause severe economic loss to commercial fishing industries. In the 1950s one species of sea lamprey threatened the entire Great Lakes fishing industry. The lamprey was controlled by chemicals that killed newly hatched larvae.

Lampreys reproduce by laying eggs in nests hollowed out in the gravelly bottom of freshwater streams or lakes. Eggs are fertilized externally and hatch into wormlike larvae that burrow into the gravel. The larval lamprey remains burrowed with its head protruding for three years, feeding on microorganisms. It then changes into an adult, a process called *metamorphosis*. The adults of most species swim into the ocean to feed and return to fresh water to reproduce. Some species remain in fresh water all their lives.

35.6 Hagfishes

Hagfishes are bottom dwellers that live only in cold ocean water. They have 5 to 15 pairs of gill openings. Hagfishes have mucus-secreting glands all over their bodies and so are sometimes known as *slime eels*. Hagfishes have poorly developed eyes that are covered with skin. They have a slitlike, toothed mouth but lack the lamprey's oral disc.

Hagfishes locate their food by scent. They are mainly scavengers that feed on dead or dying fish and marine invertebrates. Hagfishes feed much like lampreys, drilling a hole and sucking the blood and insides from the animal. When not feeding, hagfishes live burrowed in the ocean floor with just the tips of their heads protruding.

Hagfishes are *hermaphrodites*—that is, a single fish has both male and female sex organs. *A hagfish may produce sperm one season and eggs the next.* Eggs are fertilized externally. The young of the hagfish hatch from the egg as miniature versions of the adult.

Section Review

1. **Evaluating Ideas**   State two characteristics of agnathans.
2. **Inferring Relationships**   Why is the presence of the lamprey in an area a threat to the local fishing industry?
3. **Analyzing Information**   Compare the lamprey and hagfish life cycles.

Thinking Critically

Cartilaginous Fishes

Sharks, rays, and skates are members of the class Chondrichthyes (kahn DRIHK thee eez). *Chondrichthyes* means "cartilage fishes": all members of this class have skeletons made of cartilage. Unlike the jawless agnathans, sharks and related fishes have hinged jaws lined with rows of teeth that are continuously replaced when worn or lost. Their skin is covered with small, pointed teeth, giving the skin the texture of rough sandpaper.

Sharks, skates, and rays have five to seven pairs of gills and a two-chambered heart. A spiral membrane or valve extends through the intestine. The valve delays the passage of food through the intestine, and furthers digestion. The fishes have separate sexes, and fertilization of eggs is internal.

Fossil remains indicate that fishes similar to modern chondrichthyes existed over 100 million years ago. Approximately 625 living species have been identified. Most of these species live in salt water.

35.7 Sharks

Sharks are carnivorous, or meat-eating, fish with torpedo-like bodies that are well-adapted to a predatory life. Sharks live in every ocean and are particularly abundant in warm seas. The whale shark is the largest of all fishes. It grows to about 18 m (60 ft.) long and weighs about 14 metric tons (15.4 tons).

Section Objectives

- *List* the major characteristics of cartilaginous fishes.
- *Name* three features that contribute to the shark's success as a predator.
- *Distinguish* skates and rays from sharks.

Figure 35–6. The sand tiger shark inhabits warm, shallow Atlantic waters. Small fish called *remoras* (lower left) travel with the shark and feed on its leftovers. Remoras attach themselves to the shark's body by means of adhesive discs on the top of their heads.

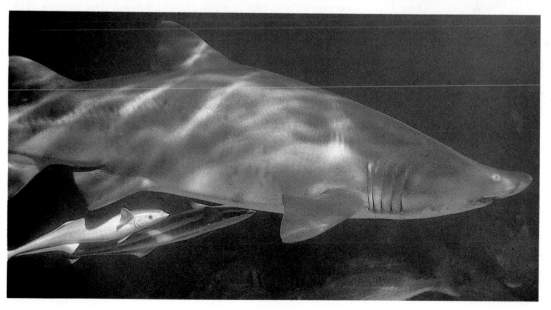

Figure 35–7. This illustration shows the position of the lateral line system of the shark.

Structure Sharks are powerful swimmers that can move rapidly when excited. Scientists estimate that blue sharks can swim 69 km (43 mi.) per hour for short bursts. Their rapid speed is made possible by strong muscles and streamlined bodies that are stabilized by two pairs of fins. The **pectoral fins** grow on the sides just behind the head. The **pelvic fins** grow farther back on the underside of the body. Two **dorsal fins** extend along the back, one behind the other. Sharks also have a vertical **caudal fin,** which is an expansion of the tail. Because sharks are heavier than water, they will sink if they do not continually move forward.

Cone-shaped toothlike structures called **placoid scales** cover the shark's tough leathery skin. Each scale consists of an enamel-like outer layer and a tooth, called a denticle, that projects from the center. Modified scales form the two rows of backward-pointing teeth in the animal's jaws. The backward slant of the teeth makes it possible for the shark to hold food more securely in its jaws.

Senses Sharks have keenly developed senses. As much as two-thirds of the shark's brain is given over to the sense of smell. Sharks can smell the odor of blood as far away as 0.4 km (0.25 mi.), in concentrations as small as one part of blood in 1 million parts of water. The eyesight of sharks is not as well developed as their sense of smell, but they can see moving objects as far away as 15 m (50 ft.).

Sharks also detect movement and locate objects through a system of fluid-filled canals called a **lateral line system.** This system extends down the head and along the side of the shark. Openings to the body's surface occur at intervals.

Vibrations transmitted through the ocean water jostle the fluid in the lateral line system. The movement of the fluid stimulates special receptor cells in the canals that send nerve impulses to the brain. Combined with the animal's other sense organs, the lateral line system makes sharks keen monitors of their environment.

Reproduction Unlike most fishes, the eggs of sharks are fertilized inside the female's body. The male grasps the female with his teeth and inserts the sperm into her with two organs called *claspers.* In most species the eggs develop inside the mother, which later gives birth to live "pups." A few species lay eggs, which may take as long as 15 months to hatch. The eggs of the whale shark are among the largest in the animal kingdom. They may measure up to 30 cm (12 in.) in length and 14 cm (5.5 in.) in width.

35.8 Rays and Skates

Unlike sharks, rays and skates have flat, broad bodies well suited for life on the bottom of the ocean. Their pectoral fins are greatly enlarged and flap like wings when the fish are swimming. The gill openings are on the underside of the head. Water for breathing enters the body through openings called **spiracles** on the top of the head. The spiracles move water to the gills.

Rays are typically less than 1 m (3.3 ft.) long. The giant manta ray measures as much as 7 m (23 ft.) in breadth. Most of the 350 species of rays are harmless to humans. Most rays eat smaller fishes and invertebrates. Some have unique methods of defense and attack. The sting ray has a long, slender tail with sawlike spines that can inject poison. Electric rays have powerful organs that emit an electric charge, stunning their prey.

Skates are similar to rays, though most are somewhat smaller. Their sandlike coloration enables them to blend in with the ocean bottom. When a source of food passes overhead, a skate leaves its hiding place, swims above the other animal, and settles down upon it, pinning the victim between itself and the ocean floor.

Figure 35–8. The manta ray on the left and the skate on the right exhibit flattened bodies suited for living on the ocean floor.

Reading Critically

Comparing Information How are the attack patterns of rays and skates different?

Section Review

1. **Comparing Ideas** What do sharks and skates have in common with lampreys and hagfishes?
2. **Analyzing Structures** What features do sharks possess that help them to swim rapidly?
3. **Identifying Relationships** How does a shark's lateral line system help it to locate food?
4. **Synthesizing Conclusions** What physical features of rays make them well suited for life as bottom dwellers?

Thinking Critically

Section Objectives

- *Distinguish* bony fishes from the other main classes of fishes.
- *Label* the main skeletal structures in a diagram of a typical bony fish.
- *Describe* how fishes respire.
- *Explain* what is meant by *spawning*.
- *List* three patterns of fish migration and give an example of each.

Bony Fishes

The vast majority of the world's fishes belong to the class Osteichthyes (ash tee IHK thee eez). *Osteichthyes* means "bony fishes." As the name indicates, these fishes have skeletons made of bone instead of cartilage. Like sharks, skates, and rays, however, bony fishes have jaws and scaly skin.

35.9 Characteristics

Bony fishes number about 20,000 species, or 95 percent of all fish species. The species differ greatly in appearance and behavior. Some are as thin as straws. Others have protective coloring and shapes that make them barely distinguishable from the rocks in which they hide. Some species are sluggish and move as little as possible. Others move rapidly in pursuit of prey. Some species live solitary lives, while other species live and travel together in large groups, called *schools*.

Moving together in schools protects the individual members from predators. A school that normally spreads out over several hundred meters may, in the presence of danger, condense to form a sphere only a meter (3.3 ft.) in diameter. When this happens, the school may resemble a single, large fish to a predator. Or the predator, unable to concentrate on a single individual, may not be able to catch any fish at all. About 20 percent of fish species travel together in schools.

Figure 35–9. Bony fishes vary greatly in their protective adaptations to underwater life. The pipefish (left) is hard to see among aquatic grasses, while the leaf fish (center) resembles a leaf floating on the water. Hussars (right) gain protection by traveling in large schools.

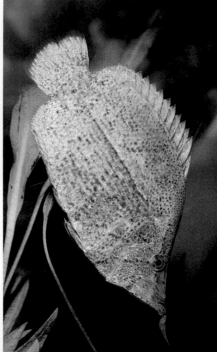

Scientists divide bony fishes into three major groups: lobe-finned fishes, lungfishes, and ray-finned fishes. The first group, the **lobe-finned fishes,** have dorsal and pectoral fins with large fleshy bases supported by leglike bones. Only one living species is known, the *coelacanth* (SEE luh kanth). Lobe-finned fishes were considered extinct until 1938 when a coelacanth was caught off the coast of South Africa.

Lungfishes use lungs as well as gills for breathing. *Lungs are* the internal respiratory organs used by all air-breathing land animals. The three surviving genera of lungfishes differ in the amount of time they can survive out of water using only their lungs. The Australian lungfish can survive in oxygen-poor water by coming to the surface to gulp air, but it cannot live out of water. The South American and African lungfishes bury themselves in mud when the streams in which they live dry up. They respire through their lungs for periods of up to two years until rains come and the streams fill up again.

Ray-finned fishes have fins that are supported by a number of long bones called *rays.* Most fishes, including perch, bass, and all the familiar fishes of the world, belong in this category. Ray-finned fishes evolved about 400 million years ago. Scientists speculate that they arose in freshwater habitats and some later migrated to the oceans. They soon replaced cartilaginous fishes as the dominant kind of fish on Earth.

35.10 The Trout: A Typical Bony Fish

The trout is a bony fish that lives in northern lakes and rivers of the United States or returns from the sea to breed in northern streams. One species, the brook trout, grows to about 46 cm

Figure 35–10. This illustration shows the three major groups of bony fishes: the coelacanth, the only living lobe-finned fish (top left); the lungfish (bottom left); and the ray-finned fish (right), here represented by a perch.

Biofact

Q: *How do fish sleep?*

A: Fish have no eyelids, so they cannot close their eyes to sleep. Some rest on the bottom; others doze in mid-water. Some fishes, such as catfishes and some eels, feed at night and sleep during the day.

(18 in.) long and has light markings on a dark background. The trout's external and internal anatomy is in many ways representative of all bony fishes.

External Structure As Figure 35–11 shows, the trout has an elongated body. Its mouth, nostrils, and eyes are located on its head. The trout has two sets of gills, one on either side of the body. A protective flap of tissue called an **operculum** covers the gills.

The trout's fins stabilize and maneuver the fish and propel it foward. The forwardmost pair are the pectoral fins. Midway along the sides of its body are the paired pelvic fins. The pectoral and pelvic fins help the fish to steer and brake. Two dorsal fins extend from the trout's back. An **anal fin** extends from its ventral surface, near its anal opening. The trout's deeply forked caudal fin forms part of the tail and adds force to the fish's swimming movements.

A trout swims by moving its body from side to side while swinging its tail in the opposite direction. The paired fins help change course. The caudal fin provides the power; by pushing against the water, it forces the fish forward.

Figure 35–11. The external and internal anatomy of the female trout is shown in the illustration below.

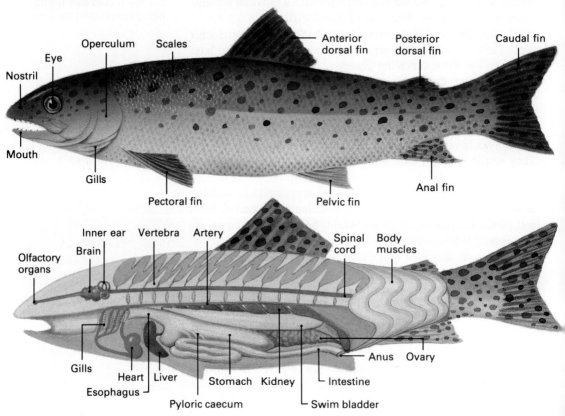

Most fishes have skin covered by thin overlapping outgrowths called **scales.** The trout's scales are thin, bony, and rounded at the edges. Fishes are born with a certain number of scales. Though the scales enlarge throughout the life of the fish, new ones are never grown.

Figure 35–12. The trout, like most bony fishes, has thin, flexible scales that are arranged in overlapping rows.

Skeletal and Digestive Systems   The trout's skeleton is composed almost entirely of bone. The anterior end of the vertebral column is the skull, which covers and protects the brain. Ribs project from the backbone. The spinal cord runs parallel to the backbone and nerves branch from it to various parts of the body. Trout feed on insects and fish eggs. The food moves from the throat cavity down the *esophagus*, a short tube that leads to the stomach. There the food is stored and digestion begins. Near the stomach is the *liver*, a large organ that secretes *bile*, a substance that breaks down the fats in the food. Most of the fish's digestion takes place in special intestinal pouches called *pyloric ceca*. Undigested material leaves through its anus.

Respiratory movements are studied on page 569.

Respiratory and Circulatory Systems   Like most fishes, trout obtain oxygen by means of gills. Trout have four gills, two each in *gill chambers* on either side of the head. Each gill consists of a bony *gill arch* fringed with thin-walled tissues called *gill filaments*. The gill filaments contain many small blood vessels. As the mouth and throat force water over the gills, dissolved oxygen from the water diffuses through the thin walls of the blood vessels and enters the blood.

Trout also have an organ unique to bony fishes—a gas-filled **swim bladder** in the coelom that acts as a float. Gases pass into and out of the swim bladder from the blood. As the bladder fills up, the fish becomes more buoyant and rises in the water. As the bladder deflates, the fish becomes less buoyant and sinks. Glands regulate the gas content in the swim bladder, enabling the fish to remain at a specific depth in the water with little effort.

A two-chambered heart pumps blood through a series of vessels to all parts of the body. *Arteries* carry blood away from the heart; *veins* carry blood back to the heart. The small vessels that form the connecting network between arteries and veins are called *capillaries*. The exchange of nutrients and waste products takes place in the capillaries.

Excretory System   In fishes, as in all vertebrates, the *kidney* is the main excretory organ that removes wastes from the blood. In trout the kidney also plays an important role in maintaining the proper *osmotic balance* of water and salts in the body.

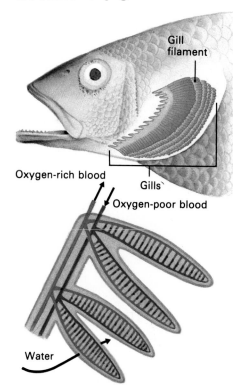

Figure 35–13. The illustration above shows how trout obtain oxygen by means of gills.

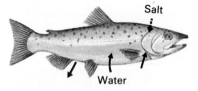

Freshwater fish

Salt

Water

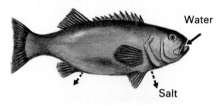

Saltwater fish

Water

Salt

Figure 35–14. To maintain a proper osmotic balance, freshwater fishes (top) must continually take up salt from the water and expel water. Saltwater fishes (bottom) do the reverse. They have cells that excrete salt and they expel only small amounts of water.

Biofact

Q: *Do walking catfish really walk?*

A: No. The walking catfish makes its way from one pond to another using its side fins and tail to help it crawl over the ground.

The concentration of salt in the bodies of freshwater trout is higher than in the water around them. Because water moves from areas of lower salt concentration to areas of higher salt concentration, trout and other freshwater fishes tend to gain water, lowering the salt concentration in the fish's cells. To maintain a proper osmotic balance, freshwater fishes have special salt-absorbing glands in their gills that take up salt from the water and transport it to cells. Also, large amounts of water are expelled as urine. The result is a system that is osmotically balanced.

Fishes that live in the ocean have the opposite problem. The concentration of salt in their bodies is lower than that in the water. As a result, marine fishes constantly lose water to the sea. To protect against dehydration, ocean fishes take in a lot of water. They drink almost continuously. Along with the water, the fishes also take in much more salt than their bodies can use. Saltwater fishes have salt-secreting cells in their gills and kidneys that rid them of extra salt and thus maintain an osmotic balance. Furthermore, they excrete a concentrated urine that has little water.

Some fishes have adaptations that allow them to move back and forth between saltwater and freshwater environments. Trout, salmon, and sturgeon are fishes that have well-developed kidneys for life in fresh water and salt-secreting cells for adjustment to life in salt water.

Nervous System   The trout's brain coordinates the information received from its sense organs. A fish's keenest sense is smell. The **olfactory organs,** which monitor smell, are located above and on each side of the mouth. Water enters the olfactory organs by way of the nostrils. Chemicals in the water stimulate certain nerve cells to send an electrical message to the brain.

Fishes have no external ears or eardrums; yet they hear. Sound vibrations arrive through the water and are transmitted through the skin and bones to an *inner ear*. The inner ear consists of a series of tubes on each side of the head that are lined with nerve cells. When stimulated, the nerve cells send impulses to the brain. Like sharks, bony fishes monitor vibrations in the water by means of a lateral line system. The sensory cells of the system can detect very low frequency vibrations in the water.

The trout's eyes can see both to the left and right at the same time—a definite advantage for an animal that has no neck to turn the head from side to side. Most fish have poor vision, however. They can probably see objects no farther than 0.5 m (1.6 ft.) away.

Some fish travel vast distances in search of food or spawning grounds. Movements like these that follow a regular pattern year after year are called **migrations**. Scientists have discovered the travel routes of many migratory species by "tagging" fish in one spot and recording where the tagged fish were later caught.

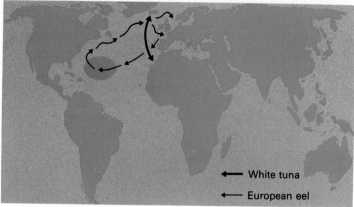

← White tuna

← European eel

Migrants such as herring, cod, and white tuna live and travel only in the ocean. These fish are called *ocean-odromous.* White tuna, for example, winter near the Azores and the Canary Islands off Africa and spawn in the spring. Then they migrate to the waters off Iceland where food is plentiful during the summer months.

Anadromous fish live in the ocean and migrate to fresh water to spawn. The

Pacific salmon spends its adult life in the ocean. When it is ready to spawn, it returns to the same stream in which it was born. Even those anadromous fish hatched in fish hatcheries and later placed in the ocean return to the same stream in which their ancestors were born.

Catadromous fish live in fresh water and return to the sea to breed. Eels are catadromous fish. The adult European eel lives in

lakes and streams in Europe. It migrates 5,000 km (3,100 mi.) to a specific spot in the Sargasso Sea in the western Atlantic to spawn. The larval eels drift with the Gulf Stream. Several years are required for the larval eels to float back to the European continent. Once there, the young eels migrate up rivers by the millions.

■ **Inferring Ideas** What advantages do fish gain by migrating every year?

Reproductive System   Like most bony fishes, trout fertilize their eggs externally. The females **spawn**—that is, they shed eggs from their bodies into nests that have been hollowed out on the floor of the river or lake bed. The males then release **milt,** which is a fluid containing sperm, over the eggs. In many species, this process takes place in special locations called *spawning grounds*. Some types of fish travel very great distances to return to the same spawning ground where they themselves were hatched.

Many of the eggs are not fertilized during spawning. In addition, a large percentage of those eggs that are fertilized do

Reading Critically

Inferring Conclusions What is unusual about the mating habits of some species of trout?

A "Fishy" Health Idea

To help prevent heart disease, most nutritionists recommend a diet that is low in red meat, eggs, and other foods that are high in cholesterol. However, Eskimos have healthy hearts although they eat large amounts of fatty meat.

Eskimos also eat large amounts of fish, and some research suggests that this helps protect them against heart diseases and disorders. Some of the oils in the fish may help prevent the formation of fatty deposits that contain cholesterol, called *plaques,* in blood vessels. Plaques can lead to heart attacks by cutting off supplies of oxygen and nutrients to the heart.

The possibility of benefits from fish oils has led to research that may help people increase these oils in their diets. A Utah biochemist has discovered that chickens lay eggs that contain fish oil if the chickens are fed a supplement of fish oil. Volunteers who ate four of these fish-oil eggs a day showed no rise in their cholesterol levels

during the experiment. However, volunteers who ate ordinary eggs did show increases. Fish-oil eggs do smell and taste "fishy." Perhaps laboratory workers will find a way to correct this problem, and fish-oil eggs will replace ordinary eggs on the breakfast table.

not develop. Even if the eggs develop and hatch, the young fishes are in constant danger of being eaten by predators. However, most species of fishes produce a large number of eggs. A female cod, for example, produces over 9 million eggs during a spawning season. Although most of these eggs are destroyed or eaten, a few survive and develop into adult fishes.

A few fish species are *live-bearers*—the eggs are fertilized internally and the young develop within the mother's body. Guppies, mollies, and swordtails are examples of live-bearers.

Section Review

1. **Evaluating Information**   Explain how trout, lampreys, and sharks differ from one another.
2. **Analyzing Function**   How do a trout's gills function?
3. **Summarizing Information**   Describe the migration pattern of the white tuna.
4. **Inferring Relationships**   How do saltwater fish maintain an osmotic balance?

Thinking Critically

INVESTIGATION 35:
How Does Temperature Affect Breathing Rate in Goldfish?

Objectives
- To *observe* the effect of temperature on the breathing rate of a goldfish
- To *record, interpret,* and *evaluate* data

Materials
goldfish, 1000-mL beaker, two 600-mL beakers, 400-mL beaker, hot plate, crushed ice, water, fishnet, thermometer, stopwatch

Prelab Preparation
1. Review the external structure and the respiratory system of bony fishes.
2. Describe an operculum.
3. Describe the structure of a gill.
4. Explain how you might tell whether a fish is breathing.
5. Define the terms ectotherm and endotherm.
6. Discuss the topic of this Investigation with your laboratory partner. Then form a hypothesis to help solve the problem.
7. State reasons for your hypothesis.
8. Identify the independent and dependent variables that will be used to test your hypothesis.
9. Make a table for recording breathing rate at 8°C, 12°C, 16°C, 20°C, and 24°C. Allow space for data from three trials to be made by each of four teams and space for the average breathing rate for each temperature.

Inquiry: Experimentation
10. Place the fish in a clean 400-mL beaker that contains 200 mL of aquarium water. Watch the fish. Describe the movements of the fish's mouth, and opercula. Explain how these movements cause water to flow over the gills.
11. **CAUTION: The hot plate and hot water can cause injury.** Label the 1000-mL beaker "Bath." Pour 500 mL of tap water into the 1000-mL beaker. Pour 500 mL of tap water into a 600-mL beaker and warm the water to about 30°C on the hot plate. Fill the other 600-mL beaker with crushed ice.
12. Add ice or hot water to adjust the tem-

perature of the bath water to 24°C. Then, place the smaller beaker containing the fish into the larger "Bath" beaker.
13. Adjust the temperature of the water in the beaker that contains the fish to 24°C by adding ice or hot water to the bath beaker, as necessary. *Why is using the water bath better than adding ice or hot water directly to the beaker containing the fish?*
14. Once the water has reached the desired temperature, wait two minutes for the fish to adjust to the change. Then record the fish's breathing rate for three one-minute trials.
15. Beginning with 20°C and working down to 8°C, repeat step 14 for the remaining temperatures.
16. Return the fish to the aquarium and clean your laboratory area.
17. Combine your data with that of three other teams to calculate the average breathing rate for each temperature.
18. Construct a line graph that shows the relationship between breathing rate and external temperature for goldfish.

Analysis
1. **Summarizing Data** Summarize the data collected during this Investigation.
2. **Analyzing Data** State your conclusion and explain how it is supported by the data.
3. **Making Inferences** Fish in northern climates survive the winter in lakes and ponds covered with ice and snow. Since the ice limits gas exchange between the water and air, how can fish survive? What evidence supports this hypothesis?

Chapter 35 Review

Summary

Phylum Chordata includes the vertebrates, or animals with backbones. The seven living classes of vertebrates are jawless fishes, cartilaginous fishes, bony fishes, amphibians, reptiles, birds, and mammals.

Jawless fishes, such as lampreys and hagfishes, attach themselves to other fishes and suck out blood and tissues. Cartilaginous fishes include sharks, skates, and rays. Sharks are powerful swimmers with a keen sense of smell.

Rays and skates have flattened bodies and most are bottom dwellers.

Although bony fishes are divided into three groups—lobe-finned fishes, lungfishes, and ray-finned fishes—all common species are ray-finned. Bony fishes, such as trout, have a special swim bladder that regulates their buoyancy in water. Fishes obtain oxygen through gills. Fertilization usually takes place externally.

BioTerms

anal fin (564)
appendicular
   skeleton (555)
axial skeleton (555)
caudal fin (560)
coelom (555)
dorsal fin (560)
endoskeleton
   (555)
gill (557)
gill slit (553)
lateral line
   system (560)

lobe-finned
   fish (563)
lungfish (563)
migration (566)
milt (566)
nerve cord (553)
notochord (553)
olfactory
   organ (566)
operculum (564)
oral disc (557)
pectoral fin (560)
pectoral girdle (555)

pelvic fin (560)
pelvic girdle (555)
placoid scale (560)
ray-finned fish (563)
scale (565)
spawn (566)

spiracle (561)
swim bladder (565)
tail (553)
vertebra (555)
vertebral
   column (555)

For each pair of terms, explain the differences in their meanings.

1. lobe-finned fishes, ray-finned fishes
2. axial skeleton, appendicular skeleton
3. notochord, vertebral column
4. dorsal fin, pectoral fin

BioQuiz   (Write all answers on a separate sheet of paper.)

Completion

1. Male trout fertilize eggs by releasing _____ over them.
2. The two chambers of a fish heart are the _____ and the ventricle.
3. The vital organs of vertebrates are found in the _____ .
4. Bony fishes are divided into three major groups: lobe-finned fishes, _____ , and ray-finned fishes.
5. The hind legs of vertebrates are attached to the _____ girdle.

Multiple Choice

6. Vertebrates differ from other chordates in having _____ .   a) a notochord. b) a vertebral column.   c) an endoskeleton.   d) an axial skeleton.
7. The function of the _____ is to protect the gills.   a) pectoral fin   b) operculum c) placoid scale   d) gill slit
8. Hagfishes emerge from the egg as   a) larvae.   b) miniature adults. c) zygotes.   d) All of the choices are correct.

9. Which of the following structures is not characteristics of all chordates? a) notochord b) nerve cord c) gill slits d) bones
10. The lamprey's mouth is a round sucking organ called a) an oral disc. b) a spiracle. c) an operculum. d) a gill slit.
11. Which of the following is hermaphroditic? a) a lamprey b) a trout c) a hagfish d) a skate
12. A shark's skin is covered with a) oral discs. b) placoid scales. c) gill slits. d) All of the choices are correct.
13. A shark's lateral line system a) detects movement. b) expels wastes. c) draws in water. d) excretes eggs.
14. Trout regulate their depth in the water through their a) anal fin. b) operculum. c) gills. d) swim bladder.

15. A special function of the kidney in trout is a) to regulate the fish's depths in water. b) to maintain oxygen intake. c) to maintain osmotic balance. d) to circulate blood.

16. Describe how trout swim.
17. How do the pectoral and pelvic girdles function in vertebrates?
18. How is the depth at which trout floats regulated?
19. How do the habitat and feeding habits of the immature lamprey differ from those of the mature fish?
20. Describe the activities that occur at a spawning ground?

Application/Critical Thinking

1. **Organizing Information** List all vertebrates you see in a single day. Write down the name and the class of each animal. For each animal, list one characteristic that is an adaptation to living on land or in water.
2. **Relating Ideas** Use your library to research data for a chart on basking sharks, hammerheads, nurse sharks, white sharks, and whale sharks. Make columns and fill in scientific names, habitats, and feeding habits. You may wish to extend the chart to include body lengths and whether or not each species has been involved in attacks on people.
3. **Inferring Relationships** Why are most fish unable to live outside the water even when oxygen is readily available?
4. **Inquiry** What are the advantages and disadvantages of the way the body temperature of fishes is regulated?

Cross-Discipline Connection

Biology and Health Use references in the school and public libraries to investigate possible benefits of including Omega-3 and other fish oils in the diet.

Discovery Through Reading

Read the article "Face-to-Face with a Living Fossil." *Discover* (March 1988) 56–57, which describes the coelacanth. Why is the coelacanth called a "living fossil"? Describe the movement of the coelacanth's fins as it swims.

Read the article "Ballet with Sting-rays" *National Geographic* (January 1989): 84–95 which describes the feeding habits of sting rays in the Caribbean Sea. What kinds of food do sting-rays normally eat and how do they locate food?

Amphibians

Outline

Malaysian horned frog

Focus

Evidence shows that the ancestors of amphibians first appeared about 370 million years ago. At that time, land plants were small, leafless organisms and no vertebrates lived on land. However, lobe-finned fishes, with lungs, gills, and limb-like fins were suited for life on shore. Their descendents became the first amphibians.

■ *What changes must occur in a tadpole before it becomes a frog that can live on land?*

■ *What structures do humans show that allow humans to exist in many different land environments?*

From Water to Land

The word *amphibian* means "double life." It is thus a fitting name for organisms such as frogs, toads, and salamanders that during their life cycle live in two worlds—the world of water and the world of dry land.

36.1 Movement to Land

The movement to land was a significant biological event that opened up new habitats and new sources of food for animals. Land also offers more oxygen to breathe, for air has 20 percent more available oxygen than water. Furthermore, land provides more shelter than water for breeding and for raising young.

The transition from water to land was not an easy one, however, because terrestrial environments are more harsh than aquatic ones. One major problem of living on land is that body structures dry out more quickly in air than in water. The external gills of fish, for example, are constantly bathed when in water. In air, the gills dry out and cannot function. Therefore, an aquatic species could not move onto land until it was equipped with respiratory organs that would not dry out in air. Similarly, the skin of aquatic animals is constantly moistened by water. Thus the skin also had to undergo modifications before a species could colonize land.

Another problem of life on land is that air is not as dense as water and so provides less support against gravity. For this reason animals living on land need strong skeletons.

A third obstacle to survival on land is the continuous fluctuation of temperature there. Animals that live in large seas and lakes are buffered by water's fairly constant temperature. Success on land requires adaptations for surviving wide variations in temperature.

36.2 Characteristics of Amphibians

Many amphibian characteristics are adaptations for living on land. One example is the amphibian's mode of respiration. Most adult amphibians have internal lungs rather than external gills. These lungs are contained in the body cavity and are constantly moistened by water condensed from air and by body fluids. Amphibians have simple saclike lungs that are not as efficient as the lungs of other land vertebrates. The oxygen obtained by lung breathing is supplemented by oxygen that diffuses directly through the amphibians' moist skin and mouth lining.

Section Objectives

- *State* three problems animals faced in making the transition from water to land.
- *Name* four characteristics of amphibians that are adaptations to living on land.
- *List* the three orders of amphibians.

Biofact

Q: *Do all amphibians have either lungs or gills?*

A: No. Salamanders of the family Plethodontidae have neither lungs nor gills. They respire almost entirely through the skin, which contains many capillary networks. Salamanders supplement this "breathing" by mouth breathing.

Reading Critically

Inferring Ideas Why do you think that the lungs of amphibians are not as well developed as those of other land vertebrates?

Figure 36–1. Many frogs have powerful hind legs that permit huge leaps (top). Toads bury themselves in mud and conserve body moisture in this way (bottom).

Thinking Critically

Amphibian skin is kept moist in several ways. Frogs, for example, have **mucus glands** in the skin. These glands secrete a slimy substance that helps keep the skin moist. Toads have drier skin than frogs. However, toads are often active only at night time and in wet areas. Some toads bury themselves in mud or wet soil. These behaviors help keep their skins from drying out.

Amphibians have skeletons strong enough to support their weight. Most have four limbs, which are specialized for various functions. Frogs and toads, for example, have strong back legs for jumping on land. Amphibian feet are clawless. In many species, the feet are webbed for swimming.

Like fishes, amphibians are cold-blooded—that is, they have no way of maintaining a constant internal body temperature. Amphibians withstand temperature fluctuations by avoiding temperature extremes. Amphibians remain active as long as temperatures are favorable for movement. They may cease activity for long periods if conditions become too hot or too cold.

Amphibians represent only a partial adaptation to land. Most species return to water to lay their eggs. The young of many species pass through a larval stage in water before beginning their life on land.

36.3 Classification of Amphibians

Biologists classify the 2,500 living species of amphibians into three orders. Tailless amphibians, such as frogs and toads, make up the order Anura (uh NYUR uh). *Anura* means "without a tail." Salamanders and other amphibians with legs and tails are placed in the order Urodela (yur uh DEE luh). *Urodela* means "visible tail." Legless amphibians called *caecilians* (sih SIHL yuhns) make up the order Apoda (A puh duh), a name that means "without legs."

Amphibians range in size from a Cuban frog only 1.2 cm (0.5 in.) long to a giant Asian salamander 160 cm (63 in.) long. Amphibians live on every continent except Antarctica, but they are most abundant in the tropics.

Section Review

1. **Evaluating Relationships** How did animals make the transition from an aquatic to a terrestrial existence?
2. **Classifying Data** Name the three orders of amphibians and give an example of each order.
3. **Evaluating Ideas** What adaptation has allowed amphibians to withstand the greater stress of gravity that is experienced when the amphibian is on land?

Frogs

The most successful amphibians are frogs. Most of the 2,000 known species live in the moist tropics, but frogs also are found in all temperate areas. Because frogs are both familiar and easy to obtain, they are often studied in biology classes as examples of vertebrate anatomy.

36.4 External Structure

Frogs have short, broad bodies; long hind limbs; and bulging eyes. Their heads and trunks are fused so they have no necks. Adults frogs do not have tails.

The smooth, moist skin of frogs contains both mucus glands and poison glands. The poison glands secrete chemicals that are distasteful or harmful to predators. Most frogs produce poison that is only mildly irritating to humans, and that does not deter snakes, the frog's major predator. One South American species, however, produces a poison that is one of the most powerful venoms known. Most frogs that produce powerful venoms have highly colored skin that warns potential predators of danger. In contrast, the majority of frogs have green, gray, or brown skin, which blends into the surroundings.

Frogs have large powerful back legs that enable them to jump and leap. Frogs have been known to cover more than 5 m (16 ft.) in a single leap. The front legs, which absorb the shock on landing, are much shorter. Most frogs have webbed feet. Tree frogs, however, have grasping feet or suckerlike pads specially adapted to life in trees.

A frog's eyes are large, round, and protruding. In most species, the eyes protrude above the top of the skull. This adaptation allows frogs to remain submerged in water and be aware of predators at the same time. Frogs can also pull their eyes into their sockets. The retracted eyes exert pressure on the top of the throat and hold food tightly in the mouth. Each eye is covered by a transparent third eyelid called a **nictitating** (NIHK tuh tay ting) **membrane** that helps protect the eyeball.

Two nostrils located at the front and top of the head open into the mouth cavity. The position of the nostrils allows the frog to breathe while almost completely submerged.

Frogs do not have external ears. Instead, they receive sounds through two **tympanic membranes,** which are circular structures located posterior to each eye. Sound and balance are sensed in the internal ear, which lies directly under the tympanic membrane. The ear is connected to the mouth by a channel

Section Objectives

- *Label* on a diagram the external body parts of a frog.
- *List* three ways frogs breathe.
- *Trace* on a diagram the flow of blood between a frog's heart and lungs.
- *Name* the major stages in the life history of a frog.
- *Distinguish* between hibernation and estivation.

Figure 36–2. A frog's nostrils and protruding eyes are located at the top of the head. This arrangement permits the frog to see and breathe while almost completely submerged in water.

Amphibians **575**

Q: *Does croaking differ among various kinds of frogs?*

A: Yes. The croaking of frogs is *species specific.* Each species of frog or toad has specific characteristics of tone, pitch, and pulse. A female of a species can recognize the male of her species because of the unique call.

called the **Eustachian** (yoo STAY shuhn) **tube.** By allowing air to enter the inner ear, the Eustachian tube helps to maintain equal air pressure on both sides of the tympanic membrane.

Frogs communicate by making a distinctive croaking sound. When air from the frog's lungs passes over bands of tissue called *vocal cords,* the vocal cords vibrate. The vibrations of the vocal cords give off sound. Male frogs have more developed vocal cords than females and use the cords to call to the females during the spring mating season. Some species have a large vocal pouch in the throat or on each side of the head that collects the air after it passes over the vocal cords. When air flows in, these pouches balloon outward. Frogs with vocal pouches make louder sounds than frogs that have no vocal pouches.

36.5 Digestive System

Frogs, like other adult amphibians, are carnivorous. They eat insects, worms, and other animals small enough to be swallowed whole. A frog uses its sticky tongue to snare insects. The

Figure 36–3. The illustrations below show the major parts of the frog's skeletal system (left) and digestive system (right).

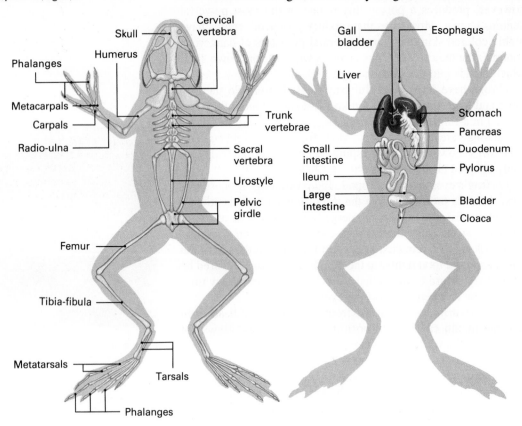

frog's tongue attaches to the front of the mouth and flips outward to catch its prey. Small teeth that line the upper jaw and **vomerine teeth** that project from the roof of the mouth aid in holding prey. In the mouth, food is moistened by saliva produced in *salivary glands.* The food then enters the esophagus, the tube that leads to the stomach. Enzymes secreted by glands in the stomach break down food further.

Food leaves the stomach through an opening called the *pylorus* and enter the **duodenum,** the first part of the small intestine. The **small intestine** is a long tube in which most of the digestion and absorption of food occurs. A thin, tough membrane called the **mesentery** holds the intestine in place. Food next passes to the second part of the small intestine, the **ileum.** From there it travels to the **large intestine,** where much of the water in the food is absorbed. Any remaining waste then enters the **cloaca,** a tube that also receives materials from the urinary bladder and the sex organs. Waste materials pass out of the frog's body through the cloacal opening.

Two organs, the pancreas and the liver, aid digestion. The **pancreas** lies anterior and slightly dorsal to the stomach and secretes digestive enzymes into the small intestine. The pancreas also secretes **insulin,** a substance that controls the level of sugar in the blood. The liver fills a large part of the body cavity. The liver produces bile which aids in fat digestion. It also stores the carbohydrate *glycogen,* a byproduct of glucose metabolism.

36.6 Skeletal System

The frog's short trunk has a backbone consisting of nine vertebrae. The *cervical vertebra,* located at the anterior end of the backbone, allows the head to move. Seven *trunk vertebrae* connect the cervical vertebra to the *sacral vertebra,* which supports the hind limbs. Attached to the sacral vertebra is the *urostyle,* a long, undivided portion of the backbone that forms a ridge along the frog's back. The urostyle consists of several fused vertebrae.

A fundamental feature of amphibians is the presence of limbs. Limbs are adaptations that made it possible for a frog to move around on land. Forelimbs are attached to the main skeletal frame at the pectoral girdle; hind limbs are attached at the pelvic girdle. The skeleton of each forelimb consists of a long *humerus,* a *radio-ulna,* and the bones of the wrist and hand. The long bone in the hind limb is called the *femur.* It is attached to a *tibia-fibula,* which in turn is connected to the bones of the ankle and the foot.

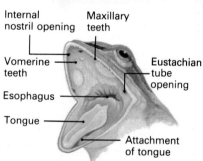

Internal nostril opening — Maxillary teeth — Vomerine teeth — Eustachian tube opening — Esophagus — Tongue — Attachment of tongue

Figure 36–4. A frog catches its prey with a quick flip and extension of its sticky tongue (top). The tongue and other parts of the frog mouth are shown in the illustration (bottom).

For a comparison of vertebrate skeletal systems see pages 894–895.

36.7 Respiratory System

For a comparison of vertebrate respiratory systems, see pages 900–901.

A frog takes oxygen into its body through its lungs, its mouth, and its skin.

When the floor of the frog's mouth is lowered, a temporary vacuum is created in the mouth. As a result, air from the outside rushes in through the nostrils to fill the vacuum. When the floor of the mouth rises and the nostrils close, air is forced on into the lungs. Often a frog requires a number of gulps of the mouth to fill its lungs.

Some oxygen diffuses into the blood through the membranes of the mouth, which are rich in blood vessels. This process is sometimes called **mouth breathing.**

BIOLOGY AND YOU:

Antibiotic Frogs

A chemical recently found in the skin of the African clawed frog may become useful in developing antibiotics for treating burn victims.

Like penicillin, this substance was found as a result of research on problems that had little to do with antibiotics. A scientist doing RNA research at the National Institutes of Health was surgically removing ovaries from African clawed frogs. During his experiments, he observed that the frogs' surgical wounds healed quickly, without becoming infected.

After careful investigation, laboratory workers found a protein in the African clawed frog's skin. The protein helps make the frog's skin immune to many different kinds of infectious bacteria, fungi, and protozoa. Scientists named the protein *manganin.*

Manganin may have adaptive value for the African clawed frog. The water in which the frog lives contains many microorganisms that can cause skin infections. Because their skin makes manganin, African clawed frogs are not threatened by skin infections even if their skins become damaged.

Unlike the African clawed frog, human skin does not produce manganin. Sometimes, even minor cuts and burns on human skin become infected when they are invaded by microorgan-

isms. If large areas of human skin are damaged, especially from burns, life-threatening infections often result. Treatment of infected burns is often difficult and may be painful for a burn victim.

Perhaps ways can be found to use our knowledge about manganins to develop antibiotics that will help human skin heal without becoming infected.

Frogs also respire by absorbing dissolved oxygen directly through the skin. Dissolved oxygen diffuses through the frog's thin skin into the blood capillaries underneath. This allows frogs to remain under water for long periods. Most carbon dioxide also leaves the frog's body by diffusion through the skin.

36.8 Circulatory System

The frog, like all amphibians, has a three-chambered heart. A wall separates the atrium into two chambers. Blood returning from the body enters the *right atrium*. Blood returning from the lungs enters the *left atrium*. Both of these chambers contract, and blood is pumped into the *ventricle*. Oxygen-poor blood from the body and oxygen-rich blood from the lungs thus mix in the ventricle. When the ventricle contracts, blood is forced out of the heart. Some goes to the lungs and some goes to the rest of the body.

Amphibian hearts differ from those of birds and mammals, which are four-chambered. Four-chambered hearts have a *left ventricle* and a *right ventricle*. Blood returning from the body enters the right atrium, is pumped to the right ventricle, and then to the lungs. It returns to the left atrium, is pumped to the left ventricle, and then to the body. There is thus a separation between the **systemic circulation**—that is, blood moving to and from the body—and the **pulmonary circulation,** blood moving to and from the lungs. The separation of blood flow to body and to lungs is called *double circulation.*

Reading Critically

Analyzing Information If frogs have lungs, how can they remain under water for long periods of time without dying?

For a comparison of vertebrate circulatory systems, see pages 898–899.

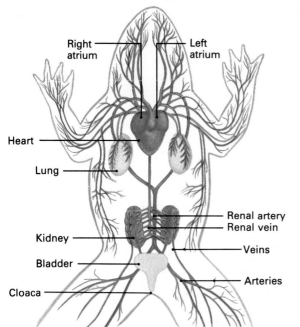

Right atrium — Left atrium

Heart

Lung

Kidney

Bladder

Cloaca

Renal artery
Renal vein

Veins

Arteries

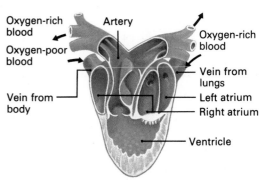

Oxygen-rich blood — Artery — Oxygen-rich blood

Oxygen-poor blood

Vein from body

Vein from lungs

Left atrium

Right atrium

Ventricle

Figure 36–5. Blood is pumped through the frog's circulatory system (left) by a three-chambered heart (above). Unlike the human heart, a frog's heart has a single ventricle.

Amphibians **579**

Frogs, like all amphibians, have no way of regulating their internal body temperatures. As the temperature of the external environment falls, their own body temperature also falls. This is why amphibians are termed "cold-blooded."

To survive extreme cold, frogs and other amphibians may bury themselves in mud or huddle together inside logs. As their body temperature falls, their respiration and level of activity slow down. What little energy they require comes from stored fat and glycogen in their bodies. Such a period of severely reduced activity in winter is called **hibernation.** As the weather warms, the frog's body gradually returns to normal.

Frogs also go through a period of inactivity during the summer, called **estivation.** To avoid hot temperatures, frogs remain immersed in water. When water is scarce, they burrow themselves in mud, where they breathe almost entirely through their skin.

Other animals go through periods of hibernation or estivation. Lungfish survive seasonal droughts by burying themselves in the mud at the bottom of dried-out ponds. Honeybees cluster together to hibernate. The queen bee is found at the center of the mass.

■ **Evaluating Ideas** Why are hibernation and estivation evolutionary advantages?

36.9 Nervous System

Adult frogs lack the lateral line system used by fishes to monitor their environment. As a result adult frogs depend more on their senses of smell, vision, and hearing. *The frog's brain is the central organ of its nervous system and processes information from the various sense organs.*

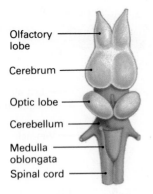

Olfactory lobe

Cerebrum

Optic lobe

Cerebellum

Medulla oblongata

Spinal cord

Figure 36–6. A frog's brain looks like a mere widening of its spinal cord. However, it functions as a true brain, processing information from the entire nervous system.

The frog's brain resembles a swollen portion of the spinal cord. The front parts of the brain are the *olfactory lobes,* which receive and interpret smell impulses. Behind these lobes is the **cerebrum,** the control center of the brain. Two *optic lobes,* located behind the cerebral hemispheres, receive and interpret impulses from the eyes. The **cerebellum** controls movement and muscular coordination. Behind the cerebellum is the **medulla oblongata,** where many of the more automatic responses of the nervous system are carried out.

Ten pairs of cranial nerves connect the brain and the sensory organs. These nerves carry information from the sense organs to the brain, which processes the information. Messages from the brain to head structures travel through some cranial nerves.

The medulla oblongata connects with the spinal cord. Nerves that carry impulses to and from the body are attached to the spinal cord.

36.10 Excretory System

A pair of dorsal kidneys are the major excretory organs of the frog. A kidney lies on either side of the backbone, directly under the skin. Blood enters a kidney through the **renal artery,** which branches into many smaller vessels and capillaries in the kidney tissue. In the kidney, wastes and excess water leave the blood and form urine. Urine drains into a urinary bladder, which empties into a cloaca that opens to the outside. Because large amounts of water enter a frog through its skin, the amount of urine that a frog excretes each day may equal 25 percent of the frog's body weight.

The skin also serves as an excretory organ. In addition to carbon dioxide, excess salts and minerals leave the frog's body through the skin.

36.11 Reproductive System

Male and female frogs are difficult to distinguish because their sex organs are internal. During the mating season, however, the thumbs of many male frogs enlarge and become black.

A female frog's two egg-producing organs, called **ovaries,** are located near the kidneys. Thousands of eggs produced by the ovaries are released directly into the body cavity. Cilia sweep the eggs into coiled tubes called *oviducts*. There the eggs are coated with a jellylike covering and stored in two *ovisacs* until they are released for external fertilization. The eggs leave the body through the cloaca.

Male frogs produce sperm in two **testes.** One yellowish testis is located on the front portion of each kidney. The sperm travel through narrow tubes into the kidneys and then through the urinary ducts to the cloaca. Sperm are released through the cloaca during mating.

Both testes and ovaries have **fat bodies** on their external surface. These bodies store fat that supplies nutrition for developing eggs and sperm.

36.12 Life Cycle

During the spring mating season, a male clasps a female from behind and presses his large black thumbs into her back. This process, called **amplexus,** stimulates the female to expel her eggs. The male then releases sperm over the eggs. The sperm are able to penetrate the jellylike coating. This covering is distasteful to potential predators and also helps regulate the temperature of the fertilized eggs.

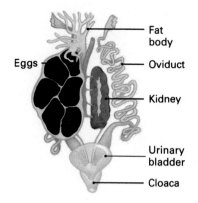

Fat body

Eggs

Oviduct

Kidney

Urinary bladder

Cloaca

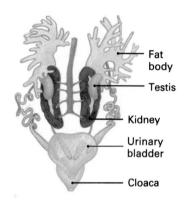

Fat body

Testis

Kidney

Urinary bladder

Cloaca

Figure 36–7. The illustrations above show the major organs of the excretory and reproductive systems of the female frog (top) and the male frog (bottom).

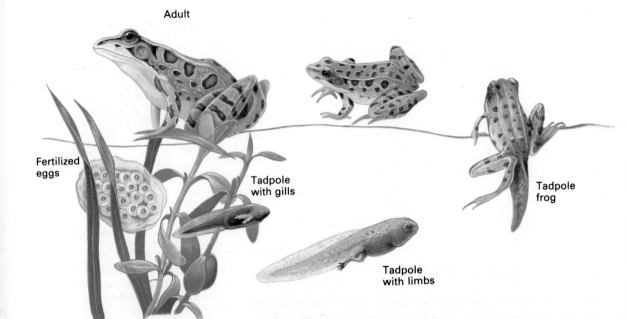

Adult

Fertilized
eggs

Tadpole
with gills

Tadpole
frog

Tadpole
with limbs

Figure 36–8. The major stages in the life cycle of a frog are shown in the illustration above.

The eggs hatch 2 to 30 days later, depending on the species and the water temperature. The eggs hatch into **tadpoles,** the larval form of frogs. *The aquatic tadpole goes through a metamorphosis, or change, as it develops into the adult amphibious frog.* Follow the life cycle of a frog in Figure 36–8.

The young tadpole begins life with a short tail, lidless eyes, and adhesive discs with which it attaches to objects. The tadpole breathes through gills and feeds on vegetation in the water. Gradually the tadpole develops limbs and its tail begins to disappear. Lungs replace gills, and the young frog leaves the water for the land. The process of metamorphosis from tadpole to frog takes a year or less for the common leopard frog and up to three years for the bullfrog.

Section Review

1. **Locating Structures**   Where are a frog's ears located?
2. **Interpreting Ideas**   How does a frog digest food?
3. **Interpreting Ideas**   How does a frog take air into its lungs?
4. **Summarizing Ideas**   Describe the route of blood through the chambers of a frog's heart.
5. **Inferring Relationships**   How does a frog keep from freezing in winter?
6. **Analyzing Information**   Compare the structure and feeding habits of a tadpole and an adult frog.

Thinking Critically

Other Amphibians

Toads, salamanders, and caecilians are amphibians that have developed various adaptations for living on land. Desiccation, or drying out, is a major threat for each animal.

36.13 Toads

Like frogs, toads belong to the order Anura. Toads resemble frogs in many ways, and the name *toad* is often applied to any species of Anura that is specially adapted to a dry environment. True toads belong to the family Bufonidae.

Toads tend to have shorter legs than frogs, squat bodies, and thick skin covered with bumps. The common American toad ranges from 2 to 25 cm. (0.8 to 10 in.) in length. The red or brown color of the skin allows these toads to blend in with the ground.

Many toads live in deserts and arid areas, but others live in moist habitats. They move about at night and bury themselves in soil during the day to avoid heat. Toads usually return to water only to reproduce. The female toad lays eggs in stringy masses, in contrast to the egg clusters of frogs. The tadpoles of toads are typically black.

36.14 Salamanders

Salamanders are amphibians with tails. Scientists believe that, of all modern amphibians, salamanders most closely resemble ancestral amphibians.

Section Objectives

- *Distinguish* toads, frogs, and salamanders from each other.
- *Describe* the characteristics and habitats of caecilians.

Reading Critically

Inferring Ideas If you saw a single organism in the water, how could you tell if it was a frog or a toad?

Figure 36–9. Amphibians that are adapted for life on land include toads (below left) and salamanders (below).

Figure 36–10. The mud puppy never loses its larval characteristics, even when it becomes mature enough to reproduce.

Figure 36–11. Like all caecilians, this Japanese caecilian has tiny scales embedded in its skin.

Most of the 300 species of salamanders live in temperate areas of the world, but some species are common in the tropics. Salamanders tend to live near water in moist places, such as under stones or rotten logs. Some species that live mainly in water are commonly called *newts*.

Most salamanders measure about 10 to 15 cm (about 4 to 6 in.) long. Their front and hind limbs are approximately the same size and are attached at right angles to the body, resulting in a slow, labored walk. Salamanders eat almost any small animal, especially worms or small arthropods.

Salamander eggs are fertilized internally. The female uses her cloaca to pick up a packet of sperm, or *spermatophore*, that the male has deposited on a leaf or stick. Aquatic species deposit the fertilized eggs in the water, and land species place them on the ground or on logs. The newly hatched young resemble adult salamanders much more closely than tadpoles resemble frogs and toads. All young salamanders have gills, but most develop lungs as adults.

Some species of salamanders never lose their larval characteristics even though they achieve sexual maturity and begin to reproduce. This type of development is called **neoteny.** The common North American mud puppies and the congo eel are examples of amphibians that reproduce while still aquatic and using gills to breathe.

36.15 Caecilians

Caecilians have long slender bodies and no limbs. Their bodies are wormlike in appearance. They burrow into the ground of tropical forests and live on worms and small invertebrates they find in the ground. Most adult caecilians either are blind or have very small eyes. Special sensory tentacles are located between their snout and their eyes. Caecilians have many vertebrae and typically measure about 30 cm (1 ft.) long. Some species, however, grow to 130 cm (4.3 ft.). Caecilians are rarely seen, and less is known about their behavior than about the other, more common, amphibians.

Section Review

1. **Analyzing Ideas**   How do toads and frogs differ?
2. **Summarizing Ideas**   Describe the preferred habitats of land salamanders.
3. **Comparing Structures**   How do the sense organs of caecilians differ from those of other amphibians?
4. **Inferring Conclusions**   How do mud puppies respire?

Thinking Critically

INVESTIGATION 36:
How Are Amphibian Embryos Cultured in the Laboratory?

Objectives
- To *evaluate* methods for culturing frog embryos
- To *observe* the early development of frogs

Materials
frog eggs, watch glass, three culture dishes, pond water, spoon or spatula, stereomicroscope, thermometer

Prelab Preparation
1. List environmental factors that can affect frog embryo development.
2. Discuss the advantages and disadvantages of culturing frog embryos in distilled water, tap water, and pond water.
3. Describe how water temperature might affect development of frog embryos.
4. Explain how you would determine the best temperature to culture frog embryos in the laboratory.

Inquiry: Lab Technique
5. Make a chart similar to the one shown for recording data.

Observations on Tadpole Development					
Days	1	2	3	4	5
Room temperature					
Warm					
Cold					

6. Place five frog embryos in a watch glass and cover them with pond water.
7. Use a stereomicroscope to observe the embryos. *Does the dark side of an embryo normally face upward or downward?*
8. *Which characteristics are common to all of the specimens? Which characteristics distinguish the specimens from each other? Can you count the number of cells in each specimen?*

9. Remove any specimens that appear to be severely injured or dead. *How will the removal of these embryos benefit the remaining specimens?*
10. Label a culture dish "Room Temperature." Add pond water that is at room temperature to a depth of about 2.5 cm. Label a second culture dish "Cold" and a third "Warm." Add cold water to the second dish and warm water to the third dish, each to a depth of about 2.5 cm. Record the temperature of the water in each of the three dishes.
11. Using a spoon or spatula, gently transfer ten embryos to each dish.
12. Store the dishes according to your teacher's instructions.
13. Use the stereomicroscope to observe your specimens on days 1, 2, 3, 4, and 7. Record all changes in the specimens and make drawings. Remove any injured or dead specimens. Replace the water in each dish with fresh culture medium, always at the same temperature.
14. Describe any differences that you observe among the cultures.

Analysis
1. **Summarizing Observations** Summarize your observations.
2. **Evaluating Methods** What temperature is best for culturing frog embryos? Why?
3. **Evaluating Methods** Why was it unnecessary to feed the embryos during the Investigation?
4. **Inferring Ideas** How might the jellylike layer that surrounds an embryo help it to survive in water that varies in temperature?
5. **Making Inferences** How might the embryo's coloration help in escaping predators?

Chapter 36 Review

Summary

Amphibians were the first vertebrates to move between water and land. They adapted to the increased dryness of the land environment, to its greater gravitational stress, and to greater fluctuations in temperature.

The frog's systems show its adaptations to living on land. Frogs have a skeleton and powerful legs for movement on land as well as in water. Adult frogs breathe mainly with lungs.

A circulatory system with a three-chambered heart moves the blood to and from the lungs. Frogs return to water to reproduce. The larvae, called tadpoles, live in water and breathe through gills before becoming adults.

Toads resemble frogs but are even more suited to life on land. Amphibians with tails include salamanders. Caecilians are legless, blind amphibians that burrow.

BioTerms

amplexus (**581**)
cerebellum (**580**)
cerebrum (**580**)
cloaca (**577**)
duodenum (**577**)
estivation (**580**)
Eustachian tube (**576**)
fat body (**581**)
hibernation (**580**)
ileum (**577**)
insulin (**577**)

large intestine (**577**)
medulla oblongata (**580**)
mesentery (**577**)
mouth breathing (**578**)
mucus gland (**574**)
neoteny (**584**)
nictitating membrane (**575**)
ovary (**581**)
pancreas (**577**)

pulmonary circulation (**579**)
renal artery (**581**)
small intestine (**577**)
systemic circulation (**579**)

tadpole (**582**)
testis (**581**)
tympanic membrane (**575**)
vomerine tooth (**577**)

For each pair of terms, explain the differences in their meanings.

1. cerebrum, cerebellum
2. duodenum, ileum
3. hibernation, estivation
4. pancreas, insulin

BioQuiz   (Write all answers on a separate sheet of paper.)

Completion

1. In the frog, insulin is secreted by the _____ .
2. The part of the frog's brain that coordinates muscular activity is called the _____ .
3. The process that leads to the release of eggs by the female is _____ .
4. Prior to fertilization, frog eggs are coated with a jellylike covering and stored in _____ .
5. The type of development in which some species of salamanders reproduce even though they still show certain larval characteristics is called _____ .

Multiple Choice

6. Solid waste matter passes out of the frog's body through its   a) Eustachian tube.   b) mucus gland.   c) cloaca.   d) small intestine.
7. In a frog, the automatic responses of the nervous system are carried out by the   a) cerebrum.   b) cerebellum.   c) medulla oblongata.   d) optic lobe.
8. Which of the following is not part of the frog's brain?   a) cerebrum   b) ileum   c) cerebellum   d) medulla oblongata
9. Food passes from the stomach to the

_____ via the pylorus.   a) duodenum
b) ileum   c) mesentery   d) renal artery

10. The _____ is the control center of the frog's brain.   a) medulla oblongata
b) cerebrum   c) olfactory lobe
d) cerebellum

11. The thin, tough membrane that holds the frog's intestine in place is the _____ .
a) mesentery.   b) ileum.   c) cloaca.
d) fat body.

12. The third eyelid in frogs is called
a) a neoteny.   b) a nictitating membrane.   c) a mesentery.   d) a tympanic membrane.

13. The membrane that supports frog intestines is a   a) neoteny.   b) nictitating membrane.   c) mesentery.   d) tympanic membrane.

14. The pancreas of frogs excretes both

digestive enzymes and   a) insulin.
b) eggs.   c) fat bodies.   d) mucus.

15. A period of inactivity by frogs during the summer is called   a) hibernation.
b) estivation.   c) amplexus.
d) neoteny.

16. How do frogs and toads protect themselves against drying out on land?
17. How can a frog breathe under water?
18. How do the limbs of frogs and salamanders differ?
19. What function do enlarged thumbs on a frog serve?
20. How are salamander eggs fertilized?

Application/Critical Thinking

1. **Inferring Relationships**   Centuries ago, if people saw toads after a rain they believed it had "rained toads." Use your knowledge to give another explanation.
2. **Evaluating Conclusions**   Caecilians spend all their lives underground. Write a paragraph explaining how some caecilian features are adaptations to underground life.
3. **Analyzing Relationships**   Extremely large or small size can be an adaptation that helps

an animal defend itself. How might you relate this theory to the size differential between the largest (23 cm) and the smallest (2.3 cm) toads?

4. **Synthesizing Conclusions**   One salamander retains larval characteristics unless the water in which it lives begins to dry up. Then it loses its gills and develops lungs. What does this indicate to you about the adaptive value of neoteny?

Cross-Discipline Connection

Biology and Literature   The witches in Macbeth use "eye of newt" and "toe of frog" to prepare their spellbinding brew. Fairy tales with amphibian themes include those about princesses kissing frogs, and there are myths about toads causing warts. Brainstorm with your classmates why amphibians are used to create negative connotations in literature.

Discovery Through Reading

Read about the tiny coqui tree frogs of Puerto Rico in the article "What's Smaller Than a Matchbox and Louder Than a Speeding Plane?" _National Wildlife_ (December–January 1987): 33. How have male and female coqui tree frogs adapted physically to their call?

CHAPTER

37

Reptiles

Outline

Adult land iguana

Focus

About 6,000 species of reptiles, including snakes, lizards, tortoises, turtles, and crocodiles, are alive today. The members of this cold-blooded group are relatives of the dinosaurs. Reptiles are widely distributed but are more common in warm tropics and deserts than in cooler areas. Modern reptiles are the descendents of the first land-dwelling vertebrates.

■ *Why are reptiles more common in warm climates than in cool climates?*

■ *What features does the iguana in the photograph show that are not seen in frogs?*

History of Reptiles

Amphibians never live far from water because their thin skins dry out quickly and their eggs must be fertilized in water. The scaly skin and internal fertilization of reptiles are adaptations that allowed reptiles to become independent of an aquatic environment. As a result, reptiles became the first vertebrates to move into new habitats on land where there was little competition with other animals for food and territory.

37.1 The Success of Reptiles

Unlike amphibians, reptiles do not need to return to water to reproduce. In reptiles, fertilization is internal, so water is not needed to transport the sperm to the egg. In addition the reptiles have a "land egg"—an egg that can protect a developing embryo on dry land. The development of such an egg allowed reptiles to reproduce in even the driest environment.

The reptile's egg, called an **amniotic egg,** has a fluid-filled sac enclosed by a protective, porous shell. The shell may be flexible like leather, or rigid and reinforced with calcium carbonate. Oxygen and carbon dioxide pass freely through the shell.

Inside the shell are four specialized membranes: the amnion, the yolk sac, the allantois, and the chorion. The **amnion** surrounds the embryo and forms a chamber filled with a saline fluid. The embryo thus floats in its own tiny sea, which also provides support for the embryo's tissues. The **yolk sac** is

Figure 37–1. The amniotic egg (below, left) is believed to have first appeared among reptiles. Young reptile hatchlings (below, right) were able to develop on land because of the protection provided by the egg's fluid-filled amnion.

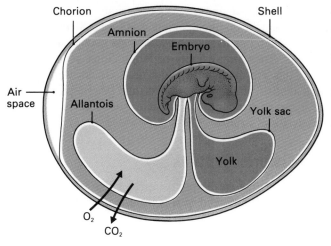

attached to the abdomen of the embryo. It forms a container for the large amount of stored food called the **yolk.** The **allantois** (uh LAN tuh wihs) makes up a sac that stores the nitrogen wastes produced by the growing cells. The allantois is rich with blood vessels. The outermost membrane, the **chorion** (KOHR ree ahn), lines the eggshell. Together the allantois and chorion control the passage of gases in and out of the egg, supply the embryo with oxygen, and remove carbon dioxide.

Unlike amphibian eggs, reptile eggs have an outer shell that protects the embryo from drying out. This adaptation helped reptiles succeed in a land environment.

Another difference between amphibians and reptiles is seen in the structure of their skins. Unlike the soft, thin skin of amphibians, the skin of reptiles is thick and contains **keratin.** Keratin is a protein that makes skin hard and waterproof. The skin of reptiles is also covered with horny, overlapping scales or plates that are also made of keratin.

37.2 The Age of Reptiles

The fossil record shows that the first reptiles appeared on Earth about 310 million years ago. These reptiles, called *cotylosaurs* (KAHD uh luh sahrs), were small lizardlike animals that fed on insects. As the Earth underwent extreme climatic changes during the Permian and Triassic periods (275 to 180 million years ago) and the land dried out, cotylosaurs evolved into a number of new kinds of reptiles. These descendants of the cotylosaurs became the dominant animals on land during the Mesozoic era, which lasted from about 225 million to 65 million years ago. For this reason, the Mesozoic era is called the Age of Reptiles.

During the Jurassic and Cretaceous periods of the Mesozoic era, reptiles were the dominant animals on Earth. Some lived on land, others swam like fishes, and still others glided through the air like birds. They ate a variety of foods. Some reptiles were *herbivores* that ate thick, lush vegetation. Others were *carnivores* that ate fish, amphibians, insects, and other reptiles. They showed many of the physical characteristics that are seen in modern species of lizards.

37.3 Prehistoric Reptiles

The most fascinating of the prehistoric reptiles were the dinosaurs. The dinosaurs ranged in size from animals as small as a chicken to the largest creatures that have ever lived on land. The largest dinosaurs were herbivores, such as the apatosaurus (uh pat uh SAHR uhs) and the diplodocus (dih PLAHD uh kuhs).

Figure 37–2. The cotylosaur was the ancestor of most modern reptiles. Only the crocodile descended from another ancestor.

These dinosaurs had immense bodies with long necks and tails. They could have easily peered over a four-story building. The diplodocus, for example, is estimated to have been more than 24 meters (80 ft.) long and to have weighed over 50,000 kg (110,000 lb.). The diplodocus had a small head with tiny teeth and weak jaws. These reptiles probably spent much of their time near shallow lakes and swamps where they fed on water plants. The water may have helped support their huge bulk.

Perhaps the fiercest of the predatory dinosaurs was the *Tyrannosaurus rex* (tih ran uh SAHR uhs REHX). This carnivorous beast walked on its hind legs and stood 6 m (20 ft.) tall. It weighed more than 8,000 kg (17,600 lb.). The *Tyrannosaurus rex* had a huge head with powerful jaws studded with sharp, daggerlike teeth 15 cm (6 in.) long.

Some dinosaurs were "walking tanks" covered with heavy, protective armor. Certain dinosaurs, such as triceratops (try SEHR uh tahps), had huge, protective spikes on its head and armor surrounding the back of the neck. Other dinosaurs, such as the stegosaurus (stehg uh SAWR uhs), had a defensive armor that consisted of two pairs of sharp spikes on its tail and two rows of large bony plates along its spine. Some scientists think

Biofact

Q: *How long did it take a diplodocus to attain its giant size?*

A: If the diplodocus were warm-blooded, it might have grown to its full length of 24 m (80 ft.) in 50 years. A cold-blooded diplodocus might have had to live 200 years before it became fully grown.

Figure 37–3. Dinosaurs were the dominant life form of the Jurassic period. A scene such as this was common about 150 million years ago.

that the bony plates were used by the animal to regulate its body temperature.

Some ancient reptiles, such as the pterodactyl (tehr uh DAC tuhl), had the ability to fly. The fourth digit of the pterodactyl's hand was extremely long. A thin flap of skin from the animal's side was attached to this long digit to form a gliding wing. Pterodactyls were about the size of turkeys but had wing spans of more than 8 m (26 ft.).

Some prehistoric reptiles, called ichthyosaurs (IHK thee uh sawrs) looked like porpoises. These reptiles lived in the ocean and were powerful swimmers. Plesiosaurs (PLEE see uh sawrs) were also marine. They had extremely long necks, and their limbs were modified into flippers.

Dinosaurs were the dominant animals on Earth for about 160 million years, then died out. The modern vertebrates most closely related to dinosaurs are birds and crocodiles. All other modern reptiles evolved from the early cotylosaurs and their descendants. A separate group of early reptiles gave rise to mammals.

Reading Critically

Synthesizing Information
What did all the different kinds of dinosaurs have in common?

Thinking Critically

Section Review

1. **Summarizing Functions** What is the function of each embryonic membrane in an amniotic egg?
2. **Identifying Ideas** What were the largest animals ever to have lived on the land?
3. **Comparing Ideas** How do endothermic and ectothermic animals differ from each other?
4. **Inferring Relationships** Why were the reptiles able to colonize the land so quickly once the amniotic egg had been developed?

Modern Reptiles

Though reptiles no longer dominate land environments, they still play a major ecological role in many of the world's biological communities. This is especially true in the tropics, deserts, and warm grasslands. Many reptiles are virtually the same as their ancient ancestors. Other groups have adapted to new environments.

37.4 Characteristics

Like their ancient ancestors, modern reptiles have a waterproof skin and produce amniotic eggs. All reptiles also have strong, bony skeletons and well-developed lungs. Most reptiles have two pairs of limbs that enable them to walk on land. The limbs of some, but not all, reptiles are positioned more vertically under the trunk than the limbs of amphibians. The limbs of reptiles are also larger, stronger, and support more weight than those of amphibians. Reptilian feet have toes with claws that can be used for digging or for climbing on trees and rocks.

The nervous system of reptiles is similar to that of amphibians. The reptile brain is small in relation to the body. For example, a crocodile 2.5 m (8 ft.) long has a brain the size of a walnut. Despite the small brain, reptiles have shown complex behavioral patterns, including elaborate courtship rituals.

The excretory system of reptiles shows modifications that minimize water loss. Water is absorbed into the body through the intestine, bladder, pairs of kidneys, and cloaca. Aquatic reptiles, which do not need to conserve water, excrete most of their nitrogenous wastes as ammonia dissolved in water. Terrestrial reptiles, which must retain water, secrete nitrogenous wastes in a drier form, as uric acid solids.

Like amphibians, most reptiles have a three-chambered heart. However, crocodiles and their relatives have a heart with four chambers, a structure more efficient at separating oxygenated and deoxygenated blood.

Section Objectives

- *List* four characteristics common to all reptiles.
- *Name* the four orders of reptiles and give distinguishing features of each.
- *Distinguish* between alligators and crocodiles.
- *Describe* the two different methods by which snakes kill their prey.
- *State* three methods by which snakes move.

For a comparison of vertebrate systems, see pages 894–905.

Figure 37–4. Scaly skin and toes with claws are typical features of reptiles. The reptile shown here is an iguana.

Figure 37–5. The tuatara of New Zealand looks almost exactly like its ancestor of 200 million years ago. For this reason, the tuatara is often called a "living fossil."

See pages 918–919 for the classification of reptiles.

37.5 Classification

Of the 16 orders of reptiles that once flourished, only 4 now remain:

- *Rhyncocephalia* (rihn koh suh FAY lee uh): This order consists of a single species, the *Sphenodon punctatus,* commonly called by its native New Zealand name of tuatara (too uh TAH ruh).
- *Chelonia* (kih LOH nee uh): Turtles and tortoises make up this order. The bodies of these reptiles are enclosed within two bony shells.
- *Crocodilia* (krahk uh DIHL ee uh): These are the crocodiles, alligators, and related species adapted for life in shallow water.
- *Squamata* (skwuh MAYD uh): This order includes lizards and snakes.

37.6 Tuataras

The tuatara represents the last surviving species of a group of reptiles that appeared on Earth more than 225 million years ago. The tuataras living today have changed hardly at all from their prehistoric ancestors. Adults are about 60 cm (24 in.) long. The tuatara has strong legs and a long tail. A scaly crest runs down its neck and back. Like some lizards the tuatara has a third **parietal** (puh RY uh tuhl) **eye** located on the top of the head. The parietal eye has both a lens and a light-sensitive surface, but no muscles, and is not used for seeing. Some scientists believe it may be used for temperature control. Tuataras live only in the Cook Strait and on North Island of New Zealand. They are an endangered species and are protected by the local government.

37.7 Turtles and Tortoises

Turtles and tortoises are another group of reptiles that have changed little through time. Some of the 150 species live only on land, while others live mainly in water. The term *tortoise* is commonly used to refer to land species and *turtle* to most aquatic species. Some turtles and tortoises are enormous. The giant land tortoise of the Galapagos Islands grows to 1.5 m (5 ft.) in length and may weigh up to 255 kg (560 lb.). Tortoises often have long life spans. Some Galapagos tortoises live as long as 150 years. Many Galapagos tortoises were on the verge of extinction at the beginning of this century, but they are being reestablished by careful breeding programs.

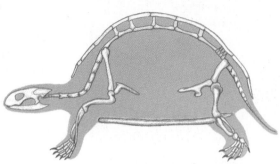

The shell is the distinguishing characteristic of turtles and tortoises. The shell is a two-part case made of modified horny scales. The top half of the shell is the **carapace** and the bottom half is the **plastron.** The shell is covered by plates called **scutes** (skyootz). Turtles and tortoises use their shells for protection, and pull their heads and limbs into their shells when threatened. Unlike other reptiles, turtles and tortoises have no teeth. Their jaws form a horny beak that crushes their food. Turtles and some tortoises are *omnivorous*. They eat both plants and animals.

Figure 37–6. Locked inside its shell, the turtle does not fit most people's picture of a reptile. The illustration above shows the hidden features of its skeleton.

37.8 Alligators and Crocodiles

The order Crocodilia includes about 250 species of alligators, crocodiles, and their smaller relatives, caimans and gavials. Crocodilians are active water-dwelling carnivores. They have broad, heavy bodies and are powerful swimmers. Their strong tails propel them through the water. The crocodilian's eyes and nostrils rise above the rest of its head. This adaptation allows a crocodilian to remain submerged and still see and breathe. A special valve between its mouth and nose passage keeps water from entering the breathing passage even when the animal opens its mouth to feed under water. Many crocodilians lie in wait for prey with only the tips of their nostrils above the water. When their prey comes within range, they use their powerful jaws and sharp teeth to capture it.

As Figure 37–7 shows, crocodilians differ from one another mainly in the structure of their head and teeth. The alligator has a broad head with a rounded snout. The crocodile has a triangular head with a pointed snout. In alligators, the teeth of the lower jaw fit inside the teeth of the upper jaw. In crocodiles, most of the upper and lower teeth mesh together.

Alligator

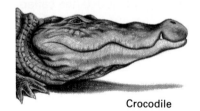

Crocodile

Figure 37–7. Crocodiles (bottom) have two protruding teeth and narrower snouts than alligators (top). Caimans and gavials have snouts that are even narrower.

Figure 37–8. Geckos have toe pads containing many tiny hooks. These hooks enable the animal to climb surfaces as smooth as a glass window.

37.9 Lizards and Snakes

Members of the order Squamata are the most successful of the modern reptiles. Together they comprise almost 4,500 species. The two major kinds of squamates are lizards and snakes.

Lizards The most obvious difference between lizards and snakes is that most lizards have legs. Some wormlike lizards, however, have no limbs at all. Lizards live in diverse habitats. Some, like most skinks, live on the ground and walk on small, weak legs. Others, like geckos, are nocturnal and may live in trees. Geckos have claws modified into pads for clinging to vertical surfaces. Many lizards run on their hind limbs. "Flying" lizards live in trees and glide from branch to branch.

Some lizards eat only plants; others eat only insects or small animals. Most lizards, however, are omnivores.

Many lizards have the capacity to regenerate lost limbs or tails. This capacity for regeneration protects the lizards by allowing them to escape from a predator by losing an appendage.

BIOLOGY AND YOU:

Snake Medicine

A fear of poisonous snakes is justified—some snake venoms can kill humans. The venom of some very deadly snakes, however, can be used to treat human diseases.

Researchers have extracted a substance called *ancrod,* for example, from the venom of the Malaysian pit viper. Ancrod stimulates the body to dissolve blood clots.

Ancrod was first used to help keep blood clots from forming in patients with artery disease. Blood clots often form in the arteries of these patients.

If a blood clot breaks away from an artery wall and blocks a vessel carrying oxygen and nutrients to the heart, the patient suffers a heart attack. By using ancrod to dissolve clots, physicians are able to avert heart attacks.

The success with patients with artery disease led researchers to use ancrod on patients with *lupus,* a disease that often strikes young people. Lupus victims accumulate blood clots in their vital organs, especially in their kidneys. The clots can cause these organs to malfunction.

Ancrod dissolves the clots and appears to have no side effects.

Researchers are now investigating the possible medical applications of chemicals in other snake venoms, as well as ancrod, in treating such varied diseases as arthritis, multiple sclerosis, and cancer.

Chameleons are tree-dwelling lizards native to Africa and Madagascar. They are capable of dramatic changes of color in response to excitement or to changes in light or temperature. These color changes often act to camouflage the chameleons, allowing them to blend in with their surroundings. Chameleons can become green, beige, or brown, and can also develop spots. Chameleons have large eyes that rotate independently of each other. Keen vision and quick reflexes enable a chameleon to catch insects with a flick of its sticky tongue.

The largest of all lizards is the Komodo dragon, so called because it comes from the Indonesian island of Komodo. These lizards may grow to be almost 3 m (10 ft.) long. Komodo dragons have extremely strong limbs and powerful claws. When they run, their limbs lift their bodies completely off the ground, and they may attain speeds of 16 km (10 mi.) per hour. Komodo dragons are highly successful carnivores. They catch and eat animals as large as small deer or wild pigs. Because of their large claws and aggressive manner, Komodo dragons have few natural enemies.

Only two species of lizards, the Gila monster of the southwestern United States and the beaded lizard of Mexico, are venomous, that is, able to inject venom, or poison, through a bite. The venom glands of the Gila monster form a row inside the lower lip at the base of grooved teeth. When it bites another animal, a Gila monster shakes its head vigorously from side to side. This action causes the venom to flow out of the mouth, through the grooves, and into the prey. The venom of a Gila monster can kill a small animal. The venom is not usually deadly to humans but can make a person extremely ill.

Iguanas are large, often colorful lizards that live in tropical areas. Many have tough, leathery skin and a large, distinctive crest on their backs. This group includes the only aquatic lizard, the marine iguana of the Galapagos Islands. This large black lizard is adapted to life in the ocean, where it eats green algae exclusively. The marine iguana maintains its salt balance by secreting salt through special glands in the nose.

Snakes Snakes are limbless reptiles that slither over the ground or live in trees. Most features peculiar to snakes are adaptations to their limbless state. Their bodies have become extremely long and muscular. They have a large number of ribs and vertebrae that make their bodies both strong and flexible. In some species, one lung is missing or reduced in size which allows room in the body cavity for the swallowing of large prey.

Both lizards and snakes periodically shed their outer layer of skin—a process called **molting.** Most snakes rid themselves

Figure 37–9. The chameleon's ability to change color is controlled by hormones that act on various pigments in the skin.

Figure 37-10. A snake molts by literally crawling out of its skin. Active snakes molt frequently, some as many as six or more times a year.

Figure 37-11. The coils of a boa constrictor (left) tighten when the boa's prey exhales. The prey soon suffocates because it can no longer take in air. Loosely-hinged jaws permit some snakes, like the parrot snake (right) to open their mouths extremely wide, and feed on large prey.

of their outgrown skin in one piece. The skin around the mouth and head loosens first. Then the snake proceeds to crawl out of its old skin, turning the discarded skin inside out as it moves.

Snakes have highly developed senses of taste and smell. When a snake darts its slender, forked tongue in and out of its mouth, it is "tasting" the air. As the tongue darts out, it picks up scent particles in the environment. The tongue returns into the mouth, where it presses up against two small hollows in the roof of the mouth. These hollows, lined with nerves sensitive to chemicals, are called **Jacobson's organ.** Jacobson's organ allows a snake to track its prey. Jacobson's organ and the sensory tongue allow a male snake to follow the scent trail of a female snake.

Snakes have relatively poor senses of vision and hearing. They have eyes on each side of the head that are covered by transparent scales. Unlike most other reptiles, snakes do not have movable eyelids. Snakes have no external ears or eardrums and can hear only a few sounds.

Most snakes are **oviparous** (oh VIHP uhr uhs)—they lay eggs that hatch outside the mother's body. However, a few snakes are **ovoviviparous.** The fertilized eggs of these snakes develop and hatch inside the mother, who then gives birth to live young.

All snakes are predators. Many snakes simply seize an animal and swallow it live. Some snakes, called *constrictors*, kill their prey by coiling their bodies around their victim. As the snake begins to slowly tighten its muscles, the pressure of constriction stops the animal from breathing and also stops the heart and circulation of blood. After the prey is overpowered, the snake swallows it whole.

The remarkable structure of the jaws allows the snake to swallow prey four to five times larger in diameter than its own body. The lower jaw is made up of two bones held together at the chin by elastic tissues. This allows each side of the jaw to be

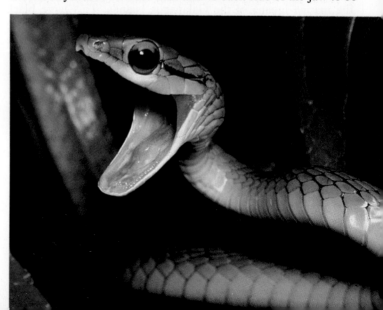

moved separately. The upper and lower jaw are similarly attached. This arrangement allows the mouth to open to an enormous size. By moving one side of the jaw forward and then the other, a snake "walks" its food down its throat. After swallowing, the snake digests the prey. Digestion is slow. A boa constrictor may take five days to digest a rat.

Some species of snakes kill their prey with venom. These snakes include cobras, sea snakes, copperheads, and mambas. Nineteen species of venomous snakes live in the United States. They include copperheads, coral snakes, water moccasins, and several varieties of rattlesnakes.

Reading Critically

Inferring Conclusions What do you think would happen to a snake if it lost its tongue?

THINKING ABOUT BIOLOGY: Locomotion in Snakes

Not all snakes crawl in the same way. In fact, snakes have three different ways to move on land: lateral undulating, straight crawling, and sidewinding.

The most rapid way of moving on land is by lateral undulations. The body of the snake forms waves that begin at the head and travel backwards toward the tail. These waves, or loops, are pressed against the ground, producing a thrust that pushes the snake forward. The entire body of the snake follows the same track. Each succeeding loop pushes against the same point, such as a pebble or a blade of grass.

Snakes may also use a straight crawling movement. Straight crawling takes advantage of the large overlapping scales located on the snake's belly. To move, the snake stretches forward with part of its body. It then lowers the stretched part to the ground. The belly scales make contact with the ground and anchor the snake as it pulls the back part of its body forward.

Sidewinding allows a snake to move over loose sand. The snake's body forms a double S-curve. The head, the center of the body, and the tail are raised. The snake's body now makes contact with the ground at only two or three points. Using the contact points for support, the snake throws the loops of its body forward and to the side. This produces a rolling, sideways form of travel.

■ **Inferring Relationships** Under what conditions might you expect a snake to use straight crawling to move?

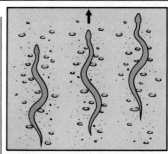
Lateral undulating

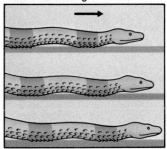
Straight crawling

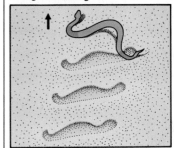
Sidewinding

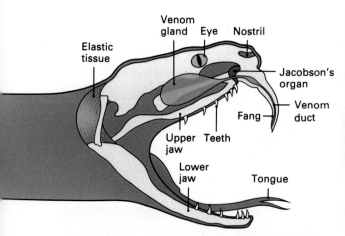

Figure 37–12. Venomous snakes, like the copperhead (above right), have venom that kills or paralyzes prey. These snakes have fangs, teeth modified for injecting venom. The illustration above shows a snake's head and a flexible jaw.

Biofact

Q: *What is the most venomous snake?*

A: A sea snake found off the northwestern Australian coast produces a neurotoxin about 100 times more powerful than that of land snakes.

In venomous snakes some of the teeth are modified as sharp **fangs** through which venom flows. Fangs are connected to special venom glands that contain venom. A venomous snake strikes at its prey with its mouth open. When the needle-sharp fangs enter the prey, venom flows into the victim. The snake then releases the victim and waits for the venom to take effect.

Venom contains poisonous proteins or *toxins*. There are two main types of toxins, each affecting the prey's body in a different way. **Hemotoxins** destroy the red blood cells and break down the walls of the blood vessels, causing heavy internal bleeding. **Neurotoxins** attack the nervous system, paralyzing the nerve cells. Cobras and their relatives have venom that is mostly neurotoxic, whereas rattlesnake's venom is mainly hemotoxic.

Some venomous snakes, called *pit vipers,* have a special type of sensory organ. Pit vipers have small heat-sensitive pits in front of their eyes. These structures can detect changes in temperature as slight as 0.003°C (0.005°F). The pits allow pit vipers to locate warm-blooded animals. Rattlesnakes, the most common venomous snake in the United States, are pit vipers. Water moccasins and copperheads are also pit vipers.

Section Review

1. **Comparing Structures**   How do the limbs of reptiles differ from those of amphibians?
2. **Classifying Data**   What are the four orders of reptiles?
3. **Analyzing Relationships**   How is an alligator distinguished from a crocodile?
4. **Summarizing Ideas**   By what two methods do snakes kill prey?
5. **Evaluating Ideas**   What is the advantage of sidewinding?

Thinking Critically

INVESTIGATION 37:
How Are Anole Lizards Adapted to Their Environment?

Objectives
- To *observe* structural and behavioral characteristics of an anole lizard
- To *identify* adaptations

Materials

live anole lizard, terrarium, live *Tenebrio* larvae (mealworms) or crickets, bits of apple, green construction paper, gauze strips, masking tape, 1000-mL beaker, 600-mL beaker, metric ruler, ice

Prelab Preparation
1. List differences among lizards, crocodiles, turtles, and snakes.
2. Describe how a lizard obtains food.

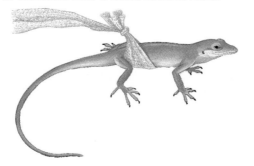

Inquiry: Exploration
3. Observe a lizard in its terrarium. Describe and record its color.
4. **CAUTION: Do not hold a lizard by its tail.** Gently remove a lizard from the terrarium and place it on the table.
5. Cut a strip of gauze about 40-cm long. Make a noose on one end of the strip. Gently slip the noose over the lizard's head and body until it comes to rest just above the back legs. Tighten the noose just enough to keep it in place.
6. Place the lizard on green construction paper. Use masking tape to secure the loose end of the gauze strip to the table top. The gauze should act as a leash, defining the area in which the lizard can move freely. *Why is this method better than letting the lizard run freely or holding the leash in your hand?*

7. Identify the eyes, teeth, tympanic membrane, and tail. Make a labeled drawing of the specimen.
8. Gently touch the surface of the lizard's back and sides. Describe the appearance, texture, and degree of moisture of the lizard's outer surface.
9. Describe the structure of the lizard's legs, feet, and toes.
10. Measure the length of the lizard's abdomen and the length of its tail. Record your results.
11. Males have a pouch of skin beneath the jaw called the *dewlap.* When inflated, this pouch may be brightly colored. Determine if a dewlap is present and record your observations.
12. Place some *Tenebrio* larvae and bits of apple near the lizard and observe the lizard's reaction. Record your observations.
13. Record any change in the lizard's color that has occurred since step 1.
14. Fill a 1000-mL beaker about one-third full with crushed ice. Gently place the lizard in a 600-mL beaker and place this beaker in the beaker of ice. Observe the animal's color after a few minutes and record your observations.
15. Gently remove the noose and return the lizard to its terrarium.

Analysis
1. **Analyzing Observations** How do the limbs and body covering of a lizard differ from those of an amphibian?
2. **Making Inferences** How are a lizard's limbs and body covering better adapted for life on land than those of an amphibian?
3. **Making Inferences** How might the length of a lizard's tail improve its chance of survival?
4. **Analyzing Observations** What evidence from the Investigation indicates that an anole lizard may change color in response to stimuli other than background color?

Chapter 37 Review

Summary

Reptiles have two distinct advantages over amphibians in coping with life on land. Reptiles have an amniotic egg that protects the embryo during development on dry land, and a hard, waterproof skin.

Reptiles originated about 280 million years ago. The first reptiles were cotylosaurs, small lizardlike animals that fed on insects. The dinosaurs are the most notable of the ancient reptiles. Some herbivorous dinosaurs weighed more than 50,000 kg (110,000 lb.). Others were carnivores. The most closely related descendants of the dinosaurs are birds and crocodiles. Some ancient reptiles could fly, and others could swim.

Modern reptiles have two pairs of limbs that are positioned vertically under the trunk. Reptilian feet have clawed toes. Modern reptiles are classified into four orders: tuataras, large, lizardlike animals from New Zealand; turtles and tortoises, which are characterized by two shells that encase their bodies; alligators, crocodiles, and related carnivores, found in shallow water; and lizards and snakes, which belong to the largest order of living reptiles.

BioTerms

allantois **(590)**
amnion **(589)**
amniotic
  egg **(589)**
carapace **(595)**
chorion **(590)**
fang **(600)**
hemotoxin
  (600)

Jacobson's
  organ **(598)**
keratin **(590)**
molting **(597)**
neurotoxin **(600)**
oviparous **(598)**
ovoviviparous
  (598)
parietal eye **(594)**

plastron **(595)**
scute **(595)**

yolk **(590)**
yolk sac **(589)**

For each pair of terms, explain the differences in their meanings.

1. hemotoxin, neurotoxin
2. oviparous, ovoviviparous
3. amnion, allantois
4. carapace, plastron

BioQuiz   (Write all answers on a separate sheet of paper.)

Completion

1. Caimans and gavials are members of the order _____ .
2. The respiratory system of snakes has only one _____ to allow for swallowing bulky food.
3. The shell that covers the turtle's back is the _____ .
4. Nutrition for the developing embryo in an amniotic egg is provided by the _____ .
5. A third eye, located on top of the head, that may be used for temperature control is called the _____ eye.

Multiple Choice

6. The venom of rattlesnakes is an example of a) hemotoxin. b) neurotoxin. c) keratin. d) molting.
7. The _____ was an ancient flying reptile. a) diplodocus b) stegosaurus c) apatosaurus d) pterodactyl
8. The protein that makes the skin of a reptile waterproof is a) plastron. b) keratin. c) amnion. d) chorion.
9. Reptiles dominated the land during the a) Mesozoic era. b) Cenozoic era. c) Paleozoic era. d) Precambrian era.

10. Animals that maintain a constant internal body temperature are a) ectothermic. b) oviparous. c) endothermic. d) molting.
11. If a reptile's eggs are hatched outside the body, the reptile is said to be a) ovoviviparous. b) oviparous. c) endothermic. d) ectothermic.
12. Which of the following reptiles has a four-chambered heart? a) an iguana b) a tortoise c) a crocodile d) a snake
13. The shells of turtles are covered by plates called a) scutes. b) carapaces. c) keratins. d) plastrons.
14. Snakes rid themselves of their skins through a process called a) metamorphosis. b) excretion.

c) constricting. d) molting.
15. The last surviving species of a group of reptiles that appeared on earth more than 225 million years ago is a a) tortoise. b) crocodile. c) pterodactyl. d) tuatara.

Writing Critically

16. How do neurotoxins and hemotoxins differ in their mode of action?
17. What two characteristics are mainly responsible for the success of reptiles?
18. How do snakes produce young?
19. When did dinosaurs dominate Earth and when did they die out?
20. What qualities of the amniotic egg allow the embryo to survive on land?

Application/Critical Thinking

1. **Analyzing Structures** Why is having no limbs an advantage for a snake? Why might this be a disadvantage?
2. **Researching Information** One of the most baffling of all scientific questions is why dinosaurs became extinct. Research two hypotheses that attempt to explain this question.
3. **Evaluating Conclusions** Discuss the advantage of the lack of external ears in snakes, and research how snakes monitor

sounds. How would you explain a snake weaving back and forth to the music of a snake charmer?
4. **Inferring Conclusions** The poisonous coral snakes in the United States are strikingly colored with red, yellow, and black rings. Some harmless snakes, such as king snakes, are colored and ringed in a similar manner. What is the advantage to a nonpoisonous snake in displaying this kind of mimicry?

Cross-Discipline Connection

Biology and Literature Reptiles have been portrayed in literature as evil. Provide evidence to support or disprove these portrayals of reptiles.

Discovery Through Reading

The article "Hidden Life of a Timber Rattler," *National Geographic* (July 1987): 128–138, describes the mysterious behaviors of the North American timber rattler. What are the rattler's behaviors near the den?

"Searching for Truth in Alligator Country," *National Wildlife* (October–November 1987): 12–19, describes efforts to maintain populations of alligators. Why were alligators considered endangered?

Birds

Outline

Arctic tern

Focus

Birds are feathered vertebrates that display extraordinary
behaviors. The Arctic tern makes an incredible yearly journey
from Alaska and other regions close to the North Pole to
Antarctica, a distance of 18,000 km (11,000 mi.). A loon
will search for food to underwater depths of 49 m (160 ft.).
Ostriches and penguins are flightless birds. A few birds mate
for life, and most care for their young.

- *What would happen if suddenly there were no more birds?*

- *What features besides wings do birds share with airplanes?*

Origin and Characteristics

Section Objectives

- *Describe* the ancestors of modern birds.
- *Tell* how birds differ from other vertebrates.
- *List* the four categories of birds.
- *Discuss* how feet and beaks are modified in different kinds of birds.
- *Explain* how the use of pesticides may bring about the extinction of some bird species.

All birds belong to the class Aves. Within this single class are tiny hummingbirds that weigh less than 101 gm (0.35 oz.) and ostriches that stand almost 3 m (10 ft.) tall and weigh more than 125 kg (275 lb.). The extinct elephant birds of Australia were even larger, possibly weighing as much as 450 kg (990 lb.).

Birds live on the high slopes of the Himalayas and on Antarctic icecaps. They flourish in tropical jungles and on city rooftops. Some birds live in deserts while others spend much of their lives soaring over the ocean, returning to land only to breed.

How are birds related to other vertebrates? Where did birds come from, and what kinds of animals were their ancestors?

38.1 Origin of Birds

Birds arose from reptiles, possibly from small tree-climbing dinosaurs that leaped from branch to branch. These dinosaurs did not have feathers. Some scientists have suggested that feathers evolved as a method of insulation for endothermic reptiles. Another theory suggests that feathered wings were an adaptation for hunting, used to trap small land animals. Whether or not feathers originally functioned for flight, insulation, or hunting, a new kind of animal evolved that had feathers but also retained some reptile characteristics. This animal was the first bird.

The earliest known bird, called *Archaeopteryx* (ahr kee AHP tuhr ihx), lived about 140 million years ago. Now extinct, *Archaeopteryx* was about the size of a modern crow. It resembled reptiles in having bony teeth set into jaw sockets, a large bony tail, and claws that were located on each wing. It was, however, covered with feathers and had a skull like a bird. For these reasons, *Archaeopteryx* is considered a link between reptiles and birds.

Other prehistoric birds, such as the aquatic diving bird *Hesperornis* and the large predator *Diatryma*, came after *Archaeopteryx* and had fewer reptilian features. By the beginning of the Cretaceous period, about 130 million years ago, the class Aves had been established on Earth.

38.2 Characteristics of Birds

The most obvious feature of birds is that they have wings and can fly. Flight is not the feature that makes birds unique, however. Birds share this ability with bats and insects.

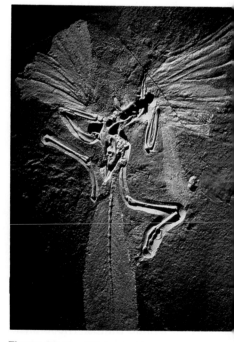

Figure 38–1. *Archaeopteryx* may have looked like a flying reptile, but feathers showed it to be a true bird. Fossil remains indicate that *Archaeopteryx* had short wings with claws at the end and was a clumsy flier.

Feathers distinguish birds from other classes of vertebrates. Some other features of birds are listed below.

- The body is divided into a head, neck, trunk, and tail.
- Bones are lightweight and filled with air.
- Air sacs are found throughout the body.
- Birds lack teeth; jaws are covered by a horny beak.
- Front limbs are modified into wings; hind limbs are adapted for perching, hopping, swimming, or other similar functions.
- Body temperature remains constant.
- The heart has four chambers.
- Reproduction involves the production of an amniotic egg that most species incubate in a nest.

THINKING ABOUT BIOLOGY: Endangered Birds

The California condor is a magnificent bird. It has a wingspan of 3 m (9.9 ft.) or more and can soar for long periods. Only about 30 of these birds are living today, however. They are an endangered species and may soon join the nearly 100 species of birds that have become extinct in the last 300 years.

Although extinction normally occurs in nature, human interference has often speeded up the process. For example, in the 1800s billions of passenger pigeons lived in the United States. These birds were ruthlessly hunted. Within a very short time, the population dropped so low that the species could not recover. The last passenger pigeon died in 1914 in the Cincinnati Zoo.

In most cases, bird species become extinct because humans cause changes in the environment, destroy food, or introduce new predators. One of the most disruptive factors has been the use of pesticides such as DDT, which remain in the environment and often become concentrated in the bodies of insects, fish, and other organisms. As birds eat these animals, pesticides build up in their bodies and interfere with calcium metabolism. As a result, eggshells are fragile, and many young birds die before they can hatch. In the United States, peregrine falcons, such as the one shown here, and brown pelicans almost

disappeared before the harmful effects of DDT were understood. Although DDT was banned in the United States in 1972, it is still used in many countries.

■ **Synthesizing Information** How could the use of DDT in other countries affect species of birds in the United States?

38.3 Classification of Birds

The 27 orders of birds include 8,600 species that are classified on the basis of characteristics that include body structure. The four most common types of birds are shown in Table 38–1.

Comparing Ideas How can a perching bird and a bird of prey be visually distinguished?

Table 38–1: Four Common Bird Types

Type	Common Examples	Types of Feet	Types of Beaks
Flightless Birds	Penguins, rheas, ostriches	Adapted for running	(Beaks vary)
Water Birds	Ducks, swans, geese	Webbed	Broad and flat for filtering / Long and pointed for fishing
Perching Birds	Sparrows, robins, other songbirds	Toes cling to branches	Short, thick, strong (seed eaters) / Long and slender for probing (insect eaters)
Birds of Prey	Hawks, eagles, owls	Sharp, curving claws	Tearing beaks

Each group of birds is adapted to a specific way of life. Legs, feet, and beaks differ, for example, according to the ecological role of the group. Perching birds that live in trees have curved toes that are able to cling to branches. Predators capture their prey with sharp, curving claws called **talons.**

Section Review

1. **Analyzing Ideas** What characteristic distinguishes birds from other vertebrates?
2. **Inferring Relationships** How are legs and feet modified to perform special tasks in the four categories of birds?
3. **Evaluating Ideas** How could you determine whether a bird population has been exposed to DDT?

Thinking Critically

● *Name* the five parts of a contour feather.
● *Explain* how a bird's skeleton and muscles are modified for flight.
● *Describe* how an egg is fertilized and provided with an egg white and shell.
● *Distinguish* between pre-cocial and altricial young.

Anatomy of a Bird

A bird is adapted for flight. Feathers, bones, muscles, and all the internal organs are strong enough and light enough to allow the bird to move easily through the air.

38.4 Feathers

Feathers are outgrowths of the bird's skin that facilitate flight and also provide insulation. Feathers evolved from the scales of birds' reptilian ancestors.

Feathers grow from small sacs in the skin called **follicles.** They first appear as small, dark **pin feathers** that have a scaly covering. As they grow, feathers burst through the scaly covering and expand into mature feathers.

Mature feathers are strong and light because of their unique structure. Feathers have a central cylinder, or **rachis** (RAY kihs), running their length. The part of the rachis that extends out of the skin is solid, while that beneath the skin is hollow. This hollow section is known as the **quill.** Branching off the rachis are many small projections called **barbs.** Barbs make up the soft, flexible part of the feather. Barbs are linked together by small lateral projections called **barbules.** Several barbs hooked together by barbules form a **vane.** When a bird strokes its feathers with its bill, any barbs that have become unhooked link together again.

Birds have four types of feathers: contour feathers, down feathers, filoplumes, and bristles. **Contour feathers** are smooth, sleek feathers that cover the head, body, and wings. Contour feathers protect and streamline the bird. The contour feathers of the wing and tail are especially large and are called *quill feathers.* **Down feathers** are soft, fluffy feathers found under contour feathers. Down feathers insulate birds. Newly hatched birds have only down feathers. **Filoplumes** are short, thin feathers that look like hair. They are also called pin feathers. **Bristles,** also short, hairlike feathers, are located near the bird's nostril. Bristles filter dust.

Many birds have a special gland, called a **preen gland,** at the base of the tail. The preen gland secretes oil. In a process called *preening,* the bird rubs its beak against the preen gland, picks up oil, and spreads the oil over its feathers. Preening serves to waterproof the feathers. The oil repels water that would otherwise seep in and leave the feathers waterlogged.

Birds, like lizards and snakes, go through a process of molting. When feathers become old or damaged, they are shed and

Figure 38–2. This Stellar's jay has its feathers ruffled to increase their insulating effect.

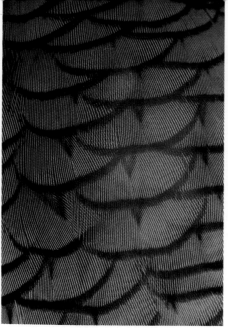

Figure 38–3. Contour feathers (left), down feathers (center), and filoplumes (right) are three major types of feathers.

replaced by new feathers. In most birds, the feathers are not shed all at once. In birds like geese or ducks, however, the loss of even a few flight feathers makes them unable to fly. Therefore, these birds lose all of their feathers at the same time. They avoid predators during molts by hiding in safe places.

Many birds have colored feathers. Sometimes coloration helps the birds avoid predators. Birds that live in trees, for example, are often camouflaged by their green or yellow feathers. Color is also important when birds mate. In many species the males are more brightly colored than the females. Their colors help attract females and warn away other males. Dull colors help conceal the females from predators when they sit on nests and incubate their eggs.

38.5 Skeleton and Muscles

The prominent parts of the bird's skeleton and muscles are modified for flight. Except for the neck, the entire axial skeleton is rigid. This makes flight mechanically efficient because the skeleton does not wobble. Individual bones are thin, strong, and filled with air pockets that make them exceptionally light.

The most noticeable part of the skeleton is the large breast bone, or **sternum.** The bottom section of the sternum forms a high, narrow ridge called a **keel.** The powerful breast muscles that move the wings are attached to the keel. The pectoralis (pehk tuh RAL uhs) muscle lowers the wing and the supra-coracoideus (soo pruh kawr uh KOY dee uhs) raises it. Slow-motion photography reveals that birds fly by moving their wings in a complex, figure-eight motion.

Biofact

Q: *How many feathers does a bird have?*

A: Whistling swans often have over 25,000 feathers. On the other hand, ruby-throated hummingbirds may have as few as 950.

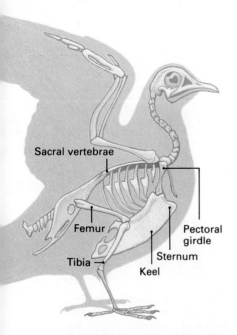

Sacral vertebrae

Femur

Tibia

Pectoral girdle

Sternum

Keel

Figure 38–4. The lightweight skeleton of a bird is an adaptation for efficient flight.

For a comparison of vertebrate systems, see pages 894–905.

The bird's powerful wing muscles enable some species of birds to fly very rapidly. Many birds fly at 50 to 80 km (30 to 50 mi.) per hour. Racing pigeons can maintain speeds of 60 km (37 mi.) per hour over long distances. Hummingbirds can hover as well as fly. To stay in one place in the air, they must flap their wings more than 200 times each second.

A group of vertebrae, called *sacral vertebrae,* are located at the lower end of the spine. Attached to these vertebrae is the pelvic girdle. Legs are attached to the pelvic girdle. The *femur* (FEE muhr) is the upper leg bone; the lower leg bone is the *tibia* (TIHB ee ah). Large muscles in the lower leg move the four toes. The ankle and foot are fused into a single structure. The outside of a bird's foot is covered by scales, keratinized coverings similar to the scales found in reptiles.

38.6 Digestive System

Birds require large amounts of energy for both flight and temperature regulation. Birds, therefore, spend much of their time searching for and eating food. Different species of birds have different diets. A seagull may eat everything from fish it has caught to garbage it finds in a dump. Eagles and hawks eat the flesh of fish and small mammals. Other birds may eat only seeds, and some drink only the nectar of flowers.

The digestive system of a bird processes a large amount of food at a time. Food is taken in through the mouth, travels down the esophagus, and enters a large crop, which is used primarily for food storage. Upon leaving the crop, food moves into a two-chambered stomach. The first chamber is the thick-walled *proventriculus* (proh vehn TRIHK yoo luhs), where food is mixed with digestive enzymes. The second chamber of the stomach is the gizzard. The gizzard functions as a substitute for teeth; it grinds up the food. A bird's gizzard has a hard, horny lining. The duodenum, the coiled intestine, and the other digestive organs of the bird are similar in structure and function to those in other vertebrates.

38.7 Respiratory System

A bird's high body temperature and level of activity require a large amount of oxygen. In addition, birds use air to help buoy them up in flight. Air is drawn into the body through the mouth or the two nostrils in the beak. The air then passes through the *trachea* (TRAY kee uh) into a pair of tubes called *bronchi.* Each bronchus leads to one of the lungs.

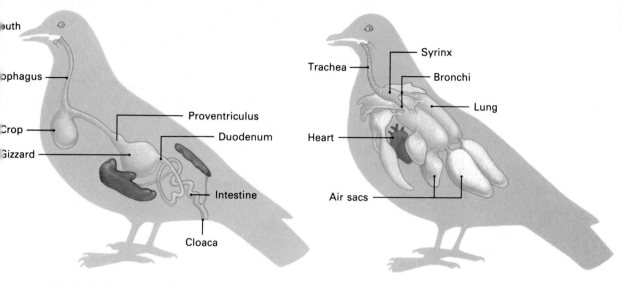

Much of the inhaled air travels into **air sacs**—cavities that make the bird lighter when filled with air. Air sacs extend into the body cavity and even into the toes. Because of the air sacs, a bird's respiratory system may take up as much as 20 percent of the body volume. The main function of the air sacs is to force air across the lung surface. Gas exchange occurs on the surface of the lungs, not in the air sacs.

Some of the air in the body is used to make sounds. Birds do not have vocal cords. They produce their calls instead by means of their **syrinx** (SIHR ihnks), or "song box." The syrinx is located at the bottom of the trachea. It contains a pair of vibrating membranes. As air passes out of the lungs, the membranes vibrate and produce sound. Muscles attached to the membranes change the pitch of the sound.

Figure 38–5. A bird's digestive system (left) processes the large amounts of food required for energy. The respiratory system (right) must deliver large quantities of oxygen for converting this food to energy.

Reading Critically

Analyzing Structures If birds have no vocal cords, how do they make sounds?

38.8 Circulatory System

Birds have four-chambered hearts. The right and left sides of the heart are completely separate. Each side of the heart is divided into two chambers, an upper atrium and a lower ventricle. The right side of the heart receives oxygen-poor blood from all parts of the body and pumps it to the lungs. After the blood is oxygenated in the lungs, it travels to the left side of the heart. From there it is pumped out to the body through the aortic arch. A bird's heart beats very rapidly, although the rate varies greatly from species to species. A mourning dove's heart rate may range between 135 and 570 beats a minute. Because a hummingbird

Characteristics and features of birds are studied in the Investigation that appears on page 617.

must deliver large amounts of oxygen to the muscles of its rapidly beating wings, its heart may beat as much as 1,000 times a minute.

38.9 Excretory System

The excretory system of a bird excretes very little water. Almost all the water is removed from urinary products before the wastes pass from the kidney to the cloaca. The primary form of nitrogenous wastes is a white solid compound called *uric acid*. Wastes from the intestine and from the kidneys are excreted together.

38.10 Nervous System

The nervous system of a bird is highly developed. The brain has three well-developed areas: the cerebellum, the midbrain tectum, and the cerebrum. The cerebellum controls flying and walking by coordinating movement. The **midbrain tectum** is the center of vision. The **optic lobes,** the place where visual impulses are interpreted, are located in this area. The cerebrum is the control center for complex patterns of behavior such as eating, mating, nest building, and care of the young. The cerebrum is also the site of the bird's learning ability and serves as the control center for its voluntary muscles.

Birds have keen senses of hearing and balance but poor senses of smell and taste. They depend more on their vision than on any other sense. Birds have extremely large eyes that detect slight movements. Although the eyes are unable to rotate, a bird still has a wide range of vision because its neck is flexible due to a large number of vertebrae. Some birds, such as owls, can rotate their necks almost 270°, three quarters of a circle. Owls and other birds that are active at night see well in the dark. They can see by starlight what humans see by moonlight.

38.11 Reproductive System

Male birds produce sperm in testes. The mature sperm pass from the testes into a long tube, called the *vas deferens*. The lower part of the vas deferens is enlarged to form a seminal vesicle where the sperm are stored until mating occurs.

The female of most bird species has only a single ovary, located on the left side. Eggs produced in the ovary are released into the body cavity and pass into an **oviduct.** The oviduct is a long tube that leads to a cloaca. After mating occurs and sperm fertilize the eggs, the eggs pass down the oviduct and are covered with **albumin,** a nutritious protein that makes up the egg

Figure 38–6. The embryo is the only living part of the egg. The yolk and albumin provide food. Other parts provide protection, waste disposal, or the exchange of oxygen and carbon dioxide.

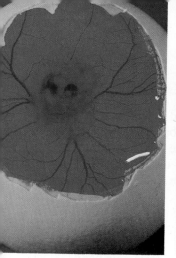
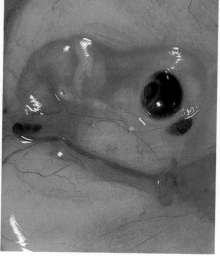
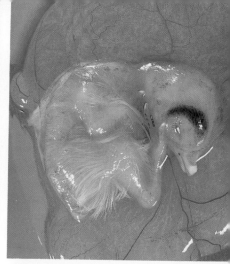

white. Then the eggs are covered by shells made primarily of calcium carbonate, also called lime. Eggs with shells leave the body through the cloaca. Eggs that are not fertilized also receive albumin and a shell. Nearly all of the eggs bought in stores are unfertilized.

The structure of the fertilized egg is shown in Figure 38–6 on page 612. You can see that the structure is similar to that of a reptile's egg but that the yolk of a bird's egg is larger.

Figure 38–7 shows the development of a bird embryo. When embryo development is complete, hatching begins. The young bird slowly pecks its way out of the shell using a special **egg tooth.** This sharp structure located on the tip of the beak is lost a few days after hatching.

The newly hatched young of birds such as chickens and ducks are well developed. Their eyes are open and they are covered with a full coat of down feathers. Within a few hours after birth these young birds leave the nest and follow their parents. Such young are called **precocial.** Songbirds and most sea birds have **altricial** young—that is, the newly hatched birds are blind, naked, and helpless. Altricial young must remain in the nest for a time because they require constant feeding and care.

Figure 38–7. These photographs show a chick embryo at 5 days (left), 8 days, when eyes are visible (center), 14 days, when limbs and feathers can be seen (top right), and a chick emerging on the 21st day (bottom).

Section Review

1. **Identifying Relationships** How are a bird's bones and feathers adapted for flight?
2. **Analyzing Function** What are the three main regions of the brain of a bird and what is the function of each?
3. **Summarizing Ideas** What are the two functions of air sacs?
4. **Interpreting Information** How do birds produce song?
5. **Synthesizing Conclusions** What advantages do precocial birds have over altricial?

> **Thinking Critically**

Section Objectives

- *Describe* some patterns of courtship behavior in birds.
- *Discuss* nest building and incubation.
- *Name* three methods by which birds navigate during migration.
- *State* the adaptive value of bird songs.

For career information, see pages 922–923.

Behavior of Birds

Reproduction in birds is accompanied by elaborate patterns of courtship, mating, nest building, incubation, and care of young. Complex behavior is also shown by the yearly movement of bird populations. Unlike the Arctic tern discussed earlier in this chapter, most birds migrate away from mating and nesting areas to warmer wintering grounds.

38.12 Courtship

Males and females of most bird species form **pair bonds**—that is, they stay with one another throughout the reproductive season. They are attracted to each other through a series of courtship displays. During these displays, one of the birds—usually the male—engages in elaborate rituals that attract a mate. Most males attract females with song. Some, such as peacocks and lyrebirds, spread out their feathers in a beautiful, colorful display. The male bower bird builds a nest of twigs and lines it with any blue object he can find. Male grebes and herons perform acrobatics in the water.

These courtship rituals allow the female to recognize a mature male of her species that is capable of reproducing. In response to male courtship, a female usually performs a series of movements indicating her readiness to mate.

38.13 Nesting and Care of Young

During or after courtship, birds build nests. Most bird nests are bowl-shaped structures made of twigs and leaves. Swallows and other birds build nests of mud on the sides of cliffs. Woodpeckers lay their eggs in trees, in holes lined with wood chips. Killdeer and other shore birds make shallow nests of pebbles. Some birds, such as monk parakeets, build large community nests in which each female has her own space. A few species make no nest at all. Falcons, for example, simply lay their eggs on bare ground.

The number of eggs laid and their sizes varies. Hummingbird eggs are no larger than a pea. Ostrich eggs may weigh 2 kg (4.5 lb.) or more. Most eggs are protectively colored.

A group of eggs in a nest is called a **clutch.** Bird eggs cannot develop unless the eggs are **incubated,** or kept warm. The female sits carefully on the clutch. Heat from her body warms the eggs. In many species, male and female parents share the job of incubation. The incubation

Figure 38–8. The peacock displays his colors to a peahen during the courtship ritual. The female's drab colors help protect her from predators when brooding eggs or guarding her young.

Birds and Planes Don't Mix

When airports are located near places where birds breed, birds are often a threat to the airplanes during take off and landing. Birds that are swept into the engine of a plane can cause a crash.

Birds can cause other types of serious damage when they collide with airplanes. A Japanese airline was spending almost $500,000 a year repairing damage that resulted from birds flying into their airplanes. The airlines asked scientists to use their knowledge of bird behavior to help solve this problem.

The scientists knew that, although birds often feed on butterflies, they avoid butterflies with a pattern on their wings that resembles large eyes. The birds react to the eye pattern in the same way they react to a predator—they flee. Experiments showed that birds also fly away from objects bearing the eye pattern. In one test, workers painted the pattern on balloons that they then placed in rice paddies. Birds stayed away.

The scientists hypothesized that the eye pattern would work as well on airplanes as it did in rice paddies. The airline took

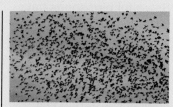

the scientists' advice and painted the pattern on the spinning fans in the engines of their airplanes. In one year, collisions of birds with these airplanes dropped by 80 percent.

Studies in animal behavior had saved both lives and money.

time ranges from a few weeks to several months. Chicken eggs hatch 21 days after they are laid. The eggs of the albatross must be incubated for three months.

38.14 Migration and Navigation

Many bird species mate, build nests, and raise their young in one part of the world and then move to another to avoid winter. A common sign of winter's approach is the sight of birds overhead, flying south. Similarly, the return of birds to the north signals the coming of spring. This regular, seasonal movement is known as **migration.** More than two-thirds of the bird species in the northern United States make an annual round trip between their winter feeding grounds in the south and their northern breeding grounds. These trips are often long and difficult. Among migrating birds, the Antarctic Adelie penguin follows an unusual pattern of behavior. These penguins travel north (away from the Antarctic) during the winter by floating on ice-

Reading Critically

Inferring Relationships How could you use flocks of birds to determine north and south?

Beautiful bird songs have intrigued both poets and scientists. Scientists record bird calls in the wild and later make *audiospectrograms* of their songs. An audiospectrogram is a graph that plots the frequency of a sound over a period of time. By looking at audiospectrograms, scientists can visualize songs and thus analyze them more carefully. The audiospectrograms shown are from three closely related species of thrushes. Different species of thrushes appear similar but their songs are very different. By studying audiospectrograms, scien-

tists found that many bird species have regional dialects—that is, birds have accents just like humans.

Many times songs mark and defend territories. For example, when a male wood thrush moves into an uninhabited area, it sings. Other males stay away. If another male wood thrush does not heed the song and enters the territory, it will be attacked. But other kinds of thrushes are safe from attack because their songs identify them as a different species.

Like thrushes, many other birds use songs for species recognition. Male birds, for instance, call to

attract females during the mating season. Newly hatched birds sing special "begging" songs when they get hungry. By analyzing audiospectrograms, scientists hope to learn more about songs—the language of birds.

■ **Inferring Conclusions** How is song mimicry of advantage to a species of bird?

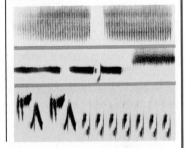

bergs. In spring they swim south back to the Antarctic. The penguins then cross several kilometers of land to their breeding ground by walking and sliding across the ice on their stomachs.

Year after year birds migrate over the same paths, called *migration routes*. Migration is guided partly by instinct and partly by learned behavior. A number of different clues guide birds during migration flights. These clues may be landmarks or they may use wind currents, the sun, and the stars. Pigeons and certain other bird species can find their way by using the earth's magnetic field.

Section Review

1. **Evaluating Behavior**   Why do males engage in courtship displays?
2. **Summarizing Ideas**   Describe three types of bird's nests.
3. **Interpreting Information**   How do birds navigate their migration routes?
4. **Analyzing Conclusions**   What is the biological significance of bird songs?

> **Thinking Critically**

INVESTIGATION 38:
What Do Animal Tracks Reveal?

Objectives
- To *relate* track patterns to bird adaptations
- To *infer* events from animal tracks

Materials
pencil, paper

Prelab Preparation
1. Name a single feature that distinguishes birds from all other animals.
2. Describe how the feet and beaks of birds are modified to perform specific tasks.
3. Using the illustrations of feet in Table 38-1 as a guide, draw the footprint that each type of foot might leave in soft soil.

Inquiry: Exploration
The illustration below shows numerous footprints found in an area of soft ground. Use this illustration to complete the Analysis in this Investigation.

Analysis
1. **Summarizing Observations** Describe the footprints. Base your description solely on your observation.

2. **Analyzing Observations** How many animals walked over this ground? How many of these animals were birds? What evidence do you have to support these conclusions?
3. **Analyzing Observations** Describe as fully as possible how these birds differ from one another. What evidence do you observe in the illustration that supports this conclusion?
4. **Analyzing Observations** What type of bird was the first to cross this area? Explain your answer.
5. **Analyzing Observations** How might footprints give evidence of an animal's overall size?
6. **Analyzing Observations** What evidence suggests that one bird began to run?
7. **Analyzing Observations** What evidence suggests that one bird may have preyed on another?
8. **Making Inferences** Describe the events that might have caused the tracks shown in the illustration. Include any assumptions, interpretations, and speculations that can be supported by evidence of the tracks.

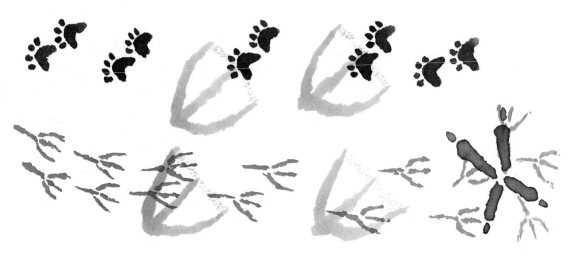

Chapter 38 Review

Summary

Birds evolved from reptiles about 140 million years ago. The first known bird, the *Archaeopteryx*, had feathers like a bird but retained a few reptilian characteristics. Birds were a well-established class by the beginning of the Cretaceous period.

Feathers distinguish birds from all other vertebrates. Birds also have bones with air pockets, horny beaks, endothermic temperature regulation, and air sacs. Four common bird types are: flightless, water, perching, and predatory.

Birds have four kinds of feathers: contour, down, filoplumes, and bristles. Feathers protect and insulate birds and enable them to fly. The bird's skeleton, muscles, and organ systems are all modified for flight.

Birds have complex behavior patterns during reproduction. Males engage in courtship displays that attract females. Birds build nests and incubate eggs in them. Many species continue to care for their young after the eggs have hatched. In winter, many species of birds migrate to warmer environments.

BioTerms

air sac (**611**)
albumin (**612**)
altricial (**613**)
barb (**608**)
barbule (**608**)
bristle (**608**)
clutch (**614**)
contour
 feather (**608**)
down feather (**608**)
egg tooth (**613**)

filoplume (**608**)
follicle (**608**)
incubate (**614**)
keel (**609**)
midbrain
 tectum (**612**)
migration (**615**)
optic lobe (**612**)
oviduct (**612**)
pair bond (**614**)
pin feather (**608**)

precocial (**613**)
preen gland (**608**)
quill (**608**)
rachis (**608**)

sternum (**609**)
syrinx (**611**)
talon (**607**)
vane (**608**)

For each pair of terms, explain the differences in their meanings.

1. contour feather, down feather
2. precocial, altricial
3. quill, rachis
4. midbrain tectum, optic lobe

BioQuiz   (Write all answers on a separate sheet of paper.)

Completion

1. Birds are able to make sound by passing air over the _____ .
2. A characteristic typical of birds of prey are sharp, curving claws called _____.
3. Feathers grow from small sacs in the skin called _____ .
4. As a substitute for teeth, birds have _____ , where food is ground up.
5. The main function of _____ is to force air across the lung surface.

Multiple Choice

6. The _____ is responsible for vision.
   a) rachis · b) midbrain tectum
   c) syrinx   d) keel
7. Feathers may have evolved for flight, hunting, or   a) mating.   b) reproduction.
   c) protection.   d) preening.
8. Males and females of most species form
   a) migration pairs.   b) a clutch.
   c) mating pairs.   d) pair bonds.
9. Jaws of birds are covered by a   a) talon.
   b) barbule.   c) horny beak.   d) bristle.

10. Feathers evolved from   a) reptile scales.
b) hair.   c) amphibian glands.
d) quills.
11. Birds fly by moving their feathers   a) in
a figure-eight pattern.   b) horizontally.
c) vertically.   d) in a circular pattern.
12. Which characteristic is common to both
reptiles and birds?   a) four-chambered
heart   b) production of an amniotic egg
c) air sacs   d) flight
13. Oil from the preen glands helps birds to
a) waterproof feathers.   b) insulate
themselves.   c) fly.   d) reproduce.
14. The legs of birds are covered with scales
made from   a) pin feathers.

b) quills.   c) protein.   d) keratin.
15. The central core of a feather is the
a) quill.   b) barb.   c) rachis.   d) vane.

Writing Critically

16. What are the four kinds of feathers, and
what is the function of each?
17. What is the adaptive value of bird songs?
18. Why is *Archaeopteryx* considered a link
between reptiles and birds?
19. What are the functions of courtship
behavior in birds before mating?
20. How is the skeleton modified for flight?

Application/Critical Thinking

1. **Inferring Conclusions** The yellow-billed cuckoo of the southeastern United States is brown on top and white underneath. Why might this color pattern be an advantage to a tree-dwelling bird?
2. **Interpreting Ideas** What might be the adaptive advantage for Canadian geese to migrate in very large flocks?

3. **Identifying Relationships** Describe the similarities and differences of the wing of a bird and an airplane.
4. **Synthesizing Conclusions** The highest flying bird is the bar-headed goose that can climb to 7,600 m (25,000 ft.). What adaptations might you expect in this bird that enables it to fly so high?

Cross-Discipline Connection

Biology and Art   Use references in the school and public libraries to investigate the work of John James Audubon. Write a report that focuses on the accuracy of Audubon's paintings and drawings of birds as well as his contributions to knowledge about birds. You may also want to research the origin and goals of the National Audubon Society.

Discovery Through Reading

Read the article "Where Will the Cranes Go?" *Newsweek* (April 3, 1989): 62–63. This article discusses both the controversy over damming rivers and the long-range environmental consequences of such actions. What is the immediate danger to the cranes' habitat? Why does the city of Denver want to build the Two Forks Dam? For what is most water used in metropolitan Denver?

Read the article "Building a Better Home," *National Wildlife* (April–May 1987): 42–49. This beautifully illustrated article describes the remarkable behavioral patterns that birds show when building their nests. What is the most obvious difference in the nests of different kinds of birds? What is the size range of bird nests? Identify the birds that build the smallest and largest nests.

BIOTECH

Saving Endangered Wildlife

The population of the great pandas of China is dwindling to fewer than 800 as human settlements encroach on their natural territory. The okapi, a giraffe-like creature that lives in the rain forests of Zaire in Africa, is losing its home to farming and the timber industry. As their habitats disappear, countless species are threatened by extinction.

Over the past few decades, zoos have become increasingly involved in the breeding of endangered species. Unfortunately, saving animals from extinction is more complex than simply supplying creatures with mates. Animals in captivity are often not compatible. The stresses associated with living in confinement often add to reproductive failure. In addition, zoos cannot presently house the large numbers of each species necessary to maintain the diverse gene pool essential for a species' long-term survival.

To counter these problems, researchers have established a computerized database, called the *International Species Inventory System* (ISIS), of animals in captivity. ISIS helps identify likely candidates for breeding programs. A British registry, the *National Online Animal History* (NOAH), offers pedigree information that indicates how closely individual animals may be related. This information is essential to conservationists because inbreeding limits the gene pool available to the next generation.

This horse was a surrogate mother for this baby zebra.

These broad-nose caimans are products of artificial breeding techniques.

The most routinely used breeding method is *artificial insemination.* It involves the nonsurgical collection of semen and its manual placement into the reproductive tract of the female. *In vitro* (outside the body) fertilization involves placing an ovum and sperm together in a glass dish filled with a nutritive medium. The resulting embryo can be implanted in the uterus of a preselected female.

Embryo transfer, another breeding method, consists of placing the embryo of one female in the uterus of another female, a *surrogate mother.* Researchers have been successful with cross-species embryo transfer between species that are closely related. For example, workers implanted a bongo embryo in the prepared uterus of an eland antelope, which later gave birth to the bongo calf.

Because the reproductive systems of exotic animals differ from one species to another, researchers have successfully adapted artificial breeding methods to only about 20 species. Advances in reproductive technology will make artificial breeding possible with a greater variety of endangered animals.

Advances in artificial breeding have saved some species from extinction.

In vitro *fertilization (above) allowed this eland to give birth to a bongo calf.*

Mammals

Outline

Humans on a photographer's safari in Africa

Focus

The more than 4,500 species of mammals live throughout the
world. Some burrow in desert sand, some swing through the
canopies of tropical forests, and some swim in arctic waters.
Mammals show adaptations that have allowed them to invade
almost all environments.

- *What mammals would humans on a photo safari expect to
  see in addition to the lions in the photograph?*

- *What kinds of small mammals would the humans find hiding
  in the grasses or flying in the air?*

Characteristics of Mammals

The class Mammalia consists of vertebrates whose young are nourished by their mother's milk. Mammals include all the most familiar domesticated animals, such as dogs, cats, horses, and cows. Mammals also include human beings, as well as the many animals that still live in the wild. Mammals have been the dominant life form on Earth for the past 65 million years. This period of time, the Cenozoic era, is called the Age of Mammals.

Fossil evidence indicates that mammals evolved more than 180 million years ago from a now-extinct order of reptiles called *therapsids* (thuh RAP suhdz). Fossil therapsid tooth and jaw fragments show a mixture of reptile and mammalian characteristics. Mammalian features are jaws that do not become unhinged, and a lower jaw formed of only two bones. Although many of the first species of mammals died out, some developed into forms that are known today. Small, insect-eating mammals coexisted with dinosaurs and later survived the conditions that led to the extinction of the giant reptiles. Most of the mammals known today had come into existence in some recognizable form by the start of the Jurassic period, 180 million years ago.

Mammals have several characteristics not found in other vertebrates:

- *The nursing of young:* Mammals have modified sweat glands called **mammary glands** that secrete the milk used to feed the young after they are born. These glands give the order its name.
- *Body hair:* Only mammals have hair that covers most of the body. The hair helps insulate the body and protect the skin from injury.
- *Live birth:* Most mammals are **viviparous**—that is, the young are born alive after developing inside the mother.
- *Extended parental care:* All mammalian young go through a prolonged period of development. They remain with their parents while learning to take care of themselves.
- *A large, well-developed brain:* More than any other single organ, the brain has enabled mammals to adapt to change and to develop complex patterns of behavior.
- *An outer ear:* Mammals are the only animals that have an outer ear, which collects sound and transmits it to the middle and inner ear.
- *Separate chest and abdominal cavities:* In mammals, a dome-shaped muscle called the **diaphragm** divides the coelom into two parts.

Section Objectives

- *List* the major characteristics that distinguish mammals from other vertebrates.
- *Name* three adaptations that help mammals maintain a high metabolic rate.
- *Distinguish* between a mammal's territory and its home range.
- *Give* three reasons why mammals migrate.

Figure 39–1. The woolly mammoth, a prehistoric animal, was hunted by early humans. A close relative of today's elephant, the mammoth died out about 10,000 years ago.

Mammals   **623**

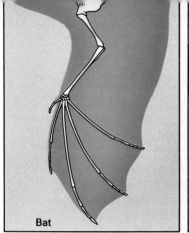

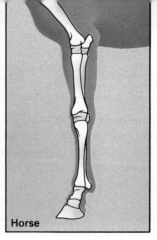
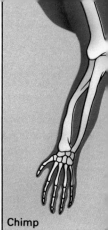

Bat
Seal
Horse
Chimp

Figure 39–2. The hands and forelimbs of mammals are adapted to various functions. Skeletal modifications form the framework for a bat's wing, a seal's paddlelike flipper, a horse's sturdy foreleg, and a chimpanzee's flexible hand.

For a comparison of vertebrate systems, see pages 894–905.

Reading Critically

Analyzing Relationships
Why would a mammal require more food in winter than in summer?

39.1 Movement of Animals

Mammals show great advances over the reptiles in the way they move on land. A mammal's legs are directly underneath its body. Thus, little energy is required to hold the body off the ground. The elbow of the forelimb is turned backward, and the knee of the hindlimb bends forward. Also, the limbs of mammals are longer and more slender than those of reptiles. These changes have made it possible for some mammals to travel on land at high speeds. The cheetah, for example, can reach incredible bursts of speed. It can run up to 113 km (70 mi.) per hour for short distances.

39.2 Respiratory and Circulatory Systems

Like birds, mammals are warm-blooded. To keep their body temperature at a constantly high level, mammals need to produce a great deal of heat. A high metabolic rate, in turn, requires plenty of food for energy. Unlike reptiles, mammals can remain active even when environmental temperatures are low. An arctic fox, for example, can run about and look for food in temperatures as low as −50°C (−58°F).

Mammals have efficient respiratory and circulatory systems that maintain their high metabolic rate. Mammals, like birds, have four-chambered hearts. The four-chambered heart allows oxygen-rich blood from the lungs to travel to other body tissues from the heart without mixing with the oxygen-poor blood returning to the heart.

The relaxation and contraction of the diaphragm muscle changes the volume of the lungs. The changes in volume result in changes in the air pressure inside the lungs. These changes in pressure cause air to move in and out of the lungs. In mammals, the breathing and food passages are separate, allowing the animal to breathe and eat food at the same time. The air and food

Have you ever wondered how bats can fly with such speed and confidence in complete darkness? Bats have an extraordinary ability to locate objects even in total darkness. Bats "see" by **echolocation**—that is, they locate objects by the reflection of sound waves. The process works somewhat like the sonar of a ship.

Bats emit extremely high-pitched sounds through the mouth and nose. Humans may hear these sounds as a series of clicks. The sound waves travel in front of the bat and make contact with an object. Part of the wave is then reflected back toward the bat, where it is received by the bat's large ears. The reflected sound, the echo, permits the bat to interpret the object's size, direction, and its distance from the bat.

Echolocation is so accurate that bats can avoid thin wires in complete darkness. Most bats use echolocation to hunt for food and to avoid obstacles. Sometimes the pitch of sounds emitted by the bats is so high that humans cannot hear it.

Not all bats echolocate, however. Fruit-eating bats have large eyes that allow them to see well even in dim light.

Bats are not the only animals that "see" by echolocation. Shrews and other nearly blind insectivores have echolocation mechanisms. Scientists studying captive porpoises have discovered that these mammals can use echolocation to locate tiny objects, detect the difference between different kinds of metals, determine the sizes of objects, and detect thin wires.

■ **Inferring Ideas** In what kind of situation might you expect bats to have difficulty using echolocation?

passages cross in a common area at the back of the mouth. When mammals swallow, a thin flap of cartilage, the *epiglottis*, moves downward and prevents food from moving into the respiratory passages.

39.3 The Mammalian Nervous System

In mammals, the constant high internal temperature permits the development of an exceptionally sensitive and complex nervous system. In proportion to its body size, a mammal's nervous system is far larger than that of any other vertebrate. In addition, a large proportion of a mammal's brain correlates and integrates incoming information. In mammals, the cerebrum is the dominant as well as the largest part of the brain. The brains of fish, amphibians, and reptiles are organized differently. In mammals, a part of the cerebrum, the *cerebral cortex*, has expanded to form a layer covering most of the forebrain. The cerebral cortex has become the major coordinating center of the brain. *The exceptional learning ability and memory of mammals are attributed to the well-developed cerebral cortex.*

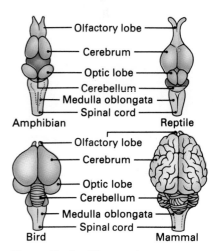

Figure 39–3. The cerebrum is associated with intelligence. A large, furrowed cerebrum is characteristic of mammals.

Figure 39–4. Young lions cannot survive without their mother's protection. When the mother hunts prey, the young watch and learn by her example.

Figure 39–5. A pronghorn buck has scent glands in his mouth. Plants that are marked with the scent alert other pronghorns that this is a boundary of the buck's territory.

39.4 Reproduction and Parental Care

All mammals show internal fertilization. The male releases the sperm inside the body of the female where it may fertilize one or more eggs. After eggs are fertilized, they develop into embryos that are nurtured within the mother's body for a time.

Male mammals can mate at any time after they reach maturity. In most species, however, a female will not mate except during her fertile period, called **estrus.** Some species have estrus periods several times a year. In other species, estrus occurs once a year and the young's birth takes place during the season most favorable for survival.

One of the most important and distinctive features of mammalian reproduction is that the young have a childhood, a distinct developmental period. When a young mammal is born, it is unable to survive in the world on its own. A young mammal requires a certain amount of parental care before it can obtain its own food and defend itself against predators. The care and protection given to the mammalian young greatly increase their chances to survive. Mammals bear relatively small numbers of young, compared with other vertebrates such as frogs and fishes. However, a larger percentage of mammal offspring survive.

39.5 Behavior

Many mammals live together in social groups for purposes of hunting or defense. A zebra herd consists of one adult male and several females and their young, while a wolf pack is made up of several males and females and their young. Some hunting animals live solitary lives. Adult tigers, for example, are found together only when they mate.

Other patterns of behavior also differ among species. Certain mammals exhibit territoriality. Others migrate or respond to cold weather by hibernation.

Territoriality Many mammals exhibit **territoriality**—that is, they defend a particular area against other animals of the same species. For example, fur seals establish a territory during their breeding season. At this time, males show behavior that discourages other males from entering their areas. Each male also displays behavior that attracts as many female seals into his own area as possible. Many mammals mark their territories with scents or body wastes.

Not all mammals defend territories, but most have a **home range**—that is, an area over which they travel during normal

Patented Beef on Your Table?

Humans have known for centuries that they could improve their livestock by controlling the breeding of their animals. They knew that they could produce herds with certain characteristics by breeding only those animals in the herd that showed those characteristics. This selective breeding has resulted in the kinds of farm animals we have today.

Scientists have accumulated much knowledge about genetics over the past four decades. They have begun to understand the biochemistry of genes. The model of DNA, the control molecule of cells, that resulted from the work of Franklin, Watson, and Crick led to a flurry of DNA and genetic research activities.

ity. Scientists asked, and found answers to such questions as "Can we find the genetic code in DNA?", and "Under what circumstances does the code change?"

As more work is done in this area, researchers are finding out more about how to influence, manipulate, and transplant the control molecules that govern the inherited characteristics of organisms. Knowing the molecular structure of genes, and finding out how genes can be altered, has had potential economic significance for companies that produce livestock. Some companies have applied for patents that would allow them to produce farm animals through genetic

engineering. These patents, if they are issued, could provide an alternative to selective breeding for desired characteristics of certain farm animals, in some cases. The possibility of producing genetically engineered farm animals has resulted in considerable controversy. In addition, it has raised many important social issues and ethical questions.

activities. A meadow mouse may have a home range of 270 m² (333 sq. yd.). A larger grazing animal, such as a whitetail deer, may have a home range of 1 to 5 km² (0.5 to 2 sq. mi.).

Migration Many mammals move regularly over large distances when food becomes scarce or when environmental conditions become unsuitable. Insect-eating bats, for example, migrate south each fall as the insect population decreases in their summer area. Caribou regularly move from summer mountain pastures to protected valley pastures for the winter. Gray whales travel each autumn from arctic waters to waters off the coast of Mexico. There the young of the herd are born in warmer waters. The whales return north in the spring.

Figure 39–6. Many mammals, such as these caribou, migrate when environmental conditions become unfavorable.

Hibernation Migration is not the only way mammals avoid problems of temperature extremes. Some species of bats, insect eaters, and rodents go into hibernation during winter months. Their metabolic rate decreases. Body temperature falls and heartbeat and breathing rates slow. In such a state, the animals use little energy and can live off stored body fat. When the outside temperature increases, they slowly resume normal activities. The body temperature of some bats approaches the temperature of the surrounding air during the day and rises when the bats become active at night, all year long.

Bears, skunks, and some other mammals spend the coldest part of the winter in a den asleep in a state of *dormancy*. Unlike true hibernators, their body temperatures decrease only slightly and they may move in and out of sleep. A few mammals, mainly rodents, avoid the extremes of summer heat or drought by moving into a state similar to hibernation called *estivation*.

Section Review

1. **Comparing Features** Name four features unique to mammals and two features common only to mammals and birds.
2. **Analyzing Conclusions** Why do mammals have a higher metabolic rate than reptiles?
3. **Comparing Ideas** Compare the ways caribou, bats, and bears meet the problem of surviving cold winter temperatures.
4. **Synthesizing Information** Explain how a home range could also be an animal's territory.

Thinking Critically

Classification of Mammals

Biologists classify the 4,500 species of mammals alive today into 18 main orders on the basis of structural differences and development of the unborn. Members of these orders live throughout the world.

Some structural differences between orders of mammals can be linked to feeding habits. The specialized teeth of mammals, for example, perform different tasks. The *incisors* at the front of the mouth are used for cutting. Behind the incisors are the *canines*, used for gripping, tearing, and stabbing. At the rear of the mouth are heavy flat *molars*, which are teeth that grind food. As Figure 39–7 shows, the number and shape of these teeth vary among mammal species.

Mammals differ in the way their young develop before birth. *Mammals can be divided into three groups: egg-laying mammals, pouched mammals, and placental mammals.*

Monotremes are mammals that lay eggs. Young monotremes develop within a protective shelled egg much as reptiles do. Pouched mammals are known as **marsupials.** Young marsupials develop within the mother's body for only a short time. After birth, they complete their development inside a special pouch, or *marsupium,* located on the mother's abdomen. Most modern mammals are **placental mammals.** In placental mammals, the young remain within the mother's body until they are able to maintain life independently. A special organ called the **placenta** connects the unborn young to the mother.

39.6 Monotremes

Only two types of monotremes are alive today, and they live in only a few isolated regions of the world. The duck-billed platypus lives only in Australia. The spiny anteater lives in parts of Australia and New Guinea.

Monotremes are considered mammals because they have hair and produce milk for their young. In other ways, the monotremes are fundamentally different from all other mammals. Monotremes show a curious mixture of characteristics. They have a cloaca, as do the lower vertebrates. Their limbs are attached to the sides of the body like the limbs of reptiles, and their feet have claws. The platypus has webbed feet and a flat tail that it uses for swimming. Unlike most other mammals, monotremes do not have true teeth. The platypus uses its flat bill to probe in the mud for worms, snails, and shellfish. The spiny anteater uses its beak to probe into anthills for food.

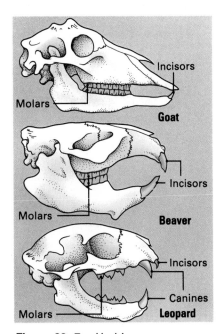

Figure 39–7. Herbivores, such as goats and beavers, have large incisors for grazing or gnawing. In leopards and other carnivores, the canine teeth are well-developed.

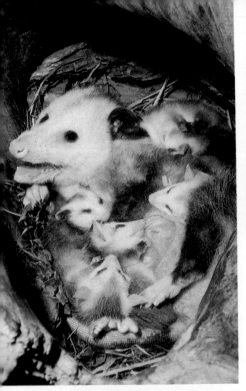

Figure 39–8. Opossums (above) are the only North American marsupial. The spiny anteater (above right) is an example of a monotreme.

The major reptilelike feature of the monotremes is that they lay eggs. Monotremes produce two to three eggs at a time. After fertilization the eggs are kept inside the mother's body and are nourished for a short period before they are laid in the nest. The female incubates her eggs by curling her body around them. The spiny anteater has a special *brood pouch* on her lower abdomen in which she keeps the eggs until they hatch.

After the young monotremes hatch, they are fed with milk secreted by their mother. The milk is produced by more than 100 specialized sweat glands on the lower abdomen. Unlike other mammals, young monotremes do not suckle. Instead, they lap up the milk as it oozes onto the mother's belly.

39.7 Marsupials

Kangaroos, koalas, and almost all other marsupials live in Australia. A few species of marsupials live in South America. North America has only one marsupial, the opossum. *The one major difference between marsupials and other mammals is that young marsupials complete their development inside their mother's pouch.*

The fertilized egg develops into an **embryo,** which remains in the female marsupial's body for only a short time. The embryos feed from the yolk in the egg and do not attach to the uterine wall. In some species, internal development lasts only a matter of days. At birth, young marsupials are still in an incomplete stage of development. They are blind, helpless, and extremely small. Newborn opossums, for example, are so tiny that more than a dozen could fit in a teaspoon.

Once inside the pouch, the young marsupial fastens its mouth onto a nipple. The nipple swells, and the young becomes firmly attached and begins to suckle. Immature marsupials are fed and protected inside the pouch until they are able to feed and care for themselves. The hind legs of the newborn marsupial are

Biofact

Q: *How do baby kangaroos first get into their mother's pouch?*

A: The babies crawl into the pouch themselves. Their mother does not help them, although she licks her body hair, which creates a path from the birth opening to the stomach pouch.

Australia and its nearby islands are home to the most unusual mammals on Earth. They include pig-footed bandicoots, red-bellied pademelons, pretty-faced wallabies, and wombats. These and other unfamiliar animals make the Australian biological region one of the most interesting in the world.

Most of Australia's mammals are marsupials or monotremes. These animals became isolated about 70 million years ago when Australia split off and drifted away from the continents of Antarctica and South America. At the time Australia separated from the larger land area, no placental mammals lived in the Australian region. Freed from competi- tion from the more intelli- gent placental mammals, the monotremes, and especially the marsupials, moved into every available habitat.

The marsupials of Australia have evolved to resemble different species of placental mammals in other areas of the world. The marsupial mouse, for example, resembles a placental mouse. Likewise, the Tasmanian devil is similar to a wolverine or badger. Similarly, each ecological role that is filled in other areas of the world by a placental mammal is occupied in Australia by a marsupial. Red kangaroos, for instance, occupy the role of grazers, just as antelopes do in the plains of the western United States. These similarities of shape and habitat between marsupials and placentals are examples of **convergent evolution,** the process by which two distantly related species come to resemble one another physically or ecologically.

Though protected for millions of years by their isolation, marsupials and monotremes are today threatened with extinction as more and more placen- tals are imported into Australia. Unless carefully protected, these fascinating mammals could disappear from the Earth.

■ **Inferring Ideas** What does convergent evolu- tion imply about the parallel development of two distantly related species?

poorly developed; actually, they are little more than embryonic buds. The front legs, however, are more fully developed and tipped with claws. A young marsupial uses its front limbs to pull itself up the mother's abdomen and into her pouch.

For the classification of mammals, see page 919.

39.8 Placental Mammals

More than 95 percent of all mammals are placentals. Early in the development of a placental mammal, the embryo becomes implanted in the wall of the mother's reproductive organ, called the **uterus.** Then the placenta forms, connecting the young mammal directly to its mother's uterus. The fluid-filled sac, the amnion, surrounds the embryo and supports it during develop- ment. Blood vessels from the amnion connect to the placenta as

Figure 39–9. Like many mammals, a newborn foal emerges from its mother still surrounded by the amnion.

well. The circulatory systems of the mother and the embryo are not directly connected. Nutrients and oxygen from the mother's blood pass across the tissues of the placenta into the blood of the developing embryo. Waste materials pass from the embryo to the mother's blood.

Because the developing young mammals get their nourishment directly from the mother through the blood, development is not limited by the fixed amount of food found in an egg. The longer period of time in which to develop permits the formation of a complex brain and nervous system. The period of time during which the young mammal develops within the uterus is known as **gestation,** or **pregnancy.** The length of gestation differs among mammals.

Placental mammals differ in size, shape, diet, and the way they move. Each order of placentals shows adaptations for a particular way of life. Some are adapted for walking; others are adapted for running, leaping, swimming, or flying. Some mammals differ so greatly in appearance that it is hard to believe they are closely related.

Insect-Eating Mammals The oldest group of placental mammals are small, highly active animals called *insectivores.* As their name indicates, these animals eat mainly insects. Their diets vary, however, and may also include snakes, fruit, birds, and other insectivores. *Biologists think that insectivores are the ancestral stock that gave rise to the other placental mammals, even to the enormous elephants and whales.*

Shrews, hedgehogs, and moles are typical members of the order Insectivora. Compared with other mammals, insectivores have small brains. They also have enormous appetites. Shrews, for example, eat more than two times their body weight daily. With their extremely high metabolic rates, insectivores would starve to death within a short time if they were deprived of food. Most insectivores live in burrows or trees and are active only at night.

Flying Mammals Bats are the only mammals that can truly fly. Without their large, folding wings, bats resemble insectivores in both habits and appearance. The bat's wing is made of a flexible flap of skin stretched over extremely long arm and hand bones. The wing is supported by the bones of the last four fingers, which are exceptionally long and thin. The thumb is usually not attached to the wing and has a curved claw used for clinging or grasping.

Bats generally fly and live in groups. They are active only at night. During the day bats sleep hanging upside down in

Figure 39–10. The thin skin of a bat's wing exposes the long hand and forearm bones that aid in flight. Bat wings vary in shape. The speediest bats have long and narrow wings.

caves, hollow trees, or even barns and attics. Most bats eat insects they catch while in flight. Some bats eat nectar, and others catch fish or frogs with their clawed hind feet.

Hoofed Mammals
Among land mammals, those with hoofs are called **ungulates.** Sheep, cattle, deer, pigs, camels, and other ungulates with an even number of toes make up the order Artiodactyla. Horses, tapirs, rhinoceroses, and other ungulates with an odd number of toes belong to the order Perissodactyla.

Ungulates walk on tiptoe. The weight of the animal is not supported on the entire foot, but only on one or more of its toes. The toes that touch the ground are broad, and the claw is enlarged, forming a hard, protective *hoof.* Ungulates' main means of defense is their ability to run.

Hoofed mammals generally live together in herds. The young are well developed at birth and can move with their herd within a day or two after they are born.

Hoofed mammals are herbivores. All animals in the order Artiodactyla except the pig and the hippopotamus have a four-chambered stomach. The first chamber is the *rumen,* which contains bacteria and other microorganisms that digest cellulose. Animals with this chamber are called **ruminants.**

Trunk-Nosed Mammals
In prehistoric times, huge herds of mammoths and mastodons roamed through Europe, Asia, and North America. Today only two living representatives of the order Proboscidea remain, the African elephant and the Asian elephant. These herbivores are noted for their enormous size and their long, grasping trunk. The trunk is really an elongated nose and upper lip. An elephant uses its trunk to take up water to drink, to spray water over its body, and to collect food and place it in its mouth. The long ivory tusks of some elephants are highly modified upper incisors.

Carnivorous Mammals
Carnivores hunt other animals for food. This order includes land predators, such as tigers, lions, and wolves, as well as marine mammals, such as seals and walruses. Their long, sharp canine teeth are specialized for capturing prey and tearing flesh. Carnivores are intelligent and have keen senses of smell, vision, and hearing. On their cheeks are whiskers, called *vibrissae,* that are sensitive to touch.

Scientists generally divide carnivores into three subgroups: the cat family, the dog family, and the seal or sea lion family. The powerful limbs of land carnivores enable them to leap onto prey from trees or chase their prey across the ground. Their feet have thick pads that absorb the shock of landing or

Biofact

Q: *What are vampire bats?*

A: Vampire bats live only in the tropics. These bats feed on the blood of other mammals, especially horses and cattle. With its front teeth, a vampire bat makes small cuts in a victim's skin. Then the bat laps up the victim's blood with its tubelike tongue.

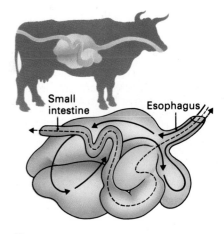

Figure 39–11. Food swallowed by ruminants passes through two of four stomach chambers, then returns to the mouth and is rechewed as cud. On its second swallowing, the food passes through all four stomach chambers.

running. Most members of the cat family have sharp retractable claws for capturing their prey. Members of the dog family have lean, muscular bodies and slender legs. Some members of the order Carnivora are not strictly carnivores. Raccoons and bears, for example, are **omnivores;** they also eat plant materials.

Seals, sea lions, and walruses have streamlined bodies and a thick layer of insulating fat called *blubber*. Seals, sea lions, and walruses use their hind limbs as paddles to propel themselves through the water. The canine teeth of walruses have become long, heavy tusks. Members of the seal family eat a wide variety of foods, including mollusks, fish, and birds. Though adapted to a life spent mainly in the water, marine carnivores mate, bear young, and rest on land.

Whales and Related Aquatic Mammals

Whales, porpoises, and dolphins are other mammals that live their whole life in the sea. These mammals are called **cetaceans** (sih TAY shuhns); they belong to the order Cetacea. Cetaceans are probably descendants of land mammals that returned to the sea about 50 million years ago and adapted to an aquatic life. They have many adaptations that facilitate a life in water. Like fish, cetaceans have long, streamlined bodies. Underneath their skin is a thick layer of blubber. These mammals have completely lost their hindlimbs. The toes of their forelimbs have fused to form flat, paddlelike flippers used for steering and balance. Although cetaceans live in water, they must come to the surface regularly to breathe. The cloud of water vapor that whales exhale is called a *blow* or *spout*. Cetaceans are extremely intelligent animals that communicate by making sounds.

Scientists divide whales into two major groups—those that have teeth and those that do not. Toothed whales include dolphins, porpoises, and sperm whales. These whales use their

Figure 39–12. Baleen whales (top) filter plankton from sea water with thin plates that hang from the upper jaw. Toothed whales (bottom) usually have teeth only in the lower jaw. The teeth are used to catch prey.

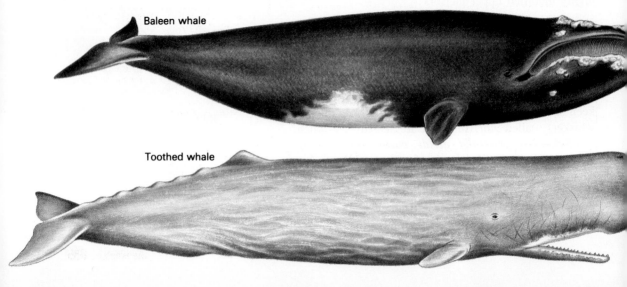

Baleen whale

Toothed whale

Table 39–1: Major Orders of Mammals

	Order	Examples	Characteristics
Egg-Laying Mammals			
	Monotremata ("one opening")	Platypus, spiny anteater	Mothers have no nipples; no teeth
Pouched Mammals			
	Marsupials ("pouched")	Kangaroo, koala, opossum	Young poorly developed at birth; remain attached to nipple inside mother's pouch until fully developed
Placental Mammals			
	Insectivora ("insect-eating")	Shrew, hedgehog, mole	Insect eaters, high metabolic rate
	Chiroptera ("hand-winged")	Bat	Only true flying mammals; nocturnal; sharp teeth; large ears; insect or nectar eaters
	Artiodactyla ("even-number toed")	Sheep, cattle, deer, pig, camel	Ungulates with even number of of toes, most have four-chambered stomach; herbivores
	Perissodactyla ("odd-number toed")	Horse, tapir, rhinoceros	Ungulates with odd number of toes; herbivores.
	Proboscidea ("trunk-nosed")	Elephant	Trunk-nosed mammals; large size, massive legs; herbivores; enlarged upper incisors form tusks
	Carnivora ("flesh eater")	Cat, dog, bear, seal	Meat eaters or omnivores; predators; most have sharp incisor teeth, claws, powerful limbs
	Cetacea ("whales")	Whale, dolphin, porpoise	Aquatic mammals; streamlined bodies; paddlelike forelimbs, no hindlimbs; mouths contain teeth or baleen
	Sirenia ("mermaidlike")	Dugong, manatee	Aquatic mammals; paddlelike forelimbs, no hindlimbs, flat tails; herbivores
	Rodentia ("gnawers")	Rat, mouse, squirrel, porcupine, beaver	Small gnawing mammals; one pair of upper incisors
	Lagomorpha ("hare-shaped")	Rabbit; hare	Gnawing mammals; two pairs of upper incisors; long hind legs for leaping
	Edentata ("toothless")	Armadillo, anteater, tree sloth	Toothless or with molars only; insect eaters; powerful forelimbs
	Primates ("first")	Lemur, monkey, ape, human	Most species tree dwellers; opposable thumbs; most with frontal eyes; capable of standing erect

Figure 39-13. Manatees belong to the order Sirenia. They are found in the Caribbean Sea and in rivers and coastal waters of West Africa and of North and South America.

Reading Critically

Inferring Relationships
What would happen to a rodent's teeth if they were completely covered in enamel?

teeth to catch prey such as seals, birds, squid, fish, and porpoises. They swallow their prey whole. Whales without teeth are called *baleen whales* because they have hundreds of thin plates called *baleen* in their mouth. Whales use the baleen to filter out plankton from the water. Baleen whales include right whales and the blue whale, which is the largest animal that has ever lived. Blue whales grow up to 30 m (100 ft.) in length and weigh more than 91 metric tons (100 tons).

Sea Cows Sea cows are aquatic mammals unrelated to whales. Today only two species are known, the dugong and the manatee. Dugongs live in warm coastal waters, and manatees live both in tropical coastal waters and in rivers. Sea cows are herbivores that feed on algae or aquatic plants. The animal has a torpedo-shaped body, 3 to 4 m (10 to 13 ft.) in length. Like whales, sea cows have lost all traces of hindlimbs and have short forelimbs and flat horizontal tails.

Gnawing Mammals Rodents are distinguished from other mammals by their teeth, which are highly specialized for gnawing. All rodents have two pairs of large, curving incisors that grow constantly. The incisors have hard enamel only on the front surface. As the rodent gnaws, the back surface of the tooth wears away faster than the front, thus keeping a chisel-sharp edge on these teeth.

Rodents number more than 3,000 species, which makes them the largest order of mammals. *Three factors account for the rodents' remarkable worldwide distribution: their intelligence, their small size, and their rapid rate of reproduction.*

Most rodents—including mice, hamsters, guinea pigs, rats, and squirrels—are small animals. Larger rodents include prairie dogs, porcupines, and beavers. The largest rodent is the South American capybara, which grows up to 1.2 m (4 ft.) long.

Rodentlike Mammals Rabbits and hares resemble rodents in many ways, but are not closely related to rodents. Rabbits and hares belong to the order Lagomorpha and are called *lagomorphs* (LAG uh mawrfs). Both rabbits and hares have long hind legs that are specialized for leaping and hopping. Like rodents, rabbits and hares have teeth adapted for gnawing. Lagomorphs, unlike rodents, have an additional pair of teeth posterior to their upper incisors.

Both rodents and lagomorphs have a special intestinal pouch called the **cecum** that contains cellulose-digesting microorganisms. Like the rumen of ungulates, the cecum is an adaptation to a diet that consists mainly of grains and tough grasses.

Toothless Mammals   Armadillos, anteaters, and tree sloths make up the order Edentata (ee dehn TAHD uh). *Edentata* means "toothless," but only the anteaters completely lack teeth. The other species have molars only. Most edentates have specialized features that are adaptations for an insect diet. The anteater, for example, uses its powerful clawed forefeet to rip open termite and ant nests. Then it inserts its long, sticky tongue into the nest to capture the insects. The largest of the edentates, the giant anteaters, weigh as much as 25 kg (55 lb.) and measure over 2 m (6 ft.) in length. The giant anteater lives only on the ground, although other anteater species live in trees. Armadillos have a unique protective shield formed of small bony plates.

Primates   Lemurs, monkeys, apes, and human beings belong to the order Primates. Most primates are tree dwellers, and many of the features characteristic of primates were originally adaptations for life in the trees. Sensitive grasping hands with opposable thumbs and feet with big toes are aids in climbing and swinging through trees. Most primates have a flattened face with both eyes directed forward. The eyes of primates can focus and can discern color. Because the fields of vision slightly overlap, their eyes can also perceive depth. Generally, young primates are cared for by their parents for a longer period after birth than most other mammals.

The outstanding feature of primates is their highly developed brain. *Primates are distinguished from other mammals mainly by their active life, their curiosity, and their exceptional ability to learn.*

Of the apes, only gibbons and orangutans live in trees. Gorillas spend their days on the ground but sleep in trees at night. Apes can stand upright and walk for short distances on their hind legs. More often, they lean forward and balance on the knuckles of their hands when they stand or move. Except for the orangutan, apes live in highly developed social groups. They communicate with each other through a large number of sounds.

Figure 39–14. Monkeys use their tails and all four limbs to get from place to place. Gibbons swing with long arms. Gorillas usually walk half erect. Only humans walk fully erect at all times.

For career information, see pages 922–923.

Section Review

1. **Inferring Relationships**   Compare the structure and function of herbivore and carnivore teeth.
2. **Comparing Events**   Compare three kinds of development that occur in mammals and give an example of each.
3. **Comparing Ideas**   Compare rodents and lagomorphs.
4. **Synthesizing Information**   How does convergent evolution help explain the similarities between the Tasmanian devil and the badger?

> **Thinking Critically**

Animal Rights

Laboratory animals are often used for many kinds of research such as medical experimentation. Testing the effects of chemicals that are used in commercial products may also involve the use of laboratory animals.

The question of whether or not animals should be used for scientific experiments and for testing commercial products has raised controversy. Some people argue that no vertebrate animal should suffer pain and death for the purpose of human advancement. Others consider bans on the use of animals for tests and experiments a serious threat to potentially life-saving research. Research that involves animals is an ongoing part of the investigation of life-threatening human dis-

eases. Proponents for using laboratory animals argue that the benefits of enhancing and extending human life justifies the use of these animals in experiments and testing. Proponents also point out that laboratory animals have been used in research that has resulted in the polio vaccine, heart transplant surgery, and coronary bypass surgery. Regulatory agencies and manufacturers are concerned that without animal tests, harmful products could be marketed to the public.

Defenders of animal rights respond that many experiments are unnecessarily abusive to the animals. They point out that using animals for testing and experimentation is sometimes unnecessary and that the reasons for

many experiments are trivial and do not justify the possible pain and suffering that the animals might endure.

Analyze the Issue

1. List the arguments both for and against the use of animals for experiments and testing.

2. Is there a difference between animal experimentation for developing a vaccine against a human disease and for developing a new line of cosmetics? Support your view.

3. What philosophical questions are raised when human and animal rights are compared?

INVESTIGATION 39:
How Are Mammals Distinguished From Other Vertebrates?

Objectives
- To *observe* the structural features of vertebrates
- To *distinguish* among vertebrate classes on the basis of their features

Materials
labeled vertebrate specimens, photographs, drawings, reference books, colored pencils

Prelab Preparation
1. Make a table that has seven vertical columns. Label each column with the name of a different class of vertebrate. Some characteristics may appear in more than one column.
2. Using your textbook for reference, add to your list of characteristics. Use a blue pencil to circle any characteristic that is common to all the classes.
3. Use a green pencil to circle any characteristic that is common to more than one class but not all the classes.
4. Use a red pencil to circle any characteristic that is unique to a single class.
5. Review dichotomous keys, the topic of Investigation 18 on page 293. Use the characteristics in your table to make a dichotomous key that can be used to identify the class of an unknown vertebrate.
6. Make a second table similar to the one shown below. In the first column, "Characteristics," list the characteristics that can be used to distinguish vertebrate classes.

Inquiry: Observation
7. Follow your teacher's instructions for observing the first specimen. Record the animal's name or identification code in the space at the top of a column. Observe the specimen and indicate the presence of a characteristic by placing an "X" in the correct box.
8. Repeat step 7 for each specimen.
9. Use your dichotomous key to identify the class of each specimen. Record each class at the bottom of your table.
10. Exchange your dichotomous key with that of another team. Use the other team's key to identify the class of each specimen. Note any differences in identification of classes as a result of using the other team's key.
11. Discuss your key with the other team, making modifications to the keys, if necessary.

Analysis
1. **Analyzing Observations** What characteristics distinguish the mammals in this Investigation from other vertebrates?
2. **Analyzing Observations** Which characteristics common to the mammals in this Investigation are shared with some, but not all, vertebrate classes?
3. **Making Inferences** How do the characteristics unique to mammals improve their chances for survival?

Specimen name							
Characteristics							
Vertebrate class							

Chapter 39 Review

Summary

Mammals are the only vertebrates that nurse their young. The young remain with the parent through childhood. Mammals are also unique in having large, well-developed brains, body hair, outer ears, and a diaphragm.

Some mammals live together in complex social groups, while others hunt independently. Some mammals hibernate or go into a state of dormancy during periods of extreme cold; others migrate to more favorable areas.

Mammals are grouped into 18 major orders on the basis of embryonic development, tooth structure, feeding habits, and habitats.

Young monotremes hatch from eggs. Young marsupials spend only a short time inside their mother's body. After birth, they complete their development inside their mother's pouch. Most mammals, however, are placentals, which develop inside the fluid-filled amnion.

The major placental orders include insect eaters, bats, hoofed mammals, elephants, carnivores, whales and related aquatic mammals, sea cows, rodent, rabbits and hares, toothless mammals, and primates. The primate order includes not only monkeys and apes but also human beings.

BioTerms

cecum (636)
cetacean (634)
convergent
  evolution (631)
diaphragm (623)
echolocation (625)
embryo (630)
estrus (626)
gestation (632)
home range (626)

mammary
  gland (623)
marsupial (629)
monotreme (629)
omnivore (634)
placenta (629)
placental
  mammal (629)
pregnancy (632)
ruminant (633)

territoriality (626)
ungulate (633)

uterus (631)
viviparous (623)

For each pair of terms, explain the differences in their meanings.

1. monotreme, marsupial
2. ungulate, ruminate
3. estrus, gestation
4. gestation, pregnancy

BioQuiz   (Write all answers on a separate sheet of paper.)

Completion

1. In mammals, the coelom is divided into two parts by a dome-shaped muscle called the ____ .
2. Most female mammals will mate only during their fertile period, called ____ .
3. The oldest group of placental mammals are called ____ .
4. The first chamber of a four-chambered stomach is called the ____ .
5. Mammals that live their entire life in the sea are called ____ .

Multiple Choice

6. ____ belong to the order Cetacea.
   a) Horses b) Gorillas c) Whales
   d) Rodents
7. Bats can locate objects in total darkness by using a) territoriality. b) pregnancy.
   c) echolocation. d) its home range.
8. Animals that eat both meat and plant materials are a) carnivores. b) omnivores. c) herbivores. d) vegetarians.
9. Mammals are the only animals that have
   a) an outer ear. b) mammary glands.

c) a diaphragm.   d) All choices are correct.

10. Pouched animals are   a) monotremes.
    b) ruminates.   c) marsupials.
    d) omnivores.

11. Which is not characteristic of mammals?
    a) mammary glands   b) hair   c) single chest and abdomen cavity   d) an outer ear

12. During estrus most mammals   a) hibernate.   b) migrate.   c) become extinct.   d) reproduce.

13. Which of the following is used by mammals to avoid temperature extremes?
    a) hibernation   b) dormancy   c) migration   d) All choices are correct.

14. Why are monotremes classified as mammals?   a) They have teeth.
    b) They have hair and produce milk.

c) They give birth to live young.
d) They have a four-chambered heart.

15. Young develop in the uterus during
    a) estrus.   b) estivation.   c) gestation.
    d) All choices are correct.

Writing Critically

16. What limb adaptations in mammals allow them to move faster than reptiles?

17. Why do most marsupial and monotreme species live only in Australia?

18. How do baleen whales differ from toothed whales?

19. What do tigers, wolves, and seals have in common?

20. How do you account for the large population of rodents in the world?

Application/Critical Thinking

1. **Analyzing Information**   Research how the mermaid legend might have come about.

2. **Observing Behavior**   For a week, record the specific ways a pet dog or cat communicates its needs to humans or to other animals in the household.

3. **Inferring Relationships**   Spider monkeys have eyes that can focus on a single point, discern color, and view objects in three dimensions. Explain how these adaptations are of benefit to this tree-dwelling monkey.

4. **Analyzing Conclusions**   When hunting seals, a polar bear covers its black nose with its white paw. Explain the hunting strategy in terms of evolutionary adaptation or learned behavior.

Cross-Discipline Connection

Biology and Language Arts   Use library references to look up phrases referring to characteristics of mammals, such as "stubborn as a mule," "dog tired," and "hungry as a horse." Compile a list of phrases to share with the class.

Discovery Through Reading

"Seals and Their Kin," *National Geographic* (April 1987): 474–501, summarizes seal behavior. What are three problems of survival facing seals and what can humans do to help?

Read the article "Madagascar's Lemurs: On the Edge of Survival," *National Geographic* (August 1988): 132–161 about the mysterious lemurs on Madagascar. When did lemurs first appear on Earth? How many species of lemurs have disappeared since humans appeared on Madagascar?

Summary

The phylum Chordata includes the vertebrates, animals with backbones. The seven living classes of vertebrates are the jawless fishes, cartilaginous fishes, bony fishes, amphibians, reptiles, birds, and mammals.

Jawless fishes are parasites on other fishes. Cartilaginous fishes are usually predators and include the sharks and rays. Bony fishes are divided into three groups: lobe-finned fishes, lungfishes, and ray-finned fishes. Bony fishes have a swim bladder that allows them to swim at various levels under water. Fishes obtain oxygen through gills. Fertilization is usually external.

Amphibians develop in water and have adaptations that allow them to live on land. Frogs, for example, have skeletons that can support the body on land and legs that are suited for movement both on land and in water. Amphibians have lungs and a three-chambered heart. However, amphibian eggs are released, fertilized and develop in water. Fertilization is external and the larvae that hatch respire through gills.

Reptiles, unlike amphibians, have amniotic eggs that prevent the embryo from drying out. Reptiles also have dry, scaly skin. Dinosaurs are extinct reptiles whose closest living descendants are the birds and crocodiles. The four living orders of reptiles are represented by the tuatara, turtles and tortoises, crocodiles and alligators, and lizards and snakes.

Birds and mammals are warm-blooded. Birds have feathers and four-chambered hearts. The bodies of birds show adaptations that make flight possible. Bird reproduction involves complex behavior patterns. Fertilization of eggs is internal.

Mammals are covered with hair. They are the only vertebrates that nurse their young. The young remain with one or both parents for an extended period. Mammals have well-developed brains, and their complex behavior patterns sometimes include interaction in social groups. Some mammals, however, hunt independently. Mammals are classified into three groups: egg-laying, pouched, and placental mammals, which have the largest number of species.

Synthesis

Synthesis Statement

The oldest group of vertebrates, the fishes, are cold-blooded animals that have skeletal, respiratory, and other organ systems that have allowed them to be successful in a water environment. Amphibian adaptations have made it possible for members of this group to live in many areas on land. However, amphibian eggs must be fertilized in water and the larvae develop in water. Reptiles, birds, and mammals are not dependent on water for fertilization and development of their eggs. Warm-bloodedness and complex behavior patterns are characteristics of birds and mammals.

Synthesis Questions

Apply your understanding of this unit to the following questions.

1. Birds and mammals are among the dominant groups of animals on land. Describe the features of birds and mammals that have allowed these two groups to be successful land-dwelling animals. What adaptations are shared by both birds and mammals? What adaptations distinguish birds from mammals?

2. More than 95 percent of all mammals are placental mammals. Compare the reproduction of mammals to that of fishes, amphibians, reptiles, and birds. Name some advantages of placental development that may account for the success of placental mammals on land.

3. The number of offspring produced by breeding pairs of vertebrate species varies widely. Compare the relative number of fertilized eggs that are produced by fishes, amphibians, reptiles, birds, and mammals. Offer an explanation that may account for the differences in the structure of the eggs produced by each of these groups.

4. Each vertebrate group has adaptations that allow it to succeed in a particular environment. Compare the adaptations found in the different vertebrate groups and relate them to the environments in which the group is found.

5. List the characteristics of areas where you would be likely to find amphibians. How are these places different from the ones where you might expect to find reptiles? What features help explain why amphibians and reptiles are usually found in different kinds of environments?

6. Compare the mammalian nervous system to that of fishes, amphibians, reptiles, and birds. Explain how the mammalian nervous system has contributed to the success of the mammals.

7. The digestive systems and metabolism vary considerably among vertebrates. Give reasons why birds and mammals spend more of their time seeking and consuming food than do fish, amphibians, and reptiles.

8. Use a separate piece of paper to draw a concept map like the one below. Place each of the following in the appropriate circle: bird, lizard, toad, bat, and shark.

    Then draw lines from these circles to the ones that indicate warm-blooded or cold-blooded.

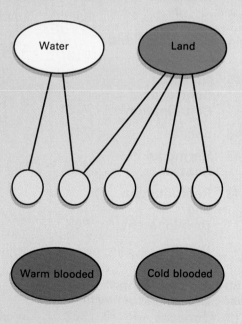

10 HUMAN BIOLOGY

Unit Outline

Unit Focus

The photograph of a large group of people shows both the similarities and differences among humans. However, each individual is distinct and can be recognized by a set of unique features. These unique features allow humans to distinguish familiar individuals from strangers in a crowd.

- *What biological features make humans different from other organisms?*

- *What features make each human individual different from all other humans?*

A crowd of spectators exhibits human diversity.

Overview of Human Biology

Outline

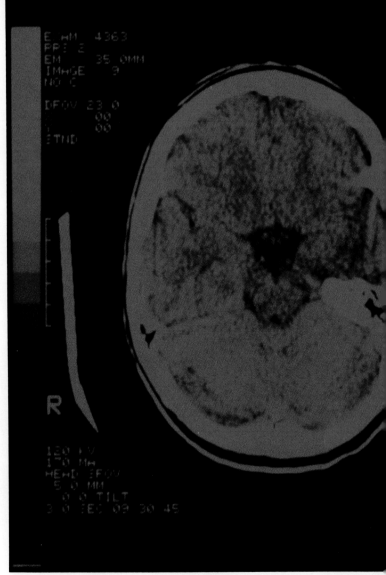

CAT scan of a human brain

Focus

Humans are complex organisms with a number of unique characteristics and features. Among these is the human brain, the most complex biological structure known to exist. Over the last 700 years, researchers have learned a great deal about how the human body is organized and how the human body works.

■ *How is the human organism different from other forms of life?*

■ *What are the advantages of having a complex brain?*

Human Characteristics

Scientists classify humans as members of the kingdom Animalia, phylum Chordata, class Mammalia and order Primates. The animals we resemble most closely are the monkeys, apes, and more than 200 other types of the order Primates. *The traits that make us distinctly human are mostly refinements of traits found in other primates.*

Section Objectives

- *Name* four characteristics humans share with other primates.
- *List* the traits that characterize humans.
- *Identify* the human body structures that show adaptation to upright posture.
- *Summarize* the major behavioral characteristics of humans.

40.1 Physical Characteristics

We share many physical characteristics with other primates, because humans and other primates developed from a common ancestor. This ancestor, now extinct, lived an *arboreal,* or tree-dwelling, existence. The evolution of some primate traits into human traits came about much later.

Primate Traits One important characteristic of all primates is a complex and highly developed brain. Compared to other animals, primates have brains that are larger in relation to their overall body size.

Primates also have sophisticated eyes that distinguish minute details—an adaptation to the ancient dim forests. The keen vision of primates is due in part to the position of the eyes at the front of the face. This position produces *stereoscopic vision,* or the ability to perceive objects in three dimensions. Special eye cells called *cones* also contribute to primates' keen vision. These cells distinguish color and enable the eye to see sharp images.

A third primate characteristic is a hand with five digits. These digits include an **opposable thumb**—that is, a thumb that can be positioned opposite the fingers to grasp branches and objects.

Long arms with flexible shoulder and wrist joints are another feature of primates. Two bones in the forearm enable primates to rotate their hands a full semicircle; shoulder joints enable them to move their arms in many directions. Together, these structures and the grasping hand permit primates to swing from branch to branch. Some primates are able to maintain an upright sitting or standing posture during certain activities such as feeding.

Primates also share the same four types of teeth—*incisors* for cutting, *canines* for tearing, and broad *premolars* and *molars* for grinding and chewing. Together these teeth enable primates to eat both plants and other animals.

Figure 40–1. This orangutan in Milwaukee County Zoo uses its opposable thumb to hold the apple it is eating. This and its upright posture link it to humans.

Human Traits The earliest humans showed so many ape-like features that scientists sometimes have difficulty telling whether fossil bones are those of an ape or a human. As evolution continued, however, humans developed distinctive physical and behavioral traits that characterize them as a species.

The most important human feature is a brain larger than that of any other primate. Chimpanzees, for example, have a brain capacity of about 500 cm³ (30 cu. in.). Humans, however, have an average brain capacity of about 1,400 cm³ (85.5 cu. in.). The expansion of the human brain resulted in the vertical forehead typical of humans.

The ability to stand and walk upright under all conditions is another distinctly human trait made possible by several specially adapted structures. The *pelvis*, the girdle of bone that includes the hip bone, is wide and slightly curved. This permits it to

Figure 40–2. A comparison of human and ape skeletal features shows the characteristics that distinguish humans as a species. These include (from left) an S-shaped spine, arch-shaped jaw, wide pelvis, large hand with well-opposed thumb, and a flat foot with nonopposable large toe.

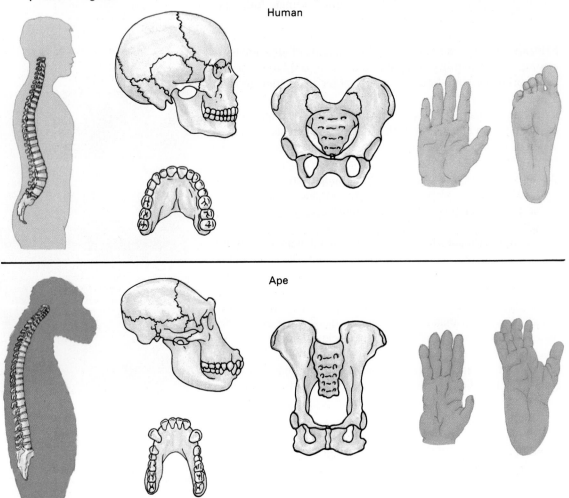

Human

Ape

support the upper part of the body. The broad rear of the pelvis provides a large area for anchoring the walking muscles. The S-shaped spine rising from the pelvis provides support and balance. The head sits erect at the top of the spine. Even the human foot is designed for standing and walking upright. Basically flat, it contains an arch for support. The large toe is not opposable, but lies parallel to the other toes. In this way the large toe is adapted for walking instead of grasping. *More than any other characteristic, upright posture with the erect head creates the distinctly "human" appearance.* This posture, with the eyes at a high level, enables humans to see distant objects.

Human teeth and jaws are also distinctive in size and shape. The canine teeth of monkeys, apes, and other primates are long and sharp. These canines are useful for tearing food. Human beings have smaller, more even teeth than other primates. Human canines are only slightly longer than the incisors and are used to hold food as well as to tear it. The premolars and molars, the back teeth that are specialized for chewing and grinding, are broader than they are in other primates. The human jaw is shaped like an arch, while the jaw of other primates has a rectangular shape.

Reading Critically

Comparing Ideas Based on the shape of the teeth and jaws, how is the eating pattern of humans different from other primates?

40.2 Behavioral Characteristics

Although the physical characteristics of all primates are somewhat similar, behavioral characteristics vary greatly between humans and other primates. The reason for this difference is the enlarged human brain. The brain enables humans to process and remember a great deal of information. These mental abilities also enabled humans to develop a system of symbols that make spoken and written language possible. The use of language, in turn, allows people to share their information and ideas. Using this sophisticated brain, humans have been able to create and use tools. With the ability to speak to one another and use tools, humans have altered their social organization from a simple agrarian structure to complex societies that depend greatly upon scientific technology.

Section Review

1. **Listing Ideas** Name four primate characteristics.
2. **Analyzing Information** Name five characteristics that distinguish humans from other primates.
3. **Evaluating Ideas** What behaviors characterize humans?
4. **Evaluating Information** How could an archaelogist determine if a set of bones were human or ape?

Thinking Critically

Section Objectives

- *Describe* the plan of the human body.
- *List* the different types of epithelial tissue and tell where in the body each is found.
- *Distinguish* among connective, muscle, and nervous tissue.
- *Identify* the major systems of the body and the functions they perform.

Organization of the Body

The human body is organized in much the same way as the bodies of other *vertebrates,* or animals with a spinal cord. In overall structure the human body is bilaterally symmetrical, which means the body has two sides that, in most ways, are mirror images of each other. The organs of the human body are formed of specialized cells and are organized into complex systems that perform specific functions.

40.3 Plan of the Body

The human body is divided into four major parts—the head, neck, trunk, and limbs. The body is built around a jointed bony skeleton covered with layers of muscle and skin. Inside the trunk of the body is a cavity called the **coelom** (SEE luhm). The coelom is divided into two smaller cavities by the **diaphragm** (DY uh fram), a dome-shaped sheet of muscle. The **thoracic** (thaw RAS ihk) **cavity** lies above the diaphragm and contains the heart, lungs, and esophagus. The **abdominal cavity** lies below the diaphragm and contains the organs of digestion, reproduction, and excretion. The **cranial cavity** is inside the skull and contains the brain.

40.4 Tissues of the Body

The organs of the body are formed from four types of tissue: epithelial (ehp uh THEE lee uhl), connective, muscle, and nervous. Most types of tissue have several forms that perform different functions.

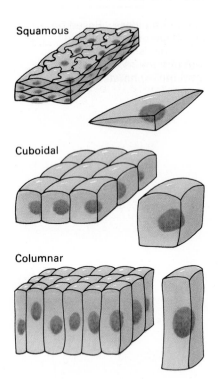

Squamous

Cuboidal

Columnar

Figure 40–3. Three types of epithelial tissue cover the inner and outer surfaces of the body. This tissue, classified according to the shape of its cells, is squamous, cuboidal, or columnar.

Epithelial Tissue   Tissue composed of one or more layers of cells protects all internal and external body surfaces. Such tissue is called **epithelial tissue.** *Squamous epithelium* is composed of flat, irregularly shaped cells. Squamous cells form the top layers of the skin, the protective covering of the heart and lungs, and the lining of blood vessels. *Cuboidal epithelium* is made up of cells that are basically cube shaped. They are found in many glands and in the ducts of some organs, such as the kidney, as well as in the middle ear and the brain. *Columnar epithelium* is composed of cells that are long, narrow, and tightly packed. They line much of the digestive system and the upper respiratory tract. Many columnar epithelial cells have tiny hairlike extensions called **cilia** (SIHL ee uh). The wavelike motion of cilia helps move substances along these surfaces.

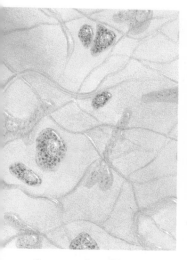

Figure 40–4. Connective tissue consists of cells embedded in a matrix. Loose connective tissue (left) has a semifluid matrix. The cells of fat tissue (right) contain large droplets of fat.

Connective Tissue The most widely distributed tissue in the human body is **connective tissue.** It joins, supports, and protects the other types of tissue. Connective tissue is composed of relatively few cells embedded in a thick, nonliving material called the **matrix** (MAY trihks). The matrix contains many tiny fibers made of proteins and carbohydrates.

Many kinds of connective tissue are found in the human body. Cartilage is a flexible but tough connective tissue consisting of small clusters of cells embedded in the matrix. Bone is a connective tissue that consists of cells in a matrix that contains hard crystals. Loose connective tissue is found under the skin and around nerves, blood vessels, the heart, and the lungs. Its matrix is semifluid. Liquid connective tissue forms blood and lymph, a clear fluid that is derived from blood. The matrix in blood and lymph is a liquid called plasma. Fat tissue is composed of cells in which large droplets of fat are stored. This fat can be used for energy when needed.

Muscle Tissue Specialized cells with the ability to contract and thereby produce movement make up **muscle tissue.** Muscle tissue is classified into three types. *Skeletal muscles* are attached to bones and move the skeleton. *Smooth muscles* are found in the walls of many internal organs, such as the digestive organs. *Cardiac muscle* is found only in the heart.

Nervous Tissue Cells that can transmit messages throughout the body make up **nervous tissue.** These cells are found in the brain, spinal cord, nerves, and sensory organs. Nervous tissue provides information about the environment. It also controls many body functions.

Reading Critically

Comparing Information
How is connective tissue different from epithelial tissue?

Biofact

Q: *Does a body organ ever consist of more than one type of tissue?*

A: Yes. All organs contain the four different types of body tissue.

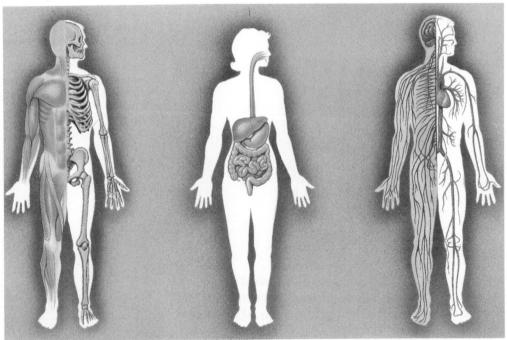

| Muscular and skeletal systems | Digestive system | Nervous and circulatory systems |

Figure 40–5. Each body system consists of a group of organs that work together.

The systems of the human body and those of other representative vertebrates are diagrammed on pages 894–905.

40.5 Systems of the Body

Tissues are organized into larger units called organs. Organs that work together to perform a particular function form a *system*. All body systems are interrelated and operate in unison.

- The **skeletal system** moves, supports, and protects the body. Blood cells are manufactured inside bones, and calcium and phosphorus are stored in bone tissue.
- The **muscular system** works with bones to make the body move. Muscles also protect some of the body's organs.
- The **digestive system** includes the tube running from the mouth through the trunk and several accessory organs. In this system, food is broken down into essential nutrients, nutrients are absorbed, and solid wastes are eliminated.
- The **circulatory system** transports nutrients, gases, and chemicals to all parts of the body. It also collects waste products from cells. Blood is circulated through blood vessels by the pumping action of the heart. The **lymphatic system,** part of the circulatory system, collects fluid from tissue and returns it to the blood. Both systems also help fight disease.
- The **respiratory system** takes oxygen into the body and eliminates carbon dioxide and water.

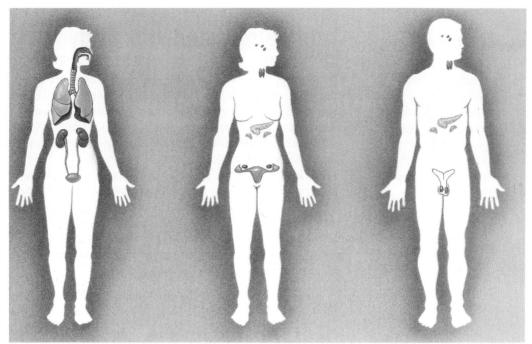

Respiratory and excretory systems

Endocrine and female reproductive systems

Endocrine and male reproductive systems

- The **excretory system** removes cellular wastes from the blood. It also maintains the body's fluid and chemical balance. Wastes leave the body through the **urinary system,** a part of the excretory system.
- The **nervous system** monitors the outside environment and controls and coordinates body activities.
- The **integumentary system** forms the body's outer protective layer. It consists of the skin, hair, and nails.
- The **endocrine system** helps control body functions through chemicals called *hormones*. Hormones regulate functions such as growth and maturation.
- The **reproductive system** provides a means of producing offspring in order to maintain the species.

The structure of human cheek cells is investigated on page 657.

Section Review

1. **Identifying Structures**   What are the three types of epithelial tissue? Give an example of where each is located.
2. **Identifying Function**   What four tissue groups make up the human body? What is the function of each?
3. **Identifying Function**   Name four systems of the body and give a major function of each.
4. **Analyzing Information**   How is the coelom divided in the human body and what systems are separated by this division?

⟨ **Thinking Critically** ⟩

- *Distinguish* between transplants and prostheses.
- *List* some organs that are commonly transplanted.
- *Name* several products of biomedical engineering.
- *Describe* how computers can help paralyzed muscles move.

Technology and the Body

The human body is often compared with a complex machine. However, there is one major difference between the two. When a machine breaks down, it can be shut off until repairs are made. New parts can be ordered to replace worn-out ones. A human body cannot be shut off when repairs are needed, and new parts cannot simply be ordered.

Science, however, is finding ways to treat human disorders and replace some body parts. One solution may be an organ transplant—the replacement of a body part with an identical part from another person. Another solution may be replacement with an artificial part, or **prosthesis** (prahs THEE sihs). The design and development of artificial body parts is called **biomedical engineering**.

40.6 Organ Transplants

The first kidney transplant, accomplished in 1954, was a major milestone in transplant surgery. Since then about 64,000 patients have received kidney transplants. Other body parts that can be transplanted include blood, heart, lungs, cornea, liver, skin, and bone. Scientists are also studying ways to transplant the small intestine and brain tissue.

Until 1978 many transplants failed because the recipients' bodies rejected the new organs. Rejection occurred because the body recognized a transplanted organ as a foreign substance and attacked, or rejected, the organ as it would attack invading viruses or bacteria. To prevent rejection, doctors administered drugs that suppressed all the body's natural defenses. However, these drugs left the organ recipient susceptible to infections of all types. Today transplant recipients are given *cyclosporine*, an antibiotic drug that suppresses only the defenses against a transplanted organ. Since it was introduced in 1978, cyclosporine has doubled the number of transplanted organs that survive for at least a year.

40.7 Artificial Replacement Parts

Since the early 1970s, biomedical engineers have developed an amazing array of artificial parts—limbs, joints, bones, teeth, blood, hearts, and even skin. Often these prostheses involve innovative uses of modern materials and electronic equipment. For example, silicone is used in artificial skin and plastics are used in artificial joints. Researchers are also designing limbs

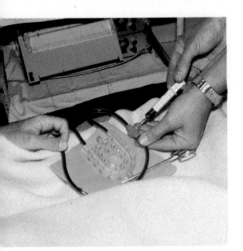

Figure 40–6. Artificial organs can now take the place of some diseased or malfunctioning organs in the human body. Here surgeons prepare to implant an artificial pancreas.

Spinal injuries have caused more than 400,000 Americans to become paralyzed. In many spinal injuries, the brain and limbs are not damaged. The problem is that the connection between these body parts has been broken because of a broken neck or back. Muscles that move limbs get their commands from the central nervous system. Generally the commands travel by way of nerves in the neck and spine. When the nerves are severed, paralysis results.

Because paralysis victims are inactive, their muscles begin to deteriorate. The process of muscle deterioration leads to other problems, such as diseases of

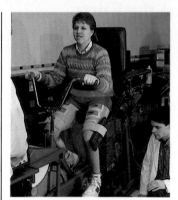

the heart and circulatory system and weakness of the bones.

Computers may soon end some of these problems. In certain experiments, researchers have enabled paralysis victims to move their legs. The researchers strap the patient's feet to the pedals of a stationary bicycle, then use a com-

puter to produce electrical impulses that in turn trigger movement in the paralyzed muscles. This procedure allows some paralysis victims to pedal the bicycle at a rate of more than 19.2 km (12 mi.) per hour. Researchers have also used computers to help paralyzed people walk. A small portable computer provides the impulses to the muscles.

Computers may soon be used with a pedal-operated wheelchair and a special tricycle. With this equipment, paralysis victims can move around indoors.

■ **Inferring Relationships** How does the computer assist the brain to make paralyzed legs move?

equipped with high-powered batteries and microprocessors, tiny devices that receive and channel electrical signals.

The chief aim of biomedical engineers is to design prostheses that behave like normal human parts. Some prostheses come close to achieving this goal. The Utah Arm, for example, is an artificial limb equipped with microprocessors. When attached to a person who has lost an arm, the electronic equipment picks up nerve impulses generated by the wearer's muscles. Then the microprocessors translate the impulses into movements almost identical to those of a natural human arm.

Research is also under way on artificial organs that are part transplant and part prosthesis. One example is an artificial replacement for the pancreas, an important organ of digestion. Part of the artificial pancreas consists of pancreatic cells from rats that produce essential digestive juices. These cells line a system of artificial tubes in a frame of metal and plastic.

Reading Critically

Identifying Information
How does a computerized prosthetic arm interact with the body?

Performance Hinges on the Knees

Watch a football player maneuver from a tight end position. Watch a weightlifter raise a heavy metal barbell. Watch an aerobic dancer execute a series of jumps. All three move in patterns that would not be possible if knees did not bend.

The knee is a hinge joint that is located where the upper and lower leg bones meet. This joint works remarkably well when the human body is moving forward—or sitting in a chair. Many activities, however, require some degree of side-to-side motion as well. Lateral pressure places stress on the knee and the ligaments that hold the upper and lower leg bones together. Excessive twisting and turning can damage the ligaments. The cartilage at the ends of the bones and the supportive tendons can also be injured.

Some activities are especially hard on knees. With every step, a jogger can exert on the knee a force of up to four times the body's weight. Football players frequently suffer knee injuries because their sport requires them to make quick lateral moves that often damage ligaments in the knee joint.

Chances of knee injury can be reduced by warming up slowly before exercising and wearing shoes that offer support and cushioning. Avoiding deep knee bends that stretch ligaments and choosing a resilient surface when exercising can also help reduce risk.

To learn more about artificial body parts, see the BioTech feature on pages 710–711.

Many researchers believe that transplants work better than prostheses for organs that chemically control the activities of body cells. Many also believe that transplants may always be preferred for certain organs, including the kidneys, liver, and heart. At present, however, artificial parts are superior to transplants for organs such as the arm in which strength and mechanical accuracy are most important.

Thinking Critically

Section Review

1. **Comparing Ideas**   Compare a transplant and a prosthesis.
2. **Organizing Ideas**   Name five organs that can be transplanted.
3. **Identifying Information**   List four types of prostheses.
4. **Synthesizing Conclusions**   What changes in medicine and science have made transplants and prostheses possible?

INVESTIGATION 40:
How Can You Observe Cheek Cells?

Objectives
- To *prepare* cheek cells for microscopic examination
- To *observe* human cheek cells

Materials
slide, coverslip, toothpick, compound light microscope, lens paper, medicine dropper, methylene blue, paper towel

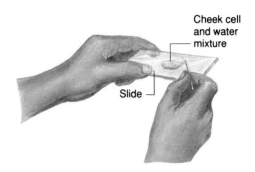

Cheek cell and water mixture

Slide

Prelab Preparation
1. Describe three kinds of epithelial tissue. Which of the three types is likely to be found lining the inside of the cheek?
2. Explain why stains are used to study cell structures. Give an example of your previous use of a stain to study cells.

Inquiry: Lab Technique
3. Put a small drop of water in the center of a glass slide.
4. Gently roll the flat end of a toothpick along the inside wall of your cheek. Cells will easily come off the surface and stick to the toothpick.

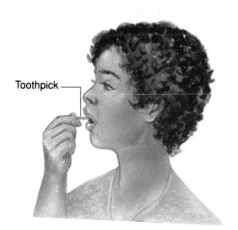

Toothpick

5. Roll the same end of the toothpick into the water on the slide. Mix carefully and add a coverslip.

6. Place the slide on the stage of the microscope and use low power to find an individual cell. Make a drawing of the cell and label what you observed.
7. Switch to high power. Make a labeled drawing of the cell as seen with the high-power lens.
8. **CAUTION: Methylene blue will permanently stain clothing, books, and papers.** Remove the slide from the microscope stage. Place one drop of methylene blue at one edge of the coverslip. Place a small piece of paper towel at the opposite edge. As the paper towel absorbs the water, the stain is pulled beneath the coverslip. Use a paper towel to absorb any excess stain.
9. Locate a cell using low power. Switch to high power. Draw and label the visible parts of the stained cell.
10. Describe the shape of a cheek cell.
11. Compare and contrast the appearance of the stained and unstained cheek cells.
12. Compare the stained cell's appearance at low power with the cell's appearance at high power.
13. List the cell structures that can be seen at high power.

Analysis
1. **Analyzing Observations** Which cell part absorbed the most stain? Explain.
2. **Inferring Ideas** How is the shape of the cheek cell well-suited to its function?

Chapter 40 Review

Summary

Humans share many characteristics with other primates such as an opposable thumb, color and stereoscopic vision, and four different types of teeth. However, human beings differ from other primates in having an enlarged brain and upright posture.

Humans are the only animals with a formal language. They also make and use tools. Human social patterns differ significantly from those of lower animals.

The human body consists of epithelial, connective, muscle, and nervous tissue. These tissues compose the following interrelated systems: skeletal, muscular, digestive, circulatory, lymphatic, respiratory, excretory, urinary, nervous, endocrine, reproductive, and integumentary.

Scientists are learning how to replace damaged body parts with transplanted organs and artificial parts.

BioTerms

abdominal
  cavity (650)
biomedical
  engineering (654)
cilia (650)
circulatory
  system (652)
coelom (650)
connective
  tissue (651)
cranial cavity (650)
diaphragm (650)
digestive
  system (652)

endocrine
  system (653)
epithelial
  tissue (650)
excretory
  system (653)
integumentary
  system (653)
lymphatic
  system (652)
matrix (651)
muscle tissue (651)
muscular
  system (652)

nervous
  system (653)
nervous tissue (651)
opposable
  thumb (647)
prosthesis (654)
reproductive

system (653)
respiratory
  system (652)
skeletal system (652)
thoracic cavity (650)
urinary system (653)

For each pair of terms, explain the differences in their meanings.

1. muscle tissue, nervous tissue
2. abdominal cavity, thoracic cavity
3. muscular system, skeletal system
4. lymphatic system, circulatory system

BioQuiz   (Write all answers on a separate sheet of paper.)

Completion

1. The _____ system takes in oxygen and expels carbon dioxide.
2. The _____ tissue is designed to receive and transmit messages.
3. The coelom is divided into two smaller cavities by the _____ .
4. Many columnar epithelial cells have _____ that help move substances.
5. Connective tissue is composed of cells embedded in a _____ .

Multiple Choice

6. The _____ system regulates body activities by producing chemicals.
   a) excretory b) endocrine
   c) nervous d) digestive
7. Tissue that covers all external and internal body surfaces is a) nervous tissue. b) muscle tissue. c) epithelial tissue d) connective tissue.
8. The heart, lungs, and esophagus are contained within the a) abdominal

cavity. b) thoracic cavity.
c) coelom. d) cranial cavity.
9. Which of the following is not a type of muscle tissue? a) skeletal b) smooth c) cardiac d) cuboidal
10. The coelom is found inside the a) head. b) limbs. c) trunk. d) neck.
11. Stereoscopic vision allows primates to see a) dimly lit objects. b) colors. c) sharp images. d) three dimensions.
12. Severing the nerves to body limbs causes a) prosthesis. b) paralysis. c) rejection. d) impulses.
13. Bone consists of cells in a matrix that contains a) plasma. b) hard crystals. c) fat droplets. d) lymph.
14. Which system manufactures blood cells? a) circulatory b) respiratory c) skeletal d) endocrine

15. Today, many damaged body parts can be replaced with an artificial part called a) a prosthesis. b) an organ. c) a microprocessor. d) a silicone implant.

Writing Critically

16. What behavioral characteristics distinguish humans from other primates?
17. What are the structural differences among the three types of epithelial tissue?
18. How do the functions of connective tissue, muscle tissue, and nervous tissue differ?
19. Why does the body frequently reject a transplanted organ?
20. What are the organic and the artificial parts of the artificial pancreas?

Application/Critical Thinking

1. **Researching Information** Use information from your library to make a time line that shows the important advances in the techniques of organ transplant.
2. **Synthesizing Ideas** Monkeys are frequently used instead of humans in both medical and behavioral experiments. Write a report on the pros and cons of this practice. In what ways are monkeys valid substitutes for humans in experiments? In what ways are they not valid substitutes?
3. **Inferring Relationships** Skin and liver cells reproduce throughout a person's lifetime, but muscle and nerve cells do not. Assume that a person has suffered skin and nerve injuries. Explain what difference might exist in the healing processes of these two types of tissue.

Cross-Discipline Connection

Biology and Computer Science For years, humans have tried to develop a computer-controlled robot that can function as similarly as possible to a human. Use the library to investigate current achievements in the field of robotics. Write a report that describes the most sophisticated robot engineered and developed to date.

Discovery Through Reading

The article "Transplants Come of Age," *Forbes* (April 27, 1987): 86–90, focuses on how the number of transplants have increased. What developments have increased the number of transplants? What is currently the biggest obstacle facing the continued increase in transplants? What might be some solutions to this problem?

Support, Movement, and Protection

A gymnast demonstrates muscular coordination and control

Focus

Bones and muscles support the body, protect internal organs, and make movement possible. Skin prevents harmful organisms from entering the body and prevents internal tissues from drying out. Skin also contains organs that help regulate body temperature and organs that pick up information about the environment.

- *Compare the different joints in your body to those found in familiar items that you use every day?*

- *Why is a cut in the skin potentially dangerous?*

The Skeletal System

Section Objectives

- *List* the functions of the skeleton.
- *Summarize* the process of bone development.
- *Describe* the structure of a long bone.
- *Name* the main types of joints and give an example of each.

The human skeleton is a remarkable structure. Its materials are strong and light. Bone is as strong as cast iron but several times lighter and considerably more flexible. The skeleton's design is simple and efficient. Many bones are hollow cylinders, a shape that provides the greatest strength while using the least amount of material.

41.1 Functions of the Skeleton

The skeleton serves several vital functions. *Along with muscles, the skeleton makes possible a wide range of movements. It supports the body and protects internal organs.* Bones store calcium and phosphate, which are taken up by the blood when needed. Also, tissue called **marrow** inside some bones produces red and white blood cells.

41.2 Structure of the Skeleton

The adult human skeleton is an *endoskeleton,* or internal skeleton, consisting of about 206 bones as well as connective tissues called *cartilage* and *ligaments*. The skeleton has two main divisions—the *axial skeleton* and the *appendicular skeleton*.

The **axial skeleton** forms the body's central framework of support and protection. It consists of the skull, the face, the vertebral column, and the rib cage. The skull protects the brain. The vertebral, or spinal column, holds the body upright and protects the spinal cord. The vertebral column includes the vertebrae, the sacrum, and the coccyx. As Figure 41–1 on page 662 shows, the vertebral column has five regions: cervical, thoracic, lumbar, sacral, and coccygeal. The rib cage consists of 12 sets of ribs and the *sternum,* or breastbone. These bones protect the heart, lungs, and other organs in the thoracic cavity. Each of the ribs is attached to the vertebral column. Seven pairs of ribs, called *true ribs,* are also attached to the sternum by cartilage. The other five pairs do not attach or attach indirectly to the sternum and are therefore called *false ribs*.

The **appendicular skeleton** consists of 126 bones in the *pectoral girdle,* the *pelvic girdle*, and the arms and legs. The pectoral girdle—the bones of the shoulder area—provides support for the arms and allows them a wide range of movement. Muscles attach the pectoral girdle to the axial skeleton. The pelvic girdle—bones of the hip area—attaches directly to the lower part of the vertebral column.

The skeletal system of the human body is diagrammed on page 895.

Biofact

Q: *What is a slipped disc?*

A: Discs of cartilage serve as cushions between vertebrae. Extra pressure on the vertebrae may force a disc to break. This condition, which can cause pain and even paralysis, is called a herniated, or ruptured, disc. When a disc protrudes and presses on nerves, this is known as a slipped disc.

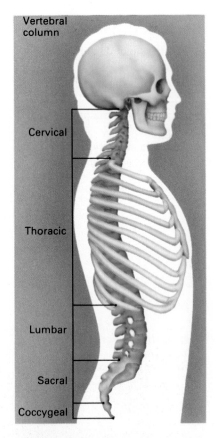

Vertebral column

Cervical

Thoracic

Lumbar

Sacral

Coccygeal

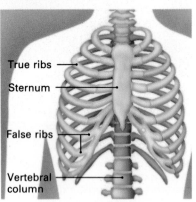

True ribs

Sternum

False ribs

Vertebral column

Figure 41–1. The vertebral column (top) and the rib cage (bottom) are two major subunits of the axial skeleton. The entire skeleton (right) consists of 206 bones.

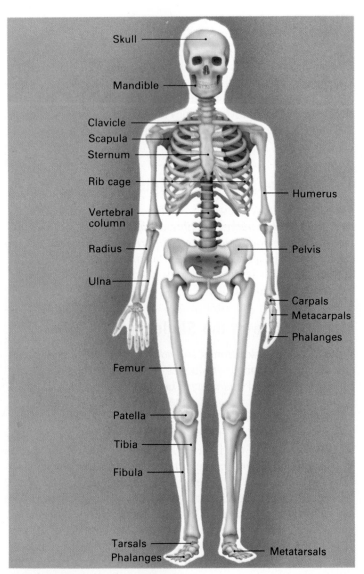

Skull

Mandible

Clavicle

Scapula

Sternum

Rib cage

Vertebral column

Radius

Ulna

Humerus

Pelvis

Carpals

Metacarpals

Phalanges

Femur

Patella

Tibia

Fibula

Tarsals

Phalanges

Metatarsals

41.3 Structure of Bones

Bones are classified according to their shape. A bone's shape is closely related to its function. For example, *long bones* in the arms and legs support weight and are involved in movements such as walking and lifting. *Flat bones,* such as the sternum and skull, have a large surface area that protects the underlying organs. The *short bones* of the wrists and ankles allow great flexibility and precise movements.

Although bones vary greatly in shape, they all have a similar structure. Bone consists of living and nonliving materials.

The living cells that make up the bone are called **osteocytes** (AHS tee uh sytz). Osteocytes are embedded in a network of tough protein fibers called *collagen*. The nonliving part of bone, the mineral portion, consists mainly of compounds containing calcium and phosphorus that surround the osteocytes and make bones hard. A protective fibrous membrane, the **periosteum** (pehr ih AHS tee uhm), covers all bones and helps connect them to muscles. Its rich blood supply nourishes the bone.

Figure 41–2 shows the internal structure of a typical long bone—the femur, or thigh bone. The middle portion, called the *shaft,* is composed of a central cavity surrounded by hard bony material. This hard material is *compact bone*. Small channels, known as **Haversian** (huh VUR shuhn) **canals,** run through this compact bone. Haversian canals contain blood vessels that nourish the osteocytes. The central cavity in long bones is filled with *yellow marrow,* which stores fat. The shaft is separated from the end of the bone by an *epiphyseal* (ehp uh FIHZ ee uhl) *line,* which marks the area where growth formerly took place.

In flat bones and at the ends of long bones, the hard material is very thin. Under this thin, hard material is *spongy bone,* which consists of tough material that resists shearing forces. In certain parts of the skeleton the spongy bone contains *red marrow* that is soft and spongy. It is in the red marrow that red blood cells and white blood cells are manufactured.

41.4 Development of Bones

During early embryonic development, the skeleton consists of only cartilage. During the second month of development, the cartilage starts to be replaced by bone through a process called **ossification** (ahs uh fuh KAY shuhn). During ossification bone cells replace cartilage cells, and calcium compounds from the blood are deposited around the cells. Some cartilage, however, never ossifies. For example, the tip of the nose and the outer portion of the ear contain cartilage throughout life.

Portions of the skull ossify after birth. Skull bones form directly from embryonic connective tissue without cartilage forming first. At birth the large, flat skull bones cover the brain, but they do not meet. The spaces between the bones, called *fontanels,* are covered by a tough membrane. Ossification is completed over a two-year period after a child is born.

A person grows as bones lengthen. In long bones, growth takes place at both ends of the bone in regions called **epiphyseal plates.** An epiphyseal plate is a layer of cartilage that contains cells that undergo mitosis. Divisions of these cells increase the amount of cartilage, and thus the length of the bone increases.

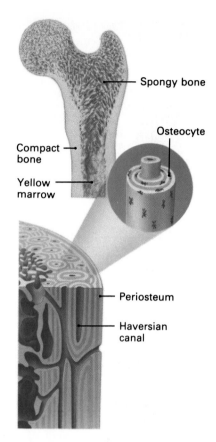

Figure 41–2. A typical long bone (top) has a shaft of compact bone surrounding a center of yellow marrow. Haversian canals like the one shown fill the compact bone.

Reading Critically

Analyzing Structure What would happen to leg growth if the epiphyseal plates on the femur were absent?

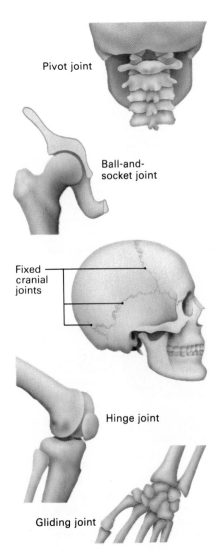

Pivot joint

Ball-and-socket joint

Fixed cranial joints

Hinge joint

Gliding joint

Figure 41–3. Each type of movable joint permits a different kind of movement. The fixed joints in the skull do not allow any motion.

The career of athletic trainer is described on pages 926–927.

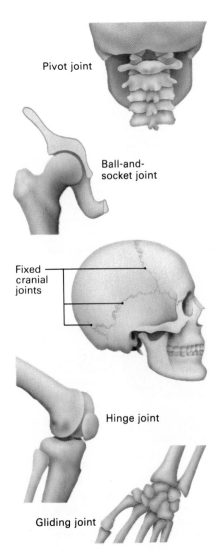

> **Thinking Critically**

At the same time, calcium is deposited around the cartilage cells in the portion of the plate closest to the shaft. Bone cells then develop in the portion of the plate closest to the shaft. As the bone cells ossify, the bone gets even longer. The plate continues to produce new cartilage cells until growth stops, at which time the plate itself is replaced by bone. Although bones grow in width throughout life, growth in length is largely complete by the time a person is 25 years old, if not sooner.

41.5 Joints

Because bones do not bend, movement can occur only where bones meet. The point where two or more bones meet is called a **joint.** Joints are of two kinds: movable and immovable. A joint that permits movement is a *movable joint*. Some movable joints, such as the shoulder joint, allow full movement. Others, such as the knee, are only partially movable. *Immovable joints* exist in bones that are fused together, as in the skull.

The body has four major types of movable joints. *Hinge joints*, such as the knee, allow forward and backward movement. *Pivot joints*, such as the joint between the first and second vertebrae, permit a rotating movement. *Ball-and-socket joints*, such as the hip, allow the widest possible movement. *Gliding joints* in the wrist and ankle allow sliding movement.

Cartilage and a special lubricant called **synovial** (sih NOH vee uhl) **fluid** keep joints moving smoothly. Bones are held together at a movable joint by **ligaments,** which are strong bands of connective tissue.

Athletes and other active people frequently dislocate or sprain joints. Stretching or tearing ligaments causes a *sprain*. Joints may also become swollen and painful in a condition called *arthritis*. The most painful and crippling type is *rheumatoid arthritis*, in which the membranes that produce synovial fluid become inflamed. The cartilage at the ends of the bones is destroyed, and the bones may fuse and prevent movement. In *osteoarthritis*, which is common among elderly people, cartilage wears away, and the bones rub together.

Section Review

1. **Identifying Function**   What are the functions of the skeleton?
2. **Analyzing Ideas**   Explain how the skeleton changes during embryonic development.
3. **Organizing Ideas**   Describe three types of bone.
4. **Evaluating Information**   Why is a hinge joint well-adapted to function as a knee?

The Muscular System

Section Objectives

- *Distinguish* among the three types of muscle tissue.
- *List* the main steps in a muscle contraction.
- *Describe* how skeletal muscles cause movement.

Bones would be virtually useless if there were no muscles. However, only some muscles move bones. Others assist in circulating blood and in digesting food. The body has more than 600 muscles, accounting for about 40 percent of the body weight of a healthy person.

41.6 Functions of Muscles

A **muscle** is an organ made up of many muscle cells. Muscles attached to bones cause movement at joints. Some muscles are always working in the body whether a person is conscious of this effort or not. For example, the heart beats and the eyelids open and close. Though movement is the chief function of muscles, they also protect some internal organs. Additionally, sitting and standing require some muscles to be active.

41.7 Types of Muscles

Muscle tissue is made of special cells that have the ability to contract and relax. *Three types of muscle tissue make up the muscular system: skeletal, smooth, and cardiac.* Each differs in structure and task.

Skeletal Muscle   Muscles that move bones are called **skeletal muscles.** They attach to bones either directly or by means of strong bands of nonelastic connective tissue called **tendons.** Because skeletal muscles are generally under a person's conscious control, they are also called *voluntary muscles*. However, they sometimes move without conscious control, such as when a person responds to sudden danger.

Muscle cells are called **muscle fibers.** Skeletal muscle fibers have a long tapering shape. Each fiber contains many nuclei and 1,000 to 2,000 full-length protein threads called **myofibrils** (my oh FY bruhlz). Tiny units called **sarcomeres** (SAHR koh mihrz) can be seen forming bands across the myofibrils. These units lie in single file in a way that gives myofibrils a striped, or *striated*, appearance. For this reason skeletal muscle is also called *striated muscle*.

Smooth Muscle   **Smooth muscle** is made up of spindle-shaped cells with one nucleus each. Most smooth muscles function in the organs of the digestive, respiratory, and circulatory systems. Smooth muscles are not under conscious control, so they

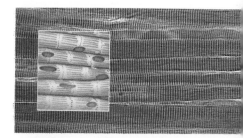

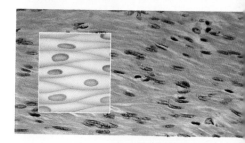

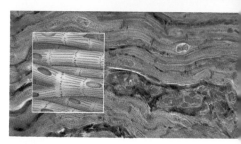

Figure 41–4.   Distinctive shapes distinguish the cells of skeletal muscle (top), smooth muscle (center), and cardiac muscle (bottom).

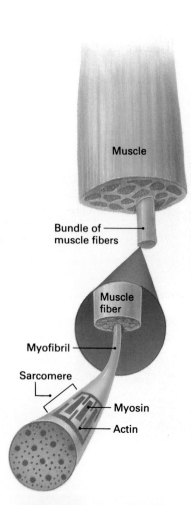

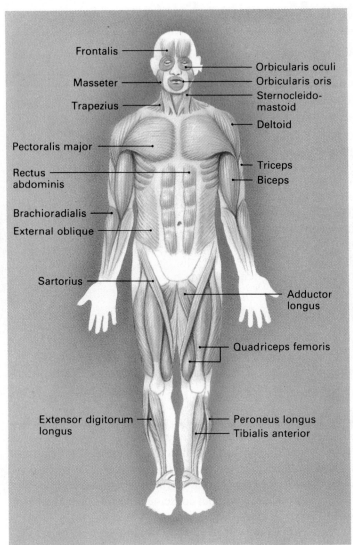

Figure 41–5. Each skeletal muscle (top) consists of individual fibers (center). These fibers, in turn, are composed of myofibrils containing sarcomeres (bottom). The skeletal muscle system is shown to the right.

are called *involuntary muscles*. They do not respond as quickly as voluntary muscles, but they do not tire as easily. These muscles lack the striations of skeletal muscles.

Cardiac Muscle   **Cardiac muscle** is involuntary, striated muscle that is found only in the heart. The tightly packed cells of cardiac muscle have one or two nuclei each. Unlike other types of muscle, cardiac muscle does not receive impulses from the nervous system. Instead, the heart has its own regulator, a tiny block of special muscle fibers called the *sinoatrial node* that cause the muscle cells to contract.

41.8 How Muscles Contract and Relax

How muscles contract and relax has been the subject of many scientific studies. Most of these studies have been done on skeletal muscles. Contraction of skeletal muscles takes place within a sarcomere. As Figure 41–6 shows, two different types of protein filaments are involved: actin and myosin. Thin *actin filaments* are twisted into double strands and are attached at the ends of a sarcomere. Thick *myosin filaments* lie in the middle of the sarcomere. Myosin filaments are also twisted into a rope-like structure that has two globular "heads" on the end of the compound myosin filament. When a muscle is relaxed, the actin and myosin filaments overlap slightly.

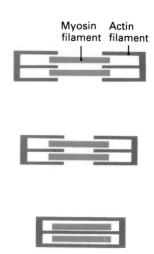

Myosin   Actin
filament filament

Figure 41–6. A muscle contracts as actin and myosin filaments slide past one another (top). Each individual sarcomere must shorten (left) in order to contract the muscle fiber.

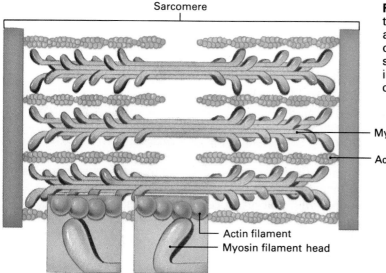

Sarcomere

Myosin filament

Actin filament

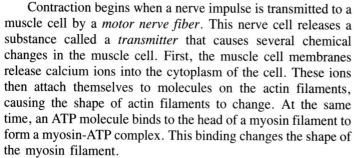

Actin filament
Myosin filament head

Contraction begins when a nerve impulse is transmitted to a muscle cell by a *motor nerve fiber*. This nerve cell releases a substance called a *transmitter* that causes several chemical changes in the muscle cell. First, the muscle cell membranes release calcium ions into the cytoplasm of the cell. These ions then attach themselves to molecules on the actin filaments, causing the shape of actin filaments to change. At the same time, an ATP molecule binds to the head of a myosin filament to form a myosin-ATP complex. This binding changes the shape of the myosin filament.

The actin filaments then slide past the myosin filaments. This movement shortens the sarcomere and causes the muscle to contract. Exactly how this happens is not clear. According to the most widely accepted theory, the change in shape of the two

Biofact

Q: *What is rigor mortis?*

A: Soon after death a person's skeletal muscles contract and do not relax. The body becomes rigid—a state called rigor mortis.

Playing Hard and Fast

A well-exercised body shows increased muscle tone and lung capacity, a healthier heart, and more resilient blood vessels. Exercise done without precautions, however, may cause serious injury, especially to an unconditioned body.

When muscle tissue has been stretched beyond its ability to recover, small blood vessels in muscle tissue hemorrhage. Muscle soreness after exercise may be a symptom of this hemorrhaging.

Extended periods of exercise may cause soreness in muscles that is the result of a buildup of lactic acid, a product that forms when muscle cells are forced to work without an adequate supply of oxygen. Exercising more slowly may allow the lactic acid to be metabolized during exercise and reduce or eliminate after-exercise soreness.

Muscles surrounding the body's joints are especially vulnerable to injury during exercise. The pain of a sprained ankle or knee comes from stretched or torn ligaments and from the swelling caused when fluid escapes the twisted joint and fills the surrounding tissues.

Even the skin is not immune to injury during exercise. Blisters form at points of friction between shoes and the skin, filling with a fluid that protects the fragile underlying tissues. Perspiration that remains on the skin too long can cause rashes.

Many such injuries can

be avoided. The fibers in regularly exercised muscles can stretch to a greater length and recover quickly, making them less prone to hemorrhaging. Lung capacity increases with regular exercise, therefore, more oxygen can be delivered to muscles when muscles are contracting. When muscles and tendons surrounding a joint are in good condition from regular exercise, they can absorb some of the force of a blow to a joint.

Reading Critically

Inferring Relationships Why might you be unable to contract your muscles if the supply of ATP was very low?

filaments enables the heads of the myosin filament to form attachments, or cross-bridges, with the actin filaments. After forming one cross-bridge, each myosin head appears to swivel and begins to form new cross-bridges with the actin filament. The attachment of each myosin head to an actin filament is made, broken, and re-formed five times per second. The energy for the pulling, releasing, and reattaching comes from the ATP. The result of these sequential attachments is that the actin filament is pulled by the myosin head so it slides along the myosin filament. The ends of the sarcomere are thus drawn together, causing the sarcomere to shorten. Many sarcomeres contracting at the same time cause a muscle to contract.

When an impulse to a muscle cell ends, the calcium ions leave the cytoplasm. The filament then returns to its original shape and position. The muscle is then relaxed.

Interference with the biochemistry of muscles and muscle action can lead to both simple and severe health problems. A *cramp* occurs when a muscle cannot relax. In a disorder called *myasthenia gravis,* the muscles have insufficient transmitter. They do not contract properly, and the victim has problems with speaking, eating, and other voluntary movements. In an inherited disorder called *muscular dystrophy,* muscle tissue degenerates and is replaced by fatty tissue. The *Duchenne* type is the most severe and accounts for 90 percent of all cases. No cure for muscular dystrophy has yet been discovered.

41.9 How Muscles Cause Movement

When a skeletal muscle contracts, it creates a pulling action that results in movement. *Muscles can only pull; they cannot push.* For this reason, muscles work in opposing pairs. A muscle pair is termed *antagonistic* if, for example, the contraction of one muscle bends a joint and the contraction of the other straightens the joint. A muscle that bends a joint is called a **flexor,** and a muscle that straightens a joint is called an **extensor.**

Most skeletal muscles are attached to two bones. During contraction one bone serves as an anchor. The point at which the muscle is attached to the anchoring bone is the **origin.** The point at which the muscle is attached to the moving bone is the **insertion.** Between these two points is a joint. Contraction of a muscle thus causes movement at the joint.

Two muscles of the upper arm—the *biceps* and the *triceps*—illustrate how antagonistic muscles produce movement. The biceps has its origin at the shoulder and its insertion on the *radius,* a bone of the forearm. When the biceps contracts, the forearm is drawn toward the front of the shoulder. If no antagonistic muscle opposed the biceps, the arm would remain bent. However, the *triceps* on the back of the upper arm has its origin on the *humerus* of the upper arm and its insertion on the ulna. When the triceps contracts, it straightens the arm.

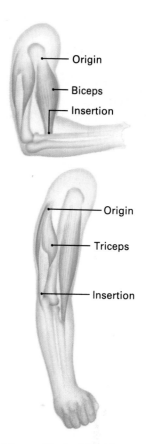

Figure 41–7. The biceps and the triceps are an antagonistic pair of muscles. Which muscle must contract to bend the arm?

Section Review

1. **Summarizing Ideas**   Describe three types of muscle.
2. **Inferring Relationships**   What role does calcium play in muscle contraction?
3. **Evaluating Relationships**   What would happen if your tricep muscle were completely severed?

> **Thinking Critically**

- *List* several functions of the skin.
- *Explain* the function of melanin.
- *State* the functions of sebaceous glands and sweat glands.
- *Describe* the effects of sunburn on the skin.

The ability of skin to perceive touch is explored on page 673.

Biofact

Q: *What forms fingerprints?*

A: The dermis attaches to the bottom of the epidermis, forming unique interlocking ridges and indentations called whorls, loops, double loops, and arches. The palms, soles of the feet, and toes also have distinctive identifying prints.

The Integumentary System

Bones, muscles, and body organs are covered by the largest single organ, the skin. The skin is also called the **integument.** Along with the hair and nails, it makes up the *integumentary system.*

41.10 Functions of the Integumentary System

The skin performs many functions for the body, the most important of which is protection. The unbroken skin prevents harmful organisms from entering the body. It also cushions the body against physical injury. The skin is a sense organ containing receptors for touch, heat, cold, pressure, and pain. It is also an organ of elimination because it rids the body of certain waste materials through sweat. In addition, sweating cools the body and so helps control body temperature. Blood vessels near the skin's surface also allow heat to escape. When exposed to direct sunlight, components of the skin produce vitamin D. In addition, skin acts as a waterproof covering that keeps fluids inside the body.

41.11 Structure of the Integumentary System

Skin consists of all four types of body tissue: nervous, muscle, connective, and epithelial. As a result, it is elastic, flexible, and responsive. Its thickness depends upon its function. For example, an extremely thin layer of skin covers the eardrums, which must be sensitive to sound waves. In contrast, thick skin covers the soles of the feet.

Layers of Skin   The skin, shown in Figure 41–8, consists of two layers. The thin outer layer is called the **epidermis.** The thick inner layer is called the **dermis.**

The epidermis itself has two layers. The top one is actually about 20 layers of dead, scalelike, flattened cells. These cells die quickly because they are cut off from their food supply. They contain a protein called *keratin,* which makes them waterproof. The body loses several thousand of these cells each day, and new cells are produced by mitosis in the lower epidermal layer. As the surface cells disappear, those in the lower layer become the outer surface. It takes about 27 days for all of the outer skin cells to be replaced. In addition to these skin-generating cells, the lower layer has cells that contain melanin, the pigment that makes skin dark. Every person has approximately

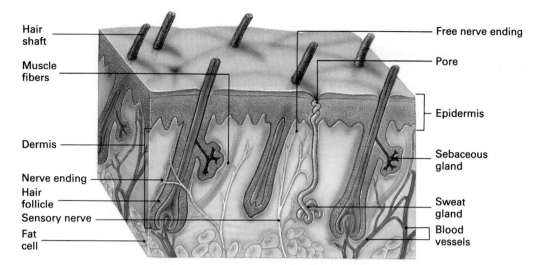

Hair shaft

Muscle fibers

Dermis

Nerve ending

Hair follicle

Sensory nerve

Fat cell

Free nerve ending

Pore

Epidermis

Sebaceous gland

Sweat gland

Blood vessels

Figure 41–8. Although the skin is barely 4 mm (0.16 in.) thick, it is the largest organ of the body.

the same number of these cells. Therefore, skin color differences result from variations in the amount of pigment produced by these cells.

The dermis is composed mainly of connective tissue, which gives the skin its strength and elasticity. Blood vessels, nerves, hair roots, and oil and sweat glands are all located in the dermis.

Subcutaneous Layer A protective layer of loose fatty tissue and dense connective tissue called the *subcutaneous layer* attaches the dermis to the bones and muscles. Although not technically part of the skin, the subcutaneous layer, like skin, helps protect the body against injury and heat loss.

Glands *Sebaceous glands*, or oil glands, secrete *sebum*, an oil that reaches the skin's surface through the places where hair emerges from the skin. The oil prevents hair and skin from drying out and helps waterproof the skin. A condition called *acne* commonly occurs during adolescence. Acne occurs when oil mixes with dead cells and plugs up sebaceous glands, causing blackheads. In addition, inflammation of oil glands causes pimples. Acne may be related to hormonal changes that take place during adolescence.

More than 2.5 million *sweat glands* exist in the dermis. Most consist of a tiny duct that opens to the skin's surface and rids the body of excess water and certain wastes. The evaporation of sweat also acts to cool the body when it becomes overheated.

Hair and Nails Hair is present on the skin over the entire body, except on the soles of the feet, the palms of the hands, and the lips. Hair is manufactured in **hair follicles,** which are small folds of epidermis that extend into the dermis. Tiny blood

---

Reading Critically

Inferring Relationships What would happen to skin that had no sebaceous glands?

THINKING ABOUT BIOLOGY: The Dangers of Tanning

Many people believe that a suntan makes them look healthy and young. Excessive sun bathing can be harmful, however.

Suntan is actually the body's attempt to protect skin cells from an overdose of ultraviolet rays. When skin is exposed to the sun's rays, a brown skin pigment called *melanin* absorbs the harmful ultraviolet rays. Exposure to these rays stimulates melanin production. The result is a darker brown skin color, or suntan.

Damage occurs because tanning without burning is almost impossible. Melanin cannot always absorb all the ultraviolet rays. Too much ultraviolet light can kill or shock some cells and prevent mitosis in others. It can damage enzymes, cell membranes, and blood vessels in the skin. The damaged blood vessels cause the redness and chills that accompany sunburn. In severe cases of sunburn, materials from dead skin cells enter the blood and can cause sun poisoning. The ultraviolet rays can damage the genetic material in skin cells and cause cancer.

Moderate exposure can be helpful. Sunlight stimulates the production of vitamin D and may help acne victims by removing excess skin oil. However, exposure must be gradual.

Several days are needed for melanin to reach the skin's surface where it provides protection, so a sunbather's goal should be to get enough sunlight to stimulate melanin production but not enough to cause redness.

Sunscreens prevent the absorption of too many harmful rays. These products have numerical ratings. A rating of 2 means a person can be in the sun twice as long with the lotion as without it. A rating of 15 provides more protection.

■ **Inferring Relationships** How does the amount of melanin in the skin relate to the rate of skin cancer?

vessels at the base of the follicle nourish the hair root. A group of actively dividing cells near the base produce new hair. The hair *shaft,* which extends above the skin's surface is composed of dead epidermis.

Nails are mainly dead cells composed of keratin that protect the tips of fingers and toes. At the base of the hard *nail plate* is a whitish, semicircular area called the *lunula.* Cell division takes place in the root of the nailbed.

Section Review

1. **Summarizing Ideas**   Describe the functions of skin.
2. **Identifying Relationships**   What is the role of melanin?
3. **Analyzing Ideas**   Describe the function of sweat glands.
4. **Comparing Ideas**   Contrast the functions of sebaceous and sweat glands.

Thinking Critically

INVESTIGATION 41:
Are Some Areas of the Skin More Sensitive than Others?

Objectives
- To *measure* the distance between touch receptors
- To *test* a hypothesis through controlled experimentation
- To *record, interpret,* and *evaluate* data

Materials
piece of cardboard measuring 18 cm x 30 cm, scissors, 11 straight pins, metric ruler

Prelab Preparation
1. List sense receptors found in the skin.
2. If two objects are so close together that only one touch receptor is stimulated, how many objects would the person sense?

Inquiry: Lab Technique
3. Cut the piece of cardboard into six 3 cm x 5 cm rectangles.
4. Insert two pins 2 mm apart halfway through one piece of cardboard. Repeat this procedure using four of the remaining rectangles, placing the pins 5 mm, 1 cm, 2 cm, and 3 cm apart, respectively. Push one pin through the center of the last rectangle. Each rectangular "touch tester" will be used to place pin points on the skin of your partner.
5. *How could the touch testers made in step 4 be used to find the distance between touch receptors?*

Distance between pins	Number of pins perceived
2 mm	
5 mm	
1 cm	
2 cm	
3 cm	

6. Make a table like the one shown. Use the table to record whether or not two pin points could be perceived by your laboratory partner.

7. **CAUTION: The student who is the subject of the experiment must remain motionless. The student who does the testing must apply the pins gently so that the subject's skin is not pierced.** Using the touch testers in any order, gently touch both pins to the back of your lab partner's neck. When your partner feels two pins, record a (+) in the table. Record a (−) when only one pin is felt. Repeat the test for a total of three trials.
8. Exchange roles and repeat the test.
9. *What is the minimum distance between pins at which they can be consistently sensed as being two points?*
10. Since the subject expects to feel two pins, a possible source of error may arise. *How could using the rectangle with the single pin reduce this source of error?*

Inquiry: Experimentation
11. After discussing the question that is the topic of this Investigation with your partner, state your hypothesis and explain the reasons that support the hypothesis.
12. Design a controlled experiment that tests your team's hypothesis.
    a. Identify the dependent and independent variables in your experiment.
    b. List the steps in your experiment in which you must be especially careful to avoid error.
13. After having your design approved by your teacher, conduct your experiment. Record your data in a table.
14. Make a bar graph that shows the average distance between touch receptors for the body areas that you tested.

Analysis
1. **Inferring Conclusions** What conclusion can be drawn about your hypothesis? Do the data support your conclusion? Explain your answer.
2. **Making Inferences** What might be the adaptive value of having some areas of the body that are more sensitive to touch than others?

Chapter 41 Review

Summary

The three body systems that together provide support, movement, and protection are the skeletal, muscular, and integumentary systems.

Bones develop and grow through a process called ossification. Several types of bones make up the skeleton, including long bones, flat bones, and short bones. Movement occurs between bones at joints.

The body has three types of muscle tissue: skeletal, smooth, and cardiac. Contraction of a skeletal muscle occurs when a nerve impulse causes chemical changes in muscle cells. When the impulse stops, the muscle relaxes.

Skin covers all outer body surfaces. It consists of the epidermis and the dermis. New cells are produced in the epidermis. Skin pigment, called melanin, is found in the epidermis. Glands, nerves, blood vessels, and hair follicles are found in the dermis. A subcutaneous layer under the dermis attaches the skin to the tissues below.

BioTerms

appendicular
  skeleton (**661**)
axial skeleton (**661**)
cardiac muscle (**666**)
dermis (**670**)
epidermis (**670**)
epiphyseal
  plate (**663**)
extensor (**669**)
flexor (**669**)
hair follicle (**671**)

Haversian
  canal (**663**)
insertion (**669**)
integument (**670**)
joint (**664**)
ligament (**664**)
marrow (**661**)
muscle (**665**)
muscle fiber (**665**)
myofibril (**665**)
origin (**669**)

ossification (**663**)
osteocyte (**663**)
periosteum (**663**)
sarcomere (**665**)

skeletal muscle (**665**)
smooth muscle (**665**)
synovial fluid (**664**)
tendon (**665**)

For each pair of terms, explain the differences in their meanings.

1. cardiac muscle, smooth muscle
2. flexor, extensor
3. ligament, tendon
4. appendicular skeleton, axial skeleton

BioQuiz   (Write all answers on a separate sheet of paper.)

Completion

1. Bones are covered by a protective membrane called the _____ .
2. The _____ is a layer of fatty tissue under the skin.
3. Muscles that work in opposition to one another are called _____ .
4. Haversian canals are small channels containing blood vessels, which run through compact _____ .
5. Tough bands of connective tissue that hold bones together at joints are called _____ .

Multiple Choice

6. Muscle that bends a joint is called
   a) an insertion. b) an extensor.
   c) a flexor. d) a smooth muscle.
7. A muscle is attached to a moving bone at the a) origin. b) epiphyseal plate. c) insertion. d) extensor.
8. Mature bone cells are called
   a) cartilage. b) epidermis.
   c) myofibrils. d) osteocytes.
9. Cartilage is replaced by bone in a process called a) ossification. b) insertion.
   c) atrophication. d) contraction.

10. Joints are able to move smoothly due to cartilage and a) smooth muscle. b) periosteum. c) synovial fluid. d) marrow.
11. Which of the following is not a voluntary muscle? a) cardiac b) biceps c) triceps d) quadriceps
12. A substance that starts a muscle contraction is a) marrow. b) integument. c) synovial fluid. d) transmitter.
13. A protein that helps make epidermis cells waterproof is a) melanin. b) osteocyte. c) keratin. d) pigment.
14. The structures that give striated muscle its striped appearance are a) muscle fibers. b) myofibrils.

c) actin filaments. d) sarcomeres.
15. The thin outer layer of the skin is called a) dermis. b) epidermis. c) the subcutaneous layer. d) connective tissue.

Writing Critically

16. Why does skeletal muscle appear to be striped?
17. What is the difference between the origin and the insertion of a muscle?
18. How is the structure of a hair follicle related to its function?
19. How does a skeletal muscle contract to cause movement?
20. What are the four kinds of movable joints in the body?

Application/Critical Thinking

1. **Evaluating Ideas** Since the skull is well-suited to protect the brain, why is it necessary for athletes to wear helmets when playing certain sports?
2. **Researching Information** Do library research and write a report about exercise and its effects on the human body. Include one or more of the following topics: resistance, aerobic, or anaerobic exercises; conditioning; and muscle building.
3. **Inferring Conclusions** Muscle fibers will contract completely if they receive

an impulse, or they will not contract at all. This is called the *all-or-none* law of muscle contraction. Given this fact, explain how the force of a muscle contraction is controlled so a pencil is not lifted with the same force as a 23-kg (50-lb.) weight.
4. **Synthesizing Conclusions** Would examination of the marrow cavity of a deer's leg bones help determine whether or not starvation was the cause of the deer's death? Why would this be a valid investigation?

Cross-Discipline Connection

Biology and Health Research a bone condition called *osteoporosis*, in the school library. Investigate what causes it, how it can be prevented, and how it is treated.

Discovery Through Reading

Read the article "Living with Arthritis," *Newsweek* (March 20, 1989): 64–70. What do scientists now hypothesize as a cause of rheumatoid arthritis? Name three forms of arthritis.

Read the article "Smooth-Muscle Cells: Twist and Clout," *Science News* (June 20, 1987): 389. Describe the research that provides new insights into the working of smooth-muscle cells discussed in this article.

Nutrition and Digestion

Outline

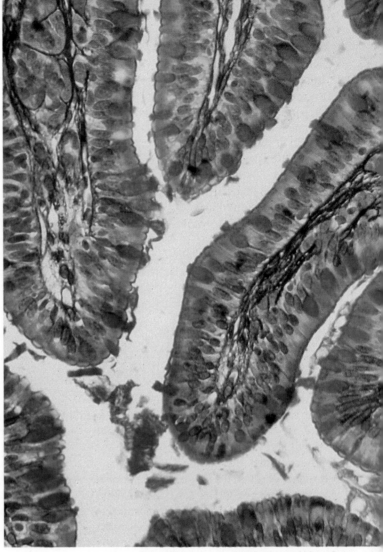

**Cells lining the human intestine stained to
show detail, × 100**

Focus

Energy and building materials exist in food only in potential
form. Most foods must be chemically broken down into small
units and absorbed into the bloodstream before the energy can
be released and the materials in food can be used for growth,
repair, and maintenance of the body.

■ *All organisms, including humans, require food. How is
food similar to the gasoline needed to keep an automobile
running? How is it different?*

■ *From what source will the body get energy if no food is
taken in for several days?*

Food and Nutrition

Section Objectives

- *Describe* the roles of proteins, carbohydrates, fats and oils, vitamins, and minerals.
- *Name* three ways in which water is important to the body.
- *Define* the term *Calorie*.
- *List* the problems associated with high levels of salt, sugars, and saturated fats in the diet.

When you sit down to a meal, you immediately notice the appearance, aroma, and taste of the foods. The most important thing about the food, however, is whether it provides the proper **nutrients,** the substances needed for body growth and maintenance. *Your daily diet should include the proper amounts of carbohydrates, fats and oils, proteins, vitamins, minerals, and water.* All the nutrients required for the functioning of the body can be obtained by drinking water and eating the proper amount of food from four basic food groups. These groups are the milk group, the meat group, the fruit and vegetable group, and the grain and grain products group. Figure 42–1 shows some of the foods in each of these groups.

42.1 Proteins

Proteins are the major building blocks of body tissue. The body requires proteins for growth and tissue repair. Proteins called **enzymes** act as catalysts in chemical reactions in the body. The body can even use proteins to supply energy if its supplies of carbohydrates and fats have been used up.

Proteins consist of long chains of molecules called *amino acids.* The body requires 20 kinds of amino acids, which are divided into two groups based on dietary requirements. The *nonessential amino acids* are those that the body can make from other amino acids. The *essential amino acids* must be obtained directly from food and so are required in the diet. There are 12 nonessential and 8 essential amino acids.

Testing for some organic compounds in foods is the topic of the Investigation on page 689.

Figure 42–1. The four basic food groups are (left to right) meat, milk, fruits and vegetables, and bread and cereals.

"Watch out for the three S's" could very well be the most important diet guideline for most Americans. It means "Be careful of *s*ugars, *s*alt, and *s*aturated fats."

On the average, Americans get about 40 percent of their Calories from fat, over a third of this from such saturated fats as butter and meat fat. A high level of saturated fat in the diet has been linked directly to excessive blood *cholesterol,* a fatty organic compound. Together, saturated fat and cholesterol are considered a major cause of heart and blood vessel diseases.

Forty-five percent of the Calories come from carbohydrates. Refined and processed sugars account for more than a third of the carbohydrate Calories. These Calories provide no additional nutritional value.

For a healthful diet, a person should get about 58 percent of his or her Calories from carbohydrates and fewer from fats. The types of fats and carbohydrates a person eats are also important. Saturated fats should be no more than 10 percent of the Calories. Complex carbohydrates, such as whole

grains, fruits, and vegetables, should make up 48 percent of the Calories, and refined sugar, no more than 10 percent.

Salt abounds in Americans' food. Studies show that a person may need as little as a quarter gram of salt a day; yet Americans average 6 to 18 grams. A salty diet may contribute to high blood pressure, or hypertension, which in turn contributes to heart attacks and strokes.

■ **Summarizing Ideas**
How can Americans improve their diets?

Biofact

Q: *Why are whole grain flours more healthful than bleached flour?*

A: Whole grains contain the seed coat, or husk, of the grain. The husk contains fiber, vitamins, and protein. During refining of bleached flour, the husk is removed.

Complete proteins contain the 8 essential amino acids. From these, the body can synthesize the 12 nonessential amino acids. Meat, eggs, and dairy products contain complete proteins. *Incomplete proteins* do not contain all the essential amino acids. Most plant proteins are incomplete. However, a carefully planned diet that combines plant proteins can provide all the essential amino acids.

42.2 Carbohydrates

Carbohydrates supply most of the body's energy needs. The simplest form of carbohydrate is a *monosaccharide*, or a simple sugar molecule. Glucose, fructose, dextrose, and galactose are monosaccharides. They exist in such foods as fruits, honey, syrups, artichokes, and onions. *Disaccharides*, or double sugars, consist of two monosaccharides. Disaccharides include sucrose, or cane sugar; and lactose, which is found in milk.

Complex carbohydrates called *polysaccharides* consist of many simple sugar molecules. Starches and cellulose are two important polysaccharides. Starches are found in cereal grains

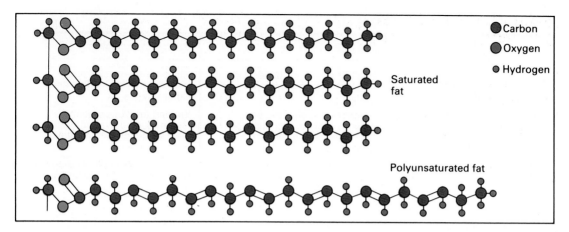

● Carbon
◐ Oxygen
• Hydrogen

Saturated fat

Polyunsaturated fat

Figure 42–2. A molecule of saturated fat (top) contains as many hydrogen atoms as it can hold. A molecule of unsaturated fat (bottom) has fewer hydrogen atoms because some of its carbon atoms are double-bonded.

and such vegetables as potatoes, beans, and corn. Cellulose is present in all plant tissues but cannot be digested by human beings. However, cellulose provides the body with **fiber,** which aids digestion by stimulating the muscles of the digestive tract.

42.3 Fats and Oils

Fats and oils are highly concentrated sources of energy. They provide twice as much energy per gram as do carbohydrates or protein. The body stores fats for use when carbohydrates are not available. Fats also form part of cell membranes and organelles. Thus, they are a structural material of the body.

Fats exist in two forms—saturated and unsaturated. Both forms consist of hydrogen, carbon, and oxygen atoms. In *saturated fat,* all the carbon atoms are joined by single bonds, and so the molecules contain the maximum number of hydrogen atoms. It is saturated with hydrogen. An *unsaturated fat* has at least one double bond between carbon atoms. For every double bond, two hydrogen atoms are missing. A molecule with two or more double bonds is called *polyunsaturated*. Animal fats are saturated fats. Butter, lard, and other saturated fats are solids at room temperature. A liquid fat is called an *oil*. Plant oils are unsaturated fats. Corn oil, olive oil, sunflower oil, and other unsaturated fats are typically liquid at room temperature.

42.4 Vitamins

Vitamins are organic substances that act as *coenzymes*—that is, they assist enzymes during chemical reactions. Although vitamins do not provide energy, they are necessary for normal growth and body activity. Vitamins are classified as either *fat-soluble* or *water-soluble*. Fat-soluble vitamins—vitamins A, D,

| **Reading Critically** |

Inferring Relationships Why does storing fat make humans more mobile?

Table 42-1: Vitamins and Minerals

Vitamin or Mineral Sources	Use by the Body	Deficiency Symptoms
A Fish liver oils, liver, eggs, butter, yellow and green vegetables, fruits	Healthy skin, eyes, bones, teeth, urinary tract, and epithelial tissue	Night blindness, skin and mucous membrane disorders, kidney stones
B₁ (thiamine) Organ meats (liver, brain, kidney, heart), whole grains, most vegetables	Proper functioning of heart, nervous system, and digestive tract; energy release from food; growth	Beriberi (nervous system disorder), cardiovascular disorders, indigestion, fatigue
B₂ (riboflavin) Liver, poultry, milk, eggs, cheese, fish, green vegetables, whole grains	Metabolism of proteins, carbohydrates, and fats; tissue repair; healthy skin	Dim vision, premature aging, poor growth, sore mouth and tongue
Niacin Meat, whole grains, potatoes, leafy vegetables, yeast	Growth, healthy nervous and digestive systems, carbohydrate metabolism	Pellagra; nervous, digestive, and skin disorders
B₁₂ (cobalamin) Liver and other meats, eggs, cheese, yogurt, milk	Red blood cell production, healthy nervous system	Pernicious anemia
C (ascorbic acid) Citrus and other fruits, leafy vegetables, tomatoes, potatoes	Healthy blood vessels, bones, teeth, cartilage; resistance to infection; healing of wounds	Scurvy, easy bruising, bleeding gums, swollen tongue and joints
D Liver, fish oils, eggs, milk, sunlight	Growth, healthy bones and teeth, metabolism of calcium and phosphorus	Rickets, poor teeth and bones
E Whole grains, leafy vegetables, milk, butter, vegetable oils	Healthy cell membranes, possibly for reproductive functions	Red cell rupture, muscular dystrophy, sterility (in lab animals)
K Leafy vegetables, soybeans; made by intestinal bacteria	Normal blood clotting, proper liver functioning	Hemorrhages
Calcium Milk, cheese, whole grains, meat, leafy vegetables, peas and other legumes	Muscular and nervous system functioning, bone and tooth development, blood clotting, cell membrane permeability	Soft bones, poor teeth, failure of blood to clot
Iodine Seafoods, iodized salt	Cellular respiration (control of body functions)	Goiter
Iron Liver, red meat, egg yolk, whole grains, prunes, nuts	Healthy red blood cells	Anemia
Magnesium Milk, whole grains, legumes, nuts, meat	Healthy bones and teeth, carbohydrate and protein metabolism	Improper nerve and muscle functioning
Phosphorus Milk, whole grains, meats, nuts, legumes	Tooth and bone development, ATP production, nucleic acids	Poor teeth and bones
Potassium Whole grains, fruits, legumes, meat	Nerve function, cell activities	Improper nerve and muscle functioning
Sodium Seafood, table salt	Water balance, proper nerve and muscle functioning	Muscle and nerve disorders, dehydration

E, and K—are stored in the body's fatty tissue. Water-soluble vitamins—all the B vitamins and vitamin C—can be dissolved in water but cannot be stored in the body. They must be obtained directly from food.

Excessive amounts of vitamins A and D may cause disorders of the bones and other body tissues. Vitamin deficiencies cause many types of disorders. A well-balanced diet provides the proper amounts of all the necessary vitamins daily.

42.5 Minerals

Minerals are inorganic substances that form an important part of living tissue. Like vitamins, minerals do not supply energy but help regulate body functions. Teeth and bones require calcium and phosphorus. Iron is the central atom in the oxygen-carrying molecules of the blood. Magnesium, calcium, and zinc help regulate nerve and muscle function. Table 42–1 lists vitamins and minerals, their uses, and the results of deficiencies.

42.6 Water

About two-thirds of the body's weight is water, most of it in the cytoplasm of cells. Blood plasma, tissue fluids, and body cavities contain the remainder. Water is required for many body functions. Most chemical reactions in the body can take place only in a water solution. Water carries nutrients to the blood plasma and into body cells. Water also forms the major part of urine and sweat, which help rid the body of wastes.

42.7 Calories

The energy value of food is commonly measured in **Calories.** One Calorie is the amount of heat energy needed to raise the temperature of one kilogram of water 1°C. The energy potential of food and the daily energy requirements of individuals are stated in Calories. A teenage boy needs about 3,000 Calories daily, and a teenage girl, about 2,000.

Biofact

Q: *Are Calories related in any way to the nutritional value of food?*

A: No. Calories are merely a measure of heat energy available from food. Nutritional value pertains to the nutrients in food.

Section Review

1. **Summarizing Ideas** How do vitamins affect health?
2. **Relating Ideas** How does water help the body function?
3. **Evaluating Information** Which presents the greater short-term risk: a diet consisting of no meat or dairy products and few types of plants or a diet of small amounts of meat and dairy and a large number of differing plants?

> Thinking Critically

- *Identify* the main structures in a diagram of the digestive system.
- *Distinguish* between mechanical digestion and chemical digestion.
- *Summarize* the digestive processes that take place in the stomach.
- *Describe* the process of digestion in the small intestine.

The Digestive System

Food can be used by the body only after it has been broken down into small molecules. The process by which food is changed into a form the body can use is **digestion.** Digestion takes place in a continuous tubelike passageway that extends from the mouth to the *anus*. This passageway is known as the **alimentary canal,** or **digestive tract.** The alimentary canal and other organs associated with digestion make up the digestive system.

The digestive system serves two major functions. The first, of course, is digestion—the breaking down of food into molecules the body can use. The nutrient molecules must then get to the cells where they are needed. Therefore, the second major function of the digestive system is **absorption.** Absorption is the movement of nutrient molecules into blood vessels or other vessels. The blood carries these nutrients to the cells, which use the nutrients for energy, growth, and repair.

Digestion takes two forms—mechanical and chemical. *Mechanical digestion is the physical tearing and grinding of food into smaller pieces.* Mechanical digestion thus increases the amount of surface area of food exposed to the action of digestive enzymes. These enzymes help bring about the second form of digestion. *Chemical digestion changes food particles into molecules the body can use.*

42.8 The Mouth

Mechanical and chemical digestion both start in the mouth, or *oral cavity.* Food is bitten, cut, and torn by the *incisors,* the sharp teeth at the front of the mouth, and the teeth next to them, the *canines.* Strong muscles of the jaws and tongue move the food into position for chewing. Food is then crushed and ground by the broad, flat surfaces of the premolars and the molars at the rear of the mouth.

While in the mouth, food is moistened by **saliva,** a mixture of *mucus* and a digestive enzyme called *ptyalin* (TY uh lihn), or *salivary amylase.* Saliva is produced by three pairs of **salivary glands.** The largest of these are the *parotid glands* located in the cheek region. The *sublingual glands* are in the floor of the mouth under the tip of the tongue, and the *submaxillary glands* are along the lower jaw.

Saliva lubricates food so that it moves smoothly through the digestive tract. Saliva may also kill some bacteria in the mouth. Ptyalin starts the breakdown of starches to glucose. However, because food remains in the mouth for such a short time, ptyalin

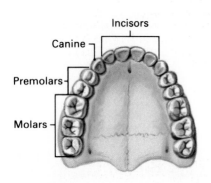

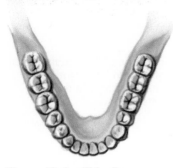

Figure 42–3. This diagram shows the location of canines, incisors, premolars, and molars in the upper and lower jaws.

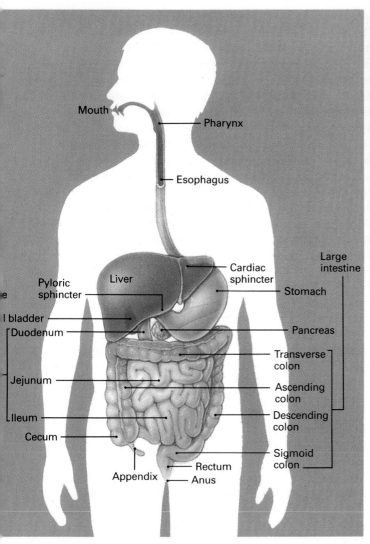

Mouth
Pharynx
Esophagus
Liver
Cardiac sphincter
Large intestine
Pyloric sphincter
Stomach
l bladder
Duodenum
Pancreas
Jejunum
Transverse colon
Ascending colon
Ileum
Descending colon
Cecum
Sigmoid colon
Appendix
Rectum
Anus

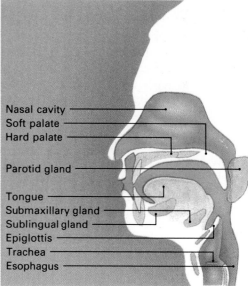

Nasal cavity
Soft palate
Hard palate
Parotid gland
Tongue
Submaxillary gland
Sublingual gland
Epiglottis
Trachea
Esophagus

Figure 42–4. After food passes through mouth and pharynx (above), involuntary muscles move it through the rest of the digestive system (left).

The digestive systems of several representative vertebrates are shown on pages 896–897.

acts on less than 5 percent of the starches. The food and saliva eventually form a moist, soft ball called a **bolus.**

When you swallow, your tongue presses against the **hard palate,** the bony plate in the roof of the mouth. The pressure forces the bolus to muscle tissue called the **soft palate.**

42.9 The Pharynx and Esophagus

From the soft palate area, the bolus moves into the **pharynx** (FAIR ihnks), a common passageway for food and air. As the bolus is forced to the back of the mouth, the soft palate closes off the nasal cavities. At the same time, a flap of tissue called the

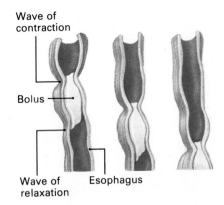

Figure 42–5. A continuous wave of muscle contractions called *peristalsis* moves the bolus through the esophagus.

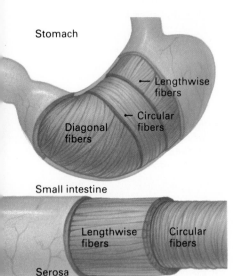

Figure 42–6. The stomach (top) has three layers of muscle that together produce a grinding motion. Only two layers, circular and lengthwise muscle, are found in the small intestine (bottom).

epiglottis (ehp uh GLAHT ihs) seals off the *trachea,* or windpipe. The **larynx** (LAIR ihnks), or voice box, at the top of the trachea moves up against the bottom of the epiglottis. Food can then pass quickly through the pharynx, across the trachea, and into the **esophagus** (ih SAHF uh guhs), the muscular tube leading to the stomach. If a person attempts to breathe while swallowing, food gets into the trachea. An automatic coughing reflex then helps clear the trachea.

Until food enters the pharynx, voluntary muscles control the process of mechanical digestion. Once a swallow has started, however, it cannot be stopped because involuntary muscles take over in the pharynx. A strong contraction of a muscle around the pharynx propels food into the esophagus. This contraction starts a wavelike motion called **peristalsis** (pehr uh STAWL sihs), which moves food along. Peristalsis results from the action of two layers of involuntary muscles that form the walls of most of the digestive tract. One layer of muscles wraps around the tract, and the second layer runs along its length. While the circular muscles squeeze, the parallel ones relax. As the parallel muscles contract, the encircling ones relax. The squeezing and contracting action of the two sets of muscles always occurs above the bolus or liquid in the digestive tract, thus pushing it through the tract.

42.10 The Stomach

At the end of the esophagus is a muscular valve called the **cardiac sphincter** (SFINK tuhr). A sphincter is a muscle that controls a circular opening in the body. This valve prevents food from reentering the esophagus. Food passes through the valve into the **stomach,** a J-shaped, baglike organ with a capacity of 2 to 4 L (2.1 to 4.2 qt.). Both mechanical and chemical digestion continue in the stomach. In addition to the two layers of involuntary muscle, the stomach has a third, diagonal layer of muscle. Through the action of these three muscle layers, the stomach can actually grind food.

Chemical digestion of protein begins in the stomach. The stomach contains about 35 million glands that produce mucus and gastric secretions. The chief gastric secretions produced by the stomach are hydrochloric acid and an enzyme called *pepsin.* Pepsin is active only in a highly acidic environment. This enzyme splits protein into smaller groups of amino acids called *polypeptides.* Hydrochloric acid also dissolves minerals and kills bacteria. There is a muscular valve that controls the passage of food out of the stomach. This valve is known as the **pyloric sphincter.**

In 1822, an American Indian named Alexis St. Martin was severely wounded. A shotgun blast tore open the abdominal wall and part of his stomach.

St. Martin went to Dr. William Beaumont, an army surgeon in northern Michigan. Beaumont examined the wound and thought that St. Martin would die from it, so he merely packed the wound with cotton and waited.

St. Martin did not die. Instead, the stomach healed with a permanent opening to the outside about the size of a quarter. This opening provided Beaumont with a unique opportunity to study digestive processes by looking right into St. Martin's stomach.

Beaumont removed samples of gastric juice from St. Martin's stomach and tested them on various foods. He noted that some foods were changed chemically by the juice and others were not changed. He placed foods directly into the open stomach and determined the amount of time needed to digest each one.

■ **Inferring Relationships** What kinds of health problems might St. Martin have encountered?

What prevents the stomach from digesting itself? Mucus-secreting cells line the surface of the stomach. The mucus helps protect the stomach lining from hydrochloric acid. About 500,000 cells of the stomach lining are shed every minute. As a result of this process, the cell layer replaces itself every three days. Occasionally too little mucus or too much acid exists in the stomach. An open, painful sore called an *ulcer* may then form in the stomach lining. Ulcers may sometimes bleed severely. They can also eat completely through the stomach wall, leading to much more serious conditions.

42.11 The Small Intestine

Food leaves the stomach as a semifluid mass called **chyme.** Chyme enters the **small intestine,** a tube about 7 m (23.1 ft.) long and 3 cm (1.2 in.) in diameter.

The small intestine has three sections. The uppermost section, the *duodenum* is about 25 cm (1.2 ft.) long. The next section, the *jejunum*, is about 4 m (13.1 ft.) long. The last 2.5 m (8.2 ft.) form the *ileum*. *The majority of chemical digestion and absorption takes place in the small intestine.*

The Pancreas and the Liver The **pancreas** and the **liver** secrete digestive juices into the small intestine and so play important roles in digestion. The pancreas, located behind the

Biofact

Q: *Can a person whose stomach has been removed digest food?*

A: Yes. The stomach is the site of protein digestion and a holding area for large quantities of food. Without a stomach, a person would have to eat frequent small meals, avoid animal protein, and chew food thoroughly.

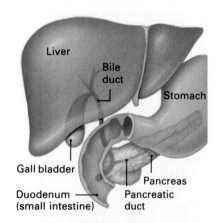

Figure 42–7. The liver secretes bile, which enters the small intestine through the gall bladder. Bile emulsifies fat, which is then digested by an enzyme produced by the pancreas.

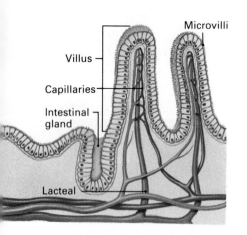

Figure 42–8. Nutrients from digested food in the small intestine pass from the villi to the microvilli, where they enter blood capillaries.

stomach, has many small lobes that secrete enzymes and sodium bicarbonate. The sodium bicarbonate neutralizes the acidity of the chyme leaving the stomach. The chief enzymes secreted by the pancreas are *pancreatic amylase, pancreatic lipase, trypsin,* and *chymotrypsin.* Pancreatic amylase continues the chemical digestion of starch that began in the mouth. It converts starches into maltose. Pancreatic lipase breaks down fats into their component molecules, fatty acids and glycerol. Trypsin and chymotrypsin break down the proteins by splitting them into smaller chains of amino acids called peptides.

The liver is the largest internal organ, weighing about 1.5 kg (3.3 lb.). It produces *bile,* which is a salt solution, not an enzyme. Bile *emulsifies* fat—that is, it breaks down large fat globules into tiny droplets. This process greatly increases the surface area of fat particles. Lipase can then act on the fat more effectively. This process is referred to as the detergent effect of bile, because detergent does the same thing to fat. Bile generally enters the duodenum from the **gall bladder,** a small sac where bile is stored.

Digestion in the Small Intestine Most chemical digestion occurs in the duodenum. A heavy layer of mucus protects the first few centimeters of the duodenum from the acidic chyme released by the stomach. If the mucus protection is not sufficient, the high acid level can cause duodenal ulcers, which are even more common than stomach ulcers.

Enzymes produced by the small intestine include *peptidases, maltase, lactase, sucrase,* and *intestinal lipase.* Various peptidases break down peptides into amino acids. Maltase, lactase, and sucrase convert disaccharides into monosaccharides. Intestinal lipase, like pancreatic lipase, splits fats into fatty acids and glycerol.

Absorption in the Small Intestine Amino acids, monosaccharides, fatty acids, glycerol, water, and minerals are all absorbed in the small intestine. *Absorption occurs quickly in the small intestine because of its lining.* The mucous lining consists of folds covered with millions of tiny projections called **villi** (VIHL eye). Each villus has a *brush border* composed of approximately 600 **microvilli,** which are extensions of the epithelial tissue covering the villi. Intestinal enzymes are not released into the cavity of the small intestine. Instead, the enzymes remain in the brush border where they act upon the food molecules. The molecules are then absorbed into the bloodstream through the microvilli walls. The lining folds, the villi, and the microvilli together increase the surface area of the small

Eating Disorders

Anorexia nervosa is an eating disorder in which afflicted persons starve themselves. In *bulimia,* on the other hand, sufferers engage in binge-purge cycles of eating followed by vomiting. Both disorders afflict young women much more frequently than they do young men. Both disorders can pose serious long-term health consequences.

Anorexia typically appears around puberty, as young women become increasingly conscious about their weight and appearance. Anorexics avoid eating. They may take laxatives or vomit to lose weight. Anorexics often exercise obsessively. Because of metabolic changes, anorexics usually cease menstruation.

An anorexic may lose 25 percent of her normal body weight. An anorexic can become so clever about avoiding food that even friends and close family members do not notice that the person is skipping meals or eating very little food at mealtimes. Anorexia can lead to severe malnutrition, heart irregularities and possibly death.

Bulimia is a lesser-known disorder and harder to recognize, because the bulimic usually maintains a normal body weight. Secretly, however, the sufferer engages in eating binges, consuming as many as 5,000 calories during one meal. The eating bout is usually followed by vomiting. This binge-purge cycle may be

repeated several times a week.

The bulimic may experience muscle weakness or paralysis, kidney disease, and irregular heartbeat. Although each of these disorders is difficult to detect during the early stages, each of them can be cured with a combination of medical treatment and family support.

intestine 600 times. The result is an absorptive area equal in size to the area of a tennis court.

Absorption occurs through the processes of diffusion and active transport. As Figure 42–8 shows, each villus contains tiny blood vessels called *capillaries,* through which monosaccharide and amino acid molecules enter the bloodstream. The blood carries these nutrients to the body's tissues. The liver converts excess glucose into glycogen, a form of starch, and stores it as a future energy source. The cells of the villi resynthesize fatty acids and glycerol into fats. The villi contain tiny vessels called **lacteals,** which absorb the fats. These fats eventually pass from the lacteals into the bloodstream.

42.12 The Large Intestine

Minerals, water, and undigested foods enter the last part of the digestive tract, called the **large intestine.** The large intestine is also known as the **colon.** *Absorption of water, minerals, and vitamins is completed in the large intestine.*

Approximately 9 L (9.5 qt.) of water pass through the digestive tract in one day. Some of the water is transported by osmosis into capillaries lining the walls of the large intestine. The solid waste material that remains is called **feces.** It stays in the body until it is eliminated through the anus. The last part of the large intestine, the **rectum,** controls the elimination of feces.

A species of bacteria called *Escherichia coli,* or *E. coli,* lives in the large intestine. These organisms and other bacteria feed on materials that the human body cannot digest. *E. coli* produce some amino acids and vitamin K.

Among the disorders resulting from digestive problems are diarrhea and constipation. *Diarrhea* is a condition in which the feces do not remain in the large intestine long enough for the water to be absorbed. *Constipation* is the opposite condition. Constipation results when the feces remain in the colon too long. As a result, too much water is absorbed. Diarrhea may be caused by bacteria or viruses, emotional stress, or eating certain foods. Prolonged diarrhea can result in dehydration and even death. Constipation may be caused by insufficient fiber and water in the diet. It results in hard, dry feces that can make defecation, the elimination of feces, painful.

Near the beginning of the large intestine is a small, fingerlike projection called the *appendix.* The appendix is a dead-end, saclike structure that has generally been considered useless in humans. However, some scientists now believe it is involved in the production of antibodies. Sometimes the appendix becomes infected and must be removed. This life-threatening and painful condition is called *appendicitis.*

Reading Critically

Analyzing Relationships In what ways is the activity of *E. coli* in the large intestine beneficial?

Section Review

1. **Comparing Ideas** What is the difference between mechanical and chemical digestion?
2. **Analyzing Function** What enzymes are found in the mouth and stomach and what are their functions?
3. **Summarizing Ideas** Describe how the absorption of food molecules occurs.
4. **Evaluating Relationships** How does the structure of the small intestine relate to its function?

Thinking Critically

INVESTIGATION 42:
Which Nutrients Are Present in Common Foods?

Objectives
- To *perform* chemical identification tests
- To *compare* the nutrient content of various foods
- To *record, interpret*, and *evaluate* data

Materials 🏠 🥽 🔥 ☣

mortar and pestle, whole milk and other common foods, Benedict's solution, hot plate, water bath, test-tube holder, test-tube rack, test tubes, Lugol's iodine, brown paper, Biuret reagent

Prelab Preparation
1. Make a data table like the one shown. Add four horizontal rows to the table.

solid substance into a powder or paste.
9. Use the condensation and incineration procedures to test a sample of each food for the presence of water and minerals.
10. Use the brown-paper procedure to test a sample of each food for the presence of fat.
11. Mix the powder or paste produced from each substance thoroughly with 20 mL of distilled water to make a solution.
12. Use Benedict's solution to test for sugar (monosaccharide) in a 5-mL sample of each food.
13. Use Lugol's iodine to test for starch in a 5-mL sample of each food.

	Water	Minerals	Fat	Monosaccharides	Starch	Protein
Main function						
Identification test						
Positive indicator						

2. In the second row of the table, briefly describe the major function of each substance shown in the top row.
3. In the third row, summarize the chemical test for each substance. Refer to the instructions for each test in Investigation 5 on page 77.
4. In the fourth row, describe the results that indicate the presence of each substance.
5. Label each of the remaining four rows with the name of a food assigned to your team for testing. Record the results of your experiment in this data table.
6. Which of the six nutrient substances shown in the first row is likely to be the most difficult to find? Explain.

Inquiry: Exploration
7. **CAUTION: Put on safety goggles and a laboratory apron.**
8. Use the mortar and pestle to crush each

14. Use Biuret reagent to test for protein in a 5-mL sample of each food.

Analysis
1. **Summarizing Results** Summarize your results.
2. **Communicating Results** Compare your results with those of other teams. Are the results obtained by your team and the other teams similar? Offer an explanation for any differences in the test results among the teams.
3. **Analyzing Data** Which foods tested by all teams contain the greatest variety of nutrients? Which foods contain only one kind of nutrient?
4. **Analyzing Data** How would tests such as these help a nutritionist plan a balanced diet?
5. **Analyzing Data** What additional information would a nutritionist require about food to plan a balanced diet?

Chapter 42 Review

Summary

Food nutrients provide the body with energy and with materials that are required for its growth, maintenance, and repair. Water aids in the breaking down of food molecules, the transport of nutrients, and the removal of waste materials.

Digestion is a mechanical and chemical process in which food is broken down into materials the body can use. Carbohydrates are broken down into monosaccharides. Fats are reduced to fatty acids and glycerol. Proteins are broken down into amino acids.

Most chemical digestion takes place in the small intestine. It may begin in other parts of the body. Water, minerals, and vitamins are absorbed in the large intestine.

BioTerms

absorption (682)	esophagus (684)	peristalsis (684)	salivary glands (682)
alimentary	fat (679)	pharynx (683)	small intestine (685)
canal (682)	feces (688)	protein (677)	soft palate (683)
bolus (683)	fiber (679)	pyloric	stomach (684)
calorie (681)	gall bladder (686)	sphincter (684)	villus (686)
carbohydrate (678)	hard palate (683)	rectum (688)	vitamin (679)
cardiac	lacteal (687)	saliva (682)	
sphincter (684)	large intestine (688)		
chyme (685)	larynx (684)		
colon (688)	liver (685)		
digestion (682)	microvillus (686)		
digestive tract (682)	mineral (681)		
enzyme (677)	nutrient (677)		
epiglottis (684)	pancreas (685)		

For each pair of terms, explain the differences in their meanings.

1. hard palate, soft palate
2. small intestine, large intestine
3. carbohydrate, protein
4. digestion, absorption

BioQuiz (Write all answers on a separate sheet of paper.)

Completion

1. The main process by which food is moved from one end of the digestive tract to the other is called _____ .
2. Chemical digestion of protein starts in the _____ .
3. Proteins called _____ function as organic catalysts in chemical reactions in the body.
4. A _____ is an organic substance that acts as a coenzyme.
5. In the stomach, proteins are digested by the enzyme _____ .

Multiple Choice

6. The processes by which absorption occurs are _____ and active transport.
   a) osmosis   b) diffusion
   c) peristalsis   d) bolus
7. A high-fiber diet helps prevent
   a) constipation.   b) appendicitis.
   c) diarrhea.   d) All are correct.
8. Bile, produced by the liver, helps in the digestion of   a) chyme.   b) fats.
   c) proteins.   d) carbohydrates.
9. Which of the following is not an unsaturated fat?   a) butter   b) olive

oil   c) corn oil   d) sunflower oil
10. Which of the following is a salivary gland?   a) parotid gland   b) sublingual gland   c) submaxillary gland   d) All choices are correct.
11. What would cause you to choke when eating?   a) a blocked sublingual gland   b) an open esophagus   c) an open trachea   d) an open pharynx
12. What valve prevents an individual from throwing up?   a) cardiac sphincter   b) epiglottis   c) pyloric sphincter   d) esophagus
13. What structures help increase the surface area of the small intestine?   a) villi   b) microvilli   c) lining folds   d) All choices are correct
14. Which of the following has not been linked to hypertension?   a) sugar

b) salt   c) saturated fats   d) cholesterol
15. Food and saliva form a moist, soft ball called   a) an epiglottis.   b) an amino acid.   c) a bolus.   d) a nutrient.

Writing Critically

16. How are mechanical and chemical digestion different?
17. What digestive processes occur in the mouth?
18. Which enzymes are secreted by the pancreas, and what do they do?
19. How might the differences between fat-soluble and water-soluble vitamins affect the diet?
20. What is the difference between complete and incomplete proteins?

Application/Critical Thinking

1. **Evaluating Data**   Record everything that you eat in a single day. Decide whether this menu represents a balanced diet. If not, plan how it may be changed to make it more nutritious.
2. **Analyzing Information**   Assume you have just eaten a hamburger on a bun with lettuce and melted cheese. Trace the pathway of the food through the digestive sys-

tem. Explain what happens to it, where it happens, the enzymes involved, and the source of these enzymes. Present this information in the form of a chart.
3. **Researching Information**   Research carbohydrate loading and write a report on your findings. Speak with a coach or health-club operator about the benefits and potential problems of this practice.

Cross-Discipline Connection

Biology and Health   Use references in your library to determine the number of Calories in some of your favorite foods. Also determine the number of Calories used by activities such

as one hour of sitting or running. Then calculate how much time different activities require in order to use all the Calories from some of your favorite foods.

Discovery Through Reading

The article "The Latest Word on What to Eat," *Time* (March 13, 1989):51–53, describes a report that calls for changes in the typical American diet. What are the amounts of fat, cholesterol,

carbohydrates, and protein recommended in the new menu? What risks does a sound diet reduce? Summarize how most Americans might change their daily diets to fit the new menu.

Circulation

Outline

***Chordae tendinae*, "heartstrings" attached to valves inside the human heart**

Focus

Every cell in the body requires a constant supply of nutrients and a constant removal of wastes. Pickup and delivery are handled by an effective transport system: a pump, carriers, and thousands of kilometers of tubes throughout the body. This system is called the *circulatory system*. In addition to carrying nutrients, oxygen, and cell wastes, this system provides natural defenses against disease.

■ *Why is a circulatory system unnecessary in a unicellular organism?*

■ *What is the difference between transport and circulation?*

The Blood

Blood is the chief carrier of the body's transport system. It carries nutrients and oxygen to body cells and transports carbon dioxide and other waste products away from the cells. Blood also combats disease and helps maintain body temperature.

43.1 Composition of Blood

A human adult has about 5 L (5.3 qt.) of blood, which makes up about 9 percent of the body's weight. Blood is a liquid connective tissue. It consists of a liquid called plasma, red blood cells, white blood cells, and cell fragments called platelets. Approximately 55 percent of blood volume is plasma. About 44 percent is red blood cells. The remaining 1 percent is white blood cells and platelets.

Plasma The straw-colored, nonliving part of blood, called **plasma,** has many functions. For example, it carries nutrients such as amino acids and glucose molecules absorbed in the small intestine to body cells. Plasma also takes waste products away from the cells and delivers these wastes to the kidneys and sweat glands so they can be safely removed from the body.

Plasma is more than 90 percent water. The remainder consists of minerals and thousands of other compounds, including many proteins. These proteins assist in blood clotting, help maintain the body's water balance, and influence the exchange of materials between the circulatory system and the body cells. Also present in plasma are nitrogenous waste products and respiratory gases. Some plasma, that with fewer proteins, seeps through blood vessel walls. It fills spaces between body tissues and bathes every body cell. This fluid is known as *tissue fluid.*

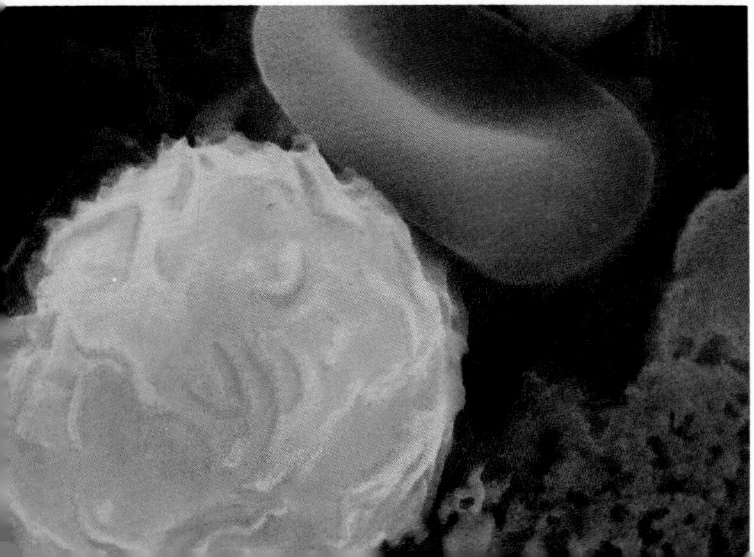

Section Objectives

- *Name* four functions of blood.
- *Describe* the functions of plasma, red blood cells, white blood cells, and platelets.
- *Summarize* the process of blood clotting.
- *List* the four primary blood types.
- *Explain* the cause of Rh disease.

Reading Critically

Summarizing Ideas Why is plasma such an important component of blood?

Figure 43–1. This photomicrograph shows human red blood cells and a white blood cell, ×5,200.

Red Blood Cells   The blood cells that transport respiratory gases are called the **red blood cells.** Red blood cells, also called *erythrocytes* or *red corpuscles,* carry oxygen from the lungs to body cells. They also transport carbon dioxide from the cells to the lungs. A red blood cell has a nucleus when it is formed in red bone marrow. However, the nucleus and other organelles disappear as the red blood cell matures. Each cell becomes a disc-shaped sac with a thick rim and thin center. Almost the entire cell fills with **hemoglobin** (HEE muh gloh bihn), an iron-containing protein molecule that is bright red when combined with oxygen. One molecule of hemoglobin carries four molecules of oxygen. Hemoglobin is therefore an effective oxygen carrier.

Red blood cells are so small that hundreds of them would be needed to encircle one strand of hair. The human body has about 25 trillion red blood cells. They are produced at the rate of over 10 billion per hour and have a life span of about 120 days. The dead cells are dismantled, and the hemoglobin is stored to be reused in new blood cells.

White Blood Cells   The **white blood cells,** also known as *leukocytes* or *white corpuscles,* are the body's main defense against viruses, bacteria, and other foreign organisms. In fighting invaders, white cells pass through blood vessel walls and into tissue fluid. They move like amoebas, attracted to the site of an infection by chemicals. The chemicals may be products of blood clotting. They may also come from bacteria, other leukocytes, or from degeneration of infected tissue. Several kinds of white blood cells are found in the blood. Some white blood cells engulf and digest the invading organisms by a process known as *phagocytosis.* Another important group of white blood cells produces antibodies, which are proteins that help to fight diseases caused by microorganisms.

Most white blood cells are manufactured and stored in red bone marrow until they are needed by the body. They are colorless, irregularly shaped cells with nuclei. Although white blood cells are larger than red cells, they are considerably less numerous—about 1 white cell for every 750 red cells.

Platelets   Cell fragments called **platelets,** or *thrombocytes,* aid in blood clotting. Within five seconds after an injury occurs, the process of clotting, or **coagulation** (koh ag yoo LAY shuhn) begins. Platelets begin to stick to the rough surfaces created by damaged tissue, such as the tissue around a cut or a broken blood vessel. Some platelets break and release chemicals that cause nearby blood vessels to constrict, thus reducing bleeding. They also release an enzyme called *thromboplastin,* which

Figure 43–2. This photograph of two activated human platelets was taken by a scanning electron microscope, magnified 15,300 times.

triggers a process involving proteins in the plasma including *prothrombin* and *fibrinogen*. In the presence of calcium, thromboplastin causes prothrombin to change into *thrombin*. Thrombin is an enzyme that promotes the conversion of fibrinogen into *fibrin*. Fibrin forms strong, elastic protein threads into a mesh that traps blood cells and platelets around the edges of the injury. The result is a blood clot. Within minutes the clot begins to shrink, pulling together the injured ends of skin and forming a *scab*.

Like red blood cells, platelets lack nuclei and are formed in red bone marrow. Platelets are about one-third the size of red cells and number about 1 to every 20 red cells. Their life span is about 7 to 11 days.

43.2 Blood Types

Occasionally an injury or a disorder is so serious that a person must receive blood from another person. *A blood transfer, or transfusion, can succeed only if blood of the recipient and donor match.* Among the factors that must be considered in matching blood is **blood type.** Blood type is determined by the presence of an antigen on red blood cells. An **antigen** is any molecule that stimulates an organism to produce antibodies. An **antibody** is a protein that attacks, or neutralizes, the antigen that triggered its production. Microorganisms, such as bacteria and viruses, possess antigens. The antigens that result in blood types, however, are inherited. The most familiar blood group system is the ABO system. Under this system, the primary blood types are A, B, AB, and O. Type A blood has antigen A, and type B has antigen B. Type AB has both antigen A and antigen B, while type O has neither of these antigens.

Types A, B, and O also contain antibodies. Type A blood contains anti-B antibodies. Type B blood contains anti-A antibodies. Type O has both anti-A and anti-B antibodies. Type AB

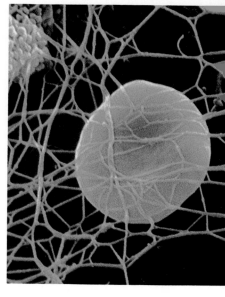

Figure 43–3. This scanning electron microscope image shows a red blood cell enmeshed in fibrin, magnified 7,700 times.

Figure 43–4. If a transfusion of type B blood were given to a person with type O blood, antibodies in the recipient's blood would attack B antigens in the donor's blood. The result would be agglutination.

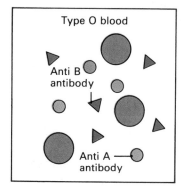

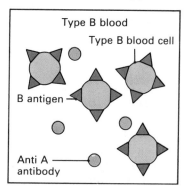

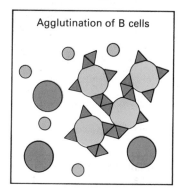

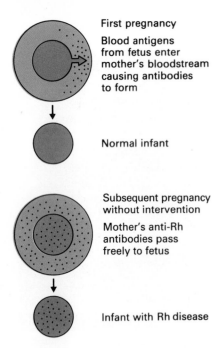

First pregnancy

Blood antigens from fetus enter mother's bloodstream causing antibodies to form

Normal infant

Subsequent pregnancy without intervention

Mother's anti-Rh antibodies pass freely to fetus

Infant with Rh disease

Subsequent pregnancy with treatment

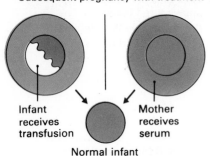

Infant receives transfusion

Mother receives serum

Normal infant

Figure 43–5. This diagram summarizes the facts regarding Rh disease.

Thinking Critically

has neither of the antibodies. If two blood types are mixed during transfusion, antibodies may cause *agglutination,* or clumping, of red cells. Agglutination results, for example, if type A blood is mixed with type B blood. Agglutinated blood cells can clog capillaries and prevent blood flow to tissues which can cause serious damage to internal organs.

When a patient needs blood, doctors must first determine what the patient's blood type is. Modern medical practice, however, requires that more than just blood type be analyzed. Other factors in donated blood must also be compatible for a transfusion to be successful.

43.3 Rh Factor

Another type of antigen is the **Rh factor,** which is present in about 85 percent of all people in the United States. These people are said to be Rh-positive (Rh$^+$). People whose blood does not contain the Rh factor are Rh-negative (Rh$^-$). The Rh factor can cause a problem to children of an Rh$^-$ woman. If the father is Rh$^+$, the child could have Rh$^+$ blood. If some of the Rh$^+$ blood antigens from the unborn child enter the mother's bloodstream, her body produces anti-Rh antibodies. During any subsequent pregnancy, the mother's anti-Rh antibodies may pass into the child's bloodstream. If the unborn child is Rh$^+$, the antibodies can cause clumping and destruction of the child's red blood cells, a condition known as *erythroblastosis fetalis,* or *Rh disease.* The Rh factor problem can be a critical one. The result may be anemia, brain damage, or even death.

Two procedures are used to overcome the problem. The Rh$^-$ mother may be given a serum containing anti-Rh antibodies within 72 hours after the birth of her first Rh$^+$ baby. The serum destroys the child's Rh$^+$ blood antigens that have entered her system before her body can develop anti-Rh antibodies. The second procedure treats the child. If the unborn child of a later pregnancy has already developed Rh disease, a blood transfusion can be given to the unborn child to remove the antibodies from its blood.

Section Review

1. **Summarizing Function** Describe the functions of blood cells and plasma.
2. **Analyzing Function** Explain the role of platelets in blood clotting.
3. **Inferring Relationships** Explain why a child with type A, B, or O blood could suffer from Rh disease.

Circulation Through the Body

Blood could not meet the body's needs if it did not move. The circulatory system, therefore, includes a pump that forces blood to move and tubes through which it flows smoothly.

43.4 The Heart

The **heart** is a muscular organ that pumps blood to all parts of the body. When a person is resting, the heart pumps about 5 L (5.3 qt.) of blood each minute. When a person is exercising strenuously, however, the heart may have to pump up to seven times that amount.

Structure of the Heart The heart is a fist-sized organ composed chiefly of cardiac muscle, nervous tissue, and connective tissue. It lies between the lungs and behind the breastbone. An average adult human heart weighs about 350–450 g (0.5–1 lb.). A tough protective sac called the **pericardium** (pehr uh KAHR dee uhm) surrounds the heart. The pericardium secretes a slippery liquid that acts as a lubricant, allowing the heart to move smoothly within the sac.

Figure 43–6. The heart is divided into a left and a right pump by a septum that runs down the middle of the heart. The two pumps beat as one.

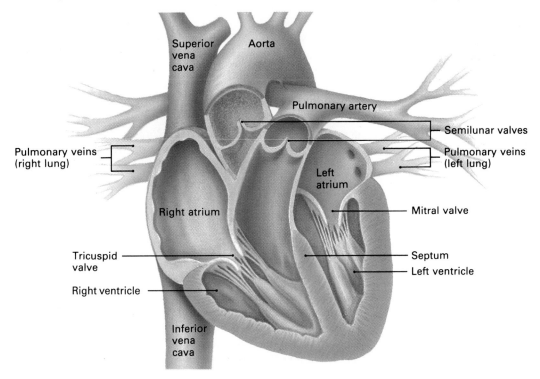

Superior vena cava

Aorta

Pulmonary artery

Semilunar valves

Pulmonary veins (right lung)

Pulmonary veins (left lung)

Left atrium

Right atrium

Mitral valve

Tricuspid valve

Septum

Left ventricle

Right ventricle

Inferior vena cava

Figure 43–7. In the circulatory system, major arteries and veins are connected to smaller and smaller blood vessels. The smallest are microscopic in size and are called capillaries.

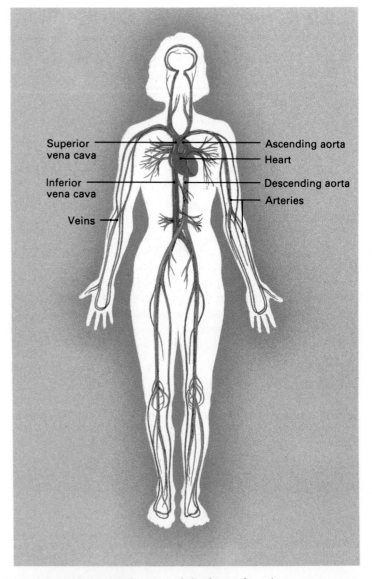

Superior
vena cava

Inferior
vena cava

Veins

Ascending aorta

Heart

Descending aorta

Arteries

The circulatory systems of the human and other representative vertebrates are shown on pages 898–899.

The right and left sides of the heart function as two completely separate pumps. An interior wall called the *septum* separates the two sides of the heart. Each side has an upper section called the **atrium** (AY tree uhm) and a lower section called the **ventricle** (VEHN trih kuhl).

As you can see in Figure 43–6 on page 697, the atrium and ventricle on each side are separated by a one-way valve. The valve on the right side is called the *tricuspid valve*. The valve on the left side is the *bicuspid*, or *mitral*, *valve*. Another set of one-way valves, called the *semilunar valves*, separate the ventricles from the large blood vessels into which blood is pumped out of the heart. All the valves prevent blood from flowing backward.

Circulation Through the Heart As shown in Figure 43–8, blood enters the right atrium through two large veins. A **vein** is a blood vessel that carries blood to the heart. The **superior vena cava** (VEE nuh   KAY vuh) brings blood from the upper regions of the body; the **inferior vena cava** brings blood from the lower body. The blood entering the heart through these veins is dark red because it is no longer oxygen-rich.

About 70 percent of the blood in the right atrium flows directly into the right ventricle. The remaining blood is forced into the ventricle by a mild contraction of the atrium. When the right ventricle contracts, the tricuspid valve closes, and blood is forced into the **pulmonary artery.** An **artery** is a blood vessel that carries blood away from the heart. The semilunar valve closes. The blood travels from the pulmonary artery into its two branches, one to each lung. In the lungs, the exchange of carbon dioxide from the deoxygenated blood and oxygen from freshly inhaled air takes place. The blood, now bright red and saturated with oxygen, enters the left atrium via the **pulmonary veins.** The path of blood from heart to lungs and back is called the *pulmonary circulation.*

The path of blood through the left side of the heart is similar to that through the right side. The contraction of the left ventricle is very powerful because it must force blood to the farthest regions of the body. Blood rushes from the left ventricle into the **aorta,** the largest artery. From the aorta, blood flows to all parts of the body through a system of increasingly smaller arteries.

Figure 43–8. Blood enters the two atria of the heart simultaneously from two different areas (left). It is then pumped to the two ventricles (center), before leaving the heart (right).

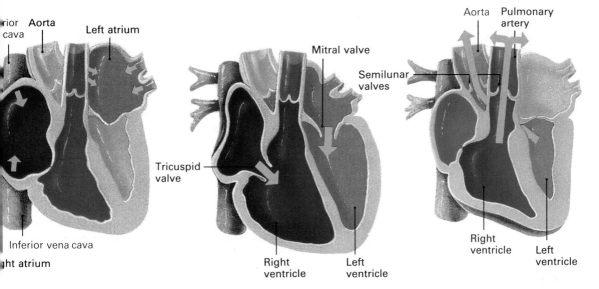

rior cava   Aorta   Left atrium   Mitral valve   Semilunar valves   Tricuspid valve   Inferior vena cava   ht atrium   Right ventricle   Left ventricle   Aorta   Pulmonary artery   Right ventricle   Left ventricle

A major cause of death in this country is a "silent killer." This condition has no symptoms and no cure, but it can be treated successfully. Sufferers may be unaware they have this condition until complications such as stroke, heart attack, and kidney failure occur. This silent disease is *hypertension,* or *high blood pressure.*

Blood pressure is the amount of force the blood exerts against artery walls. Two numbers are used to register blood pressure. The first number, called the *systolic pressure,* tells how much pressure is exerted when the heart contracts and blood spurts through the arteries. The second number is the *diastolic pressure,* which tells how much pressure is exerted while the heart relaxes. If the blood pressure is 120 over 80 (120/80), the blood is pushing against the artery walls with a pressure of 120 as the heart contracts and 80 as the heart rests. These figures are based upon how high the pressure in the arteries can raise a column of mercury similar to that in a *sphygmomanometer,* the instrument used to measure blood pressure.

Normally, blood pressure fluctuates. It is affected by such things as exercise and anxiety. In people suffering from hypertension, however, the pressure never drops to a safe level. A pressure that remains at 140/90 or more is considered high blood pressure.

High blood pressure can have many dangerous effects. Each time the heart contracts, it pushes against the artery walls. This resistance registers as the systolic pressure. The higher the resistance, the harder the heart must work. This increased pumping effort can result in heart failure.

As the heart begins to deteriorate, other problems develop. An increasing lack of oxygen to muscle tissue causes muscle fatigue and weakening. Lack of oxygen to the brain affects thinking. High pressure against the delicate walls of small blood vessels may cause them to rupture. A ruptured blood vessel in the brain causes a stroke, the effects of which can range from mild paralysis to death. High blood pressure may also affect the body's ability to get rid of waste products.

High blood pressure can be diagnosed and can be treated or controlled through diet, medication, and exercise. An estimated 24 million Americans suffer from hypertension, and most do not know they have it.

■ **Interpreting Ideas**
What does a blood pressure reading of 100/60 mean?

The Heartbeat The heart is really two separate pumps that operate simultaneously at about 70 contractions—heartbeats—per minute. Blood flows into both atria at the same time, and the atria contract together. Similarly, the ventricles contract together. A ventricular contraction is called *systole* (SIHS tuh lee). Relaxation is called *diastole* (dy AS tuh lee).

The activity within the heart causes the heartbeat, a sound usually described as "lubb dup." The "lubb" sound is related to the closing of the tricuspid and mitral valves. The shorter and higher pitched "dup" comes very shortly thereafter and is related to the closing of the semilunar valves. Certain types of heart disorders can be detected through irregularity in one or both sounds.

What causes the heart to beat regularly without any conscious control? The heart has its own automatic pacemaker. It is a small region of muscle called the **sinoatrial** (sy noh AY tree uhl), or **SA, node** in the back wall of the right atrium. The SA node triggers each heartbeat with an impulse that causes the atria to contract. Within a tenth of a second, the impulse reaches the **atrioventricular** (ay tree oh vehn TRIHK yuh luhr), or **AV, node** at the base of the right atrium. Within milliseconds, the AV node triggers an impulse that causes the ventricles to contract. In a disorder called *fibrillation,* contractions become irregular and rapid. These uncoordinated contractions affect the ventricles, and therefore the pumping of blood to the body.

43.5 Blood Vessels

Blood is carried to all parts of the body through 112,000 km (70,000 mi.) of blood vessels. Different types of vessels vary in size and structure.

Arteries have especially elastic, muscular walls. As Figure 43–10 shows, these walls consist of three layers of tissue. Arteries branch into smaller and smaller arteries until they become tiny vessels called *arterioles*. Arterioles continue to decrease in diameter until they branch into **capillaries**—vessels so narrow that red blood cells must pass through them in single file.

Capillaries are the smallest and most numerous blood vessels in the body. Every body cell is within 0.13 mm (0.005 in.) of one or more capillaries. ***Although other blood vessels transport nutrients and waste products, the actual exchange of these products between blood cells and body cells takes place through capillary walls.*** Capillary walls are only one cell thick. As a result, diffusion of nutrient molecules, waste products, and gases can take place quickly. Capillary walls also allow plasma to filter out of the blood to become tissue fluid.

Deoxygenated blood travels from capillaries into small veins called *venules*. Veins increase in size as they approach the superior vena cava and inferior vena cava. Like artery walls, vein walls consist of three layers of tissue. However, the middle layer is less muscular than that of arteries.

Blood in veins generally must flow against the force of gravity—for example, from the feet to the heart. Two features prevent blood from flowing backward, away from the heart. The first is location. Many veins run through skeletal muscles.

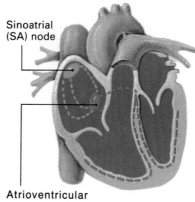

Sinoatrial (SA) node

Atrioventricular (AV) node

Figure 43–9. The sinoatrial node triggers a beat in the two atria. The atrioventricular node transmits the beat to the ventricles.

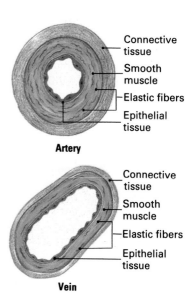

Connective tissue

Smooth muscle

Elastic fibers

Epithelial tissue

Artery

Connective tissue

Smooth muscle

Elastic fibers

Epithelial tissue

Vein

Figure 43–10. An artery (top) has a relatively thick elastic wall that stretches in response to the pressure of blood as it leaves the heart. A vein (bottom) has thinner walls that contain less elastic tissue.

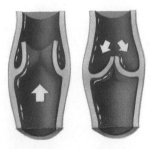

Figure 43–11. Valves in veins open under the pressure of blood flow. When pressure is relaxed, they close in a manner that prevents backflow.

Reading Critically

Evaluating Ideas Why is eating excessive amounts of foods that contain high levels of cholesterol dangerous to your health?

As the muscles contract, the veins are squeezed and blood is pushed along. The second is a series of valves that keeps the blood from moving backward.

43.6 Circulatory Subsystems

Within the circulatory system are several subsystems. The pathway of blood from the heart to the lungs and back to the heart is called the *pulmonary circulation*. The pathway of blood from the heart to other parts of the body and back to the heart is called the *systemic circulation*.

Systemic circulation also has subsystems. *Coronary circulation*, for example, supplies the heart itself with blood. The *left* and *right coronary arteries* branch off the aorta and provide the heart continuously with oxygen and nutrients. The blood returns to the right atrium by way of a large vein called the *coronary sinus*.

Heart tissue must be nourished continuously. When something prevents blood from reaching the cardiac muscle, the lack of oxygen causes the muscle cells to die. This condition, known as a heart attack, is one of the leading causes of death in the United States. A heart attack may result from a blood clot that blocks a blood vessel or from a gradual buildup of cholesterol, fibrin, and other cellular material inside the blood vessels. This buildup, called *atherosclerosis*, narrows the openings inside blood vessels.

Another part of systemic circulation is *renal circulation*, which carries blood to and from the kidneys. The *left* and *right renal arteries* branch from the aorta and enter the kidneys. Nitrogenous waste products filter out of the bloodstream into renal

Figure 43–12. Subdivisions of the circulatory system transport blood to and from the lungs, heart, liver, intestines, and kidneys.

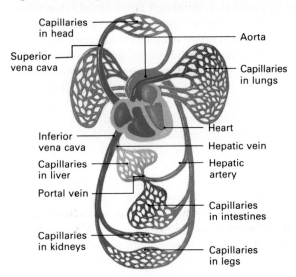

capillaries. The blood then travels through renal veins to the inferior vena cava.

Hepatic portal circulation, a third part of systemic circulation, involves the digestive tract and liver. *Mesenteric arteries* carry blood from the aorta to the intestines, where water and molecules from digested food enter the capillaries. The blood, which is now enriched with nutrients, travels via the *hepatic portal vein* to the liver, where some nutrients are stored as glycogen. The *hepatic artery* supplies the liver with oxygenated blood. Blood leaves the liver and reaches the inferior vena cava through *hepatic veins.*

43.7 The Lymphatic System

The *lymphatic system* is part of the body's circulatory system. Body fluids are carried in vessels of the lymphatic system as well as in blood vessels. Together the blood vessels and lymph vessels form the body's *vascular,* or vessel, *system.*

Lymph originates from blood plasma and tissue fluid that surrounds all body cells. It provides the medium through which diffusion of nutrients and gases occurs. Each day slightly more fluid filters out of the capillaries than is reabsorbed. Lymph and the valuable proteins it contains are collected in *lymph capillaries,* tiny vessels in almost every organ. The largest of the lymph vessels are *lymph ducts,* which empty into the two *subclavian veins* located in the neck. In this way, fluid and proteins are returned to the bloodstream.

The lymph system also helps protect the body against infection. Tiny bean-shaped organs called **lymph nodes** concentrated in the armpits, neck, and groin filter out such foreign matter as bacteria and viruses from lymph. Lymph tissue is also located in the *tonsils, adenoids, spleen, thymus gland,* digestive tract, and bone marrow. Lymph tissue also produces a type of white blood cell that helps the body fight disease.

If the lymphatic system malfunctions, excessive amounts of fluid collect in the body. This condition is known as *edema.* Generally, edema is a symptom of a more serious physical disorder.

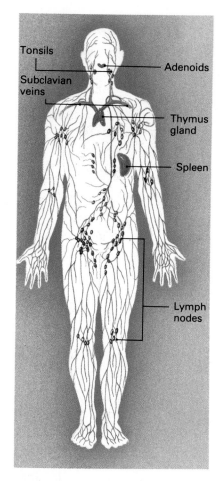

Figure 43–13. Lymph is transported through its own circulatory system. Lymph nodes are concentrated most heavily in the neck, the armpits, and the groin.

Section Review

1. **Summarizing Ideas**   Describe blood flow through the heart.
2. **Summarizing Ideas**   Describe pulmonary circulation.
3. **Inferring Relationships**   How is a capillary's structure related to its function?

> **Thinking Critically**

Section Objectives

- *Distinguish* between non-specific and specific body defenses.
- *Explain* how lymphocytes detect foreign substances.
- *Compare* the functions of B cells and T cells.
- *List* two problems that can occur with the immune system.

Reading Critically

Relating Ideas Explain why interferon could be called a nonspecific defense.

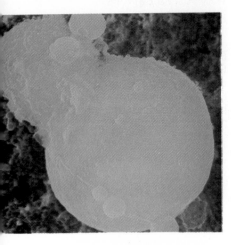

Figure 43–14. This scanning electron photomicrograph shows a small T cell attacking a tumor cell magnified 2,500 times.

The Immune System

Blood and tissue fluid carry nutrients to body cells. These substances are necessary for healthy cells. The blood also carries substances that defend the body against disease.

43.8 Nonspecific Defenses

Some defenses are called *nonspecific defenses* because they operate in the same way against all disease-causing microorganisms. *Among nonspecific defenses are the skin and mucous membranes.* They provide a mechanical barrier against **pathogens,** disease-causing agents such as viruses and some species of bacteria. If pathogens do enter the body, a type of white blood cell called a **phagocyte** engulfs and digests them. This process is known as *phagocytosis*. The dead bacteria and white blood cells may become *pus*. The presence of pus indicates an infection.

Virus-infected cells may also release the protein *interferon*. Interferon inactivates attacking viruses by preventing them from reproducing. All viruses stimulate the production of the same type of interferon, and interferon is effective against many types of viruses.

43.9 Immune Response

The body also has *specific defenses,* by which it defends itself against specific pathogens. White blood cells called **lymphocytes** constantly circulate in the bloodstream and tissue fluid, tracking down harmful microorganisms and diseased cells. When they locate their prey, they trigger a precisely targeted attack. The two main types of lymphocytes are *B cells* and *T cells.*

How do B cells and T cells recognize pathogens and foreign substances? Every body cell has molecules on its surface that identify it as "self"—that is, as part of the body. Foreign substances have surface molecules that tag them as "nonself." If a surface molecule contacted by a lymphocyte is a "self" marker, nothing happens, and the lymphocyte moves on. If the molecule is a "nonself" marker, however, the body produces an attack on the foreign substance called an *immune response*. Any molecule that triggers an immune response is an antigen.

Lymph vessels carry the antigen to a lymph node where it encounters a phagocyte that ingests it and presents it to a B cell. The B cell may then become a *plasma cell*. Plasma cells manufacture proteins that exactly fit the "nonself" surface marker of the antigen. These proteins are antibodies. Each antibody fits—or combats—just one specific antigen. This type of antibody,

Dealing With Stress

There are many different kinds of physical and emotional demands on the body that can cause the collective reactions known as stress.

Everyday living involves a certain amount of stress to which everyone reacts differently. While a certain amount of stress is normal, constant high levels of stress can affect some individuals in ways that lead to physical diseases and disorders. Stress can reduce the number of disease-fighting blood cells, leaving the body vulnerable to infections. For example, studies show that widows and widowers are much more likely to develop infections and other physical ailments during the months after the death of their spouse than they suffered when the spouse was alive. The death of a life companion produces a high amount of stress.

Another important way that stress lowers the body's resistance to infection is that the body under stress can produce up to 20 times the normal amount of the hormone *cortisol,* also called *hydrocortisone.* Over the short term, cortisol speeds the conversion of muscle glycogen into glucose, thus readying the body for quick response. Over the

long term, however, high levels of cortisol can interfere with the body's immune system. Drugs that contain cortisol-related hormones can be so effective in suppressing the immune response that they were once prescribed to prevent organ rejection in transplant patients.

called a *circulating antibody,* moves through the body fluids. If the antigen is located, the antibody hooks on and signals phagocytes to surround and destroy the antigen.

T cells do not produce circulating antibodies. They carry *cellular antibodies* on their surface. T cells either activate phagocytes or directly kill the antigen-bearing cell. T cells can recognize body cells that have been invaded by cancer and certain viruses. The cancerous cells register as "not quite self," thus allowing T cells to launch a defense.

43.10 Immunity

The body generally requires several days to form antibodies after the first attack by an antigen. Reaction to the first invasion is called the *primary immune response.* Future responses to the same antigen are rapid because of memory cells. **Memory cells** are either B cells or T cells that carry, or "remember," the antigen

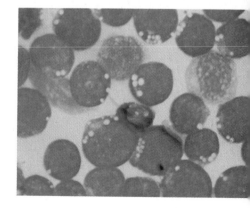

Figure 43–15. B cells like the ones above produce circulating antibodies that move through body fluids in search of a specific antigen.

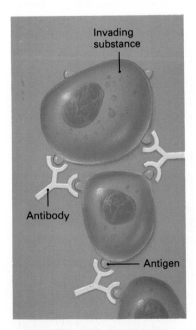

Figure 43–16. Antibodies have two locations at which they can attach to antigens. By attaching to two antigens simultaneously, they cause the cells to agglutinate.

Invading substance

Antibody

Antigen

pattern. They produce antibodies immediately if the antigen attacks again. Antibodies produced during such a *secondary immune response* are stronger and last longer than the original antibodies. Memory cells persist for the life of the individual. New memory cells are produced during each response. This process of warding off disease through antibodies is **immunity.** Immunity prevents a person from getting certain diseases, such as measles or chicken pox, repeatedly.

43.11 Problems with the Immune System

Not all "nonself" markers are harmful. Sometimes the body cannot distinguish between harmful and harmless "nonself" markers. For example, it may fail to recognize certain pollens as harmless. Reactions called *allergies* then occur. Although most allergic reactions are not medically serious, some can be life-threatening. One example is the violent immune response some people have to bee venom.

The body occasionally fails to recognize some body cells as "self" and attacks them as antigens. Such misdirected attacks occur in *autoimmune diseases. Rheumatoid arthritis* is an autoimmune disease affecting joint tissue.

The body may also lose its ability to attack invading microorganisms and diseased cells. This condition is called *immune deficiency.* In its most severe form, immune deficiency is almost always fatal. Its victims suffer from repeated infections and illnesses. The deficiency may be present at birth. More often it develops later in life. Some immune deficiencies are genetic. Others are the result of an infection. *AIDS (acquired immunodeficiency syndrome)* is an example of the latter. AIDS is caused by the human immunodeficiency virus (HIV). The virus kills T lymphocytes, destroying the body's immune system.

Rejection of transplanted organs and tissues is also caused by the body's immune system. Transplanted organs are recognized only as "nonself." Previously, drugs were used to suppress a patient's entire defense system to prevent rejection. The patient then became vulnerable to all diseases. *Cyclosporine,* a recently developed drug, suppresses transplant rejection but does not disrupt B cell immune functions.

Section Review

1. **Identifying Ideas**   Give two examples of nonspecific defenses against disease.
2. **Comparing Function**   Compare B cells and T cells.
3. **Synthesizing Information**   Why is it difficult to treat or cure autoimmune diseases?

Thinking Critically

INVESTIGATION 43:
How Does Exercise Affect Pulse Rate?

Objectives
- To *compare* the pulse rate while at rest and immediately after exercise
- To *determine* recovery time

Materials
watch with a second hand, steady bench or chair about 30 cm high, calculator

Prelab Preparation
1. Read the BioFact on page 699. Define pulse rate.
2. To find your laboratory partner's pulse, place two fingers on the inner part of his or her wrist just below the base of the thumb. Use a watch with a second hand to determine the rate per minute.
3. Prepare a data table like the one shown.

30 times a minute for three minutes.
d. Data from each team will be pooled. The group averages will be used to complete the Analysis questions.
5. After discussing the problem with your partner, form a hypothesis and explain how you arrived at your hypothesis.
6. Design an experiment that will test your hypothesis. After your design is approved by your teacher, conduct your experiment.

Inquiry: Lab Technique
7. The recorder will count the subject's resting pulse for 60 seconds and record the rate. Partners will then switch roles.
8. Repeat step 7 twice. Determine and record the average of all the trials. Record this average in the data table.
9. **Read the caution in step 4c before you**

Pulse Rates When at Rest and After Exercise

Rates per minute	Trial 1		Trial 2		Trial 3		Team average	Group average
Resting rate self/partner								
Rate after exercise self/partner								

Inquiry: Experimentation
4. Use the information below to design an experiment that measures pulse rate both at rest and after exercise.
   a. Work in teams of two students. One member will be the subject and the other member will make observations and record data. Team members will then switch roles.
   b. Resting pulse rate will be taken while the subject is sitting quietly.
   c. **CAUTION: Do not perform the following test if you have a health problem that prohibits vigorous exercise. Stop the test immediately if you feel pain or become dizzy or extremely tired.** Take the pulse rate after the subject performs the three-minute step test. The subject will step onto and off of a bench that is 30 cm high

proceed. The subject will take the three-minute step test. The recorder will take the subject's pulse rate for 60 seconds immediately after the subject finishes the test. Record the pulse rate in the data table. Switch roles and repeat.
10. Collect data from the other teams. Find and record the group averages.

Analysis
1. **Summarizing Data** Summarize your data. Explain whether or not the data support your hypothesis.
2. **Analyzing Data** State your conclusion about how pulse rate changes after exercise.
3. **Predicting Outcomes** What changes might occur in pulse rate after a person completes an eight-week physical fitness course? Explain your answer.

Chapter 43 Review

Summary

The circulatory system consists of the heart, blood, and lymph, and a vast system of blood vessels and lymph vessels. It delivers nutrients and oxygen to cells and carries waste materials from cells. Blood is made of plasma and three types of cells: red blood cells, white blood cells, and platelets.

The heart is a muscular organ that pumps blood throughout the body. It functions as two separate but coordinated pumps. The right side of the heart pumps deoxygenated blood into the pulmonary circulation. The left side pumps oxygenated blood into the systemic circulation.

Major blood vessels are arteries, veins, and capillaries. Arteries carry blood away from the heart. Veins carry blood to the heart.

Body fluids contain B cells and T cells. B cells produce circulating antibodies and T cells carry cellular antibodies.

BioTerms

antibody (**695**)
antigen (**695**)
aorta (**699**)
artery (**699**)
atrioventricular (AV) node (**701**)
atrium (**698**)
blood (**693**)
blood type (**695**)
capillary (**701**)
coagulation (**694**)
heart (**697**)
hemoglobin (**694**)

immunity (**706**)
inferior vena cava (**699**)
lymph (**703**)
lymph node (**703**)
lymphocyte (**704**)
memory cell (**705**)
pathogen (**704**)
pericardium (**697**)
phagocyte (**784**)
plasma (**693**)
platelet (**694**)

pulmonary artery (**699**)
pulmonary vein (**699**)
red blood cell (**694**)
Rh factor (**696**)
sinoatrial (SA)

node (**701**)
superior vena cava (**699**)
vein (**699**)
ventricle (**698**)
white blood cell (**694**)

For each pair of terms, explain the differences in their meanings.

1. artery, vein
2. red blood cell, white blood cell
3. antigen, antibody
4. phagocyte, lymphocyte

BioQuiz   (Write all answers on a separate sheet of paper.)

Completion

1. Blood type is determined by the _____ in red blood cells.
2. Clotting could never take place if the body did not have _____ .
3. The transfer of blood or blood parts from one person to another person is called

   _____ .
4. Blood is pumped into the _____ from the right ventricle.
5. The heart is separated into right and left sides by the _____ .

Multiple Choice

6. Bacteria in the body may be engulfed by
   a) erythrocytes. b) phagocytes.
   c) thromboplasts. d) plasma cells.
7. The pacemaker of the heart is the
   a) left ventricle. b) sinoatrial node.
   c) coronary sinus. d) pericardium.
8. Red blood cells are almost entirely filled with a) phagocytes. b) leukocytes.
   c) hemoglobin. d) thromboplastin.
9. Platelets aid in coagulation by releasing
   a) thromboplastin. b) hemoglobin.

c) corpuscles. d) fibrin.

10. The tough protective sac that surrounds the heart is the a) sinoatrial node.
    b) pericardium. c) atrioventricular node. d) superior vena cava.

11. Blood entering the heart through the inferior vena cava is a) oxygenated.
    b) coagulated. c) agglutinated.
    d) deoxygenated.

12. A blood pressure of ＿＿ would most likely be considered high. a) 140/90
    b) 120/80 c) 90/140 d) 80/120

13. Because veins move blood against the force of gravity, they contain
    a) valves. b) nodes. c) coagulants.
    d) agglutinates.

14. Which of the following could cause a heart attack? a) atherosclerosis b) high

blood pressure c) a damaged sinoatrial-valve d) All choices are correct.

15. Excessive amounts of fluid collected in the body is known as a) Rh factor.
    b) coagulation. c) edema.
    d) agglutination.

Writing Critically

16. How does tissue fluid differ from plasma?
17. How does immunity occur?
18. What two features permit blood in veins to flow *up* to the heart?
19. What might happen if an Rh-positive woman was pregnant with an Rh-negative child? Explain why.
20. Why is hypertension often called the silent killer?

Application/Critical Thinking

1. **Synthesizing Ideas** High levels of radiation destroy bone marrow. Why might a person who was exposed to high levels of radiation have a tendency to develop anemia?

2. **Researching Information** A process called *pheresis* makes it possible to collect platelets or other blood parts from a donor and then return the rest of the blood to the donor. After contacting the Red Cross or a

local hospital, report to the class what they tell you about pheresis.

3. **Inferring Conclusions** Vaccines are substances that, when injected into a person, stimulate the production of antibodies. Antiserums are injections of antibodies that have been produced by another organism. Immunity induced by vaccines occurs more slowly but usually lasts longer. Explain why.

Cross-Discipline Connection

Biology and Health   Use references in the library to write a report about the effects of diet on the health of the heart and circulatory system. List foods that have been linked to the development of heart disease and which should be avoided when possible.

Discovery Through Reading

Read the article "Stop That Germ!," *Time* (May 23, 1988): 56–64, to learn how the body's immune system fights disease. How do germs usually invade the body? What is the perfect disease for studying the immune system?

Explain your answer. Beginning with the invasion of the body by a germ, explain the 11 steps that describe how the immune system works. What are three diseases that are thought to be caused by autoimmune responses?

Artificial Body Parts

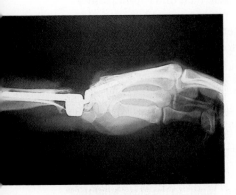

A wrist joint replacement in position

Each year thousands of people receive artificial tissues, organs, and limbs. These artificial replacements can save lives or can allow individuals to resume normal activities. Recent advances in the science of *biomaterials* have produced substances that can perform a wide range of tasks in the body. Made of polymers, ceramics, glass, and composites, these materials can be molded into various shapes. Biomaterials researchers join with specialists in physiology, immunology, and cell biology to develop substances that are tolerated by the body's immune system and do not damage cells or interfere with normal cell activity.

Physicians in burn treatment centers are using several types of *synthetic skin,* which are products of biomaterials technology. One type is a porous collagen polymer covered with a layer of silicone rubber to prevent infection and loss of fluids. As new skin cells from the patient's dermis migrate to the surface and produce new skin, the synthetic skin disintegrates. The layer of silicone is removed, and medical workers then graft small pieces of epidermis over the new skin.

Another revolutionary skin replacement is an adhesive, cellophane-like covering made from two natural compounds—keratin and chitosan. It can be

Scientists use computers to design replacement parts that can mimic natural body movements.

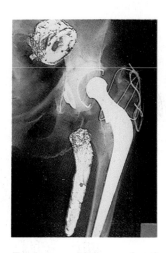

placed on a wound at the scene of an accident.

The most commonly known cardiovascular system replacement is the *artificial heart,* an interim treatment in human heart transplantation. Cardivascular conditions also are successfully treated with artificial heart valves, left-ventricle-assist devices, and artificial blood vessels. Researchers have even developed synthetic blood using various polymers. The synthetic blood helps transport oxygen in the treatment of heart attacks and strokes.

Each year thousands of people undergo *artificial joint replacement* for hips and knees that have been injured in accidents or damaged by arthritis. Researchers have developed a ball-and-socket hip joint made of metal and plastic. It has a coarse, irregular surface around which the patient's bone grows. Be-

cause this joint does not depend on a fixed bond that uses cement, it is more comfortable and permits greater movement over a longer period.

Possibly the most astounding research with artificial devices is being done on the eye. Advances in biomaterials science have led to foldable *intraocular lens implants,* which can be inserted into the eye through a very small incision. Researchers are now working on an injectable, liquid polymer lens that requires no surgery at all.

The *artificial eye* is in the early experimental stage. It uses a 64-electrode grid that is implanted in the brain and receives images transmitted by a computer—a remarkable combination of human and artificial systems.

> *Replacing human body parts is no longer a subject for science fiction.*

The artificial heart is the most familiar artificial body part.

Each year, thousands of people undergo artificial joint replacement.

Respiration and Excretion

Outline

Equipment for THE 30TH

Athletic competition places increased demands on the body

Focus

The *respiratory system* delivers the oxygen that is necessary for releasing energy from food molecules to the bloodstream. This system also removes the waste product, carbon dioxide. The *excretory system* removes other waste products of cellular metabolism from the bloodstream. Both systems are vital—the body cannot function for more than a few minutes if either system fails completely.

- *How can you tell that the athletes' bodies are using oxygen at a rapid rate?*

- *After strenuous exercise, the body often owes oxygen, called an oxygen debt, to its cells. What evidence of this debt can be seen after exercise?*

The Respiratory System

Section Objectives

- *Name* the parts of the respiratory system.
- *Describe* the structure and function of alveoli.
- *Trace* the path of oxygen from the atmosphere to a body cell.
- *List* three ways in which the human body adjusts to high-altitude living.
- *Explain* the operation of the diaphragm and intercostal muscles.

The respiratory system consists of the organs of breathing. However, breathing is only one part of respiration. **Respiration** is the process by which the body takes in oxygen, uses it to produce energy, and then eliminates some waste products of the cellular activity. Three subprocesses are involved in respiration. They are *external respiration, internal respiration,* and *cellular respiration.* In external respiration, or breathing, the body exchanges gases between the atmosphere and the blood. Internal respiration is the diffusion of gases between the blood or tissue fluid and body cells. Cellular respiration is the process by which cells break down glucose molecules to form the energy molecule ATP.

44.1 The Lungs and Breathing

The major breathing organs are two **lungs,** located in the thoracic cavity. The lungs are spongy, cone-shaped, saclike organs. Each lung weighs about 600 g (1.3 lb.). The right lung has three main divisions, or *lobes,* and is slightly larger than the left lung, which has two lobes. Both lungs are encased in a tough membrane that also lines the thoracic cavity. This double membrane, the **pleura,** secretes a lubricating fluid that allows the lungs to move smoothly. Inflammation of the pleura can lead to fluid buildup in the thoracic cavity. This condition is called *pleurisy.*

Breathing begins when the **diaphragm,** the dome-shaped muscle below the chest cavity, contracts and moves downward. The *intercostal muscles* between the ribs also contract, causing

Examples of vertebrate respiratory systems are shown on pages 900–901.

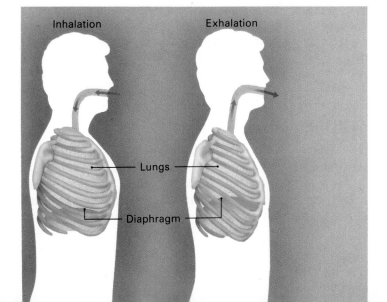

Figure 44–1. The diaphragm and intercostal muscles control the movements of the rib cage and, therefore, breathing.

Inhalation   Exhalation

Lungs

Diaphragm

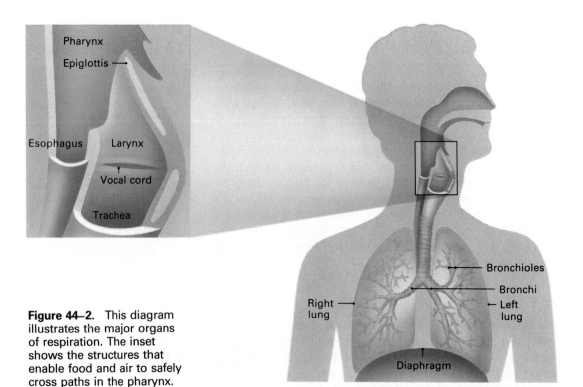

Pharynx

Epiglottis

Esophagus   Larynx

Vocal cord

Trachea

Bronchioles

Bronchi

Right
lung

Left
lung

Diaphragm

Figure 44–2. This diagram illustrates the major organs of respiration. The inset shows the structures that enable food and air to safely cross paths in the pharynx.

The effect of exercise on breathing rate and volume is investigated on page 723.

Biofact

Q: *What is a "collapsed" lung?*

A: Air pressure in the chest cavity is normally less than that outside the body. If the pressure increases because air flows into the chest cavity, perhaps because of a puncture wound in the chest wall, the lungs will not fill with air. This condition is called a collapsed lung.

the rib cage to move up and out. Together, these muscle contractions cause the chest cavity to enlarge. When the chest expands, the air pressure in the chest cavity drops. Air pressure outside the body is then greater than that inside the chest cavity. Air then flows into the lungs from outside the body, equalizing the pressure. This part of the breathing process is called *inspiration* or **inhalation.**

When the air pressure has been equalized, it causes the diaphragm and intercostal muscles to relax and return to their normal positions. This in turn reduces the size of the chest cavity. As the size of the chest decreases, the air pressure inside the chest cavity gradually becomes greater than the air pressure outside the body. Air then leaves the lungs, again equalizing the pressure. This part of the breathing process is called *expiration* or **exhalation.**

44.2 The Pathway of Air

Air enters the body through two openings in the nose called **nostrils.** From there the air flows into the **nasal cavities,** two spaces in the nose. The cavities are separated by a cartilage and bone partition called the *septum.* The cavities are lined with mucous tissue that contains many blood vessels. The mucous tissue warms and moistens the incoming air. Moisture must be present for diffusion of gases to take place within the lungs. Cilia and hairs also line the cavities and filter foreign particles from the air. The cilia move constantly, carrying these particles outward toward the nostrils.

Air travels from the nasal cavities into the back side of the *pharynx,* a tube at the rear of the nasal cavities and mouth. The pharynx is a common passageway for both food and air. While air must get into the cartilage-ringed **trachea,** or windpipe, at the front of pharynx, food must get to the esophagus at the back side of the pharynx. Therefore, food and air cross each other's paths. If food entered the air passageway, the person would choke. To ensure that food does not enter the air passageway, the body makes involuntary adjustments. During the process of swallowing, a flap of tissue called the *epiglottis* closes over the *glottis,* or the upper part of the trachea. At the same time, the *soft palate* closes off the nasal cavities. During inhalation, the glottis is open to allow air to enter the trachea.

At the top of the trachea is the *larynx,* or voice box. Two ligaments called **vocal cords** are stretched across the larynx. The larynx is called the voice box because sound is produced when air is forced between the cords. The amount of tension in the cords determines the pitch of a sound. Nine cartilage rings connected by ligaments hold the mucus-lined larynx open during inhalation and against the pressure from food passing through the adjacent esophagus. The largest of the cartilage rings appears as the *Adam's apple* in the throat.

The trachea descends to a point near the middle of the breastbone. There it divides into two branches called **bronchi** (BRAHN ky). Bronchi walls consist of muscle supported by cartilage and are lined with mucus and cilia. The bronchi reach deep into the lungs, subdividing about 25 times into smaller and smaller passageways. The first 10 subdivisions are called *secondary bronchi*. The remaining subdivisions are microscopic-sized tubes called **bronchioles** (BRAHNG kee ohlz). Bronchiole walls consist of smooth muscle and are lined with mucus and cilia. The continuous beating of the cilia in the bronchi and bronchioles carries foreign particles and excess mucus into the pharynx. This material may then be expelled by being swallowed or coughed out.

The smallest bronchioles branch into tiny ducts, which end in clusters of tiny bulges. These bulges are air sacs called **alveoli** (al VEE uh lih). Each lung has more than 300 million alveoli. Each alveolus measures from 0.1 to 0.2 mm (0.004 to 0.008 in.) in diameter. The total surface area provided by the alveoli is estimated at about 70 m² (750 sq. ft.).

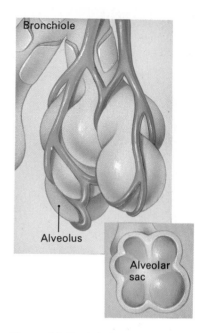

Figure 44–3. Inhaled air travels through the respiratory system to the alveoli, air sacs at the end of tiny bronchioles. Each alveolus is surrounded by blood vessels and hollow inside (inset).

Figure 44–4. The cilia lining the surface of the trachea can be seen magnified 8,000 times in this photomicrograph.

44.3 Exchange of Gases

Alveoli are completely surrounded by capillaries. *The actual exchange of gases occurs when oxygen in the air of the alveoli diffuses into the blood in the capillaries. In turn, the carbon dioxide in the blood diffuses into the air of the alveoli.* The epithelial tissue forming the walls of both the alveoli and capillaries is only one cell thick. Together, the walls of an alveolus and an adjacent capillary measure only 0.0004 mm (0.00001576 in.). The oxygen in inhaled air dissolves in the mucus on the lining of the alveoli.

In the blood, most oxygen combines with hemoglobin to form *oxyhemoglobin.* Oxygen from the oxyhemoglobin diffuses into body cells and is used in **metabolism,** the chemical and physical activities within cells. Metabolism includes the building up and breaking down of complex molecules and the releasing of energy during the breakdown. As a result of metabolism, oxygen concentration in the body cells is low, but carbon dioxide concentration is high.

Carbon dioxide, a metabolic waste product that must be eliminated, diffuses from body cells into the blood. Carbon dioxide is transported in the blood in three ways. About 5 percent dissolves in the plasma. About 25 percent enters the red blood cells and combines with hemoglobin. With help from a special enzyme, the remainder—or about 70 percent—combines with water in the red blood cells to form carbonic acid:

$$\underset{\text{(carbon dioxide)}}{CO_2} + \underset{\text{(water)}}{H_2O} \rightarrow \underset{\text{(carbonic acid)}}{H_2CO_3}$$

Almost immediately, carbonic acid separates into hydrogen ions (H^+), which combine with hemoglobin, and bicarbonate ions (HCO_3^-), which diffuse into the plasma.

$$\underset{\text{(carbonic acid)}}{H_2CO_3} \rightarrow \underset{\text{(hydrogen ion)}}{H^+} + \underset{\text{(bicarbonate ion)}}{HCO_3^-}$$

As a result of this chemical process, most carbon dioxide is transported in the plasma as bicarbonate ions.

When blood reaches the lungs, chemical reactions occur that reverse the process, releasing carbon dioxide:

$$\underset{\text{(hydrogen ion)}}{H^+} + \underset{\text{(bicarbonate ion)}}{HCO_3^-} \rightarrow \underset{\text{(carbonic acid)}}{H_2CO_3}$$
$$\rightarrow \underset{\text{(carbon dioxide)}}{CO_2} + \underset{\text{(water)}}{H_2O}$$

The carbon dioxide diffuses from the blood into the lungs. The carbon dioxide is exhaled along with water vapor.

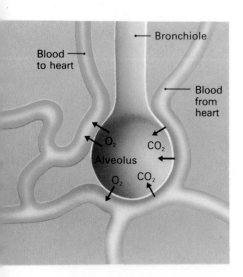

Figure 44–5. Exchange of gases occurs in the alveoli.

Reading Critically

Analyzing Relationships
What would happen if blood did not contain the enzyme that allows carbon dioxide to combine with water in the blood?

Asthma

Asthma is a noncommunicable lung disease that affects 10 million people in the United States. During an asthma attack, certain airways in the lungs narrow because of sensitivity to certain stimuli.

There are two types of asthma—*allergic* and *nonallergic.* Allergic asthma occurs when the body becomes sensitive to certain, usually common, substances such as dust, mold, pollen or animal hair. The body reacts when these substances enter the airways. Nonallergic asthma may be brought on by stress, improper exercise, or cold air.

In mild asthma attacks certain muscles contract, narrowing the airways in the lungs. In moderate attacks, excess mucus is also produced, causing further obstruction of the airways. In severe attacks, the inner walls of the airways also swell with fluids, narrowing the airways still more.

Narrowing of the airways during an asthma attack reduces the efficiency of respiration, which decreases the amount of oxygen reaching body cells. Asthmatics try to make up for this oxygen decrease by breathing faster. If the attack worsens, the increasing resistance to airflow makes it harder to exhale, thus further limiting the amount of air that can be taken in. When air cannot be exhaled effectively, it is impossible to clear the airways and the lungs of mucus. Inserting a tube

into the airways is sometimes the only way to prevent the person from suffocating.

The main treatment for mild to moderate asthma attacks is the use of *bronchodilators,* medications that open the airways and reduce their sensitivity to allergens. Most of the commonly prescribed bronchodilators are pocket-sized cartridge devices that deliver a fixed dose of medicine directly to the airways.

44.4 Regulation of Breathing

What determines when and how deeply the body should breathe? Many factors influence the control of breathing, including carbon dioxide and oxygen levels in the blood. *The level of carbon dioxide in the blood plays a vital role in regulating breathing.* Carbon dioxide affects blood acidity. Certain nerve cells are sensitive to changes in blood acidity. These nerves send messages to the *breathing center* at the base of the brain. When the carbon dioxide level in the blood is high, the messages cause the breathing center to trigger a speedup in

People who move from low altitudes to high altitudes may suffer temporarily from excessive tiredness and sleepiness. The cause of their fatigue is a lack of oxygen.

The higher the altitude, the less oxygen in the air. At sea level, hemoglobin is 97 percent saturated with oxygen. At an altitude of 3,048 m (10,000 ft.), hemoglobin is only 90 percent saturated, and at 6,096 m (20,000 ft.), only 70 percent saturated. The human body begins to feel the effects of reduced oxygen at an altitude of about 1,800 m (1.1 mi.).

Studies of people who normally live at high altitudes provide information on the long-range effects of conditions in which levels of oxygen are low. For example, the Quechua Indians of the Andes, who live above 3,600 m (more than 2 mi.), have developed very large chest and lung capacities. These people also have a higher concentration of red blood cells and hemoglobin than do people who normally live at sea level. This Indian group also has a higher breathing rate, and the capillaries in their lungs have a greater diameter.

Their hearts are much larger, particularly on the right side, and the blood pressure in the lungs is greater than it is in any other part of the circulatory system. However, the heartbeat of the Quechua Indians is slower than that of people living at sea level.

Judging from these facts, scientists theorize that a larger volume of blood is pumped with each beat of the heart in high-altitude dwellers.

■ **Analyzing Information** How do the Quechua Indians compensate for the lower percentage of oxygen in the air?

breathing rate. Conversely, a low carbon dioxide level reduces the breathing rate. Other messages reach the breathing center from *stretch receptors* in the lungs. When the lungs expand sufficiently, the stretch receptors send messages to the breathing center. The breathing center then sends messages that make the muscles relax. Stretch receptors thus operate as another kind of breathing contol mechanism.

Section Review

1. **Comparing Ideas** How do internal and external respiration differ?
2. **Identifying Relationships** What role do the diaphragm and intercostal muscles play in breathing?
3. **Identifying Relationships** What purposes do mucous tissue and cilia serve in the respiratory system?
4. **Analyzing Functions** How does the exchange of gases occur in the lungs?

> **Thinking Critically**

5. **Analyzing Information** What controls breathing rate?

The Excretory System

Respiration rids the body of water and carbon dioxide, a waste product of metabolism. Other metabolic wastes, especially nitrogen compounds, are eliminated from the body through the process of **excretion.**

Nitrogen compounds in the form of ammonia are released as the body breaks down excess amino acids. In concentrated form, ammonia is a poison. The body has two processes for making the ammonia less toxic. In one, the ammonia is mixed with great quantities of water. In the other, the ammonia is changed to a less harmful form.

The liver, operating as an excretory organ, combines the ammonia with carbon dioxide to form a less toxic compound called *urea*. Urea enters the blood and circulates throughout the body. Some urea is excreted through the skin in the form of perspiration, which is a mixture of water, minerals, and urea. Most of the urea the body produces, however, is eliminated by the excretory system.

Section Objectives

- *List* the parts of the excretory system and *state* the function of each.
- *Describe* the structure and function of a nephron.
- *Explain* the difference between filtration and reabsorption.
- *Summarize* dialysis and CAPD procedures for treating kidney disease.

44.5 The Kidneys

The **kidneys** are the major organs of the excretory system. They are two bean-shaped organs, each about 11 cm (4 1/2 in.) long, 6 cm (2 1/2 in.) wide, and 2.5 cm (1 in.) thick. They are located on either side of the spine in back of the abdominal cavity. Their combined weight is less than 0.5 kg (1 lb.). The kidneys are held in position by tough connective tissue and protected by a layer of fatty tissue.

Figure 44–6. The excretory system includes the kidneys, ureters, and urinary bladder (left). Each kidney is made up of three sections (right). The process of filtering wastes from the blood occurs in structures straddling the cortex and medulla.

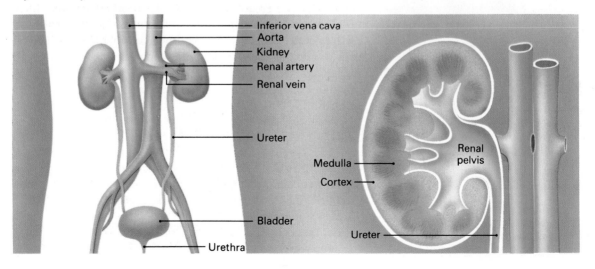

Labels (left): Inferior vena cava, Aorta, Kidney, Renal artery, Renal vein, Ureter, Bladder, Urethra

Labels (right): Medulla, Cortex, Renal pelvis, Ureter

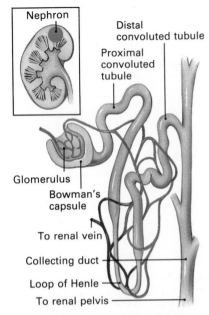

Nephron

Distal convoluted tubule

Proximal convoluted tubule

Glomerulus

Bowman's capsule

To renal vein

Collecting duct

Loop of Henle

To renal pelvis

Figure 44–7. This diagram illustrates the structures that make up the nephron and its surrounding blood vessels.

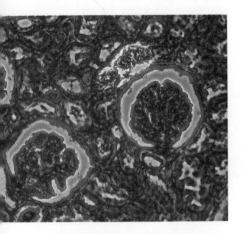

Figure 44–8. This phase contrast microscope image shows two glomeruli magnified 125 times.

The main functions of the kidneys are to remove urea and other wastes, regulate the amount of water in the blood, and adjust the concentrations of various substances in the blood. Thus, the kidneys play a vital role in maintaining *homeostasis,* or balance among elements in the body.

The cross section in Figure 44–6 on page 719 shows the three main sections of a kidney: an outer layer called the **cortex,** a middle layer called the **medulla,** and a central cavity called the **renal pelvis.** Blood enters the kidneys through *renal arteries* and leaves through *renal veins.*

The basic functional unit in each kidney, called a **nephron,** straddles both the cortex and the medulla. Each kidney contains an estimated one million nephrons.

As shown in Figure 44–7, the nephron consists partly of a **glomerulus** (glah MEHR yoo luhs), which is a mass of capillaries that form a tight ball. Each glomerulus is surrounded by a hollow, cup-shaped sac called a **Bowman's capsule.** The glomerulus and Bowman's capsule, located in the cortex, are responsible for filtering wastes from the blood. The Bowman's capsule is the first part of the **renal tubule,** much of which is a coiled tube extending into the medulla and back again. The last part of the renal tubule is called the **collecting duct.** The collecting duct is a straight tube leading to the renal pelvis. Water and mineral composition of the blood are regulated primarily by the coiled part of the renal tubule.

Filtration   The process of removing urea and other wastes from the blood is called **glomerular filtration.** The process starts as blood from the renal arteries flows into the glomerular capillaries. Blood in the glomerulus is under high pressure as it is pumped with great force from the heart into the tiny capillaries. This pressure forces water, urea, glucose, and minerals—a mixture called *filtrate*—into the Bowman's capsule. Red blood cells, white blood cells, and protein molecules do not pass out of the capillaries.

Blood passes through the kidneys at a rate of 0.25 L (0.3 qt.) per minute. In other words, all the blood in the human body passes through the kidneys once every 30 minutes. A total of 170 L (180 qt.) of filtrate is produced daily.

Reabsorption   If the kidneys only filtered the blood, a person would soon die, because along with metabolic wastes, filtration removes glucose, water, and other substances needed for life. However, these materials are returned to the blood in the renal tubule, the second part of the nephron. **Tubular reabsorption** is the process by which these vital materials are returned to the

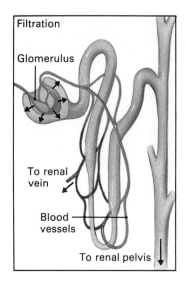
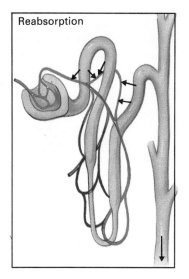
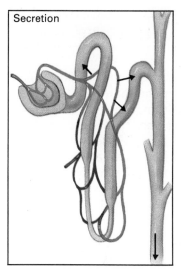

blood. Because reabsorption is important to the normal functioning of the body, the kidneys may be more accurately described as organs of regulation rather than excretion.

Reabsorption occurs as materials cross the walls of a renal tubule into a web of surrounding capillaries. Glucose and such chemicals as sodium, potassium, hydrogen, magnesium, and calcium are reabsorbed through active transport. As much as 99 percent of the water in filtrate may return to the blood through osmosis. When blood volume is low, a large amount of water is reabsorbed. When blood volume becomes normal, the rate of osmosis decreases.

In addition to reabsorption, a process called **tubular secretion** occurs in the renal tubule. In the process of tubular secretion, tubule cells actively remove certain substances from the blood and secrete these substances into the filtrate. Penicillin is an example of a substance that is secreted in this way.

Urea, other metabolic wastes, and water that remain in the renal tubule form an amber-colored liquid called **urine.** The urine from several tubules flows into a single collecting duct located in the medulla. In turn, all of the collecting ducts channel urine into the funnel-shaped renal pelvis. From the renal pelvis the urine flows into the urinary system to be removed from the body.

44.6 The Urinary System

From the renal pelvis, urine enters a long, narrow tube called the **ureter.** The ureter from each kidney connects to the **urinary bladder,** a sac of smooth muscle that can hold approximately

Figure 44–9. The kidneys perform three major functions: they remove wastes through filtration (left); return useful materials to the body through reabsorption (center); and remove substances such as penicillin through secretion (right).

Reading Critically

Identifying Relationships
Why would there be a decrease in urine output if a person had lost a large amount of blood?

400 to 500 mL (12 to 15 fl. oz.) of urine. When the bladder is full, special nerves in the bladder wall send messages to the brain. The brain's response causes sphincter muscles to relax. This relaxation in turn causes the bladder to contract. Urine is forced from the bladder through the **urethra,** a tube to the outside of the body. The process of expelling urine from the body is called *urination.*

Section Review

1. **Inferring Relationships**   What roles do the skin and lungs play in excretion?
2. **Analyzing Ideas**   Describe how the kidneys form urine and help maintain homeostasis.
3. **Summarizing Ideas**   By what two methods are wastes removed from the blood of a person whose kidneys are not functioning?

Thinking Critically

4. **Evaluating Ideas**   Compare and contrast hemodialysis and CAPD. Why are they life-saving procedures?

INVESTIGATION 44:
How Does Exercise Affect Breathing Rate and Volume?

Objectives
- To *measure* breathing rate and volume
- To *experiment* to find the effect of exercise on breathing rate and volume

Materials
watch with a second hand, lung-volume bag

Prelab Preparation
1. Define the term external respiration.
2. Explain how you would determine a person's breathing rate.
3. Explain what is meant by the term breathing volume? How might breathing volume be easily measured?

Inquiry: Lab Technique
4. Measure breathing rate by counting the number of inhalations made by your lab partner during one minute.
5. The volume of air moved through the lungs during a normal breath can be easily measured using a lung-volume bag. The bag should be completely deflated before making a measurement. Exhale normally into the bag. Twist the end to prevent gas from escaping.
6. Place the bag on a flat surface. Gently run your hand down the bag until the gas just inflates the bag. Read the volume from the gradations printed on the bag.

Inquiry: Experimentation
7. After discussing the question that is the topic of this Investigation, state your hypothesis and give reasons for your hypothesis.
8. Your experimental design will include collecting data from three separate trials. The data will be used to calculate average breathing rate and average breathing volume for each subject. A good exercise to use is two minutes of jumping jacks. Allow breathing to return to normal between trials.
9. Design a controlled experiment that tests your team's hypothesis.

a. Describe your experimental design.
b. State the reason that your experiment is a controlled experiment.
10. After having your design approved by your teacher, conduct your experiment. Record your data in a data table.
11. **CAUTION: Do not perform vigorous exercise if you have a health problem. Do not continue exercise if you feel pain or become dizzy or tired.**
12. Using the uncompleted graph below as a guide, make a bar graph for summarizing both average breathing rate and average breathing volume, at rest and after exercise, for each subject.

Effect of Exercise on Breathing Rate and Breathing Volume

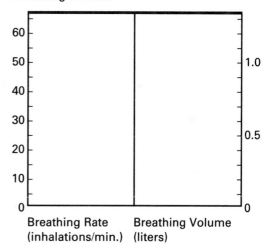

Breathing Rate (inhalations/min.)   Breathing Volume (liters)

Analysis
1. **Summarizing Data** Summarize your data.
2. **Analyzing Data** What conclusions can be drawn about your hypothesis? How does your data support your conclusions?
3. **Making Inferences** For a change in breathing rate to benefit the body, what change must also occur in the circulatory system?

Chapter 44 Review

Summary

Respiration is the process by which gases are exchanged between the atmosphere and body cells and in which cells produce energy from glucose molecules. Air passes through the nostrils, pharynx, larynx, trachea, bronchi, and bronchioles into alveoli.

Inhalation occurs when the diaphragm and intercostal muscles contract, expanding the chest cavity. Air fills the lungs because air pressure is lower inside the chest than outside the body. When the muscles relax, exhalation occurs.

The major organs of excretion are the kidneys. Their functional units, called nephrons, filter out water, wastes, and other substances from the blood. Most of the water and other substances essential to the body are reabsorbed. Some chemicals are actively removed from the blood by renal tubule cells and secreted into the filtrate. Filtrate that is not reabsorbed forms urine, which collects in the bladder and is then expelled from the body through the urethra.

BioTerms

alveolus (715)
Bowman's
   capsule (720)
bronchiole (715)
bronchus (715)
collecting
   duct (720)
cortex (720)
diaphragm (713)
excretion (719)
exhalation (714)
glomerular
   filtration (720)

glomerulus (720)
inhalation (714)
kidney (719)
lung (713)
medulla (720)
metabolism (716)
nasal cavity (714)
nephron (720)
nostril (714)
pleura (713)
renal pelvis (720)
renal tubule (720)
respiration (713)

trachea (715)
tubular
   reabsorption (720)
tubular secretion (721)
ureter (721)

urethra (722)
urinary
   bladder (721)
urine (721)
vocal cord (715)

For each pair of terms, explain the differences in their meanings.

1. inhalation, exhalation
2. respiration, excretion
3. glomerular filtration, tubular reabsorption
4. cortex, medulla

BioQuiz   (Write all answers on a separate sheet of paper.)

Completion

1. Fluids are forced out of the blood vessels in the _____ during glomerular filtration.
2. The body eliminates metabolic waste products by means of perspiration, _____, and secretion.
3. The chief waste of cells is _____.
4. The entire thoracic cavity is lined with a tough, double membrane called the _____.
5. The _____ is the largest of nine cartilage rings that holds the larynx open.

Multiple Choice

6. A major waste product that is excreted in urine is a) urea. b) protein.
   c) sugar. d) potassium.
7. The process of removing urea and other wastes from the blood is called a) excretion. b) exhalation. c) glomerular filtration. d) tubular secretion.
8. The formation of urea takes place in the a) liver. b) kidneys. c) nephrons.
   d) urinary bladder.

9. The common passageway for food and air is the a) esophagus. b) trachea. c) larynx. d) pharynx.
10. The glomeruli are surrounded by a) the medulla. b) the Bowman's capsule. c) the cortex. d) All of the choices are correct.
11. Which of the following functions is performed by the kidneys? a) filtration b) reabsorption c) tubular secretion d) All of the choices are correct.
12. A process in which a machine must perform the functions of the kidneys is a) metabolism. b) respiration. c) dialysis. d) filtration.
13. The smallest bronchioles in the lungs end in a) alveoli. b) nephrons. c) bronchi. d) stretch receptors.
14. Which of the following is not a part of the pharynx? a) epiglottis b) larynx c) vocal cord d) soft palate
15. Carbon dioxide is transported in the plasma as a) carbon monoxide. b) bicarbonate ions. c) carbon dioxide gas. d) hemoglobin.

Writing Critically

16. In what way is air pressure related to breathing?
17. How is breathing controlled?
18. How is carbon dioxide carried to the lungs for exhalation?
19. What causes blood to move from the glomerulus to the Bowman's capsule?
20. What respiratory structures are involved in external respiration?

Application/Critical Thinking

1. **Analyzing Structures** Name two ways in which the structure of alveoli helps them perform the function of gas exchange.
2. **Researching Information** Use a library to find out how successful kidney transplants are in taking over the task of excretion. Prepare a report for the class.
3. **Inferring Relationships** Firefighters sometimes die as a result of breathing extremely hot air. Use some of the facts you learned in this chapter to suggest the probable cause of death in such cases.
4. **Synthesizing Information** Uric acid is a waste product that contains nitrogen. Trace the pathway of a molecule of uric acid from a cell in the leg, where it might be produced, to its excretion from the body. Write a paragraph explaining its path and identifying the structures involved.

Cross-Discipline Connection

Biology and Mathematics   Calculate the volume of air that you inhale in a minute, an hour, a day, and a year if each breath takes in 70 ml of air.

Discovery Through Reading

Read the article "The Newest Health Hazard: Breathing," *U.S. News & World Report* (June 12, 1989): 50–51. This article focuses on how air pollution affects breathing. What is the most harmful component of polluted air? How does the body defend against this component? Describe three ways in which ozone may affect the body. What is the long term danger of breathing ozone? What affect does carbon monoxide have on the circulatory system?

Nervous Control and Coordination

Outline

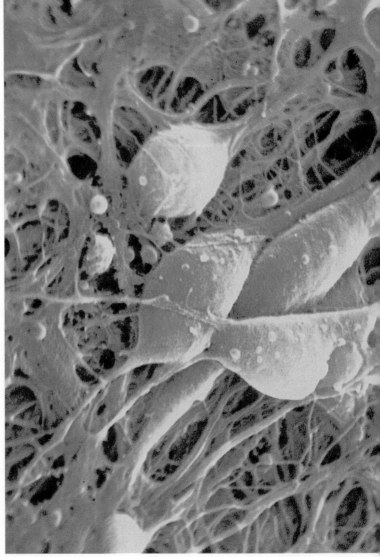

Nerve cells

Focus

Signals from nerve cells allow you to play a piano, thread a needle, throw a baseball, write in your notebook, or just sit and think. A highly developed brain coordinates activities and allows you to learn, imagine, remember, and reason. The complex system that controls and coordinates body functions is the nervous system.

- *How does the structure of the nerve cell in the photograph reflect its function?*

- *What kinds of nervous system activities can take place without the involvement of the brain?*

The Nervous System

The nervous system has two main subdivisions. One part, the **central nervous system,** consists of the brain and the spinal cord. The central nervous system receives stimuli from inside and outside the body and then coordinates the body's response. The second part of the nervous system is the **peripheral** (puh RIHF uhr uhl) **nervous system.** It provides the pathways to and from the central nervous system for electrochemical signals called **impulses.**

Three types of body structures are needed for the entire process of picking up stimuli and responding to them. They are *receptors, conductors,* and *effectors.* To understand how these different structures are coordinated, consider what happens when a doorbell rings. First, the ear acts as a receptor that picks up the sound of the ringing bell. A receptor is a cell, group of cells, or organ, that detects a stimulus. The receptor then generates impulses that travel along conductors, or nerve cells. Ultimately, the impulses reach effectors—structures that may react to the original stimulus. In this case, muscles are the effectors. The reaction to the original stimulus is to walk to the door and open it.

45.1 The Neuron

The basic functional unit of the nervous system is the nerve cell, called a **neuron.** Three types of neurons interact in the nervous system. Neurons that receive stimuli and transmit them to the central nervous system are **sensory neurons.** Neurons that carry impulses away from the central nervous system to muscles or glands are **motor neurons.** The third type of neuron, an **interneuron,** links sensory and motor neurons.

Every neuron consists of a **cell body,** which contains the nucleus and cytoplasm, and threadlike extensions of cytoplasm called **nerve fibers.** A neuron has two kinds of nerve fibers. **Dendrites** are fibers that carry impulses from other neurons or receptors toward the cell body. Dendrites are generally short, branched fibers. The second kind of nerve fiber is the **axon,** which carries impulses away from the cell body to other neurons or to effectors. As you can see in Figure 45–1, a neuron has many dendrites but only one axon. Axons are usually longer than dendrites, and any branches axons have exist only at the end of the fiber.

An axon may be wrapped in a fatty insulating layer known as a **myelin sheath.** The sheath is formed by special cells called

Section Objectives

- *Describe* the structure and functions of a neuron.
- *Describe* the changes that occur during generation of an impulse.
- *Compare* impulse transmission along myelinated and unmyelinated axons.
- *Explain* the function of a neurotransmitter.
- *Summarize* the way in which depression may be linked to neurotransmitters.

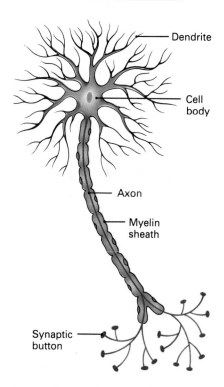

Figure 45–1. Many-branched dendrites carry nerve impulses toward a neuron cell body. A single axon carries impulses away. Axons are relatively long and are branched only at the far end.

Schwann cells. The sheath supports, insulates, and nourishes the axons. It also helps maintain the chemical balance of the axon. Gaps between the Schwann cells, called the **nodes of Ranvier** (rahn vee AY), occur about every 1 mm (0.04 in.) along the myelinated axons.

Neurons are the largest cells in the body. Some neurons may measure almost 2 m (2.2 yd.). Bundles of hundreds, or even thousands, of nerve fibers form a **nerve.** Within a nerve, each fiber carries a separate impulse, just as each wire inside a telephone cable can carry a separate phone call at the same time.

45.2 How a Nerve Impulse Travels

Impulses travel not only along the length of a nerve cell but also from cell to cell. Within a neuron the impulse is transmitted electrically. However, chemicals are generally involved in moving the impulse from cell to cell.

The Nerve Impulse   Like all cells, neurons have a certain electrical charge on the inside and outside of their cell membranes. The upper part of Figure 45–2 shows the axon of a neuron when the neuron is at its *resting potential*—that is, when it is not carrying an impulse.

The outside of the axon has about 10 times as many sodium (Na$^+$) ions as the inside. Inside the membrane are negatively charged organic ions and about 30 times as many potassium

Figure 45–2. When an axon is not carrying an impulse, it has many more sodium ions (Na$^+$) outside than inside (top). An impulse travels along the axon as sodium ions move through the cell membrane into the cell. The pink band marks the part of the axon in which the impulse is occurring (bottom).

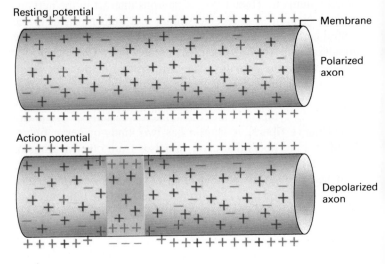

Resting potential

Membrane

Polarized axon

Action potential

Depolarized axon

+ Sodium ions (Na$^+$)
+ Potassium ions (K$^+$)
  Organic ions (−)

(K^+) ions as outside. The membrane keeps the Na^+ ions outside and the negatively charged organic ions inside. The K^+ ions move in and out of the axon freely. At resting potential, the inside of the cell membrane has a slightly negative charge, and the outside has a slightly positive charge. In this case the cell is said to be *polarized*.

When the nerve fiber is stimulated, its membrane suddenly becomes permeable to Na^+ ions at the place where the stimulation occurs. The negative ions inside the membrane then attract the Na^+ ions. Some Na^+ ions move rapidly to the inside of the cell. The presence of these positively charged ions causes that part of the interior to become more positive than the outside. These electrical changes create an *action potential*, and the neuron is said to be *depolarized*.

The membrane remains permeable to Na^+ ions for only half a millisecond. However, this brief electrical charge is enough to start the action potential moving down the nerve fiber. How does this movement occur? As you see in Figure 45–2, the positively charged ions inside the cell move toward the negatively charged area next to the region of stimulation. The positive ions cause this area to become depolarized and the membrane to become permeable to Na^+. More Na^+ ions then rush inside the membrane, causing that section of the interior to become positive. Again, positively charged ions are attracted to the adjoining negatively charged area, and thus the action potential moves along the nerve fiber.

The rapid change from negative to positive charge within the membrane is an electrical wave called a nerve impulse. *A nerve impulse can be described as the movement of the action potential along a neuron.*

As soon as an impulse passes a section of nerve fiber, the membrane once again becomes permeable only to K^+ ions. The neuron then returns to its resting potential in preparation for the next impulse. The process of returning to resting potential involves an active transport system known as the *sodium-potassium pump*. The sodium-potassium pump carries Na^+ ions to the outside and K^+ ions to the inside of the membrane.

In myelinated axons, the myelin sheath acts as an insulator against electrical impulses. Because of this insulation, the exchange of ions across the membrane takes place only at the nodes of Ranvier, where the sheath is interrupted. This periodic, rather than continuous, exchange results in a leaping of the impulse from node to node as shown in Figure 45–3. As a result, impulses travel along myelinated axons 50 times faster than they do along unmyelinated axons, sometimes as fast as 100 meters per second (224 miles per hour).

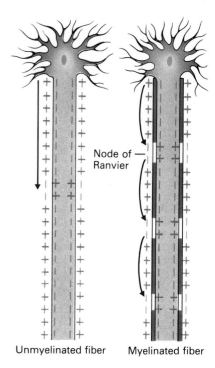

Unmyelinated fiber   Myelinated fiber

Figure 45–3. Nerve impulses travel through every part of an unmyelinated nerve fiber. In a myelinated fiber, the myelin acts as insulation, and the impulse leaps from node to node.

Reading Critically

Predicting Conclusions
What would a person's response be like if none of the axons contained a myelin sheath?

The Synapse   Impulses travel from neuron to neuron, but adjoining neurons generally do not touch one another. Therefore, an impulse must cross from the axon of one neuron to the dendrites of another. This junction is called a **synapse.** An impulse does not "jump" across the space, however. In fact, the original impulse ends when it reaches the end of an axon. At that point, however, the impulse causes the release of chemicals that generate new impulses in the next neuron.

Many axon branches terminate in tiny bulblike structures called *synaptic buttons,* which contain numerous *synaptic vesicles.* A synaptic vesicle is a tiny sac that holds chemical substances called **neurotransmitters** that stimulate nearby dendrites to start new impulses. A neurotransmitter released into the space, called the *synaptic cleft,* diffuses rapidly to nearby dendrites. There it disturbs the resting potential of the dendrites and so generates new impulses.

An impulse eventually reaches an effector cell, such as a muscle fiber. In this situation, a neurotransmitter is released from motor neurons through *motor end plates,* which are located at the ends of axons near muscle fibers. The neurotransmitter then causes the muscle to contract.

Figure 45–4. When an impulse reaches the end of an axon branch (top, left and right), a neurotransmitter is released and travels toward nearby dendrites, triggering new impulses. Neurotransmitters are also released when an impulse reaches a muscle cell (bottom, left and right), causing the muscle cell to contract.

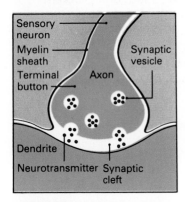

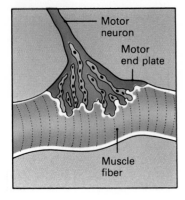

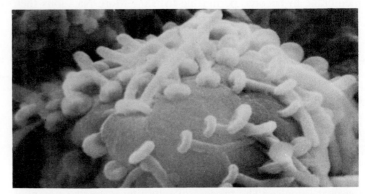

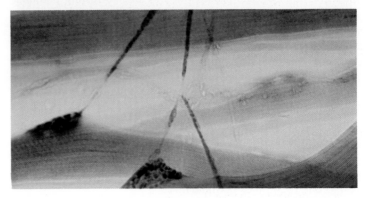

Depression is a mental disorder that affects an estimated 8 million people in the United States alone. No one knows positively that depression has a biological cause. No biochemical abnormality has yet been discovered.

Some researchers, however, are convinced that in many cases neurotransmitters are at fault. Generally, a neurotransmitter is either destroyed by an enzyme or reabsorbed by neurons almost immediately after it enters the synaptic cleft.

Reserpine, a drug used by patients with high blood pressure, causes two neuro-transmitters, *serotonin* and *norepinphrine,* to leak into the synaptic cleft. These neurotransmitters are in the part of the brain that controls emotions. Within a few days after reserpine enters a person's body, most of the serotonin and norepinephrine in that part of the brain is destroyed. Patients then often become depressed. As a result, researchers have concluded that a lack of serotonin and norepi-nephrine in the brain is related to depression.

Drugs now used to combat depression also indicate a possible link between depression and neurotransmitters. One type of drug prevents the reabsorption of serotonin and norepinephrine by neurons. The drug thus causes a buildup of sero-tonin and norepinephrine in the synaptic cleft. As a result of this buildup, impulses can be generated in the normal manner. It seems that when an abnor-mally low level of neuro-transmitters is brought to a normal level, depression is no longer a problem.

■ **Predicting Conclusions** What might be the effect of an abnormally high level of neurotransmitters?

Starting a Nerve Impulse   To "fire" a neuron—that is, to get a nerve impulse going in the first place—a stimulus must have a certain level of strength called a *threshold*. If the energy level of a stimulus falls below the threshold, the neuron will not fire. However, a stimulus with an energy level greater than the threshold does not cause a faster or stronger impulse. The neuron either fires or it doesn't, a phenomenon known as the *all-or-none* response. The intensity of a sensation depends on the number of neurons stimulated. After an impulse, the neuron must rest for about one-hundredth of a second. A stimulus, no matter how strong, cannot fire the neuron during this time.

To measure response time to different stimuli, see page 739.

Section Review

1. **Comparing Ideas**   Compare dendrites and axons.
2. **Summarizing Ideas**   Explain how depolarization occurs.
3. **Analyzing Function**   How do neurotransmitters function?
4. **Evaluating Ideas**   What is an adaptive advantage of the all-or-none response?

>Thinking Critically

The Central Nervous System

Section Objectives

- *Name* the major parts of the brain.
- *Discuss* the role of the cerebrum.
- *List* the functions of the cerebellum and the brain stem.
- *Describe* the structure of the spinal cord.
- *Compare* the functions controlled by the right and left side of the cerebrum.

Impulses travel through the central nervous system, which processes incoming sensory impulses and sends out responding impulses. *The brain and spinal cord, which make up the central nervous system, each control specific tasks.*

45.3 The Brain

The **brain** is the control center for the human body. Its 100 billion nerve cells not only coordinate and regulate body activities but also enable humans to think. The human brain weighs only about 1.4 kg (3 lb.), but it is the most complex structure on Earth. The surface is *gray matter*, which consists of about 6 million cell bodies and their dendrites packed into each cubic centimeter (0.06 cu. in.). Under the gray matter is *white matter*, formed from myelinated axons.

The brain is composed of three major structures: the *cerebrum* (suh REE bruhm), the *cerebellum* (sehr uh BEHL uhm), and the *brain stem*. Each area seems to control separate functions. However, it is not the independence but rather the interdependence of its parts that makes the brain so effective.

The Cerebrum The **cerebrum** makes up about seven-eighths of the total brain weight. Its two sides, called **cerebral hemispheres,** are joined by a bridge of 200 million nerve fibers. This bridgelike structure between the cerebral hemispheres is known

Figure 45–5. Each hemisphere of the cerebrum (left) can be divided into four lobes. The functional parts of the entire brain (right) are the cerebrum, cerebellum, and the brain stem.

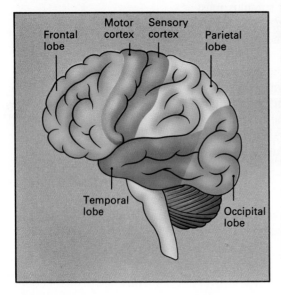

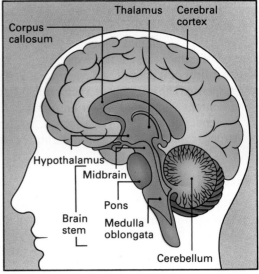

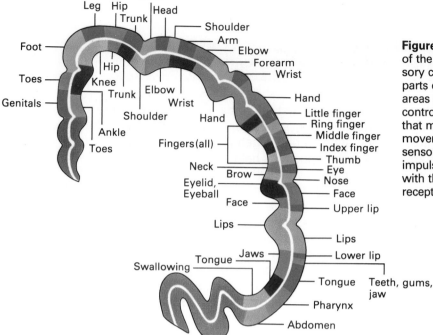

Neck
Leg Hip Head
Trunk
Shoulder
Arm
Elbow
Forearm
Wrist
Foot
Hip
Toes
Knee
Trunk Elbow Hand
Genitals
Wrist Little finger
Shoulder Hand Ring finger
Ankle Middle finger
Toes Fingers (all) Index finger
Thumb
Neck Eye
Eyelid, Brow Nose
Eyeball Face
Face Upper lip
Lips
Lips
Tongue Jaws Lower lip
Swallowing
Tongue Teeth, gums, jaw
Pharynx
Abdomen

Figure 45–6. Specific areas of the motor cortex and sensory cortex control specific parts of the body. The largest areas of motor cortex (blue) control the parts of the body that make the most complex movements. Large areas of sensory cortex (red) receive impulses from body parts with the most sensory receptors.

as the **corpus callosum** (KAWR puhs kuh LOH suhm). Deep grooves mark off four areas on each hemisphere. The four areas are the *frontal, parietal, temporal,* and *occipital* lobes.

The gray matter of the cerebrum is called the **cerebral cortex.** Its main function is to receive sensory impulses from the body and coordinate motor responses to them. Its many ridges and valleys, called *convolutions,* greatly increase the surface area of the brain. As you can see in Figure 45–6, each area on the section called the *motor cortex* controls the movement of muscles in a specific part of the body. Each area of the *sensory cortex* receives impulses from a specific part of the body. The area devoted to each body part is proportional to its sensitivity or motor capability, not to its size. For example, a large area is devoted to the hand, a sensitive area.

Each hemisphere controls the actions and sensations of the opposite side of the body. For example, the left side controls movement of the right hand; the right side controls movement of the left hand. Scientists have discovered that in most people each side also has exclusive control over certain functions.

Several important structures lie within the cerebrum. On each side of the brain is the **thalamus** (THAL uh muhs), a small structure that acts as a relay center for impulses. The thalamus processes incoming sensory impulses before sending them to appropriate parts of the cortex. It also sorts out and combines impulses from the cortex and other areas of the brain. Below the thalamus is the **hypothalamus.** Research has indicated that this

Biofact

Q: *Is brain size related to intelligence?*

A: No. Brain size among human beings is not related to level of intelligence. Previously the number of convolutions was thought to play a role in intelligence, but now even that idea is in doubt.

Both hemispheres of the cerebrum control similar activities. However, in most people, some activities are controlled by one side or the other. Usually the left side controls language. The right side governs spatial perception and musical ability.

These discoveries were made during research on patients suffering from epilepsy. Surgeons occasionally cut the corpus callosum to relieve seizures. As a result of this operation, information cannot travel from one side of a patient's brain to the other.

Researchers studied the effects of the "split-brain" operation. In one experiment, an apparatus held the patient's head while different pictures were flashed to each eye. Patients could describe only what they saw with the right eye. For example, they were shown the word *heart.* The left eye saw only *he,* and the right eye, only *art.* Patients said they saw *art.* They could not say *he.*

Although patients could not describe what they saw with the left eye, they could make a nonverbal association. For instance,

when a patient saw the word *nut* with the left eye, he or she could not say the word *nut.* But the patient could point to a nut from an assortment of objects. Researchers also found that, in tests involving spatial relationships, the right cortex was far superior to the left. Right-handed patients drew a more accurate picture with the left hand than with the right hand when space perception was involved.

■ **Interpreting Information**
What would you conclude if an individual could say only *he* and not *art*?

structure controls body temperature, thirst, hunger, salt and water balance, and emotional behavior in general. Near the corpus callosum is a network of neurons called the *limbic system.* The limbic system is thought to translate a person's drives and emotions into actions.

The Cerebellum   The **cerebellum** is located beneath the occipital lobe. The white matter that composes most of the cerebellum is covered by a thin layer of gray matter. The cerebellum coordinates voluntary muscle movements and maintains muscle vigor and body balance. Damage to the cerebellum may result in jerky, awkward movements, although the ability to make the movements is not affected.

To compare the human brain with other vertebrate brains, see pages 902–903.

The Brain Stem   The **brain stem** contains all the nerves that connect the spinal cord with the cerebrum. The principal divisions of the brain stem, as shown in Figure 45–5 on page 732, are the medulla oblongata, pons, and midbrain. The **medulla oblongata** (mih DUHL uh ahb lawn GAHT uh) is the enlarged portion of the spinal cord that enters the lower skull. It controls breathing, swallowing, digestive processes, and action of the heart and blood vessels. In the medulla, many nerve fibers crisscross. As a result, each hemisphere receives impulses from and sends impulses to the opposite side of the body. The **pons** connects the two hemispheres of the cerebellum and links the cerebellum with the cerebrum. The **midbrain** lies above the pons. It controls responses to sight, such as movements of the eyes and size of the pupils.

A complex network of nerve fibers called the **reticular formation** runs through the brain stem and thalamus. This structure plays an essential role in consciousness, awareness, and sleep. The reticular system activates the rest of the brain when a stimulus is received. However, it first filters every stimulus. For example, people can sleep through loud noises such as traffic sounds but be awakened instantly by the ring of a telephone. Researchers do not know exactly how the reticular formation

Reading Critically

Evaluating Relationships
Why could the medulla oblongata be considered the most important part of the brain stem?

BIOLOGY AND YOU:

Crack

When freebase, a potent form of cocaine, is made, a beige residue forms. This residue is called the "cookie" and is cut into small pieces that harden into pellets called *crack.*

The effect of smoking crack is rapid: a large portion of cocaine reaches the brain within 10 seconds, giving the smoker a quick and intensive high. The price for that high is, however, not a small one: crack is very addictive, probably more so than cocaine powder. The potency of this form of cocaine also makes it potentially more lethal.

Crack acts as both a local anesthetic and as a stimulant to the central nervous system. It has a numbing effect on the throat and constricts blood vessels. This raises the blood pressure and increases the heartbeat rate.

Users have been known to suffer from lethal convulsions, cardiac arrest, and respiratory failure. Even small doses and first-time use can be fatal. Long-term users risk developing *cocaine psychosis,* a disorder that resembles schizophrenia.

Although there is no easy cure for cocaine and crack addiction, a number of doctors and psychiatrists have discovered that certain drugs, such as desipramine and other tri-

cyclics closely related to it, reduce the brain's craving for cocaine.

Because crack is so addictive, it can very quickly take over a person's life—to the extent, in fact, that it is extremely difficult for a person who experiments with crack to regain control over his or her life again.

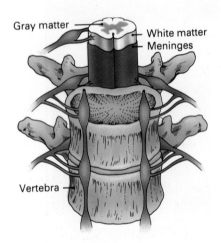

Biofact

Q: *Does the brain need much energy to operate?*

A: Yes. Compared with other organs, the brain needs a tremendous amount of energy. The brain is only 2 percent of the body's total weight, but it uses 20 percent of the body's oxygen and glucose. Because it cannot store either substance, an interruption in the supply of either one is very serious.

Gray matter —
White matter
Meninges

Vertebra —

Figure 45–7. The spinal cord is protected by the surrounding meninges and vertebral column.

Thinking Critically

functions during sleep, but they know that a lack of sleep can seriously affect a person's well-being. A person deprived of sleep becomes quick-tempered, lacks concentration and energy, and is easily distracted. Too little sleep can eventually affect sight and hearing.

Protection of the Brain The brain is protected in three ways. First, the skull helps prevent serious injury from blows to the head. Second, the brain is cushioned inside the skull by **cerebrospinal fluid.** Cerebrospinal fluid is tissue fluid that circulates constantly around the brain and spinal cord. Third, three layers of tissue known collectively as the **meninges** (muh NIHN jeez) protect the surface of the brain. The innermost layer, called the *pia mater,* follows all brain convolutions. Its rich blood supply carries nutrients and oxygen to brain cells and carries waste products away. The middle layer, the *arachnoid,* is a delicate weblike structure. Fluid between the pia mater and arachnoid serves as the pathway for exchange of nutrients and waste products. The outermost layer is a tough fibrous membrane called the *dura mater.*

45.4 The Spinal Cord

The **spinal cord** is a column of nerve tissue extending from the brain through the spinal column. In adults it is about 43 cm (17 in.) long and as thick as a pencil. The spinal cord links the brain with nerves to all parts of the body and controls involuntary movements known as *reflexes.*

Figure 45–7 shows that the center of the cord is filled with gray matter with a cross section shaped somewhat like the letter H. Cell bodies of motor neurons and interneurons are in the gray matter. The cell bodies of sensory neurons form small masses called *ganglia* outside the spinal cord. White matter around the gray matter consists of myelinated axons. Vertebrae, meninges, and cerebrospinal fluid protect the spinal cord.

Section Review

1. **Identifying Structures**   List three major brain areas and their functions.
2. **Evaluating Ideas**   How might an injury to the cerebellum affect a person's movements?
3. **Identifying Function**   What function does the reticular formation perform?
4. **Synthesizing Information**   In right side paralysis, what area of the brain may be injured?

The Peripheral Nervous System

The peripheral nervous system carries impulses to and from the central nervous system. Twelve pairs of *cranial nerves* and 31 pairs of *spinal nerves* make up the peripheral nervous system. The cranial nerves connect the brain primarily with sense organs, the heart, and other internal organs. The spinal nerves carry impulses between the spinal cord and skeletal muscles.

So far, the nervous system has been presented like a map. Another way of thinking of the nervous system is to focus on what its parts do and not on where they are located. When described in this way, the subdivisions are called the *somatic nervous system* and the *autonomic nervous system*. These systems involve both the peripheral and the central nervous systems.

45.5 The Somatic Nervous System

The **somatic nervous system** transmits impulses to and from skeletal muscles, which are usually under conscious control. For this reason the somatic nervous system is sometimes called the voluntary nervous system. Each pair of spinal nerves has motor and sensory fibers. Each pair carries impulses to and from skeletal muscles in a specific part of the body.

Not all skeletal muscle movements are voluntary. Movements called reflexes are not under conscious control. A reflex pathway, called a **reflex arc,** involves two or three neurons, as shown in Figure 45–8. The simplest arc consists of one sensory and one motor neuron. A three-neuron reflex arc includes an interneuron. The brain is not involved in either arc.

Responses such as dodging a moving object are *conditioned;* they are learned from experience. Reflexes, such as blinking, are *unconditioned.* The advantage of reflexes is speed. Reflexes may take one one-hundredth of a second—much faster than any pathway involving the brain. However, the brain may play a role in other responses to the stimulus. Typically, you quickly withdraw your hand after touching a hot object. Three neurons carry the impulses in the reflex arc, causing the jerk of your hand. Other impulses travel to the brain. The impulses to the brain may result in your conscious response, a gasp of "Ouch."

45.6 The Autonomic Nervous System

The **autonomic nervous system** controls automatic, or involuntary, functions involving glands, internal organs, and other smooth muscle tissue. The autonomic nervous system is divided

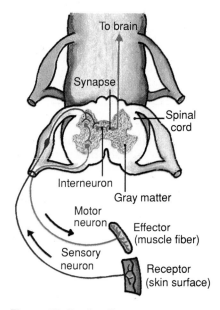

Figure 45–8. A reflex arc includes a sensory neuron, a motor neuron, and in some cases an interneuron. The spinal cord—not the brain—activates the response.

Table 45–1: The Autonomic Nervous System

Anatomic Part	Sympathetic	Parasympathetic
Iris	Dilates pupil	Contracts pupil
Salivary glands	Decreases salivation	Increases salivation
Bronchioles	Relaxes bronchioles	Constricts bronchioles
Heart	Speeds up heartbeat, increases force of contraction	Slows heartbeat
Digestive system	Slows peristalsis, inhibits pancreatic secretions, stimulates release of glucose by liver	Stimulates peristalsis, stimulates pancreatic secretions, promotes production of glycogen by liver
Urinary bladder	Relaxes bladder	Contracts bladder
Circulatory system	Constricts blood vessels of some internal organs, dilates blood vessels of skeletal muscles	Dilates blood vessels of digestive system
Hair follicles	Contracts muscles around hair follicle; body hair stands erect	No effect

into two systems. The *sympathetic nervous system* enables the body to handle stress through what is called the "fight or flight" response, in which a person either fights or runs away. Fighting and running both require extra energy. Therefore, the sympathetic nervous system causes bodily changes that channel extra glucose and oxygen to skeletal muscles, thus supplying the extra strength needed in an emergency. When stress no longer exists, the *parasympathetic nervous system* is responsible for returning body functions to normal and for maintaining them at that level. For example, the sympathetic nervous system speeds the heart to supply cells more quickly; the parasympathetic nervous system slows the heart.

Reading Critically

Evaluating Function What role does the parasympathetic nervous system play in homeostasis?

Section Review

1. **Inferring Conclusions** What is the advantage of a reflex? How is the reflex an adaptive advantage?
2. **Comparing Ideas** What is the difference between the somatic nervous system and the autonomic nervous system?
3. **Synthesizing Ideas** What is an adaptive advantage of the "fight or flight" response?

Thinking Critically

INVESTIGATION 45:
Is Response Time Affected by Stimulus Type?

Objectives
- To *measure* human response time
- To *test* a hypothesis through controlled experimentation

Materials
meter stick, bell

Response Time Conversion Table

Distance (cm)	Time	Distance (cm)	Time
1.1	.05	28.9	.24
1.7	.06	33.0	.26
2.4	.07	38.2	.28
3.1	.08	43.9	.30
3.9	.09	48.8	.32
4.9	.10	56.4	.34
7.0	.12	63.5	.36
9.6	.14	70.8	.38
12.5	.16	78.4	.40
15.8	.18	86.4	.42
19.5	.20	94.8	.44
23.6	.22	103.7	.46

Prelab Preparation
1. Review the discussion of the nervous system in your textbook.
2. Define the term reflex.
3. Explain how the functions of effectors, receptors, and conductors differ.
4. Differentiate between a fast reflex and a fast response time.

Inquiry: Lab Technique
5. Rest your forearm on a table top, your hand over the edge, and spread your thumb and forefinger about 2 cm apart.
6. Have your partner place the 0-end of a meter stick between your fingertips.
7. Without warning, your partner will release the stick and you should catch it between your fingers.
8. Measure the distance the stick falls. Make a table to record data for ten trials. Record the distance of fall in centimeters for each trial and calculate the average distance of fall for your ten trials.
9. Exchange places with your partner and repeat the test.

10. The distance the stick falls is used to indirectly measure response time. Use the Response Time Conversion Table shown in the left-hand column to convert the average distance of fall to the average response time.

Inquiry: Experimentation
11. *Does response time to an auditory stimulus differ from that of a visual stimulus?* After discussing the question with your partner, state your hypothesis.
12. Design a controlled experiment that tests your team's hypothesis. Have your partner place a small bell on one of the fingers used to hold the meter stick. When the fingers open, releasing the stick, the bell will tinkle. This sound provides an auditory stimulus signaling the release of the stick.
    a. Describe the design of your experiment.
    b. *What is the dependent variable in your experiment? What is the independent variable?*
    c. *Why is it necessary to collect data from many trials for each subject?*
13. After having your experimental design approved by your teacher, conduct your experiment. Record your data.
14. Make a line graph showing your response time for each trial. Draw one line showing response to an auditory stimulus and another showing response to a visual stimulus.
15. Indicate the average response time for each type of stimulus on your graph.

Analysis
1. **Analyzing Data** Why is it more accurate to find the average response time by converting the average distance of fall than by averaging the times for all the trials?
2. **Analyzing Data** In what ways does the graph communicate more information than the average response time?
3. **Inferring Conclusions** What conclusion can you draw in regard to your hypothesis? Explain how your data support your conclusion.

Chapter 45 Review

Summary

The nervous system is made up of the central nervous system and the peripheral nervous system. The functional unit of the nervous system is the neuron. Dendrites carry impulses from receptors toward the cell bodies. Axons carry impulses from a cell body to effectors or other neurons. An impulse is an electrochemical change in the neuron. Neurotransmitters generate impulses in adjacent neurons.

The main areas of the brain are the cere- brum, the cerebellum, and the brain stem. Different body functions are controlled by different areas of the brain.

The somatic nervous system controls skeletal muscle. The autonomic nervous system includes the sympathetic and parasympathetic systems. The sympathetic system helps the body respond to stress situations. The effects of parasympathetic nervous system are opposite those of the sympathetic nervous system.

BioTerms

autonomic nervous
    system (737)
axon (727)
brain (732)
brain stem (734)
cell body (727)
central nervous
    system (727)
cerebellum (734)
cerebral cortex (733)
cerebral
    hemisphere (732)
cerebrospinal
    fluid (736)
cerebrum (732)
corpus callosum (733)

dendrite (727)
hypothalamus (733)
impulse (727)
interneuron (727)
medulla
    oblongata (734)
meninges (736)
midbrain (735)
motor neuron (727)
myelin sheath (727)
nerve (728)
nerve fiber (727)
neuron (727)
neurotransmitter
    (730)
node of Ranvier (728)

peripheral nervous
    system (727)
pons (735)
reflex arc (737)
reticular
    formation (735)
Schwann cell (728)

sensory
    neuron (727)
somatic nervous
    system (737)
spinal cord (736)
synapse (730)
thalamus (733)

For each pair of terms, explain the differences in their meanings.

1. peripheral nervous system, central nervous system
2. cerebellum, cerebrum
3. somatic nervous system, autonomic nervous system
4. motor neuron, sensory neuron

BioQuiz   (Write all answers on a separate sheet of paper.)

Completion

1. The _____ nervous system prepares the body for emergencies.
2. Coordination is controlled by the _____ .
3. The three brain coverings are the _____ .
4. Impulses from the arms and legs to the brain are processed through the _____ .
5. Depression appears to be linked to a level of _____ .

Multiple Choice

6. A simple reaction involving only sensory and motor neurons is
   a) a synapse. b) an impulse.
   c) a reflex. d) a neurotransmitter.
7. The fatty insulation on axons is
   a) myelin. b) a dendrite.
   c) cerebrospinal fluid.
   d) a neurotransmitter.

8. Impulses are carried from other neurons toward the cell body by   a) axons.   b) dendrites.   c) myelin sheaths.   d) synaptic buttons.
9. The myelin sheath is made of   a) Schwann cells.   b) neurotransmitters.   c) synapses.   d) meninges.
10. Between a synaptic button and a dendrite is a   a) pons.   b) reflex arc.   c) synaptic cleft.   d) node of Ranvier.
11. Which of the following is not part of the brain stem?   a) thalamus   b) midbrain   c) pons   d) medulla oblongata
12. The gray matter ridges of the cerebral cortex are   a) white matter.   b) hypothalamus.   c) pons.   d) convolutions.
13. An impulse is the movement of   a) a resting potential.   b) a refractory period.   c) a synapse.   d) an action potential.
14. Breathing, swallowing, and digestive processes are controlled by the   a) cerebellum.   b) medulla oblongata.   c) cerebrum.   d) pons.
15. Which of the following is not a layer of the meninges?   a) pia mater   b) arachnoid   c) cerebral cortex   d) dura mater

Writing Critically

16. What changes within a neuron cause an impulse to travel?
17. How did the split-brain hypothesis arise? Explain what it is.
18. What is a myelin sheath? How does it affect impulse transmission?
19. How do neurotransmitters help impulse transmission?
20. How do reflex arcs differ from other impulse pathways? What is the advantage of a reflex?

Application/Critical Thinking

1. **Summarizing Ideas**   Write a paragraph describing the pathway of an impulse.
2. **Researching Information**   Do library research to learn about endorphins, the brain's own painkillers.
3. **Synthesizing Conclusions**   A driver sees a red light, lifts her right foot from the accelerator, and places it on the brake. Which hemisphere of the brain ordered this action? What areas of the brain perceived and responded to the red light?
4. **Inferring Relationships**   Large areas of the motor cortex control the movements of the tongue and the fingers. Smaller areas control the movements of the arms and the shoulders. Explain this fact.

Cross-Discipline Connection

Biology and Health   Read library references about mental illness. Write a report on those disorders caused by physical damage or dysfunction of the brain itself.

Discovery Through Reading

Read "What Is This Thing Called Sleep?", *National Geographic* (December 1987): 786–821. What is the relation of how long we sleep to how long we live?

Read "Assault on the Brain," *Psychology Today* (March 1988): 38–44, which describes research on dementia caused by AIDS. What is ADC?

CHAPTER

46

Senses

Outline

Examination of the human eye

Focus

Special receptors in the body allow you to know what is going on around you and inside you. Without them, you would not be able to avoid injuries, balance yourself, or judge your position in space. Neither would you be able to see beautiful sights, hear wonderful sounds, taste delicious flavors, and smell appealing aromas.

- *Some people are born with no receptors for pain in their skin. How does this affect their lives?*

- *What receptors in the human body are stimulated by chemicals?*

Receptors and Sense Organs

Many receptors that enable the body to obtain information from the environment are located in highly specialized organs called *sense organs*. The most familiar sense organs are the eyes, ears, nose, mouth, and skin. In addition to these, you have other sense organs that you may not be aware of. For example, receptors in your ears enable you to keep your balance. All sense organs have specialized receptors for stimuli. Most sense organs have receptors that pick up stimuli from the body's external environment. Other kinds of receptors pick up stimuli from the body's internal environment.

46.1 Types of Receptors

Sense receptors are highly selective. The receptors for taste will not respond to light, no matter how intense it is. The receptors for sight cannot be activated by sound vibrations.

Sense receptors can be classified according to the stimuli that activate them. Photoreceptors detect stimuli generated by light. The receptors for taste and smell are triggered by chemicals and are called *chemoreceptors*. *Thermoreceptors* respond to heat or cold, either inside or outside the body. *Pain receptors* generate impulses interpreted as pain. *Mechanoreceptors* respond to mechanical pressures. Such pressures may come from sound vibrations, touch, muscle contractions, or movements of joints. The pressure bends or distorts the part of the sense organ in which the mechanoreceptors are located. **Hair cells,** which have extremely fine projections like cilia, are one type of mechanoreceptor.

46.2 Sense Organs

Sense organs act as **transducers**—that is, they transform one form of energy into another form. For example, when light rays strike the inner lining of the eye, they are changed into impulses. These impulses move along a nerve to the brain's visual center where they are interpreted as sight.

Impulses from all sense organs are basically alike. *The way the brain interprets impulses from various sense organs differs.* Impulses from each sense organ travel to a different part of the brain. The impulses from a particular sense organ are interpreted in only one way, according to where they are received in the brain. For example, when the eye receives light signals, it produces impulses that the brain interprets as an image. When

Section Objectives

- *List* the main types of sensory receptors.
- *Explain* how sense organs operate as transducers.
- *Describe* how thirst is controlled by the body.
- *Summarize* how receptors and the central nervous system work together.

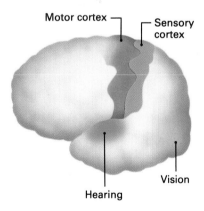

Figure 46–1. The illustration shows a sensory map of the brain. Damage to a specific area will cause problems with the activity associated with that area.

The human body has many special receptors other than those in the familiar sense organs. While some scientists claim that all these receptors are "senses," others think they are more accurately described as "controls." Regardless of the term used, the fact remains that these special receptors react to internal stimuli rather than external stimuli.

The internal controls primarily maintain homeostasis. For example, thirst is triggered by the hypothalamus, which responds to salt concentration in the blood. When the water level in the blood is low, salt becomes more concentrated. When salt concentration is high, the hypothalamus reacts by generating impulses that trigger a thirst sensation. When the water level is high, salt concentration is low, and the body eliminates more water. Similarly, chemicals in the cerebrospinal fluid and a low level of glucose in the blood seem to trigger hunger.

Another type of internal control monitors your skeletal muscles. Muscle spindles, a special type of muscle fiber, are part of skeletal muscle. The spindles contain two types of sensory neurons. One type alerts the central nervous system to a change in the stretch or contraction of a muscle. The other type registers how much stretch is involved. This constant monitoring of muscular contraction helps you maintain posture and keeps your body steady. Joint and tendon receptors work with the muscle spindles. Joint receptors register the angle of ligament movement. Tendon receptors indicate the amount of stretch in the tendons.

■ **Comparing Ideas** How are these receptors unlike those in the familiar sense organs?

Reading Critically

Analyzing Function Why are you unable to see sounds?

the ear receives pressure waves, or sound vibrations, it produces impulses that the brain interprets as sound. The brain never interprets impulses from the eye as sound or impulses from the ear as an image. Even if some other type of energy generates an impulse in a receptor cell, the brain will interpret the impulse exactly as it does all other impulses from that receptor. For example, a blow to the eye may cause you to see an image, even though the impulse was generated not by light but by mechanical pressure.

Section Review

1. **Listing Ideas** Name three familiar sense organs.
2. **Classifying Ideas** How are sense receptors classified?
3. **Identifying Ideas** The receptors in the ears convert one form of energy into another form. What are these two forms of energy?

Thinking Critically

4. **Inferring Relationships** In what way might a totally blind person "see" light?

Vision, Hearing, and Balance

The eyes and ears provide the body with its greatest protection. Because these organs are sensitive to distant stimuli, they can give early warnings about possible dangers.

46.3 The Eyes

The eye is often compared to a camera, but it is more complicated than the most sophisticated camera. Humans have *binocular vision,* the ability to view objects with two eyes. People also have *stereoscopic vision,* the ability to see objects in three dimensions—height, width, and depth. With stereoscopic vision a person can assess the speed of a moving object and determine the distance of an object in space.

Structure of the Eye   The *eye,* or *eyeball,* is an almost perfect sphere with a diameter of about 2.5 cm (1 in.). The eye is protected in a number of ways. A fatty layer within the eye socket cushions the eyeball. Eyelids and eyelashes also provide protection by preventing foreign particles from entering the front of the eye. If something touches the eyelashes or moves suddenly in front of the eye, the eyelid closes and reopens rapidly in a blinking reflex.

Each eye is moved by three sets of muscles and is lubricated by mucus and tears. The mucus is secreted by the **conjunctiva,** a delicate, blood-rich membrane that lines the inner eyelid and covers the front of the eye. Tears are produced by the **lacrimal gland** near the outer corner of the eye. When the eye closes, the eyelid spreads the mucus and tears, which moisten the eye and help remove foreign particles.

The eye has an outer wall that consists of three layers of tissue: the sclera, the choroid, and the retina. These three layers surround a jellylike substance, the **vitreous** (VIH tree uhs) **humor** that makes up two-thirds of the eyeball.

The **sclera** (SKLIHR uh) is tough, white connective tissue that forms the outermost layer. About 80 percent of the sclera, including the "white" of the eye, is opaque. The remainder is a transparent layer called the **cornea** at the front of the eye.

The **choroid** (KAWR oyd) is the middle, darkly pigmented layer of tissue. It absorbs light and so prevents reflection, which would result in fuzzy images. The choroid contains many blood vessels that nourish the eye. Toward the front of the eye, the choroid forms a colored ring, the **iris,** which gives the eye its color. In the center of the iris is an opening called the **pupil.** In

Section Objectives

- *List* the major parts of the eye and *state* the function of each part.
- *Contrast* the functions of the rods and the cones.
- *Name* several disorders that can be detected by examining the retina.
- *Trace* a vibration through the ear.
- *Explain* how the inner ear regulates balance.

To learn more about the function of the eye, see page 753.

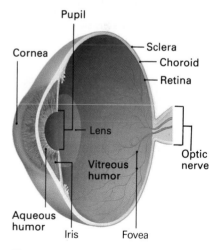

Figure 46–2. The cross-section view of the eye shows both outer and inner structures. The size of the pupil automatically adjusts in response to changes in light.

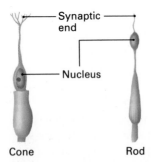

Cone   Rod

Figure 46–3. Rod and cone photoreceptor cells differ in their response to light stimulation. Without cones, a person would not see colors, only shades of gray.

Biofact

Q: *How does an animal with color vision distinguish one color from another?*

A: Colors are distinguished from one another when different types of cone cells are stimulated by different wavelengths of light.

bright light, one set of muscles in the iris contracts and causes the pupil to become smaller. In dim light, a different set of iris muscles contracts, making the pupil larger.

Behind the pupil is the **lens,** a transparent, curved structure. By changing shape, the lens helps focus images onto receptor cells at the rear of the eye. The curvature of the lens is controlled by muscles attached to the choroid. A clear, watery fluid called the **aqueous** (AY kwee uhs) **humor** fills the space between the lens and cornea. The vitreous humor fills the space behind the lens.

The innermost layer of the eye is the light-sensitive **retina.** The retina contains about 125 million receptors called **rods** and **cones.** *The rods and cones are stimulated by light to generate nerve impulses.* The rods are extremely light-sensitive and can detect various shades of gray even in dim light. However, they cannot distinguish colors, and they produce poorly defined images. The cones detect color, produce sharp images, and are important for seeing in bright light. In a tiny pit at the center of the retina is a concentration of cones. This area, the **fovea** (FOH vee uh), produces the sharpest image.

How You See Light passes through the cornea, aqueous humor, pupil, lens, and vitreous humor, and finally reaches the retina. Impulses generated by the rods and cones in the retina travel to the visual center in the occipital lobe of the brain by means of the *optic nerve.* The optic nerve from each eye consists of about 1 million nerve fibers. No rods or cones exist at the point where the optic nerve enters the retina. This area, called the *optic disc,* or blind spot, does not transmit impulses.

THINKING ABOUT BIOLOGY: What Eyes Reveal

A doctor can learn a great deal about the condition of your entire body by looking into your eyes. Using an *ophthalmoscope,* which has special lenses and a light, he or she can study the optic disc and the blood vessels of the retina.

Studying the retina may reveal many disorders that do not directly involve the eyes. For example, high blood pressure can be identified by viewing the blood vessels of the retina. The increased pressure of the blood circulating through these tiny vessels may cause some of them to burst. Diabetes may also cause changes in these blood vessels and in the vitreous humor. Changes in the size and shape of the optic disc may indicate such serious disorders as glaucoma or even brain tumor.

■ **Listing Ideas** How can regular visits to the ophthalmologist benefit your overall health?

Near the base of the brain, half of the nerve fibers from the left eye cross over and join half of the nerve fibers from the right eye. All these fibers go to the right side of the brain. Likewise, half the nerve fibers from the right eye join half from the left eye and go to the left side of the brain. Each side of the brain thus receives images from both eyes. The point at which the partial crossing-over of the fibers occurs is the *optic chiasma*.

Disorders of the Eye   Eye disorders affect more than 50 percent of the people in the United States. Among the most common of these disorders are *myopia* and *hyperopia*. In myopia, or nearsightedness, the eyeball is too long from the front to the back. Light focused by the lens falls at a point in front of the retina, resulting in a blurred image of distant objects. In hyperopia, or farsightedness, the eyeball is too short from front to back. Light is focused at a point behind the retina, resulting in a blurred image of close objects. In *astigmatism,* irregularities in the curvature of the cornea result in fuzzy images. Prescribed eyeglasses or contact lenses can correct these conditions.

In a condition called *glaucoma,* the aqueous humor cannot drain into blood vessels around the eye. Because new aqueous humor is constantly produced by the choroid, failure to drain creates excess pressure within the eye. This pressure damages the retina and optic nerve and can lead to blindness.

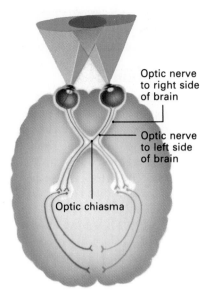

Figure 46–4.   This illustration shows the neural pathways involved in seeing. Because the fields of vision overlap, each side of the brain receives information from each retina.

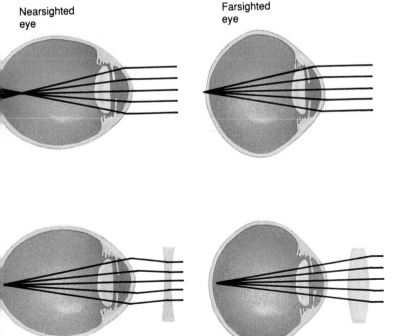

Nearsighted eye

Farsighted eye

To find out about a career as an opthalmologist, see pages 924–925.

Figure 46–5.   A concave lens corrects nearsightedness by spreading the light rays so that they focus on the retina (left). A convex lens bends light rays to correct farsightedness (right).

A Real Blast

More than eight hours of exposure to sound at 90 decibels can cause temporary hearing loss. That is noise about as loud as a lawn mower.

Listening to sound at 120 decibels immediately destroys sensitive hair cells that are the receptors for sound waves. These hair cells do not grow back, so the hearing loss is irreversible.

A potential source of excessive sound levels that are high enough to cause hearing loss is

headset stereos. Even when powered by a single AA battery, a small radio can reach 115 decibels. If a listener finds that sounds are muffled and

words are difficult to distinguish after removing a headset, hearing loss may have occurred. A ringing or a tickling sensation in the ears after removing a headset may indicate severe hearing loss. A chronic ringing in the ear called *tinnitus* may be a sign of damaged hair cells.

To prevent hearing loss from using a headset, the volume should be kept low enough to hear a normal conversation.

46.4 The Ears

The eyes have only one vital function—vision. The ears, however, perform two vital functions—hearing and balance.

Reading Critically

Inferring Relationships
What do you think would happen if the ear canal did not produce ear wax?

Structure of the Ear   The ear is divided into three major sections: the *outer ear*, the *middle ear*, and the *inner ear*. Each region has a specific function.

The outer ear consists of a cartilage flap called the **pinna** and the **auditory canal,** a tube leading to the middle ear. These structures channel sound to the **eardrum,** a tightly stretched membrane between the outer ear and the middle ear. The auditory canal is lined with hairs and special cells that secrete earwax. Together, the hairs and earwax prevent foreign particles from reaching the eardrum.

The middle ear is an air-filled space called the **tympanic cavity** inside the skull bone. A duct called the **Eustachian** (yoo STAY shuhn) **tube** connects the middle ear to the pharynx. Generally the tube is collapsed, but it opens when you yawn, swallow, cough, or blow your nose. Air pressure between the middle ear and throat is then equalized. Air pressure around you varies with altitude and can change rapidly, as when you ride an elevator or airplane. If the pressure is not equalized, the eardrum can bulge, causing pain and difficulty in hearing. Lying across the middle ear cavity are three tiny bones called the **malleus** (MAL ee uhs), or *hammer;* the **incus** (IHN kuhs), or *anvil;* and the **stapes** (STAY peez), or *stirrup.* The stapes touches a membrane called the **oval window,** located between the middle ear and the inner ear.

The inner ear contains the sensory receptors for hearing and balance. It consists of three main parts: the cochlea, the vestibule, and the semicircular canals. The organ of hearing is within the **cochlea** (KAHK lee uh), a bony, coiled tube filled with fluid and lined with hair cells. A second membrane-covered opening is located in the cochlea below the oval window. Called the **round window,** it maintains a constant pressure within the cochlea. The upper part of the inner ear consists of three **semicircular canals,** which are fluid-filled tubes positioned at right angles to each other. These canals help maintain balance by responding to head movement. A bony chamber called the **vestibule** lies between the semicircular canals and the cochlea.

How You Hear   Sound waves are generated when any object vibrates, or moves back and forth, in the air. The human ear can detect sounds between 20 and 20,000 vibrations per second.

Biofact

Q: *How does an animal distinguish one sound from another?*

A: Different hair cells in the cochlea are stimulated by different frequencies. The brain then interprets the sound according to which hair cell an impulse comes from.

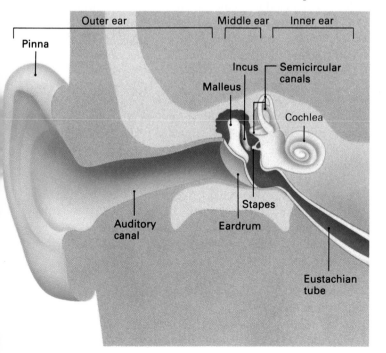

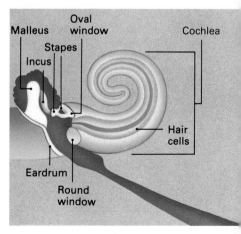

Figure 46–6. Sound waves must pass through the outer, middle, and inner ears (left) for hearing to take place. The cochlea, which contains the receptors for sound, is located in the inner ear (below).

Figure 46–7. This scanning electron micrograph magnifies the inner hair cells of the human ear 1,705 times.

The vibrations travel through the auditory canal to the eardrum; to the malleus, which touches the eardrum; and then to the incus and the stapes. The stapes touches the oval window. The oval window sets the fluid in the cochlea in motion. Stimulated by the fluid motion, hair cells in the cochlea generate nerve impulses that travel along the *auditory nerve* to the auditory center in the temporal lobe of the brain. Exactly how vibrations are transformed into impulses is not clear.

Hearing loss due to disease or injury of the auditory nerve or cochlea is called *nerve deafness*. It is the most common cause of total and permanent hearing loss. Deafness resulting from interference as vibrations pass to the inner ear is called *conductive deafness*. This condition may be caused by several problems, including excess earwax, infection, swelling and closing of the passage, rupture and inflammation of the eardrum, or immobility of the stapes due to bone overgrowth. Conductive deafness generally can be treated.

How You Balance Yourself Fluid in the semicircular canals flows when you change the angle of your head. A different canal in each ear is affected by any particular movement. For example, a movement to the right causes fluid in the right ear to flow toward the hair cells. As a result, many impulses are sent to the cerebellum from the right ear. At the same time, the movement causes fluid in the left ear to flow away from the hair cells. Few impulses are then sent to the brain from the left ear. The cerebellum interprets the two sets of impulses so you know which way your head is turned.

The **saccule** (SAK yool) and **utricle** (YOO trih kuhl), the two sections of the vestibule, also help with balance. They are lined with hair cells covered by a gelatin-like membrane embedded with small mineral grains. Gravity pulls the grains down onto the hair cells, causing them to generate impulses. The cerebellum interprets the direction of gravity and lets you know the position of your head.

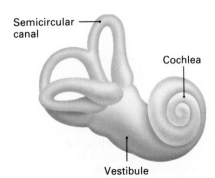

Semicircular canal

Cochlea

Vestibule

Figure 46–8. The organs of balance are located in the inner ear. Stimulation of the hair cells in the saccule, utricle, and semicircular canals provides information to the brain on changes in the rate as well as the direction of motion.

> **Thinking Critically**

Section Review

1. **Identifying Function**   How does the iris function?
2. **Comparing Ideas**   How do rods and cones differ?
3. **Identifying Relationships**   How does yawning help relieve ear discomfort in an airplane passenger?
4. **Identifying Information**   What part of the inner ear has sound receptors?
5. **Inferring Relationships**   How would destruction of the right optic area of the brain affect a person's vision?

Smell, Taste, and Touch

Smell and taste are closely associated senses. The fact that a stuffy nose makes food seem tasteless demonstrates the close relationship between these senses. Smell and taste seem to operate more simply than sight and hearing, but biologists do not yet know precisely how the receptors for smell and taste discriminate among various chemicals.

The skin, the largest organ of the body, contains several types of receptors. These receptors register touch, pressure, pain, heat, and cold. The receptors for these sensations vary in number and location over the body.

Section Objectives

- *State* one hypothesis of how smells are differentiated.
- *Explain* what taste buds are and how they may operate.
- *Identify* the various types of sense receptors in the skin.

46.5 The Nose

The *nose,* the chief sense organ of smell, contains receptors embedded in mucous membrane. About 50 million of these special cells, called **olfactory receptors,** are located in each nasal passage. Airborne substances dissolve in the mucus that covers the olfactory receptors. The receptors produce nerve impulses that travel through *olfactory nerves* to the *olfactory lobe* in the cerebral cortex.

Some biologists think that the perception of smell occurs when a specialized molecule on the receptor surface reacts with a specific chemical in inhaled air. The reaction generates an impulse that results in a particular smell. Other scientists believe that the outline, or shape, of a molecule is the cause of its particular odor. They think that a molecule of a specific shape fits into an olfactory receptor that will accept only that shape, just as a lock works with one key. These researchers believe that the thousands of odors humans can distinguish are simply combinations of seven basic odors.

46.6 The Tongue

The *tongue* is the major sense organ of taste. The chemical receptors for taste are clusters of sensory cells located in the **taste buds.** Each taste bud consists of about 40 receptor and supporting cells and an opening called the *taste pore.* The taste buds lie in bunches called *papillae,* which are visible as the bumps on your tongue. Although most of a person's 10,000 taste buds are on the tongue, a few also exist on the roof of the mouth and in the throat.

Taste buds produce one or a combination of four main taste sensations: sweet, sour, bitter, and salty. A receptor cell may be

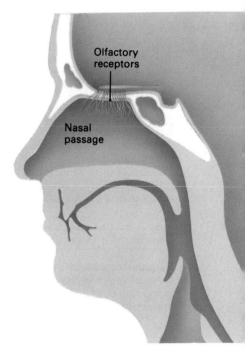

Figure 46–9. The illustration above shows the location of the olfactory receptors in the human nasal passage.

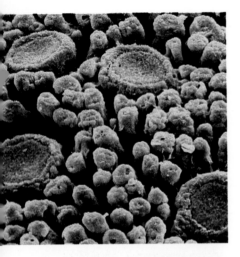

stimulated by only one taste, but most cells are stimulated by two or more tastes. This combination of different tastes may be what produces the wide variety of flavors you enjoy.

Like smell, taste depends upon chemical reactions that take place only in solution. Saliva constantly bathes taste buds, reaching receptor cells through the taste pores. Food molecules also enter the taste pores. The chemical reactions that take place somehow cause the receptor cells to generate nerve impulses. The impulses travel through three different nerves to the taste center in the cerebral cortex. No one knows precisely how taste receptors function. Some researchers think that sensory cells have sites that accept specific chemical molecules. Other researchers think that, as with smell, the shape of a molecule determines its taste. Molecules of a certain shape, they think, activate specific sites on a taste bud to produce one taste.

46.7 The Skin

The skin contains five distinct senses, most with their own type of receptor. These five senses are *touch, pressure, pain, heat,* and *cold.* Impulses travel from the various sense receptors to different areas of the sensory cortex.

Touch receptors are the ends of certain nerve fibers. Many touch receptors are located at the base of hairs and generate impulses when the hairs move even slightly. However, touch is most sensitive in the fingertips, palms, lips, and other places where hair is not present. Some touch receptors are sensitive to deep pressure, while others are sensitive to lighter pressure.

Unlike the other senses of touch, the sense of pain has no specialized receptors. Pain receptors are free ends of unmyelinated nerve fibers. Pain appears to stem from a variety of stimuli. Some parts of the body are almost pain-free. Other parts may sense only one type of pain. Sensitivity to pain may also be related to other body conditions, such as mental attitude.

Temperature receptors may be either bare nerve endings or specially shaped cells. Different types of receptors detect heat and cold.

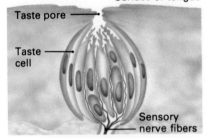

Figure 46–10. The electron micrograph (top) shows the papillae on the surface of the human tongue (× 240). The cross section of a human taste bud (bottom) shows the location of taste receptor cells and the nerve fibers that transmit the sensations.

Reading Critically

Summarizing Ideas What types of sense receptors are in the skin? Why are they important?

Thinking Critically

Section Review

1. **Identifying Function** What is the function of olfactory receptors?
2. **Analyzing Conclusions** Why is moisture necessary for smell and taste?
3. **Evaluating Relationships** Why might some people be less sensitive to pain than others?

INVESTIGATION 46:
How Does the Brain Interpret Information from the Eyes?

Objectives
- To *observe* and *analyze* the functions of the retina
- To *record, interpret*, and *evaluate* observations

Materials
unlined 3 x 5 index card, plain white paper, pencil

Prelab Preparation
1. Review the structure of the human eye.
2. Describe the function of rods and cones.
3. Describe the location and function of the optic nerves.
4. Describe the neural pathways involved in seeing.
5. On an unlined index card, draw an **X** that is about the size of the one in this sentence about one inch from the left-hand edge. Draw an **O** that is about the same size about three inches to the right of the X.

Inquiry: Exploration
6. Hold your marked index card in front of you at arm's length. Close your right eye and stare at the circle. Move the card slowly toward you while continuing to stare at the circle. Record your observations, noting the distance of the card from your eye when the X disappears.
7. Roll a sheet of plain white paper into a tube about one inch in diameter. Look through the tube with your left eye. Place your right hand, palm facing you, beside the tube. While looking through the tube with your left eye, look at your open palm with your right eye. *Why does a "hole" appear in your palm?* Repeat the procedure looking through the tube with your right eye and using your left hand.
8. Using the picture of the tiger and the cage, place the long edge of an index card between the tiger and the cage. Next, place the tip of your nose against the upper edge of the card. Look at the cage

with one eye and the tiger with the other. Record your observations.

9. Place a piece of plain white paper in front of you. Stare at the black dot on the drawing of the heart on this page for about 20 seconds. Then, immediately stare at the white paper for about 10 seconds. Record your observations.

Analysis
1. **Analyzing Relationships** What is the relationship between the disappearance of the X on the index card and the optic nerve?
2. **Analyzing Theory** How does the theory of color vision help to explain the afterimage observed with the heart illustration?
3. **Inferring Relationships** How can the phenomena that you observed with the tiger and the cage and the heart afterimage explain how you see motion in a movie?

Chapter 46 Review

Summary

The most familiar senses are sight, hearing, smell, taste, and touch. Special receptors receive stimuli in the form of light, chemicals, temperature, vibrations, and pressure. The sense organs change the energy from the stimuli into impulses that are transmitted to the brain.

Rod and cone cells in the retina of the eye make sight possible. The ear is the organ of hearing and balance. Sound vibrations are changed into nerve impulses in the cochlea. Balance is achieved by means of the semicircular canals and the vestibule.

Smell occurs through chemical reactions in the olfactory receptors, and taste is dependent upon chemical receptors in the taste buds.

The skin contains receptors for touch, pressure, pain, and temperature. These receptors are distributed throughout the body.

BioTerms

aqueous humor (**746**)	lacrimal gland (**745**)	semicircular	tympanic
auditory canal (**748**)	lens (**746**)	canal (**749**)	cavity (**748**)
choroid (**745**)	malleus (**749**)	stapes (**749**)	utricle (**750**)
cochlea (**749**)	olfactory	taste bud (**751**)	vestibule (**749**)
cone (**746**)	receptor (**751**)	transducer (**743**)	vitreous humor (**745**)
conjunctiva (**745**)	oval window (**749**)		
cornea (**745**)	pinna (**748**)		
eardrum (**748**)	pupil (**745**)		
Eustachian tube (**748**)	retina (**746**)		
fovea (**746**)	rod (**746**)		
hair cell (**743**)	round window (**749**)		
incus (**749**)	saccule (**750**)		
iris (**745**)	sclera (**745**)		

For each pair of terms, explain the differences in their meanings.

1. aqueous humor, vitreous humor
2. rods, cones
3. malleus, incus
4. olfactory receptor, taste bud

BioQuiz   (Write all answers on a separate sheet of paper.)

Completion

1. The _____ tube helps to equalize air pressure in the middle ear.
2. Ability to see height, width, and depth of an object is called _____ vision.
3. Pressure in the eye caused by the inability of the aqueous humor to drain into blood vessels can cause _____ .
4. Hearing receptors react to stimuli from _____ .
5. The tissue layer that forms the "white" of the eye is called the _____ .

Multiple Choice

6. Taste and smell would be impossible without   a) cones.   b) hair cells.   c) rods.   d) transducers.
7. The saccule and utricle are necessary for the sense of   a) sight.   b) taste.   c) balance.   d) touch.
8. Physicians can learn about a person's physical condition by examining the   a) retina.   b) pinna.   c) pupil.   d) cone.
9. Bunches of taste buds are   a) pinna.   b) utricle.   c) sclera.   d) papillae.

10. Mucus that lubricates the eye is secreted by the a) choroid. b) conjunctiva. c) lacrimal gland. d) vitreous humor.
11. Where in the eye are the sharpest images formed? a) the lens b) the retina c) the pupil d) the fovea
12. What part of the ear secretes ear wax? a) the auditory canal b) the tympanic cavity c) the Eustachian tube d) the cochlea
13. Which place is most sensitive to touch? a) the base of a hair b) the kneecap c) the fingertip d) the ear lobe
14. Because they change one form of energy into another form, sense organs are a) lacrimal glands. b) transducers. c) hollow. d) round.
15. The specialized sensory cells for seeing color are a) olfactory receptors. b) cones. c) rods. d) chemoreceptors.

16. How do muscle spindles operate as sensory receptors?
17. What are the major types of stimuli that activate sense organs? Which sense organs react to each type?
18. How is pressure on the eardrum converted to sound?
19. What controls the amount of light entering the eye? Explain how.
20. Nerve impulses being alike, how do they result in various sensations?

Application/Critical Thinking

1. **Analyzing Experiments** Test the skin for sensitivity to various sensations. You might use velvet or sandpaper for touch, a piece of ice for cold, and a metal rod slightly heated in warm water for heat. Test the same skin areas for all sensations and record which areas of the body seem most sensitive to certain stimuli.
2. **Inferring Conclusions** When driving, it is dangerous to remain in the passing lane just behind the automobile that you are passing. Obtain a driver's manual and find out where this danger zone is. Explain why this zone is dangerous.
3. **Synthesizing Conclusions** The sense of smell results from chemicals in the vapors that reach the nose from a distance. The sense of taste results from chemicals that are in solution in the mouth. Which receptors, smell or taste, are more sensitive? Explain your answer.

Cross-Discipline Connection

Biology and Optometry   Invite an optometrist to talk to your classmates about his or her profession. Ask the optometrist to describe how corrective lenses are made. Write a report on common vision impairments that can be corrected by wearing glasses or contact lenses and those vision impairments that require some other means of correction.

Discovery Through Reading

The article "The Smell Survey Results," *National Geographic* (October 1987): 514–525, summarizes the results of an international smell survey. According to the results of this survey, which have the better sense of smell, men or women?

Hormonal Control

Outline

A pilot responds quickly under stress

Focus

The *endocrine system,* like the nervous system, regulates body activities. However, the endocrine system uses chemical messengers that travel through the bloodstream and have effects on specific cells called *target cells.* The effects of these chemical messengers are usually more long-lasting than the effects of nerve impulses.

- *What is the advantage of having chemical messengers circulating in the bloodstream?*

- *Chemical messengers help the body function effectively in stressful situations. What body functions must be operating at high levels in the pilot shown in the photograph?*

The Endocrine Glands

The body contains many *glands*. Glands are cells, groups of cells, or organs that produce and secrete substances. **Exocrine glands,** such as sweat glands and digestive glands, secrete their products through tubes, or ducts. **Endocrine glands,** often called *ductless glands,* release their products directly into the bloodstream. *Endocrine glands produce powerful chemicals called* **hormones,** *which help regulate the activities of body tissues and organs.* Each hormone acts on a specific tissue or organ; that tissue or organ is the hormone's **target.**

47.1 The Thyroid

The **thyroid gland,** located in the neck on the trachea, secretes *thyroxine.* Thyroxine controls metabolic activities, including the production of proteins and ATP. Because thyroxine influences protein production, it affects the growth rate of children. This hormone is also necessary for the proper development of the nervous system.

Iodine is necessary for the production of thyroxine. A person needs 1 mg of iodine each week. Eating a moderate amount of iodized salt usually meets that need. Insufficient iodine may cause the thyroid gland to enlarge, a condition called *goiter.* Frequently a person with goiter also suffers from *hypothyroidism,* a lack of thyroxine. The result is a low metabolic rate. In adults the symptoms are low body temperature, sluggishness, weight gain, and excess fluid in the body. In infants hypothyroidism may cause *cretinism.* The effects of cretinism include mental retardation and abnormal bone growth. *Hyperthyroidism,* or an excess of thyroxine, causes a higher-than-normal metabolic rate. The symptoms of hyperthyroidism include weight loss, muscle weakness, excessive sweating, increased heartbeat rate and blood pressure, nervousness, and bulging eyes.

47.2 The Parathyroids

On the back of the thyroid gland are four tiny **parathyroid glands.** They secrete *PTH (parathyroid hormone),* which regulates the levels of calcium ions and phosphate ions in the blood. These minerals are necessary for proper bone development and for normal functioning of muscles and nerve cells. Too little calcium can make nerve cells so unstable that they send impulses without being stimulated. The result is uncontrollable muscle contractions. If muscles remain contracted, a person

- *Distinguish* between exocrine glands and endocrine glands.
- *Identify* the major endocrine glands and the hormones they produce.
- *List* the major effects of some hormones.
- *Describe* how the hypothalamus affects the anterior pituitary gland.
- *Explain* what prostaglandins are.

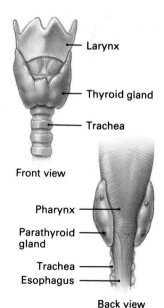

Larynx

Thyroid gland

Trachea

Front view

Pharynx

Parathyroid gland

Trachea

Esophagus

Back view

Figure 47–1. The thyroid and parathyroid glands are located on the trachea.

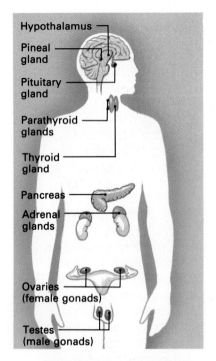

Figure 47–2. The illustration above shows the location of the major endocrine glands in the human body.

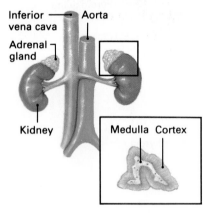

Figure 47–3. The location of the adrenal gland and its two parts (inset) are shown above.

may die because breathing stops. The calcium level sometimes is too high. Nerves and muscles then fail to respond to stimuli. Reflexes are slow, and muscle contractions are weak.

47.3 The Adrenals

An **adrenal** (uh DREE nuhl) **gland** is located on top of each kidney. Each adrenal gland has two parts. Each part functions as a separate endocrine gland. The inner part, called the **adrenal medulla,** secretes **epinephrine** (ehp uh NEHF rihn) and **norepinephrine.** These hormones produce the same effects as the sympathetic nervous system. They thus help the body respond to stress. For example, they increase blood pressure and heartbeat and breathing rates, dilate the pupils, and inhibit digestion. They also increase metabolism, sometimes as much as 100 percent.

The outer part of the adrenal gland is the **adrenal cortex,** which secretes more than 50 hormones. All belong to a group called **corticoids.** Among the corticoids are *aldosterone; hydrocortisone,* also called *cortisol;* and *androgens.* Aldosterone affects water and salt balance by controlling the reabsorption of sodium and potassium ions in the kidneys. Hydrocortisone controls the breakdown of proteins and fats into glucose, inhibits glucose uptake by cells, and aids in healing. Androgens are sex hormones. They regulate development of secondary sex characteristics.

A lack of corticoids may result in *Addison's disease.* The symptoms of this disease include low blood pressure, darkened skin, dehydration, a low level of sugar and sodium ions in the blood, and a high blood level of potassium ions. A victim will die within a few days if not treated with corticoids. Oversecretion of corticoids may result in *Cushing's disease,* characterized by high blood pressure, fat deposits in the face and back, and accumulation of tissue fluids. Excessive secretion of androgens may result in early sexual development in males and excessive facial hair and a deep voice in females.

47.4 The Pancreas

The *pancreas* is an exocrine gland that produces digestive enzymes. However, it also has special cells called the **islets of Langerhans** that function as an endocrine gland. They secrete insulin and glucagon. **Insulin** is a hormone that lowers the level of glucose in the blood. It does so by stimulating the uptake of glucose by body cells and the formation of excess glucose into glycogen in the liver and muscles. *Glucagon* triggers the breakdown of glycogen to glucose when the body needs more energy.

Prostaglandins, fatty acids that behave as hormones, are among the most powerful biological chemicals. Some scientists say they are not hormones, however, because they are produced by almost every body cell, not just by glands.

Prostaglandins appear to regulate the organs and tissues in which they are produced. They are secreted only when needed and last less than a minute before enzymes break them down. In that time, however, they may affect circulation, digestion, respiration, reproduction, and possibly even nerve control.

Scientists know some of the effects of prostaglandins but they still are not sure exactly how these chemicals operate. For example, they know that the cells lining blood vessels produce a prostaglandin called *prostacyclin.* Prostacyclin relaxes blood vessels and suppresses agglutination, or clumping, of platelets. Another prostaglandin, *thromboxane,* is produced by platelets. It constricts blood vessels and promotes agglutination. The two prostaglandins must remain balanced to assure proper blood circulation. If a blood vessel is damaged, prostacyclin production may be reduced in that area. Thromboxane can then cause the blood vessel to constrict and platelets to agglutinate there. Some scientists feel that this effect of thromboxane may be one of the major causes of strokes and heart attacks.

Prostaglandins secreted by the uterus cause uterine contractions. An excess secretion of prostaglandins from the uterus can bring on menstrual cramps.

Prostaglandins also increase the fluid and heat in joints. As a result, they contribute to arthritis pain and inflammation. Their role in arthritis has helped explain the mystery surrounding aspirin. For decades aspirin was known to provide relief to people who suffer from arthritis, but no one understood why. Scientists now know that aspirin inhibits the production of some prostaglandins and thus has a soothing effect. Prostaglandin research is under way in other areas, such as cancer and diabetes.

■ **Inferring Relationships** How might prostaglandins be involved in excessive bleeding from cuts or scratches?

In the absence of insulin, glucose cannot enter body cells. As a result, the cells use their own proteins and fat for energy. The level of glucose in the blood then becomes abnormally high. This condition, called *diabetes mellitus,* is the third major cause of death in the United States. Without proper treatment it can lead to heart disease, stroke, kidney failure, severe nerve damage, or blindness. Diabetes may also result in infections so severe that limb amputation is necessary.

The two chief forms of diabetes are Type 1, or insulin-dependent, diabetes and Type 2, or non-insulin-dependent, diabetes. In Type 1 diabetes, the islets of Langerhans produce too little or no insulin. Some researchers suspect a virus may be

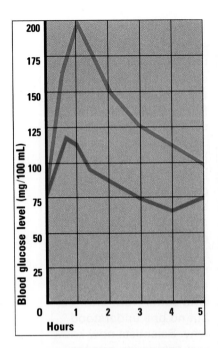

Figure 47–4. This graph compares the levels of glucose in the bloodstreams of a normal individual (blue) and a diabetic (red) during the five-hour period immediately following a typical meal.

Reading Critically

Analyzing Function In what way do gonads function as two organs?

---

involved in Type 1 diabetes. Type 1 usually first appears in people under 20 years of age and can be controlled by strict diet and daily injections of insulin. Approximately 85 percent of all diabetics suffer from Type 2 diabetes. Type 2 generally first appears in people over 40 years of age. These diabetics may have normal or even high levels of insulin, but their bodies cannot use the hormone. The causes of Type 2 diabetes are believed to be a shortage of insulin receptors on body cells or a breakdown of the immune system, which causes the body to become insulin-resistant. Heredity also appears to be a factor in both types of diabetes. Type 2 diabetes can generally be controlled through diet.

Excessive levels of insulin in the blood lead to *hypoglycemia,* a condition in which the level of glucose in the blood drops. Body cells then cannot obtain enough energy. Because brain cells need a constant supply of glucose, a victim may lose consciousness due to the lack of glucose. A diet high in protein and low in carbohydrates can help control hypoglycemia.

47.5 The Gonads

Gonads, the gamete-producing organs of the reproductive system, also produce and secrete hormones. The female gonads secrete estrogens that influence the development of female secondary sex characteristics. Among these are wider hips, enlarged breasts, and rounded body contours. The male gonads produce androgens that stimulate development of the male secondary sex characteristics. These include a deepened voice and enlarged muscles and bones. All these sex hormones play roles in reproduction, which is discussed in Chapter 48.

47.6 The Pituitary

The **pituitary** (pih TOO uh tehr ee) **gland,** located at the base of the brain, is about the size and shape of a kidney bean. It has two major sections, the anterior lobe and the posterior lobe.

The *anterior lobe* produces at least six hormones. Four are **tropic hormones**—that is, hormones that affect the secretions of other glands. Two tropic hormones, *FSH (follicle stimulating hormone)* and *LH (luteinizing hormone),* act on the gonads. These hormones will be discussed further in Chapter 48. The other two tropic hormones are *TSH (thyroid stimulating hormone)* and *ACTH (adrenocorticotropic hormone).* TSH stimulates the thyroid gland to secrete thyroxine, and ACTH affects the adrenal cortex. The anterior lobe also secretes *somatotropin,* or *growth hormone (GH).* Somatotropin has many effects on

Table 47–1: Hormones and Their Functions

Gland	Hormone	Target	Functions
Pituitary (anterior lobe)	Growth hormone (GH, somatotropin)	All cells	Maintains protein production, releases fats and glucose
	Thyroid-stimulating hormone (TSH)	Thyroid gland	Stimulates production and secretion of thyroxine
	Adrenocorticotropic hormone (ACTH)	Adrenal cortex	Stimulates production and secretion of corticoids
	Follicle-stimulating hormone (FSH)	Gonads	Plays a role in female monthly cycle, the production of female sex hormones and male gametes
	Luteinizing hormone (LH)	Gonads	Plays a role in female monthly cycle, stimulates production of sex hormones
	Prolactin	Mammary glands	Stimulates growth of gland and production of milk
Hypothalamus	Releasing hormones	Pituitary	Stimulates release of GH, TSH, LH, FSH, ACTH, and prolactin
	Inhibiting hormones	Pituitary	Inhibits release of GH and prolactin
	Oxytocin	Uterus, mammary glands	Stimulates muscle contractions during childbirth, milk release
	Antidiuretic hormone (ADH, vasopressin)	Kidneys	Controls water reabsorption
Thyroid	Thyroxine	All body cells	Stimulates metabolic rate
Parathyroid	Parathyroid hormone (PTH)	Bone	Controls level of calcium ions and potassium ions
Adrenal cortex	Aldosterone	Kidneys	Controls reabsorption of sodium, stimulates excretion of potassium
	Hydrocortisone (cortisol)	Liver, various cells	Inhibits glucose uptake, aids healing, reduces inflammation
	Androgen	Male gonads	Stimulates development of male secondary sex characteristics
Adrenal medulla	Epinephrine, norepinephrine	Various cells	Controls stress reactions: increases heart and breathing rates, raises blood pressure and glucose level, inhibits digestion
Pancreas (islets of Langerhans)	Insulin Glucagon	Liver, muscle	Stimulates glucose uptake Triggers breakdown of glycogen into glucose
Female gonads (ovaries)	Progesterone, estrogen	Female sex organs	Controls female secondary sex characteristic development, female sexual functions
Male gonads (testes)	Testosterone	Male sex organs	Controls development of male gametes and male secondary sex characteristics

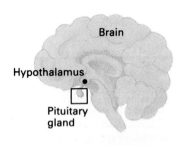

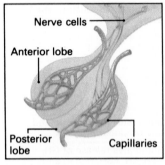

Figure 47–5. The illustration shows the location of the pituitary gland in the brain (top) and a closeup view of the gland (bottom).

Thinking Critically

metabolism. It stimulates bone and muscle growth and helps control the use of glucose and fatty acids for energy. *Prolactin,* another hormone of the anterior lobe, stimulates the mammary glands to produce milk after the birth of a child.

The posterior lobe of the pituitary does not produce any hormones, but it stores two hormones produced by the hypothalamus. They are *antidiuretic hormone (ADH)* and *oxytocin.* ADH, also called *vasopressin,* keeps the blood volume constant by controlling reabsorption of water in the kidneys. Oxytocin stimulates the contraction of uterine muscles during childbirth and the release of milk from the breasts after childbirth. Prolactin and oxytocin have no known function in males.

Most disorders associated with the pituitary gland involve somatotropin. An excess during childhood results in *gigantism,* or excessive growth. One person with the disorder grew to 2.7 m (8 ft. 11 in.). An excess during adulthood results in *acromegaly,* in which the hands, feet, and skull increase in size. Too little somatotropin during childhood results in *dwarfism,* characterized by a short body but otherwise normal proportions and normal mental and sexual development.

47.7 The Hypothalamus

The *hypothalamus,* which is a part of the brain, may be considered the master switchboard of the endocrine system. It links the endocrine system with the nervous system. The nervous system feeds information from the entire body into the hypothalamus. Based on that information, the hypothalamus then sends signals in the form of tropic hormones to stimulate or inhibit hormone secretion by the pituitary gland. At least nine such hormones have been identified. The hormones that stimulate secretions are called *releasing hormones.* Releasing hormones trigger secretion of TSH, GH, LH, FSH, ACTH, and prolactin. Hormones that slow down secretions are *inhibiting hormones.* The hypothalamus secretes inhibitors for GH, TSH, and prolactin. It also produces ADH and oxytocin and signals their release from the posterior pituitary.

Section Review

1. **Comparing Ideas**   How do exocrine glands and endocrine glands differ?
2. **Analyzing Relationships**   What happens when the body has too little insulin?
3. **Evaluating Conclusions**   What would happen if the hypothalamus stopped functioning?

Endocrine System Regulation

The endocrine system and the nervous system together control other body systems. However, the endocrine system also controls itself.

47.8 Feedback

The endocrine system controls itself through a process called **negative feedback.** This process is similar to the way a thermostat regulates a household furnace. When the temperature falls below the thermostat setting, the furnace switches on and begins producing heat. When the temperature reaches the thermostat setting, the furnace switches off. *Similarly, the level of a hormone in the blood turns its own production off and on.*

Negative feedback controls the thyroxine level in the blood. The hypothalamus plays the role of the thermostat. The hypothalamus has cells that detect the presence of thyroxine in the blood. When the thyroxine level is low, the hypothalamus secretes a releasing hormone that stimulates the pituitary to secrete

Section Objectives

- *Identify* the two general types of hormones.
- *Explain* how hormones affect their targets.
- *Describe* how a negative feedback circuit works.

To learn more about the interactive operations of the endocrine system, see page 765.

BIOLOGY AND YOU:

Estrogen by Patch

The period of time when a woman's menstrual cycle ceases is called *menopause.* After experiencing menopause, some women may suffer from a bone disorder called *osteoporosis,* which is characterized by a decrease in bone mass. The development of osteoporosis may be influenced by a drop in the level of the ovarian hormone estrogen that occurs after menopause.

Until recently, doctors administered oral doses of estrogen. However,

estrogen taken orally is altered in the digestive process and the products can cause headaches, nausea, and a risk of elevated blood pressure and gallbladder disease.

Researchers have developed a porous skin patch called a *transdermal patch* that releases estrogen through the skin directly into the bloodstream.

One advantage of the transdermal patch is that it bypasses the digestive system and thus reduces the side effects associated

with oral hormones. Also, since the transdermal patch releases hormones gradually, it mimics the body's natural hormone secretion.

TSH. TSH causes the thyroid to secrete thyroxine. When the
thyroxine level returns to normal, the hypothalamus stops secreting the releasing hormone. As a result of this feedback
mechanism, the pituitary stops secreting TSH, and the thyroid
slows down secretion of thyroxine.

47.9 How Hormones Act

There are two types of hormones: **steroids,** which are fatlike
organic compounds, and **protein hormones.** Sex hormones and
corticoids are steroids. All others are protein hormones.

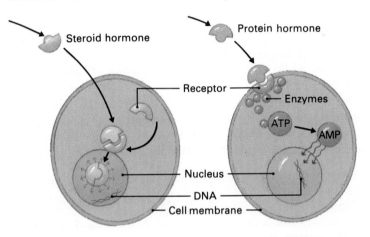

Biofact

Q: *How does the body rid itself of hormones?*

A: Excess hormones are inactivated by the liver and kidneys and may be excreted. A kidney or liver disorder may cause problems resulting from hormone buildup in the blood.

Figure 47–6. Steroid hormones (left) act directly within the cell nucleus, after passing through the cell membrane and binding with receptor molecules. Protein hormones (right) combine with receptor molecules at the boundary of the cell and work by activating enzymes inside the cell.

Steroids and protein hormones produce their effects differently. A steroid passes through the target cell membrane. It
combines with a receptor molecule and moves into the cell nucleus. There it helps determine the manufacture of specific proteins. Protein hormones affect their target cells through a two-
step procedure called a "two-messenger" system. The first
messenger, the hormone, combines with a receptor on the target
cell membrane. This combination activates an enzyme on the
membrane's inside wall. The enzyme helps change ATP into
cyclic adenosine monophosphate, or **cyclic AMP.** Cyclic AMP
triggers enzymes that bring about changes initiated by the original hormone. Thus, cyclic AMP is called the *second messenger*.

Reading Critically

Interpreting Ideas Why could steroids be described as direct-action hormones?

To find out about the controversy surrounding the use of synthetic steroids by athletes, see page 812.

Section Review

1. **Analyzing Ideas** How does negative feedback operate within the endocrine system?
2. **Listing Ideas** What are two types of hormones?
3. **Inferring Conclusions** Why is the cyclic AMP called the second messenger?

Thinking Critically

INVESTIGATION 47:
How Does the Endocrine System Work?

Objectives
- To *develop* an awareness of the principal hormones and their functions
- To *relate* endocrine glands and hormones to their target organs

Materials
unlined paper, colored pencils, ruler, reference books

Prelab Preparation
1. How do endocrine glands and exocrine glands differ?
2. Explain how a hormone affects the cells of a target organ.
3. Explain negative feedback.
4. On a sheet of unlined paper, copy the hormones, endocrine glands, target organs and target cells just as they are arranged at the bottom of this page. Be sure to leave space between the rows of terms and between the terms in each row.

Inquiry: Exploration
5. Use a black pencil to draw a box around each endocrine gland.
6. Draw a black triangle around each target that is not also an endocrine gland.
7. Draw a black circle around each hormone.
8. Use a green pencil to draw an arrow from each endocrine gland to the hormone or hormones that it produces.
9. Use a blue pencil to draw an arrow from each hormone to its target.
10. Tropic hormones stimulate their target glands to produce hormones. The hypothalamus detects increases in the levels of these hormones through the process of negative feedback. Draw a red arrow from each of these target glands to the hypothalamus.
11. The secretion of two pituitary hormones is regulated by inhibiting hormones as well as by releasing hormones. Draw an orange arrow from these hormones to the hypothalamus.

Analysis
1. **Analyzing Information** What does the diagram show about the interactions that occur in the endocrine system?
2. **Making Inferences** What endocrine glands might be malfunctioning in an individual who has very low levels of hydrocortisone?
3. **Making Inferences** How would damage to the pituitary affect the endocrine system?

Hypothalamus

Releasing   Inhibiting
hormones   hormones

Pituitary

TSH	ACTH	FSH	LH	GH	Prolactin
Thyroid	Adrenals	Gonads	Body cells		Mammary glands
Thyroxine	Aldosterone	Hydrocortisone	Androgens		
Body cells	Kidneys	Liver	Gonads		

Chapter 47 Review

Summary

Hormones secreted by endocrine glands control body functions such as metabolism, water and mineral balance, glucose balance and storage, muscle contraction, impulse transmission, and reproduction. The major endocrine glands are the thyroid, parathyroids, adrenals, pancreas, gonads, pituitary, and hypothalamus.

Hormones act upon specific tissues and organs, or targets. Tropic hormones affect other endocrine glands, causing them to secrete hormones.

The endocrine system regulates itself through negative feedback. In the process of negative feedback, the blood level of a hormone causes a gland to either stop or start secretion of that hormone.

Hormones are either steroids or protein hormones. Steroids affect cells by passing through the cell membrane and moving to the nucleus. In the nucleus the steroid influences protein production. Protein hormones attach to receptors on the cell membrane, where they activate an enzyme that helps convert ATP to cyclic AMP. Cyclic AMP then stimulates enzymes that bring about the changes initiated by the original hormone.

BioTerms

adrenal cortex (**758**)
adrenal gland (**758**)
adrenal
    medulla (**758**)
corticoid (**758**)
cyclic AMP (**764**)
endocrine
    gland (**757**)
epinephrine (**758**)
exocrine gland (**757**)
gonad (**760**)

hormone (**757**)
insulin (**758**)
islets of
    Langerhans (**758**)
negative
    feedback (**763**)
norepinephrine (**758**)
parathyroid
    gland (**757**)
pituitary gland (**760**)
protein hormone (**764**)

steroid (**764**)
target (**757**)
thyroid gland (**757**)

tropic
    hormone (**760**)

For each pair of terms, explain the differences in their meanings.

1. adrenal cortex, adrenal medulla
2. endocrine gland, exocrine gland
3. protein hormone, tropic hormone
4. epinephrine, norepinephrine

BioQuiz   (Write all answers on a separate sheet of paper.)

Completion

1. The endocrine system controls itself through a process called _____ .
2. The body's water balance is governed by the _____ .
3. Improper functioning of the _____ affects muscle contractions.
4. Endocrine glands produce _____ that help regulate the activities of the body.
5. The _____ are special cells in the pancreas that function as an endocrine gland.

Multiple Choice

6. Hypoglycemia is a condition in which excessive levels of _____ are present in the blood.   a) adrenalin   b) thyroxine   c) insulin   d) cortisone
7. Mammary glands produce milk in response to   a) insulin.   b) thyroxin.   c) prolactin.   d) TSH.
8. A lack of the hormone insulin may lead to   a) giantism.   b) overweight.   c) underweight.   d) diabetes mellitus.

9. Hormones that help the body handle stress are secreted by the a) adrenal cortex. b) adrenal medulla. c) thyroid. d) pituitary.
10. Dwarfism results from too little of the hormone _____ during childhood. a) cortisone b) thyroxine c) insulin d) somatotropin
11. Which of the following is an ingredient in the production of thyroxine? a) oxytocin b) iodine c) prolactin d) luteinizing hormone
12. Which gland connects the endocrine system to the nervous system? a) adrenal gland b) thyroid gland c) pituitary gland d) hypothalamus
13. What hormone can cause excessive hair and a deep voice in females? a) androgen b) estrogen c) cortisol d) luteinizing hormone
14. Which of the following is not linked to prostaglandin levels? a) agglutination of platelets b) arthritis pain and joint inflammation c) kidney failure d) All of the choices are correct.
15. All hormones of the adrenal cortex are a) sex hormones. b) tropic hormones. c) growth hormones. d) steroids.

Writing Critically

16. What is the difference between Type 1 and Type 2 diabetes?
17. How does the hypothalamus link the nervous and endocrine systems?
18. How does the two-messenger system of hormone activity work?
19. In what way does the hypothalamus regulate the body's water balance?
20. How do tropic hormones affect the endocrine system? Give an example.

Application/Critical Thinking

1. **Evaluating Ideas** Give one example of how the endocrine system helps maintain homeostasis.
2. **Diagramming Information** Diagram a feedback loop showing the relationship between the hypothalamus, the pituitary gland, and one other gland of the endocrine system.
3. **Analyzing Conclusions** The parathyroid gland controls the release of calcium from the bones into the bloodstream. Occasionally, tumors affect the parathyroid gland so that too much calcium is released from the bones. What do you think are some of the results of such an occurrence?
4. **Analyzing Ideas** The pituitary and hypothalamus are connected. What function of the pituitary suggests that this gland is an extension of the brain?

Cross-Discipline Connection

Biology and Chemistry Do library research to find out why taking insulin orally does not help diabetics. Why must it be injected?

Discovery Through Reading

The article "A User's Guide to Hormones," *Newsweek* (January 12, 1987):50–59, provides an overview of the hormones in the body and how they affect our lives. In 1970 scientists identified about 20 hormones. How many hormones have now been identified? What is the current definition of a hormone? What discovery leads to the conclusion that the brain is a gland?

48

Reproduction and Development

Outline

Parents with a newborn infant

Focus

Worldwide, about 141 children are born each minute, 8,500 each hour, and 74 million each year. By the time of birth, the single fertilized egg has undergone many divisions and developed for nine months within the mother. After birth, the child continues its development. Like all mammals, humans reproduce sexually. The special structures in the male and female make up the *reproductive system*.

■ *When does the process of development in humans end?*

■ *What are the advantages of such a long development period within the mother?*

The Reproductive Systems

The reproductive organs in males and females are called *go-nads*. Gonads are present at birth. They develop fully during **puberty,** a period during which boys and girls mature physically and sexually. Females usually complete puberty during the early teen years. In males, puberty generally occurs about two years later. Following puberty, gonads produce sex cells called **gametes** (GAM eets).

48.1 The Male Reproductive System

The male gonads, the **testes,** *are a pair of organs with two primary functions: to produce male gametes, called sperm, and to produce male hormones.* The testes are suspended below the abdomen in an external sac called the *scrotum,* where the temperature is lower than normal body temperature. The lower temperature is necessary for the production of healthy sperm. Inside the testes are hundreds of tightly packed, coiled tubes, called *seminiferous tubules,* where sperm are produced.

Sperm are carried from the seminiferous tubules to a coiled tube called the *epididymis* (ehp uh DIHD ih muhs). In the epididymis, sperm mature and become motile and then move into the *vas deferens.* Muscular contractions, called *ejaculations,* force sperm from the vas deferens through the *urethra,* in the *penis,* to the outside of the body.

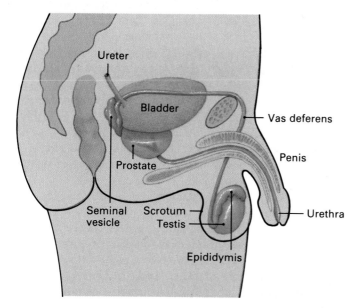

Figure 48–1. The structures of the male human reproductive system are shown here.

Ureter

Bladder

Vas deferens

Prostate

Penis

Seminal vesicle

Scrotum

Testis

Urethra

Epididymis

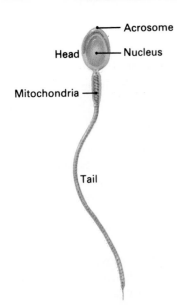

Acrosome

Head — Nucleus

Mitochondria —

Tail

Figure 48–2. The drawing shows the parts of a human sperm cell.

To compare sperm and egg cells, see page 779.

As sperm are ejaculated, they are mixed with secretions from several glands—the *seminal vesicles, Cowper's glands,* and the *prostate.* The secretions contain nutrients, hormones, and enzymes that provide the sperm with energy and the proper environment. The sperm and the secretions together form a thick, milky liquid called **semen.**

A human sperm cell is extremely tiny. Approximately 4 billion sperm could easily fit into a thimble. Each sperm cell has three parts—the head, the middle region, and the tail. The head is the cell nucleus. A small region at the tip of the head, the *acrosome,* contains enzymes that enable the sperm to penetrate the female gamete. The middle region contains the *mitochondria* that supply the cell's energy. The tail, a long, slender flagellum, uses that energy to move the sperm cell.

During puberty, cells surrounding the seminiferous tubules begin to secrete male hormones, or androgens, the most important of which is **testosterone** (tehs TAHS tuh rohn). Testosterone stimulates development of secondary male sex characteristics. Among these are strong muscles, a deep voice, and body hair. Two tropic hormones secreted by the anterior pituitary are necessary for normal functioning of the testes. *LH (luteinizing hormone)* stimulates the production of testosterone. *FSH (follicle stimulating hormone)* controls the maturation of sperm cells.

48.2 The Female Reproductive System

The female gonads, the **ovaries,** are located in the lower part of the abdominal cavity. These olive-sized organs produce the female gametes, called *ova* or *eggs.* Below the ovaries is the **uterus,** a hollow, thick-walled, muscular organ about the size of a fist. The uterine walls are lined with mucous membrane that contains many glands and blood vessels. An unborn child develops here. A duct, called a **Fallopian tube,** or *oviduct,* extends from each side of the uterus. Fringed projections at the upper end of each Fallopian tube surround each ovary. Cilia lining these projections propel the mature egg to the uterus. A tube called the *vagina* leads from the uterus to the outside of the body. Between the uterus and the vagina is a muscular ring, the *cervix.*

At birth a female has about 2 million immature eggs in her ovaries. Beginning at puberty a single egg matures and is released from an ovary each month. In general, the ovaries alternate in releasing eggs. The left ovary releases an egg one month, and the right ovary releases one the next month. Approximately 400 eggs mature during a female's lifetime. During puberty the ovaries also begin to secrete the female hormone **estrogen** (EHS

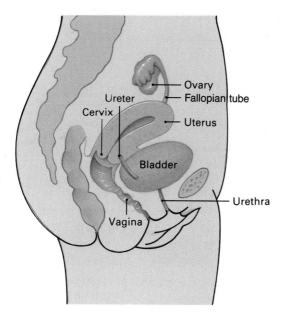

Figure 48–3. The major organs of the female human reproductive system are shown in this illustration.

Labels in figure: Ovary, Fallopian tube, Ureter, Cervix, Uterus, Bladder, Urethra, Vagina

truh juhn). Estrogen causes development of secondary female sex characteristics, such as wide hips, body hair, and enlarged breasts.

48.3 The Menstrual Cycle

The female reproductive system has three primary functions: the production of eggs, the secretion of female sex hormones, and the nourishment and protection of a new individual. Approximately every 28 days, one egg matures and is released from the ovary, and the uterus is prepared to receive it. These activities are controlled by hormones operating on a feedback system. The entire process of ovulation and related changes in the uterus operates on a regular, repeating pattern called the **menstrual** (MEHN stroo wuhl) **cycle.**

The cycle starts with the release of FSH and LH from the anterior pituitary. These hormones trigger the maturing of an egg and its **follicle,** the fluid-filled chamber around the egg. The follicle secretes estrogen, which causes the uterine lining to thicken. Estrogen also triggers an increase in LH. The LH causes the follicle to rupture and release the mature egg from the ovary surface. The process of releasing a mature egg from the ovary is called **ovulation.**

Following ovulation LH stimulates the follicle to enlarge and fill with blood vessels. The follicle is now called the **corpus luteum** (KAWR puhs LOO tee uhm), or "yellow body." It functions temporarily as an endocrine gland, producing the

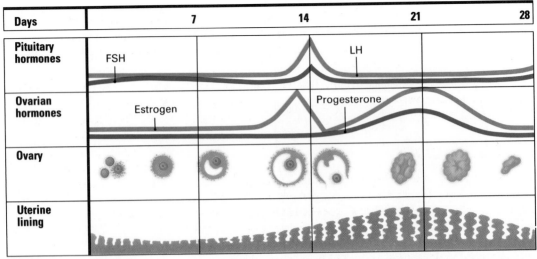

Days		7	14	21	28
Pituitary hormones	FSH			LH	
Ovarian hormones	Estrogen		Progesterone		
Ovary					
Uterine lining					

Figure 48–4. The diagram above shows the changes that take place in human females during a 28-day menstrual cycle. The cycle is counted from the first day of the menstrual flow. The timing of these changes varies somewhat among individuals.

Reading Critically

Analyzing Function What causes the corpus luteum to disintegrate? Why is this disintegration advantageous?

ovarian hormones estrogen and **progesterone** (proh JEHS tuh rohn). Progesterone causes the uterine lining to develop a rich blood supply in preparation for the uterus to receive a fertilized egg. Both estrogen and progesterone inhibit the production of *GnRH (gonadotropin-releasing hormone)* by the hypothalamus. The lower GnRH level inhibits the production of FSH and LH, thus keeping another follicle from maturing.

If an egg is not fertilized, the corpus luteum disintegrates. The cells of the uterine lining die and are sloughed off through the vagina. The discharge of dead tissue, the unfertilized egg, and blood from ruptured capillaries is called **menstruation** (mehn stroo AY shuhn). The decreased levels of FSH and LH, plus disintegration of the corpus luteum, lead to lower progesterone and estrogen levels. The lower hormone levels trigger GnRH, which stimulates FSH and LH secretion. A new cycle begins.

Males normally produce healthy sperm until about age 80. Females cease to release egg cells after **menopause.** Menopause, the time at which the menstrual cycle ceases, usually begins between the ages of 45 and 55. After menopause the pituitary does not secrete LH, and follicles do not mature. Therefore, estrogen and progesterone are not produced.

Section Review

1. **Identifying Function** List the functions of male gonads.
2. **Summarizing Ideas** What is the corpus luteum?
3. **Comparing Ideas** List the differences in the rate of production of male and female gametes.
4. **Synthesizing Ideas** Why must sperm pass through the body before ejaculation?

Thinking Critically

Fetal Development and Birth

The fusing of a sperm nucleus and an egg nucleus is called **fertilization.** When an egg is fertilized, menstruation does not occur. Instead, a nine-month **gestation** (jehs TAY shuhn) **period** begins. This period, also called **pregnancy,** is the time during which a fertilized egg develops into a child inside the mother.

48.4 Fertilization

During sexual intercourse semen is ejaculated through the male's penis into the female's vagina. Of some 400 million sperm ejaculated, less than 3,000 sperm get as far as a Fallopian tube and, of these, only about 50 reach the mature egg. In fertilization the head and middle section of the sperm enter the egg. Only one sperm can fertilize an egg. Changes occur in the egg cell membrane to prevent other sperm from penetrating it.

Since both gametes are haploid, each parent contributes half the normal chromosome number. In human beings the haploid number is 23 chromosomes. When the gametes fuse, the **zygote** (ZY goht), or fertilized egg, has 46 chromosomes.

48.5 Embryonic Development

About 36 hours after fertilization, the zygote begins to divide by mitosis. The zygote does not increase in size as a result of these divisions, called *cleavage*. The zygote then forms a hollow ball of cells called the *blastocyst*. Only one part of the blastocyst will develop into the **embryo.** An unborn child is called an embryo during the first eight weeks of development. Afterward, it is referred to as a **fetus.** The outer part of the blastocyst, called

Section Objectives

- *Describe* the fertilization process, including *in vitro* fertilization.
- *Define* the term *pregnancy*.
- *Draw* a time line showing the development of an unborn child.
- *Name* the protective embryonic membranes and their functions.
- *Summarize* the process of childbirth.

Figure 48–5. The illustration shows the fertilization of a human egg by sperm. The sperm move up through the Fallopian tube to meet the egg. The egg when fertilized (inset) continues to pass down the Fallopian tube and becomes implanted in the lining of the uterus.

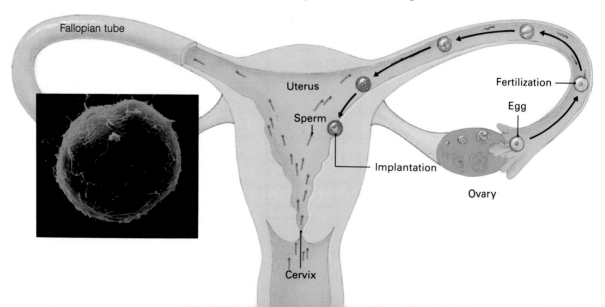

Fallopian tube

Uterus

Sperm

Fertilization

Egg

Implantation

Ovary

Cervix

Blockage of the Fallopian tubes is the chief reason many women are unable to become pregnant. The blockage prevents sperm from entering the tube and fertilizing a mature egg.

The technique known as *in vitro fertilization* (IVF) can overcome this difficulty in some cases. The term *in vitro* means "in glass" and refers to the fact that fertilization takes place in a laboratory dish rather than in the human body.

The procedure involves taking a mature egg from the woman's body when the egg is ready to be released from the ovary.

A physician removes the egg through a small incision in the woman's abdomen. The egg is placed in a laboratory dish to which nutrient has been added to keep the egg healthy. Sperm from the husband is added to the dish. After two days the material in the dish is examined to determine whether the fertilized egg is dividing. If division is taking place, the egg is implanted in the woman's uterus. If the implantation is successful, the woman becomes pregnant. Nine months later, the newborn infant joins the ranks of "test tube" babies.

IVF has made it possible for a number of childless couples to have babies. However, these successes represent only about 12 percent of the women who undergo IVF. Most failures occur during implantation. The removal of the unfertilized egg from the ovary can cause bleeding or a hormone imbalance. When that happens, it means that the lining of the uterus is not ready to accept the egg at the time of implantation, and pregnancy will not occur.

■ **Synthesizing Conclusions** Why is timing so important in the IVF process?

the *trophoblast*, is not part of the embryo.

About six days after fertilization, the blastocyst attaches itself to the lining of the uterus and the trophoblast begins to develop the structures that will allow the embryo to obtain nutrients from the mother, a process called *implantation*. The

Table 48–1: Development of Cell Layers

Cell Layer	Becomes
Ectoderm	Epidermis, including hair and nails; nervous system; epithelial tissue of the nose, mouth, and anus; enamel of the teeth
Mesoderm	Muscles, skeleton, the ducts of the excretory and reproductive systems, circulatory system, kidneys, gonads, dermis, connective tissue
Endoderm	Liver, pancreas, digestive tract, respiratory system

trophoblast also releases human chorionic gonadotropin (HCG), which maintains the thickened lining of the uterus. The presence of HCG in the urine of a woman results in a positive pregnancy test. At the beginning of the third week, the cells of the blastocyst that give rise to the embryo begin to develop three layers that will eventually develop into the various organs of the body, as shown in Table 48–1.

Four protective membranes are formed from the trophoblast. They are the *yolk sac, allantois, amnion,* and *chorion.* The yolk sac has no yolk, as it does in birds, but the blood cells and the cells that will give rise to sperm and eggs begin their development here. The allantois gives rise to the **umbilical cord.** The amnion forms a sac, which fills with fluid. This amniotic fluid cushions the embryo and keeps it moist. The outermost membrane, the chorion, forms fingerlike projections, called villi, that attach to the lining of the uterus. Blood vessels from the allantois run through the villi.

Together the chorion and allantois form the **placenta.** The placenta is a mass of tissue that secretes estrogen and progesterone, which help maintain a thickened, blood-enriched uterine lining. The placenta also serves as the point of exchange of substances between mother and fetus. The exchange takes place through the umbilical cord by which the fetus is attached to the placenta. However, the connection between the circulatory systems of the mother and child is not a direct one. The mother's

Figure 48–6. The diagram shows how the exchange of nutrients and waste matter takes place across the placenta and uterine walls.

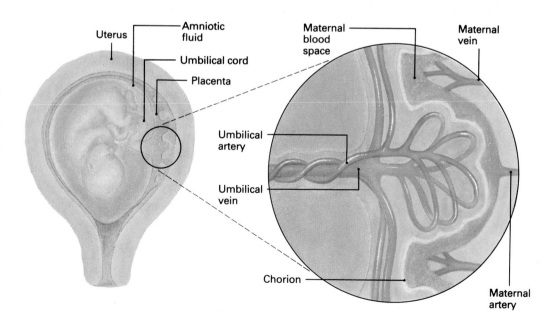

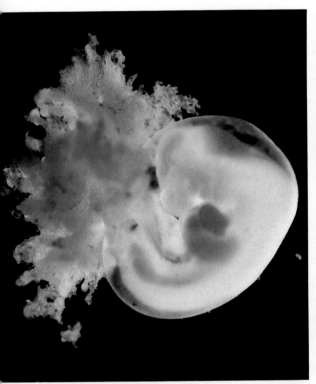
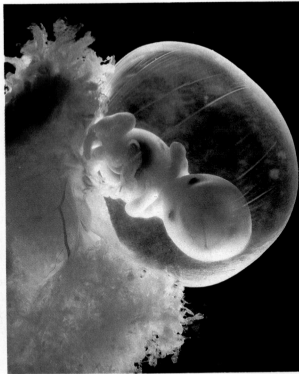

Figure 48–7. The series of photographs above show a human embryo and fetus at five stages in its development: (left to right) 5 weeks, 7 weeks, 3 months, 4 months, and $4\frac{1}{2}$ months.

body carries out the processes of digestion, excretion, and respiration for the developing child. Food and oxygen pass from the mother's bloodstream into the capillaries within the villi of the placenta. The food and oxygen then pass into adjacent capillaries belonging to the fetus and, thus, into the main bloodstream of the fetus. Waste products pass from the blood of the fetus to the blood of the mother in the same manner.

The nine-month pregnancy is commonly divided into three three-month periods called **trimesters.** During the first trimester, unorganized cells become organized into vital organs. In the second trimester, the organs and body features become more refined. After 25 weeks, development is complete. During the final trimester, most growth in body size takes place. A child born at this time would be premature but, with proper care, it would have a good chance of surviving outside its mother's body.

48.6 Childbirth

After approximately 266 days inside its mother's body, the child is ready for birth. Shortly before birth the mother's body undergoes changes that prepare it for **labor,** the process of literally

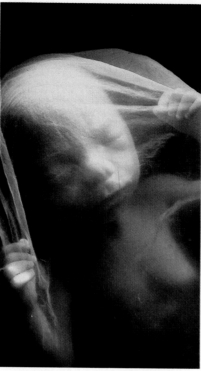
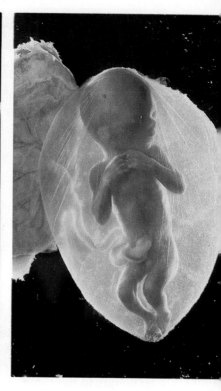

forcing the child out of her body. Contractions of uterine muscles become progressively stronger due to a decrease in progesterone, an increase in estrogen, and the release of the hormone *oxytocin* by the hypothalamus. Oxytocin speeds up contractions of the uterus. The cervix relaxes and widens from about 0.5 cm to 10 cm. As the baby enters the birth canal, the amnion breaks, and amniotic fluid escapes. Muscle contractions become very strong and finally push the infant out of the mother's body. The passing of the child from the uterus into the external environment is called **delivery.**

Before birth, the fetal blood picks up oxygen and gets rid of carbon dioxide as it circulates through the placenta. Because the lungs are not yet functional, modifications of the fetal circulatory system ensure that very little of the oxygenated blood from the placenta is diverted to the lungs. This special fetal circulation is made possible by openings between the atria of the heart and between the large blood vessels that carry blood away from the heart. These openings normally close after birth. If either remains open, it must be closed by surgery.

After delivery, the placenta separates from the wall of the uterus. The child must now support its own life processes. Carbon dioxide quickly builds up in the child's blood and triggers

Reading Critically

Analyzing Function How is the hypothalamus involved in the labor phase of childbirth?

The Boy in the Bubble

The "boy in the bubble" died in 1984, after having spent nearly 12 years in hospital quarantine. The child suffered from a rare immune deficiency that left his body defenseless against infection. Because of his disorder, he had to be isolated from direct contact with people and anything that was not sterile. His protection was the carefully controlled environment inside a germ-proof plastic bubble.

Now, doctors in France have used a remarkable technique to treat inherited immunodeficiencies while a fetus is still developing inside the womb. The procedure involves injecting millions of healthy immune cells into the umbilical cord of a fetus that has been diagnosed as having an immune deficiency. The transplanted cells reproduce in the fetus' vital organs, strengthening the immune system before birth.

The cell transplant technique was used in France to strengthen the immune system of a fetus that had been diagnosed as having a rare immune disorder. The woman carrying the fetus had lost her first child to the same disorder. The cell transplant was performed when the fetus was 30

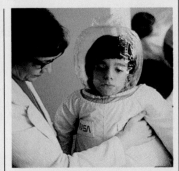

weeks old. Injections of immune cells were continued after the child was born.

For now, the child remains inside a germ-free bubble. However, doctors hope that the cell transplants will help the child's immune system develop and begin to function on its own—freeing the child from his bubble.

the respiratory center in the brain to take in oxygen. The child begins breathing on its own.

After the baby is delivered, the uterus continues to contract, expelling fluid, blood, and the placenta with its attached umbilical cord. These materials are called the *afterbirth*. By this time the mother's pituitary gland has begun releasing *prolactin*, a hormone that stimulates her mammary glands to secrete milk.

Section Review

1. **Summarizing Ideas** How is a zygote formed?
2. **Analyzing Conclusions** Explain how a fetus receives nutrients and how it rids itself of waste products.

Thinking Critically

3. **Evaluating Relationships** What would happen to an implanted embryo if levels of LH dropped sharply?

INVESTIGATION 48:
How Does Life Begin?

Objectives
- To *compare* egg cells and sperm cells
- To *observe* early stages of development

Materials
prepared slides of egg cells and sperm cells, compound light microscope, lens paper, prepared slides of early embryonic development

Prelab Preparation
1. Describe how sperm cells are produced.
2. Describe how egg cells are produced.
3. State the function of sperm cells and egg cells.
4. Explain what process results in the formation of haploid sperm cells and egg cells.
5. Define cleavage.

Inquiry: Observation
6. Place the slide of the egg cell on the microscope stage. Using low power, examine the egg cell. Make a labeled drawing of what you observe.
7. Describe the appearance of the egg cell.
8. How does the amount of cytoplasm in the egg cell compare to the size of the nucleus?
9. Switch to high power and make a second labeled drawing of the egg cell.
10. Place the slide of the sperm cells on the microscope stage. Using low power, focus on the sperm cells. Make a labeled drawing of the sperm cells.
11. Switch to high power and make a second labeled drawing of a sperm cell.
12. Describe the appearance of the sperm cell.
13. How does the amount of cytoplasm in the sperm cell compare to the size of the nucleus?
14. Obtain slides of various stages of the embryonic development of a frog or starfish. The slides might include the following stages: two, four, or eight blastomeres; blastula; early, mid-, or late gastrula.
15. Observe each slide under low power. Make labeled drawings showing each stage of development.
16. Describe each stage of embryonic development that you have observed.

Analysis
1. **Analyzing Observations** How do egg cells and sperm cells compare in size?
2. **Making Inferences** Offer an explanation for the difference in size between sperm cells and egg cells.
3. **Making Inferences** How is the shape of a sperm cell suited to its function?
4. **Analyzing Observations** Compare the early stages of development in terms of overall size, number of cells, size of each cell, and the amount of cytoplasm compared to nuclear volume.
5. **Making Inferences** What appear to be the functions of cleavage during the early stages of development?
6. **Making Inferences** Why might increasing the number of cells during the early stages of development be necessary for the later stages to proceed successfully.
7. **Making Inferences** Based on your work, suggest how fraternal and identical twins might be produced.

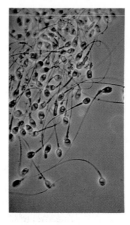 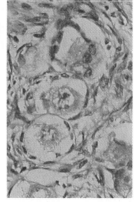

Sperm cells   Egg cells

Chapter 48 Review

Summary

Male gonads, called testes, produce sperm. Sperm are the haploid male gametes. Female gonads, called ovaries, usually produce a single, mature, haploid egg each month. These eggs are the female gametes.

The maturing and releasing of an egg follows a pattern called the menstrual cycle. Hormones control the cycle, which begins with the maturing of an egg and its follicle. Following ovulation the follicle forms the corpus luteum.

This body secretes hormones that prepare the uterus to receive a fertilized egg.

Fertilization begins a nine-month gestation period. The zygote divides to form a blastocyst. The blastocyst implants itself in the lining of the uterus. Part of the blastocyst becomes the embryo. A pregnancy is divided into trimesters, during which unorganized cells first become organized and then develop into distinct tissues and organs.

BioTerms

corpus luteum (771)
delivery (777)
embryo (774)
estrogen (770)
Fallopian tube (770)
fertilization (773)
fetus (775)
follicle (771)
gamete (769)
gestation
   period (773)

labor (776)
menopause (772)
menstrual
   cycle (771)
menstruation (772)
ovary (770)
ovulation (771)
placenta (775)
pregnancy (773)
progesterone (772)
puberty (769)

semen (770)
testis (769)
testosterone (770)
trimester (776)

umbilical cord (775)
uterus (770)
zygote (773)

For each pair of terms, explain the differences in their meanings.

1. follicle, corpus luteum
2. fertilization, pregnancy
3. embryo, fetus
4. umbilical cord, placenta

BioQuiz   (Write all answers on a separate sheet of paper.)

Completion

1. The level of _____ drops quickly when an egg is not fertilized.
2. The hormone _____ stimulates the development of female secondary sex characteristics.
3. When the female body stops producing LH, the woman experiences _____ .
4. Sperm originate in the _____ and move to the epididymis and then to the vas deferens for storage before ejaculation.
5. The tip of a sperm cell, called the _____ , contains enzymes that enable the sperm to penetrate the female gamete.

Multiple Choice

6. Puberty is characterized by the development of the a) fetus. b) gametes. c) uterus. d) gonads.
7. The hormone that controls sperm maturation in males is a) FSH. b) testosterone. c) estrogen. d) progesterone.
8. The most important male hormone is a) estrogen. b) testosterone. c) progesterone. d) FSH.
9. A zygote divides but does not increase in size during a) gestation. b) cleavage. c) blastulation. d) gastrulation.

10. The menstruation cycle starts with the release of FSH and   a) progesterone. b) LH.   c) estrogen.   d) eggs.
11. The ____ is a protective membrane that surrounds the embryo.   a) allantois b) amnion   c) chorion   d) All choices are correct.
12. The discharge of dead tissue and an unfertilized egg from the uterus is called a) gestation.   b) menstruation. c) menopause.   d) ovulation.
13. Sperm cells are supplied with energy from the   a) nucleus.   b) tail. c) acrosome.   d) mitochondria.
14. Fertilization usually occurs in the a) uterus.   b) ovary.   c) Fallopian tube.   d) cervix.

15. A human zygote has ____ chromo-somes.   a) 23   b) 46   c) 24   d) 48

Writing Critically

16. What is the procedure for *in vitro* fertilization?
17. How does a fetus get the oxygen it needs, and how does this system change at birth?
18. What are the three parts of a sperm cell, and what is the function of each?
19. What is the function of the corpus luteum?
20. When a woman reaches menopause, what changes occur in her body?

Application/Critical Thinking

1. **Analyzing Information**   Make a time line that shows the major events that occur during the development of the human fetus. Divide the time line into trimesters. Include the time at which brain waves are first detectable and when the major organs are formed. Include a graph that shows the increases in length of the average fetus during development.
2. **Synthesizing Information**   When blood from a person who belongs to group A $^-$ is mixed with blood from a person who belongs to group B $^+$, the blood cells adhere together and form clumps. This process is called agglutination. Consider a mother with type A $^-$ blood who is carrying a fetus with type B $^+$ blood. Why will agglutination not become a problem although oxygen, nutri-ents, and waste materials are exchanged between the blood of the mother and the blood of the fetus?

Cross-Discipline Connection

Biology and Language Arts Do library research to find out about folk tales and myths that surround birth, such as the myth that babies are brought by the stork and the folk tale that babies grow in garden patches. Include modern myths such as the tale about a superhu-man born on another planet. Write a report on the myths you research.

Discovery Through Reading

Read the article "The New Rules of Reproduc-tion," *U.S. News & World Report* (April 18, 1988): 66–69. This article focuses on how advances in the technology of reproduction are-finding difficulty fitting into the laws of society. Name two states and describe the laws they have about surrogate motherhood. What are two proposed uses for fetal cells? Describe one technique by which women who have already reached menopause can become mothers.

Human Diseases

Outline

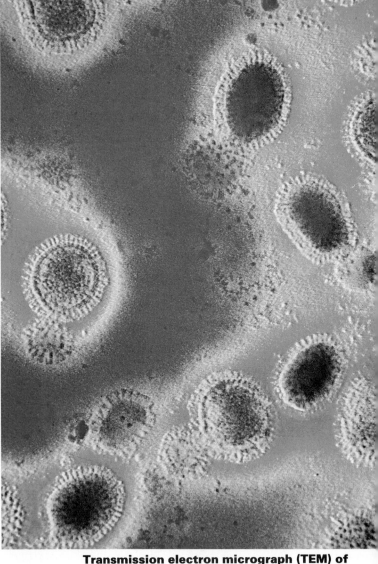

Transmission electron micrograph (TEM) of influenza virions, × 44,000

Focus

An upset stomach and an epidemic that kills millions of people are both examples of diseases. A **disease** is a condition that impairs or damages the body's normal functioning. Some diseases are caused by an organism that invades the body and other diseases result from a flaw or breakdown in the body's metabolic processes. **Pathogens** are agents of disease that include bacteria, other microorganisms, and viruses.

■ *How do pathogens enter the body?*

■ *What precautions can an individual take to reduce the risks of developing diseases?*

Infectious Diseases

In order for a microorganism to be infectious, it must be able to reproduce itself in the tissues of the host and to cause cellular damage. Infectious diseases can be grouped according to the pathogen that causes the disease.

49.1 Bacterial Diseases

Illness from bacterial infections occurs in one of two ways: by the damaging or killing of living tissue or by the production of poisonous substances, or **toxins,** that interfere with the host's metabolism. Boils and pimples result from the multiplication of bacteria in the skin. Cholera and food poisoning are caused by the production of toxins by organisms.

Bacteria usually manufacture toxins while growing and reproducing. There are two types of toxins: *exotoxins* and *endotoxins*. **Exotoxins** are proteins that are secreted by the bacteria into an organism or system that the bacteria have invaded. An **endotoxin** is a lipopolysaccharide found in the cell wall of a bacterium. Endotoxins produce fever and may damage the circulatory system.

Tetanus is a disease caused by *Clostridium* (klahs TRIHD ee um) *tetani,* a type of bacteria normally found in soil. Because *C. tetani* is a saprophytic anaerobe, it can live only in dead tissue in the absence of oxygen. These conditions are found mainly in deep puncture wounds. In such a wound, these bacteria produce an exotoxin that spreads to the nerves that control muscle movement, causing the muscles to remain contracted. This is why tetanus is also called "lockjaw."

The body defends itself against toxins by forming *antitoxins,* which neutralize the toxin's harmful effects. The body's immune system can also act directly against bacteria by surrounding the invading organism with white blood cells. These defensive blood cells are what form the unsightly white pus in a skin blemish or an infected cut.

Bacterial infections can usually be treated with chemicals, called **antibiotics,** that are capable of inhibiting the bacteria's growth. Most antibiotics directly attack the harmful bacteria without harming the surrounding tissue.

A **vaccine** contains a weakened or killed strain of a particular bacterium or virus. When the vaccine enters the body, it stimulates the formation of antibodies that are then able to combat that particular pathogen. The body also can be induced to form antitoxins, which resist the toxins released by bacteria. The preparation of antitoxins against diphtheria is based on this principle.

Section Objectives

- *Define* the term *pathogen* and *explain* how pathogens are involved in bacterial disease.
- *Compare* the mechanism of action in viral, bacterial, fungal, and protozoan diseases.
- *Describe* ways in which medical treatments are used to control and prevent disease.
- *Explain* how the body defends itself against harmful bacteria.

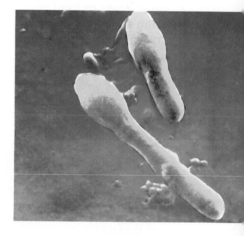

Figure 49–1. This electron micrograph shows bacteria *Clostridium tetani,* which cause tetanus in humans.

To find out how antibiotics affect bacterial growth, see page 799.

Food poisoning occurs when an individual eats something that has been contaminated by bacteria, bacterial toxins, or a toxic chemical. Some types of food poisoning result in mild symptoms of discomfort; others may be fatal. Nausea, vomiting, cramps, and diarrhea are the common symptoms of food poisoning. People get food poisoning most often from meats, poultry, seafood, home-canned foods, and dairy products.

Most cases of food poisoning are caused by one or more types of *Staphylo-* *coccus* bacteria. Like many bacteria, staphylococci release exotoxins into the food. The toxins cause the symptoms of food poisoning.

Another bacterium that causes food poisoning is *Salmonella,* which can cause illness by reproducing in the respiratory tract of the victim. People generally do not die from staphylococcus or salmonella poisoning.

People do die from botulism, a kind of food poisoning caused by *Clostridium botulinum,* an anaerobic bacterium. The spores of *C. botulinum* can develop in improperly canned food. In this oxygen-deprived environment, the spores become active bacteria that secrete botulin toxin, the most powerful toxin known. When food containing the toxin is eaten, the toxin attacks the nervous system, causing paralysis of the respiratory muscles. The victim suffocates due to this paralysis.

■ **Inferring Conclusions** Explain why eating food containing dead salmonella bacteria would not make you ill.

49.2 Viral Diseases

Some of the most common human diseases are caused by viruses. Viruses are strands of nucleic acid enclosed within a protein coat. Most viruses are too small to be seen with a conventional light microscope. The largest virus is about one-tenth the size of an average-sized bacterium. The common cold, chicken pox, rabies, and influenza are examples of viral diseases. Viruses are also responsible for some rare diseases such as St. Louis encephalitis and Lassa fever. Herpes viruses can cause cold sores, chicken pox, a genital infection, and mononucleosis.

A viral infection occurs when a virus enters a host and uses the host's cells to reproduce itself. Once the nucleic acid of the virus has been incorporated into the host's DNA, the virus may remain temporarily dormant, or it may change the behavior of the cell. The virus may take control of the cell's nucleic acid and protein-making process to duplicate itself within the cell. When this occurs, the cell virtually becomes a factory making only viruses. As many as one million virus particles may be

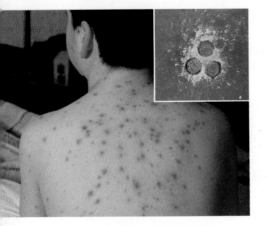

Figure 49–2. This child has the blisterlike lesions characteristic of chicken pox, which is caused by the varicella virus (inset).

produced in a single cell before the cell is destroyed. The new viruses escape to infect other cells and continue reproduction.

Particular viruses usually infect particular tissues in the body. For example, the poliovirus can live and reproduce in a person's intestines without harming the body. However, when this virus attacks the spinal cord, it causes the crippling symptoms of poliomyelitis.

The body's immune system produces defenses against viral, as well as bacterial, infections. The main defense is the body's production of cellular proteins called *interferons*. **Interferons** are proteins that inhibit the reproduction of viruses in infected cells. Interferons also stimulate the surrounding cells to resist the invasion of viral particles. Most mild viral infections, such as colds, are defeated by the body's own resistance. Medications are usually prescribed only to relieve the symptoms of the infection.

The body also can develop selective immunity to particular viruses. A case of the measles stimulates the body to produce antibodies that attack the measles virus. After the infection has passed, the body's immune system usually maintains a lifelong resistance to that virus.

Reading Critically

Comparing Ideas   How are viral infections different from bacterial infections?

49.3 Fungal and Protozoan Diseases

Although there are hundreds more fungal diseases found in plants than in animals, some fungi do infect humans. Fungi do not make their own food; they establish parasitic and saprophytic relationships with their hosts. Fungal infections can attack three areas of the body: the skin, the area deep beneath the skin, or the internal organs. Athlete's foot is an example of a fungal infection. Spores of the fungus that causes athlete's foot enter the foot through a break in the skin. As the fungus grows, the skin becomes itchy and scaly.

Figure 49–3.   The moisture in athletic lockers and shower rooms can be ideal for the growth and spread of the fungus (right) responsible for athlete's foot (left).

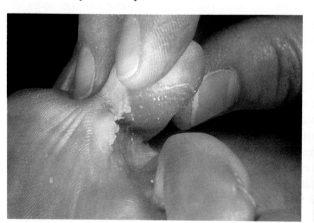
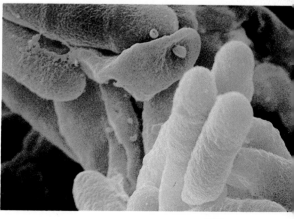

Who Gets AIDS?

The first cases of AIDS were reported in the United States in 1981. Since that time, AIDS and other HIV-related diseases have reached epidemic proportions. Evidence of HIV infection has been reported in both males and females, in every age group, in every ethnic group, and in every state in the United States.

However, because the virus is transmitted almost exclusively through behavior that individuals can modify, people can avoid becoming infected with the human immunodeficiency virus, and thus avoid getting AIDS and HIV-related diseases.

The behaviors that are most likely to lead to HIV infection are using illegal intravenous drugs, having more than one sexual partner, and having sex with a person who has had one or more sexual partners. Since HIV can be transmitted by both males and females, the virus can be acquired through both homosexual and heterosexual contact. People who show no signs of disease may harbor the virus.

Refraining from both sexual contact and the use of illegal intravenous drugs reduces the risk of contracting the AIDS virus to virtually zero. The use of latex condoms, together with spermicides, reduces but does not eliminate the risk of contracting the virus.

For information about AIDS, contact: National AIDS Information Clearinghouse, P.O. Box 6003, Rockville, MD 20850; or call: National AIDS Hotline, 1-(800) 342-AIDS.

Only about 35 of the 28,000 species of protozoans cause disease in humans. Malaria, African sleeping sickness, and amoebic dysentery are all diseases caused by protozoa. All of these diseases can be fatal.

In amoebic dysentery, the amoeba infects the host's liver, spleen, and brain. Most individuals contract the pathogen through contaminated water or uncooked vegetables. It can also be transmitted by materials contaminated by the feces of infected hosts. Less-developed countries with poor sanitation have high rates of amoebic dysentery in their populations.

Section Review

1. **Summarizing Ideas** How do bacteria cause illness?
2. **Comparing Ideas** Compare the mechanism of action in viral diseases with those of fungal and protozoan diseases.
3. **Analyzing Information** How does the body fight infectious disease?

Thinking Critically

4. **Evaluating Relationships** What would happen if a virus could not escape from the host cell?

Sexually Transmitted Diseases

A special category of diseases is passed by sexual contact. These diseases are called **sexually transmitted diseases** (STDs). STDs may be caused by viruses, bacteria, or other agents.

49.4 AIDS

Acquired immune deficiency syndrome, AIDS, is a lethal STD caused by a virus that attacks the immune system and eventually destroys the body's resistance to other diseases.

The virus that causes AIDS is called *human immunodeficiency virus (HIV)*. HIV usually invades T lymphocytes, cells that produce several infection-fighting substances. HIV may remain inactive inside the body for months or even years. During this time, an infected person may show no outward symptoms of disease. Blood tests taken before an infected person forms antibodies will not reveal the infection. When HIVs become active, the T lymphocytes become factories producing nothing but HIV. Eventually, the T lymphocytes rupture and die. The HIVs, thus freed, invade other T lymphocytes. **By destroying T lymphocytes, HIV effectively wipes out one of the body's major defenses against infection and disease. Thus, the body becomes susceptible to a number of life-threatening infections and fatal diseases.** There is no cure for AIDS.

AIDS is sometimes preceded by an HIV-caused illness called *AIDS-related complex*, or ARC. There is no way to predict when a person with ARC will develop AIDS, or if ARC will develop into full-blown AIDS.

Most infected people acquired the virus through sexual contact with an infected person, or through sharing infected needles and other paraphernalia that is used for injecting illicit intravenous drugs into the bloodstream. Newborns have developed AIDS because an infected woman can transmit HIV to the unborn fetus. Infants can acquire the virus through the infected milk of the mother during nursing. A small number of medical workers have been infected when they were directly exposed to HIV-contaminated blood. Some individuals have acquired HIV through transfusions of donated blood and blood-clotting products. However, routine testing of donated blood since 1985 has made the risk of infection from these sources negligible.

There is, at present, no evidence that HIV can be transmitted through casual contact with infected people such as through food handling, coughing, sneezing, or sharing of swimming pools, bathrooms, and telephones.

Figure 49–4. The green "dots" in the photograph are human immunodeficiency viruses. They are shown attacking a T lymphocyte cell.

49.5 Genital Herpes

Herpes simplex 2 is a virus that is transmitted through direct contact with infected genital tissue. Infection usually occurs during sexual intercourse. However, infants born to infected mothers may acquire herpes during passage through the birth canal. Herpes can damage the central nervous system of the newborn, causing mental retardation or even death.

The symptoms of genital herpes are: itching and painful blisters similar to cold sores on the penis of males and on the labia or in the vagina of females. Symptoms may also include swollen glands, fever, headaches, and fatigue. The symptoms disappear within two or three weeks but may recur repeatedly. Medication can relieve symptoms, but once the virus invades the body, it remains there. There is no cure for genital herpes.

49.6 Other Sexually Transmitted Diseases

Over 25 STDs have been identified, including vaginitis, gonorrhea, syphilis, venereal warts, pubic lice, nongonococcal urethritis, and chlamydia. Although not well understood, chlamydia is one of the most common STDs in the United States.

Table 49–1 Sexually Transmitted Diseases

Disease	Type of Infection	Symptoms	Treatment
AIDS	Viral (Human immunodeficiency virus—HIV)	Early: weight loss, frequent fevers, mild infections, weakness, enlarged lymph glands; later: susceptibility to common infections, pneumonia and cancer	Experimental, antivirals and immunostimulants to slow progress of the virus
Chlamydia	Bacterial *(Chlamydia trachomatis)*	Vaginal discharge, painful urination	Tetracycline, other antibiotics
Genital Warts	Viral *(Condylomata acuminata)*	Common skin wart on genitals	Chemical or physical removal
Gonorrhea	Bacterial *(Neisseria gonorrhoeae)*	In males: thick discharge from penis, painful urination, tender groin; in females: few symptoms	Penicillin, spectinomycin
Genital Herpes	Viral (herpes simplex type 2)	Bumps or blisters on genitals	No cure, acyclovir for symptoms
Nongonococcal urethritis	Bacterial *(Mycoplasma hominis, Ureaplasma urealyticum)*	Thin clear discharge from penis or vagina, mild pain on urination	Tetracycline, other antibiotics
Pubic lice	The louse	Itching in region of pubic hair	Creams, lotions, or shampoos containing gamma benzene hexachloride
Syphilis	Bacterial *(Treponema pallidum)*	First stage: ulcerlike lesions on genitals; second stage: rash, hair loss, sore throat, headache, nausea, low fever; third stage: heart disease, insanity, death	Penicillin, erythromycin, tetracycline
Vaginitis	Can be viral, bacterial, fungal (Candida albicans), or protozoan *(Trichomonas vaginalis)*	Thick discharge, mild pain on urination, itching	Metronidazole

Gonorrhea   Gonorrhea is caused by the bacterium *Neisseria gonorrhoeae* and is transmitted almost exclusively by sexual activity. These bacteria cannot survive outside the human body, so it cannot be transmitted through contaminated toilets or sinks.

Gonorrhea infects the entire genital and urinary tract of the male, causing painful urination and blockage of the urethra. Gonorrhea is often undiagnosed in women, as a vaginal discharge may be the only symptom. Sometimes women experience no symptoms at all. If left untreated, gonorrhea can cause permanent sterility in either males or females. Some forms of gonorrhea can be treated successfully with antibiotics, although some strains of the bacteria have proved resistant to the usual medications.

Syphilis   The spirochete bacterium *Treponema pallidum* is responsible for the disease syphilis. Cases of this disease are called *acquired syphilis* when transmitted through sexual contact. *Congenital syphilis* is passed from an infected mother to the developing fetus in her uterus. When diagnosed in its early stage, syphilis is easily treated with antibiotics. If left untreated, the disease can cause blindness, insanity, and death.

The first stage of syphilis is characterized by an open sore, called a **chancre** (SHAHN ker), usually on or near the genitals. The sore usually disappears in about a month. During this first stage, the spirochetes are susceptible to antibiotic treatment. If the disease is left untreated, the first stage is followed by the second stage, which is characterized by a skin rash as shown in Figure 49–5, loss of hair, and sores in the mouth. There may also be swelling of the lymph glands and wartlike growths around the rectum or genitals.

If untreated, syphilis will enter an inactive stage called *latency*. Most symptoms disappear, and the disease is no longer transmitted sexually. The final stages of the disease appear two to ten years after the first infection. The syphilis spirochetes may attack the skin, bones, and joints; or they may weaken the heart and blood vessels; or they may affect the brain and spinal cord. The result is often fatal heart disease and paralysis.

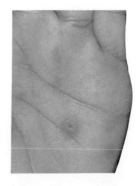

Figure 49–5.   The skin rash shown here is typical of second-stage syphilis.

Section Review

1. **Identifying Relationships**   Why do AIDS patients often develop rare forms of pneumonia and cancer?
2. **Summarizing Ideas**   What are the major stages of syphilis and what are the symptoms of each stage?
3. **Synthesizing Information**   Compare and contrast AIDS and genital herpes.

⟨Thinking Critically⟩

Section Objectives

- *Explain* the role of carcinogens in cancer.
- *Describe* the role of myelin in multiple sclerosis.
- *Describe* the symptoms of Alzheimer's disease.
- *List* behaviors that lessen the danger of developing a degenerative disease.

Degenerative Diseases

Long-term diseases that involve the deterioration or breakdown of the body's tissues and organs are called **degenerative diseases.** Degenerative diseases can be caused by a malfunction within the body's cells or can be stimulated by an outside agent. Cancer, cardiovascular diseases, arthritis, Alzheimer's disease, and multiple sclerosis are all degenerative diseases. Adults are more likely to develop degenerative diseases than children are.

49.7 Cancer

Cancer is probably the most well-known degenerative disease. **Cancer** occurs when cells grow and multiply in an abnormal, uncontrolled manner. These clumps of cells are called **tumors.** Tumors can be harmless, called **benign,** or deadly, called **malignant.** The common wart is an example of a benign, if unattractive, tumor. When a tumor grows uncontrollably, invading and destroying nearby tissue, it is malignant. A cancer is a malignant tumor.

When a tumor remains a hard mass of cells, it is called a *sarcoma* or a *carcinoma.* **Sarcomas** are tumors involving the connective tissue, such as muscle. **Carcinomas** are tumors involving the epithelial tissue, such as skin. When cells leave a tumor and move throughout the body, new tumors can form at sites distant from the original one. This spreading of cancer is called **metastasis.**

Figure 49–6. These scanning electron micrographs show a normal cell (top) and a cancerous cell (bottom). A cross section (far right) shows how a malignant tumor might metastasize.

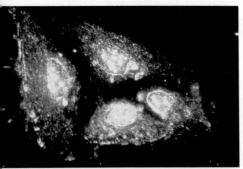

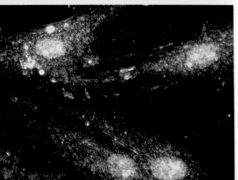

Carcinoma of the lung

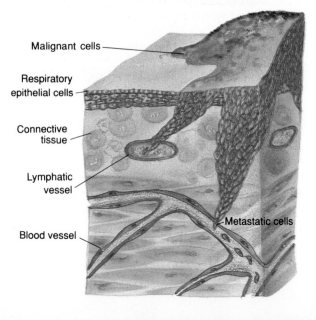

Malignant cells

Respiratory epithelial cells

Connective tissue

Lymphatic vessel

Blood vessel

Metastatic cells

Table 49–2: Major Sites of Cancer in the Human Body

Body Site	Symptoms	Precautionary Measures
Bladder and kidney	Difficult and painful urination; blood in the urine	Regular medical checkups, including urinalysis
Blood-forming organs	Fatigue; tendency to bruise and bleed easily; long-lasting infections	Regular medical checkups; analysis of blood sample
Breast	Lump or thickening in the breasts	Monthly self-examination of the breasts; regular medical checkups
Colon and rectum	Change in bowel habits; bleeding from the rectum; blood in the stool	Regular medical checkups, including examination of the colon and rectum
Larynx	Hoarseness; difficulty in swallowing	Regular medical checkups, including examination of the larynx
Lung	Persistent cough or long-lasting respiratory ailment	Avoidance of cigarette smoking; regular medical checkups
Lymphatic organs	Enlarged lymph nodes	Regular medical checkups
Mouth and pharynx	Sore that does not heal; difficulty in swallowing that persists	Regular medical and dental checkups; avoidance of smoking and smokeless tobacco
Pancreas	Yellowing of skin and eyes; severe abdominal pain	Regular medical checkups
Prostate	Difficulty in urinating	Regular medical checkups, including a rectal examination
Skin	Sore that does not heal; change in a wart or mole	Avoidance of excessive sunbathing; use of sunscreens; regular medical checkups
Stomach	Persistent indigestion	Regular medical checkups
Uterus	Unusual bleeding or discharge from the vagina	Regular medical checkups, including a Pap test

Cancer cells differ from normal cells in three main ways: (1) they divide more rapidly, (2) they do not stick together as firmly as normal cells, and (3) they dedifferentiate; that is, they look as if they have reverted to an early stage in their development.

Causes of Cancer   Cancer cannot be attributed to any single cause. Scientists think that genetic changes probably always occur in cells that are cancerous. However, the genetic change itself may not cause the cancer but only result from it. Whatever the cause of cancer, the critical factor appears to be that one or more of the proteins that regulate cell division in the body are incorrectly activated, and the cells go into a state of uncontrolled growth.

Many cancers are activated by agents that enter the body from outside. Cancer-causing agents are called **carcinogens.** *Researchers believe that the carcinogen induces a change in the enzymes found in the nucleus of the cell. The abnormal cell then reproduces itself wildly.*

Medical researchers have identified hundreds of carcinogens, including cigarette smoke, asbestos dust, benzene, X rays, and industrial chemicals. Cigarette smoking causes about 80 percent of lung cancers in the United States. Carcinogens have also been found in ordinary foods and in drinking water. Scientists estimate that at least 50 percent, and perhaps as many as 80 percent, of all cancers are caused by such environmental factors.

A few rare cancers, such as a cancer of the eye called *retinoblastoma,* have been identified as hereditary. The tendency toward cancer of the breast may also be transmitted genetically. A woman is twice as likely to develop breast cancer if her mother or aunt had the disease.

Some forms of cancer are caused by viruses. When you develop a cold or influenza, a virus has entered your cells, replicated, and caused the illness. Other viruses, such as those that cause cancer, enter the cells and seem to be dormant for a time. However, the genetic material of the virus becomes integrated with the genetic material of the cell that it has invaded. This virus can then be passed from parent to child, perhaps showing a link to the hereditary characteristics of some cancers. Medical research has now established that a virus causes leukemia, a cancer of the blood. Research has not yet proved whether such viral cancers are communicable.

Treating Cancer   The simplest solution for treating cancer is to remove the cancerous mass surgically. Use of modern anti-

Figure 49–7.   The safe removal of asbestos requires using masks and protective clothing. Asbestos fibers (inset) can cause cancer when inhaled.

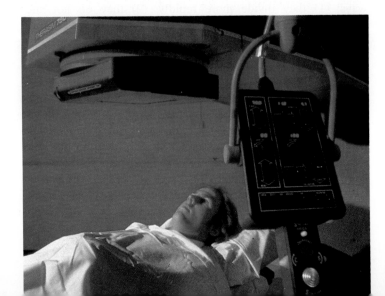

Figure 49–8.   This patient is receiving radiation as therapy for cancer.

biotics and blood transfusions has increased the success rate of surgical cancer treatment. However, surgery cannot prevent the recurrence of cancer from metastasized cells.

A second treatment for cancer is radiation therapy. The cancerous region is bombarded with X rays or radiation from radioactive elements such as cobalt. Radioactive iodine can be injected directly into the body to treat thyroid cancer. Radiation therapy is so precise that the diseased cells are destroyed without damaging surrounding healthy tissue.

The most promising cancer treatment is **chemotherapy,** which arrests cancer with highly toxic drugs. Typically, these drugs have side effects that make the cancer patient very ill. He or she may suffer severe nausea, loss of weight and hair, and other symptoms. When effective, however, chemotherapy can result in **remission,** a period of inactivity that may last for several years.

Reading Critically

Evaluating Relationships
How can a blood transfusion help fight cancer?

49.8 Multiple Sclerosis

Unlike many degenerative diseases, *multiple sclerosis (MS)* most often afflicts young adults between the ages of 20 and 40. The disease causes a gradual destruction of *myelin,* the white matter of the brain and spinal cord, but it is seldom fatal. Small, hard deposits of fatty material called **plaques** become scattered throughout the myelin, interfering with the normal functioning of nerve pathways. As more and more plaques develop in the myelin, more symptoms of the disease appear.

There is no diagnostic test and no cure for MS. Physicians determine that an individual has MS chiefly from such symptoms as double vision, unsteady walk, loss of balance, or weakness in the arms or the legs. Jerky movements of the head, legs, or arms may occur, and there may be numbness or tingling in the fingers. The symptoms of MS may lessen and disappear entirely for a time. These periods of health are usually followed by unpredictable symptoms that progressively worsen.

Researchers believe that MS is probably caused by a virus that infects the individual before the age of 15. The virus may cause an abnormal reaction in the body's immune system. MS may be affected by diet or climate. The disease is virtually unknown in the tropics and is most prevalent in northern Europe and America, where diets contain large amounts of animal fat.

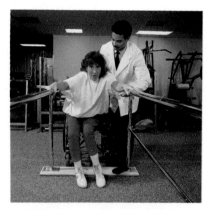

Figure 49–9. With physical therapy, many MS patients are able to reachieve a great deal of control over body movements.

49.9 Cardiovascular Disease

Cardiovascular disease is a term that covers diseases affecting the heart and blood vessels. Arteriosclerosis and high blood pressure are cardiovascular diseases that result in heart attacks and strokes. Together, these diseases are the leading cause of death in the United States.

THINKING ABOUT BIOLOGY: Alzheimer's Disease

When some elderly people began forgetting familiar relatives, began getting lost in familiar surroundings, and could no longer remember how to do simple things, society used to call them *senile*. Today, extreme memory loss has been recognized as one of the symptoms of *Alzheimer's disease*.

Alzheimer's disease causes a progressive destruction of brain cells. People with Alzheimer's disease forget recent events even though they can remember past events very clearly. As the disease progresses, memory loss steadily increases, accompanied by impairment of judgment, speech, and muscle coordination. In severe cases, individuals are incapable of caring for themselves. The body gradually weakens, becoming vulnerable to various infections.

Medical researchers have found an abnormal tangle of fibers within the brain cells of the victims of Alzheimer's disease. These deficient brain cells are apparently concentrated in a small part of the brain that controls the making and storing of memories.

Researchers have also identified an abnormal coating on brain tissues. This coating is composed of decomposing nerve endings and some non-nerve tissues. How the coating hinders the functioning of the brain is not yet clear.

The series of positron emission tomography (PET) scans below show brain activity of an individual with normal brain activity (top) and an individual with Alzheimer's disease (bottom). PET scans map the activity of neurotransmitters. As can be seen by the PET scans, individuals with Alzheimer's disease have altered brain activity.

The cause of Alzheimer's disease is unknown. Scientists suspect that a virus-like particle consisting only of a protein may block the transmission of nerve impulses between brain cells.

■ **Inferring Relationships** Why do the symptoms of Alzheimer's disease point to the brain as the site of disease?

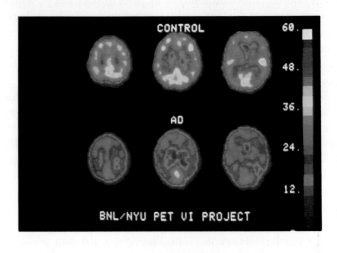

Arteriosclerosis is a cardiovascular disease that involves the arteries. Fatty deposits build up on the walls of the arteries, causing them to become clogged. These clogs decrease the amount of blood that can flow through the arteries. If the blockage becomes severe enough, the individual can experience a heart attack or stroke.

High blood pressure, or hypertension, is a dangerous disease because it has no symptoms. The cause of hypertension is unknown, but the result can be a stroke or heart attack.

Both heart attacks and strokes occur as a result of insufficient amounts of oxygenated blood reaching the affected organ. In the case of a heart attack, the heart muscle itself is damaged. In a stroke, a portion of the brain is damaged. Depending on what portion of the brain is damaged, paralysis, loss of speech, or other disabilities may occur.

Cardiovascular disease follows the same pattern as the diseases already discussed. First, there appears to be a hereditary tendency toward the disease. A man whose father or uncle suffered cardiovascular disease is more likely to be a victim, also.

Second, the onset of the disease appears to be related to external factors such as diet and exposure to toxic substances. For instance, researchers have long associated cardiovascular disease with a diet that is high in animal fats. Nicotine, the active drug in cigarette smoke, has been linked to cardiovascular disease in clinical studies. In addition, any degenerative disease may be stimulated by viruses or other disease-causing agents, although vulnerability to these agents varies from individual to individual.

A few precautions may reduce the chances of developing a degenerative disease. Regular exercise and a diet low in animal fats help maintain resistance to these and most other diseases. Harmful habits such as smoking and excessive use of alcohol clearly increase the chances of developing a degenerative disease. Paying close attention to any changes in the body and periodic checkups by a physician may allow detection of disease in its early stages and substantially increase the chance of successful treatment and a full recovery.

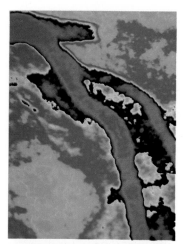

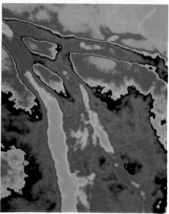

Figure 49–10. These X rays show an artery from an individual with arteriosclerosis (top) and a healthy individual (bottom). The artery on top is clogged with fatty deposits that greatly decrease the flow of blood through the heart and body.

Section Review

1. **Relating Ideas** How could carcinogens and heredity both be involved in the development of cancer?
2. **Evaluating Ideas** Describe the symptoms of MS. How do you think people with MS could minimize their symptoms?
3. **Inferring Relationships** How are certain behaviors related to degenerative diseases?

> **Thinking Critically**

- *Explain* how hereditary diseases are passed from parent to child.
- *Identify* the cause of Tay-Sachs disease.
- *Describe* how hereditary diseases are related to inborn errors in metabolism.

Hereditary Diseases

Hair color, skin color, and eye color are not the only traits that children inherit from their parents. A disease can also be inherited. Genetically transmitted illnesses are called **hereditary diseases.** *Many hereditary diseases are caused by the body's inability to correctly perform certain chemical processes. These malfunctioning processes are sometimes called* **inborn errors of metabolism.** The diseases are usually autosomal recessive, which means that both parents are heterozygous *carriers* for the error and are thus symptom free. The symptoms of the error show up only in the recessive homozygote. In some hereditary diseases, the genetic defect is an autosomal dominant. In these cases, one of the parents also has the disease.

49.10 Cystic Fibrosis

An error in one allele causes *cystic fibrosis (CF),* the most common fatal genetic disease in the Caucasian population in the United States. CF is a disease that is found predominantly in northern European Caucasians. CF is a homozygous recessive disease; one in 20 Caucasian individuals is a carrier of the defective gene. Only those individuals who inherit a defective gene from both parents develop CF.

CF is a disease characterized by the production of abnormally thick mucus. The thick mucus forms plugs that clog the lungs and digestive system. Because the plugs of mucus block the bronchial tubes, children with CF must struggle for every breath. While normal mucus sweeps away bacteria in the lungs, the thick mucus of CF children traps bacteria, increasing the occurrence of lung infections.

These plugs of mucus also prevent the liver and pancreas from secreting the enzymes necessary for the digestion of food. Untreated CF victims digest only part of their food and may suffer from poor nutrition, even when they have a healthful diet. There is no cure for CF; it is only possible to lessen its symptoms.

An early symptom of CF in infants is an unusual amount of salt in the perspiration, saliva, and tears. This excess salt is a direct result of the genetic abnormality. Scientists believe that the mucus of individuals with CF is thick and viscous due to an abnormal form of the enzyme NADH dehydrogenase. Because this enzyme is abnormal, the mitochondrial electron transport chain breaks down, causing the thick mucus. The absence of the enzyme also means that chlorine ions are not transported across membranes. The chlorine ions are eliminated from the body in the form of salt.

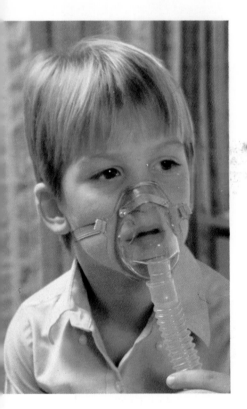

Figure 49–11. This child with cystic fibrosis is inhaling oxygen in an effort to ease his breathing.

Table 49–3: Some Genetic Diseases

Disease	Transmission	Characteristics
Cystic fibrosis	Autosomal recessive	Difficulty breathing, thickened mucus, digestive problems
Duchenne muscular dystrophy	Sex-linked	Wasting of muscles
Gaucher disease	Autosomal recessive	Enlarged liver and spleen, neurologic problems
Hemophilia	Sex-linked recessive	Failure of blood to clot normally, arthritis due to severe joint hemorrhaging
Huntington disease	Autosomal dominant	Progressive mental retardation, irregular jerking movements
Hurler syndrome	Autosomal recessive	"Gargoyle" appearance, mental retardation, dwarfism, enlarged liver and spleen, hearing and corneal defects
Lesch-Nyhan	Sex-linked	Cerebral palsy, mental retardation, self-mutilation
Marfan syndrome	Autosomal dominant	Elongated extremities, dislocation of lens of eye, cardiovascular abnormalities
Phenylketonuria	Autosomal recessive	Mental retardation, microcephaly
Tay-Sachs	Autosomal recessive	Progressive physical and mental retardation, blindness, death

Scientists have recently identified the gene that encodes the transmembrane protein. Because this gene differs in individuals with CF, scientists can improve cystic fibrosis diagnosis and work more effectively toward finding a cure.

49.11 Tay-Sachs Disease

Some hereditary diseases are found more frequently in some ethnic groups than others. *Tay-Sachs disease,* a metabolic disorder that results in deterioration of the brain and death by the age of four, afflicts the Ashkenazi Jews, who originate in Middle Europe. One in 30 is heterozygous for the disease. Children who are homozygous recessive for Tay-Sachs are missing an essential enzyme, hexosaminidase, that metabolizes lipids in the brain.

In the absence of this enzyme, the lipids accumulate in the nerve cells of the brain, destroying their normal function. A

Reading Critically

Analyzing Relationships
Why is Tay-Sachs disease found within a specific ethnic group?

baby with Tay-Sachs disease appears normal at birth; by eight months symptoms begin to appear. The child loses the ability to crawl and eventually suffers blindness, convulsions, and paralysis. There is no cure for the disease, and no effective treatment.

49.12 Sickle-cell Disease

Sickle-cell disease is an incomplete dominant hereditary disease that also affects an ethnic group. About 9 percent of blacks in the United States are heterozygous for the abnormal sickle-cell gene. Sickle-cell disease involves the production of abnormal hemoglobin. The defect in the hemoglobin is due to the incorrect substitution of one valine molecule for one glutamine molecule out of a total of about 300 amino acid molecules. When oxygen is scarce, the defective hemoglobins become insoluble, clumping together and forming rigid, rodlike structures. When red blood cells contain enough of the defective hemoglobins, they become sickle shaped and stiff, unlike the normal disk-shaped, flexible red blood cells.

Because of their rigidity and shape, sickle-shaped red blood cells do not move easily through small blood vessels. Instead they often block capillaries. When the sickle cells congregate in the hands and feet, the person may experience extreme pain. Sickle-cell disease also causes damaging blood clots in the internal organs.

Sickle-cell disease is usually fatal to those who are homozygous for the disease. However, people who are heterozygous for the sickle-cell allele exhibit few if any symptoms. One side effect of the heterozygous condition is that susceptibility to malaria is greatly decreased. Interestingly, the frequency of the sickle-cell allele is extremely high in areas of Africa where malaria is prevalent. For people living in areas in which malaria is prevalent, being heterozygous for the sickle-cell allele is a beneficial trait.

Figure 49–12. Many couples seek genetic counseling to determine if either individual or both individuals are carriers for a genetic disease.

Thinking Critically

Section Review

1. **Synthesizing Information** Why must an individual be homozygous for CF in order to have the disease?
2. **Identifying Relationships** What causes the red blood cells of individuals with sickle-cell disease to become misshapen?
3. **Inferring Relationships** Why do infants with Tay-Sachs disease develop severe mental retardation?
4. **Inferring Conclusions** Using what you know about natural selection, explain how being heterozygous for sickle-cell disease may have survival value.

INVESTIGATION 49:
How Do Antibiotics Affect Bacterial Growth?

Objectives
- To *use* aseptic technique to culture bacteria
- To *evaluate* the effect of antibiotics on bacterial growth

Materials
Wax pencil, petri plates with sterile nutrient agar, pipette with bulb, Bunsen burner, *Serratia marcescens* stock culture, four antibiotic disks, incubator, metric ruler

Prelab Preparation
1. Describe the roles that bacteria play in the biosphere.
2. Explain why some bacteria are considered pathogens.
3. Explain why you should treat harmless bacteria as though they were pathogenic.
4. Discuss the methods people use to control bacteria in their bodies and in the environment.
   CAUTION: **Put on an apron, safety goggles, and rubber gloves. Treat all bacterial cultures as if they were pathogenic.**

Inquiry: Lab Technique
5. Use a wax pencil to mark the bottom of your petri plate in quadrants.
6. Using aseptic technique as demonstrated by your teacher, open the dish slightly and use a pipette to place 0.1 mL of the stock culture in the center of the petri plate. Place the plate on the lab bench or desktop and briskly agitate the plate back and forth to spread the bacterial culture over the plate.
7. Describe the specific procedures you used to prevent the contamination of the stock culture tube, the petri dish, yourself, and the environment.

Inquiry: Experimentation
8. *Do antibiotics kill bacteria?* After discussing the question with your partner, formulate a hypothesis about the effect of antibiotics on bacteria.

9. Using a separate disk for each antibiotic, design a controlled experiment that tests your team's hypothesis.
   a. Describe the design of your experiment.
   b. Explain why your experiment is a controlled experiment.
   c. Explain the steps you will take to ensure that you maintain aseptic technique throughout your experiment.
10. List the data that you plan to collect during your experiment.
11. Design a table for recording your data.
12. After your experimental design has been approved by your teacher, conduct your experiment.
13. Present your data in a table and on a graph.

Analysis
1. **Inferring Conclusions** Do the data support your hypothesis? Explain your answer.
2. **Analyzing Data** Describe and evaluate the data you are using to support your conclusion.
3. **Synthesizing Data** Do you have data to show that the inhibition is due to the antibiotic rather than the paper disk? If so, describe it.
4. **Predicting Conclusions** The antibiotics you used in your experiment were used on a nonliving surface. How might the effects of the antibiotics change when they are introduced into living tissue?

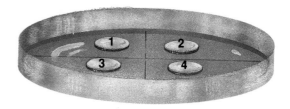

Chapter 49 Review

Summary

Disease in humans can be caused by a variety of pathogens and circumstances. Many diseases are caused by viruses or bacteria.

STDs can be fungal, protozoan, viral or bacterial. They are similar in that they are all transmitted by direct sexual contact. AIDS and herpes are both viral diseases that are transmitted by sexual contact, while gonorrhea and syphilis are bacterial infections with the same mode of transmission.

Degenerative diseases can be caused by a variety of agents; their common link is that they all involve the deterioration of the body's organs or tissues. Some of these diseases are believed to be due to viral infection, and others to a malfunction in the body's cells.

Hereditary diseases are genetically transmitted. Most of these diseases are caused by inborn errors in the metabolism that result in the body's being unable to carry out vital chemical processes. Hereditary diseases are, as yet, incurable.

BioTerms

antibiotic (**783**)
benign (**790**)
cancer (**790**)
carcinogen (**792**)
carcinoma (**790**)
cardiovascular disease (**793**)
chancre (**789**)
chemotherapy (**793**)
degenerative disease (**790**)
disease (**782**)

endotoxin (**783**)
exotoxin (**783**)
hereditary disease (**796**)
interferons (**785**)
inborn errors of metabolism (**796**)
malignant (**790**)
metastasis (**790**)
pathogen (**782**)
plaques (**793**)
remission (**793**)

sarcoma (**790**)
sexually transmitted disease (**STD**) (**787**)

toxin (**783**)
tumor (**790**)
vaccine (**783**)

For each pair of terms, explain the differences in their meanings.

1. endotoxin, exotoxin
2. benign, malignant
3. chancre, plaques
4. carcinoma, sarcoma

BioQuiz   (Write all answers on a separate sheet of paper.)

Completion

1. Poisonous substances, or _____ , are produced by bacteria that damage the host's metabolism.
2. Disease-causing microorganisms are _____ .
3. Tumors involving epithelial tissue are called _____ .
4. The use of highly toxic drugs to treat cancer is called _____ .
5. A _____ is a condition that damages the body's normal functioning.

Multiple Choice

6. The spread of cancer cells to distant sites of the body is called   a) malignant.
   b) metastasis.   c) a chancre.
   d) a carcinoma.
7. Children with _____ produce large amounts of mucus.   a) Tay-Sachs disease   b) sickle-cell disease
   c) cystic fibrosis   d) Huntington disease
8. Proteins secreted by bacteria into an organism are   a) endotoxins.   b) exotoxins.
   c) antibodies.   d) antitoxins.

9. HIV attacks   a) platelets.
   b) T lymphocytes.   c) muscle cells.
   d) red blood cells.
10. Which of the following is not a
   degenerative disease?   a) cancer
   b) arthritis   c) multiple sclerosis
   d) muscular dystrophy
11. Which of the following is not a known
   carcinogen?   a) cigarette smoke
   b) asbestos   c) sugar   d) X rays
12. A disease found most commonly in the
   African-American population is
   a) Tay-Sachs disease.   b) cystic fibrosis.
   c) malaria.   d) sickle-cell disease.
13. Which of the following diseases is not
   caused by a virus?   a) AIDS   b) chicken
   pox   c) measles   d) tetanus
14. Athlete's foot is caused by a   a) fungus.
   b) protozoan.   c) bacterium.   d) virus.

15. Which of the following is not a sexually
   transmitted disease?   a) syphilis
   b) gonorrhea   c) cancer   d) herpes

Writing Critically

16. How do viruses cause disease in a host
   organism?
17. How are the causes of cancer and multiple sclerosis alike?
18. Describe how a fatal hereditary disease
   could be passed on if it is autosomal
   dominant.
19. Compare AIDS with herpes in regard to
   causative agent, means of transmission,
   effect, and treatment.
20. Leukemia is one of the most difficult
   forms of cancer to treat. Explain why
   this is so.

Application/Critical Thinking

1. **Inferring Relationships**   Scientists know
   that the ozone layer of the atmosphere filters many harmful ultraviolet rays. If the
   ozone layer continues to be destroyed,
   how might its absence affect the rate of
   certain kinds of cancer?
2. **Analyzing Conclusions**   If an individual
   accidentally swallowed a sample of poliovirus, would he or she develop polio? Explain.

3. **Researching Information**   Use your
   library to find out more about AIDS.
   Write a paragraph about how it is moving
   into the heterosexual population.
4. **Synthesizing Information**   Children who
   have had chicken pox often develop shingles as adults. Shingles are caused by the
   same virus as chickenpox. How is this
   virus like herpes simplex type 2?

Cross-Discipline Connection

Biology and History   Choose one important
person in history who had poliomyelitis and
research how the disease affected his or her
life. Report your findings to the class.

Discovery Through Reading

The article "Watch Out for the Tick Attack,"
Consumer Reports (June 1988):381–385, explains Lyme disease. What methods of prevention does the article suggest to protect against
Lyme disease?

The article "Medicine's New Vision,"
National Geographic (January 1987): 2–41,
describes medical technologies that allow doctors to "see" inside the human body. Name the
techniques described in the article.

Alcohol, Other Drugs, and Tobacco

Outline

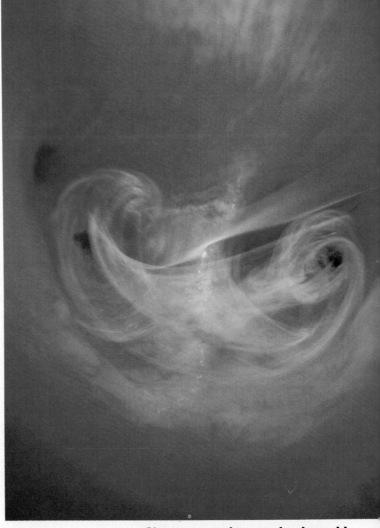

Cigarette smoke entering bronchi

Focus

For thousands of years, people have known that certain chemical substances called **drugs** have a marked effect on the body and mind. Today, a great many drugs are used medically to prevent and fight disease and to reduce pain. However, a number of drugs are misused by people who are seeking to escape problems and stressful situations. Misusing drugs is almost always harmful, endangering an individual's health and sometimes endangering other people also.

■ *What kinds of pressures may lead a person to experiment with drugs?*

■ *What is the analogy between using harmful drugs and putting diesel fuel into a regular gasoline engine?*

Psychoactive Drugs

A **psychoactive drug** is one that affects the central nervous system. Alcohol is an example of such a drug. Many other drugs, ranging from diet pills to LSD, also belong to this category. Because psychoactive drugs produce a false sense of well-being and relief from tension, they are the drugs most commonly misused.

50.1 Drug Abuse

Drug abuse occurs when a person takes excessive amounts of a psychoactive drug for nonmedical reasons. Many psychoactive drugs lend themselves to abuse because when used regularly, they can cause a state of dependence called **addiction.** Psychological addiction occurs when a user has an emotional need for a drug and uses it to maintain a state of well-being. Physical addiction exists when the body needs the drug in order to work properly. A characteristic of addiction is **withdrawal,** a painful reaction when the drug is discontinued. This condition causes severe tremors, severe sweating, and feelings of anxiety, and may progress to physical ailments, such as cramps or muscle pain, nausea, vomiting, and convulsions.

Continued use of a psychoactive drug often leads to **tolerance,** a condition in which larger and larger doses of the drug are needed to produce the desired effect. Drug tolerance is dangerous because taking ever larger doses of a drug may result in a fatal overdose.

50.2 Alcohol

The psychoactive ingredient in beer, wine, and other alcoholic beverages is ethyl alcohol, or ethanol (C_2H_5OH). Of all the types of alcohol, only ethyl alcohol can be consumed with relative safety. *However, ethyl alcohol is a drug—in fact, one of the most widely used and abused of all psychoactive drugs.* People who consume alcohol excessively can cause themselves serious physical harm.

Effects of Alcohol When a glass of beer or wine is consumed, most of the ethyl alcohol it contains is absorbed in the small intestine. However, about 20 percent passes directly into the blood through the walls of the stomach less than two minutes after consumption. From the blood, ethyl alcohol diffuses into tissue fluid and affects every cell in the body.

Section Objectives

- *List* the characteristics of drug abuse.
- *Describe* the effect of alcohol on the central nervous system.
- *Summarize* the stages leading to alcoholism and the health problems caused by excessive drinking.
- *Explain* how researchers have been able to diagnose alcoholism.
- *Distinguish* between the effects of hallucinogens, stimulants, and depressants.

For information about a career as a drug counselor, see pages 930–931.

Drinks in One Hour	Body Weight in Pounds								Influence
	100	120	140	160	180	200	220	240	
1	.04	.03	.03	.02	.02	.02	.02	.02	Possibly Impaired
2	.06	.06	.05	.05	.04	.04	.03	.03	
3	.11	.09	.08	.07	.06	.06	.05	.05	Impaired
4	.15	.12	.11	.09	.08	.08	.07	.06	
5	.19	.16	.13	.12	.11	.09	.09	.08	
6	.23	.19	.16	.14	.13	.11	.10	.09	
7	.26	.22	.19	.16	.15	.13	.12	.11	Legally Impaired
8	.30	.25	.21	.19	.17	.15	.14	.13	

Subtract .015% for each hour of drinking. One drink is 1 oz. of 80 proof liquor at 40% alcohol, 12 oz. of beer at 4.5% alcohol, or 4 oz. of wine at 12% alcohol.

Figure 50–1. The chart shows the blood alcohol content and the level of impairment that result after consuming 1 to 8 drinks.

Alcohol is oxidized in the liver and in body cells at a fairly constant rate of 29.6 mL (1 oz.) per hour. Oxidation changes an ounce of ethyl alcohol into water, carbon dioxide, and about 200 calories of heat energy. When a person drinks more alcohol than the body can oxidize, the excess alcohol accumulates in the blood and tissue fluid. The excess alcohol acts as a **depressant,** a drug that slows the functions of the central nervous system.

Even a small amount of alcohol affects the cerebral cortex, the part of the brain that controls thought, judgment, and self control. By suppressing these functions, alcohol produces feelings of relaxation and freedom from tension. A higher concentration of alcohol in the blood slows the brain centers governing speech, vision, hearing, coordination, and balance. As a result, the drinker may experience slurred speech, double vision, and staggering. If the concentration of alcohol in the blood reaches high enough levels, it can suppress the brain centers governing breathing and the heartbeat, causing death.

Biofact

Q: *What is fetal alcohol syndrome and what are some of its symptoms?*

A: Babies born of mothers who drink alcohol during pregnancy frequently have a condition called *fetal alcohol syndrome.* Babies with this disorder have small heads, low birth weight, retarded growth, and mental retardation. Many also suffer from heart murmurs, hernias, and urinary tract abnormalities.

Alcoholism Addiction to alcohol, or **alcoholism,** is the major drug abuse problem in the United States. About 10 million adults and 3 million teenagers are alcoholics. More than 200,000 people die of alcoholism each year. Alcoholism is a form of drug addiction. However, it is a treatable disease.

Alcoholism develops gradually through several stages. During the early stages, an individual drinks to be sociable but soon consumes larger amounts of alcohol and may experience blackouts. The individual continues to function during a blackout, but later cannot remember his or her actions. In advanced stages the individual loses control of the amount of alcohol consumed and eventually becomes intoxicated every day. In addition, a form of mental illness called *alcoholic psychosis* may occur. An individual with alcoholic psychosis becomes confused and may not recognize family members. In extreme cases, the individual may see or hear things that do not exist and develop uncontrollable trembling called **delirium tremens,** or **DTs.**

People who drink excessive amounts of alcohol over long periods of time also develop serious health problems. For example, many alcoholics suffer from a lack of vitamins because they do not eat properly when drinking heavily. A lack of nutrients may cause malnutrition and lead to abnormalities in the heart and circulation and inflammation of the stomach lining. In addition, alcohol is readily converted to energy, preventing the body from breaking down other nutrients, such as sugars, amino acids, and fatty acids. These nutrients are stored as fats in the liver. After several years of heavy drinking, liver cells are filled with fat and begin to die. Once in this condition, the liver may become inflamed, a condition called *alcoholic hepatitis*.

Biofact

Q: *Is alcoholism related to a person's genetic makeup?*

A: Research results are inconclusive, although some alcoholics seem to inherit a tendency for the disease. This tendency may take the form of a difference in the ability to metabolize alcohol.

THINKING ABOUT BIOLOGY: A Way to Diagnose Alcoholism

Diagnosing alcoholism before it reaches advanced stages is a difficult problem. Alcohol is absorbed and oxidized so rapidly that it quickly disappears from the bloodstream. Also, alcoholics generally deny to themselves or anyone else that they are drinking too much. As a result of this denial, physicians facing symptoms similar to those of alcoholism have had no sure way to make an accurate diagnosis.

Recently, however, experiments have indicated that the results of standard blood chemistry tests can be used to pinpoint alcoholics. In one experiment, researchers took blood from test groups of known alcoholics and nonalcoholics. Typical blood tests measure 25 separate chemicals in the blood. Instead of analyzing the test results of these 25 chemicals individually, however, the researchers looked for distinct patterns among the results. By doing a mathematical analysis of many blood chemicals and how they relate to each other, the researchers found one pattern associated with alcoholism and another associated with non-alcoholism. These patterns were then used in analyzing blood tests of other individuals. The researchers found they could identify severe cases of alcoholism 100 percent of the time, less severe cases 94 percent of the time, and nonalcoholics 100 percent of the time.

■ **Evaluating Information** What are the advantages of this test?

Figure 50–2. Law enforcement officers use breath-analyzing devices like the one shown to determine the level of alcohol in a driver's bloodstream.

If heavy drinking continues, a liver condition called **cirrhosis** may develop. In cirrhosis, functioning liver cells are replaced with useless scar tissue, and the liver gradually shrinks into a small, hard mass. In this form, the liver can no longer eliminate body wastes, produce blood clotting factors, or carry out its other functions.

50.3 Other Psychoactive Drugs

Psychoactive drugs include a variety of substances other than alcohol. The caffeine found in coffee is a psychoactive drug, as are heroin and the drug in marijuana. Some psychoactive drugs, while used in controlled doses to treat pain and disease, cannot be sold to or used by the general public. Abuse of both legal and illegal drugs can lead to many serious health problems.

Hallucinogens Drugs that distort the way the brain translates impulses from the sensory organs are called **hallucinogens** (huh LOO suh nuh jehnz). These distortions may take one of two forms. The brain may alter messages about something real, producing an illusion. The brain also may produce images with no basis in reality called *hallucinations*. Hallucinogens include LSD (lysergic acid diethylamide), mescaline, and peyote.

The effects of hallucinogens depend upon a variety of factors, such as the chemical used, the dosage, and the user's emotional state. Sometimes users see vivid images and have feelings of well-being. Users also claim that hallucinogens make them more creative and perceptive, although research has not supported these claims. However, people using hallucinogens may also experience depression, terror, and fear of dying.

LSD is an especially dangerous hallucinogen because its effects are so unpredictable. LSD may also make users feel that nothing can harm them. In this state of mind, users may take physical risks, such as stepping in front of a car, that lead to injuries or death.

Hallucinogens have a high potential for abuse. They do not create physical dependence but may produce psychological dependence. Hallucinogens do not have any currently acceptable medical use.

Stimulants Certain drugs are called **stimulants** because they stimulate the central nervous system and thereby speed up body processes. One common stimulant is the caffeine found in coffee, tea, some soft drinks, chocolate, and some diet pills. Amphetamines are a group of strong stimulants often called "speed." Other stimulants include nicotine and cocaine.

Deadly Designs

A certain group of drugs is more potent, addictive, and deadly than drugs such as cocaine and heroin. These drugs are called *designer drugs.*

An unscrupulous chemist produces a designer drug by slightly altering the molecular structure of a prescription or illegal drug that produces a "high." The compound formed by this slight alteration is called an *analog.* Certain analogs are 2,000 to 6,000 times more powerful than the drug on which they are based.

Designer drugs are extremely dangerous. Since they are made without any regulation or control, there is no assur-ance that they will not cause serious health prob-lems or death even for first-time users.

Among the deadliest of designer drugs are the analogs of *fentanyl.* More than 1,000 chemical analogs of fentanyl have been identified so far, most of which are much more powerful than heroin. Because the strength and quality of these analogs are unknown, many users have suffered major health problems, and even death, from using these drugs. As little as one dose has caused per-manent brain damage in people who have experi-mented with these drugs.

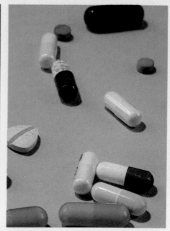

The common street names for analogs of fen-tanyl are China White and Synthetic Heroin. Street names for the analogs of certain hallucinogens and stimulants include MDMA, Ecstacy, Adam, and

The amphetamines are among the most commonly used of all stimulants. These drugs stimulate the cerebral cortex by re-placing neurotransmitters at the synapses. Their chief effect is to cause the body to react as if it were in danger. Thus ampheta-mines speed up metabolism, blood pressure, heartbeat and res-piratory rates. They also cause pupils to dilate, reduce the appe-tite, and produce a feeling of alertness and confidence.

Long-term use of stimulants can be dangerous. Because stimulants produce feelings of energy, users may not realize how exhausted they are. Excessive use of amphetamines for long periods can even cause mental problems resembling schiz-ophrenia, a condition in which a person loses touch with reality. In extreme cases, individuals may become violent.

Cocaine is a stimulant made from the leaves of the coca plant. Cocaine users take cocaine by inhaling it through the nose or by injecting it into a vein. The effects of cocaine resemble those of amphetamines, but inhaled cocaine also damages the membranes of the nasal passages. Ulcers form and holes may penetrate the septum. An even more addictive form of cocaine is *crack* or *rock* cocaine. Crack is cocaine that has been mixed with other substances and formed into chips. The chips are put in a pipe and smoked, delivering a large quantity of cocaine to the brain in seven seconds.

Depressants   Depressants are drugs that slow down the action of the central nervous system. This group of drugs includes alcohol, calming drugs called *tranquilizers,* and more powerful relaxants called *barbiturates.*

In small doses, depressants decrease awareness and relieve tension and inhibitions. Larger doses are used to treat sleep disorders and anxiety. However, excessive doses of depressants may result in a coma, a condition of deep unconsciousness. Depressants taken in combination with alcohol can be deadly. The depressant effects of both drugs can stop respiration.

Phencyclidine hydrochloride, also known as PCP or angel dust, is another depressant. However, it may also act as a hallucinogen or a stimulant. PCP is an extremely dangerous drug that can cause confusion, delirium, paralysis, and violent behavior.

Depressants may cause serious physical and psychological dependence. Withdrawal can be so severe that convulsions and death result.

Inhalants   A broad group of chemicals produce psychoactive vapors that can be inhaled. Nitrous oxide, also called "laughing gas," ether, and chloroform all have been used medically as anesthetics. When inhaled they produce a short-term effect similar to alcoholic intoxication.

Highly toxic are the fumes from a large group of organic solvents. These inexpensive and easily available substances include gasoline, paint thinners, glue, and cleaning fluids. Prolonged use results in irreversible brain and liver damage.

Marijuana   Marijuana is the dried leaves, flowers, or stems of the hemp plant *Cannabis sativa.* The psychoactive ingredient in marijuana is Δ9-THC (delta-9-tetrahydrocannabinol), which may act as a hallucinogen, stimulant, or depressant. Hashish is made from the dark, sticky resin of the hemp plant. It contains more THC than marijuana and is therefore more powerful.

Marijuana affects users in various ways. In some cases, the drug produces a sense of well-being and enhances the senses of taste, smell, sight, and hearing. If an individual is upset or depressed, however, marijuana may intensify those feelings. While under the influence of marijuana, a person may experience loss of judgment, loss of inhibitions, and distorted vision and hearing. Although marijuana does not seem to cause physical addiction, users may become psychologically addicted.

Narcotics Drugs that dull the senses and relieve pain by depressing the cerebral cortex are called **narcotics.** They also affect the limbic system, the body's mood-regulating center. One group of narcotics, called *opiates,* is derived from the opium poppy. Opiates include codeine, morphine, heroin, and opium.

Reading Critically

Analyzing Effects Why do narcotics cause changes in mood?

Many opiates are used as pain relievers and cough suppressants. Codeine, for instance, is found in some cough medicines. Morphine, which is a stronger drug than codeine, is used to dull severe pain. Heroin, which is stronger and more addictive than other opiates, is not used in medicine. However, it is the narcotic most widely abused.

Heroin can be inhaled or injected under the skin or into a vein. It induces a feeling of happiness, relieves pain, and affects the body much as a depressant would. Tolerance and addiction develop rapidly. For a heroin addict, withdrawal symptoms appear just a few hours after the last dose and may last for several days. Feelings of anxiety and general discomfort may progress to dilation of the pupils of the eye, diarrhea, and pain in the abdomen, muscles, and joints.

One method of treating heroin addiction is to substitute another narcotic agent, methadone, for the heroin. Methadone, like heroin, is addictive. An advantage is that methadone is taken orally, thus avoiding needle infections. Also, methadone is three to six times longer-lasting than heroin, so that the dosage can be given once a day. Methadone treatment is effective only when administered as part of a multiple program that also includes vocational and psychological guidance.

Section Review

1. **Relating Ideas** What are addiction and withdrawal?
2. **Evaluating Ideas** How does alcohol affect the central nervous system and the liver?
3. **Analyzing Conclusions** How have researchers been able to diagnose alcoholism?
4. **Comparing Ideas** Compare stimulants and depressants.
5. **Identifying Ideas** What is a hallucinogen?
6. **Synthesizing Conclusions** Explain why methadone treatment does not cure heroin addiction.

Thinking Critically

- *Identify* several components of tobacco smoke.
- *Describe* some effects of tobacco smoke.
- *Explain* why tobacco smoke may seriously affect nonsmokers.
- *Discuss* several diseases caused by or related to smoking.

The effect of smoke on air passages is the topic of the investigation on page 813.

Tobacco

Like any psychoactive drug that is misused, tobacco poses a serious health threat. Tobacco smoke is a combination of heated gases and suspended particles that contains more than 1,200 poisonous chemicals. One element in tobacco is **nicotine,** a colorless, oily psychoactive drug. *Tars* make up the particles in tobacco smoke. They also form a sticky coating on the lining of the bronchial tubes and can interfere with breathing.

50.4 Effects of Tobacco

Some gases in cigarette smoke, such as hydrogen cyanide, are strong poisons. Carbon monoxide, another of the gases, is thought to contribute to cardiovascular disease among smokers. Carbon monoxide reduces the amount of oxygen carried by hemoglobin, causing shortness of breath. In addition, the action of the cilia that line the respiratory passages may be inhibited for up to eight hours after being exposed to smoke. Constant exposure eventually destroys the cells that produce cilia and mucus in the respiratory tract. A smoker is then more susceptible to respiratory infections.

The carbon monoxide level in the blood returns to normal within eight hours after a cigarette-user stops smoking. The cilia require one to nine months to regrow after smoking stops.

Nicotine has a different effect than carbon monoxide. In small doses it acts as a stimulant and speeds up the transmission of nerve impulses. In high dosages, however, it has an inhibiting effect on nerve impulses. Nicotine also stimulates the adrenal glands. As a result, blood pressure rises, the heartbeat rate increases, and blood vessels constrict.

The smoker is not the only person affected by tobacco smoke. The smoke from a cigarette consists of mainstream smoke, which the smoker breathes in, and sidestream smoke from the tip, which is not drawn through the cigarette. Sidestream smoke contains twice as much tar and nicotine and five times as much carbon monoxide as mainstream smoke. Nonsmokers breathe this smoke into their lungs whenever they are in the vicinity of a smoker.

50.5 Diseases Related to Smoking

Smoking is involved in about 30 percent of all heart disease in the United States. Nicotine increases blood pressure and the heartbeat rate, causing stress on the circulatory system.

Biofact

Q: *Is "smokeless" tobacco any less harmful than smoking?*

A: Nicotine is also absorbed by the body from chewing tobacco and from dipping snuff. Chewing tobacco and snuff are equally as addictive as tobacco that is smoked, and lead to an increased risk of mouth and throat cancers.

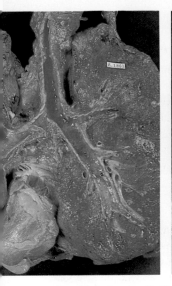 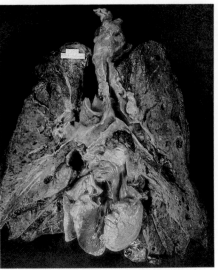 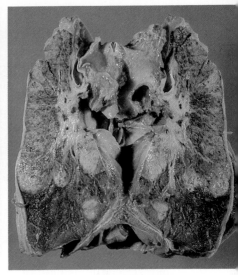

Smoking is also believed to contribute to 80 percent of all cases of lung cancer. Lung cancer is the leading type of cancer death in the United States, accounting for 120,000 deaths each year. The risk of developing lung cancer is directly related to the length of time a person has been smoking and the number of cigarettes smoked each day. Cancer of the mouth, larynx, esophagus, stomach, and urinary bladder are also more common in smokers than in nonsmokers.

Emphysema and chronic bronchitis are also related to smoking. Chronic bronchitis involves inflammation of the bronchial tubes and an increase in the production of mucus. A chronic cough and breathing difficulties result. Chronic bronchitis is often followed by emphysema. Emphysema is a disease marked by rupture of the alveoli, the tiny sacs in the lungs where gases are exchanged. Because the surface area for gas exchange is reduced, a person suffering from emphysema cannot get rid of carbon dioxide or take in oxygen efficiently. Eighty percent of all emphysema cases are related to smoking.

Figure 50–4. The photo on the left shows a healthy heart and lung, photographed from the back. Compare this with the photos of a lung of a person suffering from emphysema (center) and cancer (right).

Reading Critically

Inferring Relationships
Why are diseases that cause breathing difficulties often related to smoking?

Section Review

1. **Relating Ideas**   How do the carbon monoxide and nicotine in cigarette smoke affect the body?
2. **Summarizing Ideas**   What are tobacco tars? Describe what they do.
3. **Summarizing Ideas**   List and describe several diseases related to smoking.
4. **Evaluating Conclusions**   Why might a nonsmoker living with a smoker develop diseases associated with smoking?

Thinking Critically

Anabolic Steroids

Anabolic steroids are synthetic male hormones. When they were developed, researchers hoped that anabolic steroids might be used in medicine to stimulate the body to make more of the proteins that direct tissue growth and repair. This application, if it could be achieved, would help speed the healing of fractured bones and injured muscles and tendons.

However, additional research showed that the effectiveness of anabolic steroids in speeding the healing process was questionable. Anabolic steroids proved to have serious side effects. These effects commonly include atrophy of the testes, increased risk of heart disease, and liver and kidney disorders. Steroids may also cause impotence in males and masculinization in females. These side effects may be worse in young people whose growth is not yet complete.

Steroid use can also cause psychological problems. Users may experience increased hostility and aggressiveness.

One especially dangerous effect is an increased tolerance to pain. People who take steroids sometimes continue strenuous physical activity even after injury, causing serious damage to their bodies and even, possibly, death.

Many people, however, choose to ignore the dangerous side effects in favor of certain benefits: the rapid increase in muscle tone and bulk. Some bodybuilders, swimmers, football players,

and track athletes believe that increased strength and performance are worth the risk. They are not willing to sacrifice a competitive advantage to opponents who use steroids.

Analyze the Issue

1. State the information that a person might consider in deciding whether or not to use anabolic steroids.

2. What issues and ethical questions arise from the development of drugs, such as steroids, that artificially enhance athletic performance?

3. What part, if any, do you think athletic organizations should play in controlling the use of steroids by athletes?

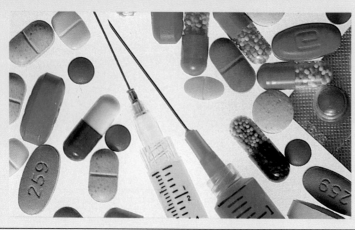

INVESTIGATION 50:
How Does Smoking Affect Air Passages?

Objectives
- To *use* a model that simulates the collection of substances along the air passages as a result of smoking
- To *infer* the effect of smoking on cells

Materials

cigarettes, matches, glass tubing, glycerine, rubber tubing, aspirator, rubber medicine dropper bulb, scissors, burette clamp, ring stand, cork, cork borer

Prelab Preparation
1. Identify substances that are normally found in cigarette smoke.
2. Name substances in cigarette smoke that may be harmful to the body tissues.
3. Read the procedure described in steps 4–8 below. In the apparatus described, identify the part of the human body represented by the glass tubing.

Inquiry: Exploration
4. Carefully bore a hole that has a slightly larger diameter than the glass tubing through the cork.
5. **CAUTION: Handle the glass tubing with care, as it can break and cause cuts.** Lubricate a 15-cm length of glass tubing with a few drops of glycerine. Then slide the glass tubing about halfway through the hole in the cork.
6. Cut the closed end off the top of the rubber bulb of a medicine dropper and use it as a holder for the cigarette.
7. Use a short piece of rubber tubing to connect the cut end of the holder to one end of the glass tubing.
8. Connect a 20-cm piece of rubber tubing to the aspirator. Use a second short piece of tubing to connect the aspirator to the open end of the glass tubing.
9. Use a burette clamp to hold the apparatus by the cork at the appropriate level on the ring stand, as shown in the illustration.
10. Place a cigarette in the rubber holder.
11. Ignite the cigarette by placing a lighted match at the tip of the cigarette and

use the rubber tubing connected to the aspirator to draw air through the system. Continue to draw air through the system in this way to "smoke" the cigarette.
12. Use the apparatus to "smoke" two or three cigarettes. *What appears on the inside of the glass tubing as the cigarettes are smoked?*
13. Gently touch the glass tubing. *How has the temperature of the glass changed since beginning the Investigation?*
14. Disconnect the glass tubing and smell the open end. Describe the scent.

Analysis
1. **Analyzing Observations** What evidence from your experiment indicates that substances in cigarette smoke coat the air passages?
2. **Making Inferences** What effect might these substances have on the cilia that line human respiratory passages?
3. **Making Inferences** How could a scientist determine what chemicals are present in cigarette smoke?

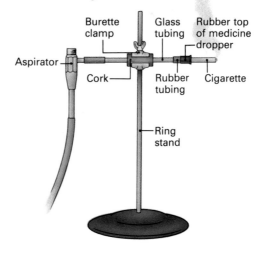

Chapter 50 Review

Summary

Psychoactive drugs are those drugs that affect the central nervous system. These drugs are often abused. Using these drugs may lead to physical dependence, psychological dependence, or both. The body may also build up a drug tolerance. Tolerance is a condition in which the body becomes "used to" a drug. As a result, increasing amounts of the drug are required to produce the same effect.

Alcohol is a depressant that slows down body processes. When a person consumes more alcohol than the body can oxidize, the excess alcohol affects the central nervous system. Thought, judgment, and self-control are affected first. Increased amounts of alcohol disturb speech, vision, balance, and eventually respiration. Addiction to alcohol, called alcoholism, is a treatable disease. Other psychoactive drugs are hallucinogens, stimulants, inhalants, marijuana, and narcotics. Many of these drugs are illegal because they impair judgment and may make users dangerous to themselves and to others.

Tobacco contains the drug nicotine, plus tars and gases. Tobacco has been linked to cancer, cardiovascular diseases, chronic bronchitis, and emphysema. Smoke affects not only the smoker but also anyone nearby who inhales the side-stream smoke.

BioTerms

addiction **(803)**
alcoholism **(804)**
cirrhosis **(806)**
delirium tremens
  (DTs) **(805)**
depressant **(804)**
drug **(802)**
drug abuse **(803)**

hallucinogen **(806)**
narcotic **(809)**
nicotine **(810)**
psychoactive drug
  (803)
stimulant **(806)**
tolerance **(803)**
withdrawal **(803)**

For each pair of terms, explain the differences in their meanings.

1. addiction, withdrawal
2. depressant, stimulant
3. hallucinogen, psychoactive drug
4. drug, narcotic

BioQuiz   (Write all answers on a separate sheet of paper.)

Completion

1. The most addictive and abused narcotic drug is _____ .
2. Alcohol can rapidly affect the body because it is absorbed into the bloodstream from the _____ .
3. Cirrhosis is a disease of the _____ caused by excessive drinking.
4. Narcotics affect the _____ , the body's mood-regulating center.
5. A substance in cigarettes that makes blood vessels constrict and the heart beat faster is _____ .

Multiple Choice

6. Excess alcohol in the body acts as a
   a) depressant.   b) stimulant.
   c) narcotic.   d) hallucinogen.
7. _____ drugs affect the central nervous system.   a) Narcotic   b) Hallucinogenic   c) Psychoactive   d) Depressant
8. Drugs that cause the body to react as if it were in danger are   a) barbituates.
   b) amphetamines.   c) hallucinogens.
   d) stimulants.
9. The drug that is made from the dark, sticky resin of a hemp plant is

a) hashish. b) marijuana. c) ether.
d) heroin.
10. The drug that is sometimes used to treat heroin addiction is a) hashish. b) marijuana. c) nicotine. d) methadone.
11. Which of the following does not contain caffeine? a) chocolate b) tea c) cigarettes d) coffee
12. When a user stops taking drugs, he or she may undergo symptoms of a) withdrawal. b) addiction. c) depression. d) psychosis.
13. LSD, mescaline, and peyote are all a) barbituates. b) hallucinogens. c) amphetamines. d) inhalants.
14. Which of the following does not cause physical dependence? a) alcohol b) depressants c) marijuana d) All

choices are correct.
15. The ingredient in cigarette smoke that may contribute to cardiovascular disease is a) nicotine. b) carbon monoxide. c) carbon dioxide. d) tar.

16. What causes an alcoholic's liver to deteriorate?
17. Why is it dangerous to mix alcohol and barbituates?
18. Why are smokers susceptible to respiratory infections?
19. How might some people abuse both stimulants and depressants at the same time?
20. What are the effects of each of the major categories of drugs?

Application/Critical Thinking

1. **Relating Ideas** Alcohol inhibits the production of antidiuretic hormone (ADH). ADH increases permiability of the kidney's collecting ducts so that large amounts of fluid return to the blood. How does using alcohol affect urine output?
2. **Predicting Outcomes** HCl secretion in the stomach increases when the hormone gastrin is present. Explain how the consumption of alcohol caffeine, which stimulates gastrin secretion, affect HCl levels.
3. **Synthesizing Conclusions** The hemoglobin of smokers carries more carbon monoxide and less oxygen than that of nonsmokers. How might smoking affect heart muscle?

Cross-Discipline Connection

Biology and Social Studies   Discuss the contracts between students and parents proposed by MADD (Mothers Against Drunk Driving) and SADD (Students Against Driving Drunk). How do contract agreements provide support among members of a group?

Discovery Through Reading

Read the article "Alcoholism's Elusive Genes," *Science News* (July 30, 1988): 74–75, 79. This article addresses the question of an inherited tendency for alcoholism. Describe the two types of predisposition to alcoholism. Describe the personality types for individuals expressing both types of predisposition.

"The Perils of Pot," *Discover* (June 1988): 18, discusses the effects of smoking marijuana. List the physiological effects of smoking marijuana. How do the amounts of carbon monoxide and tar in the lungs compare after smoking a marijuana and a tobacco cigarette? What symptoms do babies born to marijuana-smoking mothers show?

Summary

Human tissues form complex organs which function as integrated organ systems. An internal bony skeleton supports the body and is held together by ligaments. Striated muscles are attached to bones by tendons and move bones through contraction. The muscular system also includes smooth, involuntary muscles and cardiac muscle. Skin covers the body and also excretes waste and helps regulate body temperature.

The digestive system breaks down food mechanically and chemically. Most chemical digestion takes place in the small intestine where most food is also absorbed. The circulatory system carries nutrients and oxygen to all the body cells. This system also removes wastes and transports disease-fighting cells and substances. The heart pumps blood through arteries and receives blood from veins. The exchange of materials takes place through capillary walls. Blood consists of plasma and formed elements that include red and white blood cells and platelets. Lymphocytes produce or carry antibodies, which function in immunity, thus protecting the body from disease.

Exchange of gases between the air and the bloodstream occurs through lung alveoli. A pair of kidneys remove metabolic waste and regulate the amount of water in the cells of the body.

The nervous system coordinates and controls body activities. Neurons carry electrochemical impulses to and from the central nervous system. The peripheral system includes sympathetic and parasympathetic systems that govern the "fight or flight" response. Complex sense organs monitor the environment. Specialized regions of the human brain control and regulate different activities and make thinking possible.

Reproduction in humans is sexual. After fertilization, the egg develops into an embryo that is attached to the uterus wall by a placenta. Materials diffuse to and from the mother's bloodstream through the placenta. Birth occurs after nine months of gestation.

Human diseases include infectious diseases caused by viruses, bacteria, fungi, and protozoa; STDs; degenerative diseases; and hereditary diseases. The use of alcohol, some other drugs, and tobacco have harmful effects on the body.

Synthesis

Synthesis Statement

The human body shows complex and coordinated activities that allow humans to succeed among the vast array of other living things in the physical world. Although the body systems are often studied separately, each one works with and often influences and depends on all the others. Upsets in the functioning of any body system, whether through improper diet, invasion by pathogens, inborn errors of metabolism, degeneration of tissues, or substance abuse, results in disease.

Synthesis Questions

Apply your understanding of this unit to the following questions.

1. Describe the relationship between the circulatory system and the respiratory systems. What is the adaptive value of separate respiratory and circulatory systems?

2. Which human system is most strikingly different from that of other mammals? Describe how this system has played a role in the evolutionary success of humans.

3. Humans are capable of living in many different environments including some with extreme climates. What adaptations do humans show that allow them to live in various environments and climates?

4. Identify the human organs that would be most difficult to replace with an artificial body part. Why do these organs pose such great challenges to scientists who design artificial body parts?

5. The human body is organized into a dozen different systems. Explain why the body plan of the human body is an effective design for housing the different systems.

6. Syphilis and AIDS are sexually transmitted diseases that affect many parts of the human body. Identify the body systems that may be affected by syphilis and AIDS and explain how each of these diseases affects each system.

7. Humans are quite large compared to many other organisms. Describe the biological problems that result from the relatively large size of humans. Explain why humans could not double their size without major changes occurring in their overall structure.

8. The pituitary gland produces several different hormones. What systems of the body might be affected if a tumor destroyed all or part of the pituitary gland? Explain what the results of the loss of pituitary function might be on each of the systems you have named. Offer an explanation that may account for different consequences in each sex.

9. Use a separate piece of paper to draw a concept map like the one below. Place each of the following terms inside the appropriate figure: long term control, short term control, and body systems. Identify the systems that are responsible for long-term and short-term control. Also identify the arrow that shows feedback.

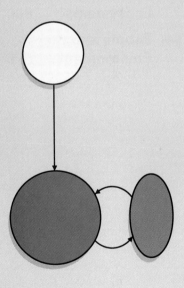

UNIT 11

ECOLOGY

Unit Focus

Each organism interacts with other organisms in a vast interrelated web of life. All organisms interact with the environment and have an impact on this environment.

- *How do the regular patterns created by contour farming show the impact of humans on the Wyoming grassland environment?*

- *What problems were humans trying to solve when they cultivated the land in these patterns?*

Contoured farmland in Wyoming

Introduction to Ecology

Outline

A beaver changes its environment

Focus

Every organism exists in an environment. The study of environments and the relationships of living things to their environment is called **ecology**. An ecologist is a person who studies environments and the relationships that exist in them. Even a small change in an environment or a change in the activities of one kind of organism can have widespread effects on this complex network of relationships.

■ *What physical changes does a beaver make in its environment?*

■ *How do these changes benefit other organisms in the area?*

Organization of the Biosphere

Life on Earth extends from the ocean depths to a few kilometers above the land's surface. The great biological drama, the struggle for survival, is played out entirely within this thin and fragile space. Ecologists call this area where life exists the **biosphere.** The biosphere is an extremely complex system and a difficult one to understand. To unravel the mystery of how millions of diverse species live together in the biosphere, ecologists divide it into smaller, more easily studied units. These units are called ecosystems.

51.1 Ecosystems

An **ecosystem** is a physically distinct, self-supporting unit of interacting organisms and their surrounding environment. A forest, for example, is an ecosystem. Its physical boundaries are the areas where trees give way to other types of vegetation. A forest is considered self-supporting because plants change energy from the sun into chemical energy. Forest animals then eat the plants and are eaten by other animals, thus transferring energy from organism to organism. When forest plants and animals die, their bodies are decomposed by microorganisms, and the chemicals released by this decomposition are then reused by other living things. By these four processes—production of chemical energy from sunlight, transfer of energy, decomposition, and reuse of nutrients—an ecosystem sustains itself year after year. A forest is an example of a physically distinct, self-supporting part of the biosphere. Therefore, a forest is considered an ecosystem.

Many kinds of ecosystems exist on Earth. They vary in composition and size. An ecosystem can be as large and complex as a jungle or as small and simple as a tiny patch of garden. Meadows, rivers, and tide pools are examples of ecosystems. Bogs found in the middle of a forest and the waters of mountain lakes are also ecosystems.

An ecosystem consists of two sets of environmental factors: biotic factors and abiotic factors. An ecosystem's **biotic factors** are all of its living organisms. Most ecosystems contain many organisms of many species. The individuals of some species are easy to see, such as a hawk or an oak tree, but many are not visible to the naked eye, such as the microbes that exist everywhere. **Abiotic factors** are the nonliving parts of the ecosystem. These factors include light, soil, water, wind, temperature, and nutrients.

Section Objectives

- *List* some effects of abiotic factors on ecosystems.
- *Explain* how populations of organisms are organized into a community.
- *State* the difference between an organism's habitat and its niche.
- *Discuss* the importance of the relationships among members of a community.

For information on careers, see pages 934–935.

Figure 51–1. The boundary between a forest ecosystem and a sand dune ecosystem is clearly visible in this photograph.

If you had been in Borneo one day in 1955, you would have seen a strange and surprising sight. The skies over many villages were filled with parachutes dropped by the British Royal Air Force. The parachutes were carrying cats. The need for "Operation Cat Drop" arose after the World Health Organization attempted to rid the area of malaria. To control the population of malaria-carrying mosquitoes, the villages were sprayed with two potent pesticides. These insecticides wiped out the mosquitoes, but they also created many other problems.

Two of the normal inhabitants of the village huts were cockroaches and lizards, called geckoes. The cockroaches, contaminated by the insecticides, were eaten by the geckoes. In turn, the lizards were eaten by the cats. A a result, the cats were poisoned by the accumulation of pesticides. Without cats the village rat population increased dramatically. Because rats carry bubonic plague and typhus, the villagers were threatened by these serious, and often fatal diseases. Operation Cat Drop restored the cat population. Soon the rat population was under control and the disease threat eliminated. Operation Cat Drop shows scientists that disturbing one part of an ecosystem's biotic community may have unexpected and far-reaching effects on its other members.

■ **Analyzing Relationships** What did Operation Cat Drop show about the relationships among organisms?

Figure 51–2. Cactus plants (top) thrive in sunlight so bright it would kill most other plant species. Violets (bottom) grow best on a shady forest floor.

Light and Temperature Light and temperature are two of the most important abiotic factors. Plants such as the barrel cactus grow best in the high-intensity light of the desert. Nettles on a forest floor, however, are adapted to low-intensity light. In addition, the distribution of organisms in a lake or ocean is directly related to how deep light penetrates the water. For instance, some algae live near the surface of a lake where the light is bright, while other kinds of algae live near the bottom in areas of little light.

Temperature is equally important. Some organisms, such as lemmings and dwarf willows, are adapted to the cold arctic wastelands, where the temperatures during the growing season are often no higher than 5°C (41°F). Gila monsters and many other cold-blooded animals live in the desert where summer temperatures are often above 38°C (100°F).

Water and Soil Water and soil are two additional important abiotic factors. Individual organisms differ in their need for water. Many animals, such as the kangaroo rat, live in a desert environment, where water is scarce. Many other animals and plants, however, live in water.

Soil variations are also important. An example is the plant genus *Ammophila*. *Amm* is Latin for "sand"; *philos* is a Greek word meaning "to love." *Ammophila* lives on sand dunes because it requires sandy soil. Other plants, such as basswood trees, require a nutrient-rich soil in which to grow. Earthworms need a soil rich in oxygen, but some bacteria are able to live in soil with no oxygen at all. Chemical variations and soil acidity help determine where an organism will live and how well it will thrive. In addition, the animals themselves affect the composition of the soil, because they add their own organic materials to the soil's original composition.

51.2 Communities and Populations

An ecosystem's biotic factors—the plants, animals, and other organisms in an ecosystem—interact with one another. Because of this, ecologists say that these living things are members of the same biotic **community.** A community is a group of organisms that coexist. *Members of a community form a system of production, consumption, and decomposition.*

To better comprehend communities, ecologists often divide them into smaller units called populations. A **population** is a group of many individuals of a single species that occupy a common area and share common resources. For instance, all the maple trees in a maple-basswood forest are members of the same population. This is also true of all the trout in a mountain lake. All of the populations of a self-sustaining area make up a biological community.

The number of populations within a community varies. A tropical rain forest or a coral reef contains thousands of populations. Other communities, such as deserts, contain relatively few populations.

51.3 Habitats and Niches

Ecosystems are made up of interacting communities, and communities are composed of interacting populations. Likewise, populations are composed of interacting individuals. Each individual organism lives in a specific environment and pursues a specific way of life.

The part of an ecosystem in which a particular species lives is called its **habitat.** For example, the habitat of a California condor is the dry hills in certain parts of southern California. The habitat of a gray whale is the coastal waters of the western Pacific Ocean. An organism may inhabit an entire ecosystem, such as a woodpecker in an oak forest. The oak forest is the

Figure 51–3. The number of populations inhabiting a community can be extremely large. A coral reef, with its many plant and animal species, is an excellent example.

Figure 51–4. The giant panda has a very limited ecological niche. Its diet consists largely of bamboo shoots.

Reading Critically

Inferring Conclusions Is the niche of a human narrow or broad? Explain your answer.

woodpecker's habitat. However, the habitat of other organisms may be a small part of the ecosystem, such as that of the amoeba, which lives in a few square millimeters of ooze on the bottom of a pond.

The way of life a species pursues within its habitat is called its ecological **niche.** An organism's niche is composed of both biotic and abiotic elements. These include how much moisture it requires, what it eats, where it lives, when and how it reproduces, and other such factors that make up its life. The niche of an armadillo, for example, includes such elements as the necessary food, water, and light. Its niche also includes temperature and space. In short, the total way of life of the armadillo is known as its niche.

Some niches are very broad. Rats, for example, live in houses, sewers, barns, ships, or even in open fields. They eat a varied diet, which may include grain, processed food, garbage, or other animals. They can reproduce when the temperature is hot, cold, or moderate, and may reproduce several times during a year.

In contrast, some niches are narrow. Pandas, for instance, are found in only a few isolated regions in China. They are very sensitive to changes in their environment and will not mate unless conditions for reproduction are perfect. They usually mate just once a year. Their diet consists almost exclusively of bamboo shoots. The panda, unlike the rat, has a very limited ecological niche.

Even when they may appear to, niches do not overlap. For example, five different kinds of warblers can live harmoniously in a single spruce tree. However, one species feeds mainly in the upper branches and another in the lower branches. The third species feeds primarily close to the trunk. The other two feed near the ends of the branches but in different parts of the tree. Although all five different kinds of warblers live in the same tree, each occupies a different niche. None of the warblers competes directly for limited food, water, or space.

Section Review

1. **Evaluating Ideas** Explain why a forest is considered an ecosystyem.
2. **Analyzing Conclusions** In what ways does an ecosystem sustain itself year after year?
3. **Relating Ideas** How do the amounts of available light and water affect an ecosystem?
4. **Summarizing Ideas** What is a community? A population?
5. **Comparing Ideas** What is the difference between an organism's habitat and its niche?

Thinking Critically

The Flow of Materials

All organisms need certain chemicals in order to live. Chief among these are water, oxygen, carbon, and nitrogen. Organisms use these substances in the molecules that supply their nutrients and make up the materials of their bodies. When organisms die, these chemical materials are returned to the earth and the atmosphere. Other organisms then take up and use these same chemicals. *The continuous movement of chemicals throughout the ecosystem is called recycling.* The pathway through which a chemical substance is recycled is its **biogeochemical cycle.**

Section Objectives
- *Explain* what is meant by a biogeochemical cycle.
- *Describe* how water is recycled throughout a given ecosystem.
- *Show* the pathways taken by oxygen and carbon during recycling.
- *Define* nitrogen fixation, ammonification, nitrification, and denitrification.

51.4 The Water Cycle

The water cycle is an example of a biogeochemical cycle. Heat from the sun evaporates water from oceans, lakes, moist soil, the leaves of plants, and the bodies of animals. Water molecules from these sources are carried into the atmosphere by air currents. There they condense around dust particles and eventually fall to Earth as precipitation in the form of rain, snow, hail, or fog.

Rain replenishes Earth's oceans and lakes. Plants release some of the water from their leaves through *transpiration*. Some water filters down through the soil until it reaches solid rock. By means of seepage and underground streams, this groundwater eventually reaches streams, lakes, and oceans, where much of it is recycled by the process of evaporation.

For information about the effect of algal blooms on freshwater oxygen levels, see pages 362–363.

51.5 The Oxygen-Carbon Cycle

Oxygen and carbon make up much of the body's carbohydrates, proteins, and fats. They are also involved in many chemical reactions. Like water, carbon and oxygen are recycled throughout the ecosystem. Their recycling pathways are so closely related that they are considered part of the same biogeochemical cycle, called the **oxygen-carbon cycle.**

The oxygen-carbon cycle is driven by photosynthesis and respiration. In photosynthesis plants take in carbon dioxide (CO_2). The oxygen is then released into the atmosphere as a gas, and the carbon is used to make glucose. The glucose and carbohydrates made from glucose are used by animals that eat the plants. Organisms release chemical energy from the breakdown of glucose during respiration. After additional chemical changes, some of the products of glucose metabolism become

Biofact

Q: *How much carbon is incorporated into sugar by plants each year?*

A: Photosynthesis produces 50 to 60 billion metric tons (4 to 7 trillion pounds) of sugar annually.

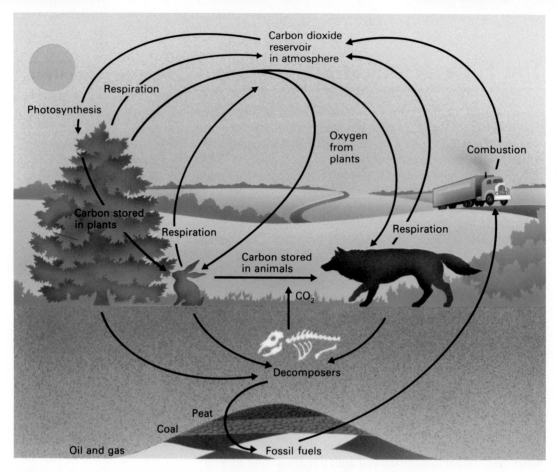

Figure 51–5. Carbon dioxide and oxygen are constantly recycled through plants, animals, and the atmosphere.

part of the animal itself. When these plant eaters are eaten, the carbohydrates are passed on.

During the process of respiration, unused carbon is returned to the air as CO_2 or is released in solid waste. Decomposers break down wastes and dead tissue, releasing more CO_2.

51.6 The Nitrogen Cycle

Nitrogen, a component of proteins and DNA, is also cycled throughout the biosphere. Over 78 percent of the air is nitrogen gas (N_2), but nitrogen in this form is useless to organisms. *Most living organisms use nitrogen only in the form of nitrates (NO_3^-), nitrites (NO_2^-), or ammonia (NH_3).* Atmospheric nitrogen must be converted, or fixed, into usable molecules.

The conversion of nitrogen gas (N_2) to nitrate (NO_3^-) is known as **nitrogen fixation.** Nitrogen fixation is carried out mainly by bacteria found in the roots of *legumes,* such as peas and beans. These bacteria take atmospheric nitrogen (N_2) and change it to nitrates, which the plants can then use. When animals eat these plants, the animals acquire usable nitrogen.

Reading Critically

Predicting Outcomes
What do you think would happen if there were no legumes on Earth?

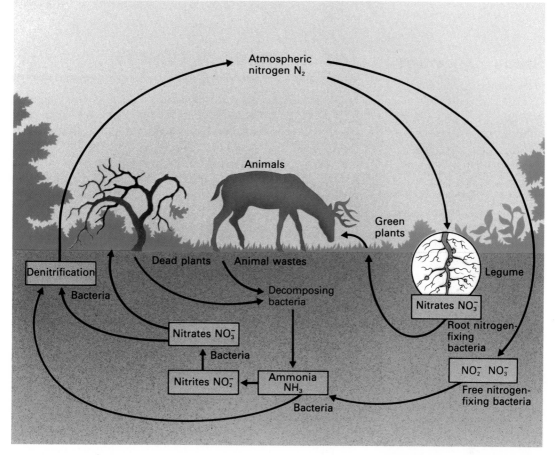

When plants and animals excrete waste or die, microorganisms convert their nitrogen compounds to ammonia—a process called **ammonification** (uh moh nuh fih KAY shuhn). Then, because most plants cannot use ammonia, it is converted into nitrate (NO_3^-) in a two-step process called **nitrification** (ny truh fuh KAY shuhn). One group of soil bacteria changes the ammonia to nitrites; another group of bacteria then converts the nitrites into nitrates.

Other bacteria convert ammonia, nitrite, and nitrate back into nitrogen gas—a process known as **denitrification.** Thus nitrogen gas (N_2) is returned to the atmosphere.

Figure 51–6. Certain bacteria convert atmospheric nitrogen into a form that organisms can use. Other kinds of bacteria recycle nitrogen from living things back into the atmosphere.

Section Review

1. **Identifying Systems**   How is underground water recycled?
2. **Organizing Ideas**   What are the events in the oxygen-carbon cycle?
3. **Relating Ideas**   How does nitrogen fixation make nitrogen available to plants?
4. **Synthesizing Information**   Why are cycles important?

> **Thinking Critically**

Section Objectives

- *Name* the trophic levels within an ecosystem.
- *Distinguish* among herbivores, carnivores, omnivores, and scavengers.
- *Discuss* the differences between food chains and food webs.
- *Draw* an energy pyramid, pyramid of mass, and pyramid of numbers for a typical ecosystem.

Figure 51-7. This jackal and hyena act as scavengers when they feed on the remains of animals left behind by predators.

The Transfer of Energy

Individual organisms within a biotic community survive either by producing food or by feeding on other organisms. Plants, the chief producers, make food by the process known as photosynthesis. This food may be consumed by animals. Food energy thus moves from one organism to another. The process of the transfer of energy is not haphazard, however. It is part of an organized system of energy flow throughout the ecosystem.

51.7 Trophic Levels

A plant is eaten by a rabbit, which in turn is eaten by a coyote. Events such as these take place each day throughout the biosphere. Each of these organisms—plant, rabbit, and coyote—belongs to a distinct level of feeding within the ecosystem. The various levels are referred to as **trophic** (TROHF ihk) **levels.**

Plants are at the first, or lowest, trophic level in an ecosystem. Plants produce their own food, so ecologists refer to them as *producers.* An animal that eats a plant is acting as a *primary consumer,* also called a *first-order consumer.* An animal that eats primary consumers is called a *secondary consumer,* or *second-order consumer.* An animal that eats a secondary consumer is a *tertiary consumer.* In the example above, the plant is the producer, the rabbit is the primary consumer, and the coyote is the secondary consumer. The particular species found at each trophic level vary from community to community, but the overall pattern remains the same.

Sometimes animals are referred to by the type of food they eat rather than by their trophic level. Animals that eat only plants are called **herbivores.** Animals that eat only animals are called **carnivores.** Animals that eat both plants and animals are **omnivores. Scavengers** are animals that feed only on dead organisms. A scavenger may be a herbivore, a carnivore, or an omnivore. Crayfish, which live in ponds and streams, are primarily scavengers. Vultures and certain canines, such as jackals, are also scavengers.

Organisms at all trophic levels die. Decay organisms then act upon their bodies, breaking down tissues into small molecules. These organisms, such as bacteria and fungi, are called **decomposers** because they break down the dead plant and animal tissue and return the nutrients to the soil. In addition, many decomposers feed on materials that would not be considered food at any other trophic level. Among these are animal wastes and the cellulose found in plants.

51.8 Food Chains

As you have seen, organisms at one trophic level feed upon organisms at a lower level. The sequence of one organism feeding upon another at a lower trophic level is called the *food chain*.

Figure 51–8 shows an example of a food chain in the northern Atlantic Ocean. Some types of plankton are producers. These producers are eaten by small herbivorous invertebrates called *copepods*. The copepods are in turn eaten by sand eels, which are in turn eaten by herring. Herring are then caught and ultimately eaten by human beings. This food chain has five levels—plankton, copepod, sand eel, herring, and human.

Most food chains involve no more than four or five trophic levels. In the example above, however, a tapeworm in a human being would add another level.

51.9 Food Webs

Ecosystems almost always contain more than a single food chain. Most food chains also overlap because many organisms eat more than one type of food. As a result, the relationships between various trophic levels are often very complex. In most ecosystems the food chains are intertwined to form a *food web*—a network of interacting food chains.

A relatively simple food web is shown in Figure 51–9. In this particular community, a small meadow, plants are eaten by primary consumers, including mice, rabbits, grasshoppers, and other insects. The grasshopper may be eaten by a secondary consumer, such as a lizard or a bird. The mouse may be eaten by a hawk or a snake. The hawk may also eat the rabbit, the lizard,

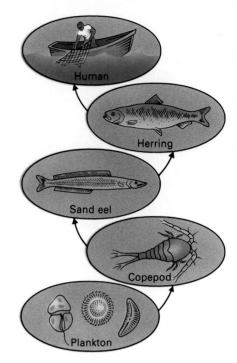

Figure 51–8. Food chains include producers, herbivores, and carnivores. What are the producers in this food chain?

Figure 51–9. Because an organism can represent more than one trophic level, a food web is more complicated than a food chain.

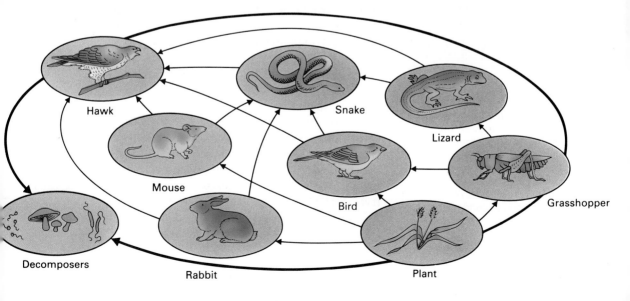

the bird, or the snake. When these organisms die, decomposers act to release carbon, nitrogen, and other essential substances for reuse by other organisms.

In the example described, the hawk is both a secondary and a tertiary consumer. In a food web, a single organism may act at several different trophic levels. When you eat a roast beef sandwich, you are consuming on two different trophic levels at the same time. The bread is composed of wheat, which is made from a producer. The roast beef is made of the muscles of cattle, which are primary consumers. So when you eat a roast beef sandwich, you are acting as both a primary and a secondary consumer.

51.10 Ecological Pyramids

When a head of lettuce grows in the sun, it captures some of the sun's energy. However, all of this energy is not passed on to the rabbit that eats the lettuce. The lettuce plant undergoes metabolism, which uses energy. The amount of energy a plant stores—the amount available to the hungry rabbit—is much less than the plant initially got from sunlight. The bobcat that eats the rabbit will receive only a portion of the energy that the rabbit gained from the lettuce. One reason for this is that the rabbit used some of the energy gained from the plant to meet its own metabolic needs.

The energy available for use by organisms at each trophic level averages only about 10 percent of the preceding level. This means that as much as 90 percent of the energy is used up or lost during metabolism. In a pond ecosystem, for example, for every 1,000 kilocalories of energy taken in as light by the algae, which are the producers, almost 900 kilocalories are lost as heat during metabolism. Only 100 kilocalories are available to the minnows that eat the algae. Bass, the secondary consumers that eat minnows, receive only 10 kilocalories, or only 0.01 of the original energy input. If a human catches and eats the bass, the energy he or she receives is only 1 kilocalorie, or only 0.001 of the energy initially stored by the algae.

To visualize this decrease in available energy in an ecosystem, ecologists create diagrams called **ecological pyramids.** One of the most important of these is the *energy pyramid.* An energy pyramid shows the amount of energy, measured in calories, contained in the bodies of organisms at each trophic level. Figure 51–10 shows an energy pyramid. Notice that at each level, less energy is available.

A *pyramid of biomass* can also be useful for visualizing an ecosystem. **Biomass** is the mass of an organism after all the water

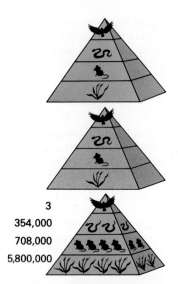

3
354,000
708,000
5,800,000

Figure 51–10. A pyramid of energy (top), a pyramid of biomass (center), and a pyramid of numbers (bottom) illustrate relationships among trophic levels. From top to bottom, the levels in each pyramid represent tertiary consumers, secondary consumers, primary consumers, and producers.

Nature's Energy Transfers

Imagine that, in place of a steak, a diner ordered the grain it took to fatten the cow that produced a steak. The grain that the diner was served might take up most of the room in a small restaurant.

The diner, the cow, and the grain are each on different levels of an ecological pyramid. The cow feeds directly on producers—the green plants that convert sunlight energy into the energy found in the chemical bonds of organic molecules.

Because they are living things, producers use some of these molecules as parts of their structure. Others are broken down to provide energy for the producer's metabolism. Although metabolism is efficient, some energy is lost in this process as heat, which escapes into the atmosphere.

Producers that are seed plants package some of the sunlight energy in molecules that are stored in their seeds. The grains that are fed to beef cows are the seeds of the producer. The cow, then, is on the second level of the pyramid. The grains provide the molecules that the cow uses for its own structure and metabolism. Some of these molecules will become steak, and some

will be used for the cow's metabolism.

About ten percent of the energy of a lower level on an ecological pyramid is transferred to the level above it. Therefore, a beef cow must eat many times its weight in grain to produce steak. By bypassing the cow and eating the grain, a diner may, perhaps, have more meals.

has been removed. In such a pyramid, the biomass of all the individuals of a trophic level are added together. The pyramid of biomass in Figure 51–10 shows how, in general, biomass tends to decrease along with energy transfer.

Another useful pyramid is the *pyramid of numbers*, also shown in Figure 51–10. A pyramid of numbers is used to show that the number of organisms feeding at each trophic level also tends to decrease.

Section Review

1. **Relating Ideas** Explain how energy is transferred in an ecosystem.
2. **Comparing Ideas** Distinguish carnivores from scavengers.
3. **Relating Ideas** Illustrate three ecological pyramids.
4. **Comparing Ideas** Compare food chains and food webs.

Reading Critically

Analyzing Ideas Where does all the energy go if only 10 percent is transferred from level to level?

Thinking Critically

Section Objectives

- *Tell* what causes competition among organisms in ecosystems.
- *Distinguish* among mutualism, commensalism, and parasitism.
- *Discuss* the difference between circadian and annual rhythms.
- *Explain* the different kinds of symbiotic relationships and give examples of each.

Biotic Relationships

All organisms must live side by side with many other organisms. The evolutionary process has shaped ecosystems so that each ecosystem's organisms constantly interact with one another. Many different kinds of interactions exist among the organisms in an ecosystem. The result is a dynamic system that supports each population's requirements for natural resources.

51.11 Competition and Predation

In any ecosystem factors such as food, space, and water are found in limited quantities. *Competition* is the struggle among organisms for limited natural resources. When organisms compete with members of their own species, they undergo *intraspecific competition*. When organisms compete with other species, they show *interspecific competition*.

Competition resulted in the evolution of animals with distinct patterns of consumption. Some animals eat only plants; others eat animals. Animals that seek out and kill other animals for food are **predators.** The organisms they consume are *prey*. You might think that all of the prey in an area would soon be wiped out by predators. Ecologists know, however, that predators and prey coexist in a balanced relationship that keeps the population of each relatively constant year after year.

51.12 Symbiosis

Competition and predation are not the only ways that organisms interact with one another. Organisms also engage in symbiotic relationships. **Symbiosis** (sihm by OH sihs) means "living together." *A symbiotic relationship is a permanent, close relationship between two organisms of different species that benefits at least one of them.* The three types of symbiosis are mutualism, commensalism, and parasitism.

Mutualism   **Mutualism** is a symbiotic relationship in which two organisms live together or cooperate with each other for mutual benefit. For example, termites eat wood but are unable to digest its cellulose. The cellulose is digested by protozoa that live in the termite's gut. Termites benefit from the presence of the protozoa by getting food digested, and the protozoa benefit by being protected by the termite's body. In fact, under normal conditions the protozoa would be unable to live outside of the termite's body. The termite-protozoa relationship is mutualistic.

Figure 51–11. An animal's size has nothing to do with whether it eats plants or other animals. The elephant, one of the largest animals, is an herbivore.

Similarly, a lichen is a mutualistic organism composed of an alga and a fungus living intertwined with one another. The alga produces sugars for itself and for the fungus. The fungus receives food and, in turn, covers the alga, thus protecting it from the environment and providing it with moisture.

Commensalism **Commensalism** is a symbiotic relationship in which one organism benefits and the other is neither helped nor harmed. Commensalism occurs, for example, in tropical rain forests. Large trees often have many small plants called *epiphytes* growing on them. These plants do not damage the supporting tree but, by living high in the air, receive more sunlight than if they grew on the deeply shaded forest floor. Epiphytes get water from rain or vapor. They get minerals from dust and from leaves that fall from their support trees. A commensal relationship exists between the epiphytes and the tree because the epiphytes benefit while the tree is neither harmed nor helped. Many species of orchids are epiphytes.

Parasitism **Parasitism** is a symbiotic relationship in which one organism benefits and the other is harmed to some extent. In a parasitic relationship, one organism, called a *parasite,* lives in or on another organism. The parasite obtains food from the other organism and harms it in the process. The organism that is harmed is called the *host.*

Mistletoe is a parasitic plant that lives on hosts such as oak and cedar trees. Mistletoe contains chlorophyll and thus is able to make its own food, but it obtains minerals and water from its host. To do this, it invades the host's tissues and causes severe damage.

51.13 Biological Rhythms

Organisms are affected not only by their relationships to other organisms but also by their relationship to the physical environment. Some environmental phenomena, such as day length, seasonal temperature, and phases of the moon, recur at regular intervals. Many organisms respond to these naturally recurring phenomena by undergoing physiological changes called *biological rhythms.*

The pattern of changes that occurs in organisms every 24 hours is called a **circadian** (suhr KAY dee uhn) **rhythm.** *Circa* is Latin for "about"; *dia* is Latin for "day." Sleep and wakefulness in humans is a circadian rhythm. Organisms that are active during the day are called **diurnal.** Organisms active at night are called **nocturnal.**

Figure 51–12. Oak trees are sometimes draped in Spanish moss (top). Both species thrive in this mutualistic relationship. Mistletoe (bottom) also grows on oaks, but this parasite damages the host.

One of the most interesting examples of a mutualistic relationship is the symbiosis of ants and acacia trees in Central and South America. For a long time, scientists knew that *Acacia cornigera,* the bull thorn acacia, housed large numbers of ants. Careful study of this relationship has revealed the reason.

The acacia tree provides a home for ants in the form of large thorns on its stem. Sometimes 10 or 15 ants can fit into one thorn. The tree also produces special growths on its leaves called *beltian bodies.* Chemical analysis of these structures revealed that they are full of glycogen, which is also called animal starch. The plant has a biochemical pathway that produces food that is used by ants.

The acacia derives benefits, too. Ants, protective of their food and housing, attack any predators that attempt to eat the acacia. In addition, the ants destroy other plants that, if allowed to grow, would shade the acacia and cut off its light. Bull thorn acacias are often found standing alone in open clearings because the ants have mowed down all the

surrounding vegetation.

■ **Analyzing Relationships** Why is the relationship between the ant and the acacia considered to be mutualistic?

The internal chemical mechanisms that control circadian rhythms are called *biological clocks*. Although almost all organisms in the plant and animal kingdoms exhibit regular cycles of change, no one knows exactly what a biological clock is.

Another type of biological rhythm is the annual rhythm. An *annual rhythm* is the pattern of a physiological change that occurs once a year. Flowering, egg-laying, mating, and seed germination may show annual rhythms. **Hibernation,** the reduction of activity by warm-blooded animals in winter, is based on an annual rhythm. **Estivation** (ehs tuh VAY shun), the reduction of activity by animals in summer, is another change that occurs annually.

Reading Critically

Comprehending Ideas
Why are hibernation and estivation considered annual rhythms?

Thinking Critically ⟩

Section Review

1. **Inferring Ideas**   What factors cause competition?
2. **Comparing Ideas**   Compare mutualism and commensalism.
3. **Comparing Ideas**   Compare circadian and annual rhythms.
4. **Evaluating Conclusions**   How might estivation benefit one active species in an ecosystem?

INVESTIGATION 51:
How Can You Explore a Soil Community?

Objective
- To *observe* a soil community

Materials 🔲🗂🧤🕯️⚗️🧤

plastic bags, rubber bands, test tube, pan, forceps, hand trowel, petri dish of nutrient agar, commercial anesthetic prepared for insects, sterile water, inoculating loop, triple-beam balance, metric ruler

Prelab Preparation
1. List the trophic levels that are present in most communities.
2. Define the term pyramid of biomass.
3. Make a table similar to the one shown.
4. Explain the ecological use of the term litter.

10. After separating the animal and plant material, use the triple-beam balance to find the mass of the animal material and the mass of the plant material. Record your results.
11. Repeat steps 6 and 7 for the soil sample.
12. Place a sample of soil about the size of a pea into a test tube that contains about 5 mL of sterile water.
13. Sterilize an inoculating loop. Inoculate the nutrient agar with the soil-water mixture. Incubate the dish at room temperature for 48 hours. Record your observations.
14. Share your observations with two other teams that collected samples from different locations.

Sample	Animal/ Plant	Mass	Number Observed	Description
Soil Surface	Animals	⬛		
	Plants			
Litter	Animals			
	Plants			
Soil	Animals			
	Plants			

Inquiry: Exploration
5. Collect litter from a 25-cm-square area and place it in a plastic bag and seal the bag.
6. Observe the surface of the soil and record your observations in your table.
7. Using a hand trowel, remove a 15 x 15 x 15-cm sample of soil. Place the soil in a plastic bag and seal the bag.
8. In the laboratory, place a few drops of anesthetic into the bag of litter, close the bag, and wait 5 minutes. *What is the purpose of adding anesthetic to the bag?*
9. Pour the litter into the pan and search it for organisms. Record your observations in your data table.

Analysis
1. **Summarizing Observations** Compare the number and variety of animals in the litter with the number and variety of animals in the soil.
2. **Analyzing Observations** Does a pyramid of biomass exist in this community? Explain.
3. **Analyzing Observations** What trophic levels are found in this community?
4. **Making Inferences** Is there evidence of an ecological balance in this community? Explain.
5. **Comparing Observations** How does the community you investigated compare to the communities studied by other teams?

Chapter 51 Review

Summary

Ecology is the study of the relationship of organisms to their environments. Ecosystems are physically distinct, self-supporting systems of interacting organisms and their environment. Ecosystems are composed of communities of organisms and the abiotic, or nonliving, factors in the environment such as light, water, soil, and temperature. Within an ecosystem, an organism occupies a physical region, called its habitat. Each species also has a specific niche, or way of life.

Abiotic factors play an important role in determining where organisms live. Organisms depend upon a continuous supply of recycled nutrients, such as water and carbon. Organisms can be producers, consumers, or decomposers. All organisms occupy a trophic level, and all are members of a specific food chain. Permanent, close relationships between different species are called symbiotic. Organisms respond to regularly reoccurring phenomena in patterns called biological rhythms.

BioTerms

abiotic factors (**821**)
ammonification (**827**)
biogeochemical
  cycle (**825**)
biomass (**830**)
biosphere (**821**)
biotic factors (**821**)
carnivore (**828**)
circadian
  rhythm (**833**)
commensalism (**833**)
community (**823**)
decomposer (**828**)

denitrification (**827**)
diurnal (**833**)
ecological
  pyramid (**830**)
ecology (**820**)
ecosystem (**821**)
estivation (**834**)
habitat (**823**)
herbivore (**828**)
hibernation (**834**)
mutualism (**832**)
niche (**824**)
nitrification (**827**)

nitrogen
  fixation (**826**)
nocturnal (**833**)
omnivore (**828**)
oxygen-carbon
  cycle (**825**)

parasitism (**833**)
population (**823**)
predator (**832**)
scavenger (**828**)
symbiosis (**832**)
trophic level (**828**)

For each pair of terms, explain the differences in their meanings.

1. abiotic factors, biotic factors
2. community, population
3. herbivore, omnivore
4. habitat, niche

BioQuiz   (Write all answers on a separate sheet of paper.)

Completion

1. The conversion of ammonia to nitrogen gas is called _____ .
2. A group of _____ in an area make up a community.
3. Factors such as light, temperature, and soil are examples of _____ factors.
4. Two jaguars seeking the same food is an example of _____ .
5. Organisms that are active at night are _____ .

Multiple Choice

6. A symbiotic relationship in which both organisms benefit is called
  a) parasitism. b) commensalism.
  c) mutualism. d) predatory.
7. Warm-blooded animals undergo _____ in the summer by slowing down their metabolism. a) hibernation b) estivation
  c) commensualism d) symbiosis
8. A _____ is an example of a scavenger.
  a) panda b) zebra c) jackal d) lichen

9. An organism's way of life is its
   a) community. b) habitat. c) niche.
   d) ecosystem.
10. The pathway through which a chemical
   substance is recycled is its a) biogeochemical cycle. b) biosphere.
   c) ecosystem. d) ecological pyramid.
11. Nitrogen fixation is carried out by bacteria found in the roots of a) trees.
   b) algae. c) lichens. d) legumes.
12. Members of the same species make up a
   a) community. b) niche.
   c) biosphere. d) population.
13. In the symbiotic relationship of _____ ,
   one organism benefits but the other is not
   harmed. a) mutualism b) parasitism
   c) commensalism d) predation
14. At each higher trophic level about _____
   percent of the energy is lost. a) 10

b) 30 c) 50 d) 90
15. An example of an abiotic factor in an
   ecosystem is a) a rabbit. b) water.
   c) a mushroom. d) a bacterium.

Writing Critically

16. What two requirements are necessary in
   order to identify an area as an ecosystem?
17. How do the three types of symbiotic
   relationships differ?
18. Is it possible for an organism to eat at
   more than one level on a food chain?
   Explain your answer.
19. What chemical transformations take place
   during nitrogen fixation, nitrification, and
   denitrification?
20. How do competition, predation, and
   symbiosis differ?

Application/Critical Thinking

1. **Inferring Conclusions** In the grasslands
   of Africa, many species of animals coexist
   in the same area although they all eat plants.
   Suggest reasons for these harmonious relationships in the face of limited natural
   resources.
2. **Synthesizing Information** Some ecologists who are concerned with food shortages
   suggest that people eat less meat and more
   grains and beans. This is called "eating

lower on the food chain." Considering the
flow of energy in the biosphere, explain
why this practice conserves energy.
3. **Analyzing Conclusions** Parasites do not
   usually cause the death of their hosts. Those
   that destroy the host are probably not as well
   adapted as those that do not. Write a paragraph that explains why it is advantageous
   for a parasite to do as little harm to the host
   as possible.

Cross-Discipline Connection

Biology and Economics Compare prices of
plant products, such as margarine, with animal
products, such as butter. What ecological principle explains the differences?

Discovery Through Reading

Read the article "The Anemone Is Not Its
Enemy," *National Wildlife* (October–November 1987):22–25. Describe the relationship
that has developed between the clownfish and
the sea anemone.

   "They've Got Rhythm," *National Wildlife*
(December–January 1987): 34–37, describes
the amazingly accurate biological clocks in
plants and animals. What is a biological
rhythm? What is chronobiology?

Succession and Biomes

Outline

A community of lichens and mosses on a rock in Antarctica

Focus

A variety of communities exist in the sand dunes of the Pacific coastline, the oak-hickory forests of New England, the jungles of Borneo, the treeless mountaintops of the Swiss Alps, and the thousands of other biological communities that are found on Earth. Communities change through natural processes and through disasters such as fires and hurricanes. Communities form even larger ecological units.

- *What factors influence the kinds of communities that are found in a particular area?*

- *What kinds of events might cause a change in an ecological community?*

Ecological Succession

You may have walked through a maple forest that was hundreds of years old. If your grandmother and grandfather had walked in the same forest, they probably saw the same kinds of plants and animals that you saw. However, ecologists know that the area was not always a maple forest. A thousand years ago it might have been a meadow or even a shallow lake.

Just as individual organisms grow and change with time, so do the ecological communities of the earth on which we live. A community is a group of different types of organisms that coexist. Such communities replace, or succeed, each other in a predictable, orderly way. The process of replacement is called **ecological succession.**

52.1 The Process of Succession

The complete process of succession may take hundreds, even thousands, of years and always involves a number of intermediate communities. Two hundred years ago a maple forest might have been an oak forest. Three hundred years ago the oak forest might have been a grassland. A thousand years ago the grassland might have been a shallow lake. Each of these intermediate communities is called a **seral community.**

Seral communities replace one another for an interesting reason. *Each seral community alters the physical factors of the area in a way that makes it impossible for the community to regenerate itself.* For example, a pine forest grows and shades the forest floor. New pine seedlings, however, are unable to germinate in the shade created by their parents. Thus, the very existence of a pine forest often ensures that no more pines will grow. However, this shady environment makes it possible for organisms of another seral community to grow, because the new organisms—oaks, for instance—have different requirements.

The replacement of one seral community by another continues until a **climax community** forms. A climax community is a relatively stable, almost permanent, community. A climax community differs from a seral community in that it creates conditions in which its young can regenerate the community.

In any area the kinds of plants and animals that make up a climax community are determined by temperature, soil conditions, rainfall, and other physical factors. In the north central and northeastern United States, maple forests form a common climax community. In parts of Arizona, the saguaro cactus is the climax vegetation; in southern Florida, the sawgrass.

Section Objectives

- *Distinguish* between a seral community and a climax community.
- *Outline* primary and secondary succession.
- *Explain* what takes place during the primary succession of a lake to a forest.
- *Name* the stages in secondary succession by which a vacant field becomes a forest.
- *Explain* the role of weeds in ecological succession.

Figure 52–1. Tall pine trees produce conditions that discourage young pines from growing in their shade. The young trees growing below these tall pines are oaks and sweetgums.

In reality, natural climax communities may never form in an area. It often happens that one of the seral communities remains as the end result of succession. This happens when land is subject to repeated natural occurrences such as fire or grazing that keep the successional process from reaching a climax. *Some communities are sustained by natural disasters.* For example, a prairie that is not periodically burned by wildfires will soon become a forest.

52.2 Primary Succession

Primary succession takes place in areas that have not supported communities before. The development of communities on bare rock, lava flows, sand dunes, and lakes are examples of primary succession. Bare landforms and waters that do not contain living organisms soon give way to seral communities and, ultimately, to a climax community.

From Lake to Forest Imagine a lake that has recently been carved by a glacier out of solid rock. Its water is perfectly clear. This lake is so new that it contains no sediment and no living organisms of any kind.

This lake may remain free of life for a short period of time, but soon dust blows into it, and soil slides in after a heavy rain. In addition, sediments are carried into the lake by the rivers that feed it. Wind-borne spores of bacteria, algae, fungi, and protozoa fall into the lake. These germinate and grow in the sediment that has settled there. These organisms are called **pioneer species** because they are the first to inhabit a community. Pioneer species are adapted to life in low-nutrient conditions. They grow, thrive, and eventually die, adding new nutrients, such as carbon and nitrogen, to the lake. The process of adding nutrients to an ecosystem or community is called **eutrophication** (yoo trahf ih KAY shuhn).

As eutrophication proceeds, the lake can support a few plants such as water lilies and quillworts. These plants take root in the shallow water at the lake's edge. They catch and hold soil. Some animals, such as frogs and insects, find suitable habitats in the plants at the lake's edge.

As the water lilies, quillworts, and insects die and decompose, their remains further eutrophicate the lake. The decaying organic matter collects on the lake's edge and bottom. The lake gradually becomes shallower. Cattails and rushes invade the shallow water. They grow tall and eventually shade out the water lilies.

After a while vegetation grows throughout the lake and the lake becomes a *marsh*—another seral community in primary succession. As the marsh becomes drier, willow trees start to invade its borders. Thus, another seral community, a willow community, forms. Over time other communities, such as a birch forest, a pine forest, and an oak forest, replace one another on the site once occupied by the lake. A climax forest, perhaps one dominated by beech trees, finally forms and primary succession is complete. The process may take as little as 500 years or as long as 10,000 years or more, depending on the initial condition of the area.

Sand Dunes

Another type of primary succession occurs on sand dunes. In parts of Wisconsin, Indiana, and Michigan, for example, sand dunes run parallel to Lake Michigan's shoreline. The dunes nearest the shore were formed recently. The dunes farther back were formed at an earlier time. As you walk away from the lake, you cross a series of progressively older and older dunes, but in effect, you are walking into the ecological future. The dunes closest to the lake contain the pioneer and early seral communities. Those dunes located farthest from the lake support the ecological communities that are in the final stages of succession.

Lake during its early stages

Lake has become a marsh

Climax community forms

Figure 52–2. As a lake (top) fills with vegetation, it gradually turns into a marsh (center). The marsh eventually becomes a forest (bottom).

Primary succession on sand dunes begins when wind and waves deposit organic matter on the bare sand. Grasses then root in the soil, stabilizing the sand and adding nutrients. Soon the seeds of shrubs carried by wind and water germinate, grow, and replace the grasses.

The shrubs add nutrients to the land. Pine trees then begin to grow. Birds called brown creepers, and other animals that live in association with large trees, begin to inhabit the area. When the pine trees become tall, they shade the ground, killing both the shrubs and their own seedlings. But oak seedlings, which need some shade in which to germinate, begin to flourish. The oaks eventually give way to a climax community dominated by maples. Primary succession on sand dunes takes about 1,000 years.

BIOLOGY AND YOU:

Stone Walls in the Forest

People who walk in the forests of the northeastern United States often come upon walls that are made of piles of large stones. It seems curious that anyone would build a wall in the middle of a forest.

A good detective would find evidence that the walls had been there for many years. Lichens encrust the stones. Some stones are crumbling from the activity of lichens that established themselves years before. Mosses grow in the crevices and, here and there, a weed or a wildflower grows. Soil is forming in the walls.

These walls were not always in the middle of forests. The people who piled the stones were marking the boundaries of their pastures and farms. They had cleared the land, and their cattle grazed in the open fields, and their crops grew in cultivated patches.

The people worked to keep weeds and small shrubs from overtaking the land. The land had to be tilled and the crops had to be weeded. Corn was a popular crop because corn grows rapidly, leaving little opportunity for some weeds to grow.

The corn could also be fed to the cows. The cows, in turn, kept the grasses short by grazing. The people who lived in these areas and farmed the land and tended the cows also built the walls. The walls are not high, but they are high enough to

mark the end of one property and the beginning of another.

Many of the farms are gone now. Weeds replaced crops, and bushes and shrubs replaced grasses that once grew in the pastures. Eventually, trees grew, and the once-cleared land slowly became a forest once more. However, the stone walls still remain—for people who walk in the woods to rest on, and look at, and think about.

52.3 Secondary Succession

When ecological succession takes place in an area where a community once stood rather than in a barren area, the process is called **secondary succession.** *Secondary succession often occurs after natural disasters such as fires, landslides, or floods.*

One example of secondary succession is *old-field* succession, a process by which climax communities are reestablished on abandoned farmland. Early settlers in the northeastern United States cleared land for farming, cutting down extensive oak-hickory forests in some regions. Later, these farms were abandoned. Today oak-hickory forests again grow on the once-farmed land because secondary succession has taken place.

However, when the fields were first abandoned, they did not immediately return to oak-hickory forest. Oak and hickory seedlings need cool shade and moisture to germinate and grow, but the soil in the abandoned fields was sunlit and dry. Only a few weeds, such as crabgrass, grew in the bright, dry conditions. These weeds became the pioneer species in the process of secondary succession.

As generations of pioneer plants died, nutrients were added to the soil. Thus, the crabgrass prepared the ground to support other species of plants. Six to eight years after it had been abandoned, the soil was shaded by shrubs.

Conditions were then favorable for the survival of pine seedlings. Little pines soon grew throughout the field. About 25 years later, the abandoned field became a pine forest community that flourished for the next 50 years.

The deep shade and moist conditions of the pine forest floor, however, were less favorable for pine seedlings than they were for oak and hickory trees. Over the next century these hardwood trees gradually replaced the pines. Eventually, the pine trees died out altogether and a climax community of oak and hickory was again established on the field. Thus, in a period of about 200 years, secondary succession had run its course.

Figure 52–3. An abandoned cornfield (top) is overrun with crabgrass. Five years later (bottom), broom sedge has replaced the crabgrass. Eventually, the crabgrass will be crowded out by pines.

Section Review

1. **Comparing Ideas** Compare primary and secondary succession.
2. **Evaluating Relationships** What conditions usually set the stage for secondary succession?
3. **Analyzing Information** What is the ecological role of weeds?
4. **Analyzing Conclusions** How does secondary succession proceed in an abandoned farm field?

⟨ **Thinking Critically** ⟩

- *Tell* what a terrestrial biome is and *name* the major ones.
- *State* how the environment of the tundra affects the kinds of plants and animals that live there.
- *Compare* a grassland, a desert, and a tundra.
- *Describe* the plants that thrive in a tropical rain forest.
- *Tell* the effects of farming on the tropical rain forest.

Terrestrial Biomes

Climax communities found in similar climates are remarkably alike. A forest in southern Wisconsin, for instance, looks like one in northern Germany where the climate is about the same. Other areas, such as China, also have forests resembling those in Germany and Wisconsin. The species that make up each of these forests may differ, but all are composed of flowering trees that lose their leaves in the fall. These communities are members of a larger ecological unit called a **biome.** A biome is an extensive area of similar climate and vegetation.

The biome's abiotic factors determine what plants and animals live there. The major influences are temperature, light intensity, and the patterns of rainfall, which determine the availability of water. Though scientists disagree about the number of biomes on Earth, the ones that are most generally agreed upon are shown in Figure 52–5.

52.4 Tundra

The **tundra** is a biome of the cold regions like the crest of the Rockies and near the North Pole where the vegetation grows close to the ground. This biome covers a vast expanse of land just south of the permanent ice of the pole.

Arctic tundra is a gently rolling plain with a cold, dry climate. Winters are long and severe. Only 10 to 40 cm (4 to 16 in.) of precipitation fall each year, most of it as snow. Summers in the tundra are cool and very short. Even in the warmest times of the year the surface of the ground thaws only to a depth of about one meter (3 ft.). Below this the ground is permanently frozen. This permanently frozen ground is called *permafrost.*

The most common forms of plant life in the tundra are lichens, mosses, and other small plants that can withstand extreme cold. Most tundra plants, even willow trees, are short. Almost all are less than 10 cm (4 in.) high. The plants are short, an adaptation that helps them to avoid the icy winds.

Polar bears, musk ox, reindeer, and caribou are some of the large animals that live in the tundra. Polar bears are solitary hunters that stalk the ice caps north of the tundra for food. Caribou and reindeer form huge herds that migrate back and forth across the land. They feed mostly on lichens that cling to the soil. Small rodents, called lemmings, live in the tundra together with arctic foxes, arctic hares, and grouse-like ptarmigans. In the summer months, mosquitoes emerge in uncountable millions, making life in the tundra unbearable.

Figure 52–4. The Brooks Mountains region of Alaska presents a scene typical of the tundra. The landscape is bleak, the land is gently rolling, and the vegetation grows close to the ground.

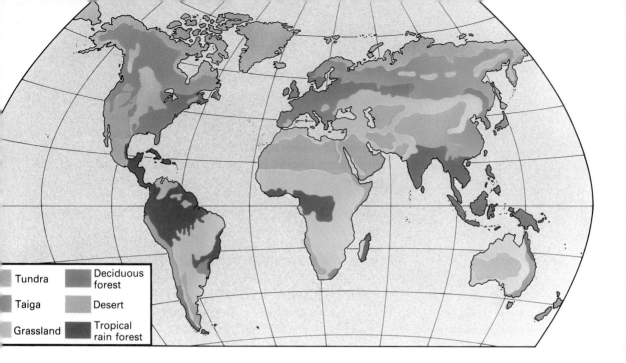

Tundra		Deciduous forest
Taiga		Desert
Grassland		Tropical rain forest

52.5 Boreal Forests

The **boreal forest** is a biome dominated by evergreen trees. It covers the northern reaches of North America, Europe, and the Soviet Union. This biome is also referred to as the *taiga* (TY guh). The taiga's summers are short and warm. The winters are long, snowy, and cold. About 20 to 60 cm (8 to 24 in.) of rain fall annually in this biome, which is also characterized by moist, spongy areas called *bogs*.

The dominant plants in the taiga are cone-bearing trees, such as white and black spruce and balsam fir. They retain their needlelike leaves throughout the harsh winters and reproduce and grow during the short growing season. These *conifers* form vast forests that cover hundreds of thousands of square kilometers. Much of the world's commercially available timber grows in the coniferous forest.

The animal most common to this biome is the moose. The coniferous forest contains so many moose that ecologists jokingly call it the "spruce-moose" biome. Other animals include bears, lynxes, elk, mule deer, and wolves. Smaller animals, such as porcupines, wolverines, hares, bobcats, and many kinds of rodents, also live in this area. During the summer, birds are numerous, particularly warblers.

On a spring evening, one can watch the dancing lights of the aurora borealis. This display of colored lights, often seen in the northern sky, is caused by the interaction of the earth's magnetic field with solar winds generated by the sun.

Figure 52–5. The worldwide distribution of six major biomes is shown on the map above.

Figure 52–6. The moose, a major inhabitant of the boreal forest, is the largest member of the deer family.

52.6 Deciduous Forests

The **deciduous** (dih SIHJ oo wuhs) **forest,** also called the *temperate forest,* is a biome dominated by deciduous trees. These are trees that shed their leaves each year. The deciduous forest covers the eastern half of the United States from southern Maine to northern Florida. It is also the dominant biome of Europe and eastern China. The deciduous forest receives rainfall year-round, measuring 60 to 100 cm (24 to 40 in.) of precipitation annually. Winters in this biome can be long, though not as long or severe as those of the boreal forest.

Maples, beeches, elms, oaks, hickories, and basswoods grow in many parts of the northern deciduous forest. In the southern hemisphere, other species of deciduous angiosperms replace the typical northern species.

Reading Critically

Listing Information What are the major characteristics of a temperate forest?

Figure 52–7. Trees that shed their leaves each year make up deciduous forests. In the fall such forests present a brilliant display of colors.

Plants in deciduous forests occupy one of four layers of vertical stratification. Some plants grow on the *forest floor,* the bottom-most level. Most are adapted to low light conditions. Many, however, flourish in the spring before the trees have produced leaves that intercept the light. Plants, such as shrubs and small trees, grow beneath the taller trees in the *understory.* The taller trees form the *canopy* layer where most of the incoming sunlight is captured. Some trees grow above the canopy and form the *emergent* layer.

The animal life of a deciduous forest is varied. White-tailed deer can be found in great numbers in this biome. Other animals include foxes, bears, wildcats, and small mammals such as mice and ground squirrels. Salamanders, snakes, lizards, rabbits, and chipmunks also live in the deciduous forest.

52.7 Grasslands

Grasslands—a biome dominated by grasses—occur where the precipitation is between 10 and 60 cm (4 and 24 in.) yearly. *Grasslands make up the largest of the several biomes found in the United States.* They cover much of the central part of the country. They are also found in central Africa and in parts of many other countries. Distinctive kinds of grasslands are given special names: *prairie* in the United States, *steppe* in Russia, *veldt* in Africa, and *pampas* in Argentina.

Spring in the grasslands is warm and wet, but it is usually followed by a scorching dry season. In many grasslands, the winters can be cold and snowy. Where rainfall is moderate, grasslands provide grazing lands for sheep and cattle. Where more moisture is available, grasslands are planted with wheat, oats, barley, and corn. Much of the world's population depends upon these areas for food.

Figure 52–8. The prairies of the midwestern United States are a familiar example of a grassland biome.

The grasslands of the United States are home for many large animals, such as bison and antelope. Smaller animals, including prairie dogs, coyotes, and badgers, are also characteristic of United States' prairies.

A **savannah** is a special kind of grassland located in a tropical or subtropical area. In a savannah trees are usually scattered throughout the grassy area. Unlike northern grasslands, savannahs remain warm all year. The largest and most famous savannah is the Serengeti Plain of East Africa. Within a single section of the Serengeti live grazing animals such as African buffalos, antelopes, gazelles, elephants, wildebeest, zebras, and giraffes. Numerous carnivores, including lions, cheetahs, wild dogs, and leopards, prey on the various grazing animals. Hyenas, jackals, and vultures are examples of meat-eating scavengers that also prowl the Serengeti.

52.8 Tropical Rain Forests

Tropical rain forests exist in equatorial areas where rainfall is high, sometimes over 500 cm (200 in.) annually. Most of the plants that grow in this biome are flowering trees. Plant growth is extremely rapid. The canopy in the rain forest is very thick, and little light reaches the forest floor. As a result many *epiphytes,* plants that use other plants for support, grow high up on the trees. Vines are also extremely common in a rain forest, as are ferns.

Large numbers of insects and other invertebrates live in tropical rain forests. Suprisingly, far fewer vertebrates live in rain forests than live in other biomes. Birds, monkeys, snakes,

Figure 52–9. Bamboo grows abundantly in this tropical rain forest in Hawaii.

THINKING ABOUT BIOLOGY: Destruction of the Rain Forest

The tropical rain forests of the world cover vast areas of land. Much of South America, southeast Asia, and central Africa are covered by tropical vegetation. Today, however, rain forests are threatened with destruction by the encroachment of human beings. Destruction of the rain forests may result in increased carbon dioxide in the atmosphere and may even change the distribution of rainfall throughout the world.

In order to meet the world's growing demand for food, many nations have opened up the rain forests to farming. Huge bulldozers tear down the thick vegetation and foresters cut down the trees. Yet the farms that result from this clearing of the land are often found to be unsuccessful because their soil is unfit to grow many kinds of crops.

The soils in tropical rain forests are extremely low in nutrients. Nutrients that enter the soil are quickly taken up by the many native plants that grow there.

Some tropical soils, called *laterite* soils, are claylike and may become hard as a brick when exposed to the hot tropical sun. Due to these factors, farmland in tropical areas produces crops for only three to five years. The land must then lie fallow for ten to fifteen years before even one or two more crops will grow.

Because the soil wears out so quickly, farmers will cultivate an area for three to five years and then move on to the next patch of cleared land. Each time they abandon a farm, they leave behind them a legacy of destroyed trees and wildlife as well as barren land.

■ **Synthesizing Conclusions** Why would destruction of rain forests increase the levels of carbon dioxide in the atmosphere?

---

and lizards are the chief vertebrate representatives. The *arboreal,* or tree-living, habit is common in the rain forest. Even large predators, like jaguars and panthers, spend time in trees.

Tropical rain forests are not jungles. *A jungle is a community within a rain forest.* Jungles grow on the edges of rivers and have very thick, almost impassable, vegetation.

52.9 Deserts

Deserts exist in areas where annual precipitation is less than 20 cm (8 in.). However, even this sparse rainfall is not evenly distributed throughout the year. In deserts in the United States, rain falls primarily in the winter; the rest of the year is often dry. In some places, such as the Sahara desert of northern Africa and

the Gobi desert of Mongolia, rain may fall only once every several years.

Desert plants in these dry environments are adapted to water conservation. Some plants, such as mesquite and creosote bush, grow long root systems that tap water deep in the ground. Other plants, such as cactuses, have shallow root systems. They store water in swollen stems and leaves. These plants have a thick outer covering that keeps the stored water from evaporating. Some desert plants are tiny, fast-growing plants that germinate, flower, produce seeds, and die all within a few weeks, sometimes even within a few days. The life cycles of these plants correspond to the short period when water is available.

The desert supports a wide variety of animal life including insects, reptiles, birds, and small mammals. Many desert animals are active at night. During the heat of the day, these nocturnal animals hide in the crevices of rocks or rest in cool, underground burrows. They venture out only when the evening brings cooler temperatures. Iguanas, Gila monsters, and horned lizards are among the many reptiles found in the deserts of the United States. Kangaroo rats, scorpions, and spiders are also common.

Figure 52–10. The saguaro cactus in the deserts of the southwestern United States and northern Mexico may reach 15 m (50 ft.).

For information about mapping ancient climates, see pages 282–283.

Section Review

1. **Comparing Ideas**   Compare a biome and a community.
2. **Analyzing Information**   Which two biomes have the lowest annual precipitation? Which has the highest?
3. **Contrasting Ideas**   How does a jungle differ from a tropical rain forest?
4. **Synthesizing Conclusions**   Even though they are unsuitable for farming, why are rain forests important to everyone in the world?

> **Thinking Critically**

- *Name* the two kinds of aquatic biomes and *explain* how they differ.
- *Discuss* the characteristics of the three ecological zones of the marine biome.
- *State* the most important factors that determine the distribution of organisms in a river and in a lake.
- *Explain* why the estuarine habitat is considered a fragile community.

For career information, see pages 932–933.

Figure 52–11. The marine biome is divided into three zones. Not shown in the diagram are the huge mountains that rise from the ocean floor. Many of them are volcanic.

Aquatic Biomes

Earth is the water planet. Oceans cover more than three-quarters of the earth's surface. Lakes and ponds dot the land. Rivers and brooks flow from the mountains to the sea. In each of these aquatic habitats, life abounds.

Ecologists divide the watery world into two biomes based upon *salinity*—that is, the amount of salt dissolved in the water. The *marine biome,* with a salt content of about 3.5 percent, includes the world's oceans. The *freshwater biome* comprises bodies of water with little or no salt, such as lakes, ponds, and rivers. A special aquatic community, the *estuary,* includes coastal habitats that are covered with a mixture of fresh and salt water.

52.10 The Marine Biome

The marine biome contains 99.9 percent of the earth's surface water. The distribution of life in this biome is affected by water temperature and by the availability of sunlight and nutrients. These factors vary from area to area.

Organisms in the marine biome live as one of three life forms: plankton, nekton, or benthos. **Plankton** are tiny animals and algae that float near the water's surface. **Nekton** are organisms, such as cod and sharks, that swim freely. **Benthos** are organisms, such as sponges and oysters, that live on the bottom. All of these marine organisms are distributed throughout three distinct ecological zones: the intertidal zone, the neritic zone, and the open sea zone.

The **intertidal zone** is that part of the seashore located between high and low tide. Organisms of the intertidal zone are covered with salt water at high tide and uncovered at low tide.

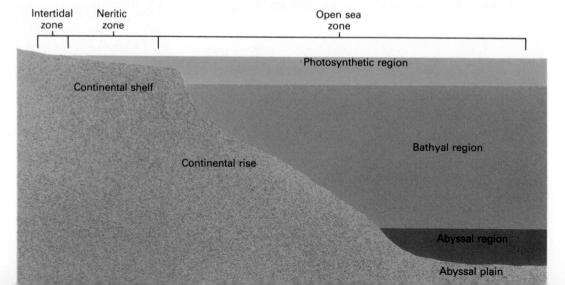

Intertidal zone   Neritic zone   Open sea zone

Photosynthetic region

Continental shelf

Continental rise

Bathyal region

Abyssal region

Abyssal plain

In addition to coping with this dramatic change, these organisms must withstand the powerful pounding of the surf. Despite these apparent hardships, the intertidal zone is crowded with life. Algae, barnacles, snails, and starfish are abundant.

The **neritic zone** is the region of open water close to shore. The water here is shallow compared to the deep seas, and light penetrates to the bottom. Many kinds of plankton live in the neritic zone. They form a plentiful supply of food for the variety of fish including cod and flounder found here.

The largest of the three marine biome zones is the **open sea zone.** The open sea zone has three regions: photosynthetic, bathyal (BATH ee uhl), and abyssal (uh BIHS uhl). The **photosynthetic region** is the area where most of the light penetrates. It extends from the ocean's surface to a depth of about 200 m (660 ft.). Plankton float near the surface in this region. Sharks, whales, large fish, and squid swim below. The **bathyal region** is the region of underwater twilight, extending from 200 m to 2,000 m (660 ft. to 6,600 ft.) deep. Little light reaches this area. It is home to strange organisms. Among these are fish that produce light biochemically through a process called *bioluminescence.* The **abyssal region** lies below 2,000 m (6,600 ft.). Life forms here are adapted to withstand extreme pressure. Dead organisms that sink to the bottom of the ocean provide food for the life forms in this zone. No light reaches this zone.

52.11 The Freshwater Biome

Lakes, ponds, rivers, streams, and brooks are typical habitats within the freshwater biome. The bodies of water that make up the freshwater biome contain relatively little salt. In rivers and streams, the rate of water flow, which determines the dissolved oxygen content, is a major factor in determining the types of organisms existing there. In lakes and ponds, the amount of nutrients is important in determining the forms of life to be found.

Lakes and Ponds A *pond* is a small, shallow depression in the land filled with fresh water. A *lake* is a larger body of water and may be quite deep. *The nutrient content of ponds and lakes changes over time.* Initially, these bodies of water have few nutrients. Their waters are clean and clear, and they support little life. In this state, lakes and ponds are called **oligotrophic,** (ahl uh goh TRAHF ihk). Lakes or ponds where nutrients are abundant are called *eutrophic* (yoo TRAHF ihk).

Plankton in eutrophic lakes use a tremendous amount of oxygen. Often there is only a little oxygen left over to support other forms of life. Fish such as catfish, carp, and certain bass,

Figure 52–12. Lakes rich in vegetation are also rich in nutrients. Such lakes are called eutrophic.

Figure 52–13. This estuary formed by the Delaware River has been designated as a wildlife refuge.

Reading Critically

Inferring Conclusions Why is such a diversity of life found in an estuary?

are well-adapted for survival in these oxygen-poor, nutrient-rich waters. However, oligotrophic lakes contain little plankton. Fish such as lake trout thrive in these oxygen-rich waters.

Rivers and Streams Organisms that live in rivers, streams, brooks, and creeks are adapted to life in flowing water. In slow-flowing streams, algae, mosses, and flowering plants are attached to the bottom of the stream, or its *bed*. Plants, such as water hyacinths, float on the surface. Catfish, frogs, and many invertebrates thrive in this environment.

52.12 Estuaries

An **estuary** is formed where rivers and streams meet the ocean. The salinity of an estuary is intermediate between that of the sea and a river. An estuary may be a mud flat, a salt marsh, or even a mangrove swamp. Most scientists consider estuaries as communities; others think all the world's estuaries make up a special kind of biome.

Changing conditions allow estuaries to support a great diversity of organisms. Fluctuation in water levels and the mixing of salt water and fresh water create a variety of habitats for organisms to live in. Also, estuaries are rich sources of nutrients. Clams, crabs, oysters, barnacles, and a variety of sea worms live in silt deposited by the incoming rivers. Large plants such as march grasses, eel grass, and filamentous algae are important producers in the estuary. Minnows and other tiny fish dart through the shallows. Shore birds are plentiful. Many marine animals spend their early lives here.

Individual estuaries are fragile communities. A sudden shift in a river's course can destroy an estuary. A particularly savage storm can overturn sand, uproot plants, and displace attached animals. New estuaries are constantly being formed as others are eliminated by natural catastrophes.

Section Review

1. **Listing Ideas** What are the two aquatic biomes?
2. **Comparing Ideas** How do the salinity of a marine biome, a freshwater biome, and an estuary differ?
3. **Listing Ideas** Name three ocean zones.
4. **Comparing Ideas** Compare oligotrophic and eutrophic lakes.
5. **Evaluating Information** Why is there a great diversity of organisms in estuaries?

Thinking Critically

INVESTIGATION 52:
How Does Altitude Affect a Climax Community?

Objectives
- To *analyze* data relating to mountain vegetation zones
- To *relate* altitude to climate and climax vegetation

Materials
graph paper, two colors of pencils

Prelab Preparation
1. List abiotic factors that determine which organisms can live in a particular biome.
2. Define the terms biome and climax community.

Inquiry: Observation
3. Use graph paper to make a graph that represents altitude on the horizontal axis in 300-m increments ranging from 1600 m to 4000 m. Represent the mean annual temperature on the right vertical axis in increments of 2° from −2° to 14°. Represent precipitation on the left vertical axis in 10-cm increments from 10 cm to 90 cm.

4. Use information from the table in this Investigation to plot a graph. Use a blue pencil to plot the precipitation for each altitude and a red pencil to plot the mean annual temperature for each altitude.
5. Make a bar graph with the same altitudes represented on the horizontal axis. Represent each kind of vegetation on the right vertical axis.

Analysis
1. **Summarizing Ideas** State the relationship between altitude and precipitation and the relationship between altitude and temperature.
2. **Analyzing Relationships** How is a mountainside similar to a series of small biomes?
3. **Inferring Ideas** How might the distribution of vegetation on this mountainside differ from that found on one that is located 200 km further south?

Climate and Vegetation in the Rocky Mountains of Central Colorado

Altitude (m)	Mean Ann. Temp. °C	Annual Total Precip. cm	Distribution of Climax Vegetation						
			Sedge	Douglas Fir	Grass	Subalpine Fir	Juniper	Englemann Spruce	Ponderosa Pine
1600	12	40			x		x		
1750					x		x		
1900	10	50			x		x		x
2050							x		x
2200	8	60							x
2350				x					x
2500	6	70		x					x
2650				x					
2800	4	75		x					
2950				x		x		x	
3100	3	65				x		x	
3250						x		x	
3400	1	50	x		x				
3700	0	30	x		x				
4000	−2	15							

Chapter 52 Review

Summary

Biological communities undergo a process of ecological succession. This process involves the replacement of one group of species by another group that is more adapted to life in a given area.

Two types of ecological succession occur. Primary succession takes place where no community existed before. Secondary succession takes place on land that has previously supported communities. During succession, the land is occupied by a number of seral communities before a climax community finally becomes established.

Large geographic areas that have similar climate and vegetation are called biomes. Tundra, boreal forests, deciduous forests, grasslands, tropical rain forests, and deserts are the major terrestrial biomes. The two biomes that make up the aquatic world are the marine and freshwater.

BioTerms

abyssal region (**851**)
bathyal region (**851**)
benthos (**850**)
biome (**844**)
boreal forest (**845**)
climax
    community (**839**)
deciduous
    forest (**846**)
desert (**848**)
ecological
    succession (**839**)

estuary (**852**)
eutrophication (**841**)
grassland (**847**)
intertidal zone (**850**)
nekton (**850**)
neritic zone (**851**)
oligotrophic (**851**)
open sea zone (**851**)
photosynthetic
    region (**851**)
pioneer species (**841**)
plankton (**850**)

primary
    succession (**840**)
savannah (**847**)
secondary
    succession (**843**)

seral
    community (**839**)
tropical rain
    forest (**847**)
tundra (**844**)

For each pair of terms, explain the differences in their meanings.

1. boreal forest, deciduous forest
2. intertidal zone, neritic zone
3. nekton, plankton
4. primary succession, secondary succession

BioQuiz   (Write all answers on a separate sheet of paper.)

Completion

1. The frozen layer of soil found in the tundra is called the _____ .
2. The Serengeti is an example of a type of grassland called _____ .
3. A community formed where a river or stream meets an ocean is called an _____ .
4. In _____ on sand dunes, the primary pine community gives way to the oak community.
5. _____ succession is when climax communities are reestablished on abandoned farmlands.

Multiple Choice

6. Organisms such as algae and tiny animals that float on the ocean's waters and provide food for other organisms are
a) nekton. b) plankton. c) a pioneer species. d) photosynthetic.
7. Bioluminescent organisms are found in the a) abyssal region. b) neritic zone. c) bathyal region. d) All choices are correct.
8. The _____ is known as the "spruce-moose" biome. a) tropical rain forest   b) tundra c) boreal forest d) deciduous forest

9. The organisms that first inhabit an area are called the _____ species. a) seral b) pioneer c) primary d) oligotrophic
10. A lake that has clear water with few nutrients is called a) eutrophic. b) oligotrophic. c) neritic. d) bathyal.
11. A lake that has abundant nutrients is called a) eutrophic. b) oligotrophic. c) neritic. d) bathyal.
12. The biome that has less than 20 cm (8 in.) of annual precipitation is the a) desert. b) tundra. c) boreal forest. d) grassland.
13. Plankton is found in the _____ region. a) photosynthetic b) abyssal c) bathyal d) benthic
14. The longest and coldest winters occur in the a) deciduous forest. b) boreal forest. c) tundra. d) taiga.
15. The uppermost layer of stratification found in forests is the a) benthos. b) understory. c) emergent. d) canopy.

Writing Critically

16. How do climax communities and seral communities differ in their to stability?
17. What are the three kinds of life forms found in the marine biome and how do they differ?
18. Why is a pine forest community unable to regenerate itself and why is it succeeded by an oak forest?
19. To what physical conditions must organisms of the intertidal zone be adapted?
20. How does the climate of a boreal forest differ from that of a deciduous forest and a rain forest?

Application/Critical Thinking

1. **Synthesizing Information** Write a paragraph suggesting how the loss of water from the Colorado River has affected marine and estuarine life in the Gulf of California.
2. **Researching Information** Do library research to find out about the biology of redwood trees. Write a paper describing how these trees obtain moisture. If possible, illustrate your report with illustrations of the redwoods.
3. **Inferring Relationships** The climax communities of inland areas around Lake Michigan's sand dunes are maple-basswood forests. Succession on the dunes themselves usually stabilizes at the oak-forest stage and does not progress to a maple-basswood climax community. Write a paragraph that offers explanations why succession does not proceed to the maple-basswood stage on the dunes.

Cross-Discipline Connection

Biology and Geography   Investigate life zones at elevations increasing from a tropical rain forest to a mountain peak. Diagram the relationship between altitude and life zone.

Discovery Through Reading

Read the article "California Desert: A Wordly Wilderness," *National Geographic* (January 1987):42–77. Describe three ways that the presence of humans in the desert has damaged that environment.

Read the article "Springtime in the Rockies," *Time* (May 29, 1989):94–95. Describe Yellowstone National Park one year after the great wildfires of 1988. How much of Yellowstone was destroyed?

Populations in Ecosystems

Outline

Monarch butterflies on a fir tree in Mexico

Focus

Monarch butterflies can blanket an entire field in Mexico. In Malaysia, so many fireflies can blink on and off at one time that the dark night suddenly becomes bright with biologically produced light. These phenomena are the result of the activities of enormous biological populations. A **population** is a group of individuals of the same species inhabiting an area.

■ *What is the distribution of the human population?*

■ *What factors might influence the size of a population in a given area?*

Population Growth

Some populations are made up of less than a dozen individuals. Others are composed of millions, even billions of individuals. Every population has a specific potential for growth and is subject to environmental pressures that control how fast it grows and how large it can be.

53.1 Biotic Potential

A population's **biotic potential** is the rate at which it would produce offspring if every new individual lived and reproduced at its maximum capacity. *The biotic potential of a population is staggering.* Consider, for example, the reproductive capacity of houseflies. A female housefly usually mates seven times a year and lays about 100 eggs each time. About half of her offspring are females and most produce the same amount of eggs as their mother. If the young were allowed to reproduce unchecked, the housefly population generated by one male and one female would number more than 5 trillion (5,000,000,000,000) in a single year.

Houseflies reproduce relatively rapidly, but even the biotic potential of elephants, which bear young about every two years, is astounding. In 750 years, the descendants of a single pair of elephants would number more than 19 million. In 100,000 years, the descendants of just two elephants would fill the visible universe.

Elephants have been around for more than 100,000 years, but they do not fill the universe. Similarly, the earth is not overrun by houseflies. You need only look around to see that populations do not achieve their biotic potential. What mechanisms control a species' biotic potential and thus limit the size of its populations?

53.2 Carrying Capacity

The environment limits populations from reaching their biotic potential. To understand how the environment controls population growth, it is first necessary to understand how populations grow. Assume that a pair of warblers enters a forest where no other warblers live. At first the increase in the number of warblers is small because there is only one female to produce young. Thus, the population undergoes a period of slow growth called the **lag phase** of growth. As more females are born, they mature, mate, and give birth.

Section Objectives

- *Explain* why species do not achieve their biotic potential.
- *Distinguish* between density-independent and density-dependent limiting factors.
- *State* the difference between J-curves, S-curves, and saw-tooth curves.
- *Use* the equation for calculating changes in population size.
- *Summarize* the advantages and disadvantages of high-density populations.

Biofact

Q: *What is the biotic potential of starfish?*

A: If 100 starfish achieved their biotic potential, in 15 generations 10^{79} starfish would exist. The number 10 to the 79th power is 1 with 79 zeroes after it.

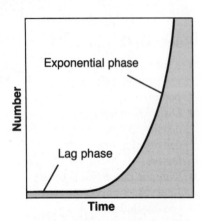

Figure 53–1. The early growth of a new population begins slowly and then explodes, forming a graph shaped like the letter "J."

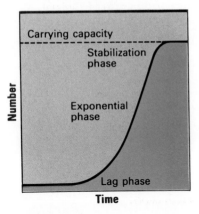

Figure 53–2. Eventually an exploding population begins to stabilize, turning the "J" curve into a curve shaped like an "S."

To see how a population of yeast cells changes with time, see page 865.

Soon the population reaches a certain size and **exponential** (eks poh NEHN shuhl) **growth** begins. This is a phase of very rapid growth in which the number of individuals repeatedly doubles in a specific time interval. For example, if a population of 100 warblers lived in the forest this year and the population was growing exponentially, 200 warblers would live in the forest next year. A year later, 400 warblers would live in the forest.

In nature, exponential growth occurs when a new habitat or a new food supply becomes available. For example, the warbler population grew exponentially some time after its arrival in a new habitat. A graph of the lag phase and **exponential phase** is shown in Figure 53–1. Ecologists call this type of population growth curve a **J-curve** because it is shaped like the letter J.

Exponential growth does not continue forever, however. The size of populations soon begins to stabilize, or reaches a **stabilization phase** of growth. This occurs because the **carrying capacity** of the environment is reached. The carrying capacity of an environment is the maximum number of individuals of a species that the environment can support. When carrying capacity is reached, the number of births and deaths becomes about equal. The population size stabilizes.

The growth of the warbler population is shown in Figure 53–2. This type of graph, which includes the lag, exponential, and stabilization phases, is called an **S-curve.**

53.3 Limiting Factors and Density

The environmental factors that stabilize population size and keep species from reaching their biotic potential are called **limiting factors.** The availability of space, food, and nesting materials are some of the limiting factors that probably affected the growth of the warbler population. Similarly, the amount of dissolved oxygen in water and water temperature are limiting factors to rainbow trout populations. The amount of sunlight is a limiting factor for the growth of daffodils. Limiting factors establish the carrying capacity of the land for each population.

Limiting factors may or may not be related to **population density**—that is, the number of individuals in a given area at a specific time. Some limiting factors operate independently of density. Others are density dependent.

Weather, landslides, fires, and floods are examples of **density-independent factors**—that is, factors whose effects are not determined by the density of a population. Imagine a desert where the temperature suddenly drops below 0°C (32°F). Both dense and sparse populations in the desert are equally affected by the freezing temperature.

In contrast **density-dependent factors** operate according to the density of the population. Food, for example, is an important density-dependent limiting factor. The more dense the population, the greater the struggle for limited amounts of food. *When a population's density is low, density-dependent factors are not limiting. As the population becomes more dense, these important factors exert a greater influence on populations.* Water, sunlight, soil nutrients, and availability of space are other density-dependent limiting factors. Stress, accumulation of waste materials, disease, and parasites are also density-dependent factors.

Predators are sometimes density-dependent limiting factors. Predators feed on other organisms and can thereby limit the size of populations. The availability of prey, predator's food, is a limiting factor on populations of predators. Figure 53–4 illustrates graphically a predator-prey relationship. It shows the population sizes of snowshoe hares and lynxes over 100 years. Lynxes prey on hares. When hares are abundant, the population of lynxes rises. As the lynxes eat more hares, hares become more scarce and then some lynxes starve to death. With fewer lynxes, the hare population makes a comeback. Thus, over the years the populations of hares and lynxes rise and fall in response to each other. Figure 53–4 illustrates these fluctuations. This kind of population growth curve, which shows the periodic growth and decline of populations, is called a **saw-tooth curve.** Over time, the populations of both predator and prey remain relatively stable.

Figure 53–3. Vegetation on a forest floor is limited to those types of plants that can grow with a minimum of sunlight.

53.4 Changes in Population Size

Ecologists are often interested in studying how populations change even after they have become stable. By doing so, ecologists detect growth trends that may be useful in managing a

Figure 53–4. Because lynxes eat hares, the populations of lynxes and hares rise and fall together, producing a saw-tooth curve.

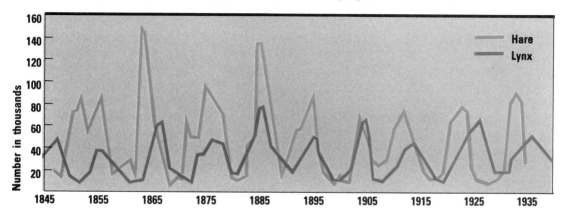

species. For example, knowing the change in the population size of rare whooping cranes enables ecologists to determine if steps must be taken to further ensure their survival. Conversely, if the size of a deer population rises too suddenly, the population may need to be decreased to maintain the ecological balance of an area.

Ecologists determine the change in population size by using the following equation:

Change in population size =
(births + immigrants) − (deaths + emigrants)

This equation can be studied using an example of caribou in the tundra. Consider a herd numbering 10,000 individuals. Assume that in a particular year 400 new caribou were born and 300 old caribou died. As the herd wandered across the icy tundra, 75

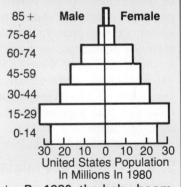

caribou *immigrated*, or joined the herd. Another 200 caribou *emigrated*, or left the herd for another. According to the equation above, then, the change in the size of the population of caribou would be as follows:

(400 births + 75 immigrants) −
(300 deaths + 200 emigrants)

The herd, therefore, lost 25 individuals during that particular year. Ecologists use equations like this to help understand the ebb and flow of population size.

In the above example, 400 births occurred among 10,000 caribou in one year. These data can be used to calculate the population's **birth rate,** the rate at which births occur. To calculate the birth rate, the number of births is divided by the population size and the result multiplied by 100. The rate is expressed as a percent. The birth rate in the above example is $\frac{400}{10,000} \times 100$, or 4 percent.

The **death rate,** the rate at which deaths occur, is calculated the same way. The death rate for caribou is 3 percent. In the above example, the **growth rate,** the rate at which the population is growing or declining, is −0.25 percent. This is arrived at by dividing the population change of 25 by the total population of 10,000 and multiplying this answer by 100. Since there was a population loss, the growth rate is a negative number. A growth rate of 0 percent would represent a completely stable population. The growth rate of this caribou population is declining but ecologists consider it relatively stable.

Populations may remain relatively stable for a long time. Sometimes, however, a severe famine or a natural catastrophe, such as a landslide or fire, nearly destroys a population. In cases like these, the population undergoes a *population crash*. On the other hand, a population may undergo a *population explosion* where the number of individuals increases dramatically. A population explosion may occur, for example, if a new food supply becomes available or if a predator is somehow removed from the area.

Figure 53–5. Birth and death rates alone do not explain annual fluctuations in the size of a caribou herd. New animals periodically join the herd, while others leave.

Reading Critically

Predicting Results What do you think would happen to a population after a population explosion occurs?

Section Review

1. **Organizing Ideas**   Give six examples of limiting factors that control biotic potential.
2. **Comparing Factors**   What is the difference between density-independent and density-dependent limiting factors?
3. **Comparing Ideas**   Compare a J-curve and an S-curve.
4. **Evaluating Information**   What would happen to the growth rate during a population crash?

Thinking Critically

The Human Population

Section Objectives

- *State* how the development of agriculture accelerated human population growth.
- *List* the factors that led to the exponential growth of human populations.
- *Explain* what happens to a human population that has reached the environment's carrying capacity.
- *Explain* why zero population growth may be difficult to achieve.

The human population has existed for over 500,000 years, a relatively short period in the earth's 4.6 billion year history. In that time, however, the human population has swelled to more that 4.5 billion individuals. How did such a large population arise? What is its future?

53.5 The History of the Human Population

By 20,000 years ago, humans had learned to build fires, construct shelters, and make clothes. The total human population then was about 3 million. This relatively small population was distributed over nearly the entire habitable earth. The sizes of their populations and the life style they adopted had a direct effect on the current size of the human population.

Our ancient ancestors were *hunter-gatherers* whose food consisted of the plants they gathered and the animals they killed. These hunter-gatherers roamed over the land in search of game. They also gathered grain as it ripened in an area, and then moved on when the grain was gone. If food became scarce, people died of starvation and its related diseases. The growth of the human population, therefore, was slow. It was in the lag phase of growth.

About 11,000 years ago, however, humans began to cultivate crops and domesticate animals. **Agriculture increased the carrying capacity of the land.** Agricultural areas provided more

Figure 53–6. Human population growth is in the exponential phase. The effects of medical advances and other human technology have made the "J" curve unusually steep.

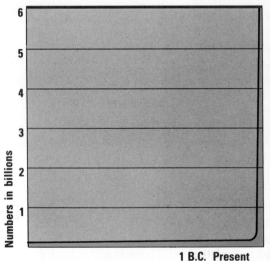

THINKING ABOUT BIOLOGY: Zero Population Growth

In 1965, the birth rate in Japan was 1.67 percent. By 1980 it was 1.37 percent. In the United States the birth rate in 1965 was 1.94 percent. In 1980 it was 1.62 percent. In both countries the birth rate dropped in 15 years. Yet because the death rate dropped as well, the populations continued to rise and, overall, became more dense.

Because populations are increasing, some nations and many private citizens have advocated a concept called *zero population growth,* a stabilized population. Zero population growth can be achieved in nations where immigration equals emigration and where each family has no more than two children. When every family has only two children, new individuals are added to the population at a rate that exactly replaces the individuals that die. The graph shows how the population of the United States would look if every family had just two children. The graph also shows the population growth if each family has three children.

Although the concept of zero population growth will theoretically stabilize a population after two or three generations, the idea is often not well accepted. Many people see large families as a source of

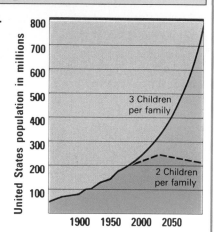

security in their old age. Various other cultural factors make the goal of zero population growth a difficult one to achieve.

■ **Synthesizing Information** Why would members of an agricultural society be against zero population growth?

---

food than when the same areas were used for hunting. With fields to tend, humans ceased wandering from hunting ground to hunting ground and settled in one place. With a stable food supply and the greater safety offered by a settled community, the human population began to increase.

It took about 500,000 years for the human population to reach 1 billion, which it did in 1840. About that time, advances in medicine began to reduce *infant mortality,* the rate at which infants died, and began to eliminate many contagious diseases. People also began to develop better systems of food production, storage, and distribution.

The population was large enough so that these technological advances enabled the population to enter the exponential phase of growth. Only 90 years later, in 1930, the population had doubled to about 2 billion. Just 45 years after that, in 1975, the human population doubled again, bringing the world population to about 4 billion.

Reading Critically

Inferring Relationships How is the settling of human communities related to increased population?

The effects of human activity on the earth's rain forests are discussed on page 76.

Biofact

Q: *What is the most densely populated part of the earth?*

A: Macao, a Portuguese province in southern China, has a density of more than 29,000 people per km² (74,000 per mi.²).

53.6 The Future of the Human Population

The human population is still in the exponential phase of growth. Because the birth rate exceeds the death rate, over 250,000 new human beings are added to the population each day or about 93 million each year. At the current rate of increase, the population doubles about every 39 years. By 2013, the human population may be close to 8 billion. Many of you reading this book will still be alive in 2051, when there may be as many as 16 billion humans on earth.

Many factors have contributed to the rise in the number of humans on Earth. Technology, for example, continues to contribute to the population explosion. A hundred years ago it was not unusual to find countries with infant mortality rates over 50 percent. Today, however, infants in even the most impoverished countries have well over an 80 percent chance to live. Furthermore, technological advances have reduced the death rate by eliminating fatal diseases such as smallpox, improving crop yields, and devising new means for distributing food.

The population explosion is also indicated by the changing rates of births and deaths. In underdeveloped countries, people depend on their children for support and security. The infant mortality rate is high because the people lack sufficient food and modern medical care. Parents must have many children to ensure that a few will survive. As a result, birth rates are highest in underdeveloped countries. The simultaneous decline in death rates causes the population of these countries to grow rapidly. In many affluent countries, such as Japan and the United States, the birth rate is actually declining, but because the death rate is declining even faster, their populations continue to grow.

As the population increases, it causes greater competition for limited natural resources. An increasing population is partially caused by problems of hunger and poverty and, in turn, worsens them. Providing for the world's population and controlling its growth are among the serious problems facing the world today.

Section Review

1. **Evaluating Ideas** How did the development of agriculture affect the human population?
2. **Analyzing Relationships** What factors besides agriculture have contributed to the dramatic rise in the human population since 1840?
3. **Evaluating Information** How can the human population grow even if the birth rate decreases?

> **Thinking Critically**

INVESTIGATION 53:
How Does Time Affect Population Growth in a Closed System?

Objectives
- To *measure* growth of a yeast population
- To *evaluate* the effect of time on population growth in a closed system

Materials
paper, pencil

Prelab Preparation
1. Explain what occurs during the lag phase and during the exponential phase of population growth.
2. Explain how biotic potential, limiting factors, and carrying capacity contribute to the stabilization phase.
3. In this Investigation, assume the following conditions. A small number of yeast cells have been placed in a test tube containing water and the nutrients necessary for growth and reproduction. Yeast cells cannot enter or leave the population and nothing is added or removed from the tube. Thus the yeast population is said to be in a *closed system.*
4. After discussing the question that is the topic of this Investigation with your partner, formulate your hypothesis and explain your reasoning.
5. What are the independent and dependent variables in this Investigation?
6. Describe the design of an experiment that would test your hypothesis.
7. Make a data table for recording population growth data over a six-day period.

Inquiry: Experimentation
8. Observe the figures at the bottom of the page that show samples of a yeast population taken over a six-day period. The lines you see appear on a special glass slide used for counting cells under a microscope.
9. Each sample represents one one-thousandth of the population present in the test tube. *How can the number of cells in the sample be used to estimate the total number of cells in the population?*
10. Count the number of yeast cells observed in the Day 0 sample. To avoid duplication, count cells touching the bottom or right-hand lines as part of that box. The cells that touch the top or left-hand lines will be included in the counts of other boxes. Record your data.
11. Repeat the procedure for the samples taken on Days 1 through 5.
12. Multiply the total number of cells found in each sample by 1,000 to find the population size. Record your data.
13. Make a line graph that shows population size in relation to time. Plot time along the horizontal axis and population size along the vertical axis.

Analysis
1. **Summarizing Data** Describe yeast population growth over time.
2. **Analyzing Data** What happened between Day 3 and Day 4? What caused this to happen?
3. **Making Predictions** How do you predict the population size will change between Day 5 and Day 10? Explain your answer.
4. **Analyzing Ideas** Name some factors that cause the population growth pattern of humans to differ from that of yeast.

Day 0

Day 1

Day 2

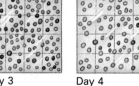
Day 3

Day 4

Day 5

Chapter 53 Review

Summary

Populations are composed of individuals of the same species living in the same area. The maximum rate of reproduction for a population is its biotic potential. A population allowed to reach its biotic potential would soon cover the earth. The growth of populations is regulated by the environment's limiting factors.

In a new area, a population grows slowly at first. The population then enters an exponential phase of growth in which its number doubles at decreasing intervals. This phase ceases when the carrying capacity of the environment is reached. Limiting factors depend on the population's density; some are independent of density.

Changes in populations are calculated by subtracting the number of deaths and emigrants from the number of births and immigrants. Dramatic changes in the sizes of populations are called population crashes and explosions.

The human population is currently in its exponential phase of growth. The number of humans now doubles about every 38 years. Providing for this growing population is one of the major problems facing the modern world.

BioTerms

biotic potential (**857**)
birth rate (**861**)
carrying
  capacity (**858**)
death date (**861**)
density-dependent
  factor (**859**)
density-independent
  factor (**858**)

exponential
  growth (**858**)
exponential phase (**858**)
growth rate (**861**)
J-curve (**858**)
lag phase (**857**)
limiting factor (**858**)
population density (**858**)
saw-tooth curve (**859**)

S-curve (**858**)   stabilization phase (**858**)

For each pair of terms, explain the differences in their meanings.

1. density-dependent factor, density-independent factor
2. exponential phase, lag phase
3. birth rate, death rate
4. biotic potential, carrying capacity

BioQuiz   (Write all answers on a separate sheet of paper.)

Completion

1. The frequency of births in a population is the population's _____ .
2. Populations achieve _____ when the number of new individuals equals the number lost by death and emigration.
3. The maximum rate at which a species reproduces is its _____ .
4. The _____ describes populations during the exponential phase of growth.
5. The period of slow growth that may precede an exponential growth phase is called the _____ .

Multiple Choice

6. The maximum number of species members that an environment can support is
   a) population density. b) carrying capacity. c) stabilization phase.
   d) limiting factor.
7. If there are 20 births, 26 deaths, 10 immigrations, and 13 emigrations, the change in population size is a) -9.
   b) 9. c) 23. d) 3.
8. Which has greatly increased the human growth rate? a) agriculture
   b) advances in medicine c) decrease in infant mortality d) All choices are correct.

9. Individuals of the same species make up
   a) a population.   b) a community.
   c) an ecosystem.   d) a biome.
10. Which of the following is not a density-dependent factor?   a) contagious diseases   b) fire   c) food   d) garbage
11. If the lynx population disappeared, the hare population could be expected to experience   a) a population crash. b) zero population growth.   c) carrying capacity.   d) a population explosion.
12. The phase of very rapid growth in which the number of individuals repeatedly doubles in a specific time interval is   a) the stabilization phase.   b) population density.   c) exponential growth.   d) the carrying capacity.
13. A periodic growth and decline of populations is   a) an exponential curve. b) an S-shaped curve.   c) a J-shaped curve.   d) a saw-tooth curve.
14. The number of individuals in a given area at a specific time is   a) carrying capacity. b) stabilization phase.   c) population density.   d) All choices are correct.
15. Which of the following is a density-independent factor?   a) food b) weather   c) disease   d) garbage

Writing Critically

16. Why does a long-term relationship between predator and prey lead to a saw-tooth type of population growth curve?
17. What are some disadvantages that face a population whose density is very low?
18. Why do organisms rarely, if ever, achieve their biotic potential?
19. What are some factors responsible for the current increases in the human population?
20. What are some causes of natural population collapses?

Application/Critical Thinking

1. **Analyzing Information** Suggest reasons why Pakistan's population has quadrupled since 1900 even though the birth rate has remained steady at 4.5 percent.
2. **Inferring Relationships** Moose first arrived in Isle Royale, an island in Lake Superior, in 1908. Because no natural predators existed, the moose population soon grew rapidly. However, the population crashed in both 1930 and 1940.

   In 1948, timber wolves arrived on the island. Since then the moose population has remained between 600 and 1,000 individuals. Explain what you think happened on Isle Royale.

Cross-Discipline Connection

Biology and Mathematics   Obtain the last 100 years of census data for your town or city and make a bar graph representing the population changes in the community.

Discovery Through Reading

Read "Population, Plenty, and Poverty," *National Geographic* (December 1988): 914–945. Which country in the article has achieved zero population growth? List three ways in which automobiles have affected the environment.

An Artificial Environment

Hydroponically grown plants

A tarantula in the insectorium

Imagine a completely enclosed artificial environment in the Arizona desert that covers more than three acres and stands six stories tall. It includes a rainforest, a savannah, a marsh, an ocean, a desert, an intensive agriculture area, and a human habitat. This ambitious project is called *Biosphere II.*

Its atmosphere functions much like that of Earth. Heat rising from the desert picks up moisture as it circulates over the artificial ocean. Warm air rises through the canopy of the rainforest. In addition to natural convection, mechanical air handlers move air as needed, providing heating and cooling in different seasons. Cooling coils in the structure cause the moisture to condense and fall as rain, which flows back into the ocean.

Like Earth, Biosphere II receives energy from the Sun. This energy is stored as sugars and starches in plants. Each of the 3,800 plant and animal species that make up the food web were chosen with great care. All wastes from the intensive agriculture area are recycled as fertilizer or broken down by organisms such as termites so that essential materials become available as plant nutrients.

The project includes eight human "biospherians" who will live and work in this self-contained world for about two years during the initial experiment. The project is built to exist for 50 to 100 years. Therefore, information can be gathered about how such closed ecological systems function over long spans of time. The human inhabitants must devote about half of each day to farm and maintenance chores. For food, they will rely on fish; rice from the aquaculture system; tropical fruits such as

Prototype of the Biosphere II space colony

bananas, papayas, citrus, figs, and guavas; grains and vegetables that are grown on the farm; and goats, pigs, and chickens that they raise inside.

Educated in the natural sciences, the biospherians are trained in all the skills they need to operate their "bio-ship". They can use computers and analytic laboratory equipment, maintain mechanical equipment, manage the aquacultural systems, monitor the wilderness ecology, and provide medical assistance. Biospherians will spend about four hours each day performing experiments and observing the interactions of the plants and animals. They will also monitor the approximately 2,000 automatic sensors placed throughout the structure. These sensors can detect changes as small as the drop in temperature of a single leaf and gas concentration in parts per trillion. A sophisticated computer program helps monitor and manage the biosphere and the scientists inside and outside who check the data and the living systems.

The cycling times are much shorter than Earth's because Biosphere II has much smaller volumes of air, water, and soil. These short cycles will provide valuable information about how biospheres operate. The Biosphere II project will help humans in their colonization of space and in their understanding of Biosphere I— Earth.

> **The Biosphere II project is an attempt to recreate the environment of Biosphere I— the Earth.**

Scientists use computers to assist them in their experiments.

People and the Environment

Outline

Conservation of Resources

54.1 Water Conservation
54.2 Soil Conservation
54.3 Wildlife Conservation
54.4 Energy Conservation

Pollution of the Environment

54.5 Air Pollution
54.6 Water Pollution
54.7 Solid Waste Disposal

Aerial view of Central Park in New York City

Focus

Hundreds of years ago, vast forests covered the eastern United States. Timber wolves stalked herds of elk and deer, and passenger pigeons were numerous. The passenger pigeon is gone forever. Many of the forests have been reduced to small patches of greenery sandwiched between skyscrapers of concrete, steel, and glass. A growing human population has had enormous impact on the environment.

■ *What characteristics of human populations pose a threat to the natural resources in an area?*

■ *In what ways can the destructive effects of human populations on the environment be minimized?*

Conservation of Resources

All the elements of nature, including sunlight, air, water, plants, and animals, are **natural resources.** People depend on natural resources to live, so maintaining the supply is vital. As the human population has grown, the demand for natural resources and the need for their conservation have grown as well. **Conservation** is the careful management, wise use, and protection of natural resources.

Conservation involves both renewable resources and nonrenewable resources. **Renewable resources** are those that can be reused or replenished if they are well managed. Air, water, soil, and wildlife are all renewable resources. Soil, for example, can be used over and over to grow crops if it is farmed properly. **Nonrenewable resources,** such as coal and oil, are resources that cannot be reused or replenished. These resources form over thousands or millions of years. Once the supplies are gone, they cannot be replaced.

Section Objectives

- *Distinguish* between renewable and nonrenewable resources.
- *State* why water conservation is necessary.
- *List* methods used to prevent soil erosion and the depletion of soil nutrients.
- *Trace* the effects of pollutants through a food chain.
- *Identify* sources of energy which may one day serve as alternates to fossil fuels.

54.1 Water Conservation

Water is naturally processed for reuse as it moves through a cycle of *precipitation* and evaporation. Precipitation is the part of the cycle in which water falls to the earth as rain, sleet, or snow. The precipitation collects in lakes, rivers, and streams as well as below the ground. The ground water, too, eventually finds its way to these same lakes and rivers. The surface water is then used to supply homes, agriculture, and industry. Some of the water evaporates back into the atmosphere where it again becomes a source of precipitation.

The earth has an abundant supply of water, but over 97 percent is salt water. In addition, the supply of fresh water is unevenly distributed. Thus, some areas have water surpluses, while others face shortages.

Some communities draw their water from natural lakes. Many other communities obtain water from reservoirs that are created by building dams on rivers. Such dams often serve other purposes as well, such as controlling floods and supplying *hydroelectric power*. This is electric power generated by transforming energy produced by water into electrical energy. Conservationists have opposed the construction of certain dams, however, because of the possible harmful ecological effects of the dams. When a reservoir is built behind a dam, for example, it destroys the habitats of the wildlife living there. This destruction can have far-reaching and unexpected effects.

Figure 54–1. Water for drinking and irrigation may come from large reservoirs created by building huge dams to trap the water.

Q: *How much water does an average American use each day?*

A: An average American uses over 304 liters (80 gallons) of water per day.

Many communities obtain their water from wells that pump up ground water. In some communities, the ground water is withdrawn faster than it can be replenished. As the ground water is depleted, the ground surface may begin to sink. In areas of the western United States, the ground water is being depleted by the heavy use of water for irrigation. It is for this reason that many conservationists believe that irrigating arid and semiarid lands may not be practical in the long run. They believe that nothing is gained if irrigation is obtained at such a high cost.

Cities near seacoasts may someday meet their water needs by taking salt out of sea water, a process called **desalination** (dee sal uh NAY shuhn). Currently, however, desalination is too expensive for large-scale use because the process requires so much energy.

In areas where water shortages occur, conservation is a necessity. One method of conserving water is by maintaining the watershed. A **watershed** is the area of land from which water drains into a particular lake or stream. Maintaining plant cover, such as trees, shrubs, and grasses, on watersheds helps prevent rapid runoff of rain water. The water then seeps into the ground and replenishes the ground water supply. Industries, farms, and individuals can conserve water by using it more efficiently.

54.2 Soil Conservation

Soil is renewable only if it is managed properly. Soil takes thousands of years to form from disintegrating rock. The soil nearest the surface, the topsoil, is most exposed to wind, water, and the organisms living on or in the soil. The bottom layer, which has been least exposed, most resembles the original rock. In between is a layer of soil containing minerals that have been

Figure 54–2. Steep hillsides are particularly exposed to soil erosion unless steps are taken to protect them from water runoff.

washed down from the topsoil. The topsoil provides the nutrients plants need to grow. Tons of valuable topsoil have been lost to **erosion,** a process in which soil is washed away by water or blown away by wind.

The rate of soil erosion increases when land is stripped of its natural vegetation. Trees, grasses, and other plants reduce erosion by protecting the soil from the direct force of rain and wind. The roots of plants bind the soil and hold it in place. Plants also absorb some rainwater and reduce the runoff rate.

Farmers use various methods to reduce erosion caused by rainwater running down sloping land. **Contour plowing** is a method of plowing across, rather than up and down, a slope. The furrows of plowed soil catch rainwater, allowing it to seep slowly into the ground. In **strip-cropping,** rows of plants, such as grass and clover, are alternated with strips of grain crops. Grass and clover hold water and retard the flow of rainwater better than grain crops do. **Terracing** is a method of converting a hillside into broad, flat steps that help hold water.

Erosion caused by wind especially affects the soil on plains. There, farmers plant rows of trees called **windbreaks** to serve as barriers to the wind.

Another major conservation problem on farmlands is the depletion of soil nutrients. Planting the same crop in a field year after year contributes to a decline in the fertility of the soil. Grain crops, for example, use up the nitrogen in the soil if they are grown in the same field for several years. Farmers maintain soil fertility by **crop rotation,** in which crops are alternated from year to year. The rotation crop is usually alfalfa, soybeans, or other legumes. The advantage of crop rotation comes from a certain kind of bacterium that lives in the roots of legumes. These bacteria restore nitrogen to the soil.

Farmers add plant remains, animal wastes, or chemical fertilizers to their fields. The overuse of chemical fertilizers, however, may prevent bacteria from producing nutrients naturally.

Figure 54–4. A wildlife refuge provides a protected habitat that helps plants and animals avoid extinction.

Figure 54–5. Large numbers of visitors have damaged the natural environment in some national parks.

54.3 Wildlife Conservation

Wildlife has decreased sharply as the human population has grown. During the past few centuries, hundreds of species of animals and countless species of plants have completely died out. Such species are called **extinct species.** The passenger pigeon and the heath hen are but two examples of extinct species. Many more species are in danger of becoming extinct. They are called **endangered species** because they may not survive in the wild unless they are protected. Endangered species include the woolly spider monkey, the blue whale, the American alligator, and the St. Helena redwood tree.

Extinctions have occurred as long as life has existed on the earth. In earlier times, however, new species have evolved as rapidly as old ones have died out. Within the last few centuries, organisms have become extinct too rapidly for new species to develop. People and their policies are responsible for this rapid rate of extinction.

One cause of animal extinctions is uncontrolled hunting, fishing, and trapping. Animals may be hunted not only for their meat, hides, and other products, but also for sale to zoos, researchers, or pet traders. The passage and enforcement of hunting and fishing laws has protected many species. Even so, illegal hunting, called *poaching,* threatens many animals, including the Siberian tiger and the black rhinoceros.

A primary threat to wildlife today is the destruction of habitats, which occurs when land is cleared for homes, farms, or other developments. Such developments threaten not only individual species but also entire ecosystems. To save wildlife in varied ecosystems, government and private organizations

The brown pelican is a fish-eating coastal bird that nests along the Atlantic, Pacific, and Gulf shores of the Americas. More than 50,000 brown pelicans once nested in Texas and Louisiana alone, but the population there dropped to almost zero in the early 1960s. By the late 1960s, California's pelican population had also declined and was not reproducing normally. In 1970 only one bird hatched at Anacapa Island, a major breeding colony. The brown pelican was placed on the United States list of endangered species in 1973.

Biologists searched for the causes of the pelican's decline. The drop in the Texas population occurred after large numbers of fish died in the Mississippi River delta. The fish had been poisoned by a pesticide called *endrin.* Thus, the pelican's food supply

had been cut off. The use of endrin has since decreased. However, the pelican may never thrive again in Texas and Louisiana because of decreased food supplies, oil spills, and the loss of habitat.

In California, biologists linked the pesticide DDT with the decline of the brown pelican. The pelican's eggs contained some traces of DDT. The eggshells were so thin that they broke while the eggs were laid or during incubation. Investigators found that a chemical company had been dumping waste DDT into the Los Angeles sewer system. The DDT contaminated the fish in the oceans and the pelicans ate many fish. The birds thus accumulated large amounts of DDT in their bodies. The process by which a substance becomes more concentrated in animals that are higher in the food chain is called *biological magnification.*

After DDT was banned in 1972, the brown pelican began to recover in California. In the early 1980s, about 2,000 pairs nested on Anacapa Island. Biologists believe that the brown pelican is making a strong comeback.

■ **Relating Ideas** How does the brown pelican story demonstrate interdependence of organisms?

have worked to establish preserves and refuges. National parks also provide homes for wildlife. However, because some parks are visited by so many tourists, the ecology of the parks is being disrupted as well.

Many of the larger zoos are attempting to contribute to wildlife conservation. Through *captive breeding programs,* scientists working in zoos hope to save such endangered species as the cheetah and the black lemur. In these programs zoologists try to create the conditions needed for the animals to mate.

54.4 Energy Conservation

About 95 percent of the energy used in the world comes from oil, coal, and natural gas. Because these substances are the fossilized remains of prehistoric plants and animals, they are called **fossil fuels.** Fossil fuels are a nonrenewable resource. The present supply took millions of years to form and cannot be replaced. As the supply diminishes, extracting the fuels becomes more difficult and more expensive. *Finding alternate sources of energy to replace fossil fuels is essential.*

At one time many people believed that nuclear energy offered the cleanest and least expensive solution to the world's ever-increasing energy needs. Nuclear energy is produced in two ways: nuclear fission and nuclear fusion. **Nuclear fission** is the splitting of atomic nuclei, a process that releases usable heat energy. The nuclear power plants in operation today use fission. **Nuclear fusion** involves fusing two hydrogen atoms to form helium. Scientists have not found a practical way to control the release of fusion energy. If a method is found, fusion could supply most of the world's energy needs.

The first nuclear power plant went into operation in the United States in 1957. Since that time the use of nuclear power to replace fossil fuels has not significantly increased. More than 25 years later, only about 4 percent of the nation's energy is provided by nuclear power. Worldwide, nuclear energy accounts for only about 1 percent of the energy supply. The use of nuclear power has been held back for several reasons. There has been much public concern over the accidental release of radioactive material into the environment and the safe disposal of radioactive wastes. Also, the cost and the complexity of building a nuclear power plant has proved to be much greater than once thought.

Other energy sources now being researched include the harnessing of water, wind, steam, and the energy of the sun. Water power provides about 2 percent of the world's energy supply. A significant increase in the use of water power is unlikely, however, because many suitable sites already have hydroelectric plants.

Wind power has been used for centuries to pump water and to grind grain. More recently large windmills have been used to generate electricity. Wind power is limited, however, because few areas have a steady enough supply of wind.

Geothermal (jee oh THER muhl) **power** can be harnessed from steam created below the earth's surface. The steam is created when water is warmed by hot rocks. Beds of hot rock below the earth's surface provide huge reservoirs of heat. In some cases steam is naturally formed by ground water that flows

Figure 54–6. A nuclear power plant includes huge towers for cooling the water used to remove waste heat from the reactor.

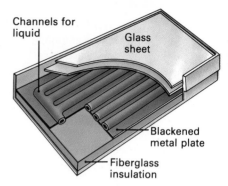

Figure 54–7. Large solar collectors are an obvious feature of a home that uses solar energy (left). Each individual solar collector (right) is designed to capture maximum sunlight.

over the rocks. This steam can be tapped by drilling and then directed to drive steam turbines. Where underground steam does not naturally occur, it can be created by injecting water into hot rocks. However, geothermal power is limited by the number of natural sites that lie near the earth's surface.

Solar energy, or energy derived from sunlight, is a safe and unlimited source of energy. Figure 54–7 shows how solar collectors absorb the sun's heat for home use. Sunlight can also be collected by devices that convert it into electricity. The use of solar energy, however, is not yet practical in areas where the sunlight is limited.

Wood, once the world's chief fuel, is still the main source of energy in many less developed countries. Growing populations in those areas have greatly reduced forest resources. If the present rate of use is not checked, these resources will one day disappear.

A small amount of electric power is produced by burning trash and other solid wastes. In addition, some treatment plants convert sewage into *methane*, a clean-burning gas. Methane has been used to power small combustion engines.

Until some of these alternate energy sources can be developed on a large scale, people must conserve fossil fuels.

Section Review

1. **Analyzing Information**   What objections have been raised to dams, irrigation, and desalination?
2. **Relating Ideas**   How does natural vegetation work to slow down the rate of soil erosion?
3. **Summarizing Ideas**   Explain how DDT harmed the brown pelican.
4. **Synthesizing Conclusions**   Why should world leaders be concerned with finding alternatives to fossil fuels?

> **Thinking Critically**

- *Distinguish* between biodegradable and nonbiodegradable wastes.
- *Name* the main sources of air and water pollution.
- *Define* the terms *eutrophication* and *thermal pollution*.
- *Identify* factors that contribute to the problem of solid wastes disposal and state one solution.

Pollution of the Environment

While conservationists labor to maintain the world's natural resources, other factors are at work that are destructive to these resources. Contamination of the environment with waste products and other impurities is called **pollution.**

Any kind of waste product is a *pollutant*. People have always produced waste products. Before industrial cities were developed, however, these pollutants were not released in huge amounts nor concentrated in small areas. In addition, the types of waste products formerly produced could be broken down naturally into harmless substances by microorganisms and reused by other organisms. Such waste products are **biodegradable** (by oh dih GRAY duh buhl). Today, many discarded products are made of metal or of newer materials, such as plastics, which are often **nonbiodegradable.** This means that they cannot be broken down by microorganisms. Because of the large quantity and types of pollutants that the industrialized nations produce, pollution is now a major problem facing the modern world. Pollution endangers human society, nonhuman organisms, and the entire physical environment.

54.5 Air Pollution

In large cities, breathing the air may be harmful to your health. It can cause headaches and burning eyes. It may contribute to the development of such diseases as lung cancer and emphysema. Air pollutants can stunt the growth of plants and eventually kill them. The pollutants in the air can even eat away at the outside surfaces of buildings.

Air pollution consists of solid or liquid particles called **particulate matter** and of various gases. The particulate matter includes dust, smoke, ashes, asbestos, and tiny particles of lead and other heavy metals. The gases of air pollution include carbon monoxide, nitrogen oxides, sulfur oxides, hydrocarbons, and excessive amounts of carbon dioxide. *The greatest source of air pollution is the burning of fossil fuels to produce electricity.* Other air pollutants are produced by the burning of fuel to drive automobiles, to heat buildings, and to supply power for industries.

Carbon monoxide, a serious air pollutant in cities, combines with hemoglobin and reduces the oxygen carrying capacity of the blood. As a result the heart and lungs must work harder to supply the tissues with oxygen when there are high levels of carbon monoxide in the air.

Figure 54–8. Factories, power plants, and automobile exhausts all contribute to the pollutant called smog, which hangs over many large cities.

Figure 54–9. Metrorail in Miami, Florida, provides a means of transportation that is less polluting than automobiles.

Air pollution is greatest in densely populated, industrialized cities. In some cities, air pollution may take the form of **smog,** a combination of smoke, gas, and fog. Smog worsens when a cool air mass settles under a warm air mass. This condition, called **thermal inversion,** is the opposite of the normal air layer arrangement. In thermal inversion, pollutants become trapped in the cool air layer which would ordinarily warm up, rise, and carry the pollutants away. If this condition persists for several days, the pollutants build up. Breathing the air may then become a major health risk.

Smog may contain large amounts of sulfur oxides from fossil fuels. These react with water vapor to form sulfuric acid. Sulfuric acid in the atmosphere falls to the ground as **acid rain,** which erodes buildings, damages crops, and kills fish and other aquatic organisms.

To reduce air pollution, governments have passed laws regulating the release of various air pollutants. Industries are required to install antipollution devices in factories. Automobile makers in the United States have been asked to install pollution control devices in cars. Cars are now designed to run on lead-free gasoline because it burns cleaner than leaded gasoline. Residents of cities have been encouraged to make increased use of public transportation as a means of reducing the number of automobiles on the road. They have also been encouraged to use non-polluting energy sources.

54.6 Water Pollution

The main sources of water pollution are sewer systems, industries, and farms. Pollutants from these sources contaminate lakes, streams, oceans, and ground water.

Most urban sewage systems remove poisonous substances before releasing sewage into lakes or streams. However, although the sewage is treated, it still contains chemicals, such as phosphates and nitrates, which are nutrients for aquatic plants.

Biofact

Q: *What is the difference between "brown air" cities and "gray air" cities?*

A: "Brown air" cities are enveloped in a brownish haze of nitrogen dioxide. This haze forms when nitrous oxide released from vehicle exhausts combines with oxygen in the air. "Gray air" cities are cities in which the main source of pollution is the burning of coal and oil. This colors the air gray.

Measuring the acidity of a water solution is the topic of the Investigation on page 883.

The Garbage Heap

Americans throw away a vast amount of garbage each year—an average of 1,500 pounds of trash per person. Most of this garbage is not recycled.

The technology exists for nationwide recycling, and large amounts of trash are recycled in many countries. The Japanese, for example, recycle more than half of their cans, bottles, and paper products. The West Germans convert about 33 percent of their unrecycled trash into usable energy at incinerator power plants. By contrast, only about 6 percent of U.S. garbage is turned into power.

Much of our garbage could be reused. Nearly 30 percent of our household trash is paper products, which can easily be

recycled. Another 13 percent is glass and metal products, which are also reusable. About 20 percent of what we throw away is organic matter such as grass clippings that can be mulched or composted. In all, as much as 80 percent of our household trash could be recycled.

The remaining 20 percent consists of materials that require expensive equipment or processes or are otherwise impossible to recycle.

Both consumers and manufacturers have become increasingly concerned about the impact on the environment of materials that cannot be recycled. Products that were formerly indestructible are rapidly being replaced by biodegrad-

able ones. Researchers are developing more and more materials that will decompose more rapidly than the synthetic materials that were produced a decade ago.

The United States is running out of places to dump its garbage. Many existing landfills are bulging. Environmental hazards and the resistance of local residents has halted the digging of many new landfills. Soon there may be no place to put garbage.

Reading Critically

Identifying Relationships
Explain why too much algae can be bad for water environments.

Algae thrive on these nutrients. Later, as the algae die and decay, they use up the water's oxygen supply. Other plants and animals cannot survive in the water without oxygen. This nutrient enrichment process, or **eutrophication,** changes the ecology of a lake or stream and often results in the death of certain fish species.

Industries dump lead, mercury, and other chemical wastes into streams and lakes. These chemicals have poisoned not only the organisms living in these lakes and streams but also people and other animals that have eaten contaminated fish.

Industries sometimes draw cold water from a lake or stream, use it for cooling purposes, and release it back into its source. Nuclear power plants are the principal users of this cooling method. When the water is used for cooling, the water itself becomes heated. This form of pollution, called **thermal pollution,** kills plants and animals that normally live in cooler water.

Oil from accidental spills and from oil industry operations is a primary pollutant of ocean waters. When released near beaches, the oil sometimes coats and kills marine animals and shore birds.

Farms contribute to water pollution through the use of chemical fertilizers and weed killers as well as through the use of chemicals, called **pesticides.** Pesticides are used to control insect pests. These products seep into the ground water and are washed into lakes and streams. Certain harmful pesticides are now banned in some nations.

54.7 Solid Waste Disposal

Solid wastes include paper products, bottles, cans, old appliances, and all the other trash that people throw away. Each year people discard billions of tons of solid wastes. These wastes accumulate in city dumps and litter streets. The disposal of solid wastes is a growing problem.

One solution to the problem of solid wastes is to recycle wastes. Products made of paper, iron, steel, glass, and aluminum can be treated in ways that make them reusable. Wasted food, grass, leaves, and other organic debris can be made into fertilizer. Some solid wastes can be burned to produce energy. The remaining wastes can be used to build up low-lying land. Wastes that are sandwiched between layers of earth create a **landfill.**

Old patterns of carelessly using and wasting resources will not work in the future. Instead, new patterns of carefully using and reusing resources will soon become essential. Not until then will people have truly learned how to live in harmony with the environment.

Figure 54–10. Oil spills from tankers and from industrial operations located near the ocean are a major threat to shorebirds and other forms of wildlife.

Section Review

1. **Identifying Ideas**   What are the main components found in the atmosphere that cause air pollution?
2. **Analyzing Information**   What chemicals in treated sewage contribute to eutrophication?
3. **Relating Ideas**   What effect does the burning of fossil fuels have on cities and on rural areas?
4. **Synthesizing Conclusions**   Propose four solutions to the problem of solid-waste disposal.

> **Thinking Critically**

Ozone Depletion: A Global Issue

In 1985, researchers discovered a "hole" in the sky over the Antarctic. The hole was the result of ozone depletion in the atmosphere. Scientists identified chemical compounds called *chlorofluorocarbons (CFCs)* as a major cause of ozone loss.

CFCs are remarkably stable compounds used as solvents in the electronics industry and as coolants in refrigerators and air conditioners. CFCs are stable compounds that rise to the ozone layer that lies 10 to 30 miles above the Earth's surface. Once there, chlorofluorocarbon molecules break down, releasing chlorine. Chlorine breaks down ozone molecules.

Because the ozone layer blocks some of the ultra-violet rays from the sun, depletion of this layer may have far-reaching effects. A prolonged increase in the amount of ultraviolet radiation reaching the Earth's surface could increase the incidence of sunburn, accelerate skin aging, and damage the eyes. Knowledge about the relationship between CFCs and the depletion of the ozone layer has led to a multinational agreement signed in 1989 that is designed to cut the global production of CFCs by 50 percent before the year 2000.

At least one state has taken action to reduce CFCs by banning automobile air conditioners that use CFCs. Actions such as this are costly, however, and may result in inconvenience to con-

sumers. Since the effects of ozone depletion may not appear for many years, the question remains whether or not people will sacrifice their lifestyle and comfort to protect the environment.

Analyze the Issue

1. Describe the process by which chlorofluorocarbons destroy the ozone layer.

2. What are the hazards that result from depletion of atmospheric ozone?

3. What policies, if any, should be put into effect to reduce ozone depletion? Should these policies be addressed to consumers, manufacturers, or both? Support your views.

INVESTIGATION 54:
How Is Water Tested for Acidity and Alkalinity?

Objectives
- To *measure* the acidity and alkalinity of water in parts per million (ppm)
- To *compare* testing techniques

Materials
two 100-mL pipettes with rubber bulbs, two 250-mL Erlenmeyer flasks, pH test paper, medicine droppers, methyl orange indicator solution, 0.01 M sulfuric acid, 0.02 M sodium hydroxide solution, phenolphthalein indicator solution, white paper, graduated cylinder, wax pencil, stirring rod, water samples (one each of pond, stream, river, tap, and rainwater)

Prelab Preparation
1. Explain where neutral, acidic, and alkaline solutions occur on the pH scale.
2. Explain how streams, rivers, lakes, and ponds become polluted by acids.
3. Make a table similar to the one shown to record data.

Inquiry: Lab Technique
CAUTION: **Wear safety goggles, rubber gloves, and a laboratory apron.**

4. Use a wax pencil to label one flask "A" for acid. Label the other flask "B" for base.
5. Use a graduated cylinder to measure 50 mL of one water sample. Pour the water into flask A.
6. Use a strip of pH test paper to find the pH of the water sample in flask A.
7. Add 3 drops of phenolphthalein to flask A.
8. CAUTION: **Acids and bases can injure the skin, eyes, and clothing.** Use the rubber bulb to carefully draw 50 mL of 0.02 M sodium hydroxide into a pipette.
9. Add one drop of sodium hydroxide at a time to flask A, gently mixing with a stirring rod until the solution turns a pale pink. Record the number of milliliters required. *Why does the solution turn pink?*

10. Multiply the number of milliliters of sodium hydroxide used by 20 to get the parts per million (ppm) of acid in the water sample. Record your results.
11. Use a graduated cylinder to measure 100 mL of the same water sample and pour it into flask B.
12. Add 5 drops of phenolphthalein to flask B.
13. If the solution changes color, go to step 14. If the solution remains clear, go to step 16.
14. Use the rubber bulb to carefully draw 50 mL of 0.01 M sulfuric acid into a pipette.
15. Add one drop of sulfuric acid at a time to flask B, gently mixing with a stirring rod, until the color disappears. Record in your data table the number of milliliters required. *Why does the solution become colorless?*
16. Add 5 drops of methyl orange indicator to flask B.
17. If the solution turns yellow, add 0.01 M sulfuric acid until the solution turns pale pink. Record the number of milliliters of acid used.
18. Total alkalinity in ppm is the sum of the milliliters of acid used in steps 12 and 14 multiplied by 10. Record your results.
19. Thoroughly clean your lab equipment and repeat steps 5 through 19 for each remaining water sample.

Analysis
1. **Summarizing Observations** Summarize the results of this Investigation.
2. **Evaluating Methods** Why would a biologist measure acidity and alkalinity in ppm rather than using the pH scale?

PPM of Acid and Base in Water

Water Sample	Flask A		Flask B		
	mL from step 6	PPM Acid	mL from step 12	mL from step 14	PPM Base

Chapter 54 Review

Summary

As the human population has grown, the demand for natural resources has also grown. Water, land, and wildlife, though renewable, need careful management to maintain the supply. Fossil fuels and other nonrenewable resources are diminishing. Alternate sources of energy must be developed.

Pollution of the environment creates a serious threat to our precious natural resources.

People need to develop better methods of dealing with the pollution resulting from the burning of fuel, the dumping of sewage, and the disposal of solid wastes.

Conservation—the careful management, wise use, and protection of natural resources—is essential for the future. Through conservation, people can maintain the supply and the quality of this planet's natural resources.

BioTerms

acid rain (**879**)
biodegradable (**878**)
conservation (**871**)
contour plowing (**873**)
crop rotation (**873**)
desalination (**872**)
endangered
  species (**874**)
erosion (**873**)
eutrophication (**880**)
extinct species (**874**)
fossil fuels (**876**)
geothermal
  power (**876**)

landfill (**881**)
natural
  resources (**871**)
nonbiodegradable
  (**878**)
nonrenewable
  resources (**871**)
nuclear
  fission (**876**)
nuclear fusion (**876**)
particulate
  matter (**878**)
pesticide (**881**)
pollution (**878**)

renewable
  resources (**871**)
smog (**879**)
solar energy (**877**)
strip-cropping (**873**)
terracing (**873**)

thermal
  inversion (**879**)
thermal pollution
  (**881**)
watershed (**872**)
windbreak (**873**)

For each pair of terms, explain the differences in their meaning.

1. nonrenewable resources, renewable resources
2. thermal pollution, thermal inversion
3. nuclear fission, nuclear fusion
4. biodegradable, nonbiodegradable

BioQuiz   (Write all answers on a separate sheet of paper.)

Completion

1. Fossil fuels are an example of _____ resources.
2. Waste products such as plastics and aluminum are _____ .
3. Nutrient enrichment of water plants through the addition of chemicals to sewage is an example of _____ .
4. Wise management, wise use, and protection of natural resources is known as _____ .
5. An area of land from which water drains into a particular lake or stream is a _____ .

Multiple Choice

6. Decaying algae in a lake reduces the lake's supply of   a) hydrogen. b) nitrogen. c) oxygen. d) water.
7. Planting windbreaks is a method of preventing   a) water pollution. b) soil erosion. c) air pollution. d) geothermal pollution.
8. Alternating the planting of grains and _____ prevents the depletion of nutrients in the soil.   a) pesticides   b) particulate matter   c) legumes   d) wildflowers

9. The illegal hunting of animals is called
   a) poaching.   b) endangering species.
   c) desalination.   d) extinction.
10. Power from steam generated below the
    Earth's surface is   a) nuclear fusion.
    b) nuclear fission.   c) hydroelectric
    power.   d) geothermal power.
11. Energy is released from the splitting of
    atomic nuclei in   a) nuclear fusion.
    b) nuclear fission.   c) particulate matter.
    d) All choices are correct.
12. Which does not reduce soil erosion?
    a) contour plowing   b) terracing
    c) watersheds   d) windbreaks
13. Pollutants becoming trapped in the cool
    air layer is called   a) thermal pollution.
    b) acid rain.   c) thermal inversion.
    d) nonbiodegradable.
14. Waste products made of paper or glass
    are best disposed of by   a) burning.

b) dumping at sea.   c) recycling.
d) using a landfill.
15. Species of plants and animals that have
    completely disappeared from the Earth
    are   a) endangered.   b) extinct.
    c) poached.   d) in captive breeding
    programs.

Writing Critically

16. What are causes and effects of acid rain?
17. How can soil erosion on sloping land be
    reduced?
18. How does the maintenance of watersheds
    help conserve water?
19. What are the limitations to the use of
    nuclear power, solar energy, and
    geothermal power?
20. Why is conservation needed?

Application/Critical Thinking

1. **Relating Ideas**   Cogeneration is a method
   of heating buildings using the heat that is a
   byproduct of the generation of electricity.
   Use your library to research cogeneration
   as an alternative energy source.
2. **Inferring Relationships**   One of the
   world's greatest art treasures, the Parthenon
   in Athens, Greece, is threatened by the effects
   of acid rain. Why is this a greater problem
   now than in the past? Research the steps

that are being taken to protect this
monument.
3. **Synthesizing Conclusions**   Goats and
   pigs were introduced to the Galapagos
   Islands by sailors who hoped those animals would breed and be a source of meat
   in the future. What do you suppose was
   the effect on the native wildlife population
   of the Galapagos? Do library research to
   help with your answer.

Cross-Discipline Connection

Biology and Social Studies   Find out what
kinds of materials are accepted for recycling in

your community. Find out how you start a
recycling program in your school.

Discovery Through Reading

Read the article "Tragedy in Alaska," *National
Wildlife* (June–July 1989): 4–9, focuses on the
environmental impact of the Alaskan oil spill

that occurred in March, 1989. What are the
three parts of a plan that is designed to clean up
an oil spill?

Summary

The biosphere extends from the ocean depths to a few kilometers above the Earth's surface. Ecosystems are physically distinct units of interacting organisms and their physical environments within the biosphere. An ecosystem's biotic factors are organisms that form populations, groups of individuals in the same species. Interactive populations of animals, plants and other organisms form communities. Mutualistic, commensalistic, and predatory relationships occur among organisms in a community or ecosystem. Each organism in an ecosystem occupies a particular niche which is its role in the ecosystem. Nutrients and energy continuously flow through an ecosystem. Communities replace other communities in a process called ecological succession.

A biome is an extensive area that includes many ecosystems. A biome's abiotic factors determine the kinds of plants and animals that can live there. There are six terrestrial biomes.

Aquatic biomes include marine, or saltwater biomes, freshwater biomes, and estuaries.

Environmental pressures control the size and growth of a population. The carrying capacity of an environment is determined by limiting factors that may or may not be related to the population's density. Change in a population is affected by emigration, immigration, birth rate, and death rate.

The natural resources of the planet are nonrenewable or renewable. Conservation of water, soil, wildlife, and energy is aimed at the wise use and protection of both kinds of resources. Contamination and pollution of the environment are major problems that threaten human society. Air and water pollution occur in both urban and rural areas. Disposal of solid wastes is another serious problem. New patterns of recycling resources and wastes may become essential for human survival.

Synthesis

Synthesis Statement

All organisms exist in environments and influence the environments in which they live. Each organism takes resources from the environment to fill its requirements and produces waste products. These waste products are often used by other living things in a continuing cycle. Organisms sometimes change the environments in which they live in ways that make it possible for other organisms to replace them. This orderly replacement of one group of organisms by another is the process of ecological succession. The impact that humans have made and continue to make on the environment has changed the environment in ways that affect the future of humans and that of all other organisms on Earth.

Synthesis Questions

Apply your understanding of this unit to the following questions.

1. Describe the effects of humans on ecological succession in an area near you. Explain how certain kinds of plant and animal communities are harmed by human actions. How might other communities benefit from human activities.

2. Two organisms often appear to share the same niche in a particular habitat. Observation always shows that each organism has its own niche. What aspect of competition does not allow two organisms to share a niche?

3. Although humans manipulate many aspects of the environment, humans are still subject to the rules of nature that govern the flow of energy throughout an ecosystem. Explain why this is so.

4. Describe how your actions and activities during a typical day affect the biogeochemical cycles of water and nitrogen.

5. How might a population boom among the members of a particular species alter the arrangement and numbers of organisms in a food chain?

6. What are some limiting factors that affect the human population? Describe some ways in which technology can and cannot help us to overcome shortages of limiting factors.

7. Ecological succession occurs in communities of all sizes. Select any area near you and describe the successional changes that you think are taking place in that area.

8. Describe some of the abiotic factors that are responsible for differences in population density between tropical rain forests and deserts and between tundra and grasslands.

9. The burning of solid wastes is often proposed as a solution to eliminate refuse that would take up valuable acreage if placed in a landfill. Offer an explanation why this might be a less than ideal solution.

10. Use a separate piece of paper to draw a concept map like the one below. Place each of the following terms inside the appropriate figure: sunlight energy, abiotic component, biotic component, heat.

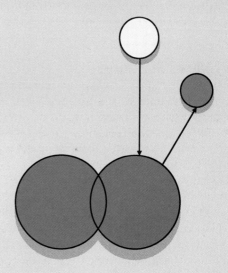

REFERENCE SECTION

Comparing Biological Systems

Invertebrates

SPONGE
Phylum Porifera, Class Demospongiae

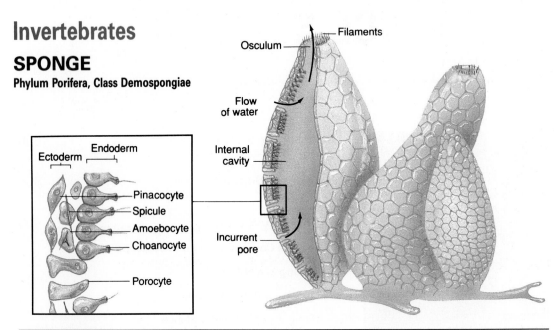

Filaments

Osculum

Flow of water

Internal cavity

Incurrent pore

Ectoderm

Endoderm

Pinacocyte

Spicule

Amoebocyte

Choanocyte

Porocyte

JELLYFISH
Phylum Coelenterata, Class Scyphozoa

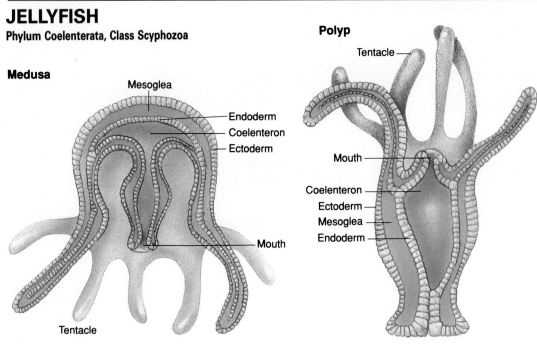

Medusa

Mesoglea

Endoderm

Coelenteron

Ectoderm

Mouth

Tentacle

Polyp

Tentacle

Mouth

Coelenteron

Ectoderm

Mesoglea

Endoderm

EARTHWORM
Phylum Annelida, Class Oligochaeta

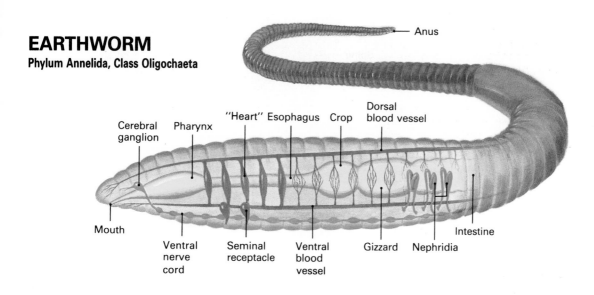

Anus

Cerebral ganglion

Pharynx

"Heart"

Esophagus

Crop

Dorsal blood vessel

Mouth

Ventral nerve cord

Seminal receptacle

Ventral blood vessel

Gizzard

Nephridia

Intestine

CLAM
Phylum Mollusca, Class Pelecypoda

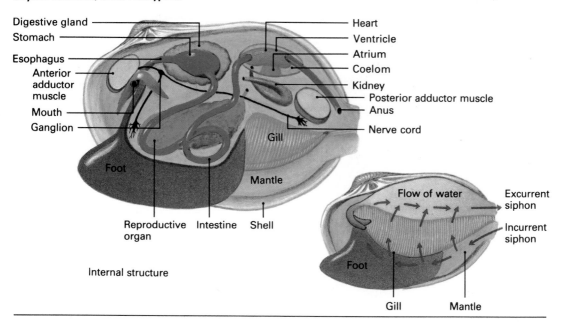

Digestive gland

Stomach

Esophagus

Anterior adductor muscle

Mouth

Ganglion

Heart

Ventricle

Atrium

Coelom

Kidney

Posterior adductor muscle

Anus

Nerve cord

Gill

Foot

Mantle

Reproductive organ

Intestine

Shell

Internal structure

Flow of water

Excurrent siphon

Incurrent siphon

Foot

Gill

Mantle

STARFISH

Phylum Echinodermata, Class Asteroidea

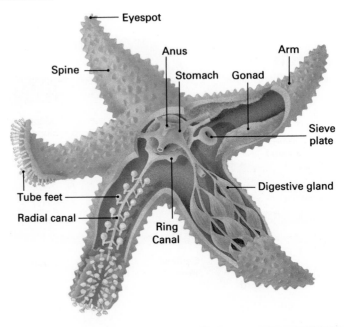

Eyespot

Anus

Arm

Spine

Stomach   Gonad

Sieve plate

Digestive gland

Tube feet

Radial canal

Ring Canal

SPIDER

Phylum Arthropoda, Class Arachnida

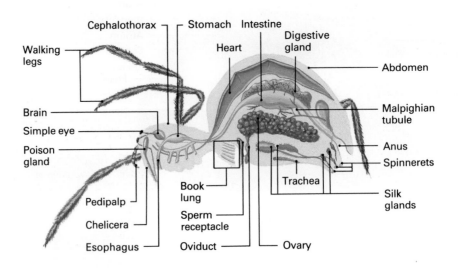

Cephalothorax   Stomach   Intestine

Digestive gland

Walking legs

Heart

Abdomen

Brain

Malpighian tubule

Simple eye

Anus

Poison gland

Spinnerets

Book lung

Trachea

Silk glands

Pedipalp

Sperm receptacle

Chelicera

Esophagus   Oviduct   Ovary

CRAYFISH

Phylum Arthropoda, Class Crustacea

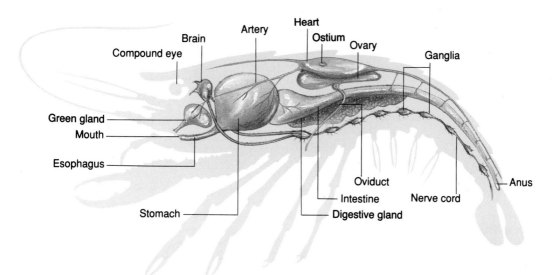

GRASSHOPPER

Phylum Arthropoda, Class Insecta

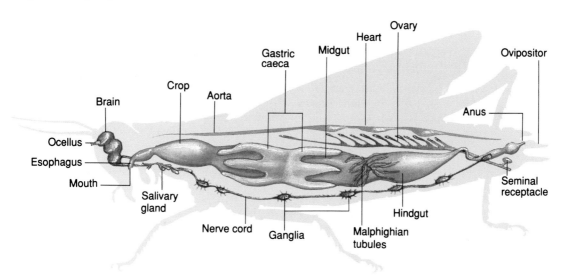

Vertebrate Skeletal Systems

FISH
Phylum Chordata, Class Osteichythyes

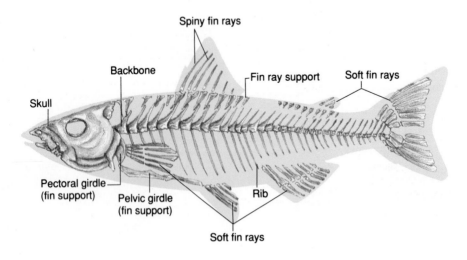

Spiny fin rays

Backbone

Fin ray support

Soft fin rays

Skull

Pectoral girdle (fin support)

Pelvic girdle (fin support)

Rib

Soft fin rays

FROG
Phylum Chordata, Class Amphibia, Order Anura

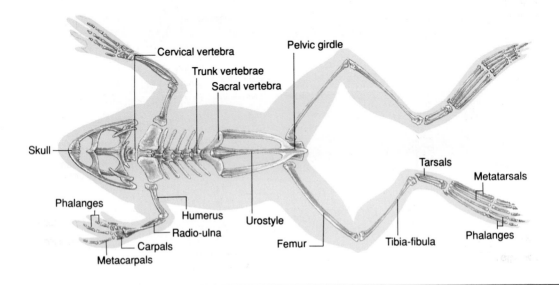

Cervical vertebra

Trunk vertebrae

Sacral vertebra

Pelvic girdle

Skull

Tarsals

Metatarsals

Phalanges

Humerus

Urostyle

Radio-ulna

Femur

Tibia-fibula

Phalanges

Carpals

Metacarpals

TURTLE
Phylum Chordata, Class Reptilia, Order Chelonia

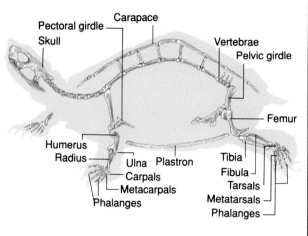

- Pectoral girdle
- Carapace
- Skull
- Vertebrae
- Pelvic girdle
- Femur
- Humerus
- Radius
- Ulna
- Plastron
- Carpals
- Metacarpals
- Phalanges
- Tibia
- Fibula
- Tarsals
- Metatarsals
- Phalanges

BIRD
Phylum Chordata, Class Aves, Order Passeriformes

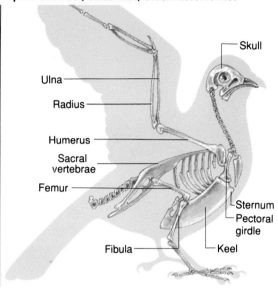

- Skull
- Ulna
- Radius
- Humerus
- Sacral vertebrae
- Femur
- Sternum
- Pectoral girdle
- Fibula
- Keel

HUMAN
Phylum Chordata, Class Mammalia, Order Primates

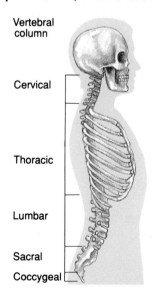

- Vertebral column
- Cervical
- Thoracic
- Lumbar
- Sacral
- Coccygeal

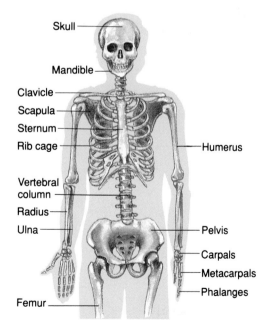

- Skull
- Mandible
- Clavicle
- Scapula
- Sternum
- Rib cage
- Vertebral column
- Radius
- Ulna
- Femur
- Humerus
- Pelvis
- Carpals
- Metacarpals
- Phalanges

Vertebrate Digestive Systems

FISH
Phylum Chordata, Class Osteichythyes

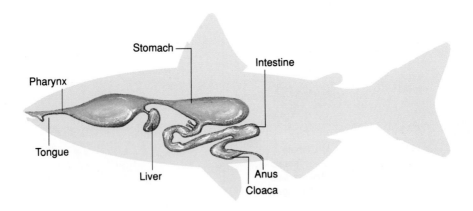

Stomach

Intestine

Pharynx

Tongue

Liver

Anus

Cloaca

FROG
Phylum Chordata, Class Amphibia, Order Anura

Gall bladder

Liver

Esophagus

Duodenum

Small intestine

Ileum

Stomach

Pancreas

Pylorus

Urinary bladder

Large intestine

Cloaca

TURTLE
Phylum Chordata, Class Reptilia, Order Chelonia

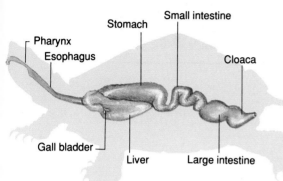

Pharynx
Esophagus
Stomach
Small intestine
Cloaca
Gall bladder
Liver
Large intestine

BIRD
Phylum Chordata, Class Aves, Order Passeriformes

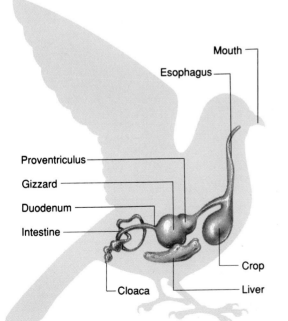

Mouth
Esophagus
Proventriculus
Gizzard
Duodenum
Intestine
Crop
Cloaca
Liver

HUMAN
Phylum Chordata, Class Mammalia, Order Primates

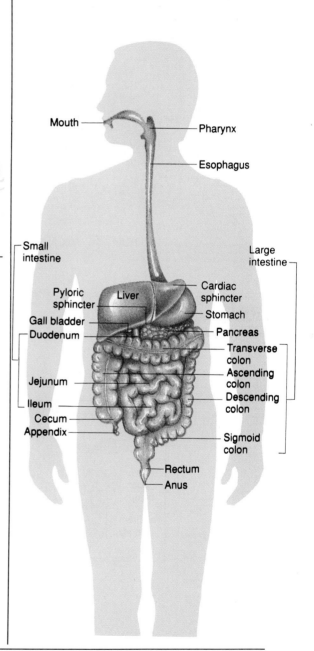

Mouth
Pharynx
Esophagus
Small intestine
Large intestine
Pyloric sphincter
Liver
Cardiac sphincter
Gall bladder
Stomach
Duodenum
Pancreas
Transverse colon
Jejunum
Ascending colon
Ileum
Descending colon
Cecum
Appendix
Sigmoid colon
Rectum
Anus

Vertebrate Circulatory Systems

FISH
Phylum Chordata, Class Osteichthyes

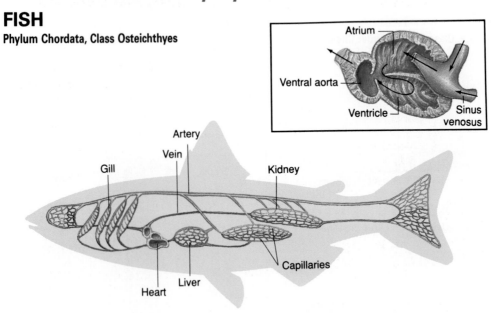

Atrium
Ventral aorta
Ventricle
Sinus venosus

Artery
Vein
Gill
Kidney
Capillaries
Heart
Liver

FROG
Phlyum Chordata, Class Amphibia, Order Anura

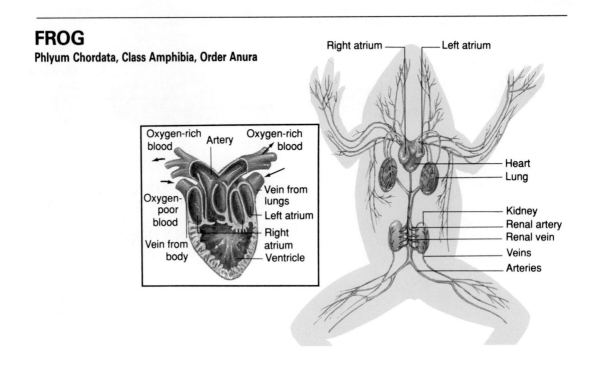

Right atrium
Left atrium

Oxygen-rich blood
Artery
Oxygen-rich blood
Oxygen-poor blood
Vein from lungs
Left atrium
Right atrium
Ventricle
Vein from body

Heart
Lung
Kidney
Renal artery
Renal vein
Veins
Arteries

TURTLE

Phylum Chordata, Class Reptilia, Order Chelonia

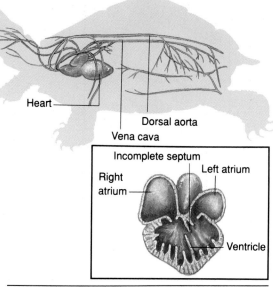

Heart

Dorsal aorta

Vena cava

Incomplete septum

Right atrium

Left atrium

Ventricle

BIRD

Phylum Chordata, Class Aves, Order Passeriformes

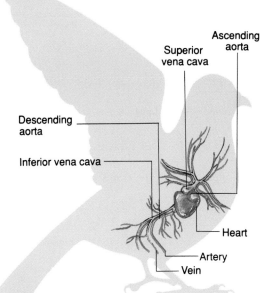

Superior vena cava

Ascending aorta

Descending aorta

Inferior vena cava

Heart

Artery

Vein

HUMAN

Phylum Chordata, Class Mammalia, Order Primates

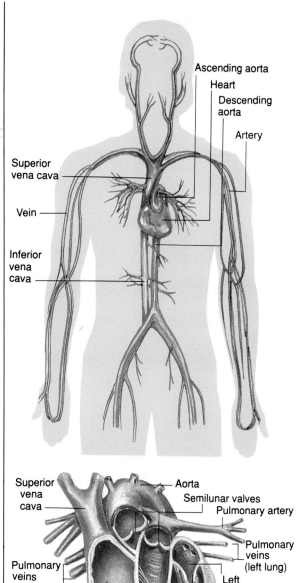

Ascending aorta

Heart

Descending aorta

Artery

Superior vena cava

Vein

Inferior vena cava

Superior vena cava

Aorta

Semilunar valves

Pulmonary artery

Pulmonary veins (left lung)

Pulmonary veins (right lung)

Left atrium

Mitral valve

Right atrium

Tricuspid valve

Left ventricle

Right ventricle

Septum

Vertebrate Respiratory Systems

FISH

Phylum Chordata, Class Osteichthyes

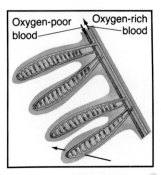

Oxygen-poor blood

Oxygen-rich blood

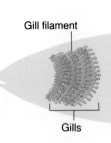

Gill filament

Gills

FROG

Phylum Chordata, Class Amphibia, Order Anura

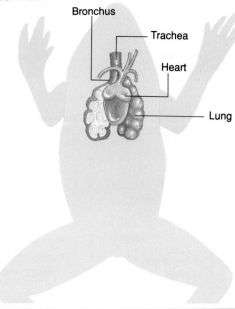

Bronchus

Trachea

Heart

Lung

TURTLE
Phylum Chordata, Class Reptilia, Order Chelonia

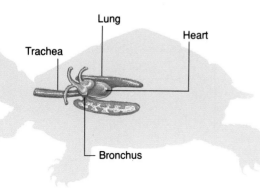

Lung

Heart

Trachea

Bronchus

BIRD
Phylum Chordata, Class Aves, Order Passeriformes

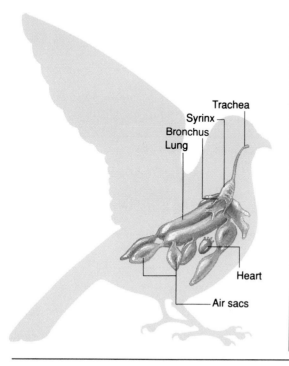

Trachea

Syrinx

Bronchus

Lung

Heart

Air sacs

HUMAN
Phylum Chordata, Class Mammalia, Order Primates

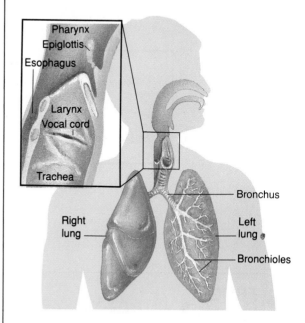

Pharynx

Epiglottis

Esophagus

Larynx

Vocal cord

Trachea

Right lung

Bronchus

Left lung

Bronchioles

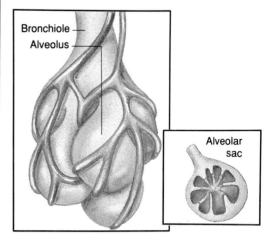

Bronchiole

Alveolus

Alveolar sac

Vertebrate Nervous Systems

FISH
Phylum Chordata, Class Osteichthyes

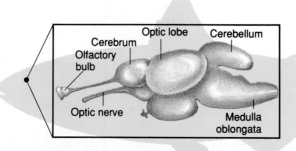

FROG
Phylum Chordata, Class Amphibia, Order Anura

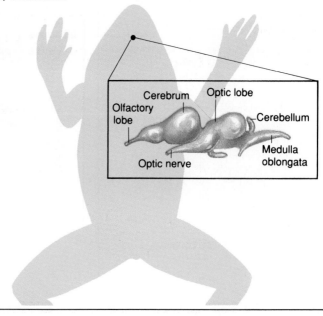

TURTLE

Phylum Chordata, Class Reptilia, Order Chelonia

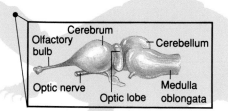

Cerebrum
Olfactory bulb
Cerebellum
Optic nerve
Optic lobe
Medulla oblongata

BIRD

Phylum Chordata, Class Aves, Order Passeriformes

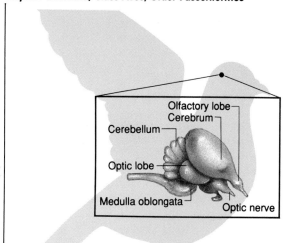

Olfactory lobe
Cerebrum
Cerebellum
Optic lobe
Medulla oblongata
Optic nerve

HUMAN

Phylum Chordata, Class Mammalia, Order Primates

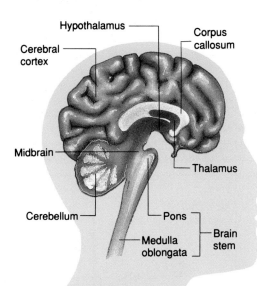

Hypothalamus
Corpus callosum
Cerebral cortex
Midbrain
Thalamus
Cerebellum
Pons
Medulla oblongata
Brain stem

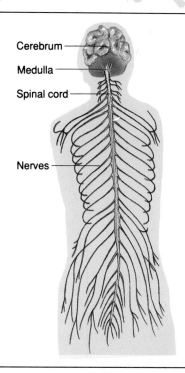

Cerebrum
Medulla
Spinal cord
Nerves

Vertebrate Reproductive/Excretory Systems

FISH
Phylum Chordata, Class Osteichthyes

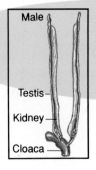

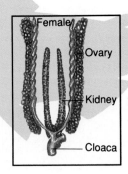

FROG
Phylum Chordata, Class Amphibia, Order Anura

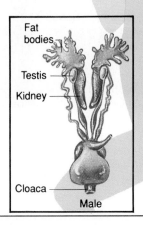

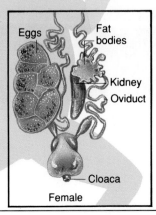

TURTLE
Phylum Chordata, Class Reptilia, Order Chelonia

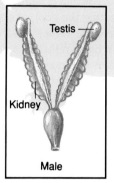

Testis

Kidney

Male

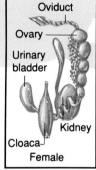

Oviduct

Ovary

Urinary bladder

Kidney

Cloaca

Female

BIRD
Phylum Chordata, Class Aves, Order Passeriformes

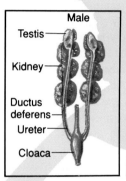

Male

Testis

Kidney

Ductus deferens

Ureter

Cloaca

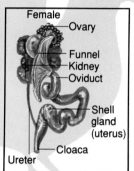

Female

Ovary

Funnel
Kidney
Oviduct

Shell gland (uterus)

Cloaca

Ureter

HUMAN
Phylum Chordata, Class Mammalia, Order Primates

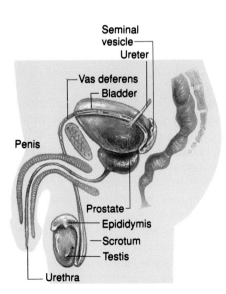

Seminal vesicle
Ureter
Vas deferens
Bladder

Penis

Prostate
Epididymis
Scrotum
Testis

Urethra

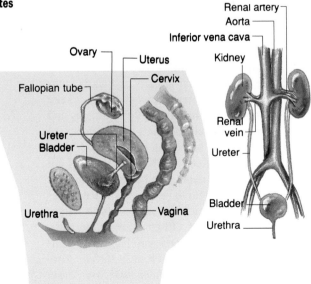

Ovary
Fallopian tube
Uterus
Cervix

Ureter
Bladder

Urethra
Vagina

Renal artery
Aorta
Inferior vena cava
Kidney

Renal vein

Ureter

Bladder
Urethra

Safety Guidelines

You can ensure both learning and enjoyment by making the laboratory a safe place in which to work. It is important that you follow safety procedures at all times. If an accident should occur, you should know exactly where to locate emergency equipment. Good safety practice means being responsible for your fellow students' safety as well as your own.

Practice the following safety measures whenever you are in the laboratory:

1. **Preparation** Study your assignment in advance. Before beginning your investigation, ask your teacher to explain any procedures you do not understand.

2. **Eye Safety** Wear goggles when handling acids or bases, using an open flame, or performing any activity that could harm the eyes. If a solution is splashed into the eyes, wash the eyes with plenty of water and notify your instructor at once. *Never use direct sunlight to illuminate a microscope. This practice is dangerous to the eyes.*

3. **Safety Equipment** Know the location of the nearest telephone and all safety equipment, including fire extinguishers, fire blankets, first-aid kits, eyewash fountains, and emergency showers. Take responsibility for your fellow students and report all accidents and emergencies to your teacher immediately.

4. **Neatness** Keep work areas free of all unnecessary items. Tie back long hair and button or roll up loose sleeves when working with chemicals or near an open flame.

5. **Chemicals and Other Dangerous Substances** When carelessly handled, chemicals can be dangerous. *Never taste chemicals or place them near your eyes.* Do not use mouth suction when using a pipette to transfer chemicals. Use a suction bulb instead.

Never pour water into a strong acid or base. The mixture produces heat and may splatter. To keep the mixture cool, pour the acid or base slowly into the water.

If any solution is spilled on a work surface, wash it off at once with plenty of water. When noting the odor of chemical substances, wave the fumes toward your nose with your hand rather than putting your nose close to the source of the odor.

Never eat in the laboratory. Counters and glassware may contain substances that can contaminate food. Do not use flammable substances near a flame. Handle toxic substances in a well-ventilated area or under a ventilation hood. Do not place flammable chemicals in a refrigerator. Sparks from the refrigeration unit can ignite these substances or their fumes.

6. **Heat** Whenever possible, use an electric hot plate instead of an open flame. If you must use an open flame, shield it with a wire screen that has a ceramic fiber center. *When heating chemicals in a test tube, never point the test tube toward anyone.* Keep combustible materials away from heat sources.

7. **Electricity** Be cautious around electrical wiring. When using a microscope with a lamp, do not place its cord where it can cause someone to trip and fall. *Never let cords hang loose over a table edge in a way that permits equipment to fall if the cord is tugged. Never use equipment with frayed cords.*

8. **Knives** Use knives, razor blades, and other sharp instruments with extreme care. *Never use double-edged razor blades in the laboratory.*

9. **Glassware** Examine all glassware before heating. Glass containers for heating

should be made of boro-silicate glass or some other heat-resistant material. *Never use cracked or chipped glassware. Never force glass tubing into rubber stoppers. Broken glassware should be swept up immediately, never picked up with the fingers. Broken glassware should be discarded in a special container, never into a sink.*

10. **Bacterial Cultures** Return all bacterial and other cultures to your teacher for proper disposal. Wash and disinfect all glassware and other equipment that has come in contact with the culture. Follow any additional instructions your teacher may give you regarding specific cultures.

11. **Dissection** *Never dissect a specimen while holding it in your hand.* Place all specimens in dissecting pans before beginning dissection.

12. **First Aid** In case of severe bleeding, apply pressure or a compress directly to the wounded area and see that the injured student reports immediately to the school nurse or a physician.

   Minor burns caused by heat should be treated by applying ice. Immerse the burn in cold water if ice is not available. Treat acid burns by applying sodium bicarbonate (baking soda). Use boric acid to treat burns caused by bases. Any burn, regardless of cause, should be reported to your teacher and referred to the school nurse or a physician.

   In case of fainting, place the fainting victim's head lower than the rest of the body and see that the person has fresh air. Report to your teacher immediately.

In case of poisoning, report to your teacher at once. Try to determine the poisoning agent, if possible.

13. **Unauthorized Experiments** *Never perform any experiment that has not been assigned by your teacher. Never work alone in the laboratory.*

14. **Cleanup** Wash your hands immediately after handling bacteria or other hazardous materials. Before leaving the laboratory, clean up all work areas. Put away all equipment and supplies. Make sure water, gas, burners, and electric hot plates are turned off.

Remember at all times that a laboratory is a safe place only if you regard laboratory work as serious work.

The instructions for your laboratory investigations will include cautionary statements where necessary. In addition you will find that the following safety symbols appear whenever a procedure requires extra caution:

Humane treatment

Laboratory apron

Sharp/pointed object

Goggles

Rubber gloves

Flame/heat

Dangerous chemical

Biohazard—disease-causing organisms

Electrical hazard

Laboratory Skills

Using a Compound Light Microscope

Parts of the Compound Light Microscope
- The *eyepiece* magnifies the image 10×.
- The *low-power objective* magnifies the image 10×.
- The *high-power objective* magnifies the image either 40× or 43×.
- The *revolving nosepiece* holds the objectives and can be turned to change from one magnification to the other.
- The *body tube* maintains the correct distance between eyepiece and objectives.
- The *coarse adjustment* moves the body tube up and down to allow focusing of the image.
- The *fine adjustment* moves the body tube slightly to bring the image into sharper focus.
- The *stage* supports a slide.
- *Stage clips* secure the slide in position for viewing.
- The *diaphragm* controls the amount of light coming through the stage.
- The *light source* provides light for viewing the slide.
- The *arm* supports the body tube.
- The *base* supports the microscope.

Proper Use of the Compound Light Microscope
1. Carry the microscope to your lab table using both hands, one beneath the base and the other hand holding the arm of the microscope. Hold the microscope close to your body.
2. Place the microscope on the lab table, at least 5 cm (2 in.) in from the edge of the table.
3. Check to see what type of light source the microscope has. If the microscope has a lamp, plug it in, making sure that the cord is out of the way. If the microscope has a mirror, adjust it to reflect light through the

Compound light microscope

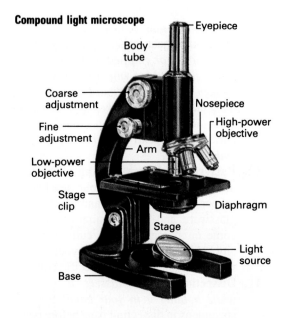

hole in the stage. **CAUTION: If your microscope has a mirror, do not use direct sunlight as a light source. Direct sunlight can damage your eyes.**

4. Adjust the revolving nosepiece so that the low-power objective is in line with the body tube.
5. Place a prepared slide over the hole in the stage and secure the slide with stage clips.
6. Look through the eyepiece and move the diaphragm to adjust the amount of light coming through the stage.
7. Now, look at the stage from eye level, and slowly turn the coarse adjustment to lower the objective until it almost touches the slide. Do not allow the objective to touch the slide.
8. While looking through the eyepiece, turn the coarse adjustment to raise the objective until the image is in focus. *Never focus objectives downward*. Use the fine adjustment to sharpen the focus. Keep both eyes open while viewing a slide.

9. Make sure that the image is exactly in the center of your field of vision. Then, switch to the high-power objective. Focus the image with the fine adjustment. *Never use the coarse adjustment at high power.*

10. When you are finished using the microscope, remove the slide. Clean the eyepiece and objectives with lens paper and return the microscope to its storage area.

Making a Wet Mount

1. Use lens paper to clean a glass slide and coverslip.
2. Place the specimen you wish to observe in the center of the slide.
3. Using a medicine dropper, place one drop of water on the specimen.
4. Position the coverslip so that it is at the edge of the drop of water and at a 45° angle to the slide. Make sure that the water runs along the edge of the coverslip.
5. Lower the coverslip slowly to avoid trapping air bubbles.
6. As the water evaporates from the slide, add another drop of water by placing the tip of the medicine dropper next to the edge of the coverslip. (Use this technique also when adding stains or solutions to a wet mount.) If you have added too much water, remove the excess by using the corner of a paper towel as a blotter. Do not lift the coverslip to add or remove water.

Wet mount

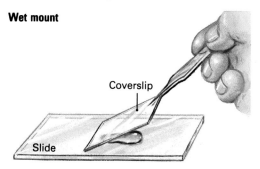

Coverslip

Slide

Lighting a Bunsen Burner

1. Before lighting the burner, observe the locations of fire extinguishers, fire blankets, and sand buckets. Wear safety goggles, gloves, and an apron. Tie back long hair and roll up long sleeves. Attach tubing firmly to outlet.
2. Turn the gas full on by using the valve at the laboratory gas outlet.

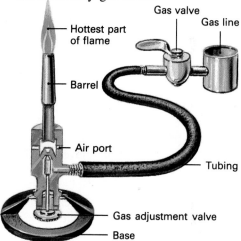

Gas valve

Gas line

Hottest part of flame

Barrel

Air port

Tubing

Gas adjustment valve

Base

3. Make a spark with a striker. If you are using a match, hold it slightly to the side of the opening in the barrel.
4. Adjust the air ports until you can clearly see an inner cone within the flame.
5. Adjust the gas flow for the desired flame height by using the gas adjustment valve either on the burner or at the gas outlet. **CAUTION: If the burner is not operating properly, the flame may burn inside the base of the barrel. Carbon monoxide, an odorless gas, is released from this type of flame. Should this situation occur, turn off the gas at the laboratory gas valve immediately. Do not touch the barrel of the burner.** Partially close the air ports before trying to relight the burner.

Using a Triple-Beam Balance

1. Make sure the balance is on a level surface. Use the leveling screws at the bottom of the balance to make any necessary adjustments.
2. Place all the counterweights at zero. The pointer should be at zero. If it is not, adjust the balancing knob until the pointer rests at zero.
3. Place the object you wish to measure on the pan. **CAUTION: Do not place hot objects or chemicals directly on the balance pan as they can damage its surface.**
4. Move the largest counterweight along the beam to the right until it is at the last notch that does not tip the balance. Follow the same procedure with the next largest counterweight. Then, move the smallest counterweight until the pointer rests at zero.
5. Total the readings on all beams to determine the mass of the object.
6. When weighing crystals or powders, use a filter paper. First weigh the paper, then add the crystals and powders and reweigh. The actual weight is the total less the weight of the paper. When weighing liquids, first weigh the empty container, then the liquid and container.

Triple-beam balance

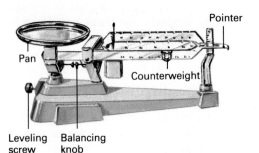

Measuring Volume in a Graduate

1. Set the graduate (graduated cylinder) on a level surface.
2. Carefully pour the liquid you wish to measure into the cylinder. Notice that the surface of the liquid has a lens-shaped curve, the *meniscus*.
3. With the surface of the liquid at eye level, read the measurement at the bottom of the meniscus.

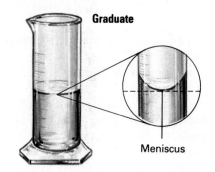

Graduate

Meniscus

International System of Units (SI) Conversion Table

The metric system is used for making measurements in science. The official name of this system is the *Système International d'Unités*, or **International System of Measurements (SI)**.

SI Units		Converting SI to English		Converting English to SI	
Length					
kilometer (km)	= 1,000 m	1 km	= 0.62 mile	1 mile	= 1.609 km
meter (m)	= 100 cm	1 m	= 1.09 yards	1 yard	= 0.914 m
			= 3.28 feet	1 foot	= 0.305 m
decimeter (dm)	= 0.1 m	1 dm	= 3.94 inches		= 3.05 dm
centimeter (cm)	= 0.01 m	1 cm	= 0.394 inch		= 30.5 cm
millimeter (mm)	= 0.001 m	1 mm	= 0.039 inch	1 inch	= 2.54 cm
micrometer (μm)	= 0.000001 m				
nanometer (nm)	= 0.000000001 m				
Area					
square kilometer (km²)	= 100 hectares	1 km²	= 0.3861 square mile	1 square mile	= 2.590 km²
hectare (ha)	= 10,000 m²	1 ha	= 2.471 acres	1 acre	= 0.4047 ha
square meter (m²)	= 10,000 cm²	1 m²	= 1.1960 square yards	1 square yard	= 0.8361 m²
				1 square foot	= 0.0929 m²
square centimeter (cm²)	= 100 mm²	1 cm²	= 0.115 square inch	1 square inch	= 6.4516 cm²
Mass					
kilogram (kg)	= 1,000 g	1 kg	= 2.205 pounds	1 pound	= 0.4536 kg
gram (g)	= 1,000 mg	1 g	= 0.0353 ounce	1 ounce	= 28.35 g
milligram (mg)	= 0.001 g				
microgram (μg)	= 0.000001 g				
Volume of Solids					
1 cubic meter (m³)	= 1,000,000 cm³	1 m³	= 1.3080 cubic yards	1 cubic yard	= 0.7646 m³
			= 35.315 cubic feet	1 cubic foot	= 0.0283 m³
1 cubic centimeter (cm³)	= 1,000 mm³	1 cm³	= 0.0610 cubic inch	1 cubic inch	= 16.387 cm³
Volume of Liquids					
kiloliter (kl)	= 1,000 L	1 kL	= 264.17 gallons	1 gallon	= 3.785 L
liter (L)	= 1,000 mL	1 L	= 1.06 quarts	1 quart	= 0.94 L
cubic decimeter (dm³)	= 0.001 m³	1 dm³	= 1.06 quarts		= 0.94 dm³
milliliter (mL)	= 0.001 L	1 mL	= 0.034 fluid ounce	1 pint	= 0.47 L
microliter (μL)	= 0.000001 L			1 fluid ounce	= 29.57 mL

Temperature Conversion

The top of the thermometer is marked off in degrees Fahrenheit (°F.). To read the corresponding temperature in degrees Celsius (°C), look at the bottom side of the thermometer. For example, 50°F. is the same temperature as 10°C. You may also use the formulas at the right to make conversions.

Conversion of Fahrenheit to Celsius:

$$°C = \frac{5}{9}(°F - 32)$$

Conversion of Celsius to Fahrenheit:

$$°F = \frac{9}{5}°C + 32$$

°F.

-40 -30 -20 -10 0 10 20 30 40 50 60 70 80 90 100 110 120 130 140 150 160 170 180 190 200 210 220 230

°C

-40 -30 -20 -10 0 10 20 30 40 50 60 70 80 90 100 110

Freezing point of water   **Boiling point of water**

Key Discoveries in Biology

500 B.C.-1 B.C.

About 500 B.C.
Greek philosopher Alcmaeon performs pioneer studies in human anatomy.

About 420 B.C.
Greek philosopher Hippocrates establishes the scientific basis of medicine.

About 350 B.C.
Greek philosopher Aristotle develops a systematic classification of animals.

Hippocrates

About 300 B.C.
Greek philosopher Theophrastus creates the first scientific classification of plants.

About 75 B.C.
Roman philosopher Lucretius applies the atomistic theory to living things and offers a particulate theory of heredity.

A.D. 1-A.D. 899

About A.D. 50
Roman naturalist Pliny the Elder compiles an encyclopedia of natural history.

About 150
Galen, a Greco-Roman physician, contributes medical theories based on the dissection of apes.

1700s

1753-58 Swedish naturalist Carolus Linnaeus establishes a modern taxonomy.

1779 Dutch naturalist Jan Ingenhousz shows that sunlight is the source of energy in photosynthesis.

1796 English physician Edward Jenner introduces vaccination.

1800s

1817 French scientist Georges Cuvier pioneers the field of comparative anatomy.

1838-39 German biologists Matthias Schleiden and Theodor Schwann establish cell theory.

1855 German physician Rudolf Virchow launches the science of cellular pathology.

1859 British naturalist Charles Darwin proposes his theory of evolution.

1862 French scientist Louis Pasteur disproves abiogenesis.

1865 Austrian monk Gregor Mendel establishes the basic laws of heredity.

1876 German physician Robert Koch establishes the anthrax bacterium as the causative agent of anthrax. Louis Pasteur develops the anthrax vaccine.

1892 German biologist August Weismann proposes the germ-plasm (gamete) theory of inheritance.

1940s

1941 American researchers George Beadle and Edward Tatum propose the one gene one enzyme theory.

1944-52 Experiments by Americans Oswald Avery (1944) and Alfred Hershey and Martha Chase (1952) prove that DNA is the genetic chemical.

1946-61 American biochemist Melvin Calvin elucidates the process of carbon fixation during photosynthesis.

1947 American geneticist Barbara McClintock proposes that genes can move between chromosome sites.

1950s

1953 American James Watson and Briton Francis Crick discover the molecular structure of DNA.

1956 American molecular biologist Arthur Kornberg synthesizes DNA in the laboratory.

1960s

1961 Americans Marshall Nirenberg and Severo Ochoa break the genetic code of DNA and messenger RNA.

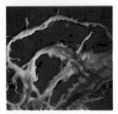

DNA strands

The key discoveries given here are only a limited selection over 2,500 years and are not meant to be a definitive list. The number of women scientists has increased dramatically over the past ten years.

900-1499

About 900
Persian physician Rhazes authors an encyclopedia of practical medicine.

About 1030
Avicenna (Ibn Sina), a Persian philosopher-physician, completes the *Canon of Medicine,* which codifies medical knowledge for 500 years.

1500s

1543 Flemish physician Andreas Vesalius publishes the first scientific textbook on human anatomy.

Drawing by Vesalius

1600s

1628 English physician William Harvey accurately describes the human circulatory system.

1665 English scientist Robert Hooke observes cell structure in the bark of the cork oak.

1676 Dutch microscopist Anton van Leeuwenhoek first sees one-celled organisms.

Hooke's microscope

1900-1919

1900 Austrian-American scientist Karl Landsteiner discovers ABO-blood types in humans.

1900 Mendel's work is independently rediscovered by three scientists—Erich Tschermak von Seysenegg, Hugo de Vries, and Carl Correns.

1902 American cytologist Walter Sutton proposes that genes are carried on the chromosomes.

1910-15 American geneticist T. H. Morgan discovers linkage and crossing over, establishing that genes exist as linear units on the chromosomes.

1920-1939

1928 British biologist Alexander Fleming discovers penicillin.

Penicillin crystals

1937 German biochemist Sir Hans Krebs discovers the citric acid cycle, the key event in cellular respiration.

1937 American geneticist Theodosius Dobzhansky initiates the synthesis of genetic and evolutionary theory.

1970s

1973 American molecular biologists Stanley Cohen and Herbert Boyer discover how to induce gene splicing.

1977 American scientists Rosalyn Yalow, Roger Guillemin, and Andrew Schally win the Nobel prize for tracking radioactive hormone in the body.

1980s

1982 American molecular biologist Robert A. Weinberg discovers an oncogene—a dormant gene capable of causing cancer when activated—in human cells.

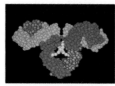

Immunoglobulin

1984 Three immunologists share the Nobel prize: Niels Jerne, in England, for his theories on how the immune system works; and Briton Cesar Milstein and Swiss Georges Kohler for their creation of monoclonal antibodies.

1987 American biologist Susumu Tonegawa wins a Nobel prize for showing that 1,000 genes direct the synthesis of up to 1 billion antibodies.

1989 Sidney Altman and Thomas Cech of the United States share a Nobel Prize for showing that RNA can actively promote chemical reactions and reproduce itself.

Five-Kingdom Classification of Organisms

Kingdom Monera

Prokaryotes (cells lack a true nucleus and membrane-bound organelles); mostly unicellular; some occur in filaments or clusters.

Phylum Schizophyta: Bacteria; about 2,500 species including eubacteria (true bacteria), rickettsias, mycoplasmas, and spirochetes; mostly heterotrophs; some photosynthetic and chemosynthetic autotrophs; asexual reproduction by binary fission.

Phylum Cyanophyta: Blue-green bacteria or cyanobacteria; about 200 species of photosynthetic autotrophs with chlorophyll *a* and accessory pigments; no chloroplasts; mostly filamentous; some unicellular; reproduction asexual by binary fission or fragmentation.

Phylum Prochlorophyta: Photosynthetic autotrophs; contain chlorophylls *a* and *b*, xanthophylls, and carotenes.

Kingdom Protista

Diverse group of unicellular and simple multicellular eukaryotes (cells have a true nucleus and membrane-bound organelles).

Phylum Mastigophora: Flagellates; about 2,500 species; mostly parasitic; includes *Trypanosoma* and *Trichonympha*.

Phylum Sarcodina: Sarcodines; about 11,500 species that move by means of pseudopodia; includes amoebas.

Phylum Ciliophora: Ciliates; about 7,200 species; locomotion by cilia, or sessile; includes paramecia.

Phylum Sporozoa: Sporozoans; about 6,000 species of nonmotile parasites; includes *Plasmodium*, the agent of malaria.

The following are often classified as divisions.

Phylum Euglenophyta: Euglenoids; about 800 species of unicellular, photosynthetic/heterotrophic organisms with chlorophylls *a* and *b;* usually having a single flagellum; reproduction is asexual.

Phylum Acrasiomycota: Cellular slime molds; about 65 species; individual amoebalike cells that aggregate and produce spores.

Phylum Myxomycota: Plasmodial slime molds; about 600 species; body consists of multinucleate plasmodium; forms funguslike sporangia and spores during reproduction.

Phylum Oomycota: Water molds; about 800 species; reproduce sexually by oogamy; flagellated asexual spores; cell walls contain cellulose.

Phylum Pyrrophyta: Fire algae; about 1,100 photosynthetic species with chlorophylls *a* and *c* and xanthophyll; unicellular; major component of marine phytoplankton; includes dinoflagellates.

Phylum Chrysophyta: Golden algae; about 12,000 photosynthetic species with chlorophylls *a* and *c* and carotenes, xanthophylls, and fucoxanthins; most are unicellular and aquatic; includes diatoms.

Phylum Phaeophyta: Brown algae; about 1,500 photosynthetic species with chlorophylls *a* and *c* and fucoxanthin; includes kelps.

Phylum Rhodophyta: Red algae; about 4,000 photosynthetic species with chlorophylls *a* and *d,* carotenes, and phycobilins; includes filamentous, multicellular seaweeds.

Phylum Chlorophyta: Green algae; about 7,000 photosynthetic species with chlorophylls *a* and *b* and carotenoids; includes unicellular, colonial, and multicellular species.

Kingdom Fungi

Eukaryotic heterotrophs that obtain food by absorption; includes saprophytes and parasites; most are multicellular, composed of hyphae; cell walls contain chitin.

Division Eumycophyta: True fungi; about 81,000 species; mostly filamentous with chitinous cell walls; reproduction may be sexual or asexual.

Class Zygomycetes: Terrestrial molds; about 600 species; reproduce asexually by spores and sexually by the fusion of nuclei from the tips of different mating strains.

Class Basidiomycetes: Club fungi; about 25,000 species of terrestrial fungi that produce spores on club-like structures called basidia; includes mushrooms, rusts, and smuts.

Class Ascomycetes: Sac fungi; about 30,000 terrestrial and aquatic species; spores form in an ascus (little sac) which results from the sexual combination of two gametes or strains; includes yeasts that reproduce asexually by budding, powdery mildews, morels, and truffles.

Class Deuteromycetes: Imperfect fungi; about 25,000 species that either do not reproduce sexually or have sexual life cycles that have not been observed; includes *Penicillium*.

Kingdom Plantae

Multicellular, eukaryotic autotrophs that carry out photosynthesis in chloroplasts; chlorophyll *a* is the photoreactive pigment; chlorophyll *b* and various carotenoids serve as accessory pigments; primarily terrestrial; cell walls contain cellulose; body has distinct tissues; life cycle of alternating sporophyte and gametophyte generations.

Division Bryophyta: Bryophytes; about 15,600 species that lack vascular tissues and true roots, stems, and leaves; obtain nutrients by osmosis and diffusion; found chiefly in moist habitats; sperm must swim to eggs; gametophyte is dominant form in life cycle.

Class Muscopsida: Mosses; about 9,500 species with small, leafy gametophytes; sporophyte nonphotosynthetic, attached to and dependent upon gametophyte.

Class Hepaticopsida: Liverworts; about 6,000 extremely tiny species; gametophytes generally leafy, with scaly upper surface; sporophyte nonphotosynthetic, attached to and dependent upon gametophyte.

Class Antherocerotopsida: Hornworts; about 100 species; gametophyte not differentiated into roots, stems, or leaves; stomata on sporophyte; sporophyte grows from basal meristem.

All of the following plant phyla are tracheophytes with true roots, stems, and leaves in the dominant sporophyte; gametophyte is greatly reduced.

Division Psilophyta: Whisk ferns; a few species of seedless plants with undifferentiated roots and leaves; sperm must swim to eggs.

Division Sphenophyta: Horsetails; about 15 species of seedless plants with hollow, siliceous stems; sperm must swim to eggs.

Division Lycophyta: Club mosses; about 1,000 diverse species of seedless plants with leafy sporophytes; some have only one type of spore; others produce microspores and megaspores; sperm must swim to eggs.

Division Pterophyta: Ferns; about 12,000 diverse species of seedless plants; sporophyte bears haploid spores on underside of fronds; spores germinate into, free-living gametophytes; sperm must swim to eggs.

Division Cycadophyta: Cycads; about 100 species of palmlike plants with slow cambial growth; gymnosperms.

Division Ginkgophyta: Ginkgo; one species only; small deciduous tree with fanshaped leaves; gymnosperms; separate sexes.

Division Gnetophyta: Seed plants similar to angiosperms; about 70 species; motile sperm; xylem with vessels.

Division Coniferophyta: Conifers; about 550 species of gymnosperms; gametophyte much reduced: male pollen is dispersed by wind; female gametophytes remain on seed cone, where fertilization and seed development take place; leaves needlelike or scale-like; most species are evergreens.

Division Anthophyta: Angiosperms; about 235,000 species of plants that produce enclosed seeds; reproductive structures are flowers; mature seeds are enclosed in fruits; gametophyte is much reduced in size; fertilization involves two sperm nuclei.

Class Monocotyledones: Monocots; angiosperms that produce seeds with one cotyledon (seed leaf); flower parts usually in threes; leaves with parallel veins; almost all are herbaceous.

Class Dicotyledones: Dicots; angiosperms that produce seeds with two cotyledons; flower parts usually in fours and fives; leaves usually with nonparallel veins that form a netlike pattern; herbaceous and woody plants.

Kingdom Animalia

Multicellular, eukaryotic heterotrophs that obtain food by ingestion; most are motile; reproduction is predominantly sexual.

Phylum Porifera: Sponges; about 5,000 aquatic, mostly marine, species of asymmetrical animals that lack distinct tissues and organs; body consists of two layers supported by a stiff skeleton; sponges are aquatic, mostly marine, and sessile; reproduction sexual or asexual.

Class Calcarea: Simple shallow-water sponges; calcium carbonate spicules; includes *Grantia*.

Class Hexactinella: Deep water sponges; silica spicules; includes Venus's flower basket.

Class Demospongiae: Large sponge; spicules of spongin and silica; freshwater and marine species; includes bath sponges and finger sponges.

Class Sclerospongiae: Spicules of calcium carbonate, silica, and spongin.

Phylum Coelenterata (Cnidaria): Coelenterates; about 9,000 aquatic species; radially symmetrical; digestive cavity with only one opening; two body layers separated by jellylike mesoglea; tentacles armed with stinging cells; two body forms: vase-shaped polyp and bell-shaped medusa; live singly or in colonies often made up of specialized individuals; reproduction sexual or asexual.

Class Hydrozoa: Hydras and related animals; freshwater hydras occur singly with only polyp form; other hydrozoans are colonial and have a life cycle with both polyps and medusae; reproduction sexual or asexual.

Class Scyphozoa: Jellyfish; marine coelenterates; dominant medusa form reproduces sexually; free-swimming larvae become sessile polyps that form new medusae asexually.

Class Anthozoa: Sea anemones, corals, and related "flower animals;" marine coelenterates with no medusa stage; sea anemones are solitary; corals are colonial organisms with either an internal or external skeleton.

Phylum Ctenophora: Sea walnut and comb jellies; about 90 species; gelatinous marine animals with eight bands of cilia; often bioluminescent.

Phylum Platyhelminthes: Flatworms; about 13,000 species; bilaterally symmetrical with three germ layers; digestive cavity has only one opening; no circulatory or respiratory systems; no coelom or pseudocoelom.

Class Turbellaria: Planarians and related free-living, carnivorous flatworms; simple nervous system with sense receptors; sexual reproduction by mutual fertilization; asexual reproduction by fission.

Class Trematoda: Flukes; parasites covered by protective cuticle; most are endoparasites; may have a complex life cycle involving more than one host.

Class Cestoda: Tapeworms; parasitic species that live as adults in the intestines of vertebrates; no digestive system; food absorbed through body surfaces.

Phylum Nematoda: Roundworms; about 12,000 mostly parasitic species; tubular and bilaterally symmetrical body form; digestive tract has two openings; pseudocoelom; reproduction is sexual.

Phylum Nematomorpha: Horsehair worms; bodies very slender, up to one meter (3.3 ft.) long; adults are free-living; larva parasitic.

Phylum Acanthocephala: Spiny-headed worms; about 500 species; parasitic with no digestive tract; head with recurved spines for attachment to host.

Phylum Rotifera: Rotifers or "wheel" animals; wormlike or spherical; complete digestive tract; crown of cilia on anterior end resembling a wheel.

Phylum Bryozoa: "Moss" animals; microscopic, aquatic organisms that form branching colonies; U-shaped row of ciliated tentacles for feeding (lophophore).

Phylum Brachiopoda: Lamp shells; about 250 species, 30,000 extinct; two shells, one dorsal and one ventral; adults sessile; feed by lophophore.

Phylum Mollusca: Mollusks; about 47,000 species of soft-bodied animals with a true coelom, a head-foot, a visceral mass, and a mantle; most are aquatic; many have one or more shells.

Class Pelecypoda: Bivalves; mollusks with two shells and a hatchet-shaped foot; no head; open circulatory system; many species sessile; includes clams, scallops, and oysters.

Class Gastropoda: Snails and slugs; aquatic and terrestrial mollusks with a locomotor belly-foot; open circulatory system; adults have an asymmetrical body twisted by torsion; most have a coiled shell.

Class Cephalopoda: Octopuses, squids, and nautiluses; marine mollusks with a large head-foot that is divided into tentacles; closed circulatory system; highly developed nervous system; shell may be internal, external, or absent.

Class Scaphopoda: Tooth shells; about 350 species; marine mollusks with tubular shells.

Class Polyplacophora (Amphineura): Chitons; closely resemble ancestral mollusk; eight dorsal shell plates with reduced head and elongated body.

Phylum Annelida: Segmented worms; about 9,000 species; body has a true coelom; longitudinal and circular muscles; fairly complex circulatory, respiratory, and nervous systems; elimination by nephridia.

Class Oligochaeta: Earthworms and related species; earthworms have paired setae, a closed circulatory system, and a cerebral ganglion; hermaphroditic; sexual reproduction by mutual fertilization.

Class Hirudinea: Leeches; mainly freshwater annelids with posterior and anterior suckers; either parasitic or free-living; reproduction sexual, usually by mutual fertilization of hermaphrodites.

Class Polychaeta: Marine worms; body with many bristles; about 6,000 species; includes sandworms.

Phylum Arthropoda: Arthropods; at least 1 million species; segmented body; paired, jointed appendages; exoskeleton; open circulatory system; complex nervous system with two ventral nerve cords and a brain.

Class Merostomata: Horseshoe crabs; four species; aquatic with fangs and book gills.

Class Arachnida: Arachnids; about 57,000 species; body has two regions, eight legs, and paired chelicerae and pedipalps; respiration by tracheae, book lungs, or both; includes spiders, ticks and mites.

Class Crustacea: Crustaceans; about 25,000 mostly aquatic species; paired mandibles and thoracic appendages; usually two pairs of maxillae; respiration by gills; includes lobsters and barnacles.

Class Chilopoda: Centipedes; about 3,000 terrestrial species; mandibles; many body segments, each with one pair of legs.

Class Diplopoda: Millipedes; about 7,500 terrestrial species; mandibles; many body segments, each with two pairs of legs.

Class Insecta: Insects, over 750,000 terrestrial and freshwater species; three body regions; three pairs of legs; head has antennae, compound eyes, and mouthparts; thorax has legs and, in many species, wings; most species undergo incomplete or complete metamorphosis; respiration by tracheae.

Order Protura: Proturans; piercing-sucking or chewing mouthparts; lacking wings, antennae, and eyes; front legs adapted as organs of touch; no metamorphosis.

Order Thysanura: Bristletails and silverfish; chewing mouthparts; two or three tails; wingless; no metamorphosis.

Order Collembola: Springtails; chewing mouthparts; wingless; compound eyes reduced or absent; no metamorphosis.

Order Ephemeroptera: Mayflies; chewing mouthparts that are reduced; membranous wings (usually two pairs); nymphs are aquatic; adults do not feed at all during their brief existence; incomplete metamorphosis.

Order Odonata: Dragonflies and damsel flies; two pairs of transparent wings; chewing mouthparts; not able to walk; incomplete metamorphosis.

Order Plecoptera: Stone flies; chewing mouthparts which are reduced in many species; two pairs of membranous wings; nymphs are aquatic; incomplete metamorphosis.

Order Orthoptera: Crickets and grasshoppers; two pairs of wings or wingless; chewing mouthparts; incomplete metamorphosis.

Order Dermaptera: Earwigs; chewing mouthparts; two pairs of wings or wingless; incomplete metamorphosis.

Order Embioptera: Web spinners; chewing mouthparts; wingless with the exception of some males; spin silk with special organs on forelegs; incomplete metamorphosis.

Order Isoptera: Termites; social insects that have chewing mouthparts; only the reproductive males and females have wings; incomplete metamorphosis.

Order Mallophaga: Chewing lice; wingless; chewing mouthparts; parasites of mammals and birds; incomplete metamorphosis.

Order Anoplura: Sucking lice; wingless; piercing-sucking mouthparts; parasites of mammals; incomplete metamorphosis.

Order Corrodentia: Bark lice, book lice; chewing mouthparts; wingless or two pairs of membranous wings; incomplete metamorphosis.

Order Hemiptera: Bugs; piercing-sucking mouthparts; two pairs of wings or wingless; incomplete metamorphosis.

Order Homoptera: Aphids, scale insects, and cicadas; wingless or winged (one or two pairs); piercing-sucking mouthparts; incomplete or complete metamorphosis.

Order Thysanoptera: Thrips; piercing-sucking mouthparts; wingless or two pairs of wings with long hairs attached to them; incomplete or complete metamorphosis.

Order Mecoptera: Scorpion flies; chewing mouthparts; wingless or two pairs of membranous wings; in some males, tip of abdomen is curved, resembling the tail of a scorpion; complete metamorphosis.

Order Neuroptera: Helgramites (dobson fly); Larva aquatic with large mandibles.

Order Trichoptera: Caddis flies; chewing mouthparts which are reduced; two pairs of wings; larvae are aquatic; adults do not feed extensively; complete metamorphosis.

Order Lepidoptera: Moths and butterflies; two pairs of broad, scaly wings; tubelike, sucking mouthparts; complete metamorphosis.

Order Diptera: Flies and mosquitoes; transparent front wings; hind wings reduced to knobby balancing organs; lapping and piercing mouthparts; complete metamorphosis.

Order Siphonaptera: Fleas; wingless; flattened body; piercing-sucking mouthparts; parasites of birds and mammals; complete metamorphosis.

Order Coleoptera: Beetles; winged (two pairs of wings, front pair serves as horny cover for membranous hind pair) or wingless; chewing mouthparts; complete metamorphosis.

Order Strepsiptera: Strepsipterans; chewing mouthparts which are reduced; females are wingless; males have two pairs of wings, with the front pair greatly reduced; complete metamorphosis.

Order Hymenoptera: Ants, bees, wasps; winged (two pairs that interlock in flight) or wingless; chewing or lapping mouthparts; some social species; complete metamorphosis.

Phylum Echinodermata: Echinoderms; about 6,000 marine species; calcium endoskeleton, tube feet, and a water-vascular system; adults radially symmetrical; includes starfish, sand dollars, and sea urchins.

Class Crinoidea: Sea lily; five rays; tube feet without suckers; most have stalklike body.

Class Asteroidea: Starfish; five rays with two rows of tube feet in each ray; eyespots.

Class Ophiuroidea: Brittle stars; five slender, delicate rays.

Class Echinoidea: Sea urchin, sand dollar; rays lacking; body spherical or oval.

Class Holothuroidea: Sea cucumber; long, thick body with tentacles; no rays.

Phylum Hemichordata: Acorn worms; about 80 species; marine; hydrostatic skeleton; dorsal and ventral nerve cords, dorsal nerve cord is hollow in some species.

Phylum Chordata: Chordates; about 43,000 species that at some stage have a notochord, dorsal nerve cord, pharyngeal gill slits, and tail.

Subphylum Urochordata: Tunicates; about 1,300 marine species; adults sacklike; usually sessile; larvae free-swimming.

Subphylum Cephalochordata: Lancelets; about 30 species of thin, fishlike marine animals; basic chordate features throughout life.

Subphylum Vertebrata: Vertebrates; about 41,700 species; bony or cartilaginous endoskeleton includes vertebrae; characterized by distinct cephalization and a closed circulatory system; excretion by kidneys; most have two sets of paired appendages.

Class Agnatha: Jawless fishes; about 60 species of lampreys and hagfishes; have suckerlike mouths; scaleless, cylindrical bodies without appendages; skeleton of cartilage; two-chambered heart.

Class Chondrichthyes: Sharks, skates and rays; about 625 mostly marine species of jawed fishes; cartilaginous skeleton; teeth replaced continuously; skin covered with tooth-derived scales; eggs fertilized internally; two-chambered heart.

Class Osteichthyes: Bony fishes; about 20,000 species of jawed fishes; bony skeletons; found in marine and freshwater habitats; body has bone-derived scales, an air-filled swim bladder, and a two-chambered heart; fertilization external in most species.

Class Amphibia: Amphibians; about 2,500 species characterized by a gill-breathing larval stage and a lung-breathing adult stage; adults have moist skin and three-chambered heart with double circulatory system; eggs usually laid in water.

Order Anura: Frogs and toads; adults are tailless with rear legs adapted to jumping; fertilization external, in water.

Order Urodela: Salamanders; adults have tails and four legs of about equal size; fertilization internal.

Order Apoda: Caecilians; legless, usually blind amphibians that live underground.

Class Reptilia: Reptiles; about 6,000 terrestrial species; fertilization occurs internally; embryo protected by a shelled, amniotic egg; skin is waterproof, covered with horny plates or overlapping scales; double circulatory system.

Order Rhyncocephalia: Tuatara; primitive four-legged species; skin covered by plates; three-chambered heart.

Order Chelonia: Turtles and tortoises; shelled, toothless species with four limbs and a three-chambered heart.

Order Squamata: Lizards and snakes; reptiles with overlapping scales and a three-chambered heart; most lizards have four legs; snakes are legless.

Order Crocodilia: Crocodiles, alligators, and related species; broad-bodied, water-dwelling carnivores with powerful tails and jaws; skin covered by bony plates; four-chambered heart.

Class Aves: Birds; about 8,600 species; winged vertebrates with feathers; endothermic (warm-blooded); double circulation and a four-chambered heart; fertilization internal; amniotic eggs usually incubated in nest; respiratory system with lungs and air sacs.

Order Rheiformes: Rheas; large, flightless South American birds.

Order Struthioniformes: Ostriches; large, flightless African birds.

Order Procellariiformes: Albatrosses, shearwaters, petrels, and other species of related seabirds with tubelike nostrils.

Order Sphenisciformes: Penguins; flightless swimming birds with wings modified as paddles.

Order Gaviiformes: Loons; diving birds with three webbed toes.

Order Pelecaniformes: Pelicans, boobies, and related water birds with four-toed, webbed feet.

Order Ciconiiformes: Storks, herons, and related long-legged wading birds.

Order Gruiformes: Cranes, coots, limpkins, rails, gallinules, and related species.

Order Charodriiformes: Auks, gulls, sandpipers, and related shore and water birds.

Order Anseriformes: Ducks, geese, swans, screamers; short-legged water birds.

Order Falconiformes: Falcons, eagles, hawks, condors, and related diurnal birds of prey.

Order Galliformes: Chickens, turkeys, pheasants, grouse, and related fowl-like birds.

Order Columbiformes: Pigeons, doves, sandgrouse, and related species.

Order Psittaciformes: Parrots; hook-billed birds that eat seeds, fruit, or nectar.

Order Cuculiformes: Cuckoos, roadrunners, and related species.

Order Strigiformes: Owls; nocturnal birds of prey.

Order Caprimulgiformes: Goat-suckers, whippoorwill, night hawk, and related species.

Order Apodiformes: Swifts and hummingbirds; weak-legged birds with strong wings.

Order Coraciiformes: Kingfisher; fishing birds.

Order Piciformes: Woodpeckers, toucans, barbets, and related birds.

Order Passeriformes: Perching birds, including all songbirds.

Class Mammalia: Mammals; about 4,500 species; young are nourished by mother's milk and receive extensive parental care; endothermic and covered by hair; double circulation; four-chambered heart; respiration by lungs; highly developed, complex brain; fertilization internal.

Order Monotremata: Monotremes, spiny anteaters and duck-billed platypus; the only mammals that lay eggs; incomplete control of body temperature; milk secreted from abdominal sweat glands.

Order Marsupialia: Marsupials, including kangaroos, wombats, and opossums; young are born in an immature state and develop further attached to a nipple in the mother's marsupium (pouch).

The following orders are placental mammals in which young undergo substantial prenatal development within the uterus. During gestation, exchange of nutrients, gases, and wastes occurs through the placenta.

Order Insectivora: Insectivores; small, chiefly nocturnal mammals that feed largely on insects.

Order Chiroptera: Bats; the only flying mammals.

Order Artiodactyla: Hoofed mammals with two or four toes; large herbivores including deer, pigs, cattle, sheep, goats, camels, antelopes, giraffes, and hippopotamuses; most are ruminants.

Order Perissodactyla: Hoofed mammals with one or three toes; large herbivores including horses, tapirs, and rhinoceroses.

Order Proboscidea: Elephants; enormous herbivores with trunk.

Order Carnivora: Carnivores; bears, cats, dogs, seals, and related predators.

Order Cetacea: Whales, porpoises, and dolphins; marine mammals with streamlined body; forelimbs adapted as flippers; no hindlimbs; nostril (blowhole) at top of head.

Order Sirenia: Sea cows; aquatic herbivores with short, paddlelike forelimbs and no hindlimbs.

Order Rodentia: Rodents; small, plant-eating mammals; one upper pair and one lower curving pair; chisel-like incisors that grow continuously.

Order Lagomorpha: Rabbits, hares, and pikas; rodentlike mammals with two pairs of upper and one pair of lower incisors.

Order Edentata: Armadillos, anteaters, and tree sloths; insect eaters with few or no teeth.

Order Primates: Primates, including lemurs, monkeys, apes, and humans; mammals with features adapted to arboreal life.

Careers in Biology

Wildlife Biologist

Wildlife biologists work to protect natural habitats, maintain reproducing populations of animals, save wilderness habitats, and restore waterways and parklands in or near cities.

Wildlife biologists specialize in a variety of areas. Some work to preserve endangered species, such as the Wyoming toad and the gray wolf, by researching the causes of the species' decline and by studying the type of habitat needed to sustain these species.

Some wildlife biologists do field research to find out about animal populations in certain areas. Others hold

Crime Laboratory Technician

A crime laboratory technician collects and analyzes evidence relating to crimes. This evidence is then used in court to help determine the guilt or innocence of the person accused of committing the crime.

Crime lab technicians are called to the scene of serious crimes. There, they methodically collect fingerprints, take photographs, and gather other kinds of evidence about a crime.

In the laboratory, the technicians analyze the collected evidence. For example, they run tests to determine blood type, and analyze handwriting samples, tool marks, or the explosives used in a crime.

Respiratory Therapist

A respiratory, or inhalation, therapist gives respiratory treatment and life support aid to patients suffering from asthma, bronchitis, emphysema, or pneumonia. They also treat victims of fires or automobile accidents and patients suffering from complications of surgery. Respiratory therapists work with such people, helping to restore their normal breathing functions and their chances for a physically normal, healthy life.

A respiratory therapist sets up and operates devices that help patients breathe, monitors the patient's vital signs, and checks to make sure that wildlife management positions or work as game wardens to enforce hunting and fishing regulations.

While most wildlife biologists work for state and federal agencies, such as the United States Forest Service, some hold positions with private companies.

Career Requirements
Individuals interested in wildlife management and research need an M.S. or a Ph.D. with a specialty in an endangered species or one group of animals. Persons with a B.A. in biology may qualify for jobs with local governments and conservation organizations or as wild-

life technicians who assist biologists in field research.

For Additional Information
Office of Public Affairs
United States Fish and
    Wildlife Service
Department of the
    Interior
1800 C Street, N.W.
Washington, DC 20240

They then must write thorough and accurate reports.

Many crimes are actually solved by crime lab technicians, and some cases are settled out of court, saving the public time and money. Crime laboratory technicians may also discover evidence that frees a person wrongly accused of committing a crime.

Most crime lab technicians are employed by city and state governments or federal agencies such as the Federal Bureau of Investigation. Others are employed by independent laboratories.

Career Requirements
Most crime laboratory technicians have a B.S. degree

in chemistry, biology, or physics. Completion of a two-year college course qualifies some students for entry-level jobs in this field.

For Additional Information
American Academy of
    Forensic Scientists
218 E. Cache La Poudre
Colorado Springs, CO 80903

all equipment is operating properly.

Under a physician's direction, a respiratory therapist may assist a patient with breathing exercises that are part of his or her recovery program.

Most respiratory therapists work in hospitals and in nursing homes. A small percentage work in

rehabilitation institutes, education, or research.

Career Requirements
Many hospitals require certification as a registered respiratory therapist (RRT). Prerequisites for certification include graduation from a two-year college program in respiratory therapy and the passing of

an examination. Respiratory therapists should have the ability to operate mechanical equipment and to work with patients who are often extremely ill.

For Additional Information
American Association for
    Respiratory Care
11030 Ables Ln.
Dallas, TX 75229

Animal Behaviorist

Animal behaviorists are scientists who study how animals behave and why animals behave the way they do. These scientists consider all the possible influences on animal behavior, such as heredity, physiology, environment, food, weather, and the behavior of other animals.

Those scientists specifically interested in how animals learn concentrate on highly intelligent mammals, such as monkeys, chimpanzees, or porpoises.

Usually, animal behaviorists study animals in captivity, but a few scientists study, track, and tag animals in the wild.

Some animal behaviorist research may

Ornamental Horticulturist

Ornamental horticulturists grow plants that are used to beautify homes and office buildings. They also grow plants that are used in the design of parks, botanical gardens, and other public places. They often develop new varieties of plants for features that have aesthetic appeal, such as slender leaves or brightly colored flowers.

When choosing plants for a large project, a horticulturist may consult with clients and travel to the planned site. Many horticulturists work in nurseries or greenhouses or for landscape firms. A growing number are employed by interior landscape design services, which select and

Aquaculturist

The job of an aquaculturist is to cultivate food animals, such as fish and mollusks, that live in water. Most aquaculturists in the United States raise trout, catfish, oysters, clams, and crayfish. Most fish and mollusk farms are small businesses owned and operated by a single family. Some large companies raise their own clams in hatcheries and also process the clams before marketing them.

Aquaculturists generally raise clams in seawater beds leased from a state or township. Workers place young "seed" clams on protected rafts. When the clams are larger, workers transfer them to the ocean bottom and cover the clams with have applications to the study of human behavior. These studies include the effects of crowding, of separating infants from their mothers, and the effects of chemical substances on behavior.

Some animal behaviorists teach in colleges or universities or seek such jobs as zookeepers, game wardens, or rangers in state or national parks.

Career Requirements
Most animal behaviorists earn a B.S. degree in general biology or zoology. They then specialize in animal behavior for the M.S. or Ph.D. degree. An advanced degree is required in order to teach in a college or university or to initiate research projects. Positions such as game wardens or park rangers usually require only a B.S. degree.

For Additional Information
Animal Behavior Society
Dept. of Psychology,
 CB 345
University of Colorado
Boulder, CO 80309

---

care for plants in large office buildings, restaurants, and shopping malls. These firms hire young people to water and fertilize plants, check for pests, and deliver plants to customers.

A horticulturist combines knowledge of plant biology with a talent for design. People who enjoy growing plants and beautifying the environment will find horticulture satisfying.

Career Requirements
Many community colleges offer two-year programs leading to an associate's degree in horticulture. More advanced horticulture work requires knowledge of plant reproduction and genetics. A B.S. degree in horticulture or in a related field is needed. Research or teaching at the college level requires an M.S. or a Ph.D. degree.

For Additional Information
American Society for
 Horticultural Science
701 North Saint Asaph
 Street
Alexandria, VA 22314

---

netting to protect them from predators.

The aquaculture industry in the United States today is a small one. However, as Americans attempt to reduce the vast amount of seafood that is imported into this country and as seafood becomes more important in American diets, the aquaculture industry will increase in importance.

Career Requirements
There are no special requirements for a career as an aquaculturist. Most people who are interested in a career in this field first accept entry-level positions. After they acquire on-the-job experience at a fish farm or clam bed, they often go into business for themselves.

Professional or technical jobs in aquaculture research generally require a bachelor's degree in biology. Courses in fish and mollusk culture are available at many community, junior, and four-year colleges in several parts of the United States.

For Additional Information
U.S. Aquaculture Federation
Box 276
Lacey Spring, VA 22833

Plant Breeder

Plant breeders use the principles of genetics to develop desirable traits in plants. The improved plant varieties resist diseases and pests, thrive in different soils and climates, and produce a large number of offspring.

Many plant breeders work at experimental farms where they develop parent lines that have desirable traits. Commercial corn breeders, for example, develop parents that produce high yields or resist corn leaf blight. Then the breeders cross-pollinate selected parents to produce hybrids that combine the two important traits. It takes many growing seasons to develop pure parent lines, to produce hybrids, and

Biophysicist

A biophysicist is a scientist who uses the knowledge and techniques of the physical sciences to answer biological questions. For example, a biophysicist might study what processes take place in a cell that allow it to "recognize" dangerous substances and help develop ways to prevent these substances from entering the cell.

Some biophysicists use X rays to study the structure of organic molecules. Others study how nerve cells conduct impulses.

Most biophysicists work on research projects in government laboratories or in universities. A few are employed by industrial laboratories.

Ophthalmologist

An ophthalmologist is a medical doctor who is legally and professionally qualified to diagnose and treat diseases and disorders of the eye. An ophthalmologist first performs a comprehensive eye examination. This makes it possible to determine whether or not there is an eye problem and may reveal the beginning of other conditions such as diabetes or high blood pressure. If a vision problem is diagnosed, the ophthalmologist may prescribe some type of corrective lenses. He or she may also prescribe drugs or perform eye surgery.

Ophthalmologists may work privately or they may work with a group to test the hybrids for the desired traits.

Plant breeders have improved nearly every important crop in the last 60 years. They have developed smooth cucumbers, tomatoes with a long shelf life, grasses with no pollen and a special dwarf wheat whose high yield may help solve the world's hunger problem. Most plant breeders work for feed companies and other private organizations. Other breeders work for government programs or at universities.

Career Requirements
Most plant-breeding jobs require a Ph.D. in plant breeding, agronomy, or horticulture. Individuals with B.S. or M.S. degrees generally work as plant-breeding technicians.

Plant breeders must be detail-conscious, since careful records must be kept on each plant.

For Additional Information
American Society of
  Agronomy
677 South Segoe Road
Madison, WI 53711

Research in the area of biophysics has contributed to many important scientific advances. Biophysicists, for instance, worked on the computer scanning equipment used to detect tumors and other diseases.

Career Requirements
Biophysicists who direct research projects must have earned a Ph.D. degree and must have a knowledge of both biology and physics. Persons with a B.A. or an M.S. degree may assist a biophysicist on a research project. For example, laboratory technicians who work with a biophysicist are generally persons with a B.A. degree.

Biophysicists must be patient and methodical. In addition, they must be creative people. Biophysicists must also have mathematical ability, since many biological systems, principles, and processes are explained in mathematical terms.

For Additional Information
Biophysical Society
9650 Rockville Pike
Bethesda, MD 20814

---

of different specialists in a health maintenance organization (HMO). An HMO is a type of health insurance in which people regularly pay a fixed amount beforehand so that they have ready access to their doctors.

New research and advances in technology are constantly changing the practice of ophthalmology. Therefore, continuing education is extremely important.

Career Requirements
The time required for an ophthalmologist to complete college, medical school, and specialty training is usually 12 years.

All states require that doctors be licensed in order to practice. To be certified in a specialty, a student must also take oral and written exams after completing a residency.

For Additional Information
American Academy of
  Ophthalmology
655 Beach Street
San Francisco, CA 94109

Paleontologist

A paleontologist is a scientist who studies fossils and other remains in the Earth's rock layers. By studying these clues, paleontologists assemble evidence of changes in a species or in an area over thousands or millions of years. The paleontologist deals with great spans of time beyond normal human understanding. Thus, part of the job of a paleontologist is helping people realize how old the Earth actually is.

Many paleontologists work for universities, teaching, acquiring rock samples, and conducting research. Paleontologists study these samples for visual evidence of the rock's age. The

Cell Biologist

A cell biologist or *cytologist* uses small tissue samples to isolate cells and study them in detail under a microscope.

Cell biologists tend to specialize in either plant or animal cells. In either case, they look for answers to the same key questions: "How do cells reproduce?," "Why do some cells become diseased and die?," and "How are cells affected by physical and chemical changes?"

Many cell biologists teach in universities while continuing their research. A growing number work for privately owned research and development laboratories or industrial companies.

Many cell biologists who work for private

Athletic Trainer

An athletic trainer is trained to give first aid to athletes who are injured in sports activities. After an athlete has been seriously injured, a trainer will work with the athlete until he or she is fully recovered.

Athletic trainers are generally hired by a team, a school, or a school district. However, an orthopedic surgeon who specializes in sports medicine may employ a trainer. A trainer working for a physician generally deals with athletes from many different sports and different teams.

Baseball, basketball, football, ice hockey, and other sports need trainers who are on hand to give first aid on the field samples also provide clues about the environment in which the rock was formed.

Vertebrate paleontologists often use fossil bones to make drawings or to construct models that show how extinct animals may have looked. Paleontologists who work for oil companies examine rock samples to determine if certain sites could contain oil and gas deposits.

Career Requirements
Most research and teaching positions in universities require a Ph.D. degree in paleontology, geology, botany, or zoology. Entry-level positions are available in private research, specifically in the oil industry, and are sometimes filled by those with an M.S. degree in geology in addition to related course work or field experience in paleontology.

For Additional Information
Paleontological Research Institution
1259 Trumansberg Road
Ithaca, NY 14850

---

laboratories focus on such topics as the hereditary information in human cells, how and why normal cells become cancerous, and aging. In studying the aging process, the cell biologist attempts to track every stage in the life of a cell.

Basic research in cell biology may yield important results for many areas of human health.

Career Requirements
An entry-level job as a technician in an industrial, government, or private laboratory requires a B.S. degree in biology. To advance in the field, however, a cell biologist must earn an M.S. or a Ph.D. degree in cell biology. A Ph.D. is also required for college teaching positions.

Cell biologists must be interested in scientific experiments and have abilities in chemistry.

For Additional Information
American Society for Cell Biology
9650 Rockville Pike
Bethesda, MD 20814

---

or on the court, and to give treatment before or after a game. If athletes need other treatment, the trainer refers them to physicians.

Trainers may be licensed physical therapists, physician's assistants, nurses with masters' degrees, or former members of the military medical corp.

Career Requirements
Athletic trainers obtain a license in an allied health profession, such as physical therapy, physician's assistant, or nursing. They also need sound knowledge of anatomy, physiology, chemistry, and physics.

The American Athletic Trainers Association offers the oral, written, and practical exams necessary for certification. Certification in this field is optional but desirable because of keen job competition.

For Additional Information
American Athletic Trainers Association and Certification Board
660 West Duarte Road
Arcadia, CA 91006

Urban Forester

An urban forester cares for trees in urban areas. Using the management and treatment skills developed in general forestry, the urban forester works to preserve and care for trees in parks and on private property. Their work is very important, since trees in urban areas have become increasingly valuable as they have diminished in number. Parks filled with healthy trees contribute to the quality of life in an urban area, and trees on private property increase the value of that property significantly.

The work of urban foresters is frequently complex and demanding. They must be able to recognize a variety of diseases in tree trunks, roots,

Epidemiologist

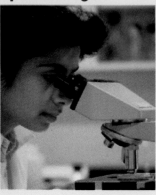

Epidemiologists study the distribution of diseases and other health disorders in populations. They also investigate the causes of widespread health problems in order to prevent or control them. For example, only a few years ago smallpox was eliminated through the work of epidemiologists.

In some ways, epidemiologists are like detectives. To understand why a disease breaks out among a group of people, epidemiologists try to answer four questions: "When did the disease appear?," "How quickly did it spread?," "What are the characteristics of the place where the disease appeared?," and "What are the characteristics of the people who developed the disease?"

Biology Teacher

A biology teacher is a professional who teaches life sciences in high school, middle school, or junior high school. Biology teachers must have a basic curiosity about all life forms and be able to present biological facts and explain complex ideas, such as evolution.

Biology teachers not only present new ideas to students but also present biological facts and help students use and understand a scientific method of problem-solving. They must keep current to bring the latest and most exciting news to the class.

Biology teachers prepare lesson plans, lead student discussions, and assign and grade homework and tests. Teaching biology requires the ability to branches, and leaves. If a tree has been attacked by insect pests or fungi, the forester may spray, dust, or inject the tree with a pesticide or a fungicide. He or she may also recommend fertilizers that will help the tree grow vigorously. An urban forester might even be called upon to try to save a tree that has been inadvertently poisoned by pesticides or by other means. Such treatment might involve treating the soil or developing new techniques to try to save the tree.

Urban foresters are generally employed by municipal agencies in managerial positions where they oversee others who work independently in the caring and preserving of trees.

Career Requirements
An urban forester must have a B.S. in forestry. Some experience in general forestry, though not a prerequisite, is helpful.

For Additional Information
National Arborist
    Association
The Meeting Place Mall
Rt. 101, P.O. Box 1094
Amherst, NH 03031

The answers to these questions usually reveal the cause of the problem. An epidemiologist, for example, many years ago discovered that people who became ill with *cholera,* a bacterial disease, had all drunk water from a polluted certain well.

Most epidemiologists are employed by universities and schools of public health. Some positions are available in hospitals and in departments of public health and other government agencies.

Career Requirements
Most epidemiologists have either an M.S., an M.D., or a Ph.D. Individuals with an M.S. degree usually coordinate investigations. Those who have earned an M.D. or a Ph.D. degree may conduct independent research or teach.

For Additional Information
The Association of
    Schools of Public
    Health
1015 15th Street, N.W.,
    Suite 404
Washington, DC 20005

motivate and communicate with students.

A biology teacher prepares laboratories so that students can gain safe laboratory experiences. He or she should be able to organize and lead field trips and arrange for guest speakers.

Since the field of biology advances rapidly, especially in a technological society, a biology teacher must be motivated to find out what new advances and new research is occurring. He or she usually belongs to professional organizations and subscribes to and reads several professional journals.

Career Requirements
All high school biology teachers must be certified to teach in accredited schools. To earn a certificate, one needs a bachelor's degree with a major in biology and some courses in education. Some states require high school teachers to have a master's degree.

For Additional Information
National Association of
    Biology Teachers
11250 Roger Bacon Drive
Reston, VA 22090

Limnologist

A limnologist is a scientist who specializes in the biology of freshwater life, especially in the biology of ponds and lakes. Many limnologists study the complex ecosystems of freshwater environments. The work of a limnologist involves investigating the physical and chemical features of bodies of fresh water in addition to the biological factors. The duties of a limnologist vary widely. They may include, for example, finding out how important a species of alga is in a lake's food chain and how the addition of chemicals to the water may affect the algal population.

Many limnologists collect data that help them to write environmental

Biometric Statistician

A statistician collects and analyzes numerical information, such as the number of offspring from a genetic cross showing a certain trait. Then the statistician uses these data to help solve problems. By analyzing records of the effects of air pollution and radiation, for instance, biometric statisticians can help determine policies.

Biometrics is the name of the field that applies mathematical and statistical techniques to biological studies. Statisticians in this field may study the effects of chemicals on genetic material in the cell. They may also investigate the causes of diseases by using public records, or

Drug Counselor

A drug counselor helps people overcome drug abuse problems or drug addiction. Counselors may be professional social workers, psychologists, or community workers interested in drug problems.

Many drug counselors are employed by private alcohol treatment centers or hospital-based programs. Others work for various programs within state or local government agencies. In some programs, clients are first isolated in rural areas away from drug sources. Later they return to city life for counseling. In other programs, counselors may work with groups of drug addicts or abusers impact statements. These reports help predict how a major change, such as building a dam, will affect the biology of a body of fresh water. Another task of a limnologist might be to gauge the effects of pollutants on the organisms that live in a pond or a lake.

Most limnologists work for universities or for government agencies. A growing number of limnologists, however, work for private companies.

Career Requirements
Positions as research assistants or technicians require a B.S. degree in limnology. Most limnologists also have an M.S. or a Ph.D. in limnology or aquatic ecology.

Limnologists must be detail-oriented and must enjoy working outdoors.

For Additional Information
American Society of Limnology and Oceanography
Virginia Institute of Marine Science
College of William and Mary
Gloucester Point, VA 23062

study fluctuations in animal populations.

Biometric statisticians are employed by any organization that needs to collect and analyze biological information. Federal, state, and local government agencies employ these professionals, as do universities, research institutions, and a variety of industries.

Career Requirements
A biometric statistician needs a B.S. degree with strong training in mathematics and the biological sciences. Biometric statisticians who analyze data, develop theoretical methods of solving problems, or consult with industry and government agencies need a graduate degree.

A prospective statistician must enjoy working with detail. He or she must be skilled in working with numbers, and be able to organize and analyze information.

For Additional Information
American Statistical Association
1429 Duke St.
Alexandria, VA 22314

rather than with individuals. Special group programs to alleviate or prevent drug abuse are conducted in some schools.

Regardless of the type of program, counselors give clients moral support and an opportunity to discuss personal or work problems. The counselor refers medical problems to a physician connected with the treatment program.

Career Requirements
No formal professional requirements exist for drug counseling. However, each state has its own requirements. In some states counselors must earn a certificate. At least one state requires drug counselors to be social workers, and several other states give preference to social workers. A Master's degree in social work is often recommended.

For Additional Information
National Association on Drug Abuse Problems
355 Lexington Avenue
New York, NY 10017

Marine Biologist

A marine biologist is a scientist who studies sea life. Most marine biologists specialize in either plants or animals, and many select a particular species to study. They record its life history and food cycles. Often they collect samples from the ocean to study in the laboratory.

Marine biologists may also study the organism's environment. They may, for example, measure the temperature and chemical composition of the water.

Some marine biologists hold positions at colleges or universities where they combine teaching careers with research. However, an increasing number of careers is becoming available in private industry. For example, the knowledge

Laboratory Technician

The laboratory technician plays a vital role in a scientific method of problem solving. Under the direction of a scientist, the technician performs laboratory tests and analyzes sample materials. The laboratory technician must also keep accurate and orderly records of test results and must compile data for the scientist who is testing a hypothesis or treating patients.

The duties of a laboratory technician vary. For example, a medical laboratory technician may work in a hospital, preparing slides from tissue samples and analyzing them under a microscope. A food tester may perform chemical analyses

Dietitian

Dietitians provide information on nutrition. They know the chemical makeup of foods and the effects of foods on the human body, and they know what nutrients—how much protein or what vitamins —are in foods.

Clinical dietitians work in hospitals or nursing homes. They often work with doctors, nurses, and other professionals in planning special diets to meet individual needs.

Some dietitians teach in colleges and some are administrative dietitians who work for commercial food service companies and give advice on the safe handling and preparation of food.

and experience of marine biologists is often needed by pharmaceutical companies that are developing drugs that are derived from marine organisms. Undoubtedly, more opportunities will exist in the future for marine biologists in other industries, especially in those industries that make use of marine resources for supplying both humans and animals with food.

Career Requirements
Entry-level positions in industry are available to those with a B.S. degree in biology, zoology, or botany. A PH.D. degree is required to teach or to initiate research projects.

Some marine biologists enjoy deep-sea diving and become certified in scuba diving in order to enhance their research.

For Additional Information
American Society of Limnology and Oceanography
Virginia Institute of Marine Science
College of William and Mary
Gloucester Point, VA 23062

on samples of additives such as preservatives and dyes.

Career Requirements
Many technicians work for industry, government, hospitals, and universities. Most positions require two years of college with courses in biology, chemistry, or physics. Some positions are open to graduates of technical training courses.

Technicians enjoy great flexibility. They can start work with a modest amount of higher education and go back to school later if they wish to specialize or advance in a special field. They can also be mobile, since there is a great demand for technicians in most areas of the United States.

Laboratory technicians must enjoy detailed work and must be careful at keeping accurate records.

For Additional Information
American Chemical Society
1155 Sixteenth Street, N.W. Washington, DC 20036

Community dietitians work with groups or individuals, usually through local government or voluntary health agencies.

Increasing numbers of dietitians are going into private practice. These dietitians plan diets designed for the special needs of individual patients.

Career Requirements
A dietitian needs a B.S. degree in dietetics, nutrition, or food science. Many dietitians also complete a 6- to 12-month internship beyond the degree. The American Dietetic Association (ADA) accredits the internship programs, which include clinical experience. The ADA offers a registered dietitian (RD) certificate to those who meet educational requirements and who pass an examination.

For Additional Information
American Dietetic Association
216 W. Jackson Blvd. Suite 800
Chicago, IL 60606

Park Ranger

Park rangers are specially trained employees of the National Park Service or a state, regional, or local park district. They protect plant and animal life in parks.

Environmental education is one of the rangers' chief duties. Rangers give lectures and present slideshows that cover such topics as the importance of forests to the environment, the relationships among animals and plants in an ecosystem, and the structure of nonvascular plants.

Park rangers also protect plants and animals from disease and from damage by visitors. Because they act as security guards in many parks, rangers are trained to use weapons. They are

Plant Physiologist

Plant physiologists develop expertise in the structure and function of plants. These scientists examine the details of plant cells and study complex plant processes such as photosynthesis. Plant physiologists also research how plant tissue is affected by the environment.

Agricultural sciences often depend on plant physiologists for accurate information about the effect of weather, fertilizers, and soil conditions on plant growth.

Many plant physiologists work on genetic engineering experiments. They are trying to find ways to alter a plant's heredity so that the plant will be hardier and produce more offspring or

Nurse-Midwife

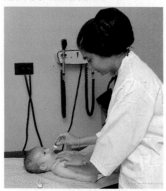

A nurse-midwife is a registered nurse who is specially trained to deliver babies. Nurse-midwives always have contact with one or more physicians who provide medical care if a problem arises.

Most nurse-midwives work in hospitals. Some may deliver babies at home if asked by the parents to do so. Others work in *birth centers,* delivery rooms with homelike settings. Unlike the home, however, the birth center has extra personnel and special equipment ready should some problem arise.

Most nurse-midwives provide prenatal care for the pregnant woman, deliver the baby, and also trained in first aid. Park rangers work mainly outdoors.

This career appeals to those people who enjoy a love of the outdoors. Park rangers must enjoy working with the public. They must also be interested in how people can function harmoniously with nature and how they can better understand natural systems.

Career Requirements

A B.S. degree with a major in park management or field natural sciences and a civil service exam are usual requirements for many park ranger positions.

Competition is keen for ranger positions. Prospective rangers should be in excellent health, like working with plants and animals, and be skilled at dealing with people.

For Additional Information

Office of Public Affairs
National Park Service
Department of the
   Interior
P.O. Box 37127
Washington, DC 20013–7127

---

display other characteristics that are commercially desirable. Developing high yields of crops is the concern of many plant physiologists.

Some plant physiologists work for large agricultural chemical companies. Others work in university laboratories or for federal and state environmental protection agencies. Many combine teaching with laboratory work. Environmental protection workers may do field work, taking samples of plants and soils.

Career Requirements

A plant physiologist needs a background in biology, chemistry, biochemistry, physics, and mathematics. Entry-level positions in plant physiology are available for those with a B.S. or M.S. in biology or botany and some coursework in plant physiology. Teaching positions at universities generally require a Ph.D. in the subject.

For Additional Information

American Society of
   Plant Physiologists
15501 Monona Drive
Rockville, MD 20855

---

follow the baby's progress for six months. If the baby has a condition that requires medical attention, the nurse-midwife recommends that the infant be taken to a physician.

Career Requirements

The American College of Nurse-Midwives certifies nurse-midwives. To become certified, an applicant must pass a written examination, must be a registered nurse (RN), and must complete a course in midwifery. The course, given by nursing schools, usually takes one to two years. Some states require that nurse-midwives be licensed. Nursing schools generally look for nurse-midwife students who are compassionate, concerned about mothers and babies, hard-working, responsible, and self-reliant.

For Additional Information

American College of
   Nurse-Midwives
1522 K Street, N.W.
Washington, DC 20005

Horticultural Technician

A horticultural technician works in a greenhouse or plant nursery and handles the daily tasks necessary to grow and ship plants commercially. Horticultural technicians generally work in a production nursery where ornamental plants are grown.

The horticultural technician performs a variety of tasks, working with a botanist, ornamental horticulturist, or plant propagator. Most technicians routinely water plants, fertilize them, and inspect them for diseases. They also prepare plants for shipping and keep records of what was done to the plants.

Some horticultural technicians become salespersons, working either in

Exobiologist

The main focus of an exobiologist's work is the search for extraterrestrial life, or life elsewhere in the universe. Although no evidence of extraterrestrial life exists at this time, some scientists predict that life could be widespread in the universe.

Exobiologists also study the way in which life began on the Earth. They hypothesize that conditions similar to those that produced life on the Earth may have occurred elsewhere in the universe and produced other forms of life.

Exobiologists search for answers to questions such as: "As our galaxy came into being, what caused the formation of the six elements needed for life—carbon, hydrogen, oxygen,

Agricultural Extension Agent

Agricultural extension agents are representatives of state and federal agencies. They are specially trained to keep farmers informed about laws that affect the farming business. They also tell farmers about new fertilizers and other products that can increase crop yields. Agricultural extension agents are aware of the technology and methods involved in organic farming and provide useful information to traditional farmers attempting to make the transition to organic farming.

A typical agent might begin the day by giving a radio broadcast on weather and crop conditions. Agents often hold the wholesale or retail market. Other horticultural technicians work in a greenhouse for a few years to gain experience in growing plants. They then begin their own nurseries or landscaping businesses.

Career Requirements
The career of agricultural technician does not require a college degree. Most horticultural technicians, however, have a high school diploma and have had some experience working with plants. A technician usually develops his or her skills while working in a plant nursery through on-the-job training. Many technicians take courses in botany or in horticulture to help them succeed in their work. Success as a horticultural technician depends on a person's liking of plants and his or her willingness and ability to continue to learn more about plants.

For Additional Information
American Society for
    Horticultural Science
101 North Asaph Street
Alexandria, VA 22314

nitrogen, sulfur, and phosphorus?," "How were organic molecules formed from these six elements?," and "What chemical events led to the first self-reproducing systems?"

To answer these questions, exobiologists conduct experiments, analyze chemicals found in ancient rocks, and use special telescopes to study the chemical composition of comets and asteroids.

Some exobiologists use radio telescopes to listen for radio signals in a search for intelligent life elsewhere in the universe.

Career Requirements
Exobiology draws on the knowledge and skills of astronomy, biology, geology, and biochemistry.

An individual who runs a research project must have a Ph.D. Persons with M.S. or B.A. degrees may serve on research teams.

For Additional Information
Extraterrestrial Research
    Division, Code LX
NASA Ames Research
    Center
Moffett Field, CA 94035

seminars on special topics, such as the effectiveness of new fungicides that help prevent crop damage.

Keeping up with current trends and using that information to help people produce food more efficiently are major challenges for extension agents. Farming is a rapidly changing business. Agents must be aware of and must continue learning about new developments through reading scientific publications, attending classes, and talking with farmers about their work.

Career Requirements
Agricultural extension agents must have a B.S. degree in agricultural science. Some states require agents to have an M.S. degree. State programs give specific training in agricultural extension work.

For Additional Information
U.S. Department of
    Agriculture
14th & Independence, S.W.
Washington, D.C. 20252

Building a Science Vocabulary

Some people have trouble studying science because they are confused by many of the strange and difficult words they read (and hear) in their science classes. Many scientific words are from Greek and Latin, because these languages were once understood by most scientists. Therefore, if you know some of the most common word parts derived from Greek and Latin, you can quickly increase your science vocabulary.

The following list will show you that many seemingly difficult scientific words are actually familiar. To use the list, first try to break down an unknown word into its parts. Then find the meaning of the parts. Also, look at some examples of other words that use the same word parts.

Word Part	Meaning	Examples
A	no, not	anarchy, asexual, atheist
AB	from, away	absorb, abstract
ABIOS	lifeless	abiochemistry, abiogenesis, abiosis
ACRO	height, extremity	acrobat, acromegaly, acrosome
ACU	needle, sharp	acupuncture, acute
AD	on, to (toward)	addict, adhere, adsorb
ADENO	gland	adenoid, adenoma, adenovirus
ALBU	white	albumin, albuminoid, albuminuria
ALGIA	pain	cephalagia, neuralgia
AMBI	both	ambidextrous, ambiguous
AMNIO	lamb	amnion, Amniota, amniotic
AMPHI	both, two kinds	amphibian, amphibious, amphipod
ANA	up, back, again	analogue, analogy, anaphase
ANEMO	wind (moving air)	anemometer, anemone, anemophilous
ANGIO	cased, closed	angioblast, angiocarp, angiosperm
ANNEL	ring	annelid, anniversary, annual
ANTH	flower	anther, antheridium, antherozoid
ANTHROP	human, mankind	anthropoid, anthropology, philanthropy
API	top, peak	apex, apical, apiculus
AQUA	water	aquanaut, aquatic, aqueduct
ARACHN	spider	arachnid, arachnoid, arachnology
ARTHRO	jointed	arthralgia, arthritis, arthropod
ASTER	star	asteroid, astronaut, astronomy
BAC	rod, stick	bacillus, bacteriophage, bacteria
BIO	life	biochemistry, biography, biology
BLASTO	germ, embryo	blastocyst, blastoderm
BRACHI	arm	brachiopod, brachium
BRONCHI	windpipe	bronchial, bronchitis, bronchoscope
BRYO	moss	bryology, bryophyte, bryozoa

Word Part	Meaning	Examples
CALCI	lime, chalk	calcification, calcify, calcium
CALYP	husk, cover	calyptrogen, calyx
CAPI	hair	capillary, capillitium
CARNA	flesh, meat	carnal, carnivorous
CARPO	wrist	carpophore, carpostome, metacarpal
CAUDA	stem	acaudal, caudal fin, caudex
CEPHAL	head	cephalic, cephalogram, encephalitis
CEREB	brain	cerebellum, cerebral, cerebrum
CHELA	claw	chelate, chelicera, cheliped
CHLOR	green	chlorine, chlorophyll, chloroplast
CHONDR	cartilage	chondriosome, hypochondria, mitochondria
CHORD	cord, string	Chordata, chordate, notochord
CHROM	color	chromatin, chromoplast, chromosome
CILIA	little hairs	ciliary muscles, ciliates, cilium
COCHL	snail	cochlea, cochleated
CORPUS	body	corpse, corpus luteum
COTYL	cup	cotyledon, dicotyledon, monocotyledon
CUTI	skin	cuticle, cutin, subcutaneous
CYST	bladder	cystitis, cystogram, cystorrhea
CYTO	cell	cytology, cytoplasm, lymphocyte
DENT, DONT	tooth	dentist, dentition, orthodontist
DERM	skin	dermatology, ectoderm, hypodermic
DORS	back	dorsal, dorsal fin, dorsolateral
DUCT	to lead	aqueduct, conduct, ductile
DYS	ill, bad	dysentery, dyslexia, dyspepsia
ECHINO	spiny	echinate, echinoderm
ECTO	outside	ectoderm, ectomorph, ectoplasm
EMBRYO	swelling (inside)	embryology, embryonic
ENDO	within	endocrine, endomorph, endoskeleton
ERYTHRO	red	erythrite, erythrocyte, erythromycin
FIBRI	hairlike	fiber, fibrin, fibrinogen, fibroblast
FLAGEL	whip	flagellate, flagellum
FOLI	plant, leaf	foliage, folio
FOLLI	sac, bag	follicle, follicular, folliculated
GAMETO	reproductive germ cell	gamete, gametocyte, gametogenesis
GASTR	stomach	gastrectomy, gastritis, gastroenteric
GEN	make, birth	generator, genetics, genital
GENY	origin, making	nosogeny, ontogeny, progeny
GERM	sprig, seed	germicide, germinal disc, germinate

Word Part	Meaning	Examples
GLOB	ball	gamma globulin, globigerina, globular proteins
GLUCO	sweet	glucose, glucosuria
GLYCO	sweet oil	glycerin, glycogen, hypoglycemia
GON	sexual	gonad, gonorrhea
GYMNO	naked	gymnasium, gymnosperm, gymnospore
HELMINTH	type of worm	helminthic, helminthoid
HEMO	blood	hemoglobin, hemolymph, hemostat
HYPER	above	hyperactive, hypercritical, hypertonic
HYPO	under	hypochondria, hypodermic, hypotonic
ICHTHY	fish	ichthyoid, ichthyology, ichthyosaur
INSULA	island	insulate, insulin, peninsula
ISO	equal	isobar, isometrics, isosceles
ITIS	inflammation	bronchitis, gastritis, neuritis
LEUCO,		
LEUKO	white	leukocyte, leukoplast, leukorrhea
LIGA	to bind	ligament, ligate, ligature
LIPO	fat	lipase, lipoid, lipoma
LOGY	study	arachnology, biology, physiology
LYMPH	clear fluid	lymph glands, lymphocyte, lymphoid
LYSIS	loosen, break down	analyze, dialysis, hydrolyze
MAMM	breast	mammal, mammillary glands
MEDI	middle	median, mediate, mediterranean
MEDULLA	marrow	medullated, medulla oblongata, medullary
MELA	black	melancholy, melanin, melanoma
MER	part	blastomere, polymer
MERI	divide	meridian, meristem
MESO	middle	mesoblast, mesoderm, mesozoic
META	among, changing	metaphase, metastasis, metatarsal
MITO	thread	mitochondria, mitosis, mitotic
MORPH	form	mesomorph, morphology, polymorphic
MUTA	change	mutagen, mutate, mutation
MYCE	nail, wart	mycelium, myceloid
MYCO	fungus	mycobacterium, mycosis
MYO	muscle	myocardium, myoclonus, myopathy
NEMATO	thread	nematocyst, nematode
NEURO	nerve, sinew	nervous, neuroblast, neuron
NOTO	back	notochord
NUCLE	walnut, kernel	nuclear, nucleolus, nucleoplasm

Word Part	Meaning	Examples
OID	like, form	hominoid, ovoid, spheroid
OL	alcohol, or an oil	ethanol, glycol, methanol
OO	egg	oocyte, oogenesis, oogonium
ORTHO	straight	orthodontist, orthodox, orthoptera
OS, OSTE	bone	ossify, osteoblast, osteomyelitis
OVI, OVO	egg	oval, oviparous, ovipositor, ovoid
PALP	lip	palpus, pedipalp
PAR	bring forth	parent, parturition
PARA	beside, beyond	parabola, paramecium, parasite
PATHO	suffer, illness	pathetic, pathogen, pathology
PED	foot	pedal, pedestrian, pedipalp
PERI	around	pericardium, Pericycle, Periosteum, peritoneum
PHAGO	eating	phage, phagocyte, phagocytosis
PHORE	carry, bearer	antrophore, gametophore
PHYLL	leaf	chlorophyll, megaphyllous, phyllomorph
PHYTO	plant	phytochemistry, phytogenesis, phytotoxic
PLASM	molded image, molded form	cytoplasm, plasmolysis, plastic
PLATY	flat, broad	plateau, platyhelminthes, platypus
POD	foot	chiropodist, hexapod, podometre, tripod
POLY	many	polygamy, polygon, polymorphic
POME	apple	pomaceous, pomade, pomegranate
PROTO	first	protoplasm, prototype, protozoa
PSEUDO	false	pseudomorph, pseudonym, pseudopodia
PTER	wing	helicopter, pterodactyl
REN	kidney	renal, reniform, renin
RETI	net	reticle, reticulate, retina
RHINO	nose	rhinoceros, rhinoplasty, rhinovirus
RHIZO	root	rhizocarpous, rhizome, rhizopod
SAPRO	rotten	saprogenic, saprophyte
SCLERO	hard	scleroderm, sclerosis
SCUTUM	shield	scutate, scute, scuttle
SEMEN, SEMIN	seed	inseminate, seminal fluid, seminar
SEPTIC	rotted	antiseptic, septic tank, septicemia
SOMA	body	chromosomes, somatic, somatoplasm
SPERM	seed	carposperm, spermatozoa, spermophile
STAMEN	threads	stamen, staminate, stamina
STIMUL	goad, prick	stimulate, stimuli, stimulus
STOMA	mouth	stomach, stomata, stomatic, stomatopod
SYM	same, similar	symbiosis, symmetry, sympathy
SYN	with	synapse, synchrony, synthetic

Word Part	Meaning	Examples
TARS	ankle, foot	metatarsal, tarsier, tarsus
TAXI	to move	geotaxic, phototaxic, taxicab
TEGMEN	cover	integument, tegula, tegular
TEN	to hold fast	tenacious, tenaculum, tenant, tenet
TENDO	stretch, sinew	tendon, tendril
TETAN	spasm	tetanic, tetanize, tetanus, tetany
THALAM	chamber	thalamic, thalamus
THALLO	spring flowers	thalloid, thallophyte, thallus
THEC	bag, sac	oothecua, spermathecua, thecate
THYRO	oblong shield	thyrocardiac, thyroid, thyroiditis
TINEA	worm	tineal, tineidae, tineoid
TOM	cut	atom, diatom, epitome, microtome
TOMY	cutting	anatomy, hysterectomy, tracheotomy
TON	stretch, tense	hypertonic, isotonic, tonic, tonus
TOXI	poison	toxic, toxicology, toxin
TRACHE	windpipe	trachea, tracheal, tracheitis
TRICH	hairlike	trichinid, trichinosis, trichite
TROPO	turning	geotropic, phototropism, tropophyte
TYMPAN	drum	tympanic membrane, tympanum, tympany
URE	urine	enuresis, urease, urea, urethra
URTICA	nettle, burn	urticaceous, urticaria, urticating
UVULA	grape	uvular, uvulatomy, uvulitis
VARIO	change	varicella, varicose veins
VASO	blood vessel, vessel	vasoconstrictor, vasodilator, vasometer
VENA	vein	vena cava, venatic, venation
VENTR	little belly	ventricose, ventricular, ventriloquist
VERMI	worm	vermiform appendix, vermifuge, vermin
VERT	to change, turn	convert, divert, invert, invertebrate
VIRU	slime, ooze	virology, virulence, virulent, virus
VORE	eating	carnivore, herbivore, omnivore, voracious
XYLO	wood	xylem, xylene, xylophone
ZOO	animal	protozoa, zoo, zoophyte
ZYGO	yoke	heterozygous, zygospore, zygote
ZYME	leaven, ferment	enzyme, zymogen, zymometer, zymotic

Glossary

Pronunciation Key

Symbol	As In	Phonetic Respelling	
a	bat	a	(bat)
ā	face	ay	(fays)
ā	careful	ai	(CAIR fuhl)
ä	argue	ah	(AHR gyoo)
ch	chapel	ch	(CHAP uhl)
e	test	eh	(tehst)
ē	eat	ee	(eet)
	ski	ee	(skee)
ėr	fern	ur	(furn)
i	bit	ih	(biht)
ī	ripe	y	(ryp)
	idea	eye	(eye DEE uh)
k	card	k	(kahrd)
o	lock	ah	(lahk)
ō	over	oh	(OH vuhr)
ô	dog	aw	(dawg)
oi	foil	oy	(foyl)
ou	mountain	ow	(MOWN tuhn)
s	sit	s	(siht)
sh	sheep	sh	(sheep)
u	love	uh	(luhv)
u̇	pull	u	(pull)
ü	mule	oo	(myool)
zh	treasure	zh	(TREHZ uhr)
ə	medal	uh	(MEHD uhl)
	effect	uh	(uh FEHKT)
	serious	uh	(SIHR ee uhs)
	onion	uh	(UHN yuhn)
	talent	uh	(TAL uhnt)

A

abdomen in arachnids, second section of the body; holds most of the organs (521)

abdominal cavity in mammals, the part of the coelom that holds digestive, reproductive, and excretory organs (650)

abiogenesis (ay by oh JEHN uh sihs) belief that some organisms form from nonliving materials (30)

abiotic factor nonliving part of an ecosystem (821)

abscission shedding of a plant's leaves (421)

absorption in the body, movement of nutrient molecules into blood vessels or other vessels during digestion (682)

abyssal (uh BIHS uhl) **region** area of the open sea below a depth of 2,000 m (1.24 mi.) (851)

acetyl CoA organic substance formed from an acetyl group and coenzyme A during aerobic respiration (132)

acid compound that releases hydrogen ions in water (70)

acid rain polluting rain, produced by the reaction of sulfur oxides from fossil fuels with water vapor in the environment to form sulfuric acid (879)

activation energy energy required to start a chemical reaction (61)

active immunity resistance to a disease that results from the body's production of antibodies (307)

active site place on an enzyme where it bonds with its substrate (74)

active transport carrier transport in which energy is used to move substances against the concentration gradient (112)

adaptation a trait in an organism that makes the organism better suited to its environment (11, 258)

adaptive radiation process by which a species adapts to a variety of habitats (264)

addiction state of dependence on a drug (803)

adenine (AD uh neen) carbon-nitrogen compound, one of the four bases of DNA (192)

adrenal (uh DREE nuhl) **cortex** outer layer of the adrenal gland (758)

adrenal gland organ that increases metabolism and helps the body react to stress (758)

adrenal medulla inner part of the adrenal gland (758)

aerobic (ehr OH bihk) **respiration** cellular process of breaking down pyruvic acid in the presence of oxygen (128)

air bladder air-filled structure that permits certain brown algae to carry on photosynthesis (358)

air sac in birds, one of several cavities that contain air, making the animal lighter (611)

albumin nutritious protein found in egg white (612–613)

alcoholic fermentation process in which the pyruvic acid formed during glycolysis is converted to ethyl alcohol (129)

alcoholism addiction to alcohol (804)

algae (AL jee) autotrophic protists (350)

algal bloom uncontrolled growth of algae (327, 354)

alimentary canal passageway from mouth to anus (682)

allantois (uh LAN tuh wihs) in reptiles, birds, and mammals, sac that stores nitrogenous wastes produced by the developing embryo (590)

allele (uh LEEL) either member of a pair of genes that determines a single trait (166)

alternation of generations life cycle involving alternating haploid (gametophyte) and diploid (sporophyte) stages (357)

altricial in young birds, the dependence upon the parents for care and feeding (613)

alveolus (al VEE uh luhs) tiny air sac in the lungs where the exchange of gases occurs (715)

amino acid organic compound, the chief subunit of protein (73)

ammonification (uh moh nuh fih KAY shuhn) process by which microorganisms convert plant or animal wastes or dead organisms into ammonia (827)

amniocentesis (am nee oh sehn TEE sihs) removal and examination of amniotic fluid to test for genetic disorders in a fetus (218)

amnion membrane that surrounds an embryo and forms a chamber filled with a saline fluid (589)

amniotic egg fluid-filled sac enclosed by a protective, porous shell (589)

amoebocyte (uh MEE buh syt) in a sponge, amoebalike cell that carries nutrients to the inner layer and takes away waste matter (475)

amoeboid movement characteristic creeping movement of amoebas, caused by the pseudopodia (339)

amplexus grasping of the female frog by the male to stimulate her to release eggs (581)

anaerobic (an ehr OH bihk) that which does not require oxygen (128)

anaerobic respiration process of breaking down glucose to form pyruvic acid, and breaking down pyruvic acid to form ethyl alcohol or lactic acid (129)

anal fin stabilizing and maneuvering appendage on the ventral surface of a fish (564)

analogous (uh NAL uh guhs) **structure** body part similar to another in function but not in structure (250)

anal pore in paramecia, opening through which undigested wastes leave the cell (342)

anaphase in mitosis, the third stage, during which chromatids separate and pull apart (147)

angiosperm (AN jee uh spuhrm) flowering plant that produces seeds in fruit and generally loses its leaves annually (400)

antenna in many arthropods, a sensory organ (524)

antennule in crayfish and other arthropods, one of a pair of appendages that maintain the organism's balance, touch, and taste (524)

anterior pertaining to the front end (474)

anther in a flower, oblong portion of a filament; place where pollen is produced (427)

antheridium (an thuh RIHD ee uhm) male reproductive structure of a moss (386)

antibiotic chemical capable of inhibiting the growth of some bacteria (324, 783)

antibody protein that attacks, or neutralizes, the antigen that triggered its production (307, 695)

anticodon (an tee KOH dahn) sequence of three bases on transfer RNA (199)

antigen (AN tuh juhn) foreign molecule that stimulates an organism to produce antibodies (307, 695)

anus opening at the end of the intestine through whi solid wastes leave the body (492)

aorta major artery that carries blood from the heart (538, 6

appendage any movable extension of the body that de not contain vital organs (519)

appendicular (ap uhn DIHK yuh luhr) **skeleton** vertebra system comprised of the pectoral girdle, the pelvic gird and their associated limbs (555, 661)

applied genetics implementation of genetic knowledge (22

applied science fields of study in which scientific findir are put to use (29)

aqueous (AY kwee uhs) **humor** clear, watery fluid betwe the lens and cornea of the eye (746)

archegonia (ahr kuh GOH nee uh) female reproducti structure of a moss (386)

artery vessel that carries blood away from the heart (699

ascospore in sac fungi, haploid spore that forms in ascus (370)

ascus in some fungi, small sac in which spores form (369

asexual reproduction production of offspring from c parent (141)

aster spindle fibers that radiate from a centriole duri mitosis in animal cells (146)

atom building block of all matter (14, 50)

atomic number number of protons in the nucleus of c atom of a specific element (52)

ATP adenosine triphosphate; molecule that stores fo energy in usable amounts (119)

atrioventricular (ay tree oh vehn TRIHK yuh luhr) **no** also AV node; in vertebrates, specialized cells in heart that transmit the heartbeat to the ventricles (701)

atrium (AY tree uhm) one of two upper chambers of heart (698)

auditory canal tube to the middle ear from the outsi (748)

Australopithecus genus name of the oldest known homi (271)

autonomic nervous system in vertebrates, system th controls involuntary responses (737)

autosome chromosome that does not determine the sex the individual (182)

autotroph (AWT uh trahf) organism that can use inorgai molecules to produce organic food molecules (129, 289

auxin hormone that tends to stimulate the elongation plant cells (445)

axial (AK see uhl) **skeleton** vertebrate support system co prised of the backbone, bones of the skull, and rib ca (555, 661)

axon long cytoplasmic fiber in a neuron; carries impuls away from the cell body (727)

B

bacillus (buh SIHL uhs) rod-shaped bacterium (317)

bacteriophage (bak TIHR ee uh fayj) virus that invades ba teria (302)

bacterium simple, one-celled organism (314)

barb one of many small projections that comprise the so flexible part of a feather (608)

rbule in a feather, one of many small lateral projections that link barbs together (608)

se compound that releases hydroxide ions in solution or accepts hydrogen ions (70)

sidia in some fungi, club-shaped, microscopic structure on which spores are formed (368)

sidiospore in a mushroom, structure formed when the basidium nucleus undergoes meiosis (369)

thyal (BATH ee uhl) **region** area of the open sea from 200 m (656 ft.) to 2,000 m (6,562 ft.) deep (851)

ign harmless, nonmalignant, non-life threatening (790)

nthos in the marine biome, organisms that are attached to some surface (850)

ateral symmetry arrangement of an organism's body parts so that one-half of the body is an apparent mirror image of the other half (474)

ary fission simplest asexual reproduction; parent cell splits to form two identical daughter cells (142, 340)

omial nomenclature in taxonomy, naming organisms by the genus and species (286)

degradable (by oh dih GRAY duh buhl) a product that can be broken down naturally (878)

genesis (by oh JEHN uh sihs) theory stating that all living things arise from other living things (30)

geochemical cycle pathway through which a chemical substance is recycled (825)

logy the study of living things (4)

luminescence production of light by living things (354)

mass weight of an organism after all the water has been removed (830–831)

me large geographic area of similar climate and life forms (18, 844)

medical engineering design and development of artificial body parts (654)

sphere all the life-supporting environments on Earth and the organisms in them (19, 821)

stereometrics study of biological form and function in three dimensions (66)

systematics study of variations in a species or population that may underlie the evolution of new species (291)

tic factor living organism in an ecosystem (821)

tic potential rate at which a population would produce offspring if every new individual lived and reproduced at its maximum capacity (857)

edal walking on two legs (271–272)

th rate rate at which births occur in a population (861)

alve class of mollusks with two hinged shells and a muscular foot (504)

dderworm immature worm in a tapeworm cyst (490)

de broad part of a leaf, containing most of the photosynthetic cells (419)

stula (BLAS choo luh) ball of cells that forms from repeated cleavages of a zygote (491)

od fluid that serves as the chief carrier of the body's transport system (693)

od type classification of an individual's blood according to the presence of an antigen on red blood cells (695)

us moist, soft ball created when saliva acts on food in the mouth (683)

book lung in arachnids, respiratory structure through which gases are exchanged (521)

boreal forest biome characterized by short summers, long winters, and an abundance of conifers and wildlife (845)

botany the study of plants (22)

Bowman's capsule in the kidney, a hollow, cup-shaped sac that surrounds the glomerulus (720)

brain control center for the vertebrate body (732)

brain stem portion of the brain where the nerves connect the spinal cord with the cerebrum (734)

bristle in birds, short, hairlike feather near the nostril; filters dust (608)

bronchiole (BRAHNG kee ohl) one of many microscopic tubes that branch off from the bronchi (715)

bronchus (BRAHN kuhs) one of the two divisions of the trachea leading to the lungs (715)

brood to guard eggs until they hatch (508)

bryophyte (BRY uh fyt) plant that lacks a vascular system and gets food and nutrients by osmosis and diffusion (383)

bud small, protective structure that holds meristematic cells and embryonic plant materials along a stem (418)

budding type of asexual reproduction in which a cell divides into two cells of unequal size; the smaller cell pinches off to become a new individual (143)

button tight mass of hyphae that comprises the first stage of a mushroom's development (368)

C

Calorie amount of heat energy needed to raise the temperature of one kg of water 1°C (681)

camouflage adaptation for defense in which an organism blends into its surroundings (543)

cancer growth and multiplication of cells in an abnormal, uncontrolled manner (790)

cap fruiting body of a mushroom (368)

capillary smallest blood vessel, where the exchange of nutrients and waste products takes place (701)

capsid outer protein coat of a virus (302)

capsule protective layer of slime surrounding the outer cell wall of some infectious bacteria (318)

carapace in some arthropods, protective outer shield or exoskeleton (524); in turtles and tortoises, dorsal half of the shell (595)

carbohydrate one of the various molecules containing carbon, hydrogen, and oxygen that supply most of the body's energy needs (71, 678)

carcinogen substance or agent that may cause cancer (792)

carcinoma a tumor composed of a mass of cells involving epithelial tissue, such as skin (790)

cardiac muscle specialized tissue responsible for heart contraction (666)

cardiac sphincter (SFINGK tuhr) muscular valve that prevents food from reentering the esophagus (684)

cardiovascular disease disease affecting the heart and blood vessels (793)

carnivore animal that eats only animals (828)

carotene orange pigment present in most green plants (122)

carrier individual who possesses a recessive allele but does not express it (215)

carrier molecule protein molecule that transports large molecules across a membrane (112)

carrying capacity maximum number of individuals in a species that the environment can support (858)

cast mold formed when a material fills the impression created by a decomposed organism (246)

catalyst substance that starts or speeds up a chemical reaction (74)

caudal fin vertical expansion of a fish's tail, used for stabilization (560)

cecum in some mammals, intestinal pouch that contains cellulose-digesting microorganisms (636)

cell functional unit, or building block, of all organisms; smallest unit that can carry on the activities of life (5)

cell body main structure of a nerve cell, containing the nucleus, cytoplasm, and nerve fibers (727)

cell cycle four-stage sequence of cell growth and division between the beginning of one mitosis and the beginning of the next (145)

cell fusion process by which cells from two different kinds of plants are joined (231)

cell membrane outer layer of lipids and proteins that protects a cell, gives it shape, and regulates what enters and leaves the cell (91)

cell plate in plants, structure formed during cytokinesis; a new cell wall forms on both sides of the cell plate (148)

cell theory a three-part explanation stating that all organisms are composed of cells, cells are the basic units of structure and function in organisms, and all cells come from preexisting cells (86)

cellular respiration process of breaking the chemical bonds of organic food molecules and releasing energy that can be used by the cell (120)

cell wall a membrane that helps to protect and support the cells of green plants, algae, fungi, and some bacteria (91)

central nervous system in vertebrates, the brain and spinal cord (727)

centrifugation (sehn trihf yuh GAY shuhn) spinning process that separates cell parts for study (43)

centriole (SEHN tree ohl) small, dark, cylindrical body located outside the nucleus of animal cells and used during cell division (96–97)

centromere (SEHN truh mihr) point at which two chromatids are joined (144)

cephalization (sehf uh lih ZAY shuhn) adaptation in which an organism's neural and sensory organs are concentrated in the anterior end (474)

cephalothorax (sehf uh luh THAWR aks) in invertebrates such as arachnids, a fused head and chest area to which legs are attached (521)

cereal grain small, one-seeded fruit of grasses (457)

cerebellum the part of the vertebrate brain that controls movement and muscular coordination (580, 734)

cerebral cortex gray matter of the cerebrum; receives sensory impulses from the body and coordinates motor responses to them (733)

cerebral hemisphere either half of the cerebrum; each co trols actions and sensations on the opposite side of the bo (732–733)

cerebrospinal fluid protective fluid that circulates around brain and spinal cord (736)

cerebrum control center of the brain (580, 732–733)

cetacean (sih TAY shuhn) a whale, porpoise, dolphin, related aquatic mammal (634)

chancre an open sore, usually on or near the genitals, appe ing in the first stage of syphilis (789)

chelicera (kuh LIHS uh ruh) in arachnids, poisonous fang clawlike appendage (521)

cheliped (KEE luh pehd) in crustaceans, one of the seco pair of appendages on the thorax part of the cephalothor (524)

chemical bond force that holds atoms together in a molecule or compound (58)

chemical equation symbols that describe what happens i chemical reaction (62)

chemical property describes how a substance acts whe combines with other substances to form different kinds matter (49)

chemical reaction process of breaking existing chemi bonds and forming new ones (61)

chemosynthesis breakdown of inorganic chemicals (318)

chemotherapy the use of highly toxic drugs for the treatm of cancer (793)

chitin (KYT uhn) in fungi, hard, water-insoluble substance the cell walls (365); in arthropods, protein-carbohydr compound that forms the exoskeleton (519)

chlorophyll (KLAWR uh fihl) green pigment in plants; nec sary for photosynthesis (122)

chloroplast plastid that stores chlorophyll (95)

chorion (KOHR ee ahn) in reptiles and birds, outermost me brane that lines an egg shell; in mammals, the membr that attaches to the uterus wall (590)

chorionic villi sampling technique involving the exami tion of a tissue sample from the fetal membrane to de genetic disorders (220)

choroid (KAWR oyd) dark layer of tissue in the middle of vertebrate eye (745)

chromatid (KROH muh tihd) strandlike structure that, pairs, comprises a chromosome during mitosis (144)

chromatin diffused material carrying hereditary informat about a cell (90)

chromosome rod- or rope-shaped body, composed of D and proteins, that carries hereditary information (90, 161)

chromosome map graphic device that shows where ge are located on a chromosome (186)

chromosome mutation change involving many genes (20

chromosome theory scientific theory stating that here tary factors, or genes, are carried on chromosomes (17

chrysalis protective covering from which a pupa emer as a butterfly (540)

chyme semifluid mass of food that passes from the sto ach to the small intestine (685)

cilia (SIHL ee uh) tiny, hairlike projections whose wave motion helps move substances along a surface (97, 3 650)

rcadian (suhr KAY dee uhn) **rhythm** a pattern of changes that occurs in organisms every 24 hours (833)

rculatory system group of organs in a body that transports materials and removes cellular wastes (652)

rrhosis condition in which liver cells are destroyed and the organ ceases to function (806)

tric acid six-carbon molecule formed during aerobic respiration by the transfer of the acetyl group of acetyl CoA to a four-carbon molecule (132)

eavage division of a zygote into halves (491)

imax community stable community whose characteristics allow for its own regeneration (839)

itellum in earthworms, a glandular area covering several segments that secretes a mucous substance that holds together mating earthworms (495)

oaca cavity that receives waste materials from the kidneys, the urinary bladder, and the sex organs, and passes them out (492, 577)

one organism or group of cells developed from one parent and genetically identical to it (230)

oning production of organisms with identical genes (230)

utch group of eggs in a nest (614)

idocyte (NYD uh syt) stinging cell in coelenterates (478)

agulation (koh ag yoo LAY shuhn) clotting of blood (694)

ccus (KAHK uhs) sphere-shaped bacterium (317)

chlea (KAHK lee uh) in the ear of mammals, a bony, coiled tube filled with fluid and lined with hair cells that functions in hearing (749)

coon in metamorphosis, protective covering around the pupa (540)

don (KOH dahn) sequence of three bases in RNA; code for a specific amino acid (197)

elenterate (sih LEHN tuh rayt) baglike invertebrate animal with tentacles, including hydra, jellyfish, sea anemones, and corals (478)

elom (SEE luhm) large, central body cavity that contains the vital organs (490, 555, 650)

lar cell in a sponge, cell that digests food (475)

llecting duct part of the renal tubule that regulates the water and mineral composition of blood (720)

lloid mixture in which the suspended particles are smaller than those in an ordinary suspension but larger than those of a solute in a solution (56)

lon last portion of the digestive tract; where absorption of water, minerals, and vitamins occurs (688)

lonial algae organisms made up of algal cells held together by a jellylike substance or cytoplasm (355)

lonial organism individual cells that live in groups and resemble a multicellular organism (16)

lony large group of bacteria descended from a single bacterium (320)

orblindness inability to distinguish certain colors (215)

nmensalism symbiotic relationship in which one organism benefits and the other is unaffected (833)

nmon name in taxonomy, name given to an organism by people of an area (285–286)

nmunity collection of interacting populations that live n the same area (17, 823)

comparative biochemistry study of molecules that make up living things (249)

comparative embryology study of embryos of different species (250)

complete flower one that contains all the essential and nonessential parts (428)

compound two or more elements that are chemically combined (53)

compound eye in arthropods, eye that has more than one lens (526)

compound leaf leaf with several separate parts attached to an extension of the petiole (419)

compound light microscope instrument that uses light and an ocular and an objective lens to magnify objects (39)

concentration amount of solute dissolved in a given amount of solvent (55)

concentration gradient difference in concentration from the highest to the lowest number of molecules in a substance (106)

condensation reaction chemical reaction in which water is produced (71)

cone in the vertebrate eye, receptor cell that can detect color and produce sharp images (746)

conjugation transfer or exchange of genetic material between organisms (322)

conjunctiva delicate, blood-rich membrane that lines the inner eyelid and covers the front of the eye (745)

connective tissue tissue that joins, supports, and protects other types of tissue (651)

conservation the careful management, wise use, and protection of natural resources (871)

contour feather in birds, one of many smooth, sleek feathers that cover the head, body, and wings (608)

contour plowing method of reducing erosion by plowing across a slope (873)

contractile (kuhn TRAK tuhl) **vacuole** in unicellular organisms, organelle that expels excess water (110, 339)

control group in an experiment, the group that is not exposed to the variable being tested (28)

controlled breeding process of selecting individuals with desired traits to produce offspring (227)

controlled experiment one in which extraneous conditions are held constant (28)

convergent evolution process by which unrelated species become more alike (265, 631)

cork cambium meristematic tissue that produces cork (413)

cornea transparent layer of tissue that covers the front of the eye (745)

corpus callosum (KAWR puhs kuh LOH suhm) in the human brain, bridgelike structure of over 200 million nerve fibers that joins the cerebral hemispheres (732–733)

corpus luteum (KAWR puhs LOO tee uhm) enlarged, blood-rich follicle that produces hormones that prepare the uterus for a fertilized egg (771–772)

cortex in plants, rigid outer layer of cells surrounding the pith (410); in the body, outer layer of an organ, such as the kidney (720)

corticoid any of a number of hormones secreted by the adrenal cortex (758)

cotyledon (kaht uhl EED uhn) embryonic leaf enclosed in a seed (400)

covalent bond electrical attraction between two atoms that share electrons (58)

cranial cavity space that houses the brain (650)

critical dark period amount of darkness a photoperiodic plant must have before it flowers (444)

crop storage chamber in many birds and some invertebrates through which food passes from the esophagus to the gizzard (496)

crop rotation method of conserving soil nutrients by alternating crops from season to season (458, 873)

crossing over process by which alleles exchange places on a chromosome (185)

cross-pollination reproductive process involving the sex cells of two plants (163)

cuticle (KYOOT ih kuhl) in plants, protective outer coating (381); in parasites such as flukes, thick protective coating that prevents digestion by the host (488)

cyanobacteria a group of blue-green bacteria that contain chlorophyll and perform photosynthesis (325)

cyclic AMP form of adenosine monophosphate that acts as a "second messenger" for many vertebrate hormones (764)

cyst (sihst) in some protists, thickened outer structure that forms when conditions are unfavorable for survival (340); in some parasites, thick-walled structure formed around the larva (489)

cytokinesis (syt oh kih NEE sihs) process during which cytoplasm divides (145)

cytokinin hormone that stimulates cell division in plants (447)

cytoplasm (SYT uh plaz uhm) material between the nucleus and outer boundary of a cell (89)

cytoplasmic streaming constant motion of cytoplasm (92)

cytosine (SYT uh seen) carbon-nitrogen compound that is one of the four bases of DNA (192)

D

dark reactions second phase of photosynthesis, in which glucose is formed (123)

data facts collected during an experiment (28)

day-neutral plant one that does not flower in response to the duration of light (444)

death rate rate at which deaths occur in a population (861)

decay element stable substance into which a radioactive isotope eventually breaks down (246)

deciduous (dih SIHJ oo wuhs) **forest** biome characterized by long winters, constant rainfall, trees that shed leaves annually, and much wildlife (846)

decomposer microorganism that breaks down dead tissue and returns the nutrients to the soil (828)

degenerative disease a long-term illness that involves the deterioration of body tissue or an organ (790)

delirium tremens (**DTs**) in extreme alcoholism, state marked by hallucinations and uncontrollable trembling (805)

delivery expulsion of a fetus into the external environment (777)

dendrite branched, cytoplasmic fiber in a neuron that carries impulses toward the cell body (727)

denitrification process in which ammonia, nitrite, and nitrate become nitrogen gas (827)

density-dependent factor environmental element whose effects are determined by population density (859)

density-independent factor environmental element whose effects are not determined by population density (858)

deoxyribose (dee ahk sih RY bohs) five-carbon sugar present in DNA (193)

dependent variable in an experiment, the condition that responds to changes in the independent variable (28)

depressant drug that slows the functions of the central nervous system (804)

dermis thick, inner layer of the skin (670)

desalination (dee sal uh NAY shuhn) process by which salt is removed from salt water (872)

desert biome characterized by very low rainfall, plant life adapted to dry conditions, and nocturnal animals (848)

development series of changes an organism undergoes as it matures (9)

diaphragm (DY uh fram) dome-shaped sheet of muscle that divides the coelom into an upper thoracic cavity and a lower abdominal cavity (415, 650, 713)

diatom (DY uh tahm) unicellular golden alga with a silica shell (354)

dicot plant with two cotyledons (402)

differentiation specialization of cells (409)

diffusion movement of molecules of a substance from areas of higher concentration of that substance to areas of lower concentration (105)

digestion process by which food is changed into a form that the body can use (682)

digestive system group of organs that ingest food, break down, absorb the nutrients, and eliminate solid waste (652)

digestive tract tubelike passageway from mouth to anus where digestion occurs (682)

dihybrid cross genetic cross involving two pairs of alleles that determine two separate traits (171)

dinoflagellate unicellular alga with a hard, stiff cell wall (354)

diploid (DIHP loyd) the basic chromosome number (2n); two from each pair of homologous chromosomes (149)

directional selection natural selection (in a species) that proceeds in a given direction (261)

disaccharide molecule formed by the condensation of two monosaccharides (71)

disease a condition that impairs or damages the body's normal functions (782)

disruptive selection type of natural selection that favors the extremes of a trait (261)

diurnal describes organisms that are active during the day (833)

divergent evolution process by which related organisms become less alike (264)

DNA deoxyribonucleic (dee AHK sih ry boh noo KLEE ihk) acid; a nucleic acid; contains instructions for cellular activity and transmits them from generation to generation (75, 191)

dominant gene that masks the other gene in a pair (164)

dormancy in plants, condition marked by minimal growth and low metabolism (445)

dorsal pertaining to the back surface of an organism (474)

dorsal fin in fishes, one of two stabilizing appendages that extend along the back (560)

double fertilization process in flowering plants in which two kinds of fertilization occur, forming both a zygote and an endosperm (431)

down feather in birds, soft, fluffy feather located under a contour feather (608)

Down syndrome genetic disorder in individuals who have an extra chromosome 23 (217)

drug chemical substance that has a marked effect on the body or mind (802)

drug abuse the taking of a drug for nonmedical reasons (803)

duodenum first part of the small intestine (577)

eardrum tightly stretched membrane between the outer and middle ear (748)

echolocation in bats, locating of objects by the reflection of sound waves (625)

ecological pyramid visual display of the decrease in available energy in an ecosystem (830)

ecological succession predictable, orderly replacement of communities in an ecosystem (839)

ecology study of the relationships of living things to their environment (820)

ecosystem distinct, self-supporting unit of interacting organisms and their environment (18, 821)

ectoderm outermost layer of body tissue (475)

ectoplasm in an amoeba, clear, thin layer of cytoplasm between the endoplasm and the cell membrane (339)

egg tooth in baby birds, sharp structure on the beak tip, used in pecking out of the shell (613)

electron negatively charged subatomic particle (51)

electron microscope instrument that creates enlarged images with a beam of electrons (41)

electron transport chain series of reactions in which energized electrons move from one molecule to another, each time releasing some energy (124)

element substance that cannot be changed into a simpler substance by chemical means (14, 51)

embryo immature form of an organism (400, 630); in humans, the developmental stage occurring during the first eight weeks (774–775)

embryo sac female gametophyte of a flowering plant (430)

endangered species species of plant or animal that may become extinct unless it is protected (874)

endergonic (ehn duhr GAHN ihk) **reaction** chemical reaction that uses more energy than it releases (62)

endocrine gland group of cells whose secretions are released directly into the bloodstream (757)

endocrine (EHN duh krihn) **system** group of organs that help control body functions through the secretion of hormones (653)

endocytosis (ehn doh sy TOH sihs) bulk transport of substances into a cell (113)

endoderm innermost layer of body tissue (475)

endodermis in plants, innermost layer of cells in the root cortex; regulates the intake of minerals and other substances (412)

endoplasm in an amoeba, thick, grainy cytoplasm that comprises most of the cell (339)

endoplasmic reticulum (ehn duh PLAZ mihk rih TIHK yuh luhm) also ER; series of canals or channels that serves as a route for materials from cytoplasm to nucleus (92)

endoskeleton internal system that functions for support of the body (510, 555)

endosperm nutritive tissue that provides a temporary food source for a new plant (431)

endospore cell formed by a bacterium to survive harsh conditions (321)

endotoxin lipopolysaccharide found in the cell wall of a bacterium (783)

energy power needed to carry on life activities (7)

energy level around the nucleus of an atom, region of space where electrons are located (57)

entomologist scientist who studies insects (534)

environment everything in an organism's surroundings that affects it in any way (11)

enzyme protein that acts as a catalyst (74, 677)

epicotyl part of an embryonic stem above the cotyledons (435)

epidermis in plants and animals, the protective, outermost layers of cells (409, 670)

epiglottis (ehp uh GLAHT ihs) flap of tissue that closes off the trachea (683–684)

epinephrine (ehp uh NEHF rihn) hormone secreted by the adrenal gland (758)

epiphyseal plate at either end of long bones, region where growth occurs (663)

epithelial (ehp uh THEE lee uhl) **tissue** tissue that covers all internal and external body surfaces (650)

equator midplane of a cell (147)

equilibrium state of balance (109)

era one of four spans into which scientists divide the time since life began (247)

erosion the wearing away of soil by water or wind (873)

esophagus (ih SAHF uh guhs) muscular tube leading from the mouth to the stomach (496, 684)

estivation (ehs tuh VAY shun) in organisms such as frogs, period of inactivity during the summer (580, 834)

estrogen (EHS truh juhn) hormone that stimulates development of certain female characteristics (770)

estrus in mammals, period of fertility in the female (626)

estuary place where a river or stream meets an ocean (852)

eukaryote (YOO KAR ee oht) cell with a nucleus (98)

Eustachian (YOO STAY shuhn) **tube** duct that connects the middle ear to the pharynx and equalizes air pressure (576, 748)

eutrophication (YOO trahf uh KAY shuhn) the process of adding nutrients to an ecosystem or community, resulting in a decrease in oxygen (841)

evolution change in living things over time (242)

excretion process of eliminating metabolic wastes (719)

excretory system group of organs that remove cellular waste from the blood and maintain the body's fluid and chemical balance (653)

excurrent siphon in bivalves, tube through which water is expelled (504)

exergonic (ehk suhr GAHN ihk) **reaction** chemical reaction that releases more energy than it uses (61–62)

exhalation emptying the lungs of air (714)

exocrine gland group of cells that produces and secretes a substance through tubes or ducts (757)

exocytosis (ehk soh sy TOH sihs) bulk transport of substances out of a cell (113)

exoskeleton an exterior skeleton (519)

exotoxin proteins that are secreted by bacteria into an organism or system that the bacteria have invaded (783)

experiment test of a hypothesis (28)

experimental group group exposed to the variable (28)

exponential (ehks poh NEHN shuhl) **growth** period of rapid growth in which the number of individuals repeatedly doubles in a given time period (858)

exponential phase period during which a population undergoes very rapid growth (858)

extensor muscle that straightens a joint (669)

extinct species kind of animal or plant that no longer exists (874)

eyepiece in a microscope, that portion of the instrument closest to the eye of the user (39)

eyespot light-sensitive structure in euglenas and planarians (338)

F

facilitated diffusion form of carrier transport in which substances move from areas of high to low concentration, requiring no energy expenditure (112)

facultative anaerobe bacterium that can live with or without oxygen (320)

Fallopian tube in females, the duct from an ovary to the uterus (770)

fang sharp tooth connected to a poison gland (600)

fat molecule composed of hydrogen, carbon, and oxygen; provides a highly concentrated source of energy (679)

fat body in frogs, structure on the ovary or testis that stores fat (581)

feces solid wastes (488, 688)

fermentation anaerobic process in which pyruvic acid is broken down into ethyl alcohol or lactic acid (129)·

fertilization process in which a male and a female sex cell combine (143, 773)

fetoscopy (fee TAH skuh pee) microscopic examination of a developing fetus in utero to detect physical abnormalities (220)

fetus in humans, the developing embryo from after the first eight weeks until birth (775)

fiber substance that aids digestion by stimulating the muscles of the digestive tract (679)

fibrous root in monocots, one of many secondary root that form a network over a wide area (411)

filament in a flower, thin, stemlike part of a stamen (427)

filoplume in birds, short, thin feather that looks like a hair also called a pin feather (608)

first polar body smaller of the cells resulting from meiosi I in female animals (151)

flagella (fluh JEHL uh) long, hairlike structures on the sur face of a cell that aid in locomotion (97, 318, 338)

flame cell excretory cell in planarians (488)

flexor muscle that bends a joint (669)

follicle in birds, one of many small sacs (in the skin) fror which feathers grow (608); fluid-filled chamber aroun an egg before it is released from the ovary (771)

F₁ first filial (FIHL ee uhl) generation; in genetics, the firs generation of offspring that results from the cros between two plants or two animals (163)

foot in clams and some other mollusks, a muscular struc ture used for burrowing (503)

forestry business of cultivating trees to provide fuel, lum ber, and other wood products (461)

fossil any preserved part or trace of an organism that onc lived (245)

fossil fuels substances that consist of fossil remains of pre historic plants and animals (876)

fovea (FOH vee uh) at the center of the retina, area wher a concentration of cones produces the sharpest image (746)

fragmentation kind of asexual reproduction in which pa of an organism breaks off and grows on its own (32 356)

fraternal twins offspring that develop from two eggs in th mother that are fertilized by two different sperm (210)

frond leaf of a fern (397)

fruit ripened ovary of a flowering plant (433)

fruiting body visible part of a fungus, containing the spor producing structures (365)

F₂ second filial (FIHL ee uhl) generation; offspring tha result from crossing two members of the first filial gene ation (163)

fungus nonmotile organism that obtains food by decon posing organic matter (365)

G

gall bladder small sac where bile is stored (686)

gamete (GAM eet) sex cell (143, 161, 769)

gametophyte (guh MEET uh fyt) in algae and plants, th haploid generation that produces gametes (356, 384)

ganglion (GAN glee uhn) concentration of nerve cells (48

gastric ceca (SEE kuh) in an insect, pocket of the stomac that secretes enzymes necessary for digestion (538)

gastrula (GAS troo luh) in animal development, indentatic of blastula cells that gives rise to differentiated tissue (49

gemmae (JEHM ee) spores produced asexually by some li erworts (387)

gemmule (JEHM YOOL) asexually produced, food-filled ba of amoebocytes that becomes a sponge (477)

gene unit of hereditary information (161)

ene frequency measure of the relative occurrence of a given allele in a population (259)

ene linkage situation in which two or more genes occur on the same chromosome (184)

ene mutation change in a single gene (201)

ene pool alleles of all the genes in all of the individuals in a population (259)

enerative cell smaller of two cells in a pollen grain (429)

ene therapy technique for replacing a defective gene (224)

enetic counseling informing couples of their chances of passing on a harmful genetic trait to their offspring (218)

enetic drift change in gene frequency of a small population due to the effects of random mating (262)

enetic engineering process of transferring DNA segments from one organism into the DNA of another species (231)

enetic equilibrium relative stability of the genetic makeup of a population (260)

enetic isolation absence of genetic exchange between populations because of geographic separation or other factors that prevent reproduction (263)

enetics study of heredity (161)

enotype (JEE nuh typ) the kinds of alleles in the cells of an organism (166)

enus in taxonomy, group of closely related species (285)

eologist scientist who studies the physical nature and history of the Earth (247)

eothermal (jee oh THER muhl) **power** energy created by steam below or near the Earth's surface (876)

eotropism plant's response to gravity (448)

erm cell mutation change in a reproductive cell (203)

erminate in a plant seed, to resume growth by sprouting (434)

erm layer any of the three layers of cells in most multicellular animals (490)

estation (jehs TAY shuhn) **period** in mammals, time in which young develop in the uterus (632, 773)

ibberellin hormone that stimulates rapid growth (447)

ll in mushrooms, thin sheet of tissue under the cap (368); in aquatic animals, respiratory organ (504, 557)

ll slits in chordates, openings in the throat region (553)

izzard digestive chamber in which organic matter is crushed (496)

omerular filtration in vertebrates, removal of urea and other wastes from the body (720)

omerulus (glah MEHR yoo luhs) in the kidney, mass of capillaries forming a tight ball within a nephron (720)

ycolysis (gly KAHL uh sihs) process of breaking a glucose molecule to form two molecules of pyruvic acid; the first step in cellular respiration (128)

olgi (GOHL jee) **body** in a cell, area for storage and packaging of chemicals (94)

onad gamete-producing organ; also produces and secretes hormones (760)

ana tiny, disklike sacs where photosynthesis begins in a chloroplast (122)

assland biome characterized by wet springs, dry summers, and many types of grasses (847)

een gland in most crustaceans, excretory organ that opens near the base of the antenna (525)

Green Revolution program to introduce high-yield crops into poor agricultural regions (459)

ground tissue in plants, relatively unspecialized tissue that cushions and protects vascular tissue (410)

growth rate rate at which a population increases (861)

guanine (GWAH neen) carbon-nitrogen compound that is one of the four bases of DNA (192)

guard cell one of two kidney-shaped cells that regulate the passage of water through a stoma in a leaf (420)

gullet in paramecia, chamber where food is stored, beneath the mouth pore (342)

gymnosperm (JIHM nuh spuhrm) type of plant that produces seeds in cones and generally keeps its leaves all year (400)

H

habitat surroundings of a particular species (823)

hair cell sense receptor in which fine, hairlike projections respond to mechanical pressure (743)

hair follicle small epidermal fold where hair is manufactured (671)

half-life the time it takes for half the isotopes in radioactive material to decay (246)

hallucinogen (huh LOO suh nuh jehn) drug that distorts sensory impressions (806)

haploid number half the diploid number; one from each pair (n) of homologous chromosomes (149)

hard palate bony plate in the roof of the mouth (683)

Hardy-Weinberg principle mathematical principle stating that the frequency of alleles in a population stays the same unless altered by some external factor (260)

Haversian (huh VUR shuhn) **canal** in the compact bone, small channel containing blood vessels that nourish the osteocytes (663)

head in some mollusks, one of the three main body parts; bears tentacles, a mouth and sensory organs (503)

heart muscular organ that pumps blood to all parts of the body (696)

hemoglobin (HEE muh gloh bihn) molecule that carries oxygen in the blood (694)

hemophilia (hee muh FIHL ee uh) hereditary disorder that prevents normal blood clotting (215)

hemotoxin poisonous protein that destroys red blood cells and breaks down vessel walls (600)

herbaceous plant monocot with a typically green stem lacking secondary growth (403)

herbivore animal that eats only plants (828)

hereditary disease a genetically transmitted illness (796)

heredity the passing of traits from parents to offspring (160)

hermaphrodite (huhr MAF ruh dyt) organism that contains both female and male gonads (476)

heterotroph (HEHT uhr uh trahf) organism that depends on other organisms for food (129, 289)

heterozygous (heht uhr oh ZY guhs) describes an individual with a dominant and a recessive gene for a trait (164)

hibernation in some animals, period of severely reduced activity in winter (580, 834)

hindgut posterior part of the digestive tract; an insect's intestine (538)

holdfast rootlike structure that anchors many brown algae (358)

homeostasis (hoh mee oh STAY sihs) self-adjusting balance among life functions, the environment, and an organism's activities (13)

home range in mammals, area over which an animal travels during normal activities (626–627)

hominid humans and their ancestors (271)

Homo erectus a large-brained hominid that lived between 1.5 million and 500,000 years ago (274)

Homo habilis hominid that is considered to be the earliest species of the genus *Homo* (272)

homologous (hoh MAHL uh guhs) **chromosome** one of two like chromosomes (149)

homologous structure body part with the same basic structure as that of another organism, suggesting common ancestry (250)

Homo sapiens scientific name of modern humans (275)

homozygous (hoh moh ZY guhs) describes an individual with identical genes for a trait (164)

homozygous dominant describes an individual having two dominant genes for a certain trait (164)

homozygous recessive describes an individual having two recessive genes for a certain trait (164)

hormone internally produced chemical that regulates the functions of tissues and organs (445, 757)

host cell cell in which a virus reproduces (301)

Huntington disease hereditary disease of the nervous system involving loss of muscle control, mental deterioration, and eventual death (212)

hybrid in genetics, individual with a dominant and a recessive gene (164)

hybridization mating of two different species, breeds, or varieties (229)

hybrid vigor improvement in quality resulting from hybridization (229)

hydrolysis breaking down of complex molecules by combination with molecules of water (73)

hydrotropism growth of a plant's roots toward water (449)

hypertonic solution solution in which the concentration of the solutes outside a cell is greater than that inside it (109)

hypha (HY fuh) one of many filaments that comprise the body of a fungus (365)

hypocotyl part of an embryonic stem above the radicle and below the cotyledons (435)

hypothalamus structure in the vertebrate brain that controls body temperature, thrist, hunger, salt and water balance, and emotional behavior (733–734)

hypothesis (hy PAHTH uh sihs) a statement that is based on observations and that can be tested (27)

hypotonic solution one in which the concentration of solutes outside a cell is lower than that inside it (109)

identical twins two offspring that develop from a single fertilized egg (210)

ileum second part of the small intestine (577)

immunity natural resistance to disease through the produc tion of antibodies (307, 706)

imperfect flower one that has the reproductive parts o only one sex (428)

imprint impression formed in a developing rock from so body structures of organisms (245)

impulse electrochemical signal in a nervous system (727)

inborn errors of metabolism the body's inability correctly perform certain chemical processes (796)

inbreeding mating of genetically similar individual (228)

incomplete dominance situation in which neither allele a pair is dominant or recessive (173)

incomplete flower one that lacks one or more of the esser tial or nonessential parts (428)

incubate to warm bird eggs to promote development of th young (614)

incurrent pore in sponges, one of many openings throug which water enters the body (475)

incurrent siphon in bivalves, tube through which wate enters the organism (504)

incus (IHN kuhs) in mammals, one of three tiny bones the middle ear (749)

independent variable in an experiment, the condition tha is changed to produce a response in the dependent var able (28)

inferior vena cava (VEE nuh KAY vuh) vessel that brin blood from the lower part of the body to the heart (699)

inhalation process of filling the lungs with air (714)

inherited passed down from generation to generatic (11)

inorganic compound one not made by living things (69)

insecticide chemical used to kill insects (543)

insertion point at which a muscle is attached to the movir bone (669)

insulin substance that controls the level of glucose in th blood, secreted by the pancreas (577, 758)

integument enclosing layer of an organism, such as th skin of the human body (670)

integumentary system group of organs that form a prote tive outer layer (653)

interbreed to mate within a population (16)

interferon (ihn tuhr FIHR ahn) protein that interferes wi viral replication (308, 785)

interneuron nerve cell that links sensory and motor ner cells (727)

interphase time between the formation of a cell by mitos and that cell's next mitosis (144)

intertidal zone that part of the seashore located betwee high and low tides (850)

invertebrate animal without a backbone (474)

ion atom that has gained or lost electrons (51)

ionic bond electrical attraction between a positive and negative ion (58)

iris colored ring of tissue that gives the eye its color (745)

irrigation process of watering crops by means other th natural rainfall (459)

irritability ability to respond to stimuli (10)

slets of Langerhans cells in the pancreas that secrete insulin and glucagon (758)

somers compounds with the same molecular formula but different arrangements of atoms (71)

sotonic (eye suh TAHN ihk) **solution** one in which the concentration of solutes outside a cell is the same as that inside the cell (109)

sotope (EYE suh tohp) atom in which the number of neutrons is different from that in other atoms of the same element (54)

J

acobsen's organ two small hollows in the roof of a snake's mouth that are sensitive to taste and smell (598)

-curve pattern formed by the combination of exponential growth and lag phases in a population (858)

oint point at which bones meet (664)

K

aryotype picture of paired human chromosomes arranged by size; used to identify chromosomal abnormalities (216, 287)

eel in birds, high, narrow ridge to which breast muscles are attached; located at the base of the sternum (609)

eratin protein that makes skin hard and waterproof (590)

idney in vertebrates, one of a pair of bean-shaped excretory organs (719)

inetic energy energy of motion (57)

linefelter syndrome genetic disorder in males with an extra X chromosome (217)

rebs cycle series of chemical reactions, involving citric acid, that occur during one stage of aerobic respiration (132)

L

abium in insects, the lower lip, which presses food against the jaws (536)

abor process during which uterine muscles contract to expel a fetus (776)

abrum in insects, the upper lip, which holds the insect's food (536)

acrimal gland structure that produces tears; located near the outer corner of the eye (745)

acteal tiny vessel in the villi that absorbs fats (687)

ag phase period of slow growth in a population (857)

andfill an area of land that has been filled by sandwiching solid wastes between layers of earth (881)

arge intestine last portion of the digestive tract, where water, minerals, and vitamins are absorbed (577, 688)

arva (LAHR vuh) form of an organism that is immature and very different from the adult organism (477)

arynx upper part of the trachea where the vocal cords are located (684)

lateral line system in a fish, system of fluid-filled canals that allows the animal to detect movement and to locate objects (560)

law of conservation principle stating that matter cannot be created or destroyed (62)

leaf base where the petiole is attached on the stem (419)

legume plant that produces seeds in pods (458)

lens transparent, curved structure that helps focus images in the eye (746)

lichen (LY kuhn) organism consisting of a fungus and an alga living symbiotically (366)

life span average length of life (9)

ligament strong band of connective tissue on the bones of a movable joint (664)

light reactions in photosynthesis, the first phase, in which light energy is trapped and materials required in the next phase are formed (123)

lignin (LIHG nihn) compound found in some plant cell walls that provides support (381)

limiting factor environmental element that stabilizes population size and keeps species from reaching their biotic potential (858)

linkage group genes that occur together on a chromosome (184)

lipid one of a group of substances that are insoluble in water; includes fats, oils, and waxes (73)

liver largest internal organ; producer of bile (685–686)

lobe-finned fish one of a group of bony fishes having dorsal and pectoral fins with large, fleshy bases supported by leg-like bones (563)

long-day plant one that produces flowers in summer, when nights are shorter than the plant's critical dark period (444)

lung one of a pair of spongy, saclike organs where gas exchange occurs (713)

lungfish one of a group of bony fishes with lungs as well as gills (563)

lymph tissue fluid that surrounds all body cells (703)

lymphatic system the part of the circulatory system that collects fluid from tissue and returns it to the blood (652)

lymph node one of many tiny, bean-shaped organs that filter foreign matter from lymph (703)

lymphocyte type of white blood cell that defends the body against disease and infections (704)

lysogenic (ly suh JEHN ihk) **cycle** period of inactivity that occurs in some viruses after they have invaded a host cell (305)

lysosome (LY suh sohm) in a cell, organelle that digests large particles (96)

lytic (LIHT ihk) **cycle** process in which a virus destroys the host cell (302)

M

macroevolution sudden appearance of a distinct species (266)

macronucleus in paramecia, the larger nucleus, which directs all functions except reproduction (341–342)

magnification apparent increase in an object's size (39)

malignant deadly, life-threatening (790)

malleus (MAL ee uhs) one of three tiny bones in the middle ear (749)

Malpighian (mal PIHG ee uhn) **tubule** in arachnids, one of many small tubes of the excretory system; removes wastes from blood (522)

mammary gland in mammals, modified sweat gland that secretes milk used to feed young (623)

mandible in crustaceans, insects, and myriapods, one of a pair of chewing jaws (524)

mantle in mollusks, thin membrane that surrounds the visceral mass (503)

marrow tissue inside some bones that produces red and white blood cells (661)

marsupial mammal that has a pouch (629)

mass measure of the amount of matter in an object (49)

mass number number of protons plus the number of neutrons in an atom (52)

mass selection raising many plants or animals and selecting the best in each generation for further breeding (228)

mating strain one of two genetically different molds that reproduce sexually (367)

matrix (MAY trihks) thick, nonliving material in which connective tissue cells are embedded (651)

matter anything that takes up space (49)

maxilla in crustaceans and some other arthropods, one of the first or second pair of mouthparts behind the mandible (524)

maxilliped in crustaceans, one of the first pair of appendages on the thorax part of the cephalothorax (524)

medulla inner layer of an organ such as the kidney (720)

medulla oblongata (mih DUHL uh ahb lawn GAHT uh) in vertebrates, enlarged portion of the spinal cord that carries out most automatic nervous responses (580, 734–735)

medusa (muh DOO suh) bell-shaped body of some coelenterates (478)

meiosis (my OH sihs) type of nuclear division in which the chromosome number is halved (149)

memory cell white blood cell that "remembers" an antigen pattern and produces antibodies (705–706)

meninges (muh NIHN jeez) three layers of tissue that surround and protect the surface of the brain and the spinal cord (736)

menopause in females, period during which the ovaries cease production of mature eggs (772)

menstrual (MEHN stroo wuhl) **cycle** in females, the regular, repeating pattern of ovulation and related changes (771)

menstruation in females, discharging of lining tissue and an unfertilized egg from the uterus (772)

meristem (MEHR uh stem) specific areas in plants at which cells divide (409)

mesentery thin, tough membrane that holds the small intestine in place (577)

mesoderm middle layer of embryonic cells, encased between the ectoderm and the endoderm of bilaterally symmetrical animals (490)

mesoglea (mehz uh GLEE uh) in coelenterates, jellylike substance separating endoderm and ectoderm (478)

mesophyll middle portion of a leaf (420)

mesothorax in insects, the second section of the three-part thorax (537)

messenger RNA also mRNA; type of RNA that carries sequences of nucleotides that code for protein from the nucleus to the ribosomes (196)

metabolism (muh TAB uh lihz uhm) sum of all the chemical reactions within cells or organisms (7–8, 716)

metamorphosis series of marked changes by which an immature organism becomes an adult (539)

metaphase in mitosis, the second phase, during which the chromosomes line up along the cell's midplane (146–147)

metastasis movement of abnormal cells from the site of a disease to a new site, as in the spreading of cancer (790)

metathorax in insects, third section of the three-part thorax (537)

microdissection kind of surgery in which biologists remove or add structures to cells (43)

microevolution slow, gradual changes in species (266)

micrometer unit of measurement equaling one-millionth of a meter (0.000039 in.) (40)

micronucleus in paramecia, the smaller nucleus, which controls reproduction (341)

microtome (MY kruh tohm) instrument that slices a specimen for microscopic viewing (42)

microtubule (my kroh TOOB yool) hollow cylinder of protein that supports and shapes a cell (96)

microvillus one of many extensions of epithelial tissue on the villi; the location where absorption occurs (686)

midbrain structure in the brain that controls responses to sight (735)

midbrain tectum in birds, the center of vision (612)

middle lamella (luh MEHL uh) in plants, layer formed between two newly formed, adjacent cell walls (92)

midgut stomach of an insect (538)

migration regular, seasonal movement of organisms (262, 567, 615)

milt in fishes, fluid containing sperm (567)

mimicry resemblance of one organism to another; an adaptation that functions for defense (265, 542)

mineral one of many inorganic substances that form an important part of living tissue (681)

mitochondrion (myt uh KAHN dree uhn) in a cell, an organelle in which energy is released from nutrients (94)

mitosis (my TOH sihs) nuclear division that results in the replication and division of the parent cell into two identical daughter cells (144)

mixture mingled molecules not chemically combined (55)

mold rock depression shaped by fossils of hard body parts (245–246)

molecular formula notation for the number of atoms of each element in a given molecule (55)

molecular weight sum of the mass numbers of all the atoms in a molecule (54)

molecule in a compound or element, the smallest particle that can have a stable, independent existence (14, 54)

molting process by which some animals periodically shed the outer layer of skin (519, 597)

monocot plant with one cotyledon (402)

monohybrid cross genetic cross involving one pair of alleles (170)

monomer basic unit of most organic molecules (71)

monosaccharide sugar molecule that cannot be broken down into smaller organic molecules; the basic unit of all carbohydrates (71)

monosomy (MAHN uh soh mee) condition in which an individual has 45 chromosomes (217)

monotreme mammal that lays eggs (629)

motor neuron nerve cell that carries impulses away from the central nervous system (727)

mouth breathing in frogs, using vessels in the mouth to diffuse oxygen into the blood (578)

mouth pore in paramecia, opening through which food passes to the endoplasm (342)

mucus gland in frogs, one of many skin glands that secrete a slimy substance that prevents drying out (574)

multicellular (muhl tih SEHL yoo luhr) **organism** organism composed of more than one cell (5–6)

multiple alleles three or more forms of a gene that can occur at one location on a chromosome and affect a given trait (213)

multiple fission nuclear division in amoebic cysts (340)

muscle organ made up of tissue that can contract (665)

muscle fiber long, tapering cell capable of contraction (665)

muscle tissue tissue with the ability to contract and thus produce movement (651)

muscular system group of organs that work with bones to move the body (652)

mutagen anything that increases the rate of mutation in cells (204)

mutant organism in which a genetic or chromosomal change is expressed (201)

mutation change in a gene or chromosome (201)

mutualism symbiotic relationship in which each organism benefits from the association (832)

mycelium (my SEE lee uhm) mass of intertwined hyphae that form the body of a fungus (365)

mycoplasma (my koh PLAZ muh) moneran that lacks a cell wall (316)

myelin sheath fatty insulating layer that surrounds the axon of some neurons (727–728)

myofibril (my oh FY bruhl) one of many protein threads that make up muscle fibers (665)

myriapod (MIHR ee uh pahd) collective name for centipedes and millipedes (520)

N

narcotic drug that dulls the senses and relieves pain by depressing the functions of the cerebral cortex (809)

nasal cavity in the nose, one of a pair of spaces where air is warmed and moistened to aid respiration (714–715)

nastic movement plant movement unrelated to the direction of an external stimulus (449)

natural resources all the elements of nature (871)

natural selection process proposed by Charles Darwin whereby those individuals well adapted to the environment survive and reproduce (258)

Neandertals Ice-Age *Homo sapiens* (275)

negative feedback process by which the endocrine system regulates itself; when the hormone level falls below a certain point, a gland is stimulated to secrete more of the hormone (763)

negative phototropism response in which an organism moves away from light (340)

nekton in the marine biome, animals that swim freely (850)

nematocyst (neh MAT uh sihst) coiled stinger in the tentacles of coelenterates (478)

neoteny type of development in which an organism retains larval characteristics but achieves sexual maturity and reproduces (584)

nephridia (neh FRIHD ee uh) in many invertebrates, pair of ciliated tubes on each segment that eliminate liquid wastes (497)

nephron in reptiles, birds, and mammals, the functional unit of the kidney (720)

neritic zone region of open water near the shore (851)

nerve collection of bundles of fibers that carry impulses to and from parts of the body (728)

nerve cord in chordates, hollow, tubular cord along the dorsal surface of the body, above the notochord (553)

nerve fiber in a nerve cell, a threadlike extension of cytoplasm that carries impulses to or from the cell (727)

nervous system group of organs that monitor the environment and control body activities (653)

nervous tissue tissue that transmits electrochemical impulses (651)

neuron basic functional unit of the nervous system (727)

neurotoxin poisonous substance that attacks the nervous system, inhibiting neuron function (600)

neurotransmitter chemical substance that transmits an impulse from one neuron to another (730)

neutron subatomic particle with no electrical charge (50)

niche way of life a species pursues within its habitat (824)

nicotine psychoactive drug in tobacco (810)

nictitating (NIHK tuh tay ting) **membrane** in frogs and some other vertebrates, a third eyelid which protects the eyeball (575)

nitrification (ny truh fuh KAY shuhn) two-step process by which ammonia becomes nitrate (827)

nitrogen fixation process by which atmospheric nitrogen is incorporated into compounds (323, 826)

nocturnal describes organisms that are active at night (833)

node of Ranvier (rahn vee AY) interruptions of the myelin sheath of a neuron (728)

nonbiodegradable describes a product that cannot be broken down by microorganisms (878)

nondisjunction (nahn dihs JUHNGK shun) failure of a chromosome pair to separate during cell division (217)

nonrenewable resources any elements of nature that cannot be replenished (871)

nonvascular plant bryophyte; plant that lacks vascular tissue (383)

norepinephrine (nor ehp uh NEHF rihn) hormone secreted by the adrenal gland (758)

nostril in the nose, one of a pair of openings through which air enters the body (714)

notochord in chordates, long, firm rod near the dorsal surface of the body (553)

nuclear envelope in a cell, double layer of lipids and proteins between the nucleus and cytoplasm (90)

nuclear fission splitting of atomic nuclei, which releases heat energy (876)

nuclear fusion joining of two atoms to form helium (876)

nuclear pore opening that allows passage of materials through the nuclear envelope (90)

nucleic acid organic compound that carries instructions for cellular activity (75)

nucleolus (noo KLEE uh luhs) spherical body of DNA, RNA, and proteins in a nucleus (90)

nucleotide DNA unit made of a nitrogen-carrying base, a sugar molecule, and a phosphate group (75, 193)

nucleus in atoms, the central core (50); in cells, the control center, containing genetic information (85)

nutrient one of many substances required for body growth and maintenance (677)

O

objective in a compound light microscope, the lens set nearest the specimen (39)

obligate aerobe bacterium that needs oxygen to live (320)

obligate anaerobe bacterium that cannot metabolize in the presence of oxygen (320)

ocular in a compound light microscope, the lens set nearest the viewer's eye (39)

olfactory organ organ that monitors odors (566)

olfactory receptor cell in the nasal passage that produces impulses in response to odors (751)

oligotrophic (ahl uh goh TRAHF ihk) describes a lake or pond that can support little life (851)

omnivore animal that eats both plant and animal materials (634, 828)

oogamy (oh AHG uh mee) differentiation of gametes into those that are distinctly male and female (346)

open sea zone in the marine biome, three-leveled area of a large body of water (851)

operational definition in an experiment, a definition that is limited to repeatable and observable phenomena (29)

operculum (oh PUHR kyoo luhm) in some gastropods, flat plate on the side of the foot, used to close off the shell (507); in fishes, flap of tissue covering the gills (564)

opposable thumb in primates, a thumb that can be positioned opposite the fingers to grasp objects (647)

optic lobes in birds, the portion of the midbrain tectum that interprets visual impulses (612)

oral disc round, sucking mouth of a lamprey (557)

oral groove in paramecia, ciliated channel that directs food particles toward the mouth pore (342)

organ structure composed of a number of tissues that work together to perform a specific task (15)

organelle structure that performs a specific function within a cell (14, 89)

organic compound compound made by organisms, containing carbon (69)

organism complete, individual living thing (5)

origin point at which a muscle is attached to an anchoring bone (669)

osculum (AHS kyuh luhm) large opening in a sponge through which water exits (475)

osmosis (ahz MOH suhs) diffusion of water through a membrane (108)

ossification (ahs uh fuh KAY shuhn) in embryonic development, process in which cartilage is replaced by bone (663)

osteocyte (AHS tee uh syt) one of many living cells that make up bone (663)

ostia in crustaceans, any of three pairs of pores through which blood enters the heart (525)

oval window membrane between the middle and inner ear (749)

ovary in plants, swollen base of the pistil (428); in animals, egg-producing reproductive organ (479, 581, 770)

oviduct long tube through which eggs travel from the ovary (612)

oviparous (oh VIHP uhr uhs) describes an animal that lays eggs that hatch outside the mother's body (598)

ovipositor in a female insect, one of a pair of pointed organs used to deposit fertilized eggs (538)

ovoviviparous describes an animal that hatches eggs inside the mother's body and gives birth to live young (598)

ovulation release of an egg from the ovary (771)

ovule in a flower, that portion of the ovary in which eggs are produced (428)

ovum female sex cell (143)

oxygen-carbon cycle interrelated recycling pathways of photosynthesis and respiration (825)

P

P parental generation; in genetics, first pair of plants or animals in a study (162)

pair bond mating relationship of a male and a female bird for the duration of a reproductive season (614)

paleontologist (pay lee ahn TAHL uh jihst) scientist who looks for and studies fossils (247)

pancreas in vertebrates, organ that secretes digestive enzymes, insulin, and glucagon hormones (577, 685–686)

parapodia (pa ruh POHD ee uh) in polychaetes, paired appendages that assist in locomotion (498)

parasite organism that benefits from a close association with another organism and harms it in the process (322)

parasitism symbiotic relationship in which one organism benefits and the other is harmed (337, 833)

rathyroid gland any of four glands on the back of the thyroid gland that regulate levels of calcium ions and phosphate ions in the blood (757)

renchyma (puh REHN kih muh) soft, spongy cells found in the center of roots and stems (410)

rietal (puh RY uh tuhl) **eye** in some reptiles, a third eye, located on top of the head; believed to be used for temperature control (594)

rticulate matter solid or liquid pollutants in air (878)

ssive immunity a type of resistance to disease acquired from the antibodies of another immune person or animal (308)

thogen disease-causing microorganism (306, 704, 782)

ctin jellylike substance that holds together layers of algal and plant cells (351)

ctoral fin in fishes, one of a pair of stabilizing appendages just behind the head (560)

ctoral (PEHK tuhr uhl) **girdle** in vertebrates, wide, flattened surface that connects the upper limbs to the axial skeleton (555)

digree record that shows how a trait is inherited over several generations (209)

dipalp (PEHD ih palp) in arachnids, one of two appendages used in chewing and in sensory perception (521)

llicle in many protists, flexible layer of protein strips under the cell membrane (341)

vic fin one of a pair of stabilizing appendages on the ventral surface of a fish (560)

vic girdle in vertebrates, fused bones that connect the lower limbs to the axial skeleton (555)

nicillin antibiotic that inhibits the growth of bacterial cells (324)

ptide bond chemical bond between amino acids (74)

rfect flower one that has both male and female reproductive parts (428)

ricardium (pehr uh KAHR dee uhm) tough, protective sac that surrounds the heart (696)

ricycle outer layer of meristematic cells around the vascular cylinder responsible for secondary root growth (412)

riosteum (pehr ih AHS tee uhm) protective membrane that covers bones (663)

ripheral (puh RIHF uhr uhl) **nervous system** the part of the nervous system that provides pathways for impulses to and from the central nervous system (727)

ristalsis (pehr uh STAWL sihs) wavelike motion that moves food along the digestive tract (684)

sticide chemical used to control insect pests (881)

tal leaf that grows between the sepals and the essential flower parts; collectively, petals form the corolla (428)

tiole (PEHT ee ohl) leaf stalk that supports the blade (419)

trified fossil one created by minerals (246)

AL phosphoglyceraldehyde; organic compound formed during the second phase of photosynthesis (126)

agocyte white blood cell that engulfs and digests a disease-causing agent (704)

agocytosis (fag oh sy TOH sihs) movement of solids or large particles into a cell (113)

pharynx in some invertebrates, muscular organ that ingests and partially digests food and also emits waste (488); in vertebrates, passageway for food and air (683)

phase contrast microscope one that uses the interference of bent and unbent light rays to show the structure of a cell (39–40)

phenotype (FEE nuh typ) an expressed trait (166)

pheromone chemical secreted by an insect, influences the behavior of other insects (542)

phloem (FLOH ehm) vascular tissue that carries sugar and other products of photosynthesis from the leaves to the rest of the plant (393)

photon unit of light energy (121)

photoperiodism (foht oh PIHR ee uhd ihz uhm) response of plants to periods of light and dark (444)

photosynthesis process by which green plants convert the energy from sunlight into chemical energy (120)

photosynthetic region area of the open sea from the surface to about 200 m (656 ft.) (851)

phototropism response of a plant to the direction of its light source (448)

pH scale means of measuring the relative concentration of hydrogen ions in a substance (70)

phycobilin (FY koh by luhn) accessory pigment found in cyanobacteria (325–326)

physical anthropologist (an thruh PAHL uh jihst) scientist who studies human fossils (247)

physical property feature of a substance that can be determined without changing its basic makeup (49)

pigment substance that absorbs light (122)

pilus (PIHL uhs) one of many short, thin extensions that bacteria use to attach themselves to food or oxygen sources or to other bacteria (318)

pin feather in birds, small, dark, immature feather with a scaly covering (608)

pinna flap of cartilage that forms the outer ear (748)

pinocytosis (pihn oh sy TOH sihs) movement of liquids and small particles into a cell (114)

pioneer species first organisms to establish themselves in an environment (841)

pistil female part of a flower (427)

pith ground tissue in the center of roots and stems (410)

pituitary (pih TOO uh tehr ee) **gland** organ at the base of the brain that secretes hormones that regulate a variety of functions (760–761)

PKU phenylketonuria (fehn ihl keet uh NYOOR ee uh); biochemical disorder that results from having two recessive alleles for the trait (212)

placenta in mammals, organ through which materials are exchanged between mother and fetus (629, 775)

placental mammals animals whose young develop in the mother's body until birth (629)

placoid scale in fishes such as sharks, one of many cone-shaped structures that cover the skin (560)

plankton (PLANK tuhn) small organisms that float near the surface of the ocean (351, 850)

plaques small, hard deposits of fatty material (793)

plasma straw-colored, nonliving part of blood (693)

plasmid (PLAZ mihd) small circle of DNA in some bacteria (232, 318)

plasmodium brightly colored, jellylike cytoplasm that comprises the body of a slime mold (345)

plastid in plant cells, organelle that stores food or contains pigment (95)

plastron ventral part of a turtle or tortoise shell (595)

platelet in mammals, cell fragment that aids in blood clotting; also called a thrombocyte (694)

pleura in mammals, tough membrane around the lungs that secretes a lubricating fluid (713)

point mutation minor change in the DNA sequence (201)

polar compound one that has opposite charges at either end of its molecules (69)

polar nuclei two central nuclei in a megaspore during egg cell formation (430)

pollen male gametophyte of seed plants (427)

pollen tube in a flowering plant, tube that grows through the stigma during fertilization (431)

pollination in flowering plants, transfer of pollen from the anther to the stigma (431)

pollution contamination of the environment with waste products and other impurities (878)

polydactyly (pahl ih DAHK tih lee) condition of having extra fingers or toes (212)

polygenic determined by several genes (214)

polymer complex molecule produced by condensation of many monomers (71)

polyp vase-shaped body of some coelenterates (478)

polyploidy (PAHL ih ploy dee) condition in which an organism has more than two complete sets of chromosomes (230)

polysaccharide carbohydrate that consists of a long chain of monosaccharides (72)

pons structure in the human brain that connects the cerebral hemispheres and links the cerebellum with the cerebrum (735)

population in a community, individuals of the same species (16, 259, 823)

population density number of individuals of the same species in a given area (858)

population genetics study of the number and kind of genes in a population (259)

population sampling genetic study of a small, randomly selected group and projection of the results to the whole population (210)

positive phototropism movement of an organism toward light (338, 448)

posterior pertaining to the hind end of an organism (474)

potential energy energy an object possesses because of its position or composition (57)

precocial describes a young bird that leaves the nest within a few hours after birth (613)

predator organism that kills and eats other organisms (508, 832)

preen gland in birds, gland that secretes oil to waterproof feathers (608)

pregnancy in mammals, time span during which young develop within the mother (632, 773)

primary growth lengthening of roots and stems (409)

primary root first root of a young plant (411)

primary succession development of a community whe none existed before (840)

principle of dominance principle stating that one gene ir pair may prevent the other from being expressed (163)

principle of independent assortment principle stating th pairs of genes segregate independently during game formation (166)

principle of segregation principle stating that members each pair of genes separate when gametes form (165)

probability likelihood that an event will occur (167)

product rule principle stating that the probability of ind pendent events occurring together is the product of t probabilities of the events occurring alone (168)

progesterone (proh JEHS tuh rohn) female hormone th helps prepare the uterus for implantation (772)

proglottid (proh GLAHT ihd) one of several sections th comprise the body of a tapeworm (489–490)

prokaryote (proh KAR ee oht) cell without a true nucle (98)

prophage (PROH fayj) viral nucleic acid that attaches its to the DNA of the host cell (305)

prophase first stage of mitosis: chromosomes coil up; ce trioles, spindle fibers, and an aster form; and centriole if present, move to opposite ends of the cells (145)

prosthesis (prahs THEE sihs) artificial body part (654)

protein basic building material of all living things (73, 677)

protein hormone one that combines with a receptor cell the target cell membrane, activating an enzyme that hel change ATP into cyclic AMP (764)

protein synthesis process by which proteins are assembl from amino acids (196)

prothallus gametophyte generation of a fern (399)

prothorax in insects, first section of the thorax (537)

proton positively charged subatomic particle (50)

protonema (proht uh NEE muh) in mosses, horizontal ph tosynthetic filament, produced by a spore (385)

protozoa (proht uh ZOH uh) complex unicellular heter trophs (336)

pseudocoelom (soo doh SEE luhm) cavity that forr between mesoderm and endoderm (490–491)

pseudopodia (soo duh POH dee uh) footlike projections some protozoa; used in locomotion (339)

psychoactive drug chemical substance that affects the ce tral nervous system (803)

puberty period of physical and sexual maturation (769)

pulmonary artery blood vessel leading from the heart the lungs (699)

pulmonary circulation blood moving to and from t lungs (579)

pulmonary vein blood vessel that brings blood from t lungs to the heart (699)

Punnett square grid or chart that shows all possible ge combinations for a cross (169)

pupa in metamorphosis, inactive stage between the larv and adult stages (540)

pupil opening in the center of the iris; where light ente the eye (745–746)

urebred describes an individual with identical members of a gene pair (164)

ure science fields of study that involve the search for new knowledge (29)

yloric sphincter muscular valve that controls the passage of food out of the stomach (684)

yrenoid (py REE noyd) small protein body that stores starch, located within a chloroplast (356)

yruvic (py ROO vihk) **acid** substance formed during the first stage of cellular respiration (128)

uill hollow section of a feather's rachis (608)

uill feather large feather on a bird's wing or tail (608)

achis (RAY kihs) cylinder that runs down the center of a feather (608)

adial symmetry arrangement of body parts around a central point (473)

adiating canal in paramecia, one of many pipelike structures that collect excess water (342)

adicle embryonic root of a plant (434–435)

adioactive isotope atom with an unstable nucleus whose known, constant rate of decay can be used to determine the age of a fossil (246)

adula (RAJ oo luh) in some mollusks, toothed organ that tears or scrapes loose bits of food (503)

ay-finned fish one of a group of bony fishes with fins supported by a number of long bones, or rays (563)

DP ribulose diphosphate, a five-carbon sugar; the major compound in the second phase of photosynthesis (126)

eceptacle base of a flower (428)

eceptor site location on the surface of a cell and on the tail of a virus at which a chemical bond forms that allows entry of the virus (303)

ecessive in a pair of genes, the gene that is not expressed (164)

ecombinant DNA new strand of DNA formed when the DNA of two different species is combined (231)

ectum last part of the large intestine in which feces is stored before it is eliminated (688)

d blood cell that part of the blood that transports respiratory gases, also called erythrocyte or red corpuscle (694)

d tide toxic growth of dinoflagellates (354)

eflex arc pathway traveled by impulses involved in involuntary movements (737)

egenerate to grow a part to replace one that is lost (476)

egeneration a type of asexual reproduction in which a complete animal develops from a body part (143)

emission a period of inactivity (793)

emote sensing gathering and recording of information about objects and phenomena from a great distance by systems that are not in contact with them (868)

enal artery vessel that carries blood to the kidneys (581)

enal pelvis central cavity of the kidney (720)

renal tubule structure in the kidney responsible for filtering wastes from the blood and for regulating the water and mineral composition of the blood (720)

renewable resources any elements of nature that can be reused or replenished (871)

replication (rehp luh KAY shuhn) duplication of a chromosome (142, 194)

reproduction process of producing offspring (10)

reproductive system a group of organs that provide a means of producing offspring (653)

resolving power the ability of a microscope to increase the visible detail in a specimen (39)

respiration process in which the body takes in oxygen, uses it to release energy (713)

respiratory system group of organs that takes in oxygen and eliminates carbon dioxide and water (652)

response any behavior of an organism that results from a stimulus (10)

reticular formation complex network of nerve fibers in the brain stem and thalamus that regulates reactions during consciousness and sleep (735)

retina in the vertebrate eye, the innermost, light-sensitive layer (746)

Rh factor antigen present in the blood of about 85 percent of the U.S. population (696)

rhizoid in molds, short extension of a stolon that anchors the mold to its food supply and absorbs food (367); in bryophytes, rootlike structure that anchors the plant and absorbs water but does not channel it to the plant (384)

rhizome in some vascular plants, underground stem that anchors the plant and absorbs water and nutrients from the soil (395)

ribose five-carbon sugar present in RNA (196)

ribosomal RNA also rRNA; type of RNA present in ribosomes; helps bind messenger RNA and transfer RNA during protein synthesis (196)

ribosome (RY buh sohm) in a cell, tiny knoblike organelle in which protein is manufactured (93)

rickettsia (rih KEHT see uh) type of bacterium that can live only inside other cells (316)

RNA ribonucleic (ry boh noo KLEE ihk) acid; a nucleic acid; copies instructions for cellular activity and carries them to the ribosomes (75, 196)

rod in the vertebrate eye, light-sensitive receptor cell that is stimulated by light (746)

root cap layer of cells at the root tip that protects the apical meristem (412)

root crop any of the various edible roots and underground stems (458)

root hair tiny outgrowth of an epidermal cell that increases the surface area of a root (411)

round window membrane-covered opening in the cochlea that maintains pressure in the inner ear (749)

ruminant mammal with a four-chambered stomach (633)

S

saccule (SAK yool) hair-lined section of the vestibule that helps maintain balance (750)

saliva glandular secretion that moistens food in the mouth, made up of mucus and the enzyme ptyalin (682)

salivary glands three pairs of glands in the mouth that produce saliva to aid digestion (538, 682)

saprophyte (SAP ruh fyt) organism that feeds on dead organisms (320)

sarcoma tumor composed of a mass of cells involving connective tissue, such as muscle (790)

sarcomere (SAHR koh mir) one of many microscopic units that comprise the bands in striated muscle (665)

savannah grassland located in a tropical or subtropical area (847)

saw-tooth curve pattern formed by the periodic growth and decline of a population (859)

scale in fishes one of many thin, overlapping structures that cover the skin (565)

scanning electron microscope (SEM); type of microscope that sends a beam of electrons across the specimen from left to right (41)

scavenger organism that feeds only on dead organisms (828)

Schwann cell one of many specialized cells that cover and produce the myelin sheath (727–728)

science body of factual knowledge that exists about the world and the method of study used to arrive at that knowledge (26)

scientific method a logical, organized method of study through which scientists establish principles (27)

scientific name in taxonomy, name consisting of the genus and the species names of an organism (286)

scientific principle best current explanation of how a part of nature works (29)

sclera (SKLIHR uh) in the vertebrate eye, tough, elastic, connective tissue that forms the outermost layer (745)

scolex (SKOH lehks) anterior end of a tapeworm (489)

S-curve pattern formed by the combination of lag, exponential, and stabilization phases (858)

scute (SKYOOT) in turtles and tortoises, one of several plates covering the shell (595)

secondary growth cumulative growth of a plant's xylem and phloem tissues (403)

secondary succession establishment of a community in an area formerly inhabited by a different community (843)

second polar body in meiosis II, the smaller of the two cells resulting from the unequal cell division that occurs in female animals (151)

sedimentary formed in layers (245)

seed coat hard, protective covering of a seed embryo (400)

selectively permeable describes materials that allow only certain substances to pass through them (108)

self-pollination reproductive process in which fertilization is carried on in a single plant (161)

semen thick, milky liquid containing sperm and glandular secretions (770)

semicircular canal one of three fluid-filled tubes in the inner ear that help maintain balance (749)

sensory neuron nerve cell that receives a stimulus and transmits it to the central nervous system (727)

sensory seta in arachnids, one of many tiny bristles on ◀ organism that detect pressure and movement (522)

sepal one of the leaflike structures that grow out from ◀ base of a flower and enclose the bud before it bloom collectively, they form the calyx (428)

seral community temporary community that alters ◀ environment, preventing its own regeneration (839)

sessile describes an organism that remains anchored in o place for most of its life (341, 472)

setae in an earthworm, pairs of bristles that aid in locom tion (495)

sex chromosome chromosome that determines the sex an individual (182)

sex-influenced trait one generally associated with a sin sex but produced by autosomal genes (215, 216)

sex-linked trait trait that is determined by alleles carri only on a sex chromosome (183)

sexually transmitted disease also STD; an illness pass on to another by sexual contact; may be caused by virus, bacterium, or other agent (787)

sexual reproduction formation of a new individual fro the union of two cells (141)

short-day plant one that flowers during spring or fa when nights are as long as or longer than its critical da period (444)

sickle-cell disease biochemical disorder caused by rece sive alleles; involves the distortion of red blood cells in sickle shapes and eventual destruction of vital orga (212–213)

sieve-tube member phloem cell through which fo passes freely (410)

simple eye in arachnids, structure that detects light b cannot form images (521)

simple leaf one with a single, undivided blade (419)

simple microscope single lens, or curved piece of glas that magnifies objects (39)

sinoatrial (sy noh AY tree uhl) **node** also SA node; in v tebrates, small region in the heart muscle that triggers t heartbeat (701)

skeletal muscle group of specialized cells that mov bones (665)

skeletal system group of organs that move, support, a protect the body (652)

slime mold organism with a mixture of traits found in p tozoa and fungi (345)

small intestine three-sectioned tube where most chemic digestion and absorption occurs (577, 685)

smog air pollution made up of smoke, gas, and fog (879)

smooth muscle group of spindle-shaped cells that provid for the involuntary movements of digestive, respirator and circulatory organs (665)

soft palate muscle tissue located behind the hard pal (683)

solar energy energy derived from sunlight (877)

solute substance that dissolves in a solvent (55, 105)

solution uniform mixture of the particles of one substan in another (55, 105)

solvent substance that can dissolve another substance (5 105)

omatic (soh MAT ihk) **cell** any body cell except one that gives rise to gametes (144)

omatic mutation change in a body cell (203)

omatic nervous system system that transmits impulses to and from skeletal muscles (737)

ori clusters of sporangia (398)

oawn in fishes, to shed eggs (567)

peciation formation of a new species (264)

pecies biological group of similar organisms that interbreed to produce fertile offspring (10, 255)

perm in sexual reproduction, male sex cell (143)

pherical symmetry ball-like arrangement of parts in a form having no top, bottom, back, front, left side, or right side (473)

picule (SPIHK yool) one of many spikes of calcium or silica that form the skeletons of some sponges (476)

pinal cord nerve tissue from the brain through the spinal column that links the brain with nerves to all parts of the body and controls involuntary movements (736)

pindle fiber temporary microtubule that helps move chromosomes during cell division (96)

pinneret in arachnids, web-spinning organ (522)

piracle (SPY ruh kuhl) in arachnids, slit in the exoskeleton that regulates the flow of air to the tracheae (521); in some fishes, opening on top of the head, through which water enters the body and is moved to the gills (561)

pirillus (spy RIHL uhs) corkscrew-shaped bacterium (317)

pirochete (SPY ruh keet) type of bacterium characterized by its large size (316)

pongin flexible protein that forms the skeleton of some sponges (476)

pontaneous generation unsupported theory that some organisms form from nonliving materials (30)

porangiophore in molds, specialized hypha that bears the spore case (367)

porangium in molds, case or structure that produces spores (367)

pore asexual reproductive cell (142)

porophyll in club mosses, narrow, clublike structure on which spores are produced (396)

porophyte (SPAWR uh fyt) organism with diploid (2n) chromosomes that produces spores (n) by meiosis (356, 384)

abilization phase period when population size levels off (858)

abilizing selection natural selection that reduces variation by eliminating extremes (261)

ain dye that colors certain tissues for easier viewing under a microscope (42)

amen male part of a flower (427)

apes (STAY peez) one of three tiny bones in the middle ear (749)

ates of matter descriptions of molecular arrangement in matter: solid, liquid, or gas (49)

atistics (stuh TIHS tihks) mathematical method of evaluating numerical data (28)

ereomicroscope type of microscope with ocular and objective lenses for each eye (39)

ernum breast bone (609)

steroid a lipid hormone that helps determine the synthesis of certain proteins after entering the cell (764)

stigma in flowers, tip of the style; produces a sticky substance that traps pollen (428)

stimulant drug that causes the central nervous system to speed up body processes (806)

stimulus any condition to which an organism can react (10)

stipe in mushrooms, stemlike structure that supports the button or cap (368)

stolon in molds, hypha that branches out along the surface of the food supply (367)

stomach organ where mechanical and chemical digestion take place (684)

stomata (stoh MAH tah) in plants, small pores that allow gas exchange (381)

strip-cropping method of reducing erosion by planting alternating rows of grass or clover between grain crops (873)

stroma fluid-filled space between the grana and the outer membrane of a chloroplast (122)

structural formula figure that shows how atoms are bonded in a molecule (72)

style in flowers, slender middle portion of a pistil (428)

subatomic particle component of an atom (50)

substrate molecule upon which an enzyme acts (74)

superior vena cava (VEE nuh KAY vuh) blood vessel that brings blood from the upper regions of the body to the heart (699)

suspension temporary mixture in which the particles eventually settle out (56)

swarm large mass of insects (536)

swim bladder in bony fishes, gas-filled organ that is in the coelom and acts as a float (565)

swimmeret in crustaceans, one of five pairs of appendages used in swimming (524)

symbiosis (sihm by OH sihs) permanent, close relationship between two organisms of different species that benefits at least one of them (322, 337, 832)

symmetry balanced arrangement of body parts around a center point or line (473)

synapse place where an impulse crosses from the axon of one neuron to the dendrite of another (730)

synapsis (sih NAP sihs) in meiosis, process during which the homologous chromosomes come together (149)

synovial (sih NOH vee uhl) **fluid** lubricant of body joints (664)

syrinx (SIHR ihnks) pair of vibrating membranes at the bottom of a bird's trachea; produces a bird's call (611)

system group of organs that cooperate in a series of related functions (15)

systemic circulation blood moving between the heart and the rest of the body other than the lungs (579)

T

tadpole larval form of a frog (582)

tail in animals, blocks of muscle tissue, posterior to the anus, surrounding the vertebral column (553)

talon sharp, curving claw of a bird (607)

taproot mature, thick primary root of many dicots (411)

target specific tissue or organ upon which a given hormone acts (757)

taste buds cluster of specialized hair cells in the tongue that act as chemical receptors for taste (751)

taxonomy science of grouping organisms on the basis of their similarities and evolutionary relationships (285)

telophase in mitosis, the fourth stage, during which a nuclear envelope forms around each set of chromosomes (147)

telson in some crustaceans, structure at the end of the abdomen; used in locomotion (524)

temperate phage bacteriophage that undergoes a long period of inactivity in a host cell (305)

tendon band of inelastic connective tissue that attaches muscle to bone (665)

tentacle long, flexible appendage (478)

terracing method of converting a hillside into broad, flat steps to prevent water loss and erosion (873)

territoriality behavior of claiming and defending a particular area against other members of the same species (626)

test cross procedure that determines the genotype of an individual whose phenotype is dominant (169)

testis sperm-producing organ (479, 581, 769)

testosterone (tehs TAHs tuh rohn) hormone that stimulates development of certain male characteristics (770)

tetrad (TEHT rad) in meiosis, structure formed when homologous pairs of chromosomes line up together (150)

thalamus (THAL uh muhs) part of the vertebrate brain that acts as a relay center for impulses (733)

thallus unspecialized, multicellular body of algae (351)

theory a scientific explanation of known facts (29)

thermal inversion condition in which pollutants are trapped in cool air under a warm air mass (879)

thermal pollution the releasing of heated water into a body of water, causing a rise in water temperature (881)

thigmotropism a response in a plant in which it curves and makes contact with a solid object (449)

thoracic (thaw RAs ihk) **cavity** portion of the coelom above the diaphragm; contains the heart, lungs, and esophagus (650)

thymine (THY meen) carbon-nitrogen compound that is one of the four bases of DNA (192)

thyroid gland in vertebrates, organ near the trachea that controls metabolic activities, including the production of protein and ATP (757)

tissue group of similar cells that perform a common function (15)

tolerance condition in which increasingly larger doses of a drug are needed to produce the same effect (803)

torsion in gastropods, twisting of the body during larval development (507)

toxin a poison that interferes with metabolism (783)

trachea (TRAY kee uh) in some terrestrial arthropods, tube that carries air directly to the cells (521); in terrestrial vertebrates, the windpipe (715)

tracheid (TRAY kee ihd) long, tapered conducting cell found in vascular plants (409)

tracheophyte (TRAY kee uh fyt) plant that gets food a nutrients from a vascular system (393)

trait genetic characteristic that is transferred from one ge eration to the next (11)

transcription process by which messenger RNA is ma from DNA molecules which serve as templates (196)

transducer structure that transforms one form of ener into another (743)

transduction (trans DUHK shuhn) transfer, by a virus, genetic information between host cells (305)

transfer RNA also tRNA; type of RNA that picks up in vidual amino acids in the cytoplasm and carries them the ribosomes (196)

transformation transfer of genetic material from a de bacterium to a live one (322)

translation process during which ribosomes attach to me senger RNA to form protein (198)

translocation transfer of food produced by photosynthe from the leaves to the rest of the plant (419)

transmission electron microscope (TEM) type of micr scope that sends a beam of electrons through the spe men (41)

transpiration water loss in plants (421)

trichocyst (TRIHK uh sihst) filament discharged by paramecium in response to certain stimuli (343)

trimester one of three three-month periods in human pre nancy (776)

trisomy (try SOH mee) condition in which an individual h an extra chromosome (217)

trochophore (TRAHK uh fawr) ciliated mollusk larva (5(

trophic (TRAHF ihk) **level** feeding level within an ecos tem (828)

tropical rain forest biome characterized by heavy rainfa rapid plant growth, and large numbers of insects a other invertebrates (847–848)

tropic hormone chemical substance that affects the sec tions of other glands (760)

tropism response in which an organism moves toward away from the stimulus (448)

tube cell larger of the two cells in a pollen grain (429)

tube foot in echinoderms, one of numerous hollow cyl ders tipped with suckers, on the underside of the ar (510)

tubular reabsorption kidney's return of glucose, wat and other vital materials to the blood (720–721)

tubular secretion process by which parts of the nephr units of the kidneys remove certain substances from blood (721)

tumor a clump of cells that grow and multiply in an abn mal manner (790)

tundra biome characterized by bleak terrain, little vege tion, and a cold, dry climate (844)

turgor (TUHR guhr) water pressure that builds in a pla cell (110)

Turner syndrome genetic disorder caused by the inhe tance of only one X, and no other, sex chromosom (217)

tympanic cavity air-filled space inside the skull bone th houses the middle ear (748)

mpanic membrane in frogs, circular structure located behind the eye that receives sounds and covers the internal ear (575)

mpanum in insects, thin, flexible membrane covering the organ of hearing; an eardrum (537)

U

ltrasound testing technique that uses sound waves to detect possible abnormalities in a fetus (219–220)

mbilical cord in mammals, blood-rich connector of the fetus to the placenta (775)

ngulate land mammal that has hooves (633)

nicellular (yoo nuh SEHL yoo luhr) **organism** organism composed of a single cell (5)

nivalve class of mollusks whose members have a single shell (506)

racil (YOOR uh sihl) pyrimidine base present in RNA (196)

reter long, narrow tube that transports urine from the kidney to the urinary bladder (721)

rethra tube through which the body expels urine (722)

rinary bladder sac of smooth muscle that collects and holds urine until it is expelled (721–722)

rinary system the part of the excretory system that filters metabolic wastes from the blood and eliminates them from the body (653)

rine amber-colored liquid consisting of urea, water, and other metabolic wastes (721)

ropod (YOOR uh pahd) in crustaceans, fused pair of appendages that functions as a flipper (524)

terus in mammals, female reproductive organ that houses a developing fetus (631, 770)

tricle (YOO trih kuhl) in the inner ear, section of the vestibule that is lined with hair cells and that helps maintain balance (750)

V

accine solution of weakened viruses that stimulates the production of antibodies (308, 783)

acuole a bubblelike storage structure within a cell (95)

ane in a feather, structure comprised of several barbs hooked together by barbules (608)

ariable in an experiment, condition that changes (28)

ariation set of differences (12)

riety subdivision of a species (289)

scular bundle grouping of vascular tissue in plants (415)

scular cambium inner layer of meristematic cells in the vascular cylinder; responsible for xylem and phloem production (412)

scular cylinder center of a root, made up of xylem, phloem, and meristematic cells; responsible for growth (412)

scular plant one that gets food and nutrients through a network of vessels (383)

scular system network of interconnected tubes and vessels that carry water, nutrients, and the products of photosynthesis throughout a plant (393)

vascular tissue in plants, internal system of interconnected tubes and vessels that transport food and nutrients (383)

vegetative body parts of a plant—roots, stems, and leaves—that carry out photosynthesis and normal growth (400)

vegetative propagation type of asexual reproduction found in plants, in which offspring separate from the parent plant to become individual plants (143, 436)

vein vessel that carries blood to the heart (699)

ventral pertaining to the abdominal surface of an organism (474)

ventricle (VEHN trih kuhl) one of two lower chambers of the heart (698)

vernalization (vuhr nuhl eye ZAY shuhn) period of low temperature required before a seed can germinate (445)

vertebra one of the bony parts of a vertebral column (555)

vertebral column backbone of a vertebrate (555)

vertebrate animal with a backbone or spine (474)

vessel member short, tubelike conducting cell found in angiosperms (409)

vestibule bony chamber between the semicircular canals and the cochlea of the ear (749)

vestigial (vehs TIHJ ee uhl) **structure** body part reduced in size and with no apparent function (250)

villus (VIHL uhs) one of many tiny projections where absorption occurs in the mucous lining of the small intestine (686)

virion (VY ree ahn) new, complete virus particle formed by viral nucleic acid and protein during a virus's reproductive cycle (304)

viroid (VY royd) smallest known disease-causing agent, consisting of a single strand of RNA (301)

virulence ability of a virus to cause disease (307)

virus microscopic form that reproduces only inside a living cell (300)

visceral mass in mollusks, part of the body that contains digestive, excretory, and reproductive organs (503)

visible spectrum array of colors formed when white light passes through a prism (121)

vital stain dye taken up by living tissues (42)

vitamin organic substance that assists enzymes (679)

vitreous (VIHT ree uhs) **humor** in the vertebrate eye, clear fluid behind the lens (745)

viviparous describes an animal that gives birth to live young which develop within the mother's body (623)

vocal cord one of a pair of ligaments stretched across the larynx, where sound originates (715)

vomerine teeth in amphibians, two teeth in the roof of the mouth that aid in holding prey (577)

W

walking leg in crustaceans, any one of the four pairs of appendages used for locomotion (524)

watershed area of land from which water drains into a particular lake or stream (872)

water-vascular system in echinoderms, a system of canals and muscular tube feet that provides a method of locomotion using water pressure (511)

white blood cell one of several types of nucleated cells found in the blood that fights viruses, bacteria, and other foreign organisms (694)

windbreak row of trees that serves as a wind barrier to prevent soil erosion (873)

withdrawal painful reaction to the cessation of drug use (803)

woody plant plant in which xylem and phloem produce cumulative layers of tissue (403)

X

xanthophyll (ZAN thuh fihl) yellow pigment present in most green plants (122)

xylem (ZY luhm) vascular tissue that transports water and minerals absorbed by the roots to the portion of the plant that is above ground (393)

Y

yolk food substance stored in egg cells and used by a deve oping embryo (590)

yolk sac structure that contains food and is attached to t abdomen of the embryo (589–590)

Z

zoology study of animals (22)

zooplankton (zoo uh PLANK tuhn) marine microscopic he erotrophs (337)

zygospore thickened, protective cell wall of a zygo (356)

zygote (ZY goht) in sexual reproduction, cell form when the nuclei of a sperm and an ovum fuse (143, 49 773)

Index

Boldface numbers refer to an illustration on that page.

R

W

X

Y

Z

Credits

H. Armstrong Roberts; 458, Photo Researchers; 459, Fred Ward/Black Star; 460, Plant Genetics; 461, Menschenfreund/Taurus Photos; 462(t), Michael Philips Manheim/Photo Researchers; 462(b), Zig Leszczynski/Photo Stan Osolinski/TSW/Click/Chicago; 468, FPG Int'l., Corp.

Unit 8: 470, 471, M. Thonig/H. Armstrong Roberts; 472, W. Gregory Brown/Animals Animals; 473(l), Robert Lee/Photo Researchers; 473(r), Runk/Schoenberger/Grant Heilman Photography; 474, Steve Solum/Bruce Coleman; 475, Jeff Rotman; 481(t), Runk/Schoenberger/Grant Heilman Photography; 481(b), R. N. Mariscal/Bruce Coleman; 482, L. Isy-Schwart/The Image Bank; 483, Visuals Unlimited/Cabisco; 486, Steve Lucas; 489(t), E. R. Degginger; 489(b), Manfred Kage/Peter Arnold; 492, Martin M. Rotker/Taurus Photos; 493, Alfred Pasieka/Taurus Photos; 494, Custom Medical Stock Photo; 496, Runk/Schoenberger/Grant Heilman Photography; 497, Hans Pfletschinger/Peter Arnold; 502, Paulette Brunner/Tom Stack and Associates; 504, 505, James Carmichael Jr./Nature Photographers; 506, Fred Ward/Black Star; 507, Y. Momautiuk/Photo Researchers; 508, Fred Bavendam/Peter Arnold; 509(t), David J. Wrobell/Monterey Aquarium Biological Photo Service; 509(b), James Carmichael Jr./Nature Photographers; 510(l), Brian Parker/Tom Stack and Associates; 510(c), E. R. Degginger; 510(r), Jeff Rotman/Peter Arnold; 512, Carl Roessler/Tom Stack and Associates; 516(t), NOAA/Pacific Marine Environment Labs Vent Program; 516(b), 517(t), Woods Hole Oceanographic Institute; 517(c), (bl), (br), NOAA/Pacific Marine Environment Labs Vent Program; 518, Kim Taylor/Bruce Coleman; 519, Hans Pfletschinger/Peter Arnold; 520, Townsend P. Dickenson/Photo Researchers; 521, Hans Pfletschinger/Peter Arnold; 523(t), E. R. Degginger; 523(b), David Scharf; 524, E. R. Degginger; 526(t), David Scharf; 526(b), Christopher Crowley/Tom Stack & Associates; 527(t), E. S. Ross; 527(b), E. R. Degginger; 528, Robert & Linda Mitchell; 532, Jim Shives/Wildlife Photobank; 534, Florida Department of Agriculture-DPI; 537, James Carmichael Jr./Bruce Coleman; 542(l), E. S. Ross; 542(r), Hans Pfletschinger/Peter Arnold; 544, Peter Fronk/TSW/Click/Chicago; 548, M. Thonig/H. Armstrong Roberts.

Unit 9: 550, 551, R. Harrington/FPG Int'l. Corp; 552, William Curtsinger/Photo Researchers; 557(l), Heather Angel/Biofotos; 557(r), Tom Stack/Tom Stack and Associates; 558, Steinhart-Aquarium/Tom McHugh/Photo Researchers; 559, Steve Martin/Tom Stack and Associates; 561(l), Zig Leszczynski/Animals Animals; 561(r), Jane Shaw/Root Resources; 562(l), Zig Leszczynski/Animals Animals; 562(c), Gary Milburn/Tom Stack and Associates; 562(r), Ron and Valerie Taylor/Bruce Coleman; 568, HRW Photo by Dennis Fagan; 572, Tom McHugh/Photo Researchers; 574(t), Stephen Dalton/Photo Researchers; 574(b), Zig Leszczynski/Animals Animals; 575, A. B. Joyce/Photo Researchers; 577, Runk/Schoenberger/Grant Heilman Photography; 578, Alan Blank/Bruce Coleman; 583(l), Jack Dermid; 583(r), Zig Leszczynski/Animals Animals; 584(t), Jack Dermid; 584(b), Tom McHugh/Photo Researchers; 588, Ken Graham/Wildlife Photobank; 589, Zig Leszczynski/Animals Animals; 593, Zig Leszczynski/Animals Animals; 594, John Markham/Bruce Coleman; 595, Zig Leszczynski/Animals Animals; 596(t), Gary Milburn/Tom Stack and Associates; 596(b), Steinhart-Aquarium/Tom McHugh/Photo Researchers; 597, John Gerlach/Tom Stack and Associates; 598(t), Zig Leszczynski/Animals Animals; 598(bl), James Carmichael Jr./The Image Bank; 598(br), Michael Fogden/Bruce Coleman; 600, Zig Leszczynski/Animals Animals; 604, David M. Stone; 605, American Museum of National History; 606, E. R. Degginger; 608, Patti Murray/Animals Animals; 609(l), (c), (r), David Cavagnaro; 613(l), Photri and Gartman Agency; 613(c), (tr), (br), Runk/Schoenberger/Grant Heilman Photography; 614, Rene Purse/Photo Researchers; 615(t), Tim Fitzharris/VIREO; 615(b), HRW Photo by William Hubbell; 616, James L. Gulledge/Lab of Ornithology; 620(t), Norman Myers/Bruce Coleman; 620(c), Susan Jones/Animals Animals; 620(b), D. Demello/New York Zoological Society; 621(t), Martin Dohrn/Science Photo Library/Photo Researchers; 621(b), Dr. Betsy Dresser/Cincinnati Zoo; 622, Bill Ruth/Aperture; 626(t), Gregory G. Dimijian/Photo Researchers; Tom Bean/Tom Stack and Associates; 627, Barrera/TexaStock; 628, Richard Farnell/Animal Animals; 630(l), Alan Roberts; 630(r), F. Prenzel, 632(t), Elizabeth Weiland/Photo Researchers; 632(b), Stephen Dalton/Animals Animals; 636, Fred Barendam/Peter Arnold; 638(t), (b), Richard Howard/Offshoot; 642, R. Harrington/FPG Int'l. Corp.

Unit 10: 644, 645, HBJ Photo by Rodney Jones; 646, Gary Retherford; 647, Peter B. Kaplan/Photo Researchers; 654, Dr. P. Galletti/Brown University; 655, National Center for Rehabilitation Engineering; 656, David Madison/Bruce Coleman; 660, Steve Powell/Allsport; 665(t), (c), (b), Eric Graves/Photo Researchers; 668, David Madison/Bruce Coleman; 676, Dwight R. Kuhn; 677(l), (lc), (rc), (r), Bruce Powell; 687, HRW by Martha Cooper; 692, Philippe Plailly/Science Photo Library/Photo Researchers; 693; Custom Medical Stock Photo; 694, James White/University of Minnesota; 695, Manfred Kage/Peter Arnold; 704, A. Liepins/Photo Researchers; 705(t), Offshoot; 705(b), Niel/Science Source/Photo Researchers; 710(t), (c), Dan McCoy/Rainbow; 710(b), Tsiaras/Medichrome/The Stock Shop; 711(t), Hank Morgan/Photo Researchers; 711(c), Patrick Guis/Gamma-Liaison; 711(b), Biophoto/Science Photo Library/Photo Researchers; 712, Cheryl A. Traendly; 715, Manfred Kage/Peter Arnold; 717, HRW Photo by Dennis Fagan; 720, Odyseaus/Peter Arnold; 726, CNRI/Science Photo Library/Photo Researchers; 730(t), 730(b), Ed Reschke/Peter Arnold; 735, Tony Freeman/PhotoEdit; 742, Vito Palmisano/Nawrocki Stock Photo; 748, Mary Kate Denny/PhotoEdit; 750, G. Bredberg/Photo Researchers; 752, Omikron/Photo Researchers; 756, Michael Melford/Wheeler Pictures; 763, CIBA; 768, Joel Gordon; 773, Dr. Sundstroem/Gamma-Liaison; 776(l), (r), 777(l), (c), Lennart Nilsson, Behold Man, Little Brown and Company; 777(r), Lennart Nilsson, A Child is Born, Dell Publishing Company ; 778, Gamma-Liaison; 779(l), John Walsh/Science Photo Library/Photo Researchers; 779(r), Martin Roetker/Taurus Photos; 782, CNRI/Science Photo Library/Photo Researchers; 783, CNRI/Science Photo Library/Photo Researchers; 784(l), Susan Gibler/Tom Stack and Associates; 784(r), CNRI/Science Photo Library/Photo Researchers; 785(l), Biophoto/Photo Researchers; 785(r), Manfred Kage/Peter Arnold; 787, NIBSC/Science Photo Library/Photo Researchers; 789, Zeva Oelbaum/Peter Arnold; 790(t), (b), Dr. Cecil Fox/Science Source/ Photo Researchers; 792(t), Dan Peha; 792(b), Manfred Kage/Peter Arnold; 793, HBJ Photo; 794, Dr. Mony de Leon/Peter Arnold; 795(t), (b), Howard Sochurek/Medichrome; 796, Jeffrey Reed/Medichrome/The Stock Shop; 798, HBJ Photo; 802, Lennart Nilsson/Behold Man, Little, Brown and Company; 806, A. Duncan/Taurus Photos; 807, Barry L. Runk/Grant Heilman Photography; 808, E. R. Degginger; 811(l), (c), (r), Martin Roetker/Taurus Photos; 812(t), HRW Photo by Richard Haynes; 812(b), Werner J. Bertsch/Medichrome; 816, HBJ Photo by Rodney Jones.

Unit 11: 818, 819, Grant Heilman/Grant Heilman Photography; 820, Rod Allin/Tom Stack and Associates; 821, Michael Fogden/Oxford Scientific/Earth Scenes; 822(t), Stephen Krasemann/Peter Arnold; 822(b), John Macgregor/Peter Arnold; 823, L. Isy-Schwart/The Image Bank; 824, Tom McHugh/Photo Researchers; 828, Mitch Reardon/Photo Researchers; 831, HRW Photo by Dennis Fagan; 832, G. Ziesler/Peter Arnold; 833(t), W. H. Hodges/Peter Arnold; 833(b), Alan Roberts; 834, Betty Kubis/Root Resources; 838, Doug Allan/Earth Scenes; 839, Grant Heilman/Grant Heilman Photography; 842, Bruce Iverson, Bsc.; 843(t), 843(b), Jack Dermid; 844, David Fritts/Animals Animals; 845, Richard Smith/Tom Stack and Associates; 846, Issac Gelb/Grant Heilman Photography; 847(t), Brian Parker/Tom Stack and Associates; 847(b), Phil Degginger/TSW-Click/Chicago; 848, Andrew Holbrooke/Black Star; 849, Katherine Thomas/Taurus Photos; 851, R. Massa; 852, Larry Lefever/Grant Heilman Photography; 856, Gregory Dimijian/Photo Researchers; 859, Grant Heilman/Grant Heilman Photography; 861, Steven Kaufman/Peter Arnold; 862, Bonnie Freer/Peter Arnold; 868(t), (b), 869(t), (c), (b), Peter Menzel; 870, Benn Mitchell/The Image Bank; 871, Charles Kennard/Stock Boston; 872, Peter Menzel/Stock Boston; 873(l), Cary Wolinski/Stock Boston; 873(r), Peter Kaufman/Peter Arnold; 874(t), Jack Dermid; 874(b), Jerome Wycoff; 875, Jack Dermid; 876, David Falconer/West Stock; 877, Jonathon Wright/Bruce Coleman; 878, Tom Stack/Tom Stack and Associates; 879, John Lopinot/Black Star; 880, Larry Lefever/Grant Heilman Photography; 881, Henry Bureau/Sygma; 888, Liano Enkelis/Stock Boston; 889(t), Boyd Norton; 889(b), SuperStock; 912(t), Historical Picture Service, Chicago; 912(b), Science Source/Photo Researchers; 913 (tl), (tr), Historical Picture Service, Chicago; 913(c), Gower Medical Publishing; 913(b), Dan McCoy/Rainbow; 920(t), Cary Wolinsky/Stock Boston; 920(c), Bruce Powell; 920(b), Jim Pickerell/FPG Int'l. Corp; 922(t), Louis Trusty/Animals Animals; 922(c), E. R. Degginger; 922(b), National Fisheries Center, U.S. Fish & Wildlife; 924(t), Martin Rogers/TSW/Click/Chicago; 924(c), Julie Houck/TSW/Click/Chicago; 924(b), Eric Kroll/Taurus Photos; 926(t), Lee Balterman/Gartman Agency; 926(c), Offshoot; 926(b), David Madison/Bruce Coleman; 928(t), 928(c), SIU/Photo Researchers; 928(b), HBJ Photo; 930(t), E. R. Degginger/Bruce Coleman; 930(c), Stuart Cohen/Comstock; 930(b), Robert Houser/Comstock; 932(t), Dave Woodward/Taurus Photos; 932(c), Beth Ullman/Taurus Photos; 932(b), Joseph Sterling/TSW-Click/Chicago; 934(t), Mac Donald/Third Coast Stock; 934(c), HBJ Photo; 934(b), Gerry Souter/TSW-Click/Chicago; 936(t), E. R. Degginger; 936(c), NASA; 936(b), HBJ Photo

Illustrations:
Joanna Adamska 657, 747, 890, 893, 894, 895, 896, 897, 898, 899, 900, 901, 902, 903, 904, 905 **Scott Thorn Barrows** 232, 652, 653, 666(r), 682, 683, 684, 686, 697, 697, 698, 699, 701, 702, 703, 706, 710, 711, 757, 758(t) **Sally Bensusen** 435(c) **Leon Bishop** 23, 35, 45, 101, 115, 135, 205, 244, 251, 267, 309, 423, 439, 451, 465, 648, 650, 651, 758(bl), 762, 764, 769, 770, 771, 773, 775, 777 **Al Carrol** xvi, 560 **James Dowdalls** 420, 473, 480, 511 **Barry Erickson** 60 **Howard Friedman** 39, 41, 89, 94(tl), 95, 98, 302, 304, 305, 308, 315, 318, 356, 365, 367, 369, 381, 383, 384, 533, 536, 537, 539, 541, 542, 892 **Biruta Ackerbergs Hansen** 108, 113, 114, 393, 394, 399, 401, 409, 411, 413, 415, 418, 421, 488, 489, 490, 491, 495, 503, 504, 525, 553, 563, 564, 565, 566, 567, 891, 892 **Science Graphics** 126, 130, 132, 133, 134, 197 **Signature Design Associates** 354, 357, 386, 412, 416 **Tracor Publications** 858, 860 **Sarah Forbes Woodward** 10, 31, 32, 33, 50, 51(tl, tc, tr), 55, 58(t, b), 59, 67, 105, 106, 109, 110, 127, 142, 143, 144, 145, 146–147, 150–151, 151(r), 161, 162, 163, 165, 166, 169, 170, 171, 172, 173, 179, 183, 184, 185, 191, 203, 209, 210, 214, 216, 217, 223, 250, 261, 265, 277, 283, 313, 340, 345, 346, 353, 454, 516, 554, 589, 590, 592, 595(br), 599, 600, 623, 624, 625, 629, 633, 634, 637, 679, 695, 696, 728, 729, 730, 732, 733, 736, 737, 760, 772, 804, 826, 827, 829, 830, 841, 845, 850, 859, 862, 863, 877 **Jean Cassels Helmer** 112, 272, 273, 274, 275, 276, 290, 403, 404, 417, 419, 427, 428, 430, 433, 434, 435(br), 436, 446, 457, 474, 476, 478, 479, 535, 576, 577, 579, 580, 581, 582, 595(tr), 607, 611, 612, 635 **Dierdre A. McConathy** 94(bl) **Teri J. McDermott** 527, 529, 555(l), 569, 585, 667(c), 707, 715, 720, 721, 723, 727, 739, 865 **Leonard E. Morgan** 8, 15, 69, 73(t, b), 86, 119, 120(b), 124, 193, 194, 195, 198–199, 218, 243, 246, 338, 339, 342, 491(tr), 662, 663, 664, 665, 666(tl), 667(tr), 669, 671, 713, 714, 716, 719, 743, 745, 746, 749, 750, 751, 752 **Precision Graphics** 44, 74, 129, 225, 517, 753 **Stansbury, Ronsaville, Wood** 92, 93, 96, 100, 123, **Carla Simmons** 34, 153, 499, 513, 601